algebra AND trigonometry

CUSTOM EDITION FOR QUEENSBOROUGH COMMUNITY COLLEGE

containing materials from

K. Elayn Martin-Gay, *Intermediate Algebra,* Third Edition

Robert Blitzer, *Algebra and Trigonometry*

martin-gay AND blitzer

Cover Art: "Matisse Dream," by George Herman.

Excerpts taken from:

Intermediate Algebra, Third Edition,
by K. Elayn Martin-Gay
Copyright © 2001 by Prentice-Hall, Inc.
A Pearson Education Company
Upper Saddle River, New Jersey 07458

Algebra and Trigonometry,
by Robert Blitzer
Copyright © 2001 by Prentice-Hall, Inc.

This special edition published in cooperation with Pearson Custom Publishing.

This publication has been printed using selections as they appeared in their original format. Layout and appearance will vary accordingly.

Printed in the United States of America

10 9 8 7 6 5 4 3 2 1

Please visit our web site at www.pearsoncustom.com

ISBN 0–536–63511–0

BA 993242

 PEARSON CUSTOM PUBLISHING
75 Arlington Street, Suite 300, Boston, MA 02116
A Pearson Education Company

CONTENTS

INTERMEDIATE ALGEBRA

Outdoor Opportunities

Geology comes from the Greek words *geo* meaning "the earth" and *logy* meaning "science" or "study." Geologists and other geoscientists study the natural resources, hazards, history, environments, and habitats of our planet. According to the National Science Foundation, over 125,000 geoscientists work in the United States, and as we continue to use up natural resources, the demand for geoscientists will increase.

People who like to work outdoors, travel, and solve puzzles make good geologists. Many spend a lot of their time "in the field" collecting data or rock specimens to be studied later in laboratories. Some geologists travel to far-flung locations to locate increasingly hard-to-find natural resources like oil, natural gas, or fresh water. Geologists must be able to take measurements, read charts and tables, use and prepare maps, and interpret data. They use these skills in activities like piecing together the geological history of a region, predicting the next eruption of a volcano, and reducing the impact of earthquakes on human life.

 For more information about careers in geology and the geosciences, visit the American Geological Institute Website by first going to www.prenhall.com/martin-gay.

In the Spotlight on Decision Making feature on page 37, you will have the opportunity to make color-coding decisions for a map of lava-heated ocean waters as a geologist.

REAL NUMBERS AND ALGEBRAIC EXPRESSIONS

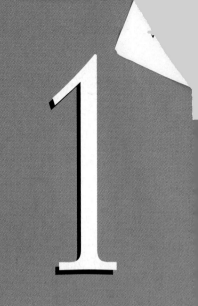

In arithmetic, we add, subtract, multiply, divide, raise to powers, and take roots of numbers. In algebra, we add, subtract, multiply, divide, raise to powers, and take roots of variables. Letters, such as x, that represent numbers are called **variables**. Understanding these algebraic expressions depends on your understanding of arithmetic expressions. This chapter reviews the arithmetic operations on real numbers and the corresponding algebraic expressions. Having done so, we will be prepared to explore how widely and diversely useful these algebraic expressions are for problem solving.

1.1 TIPS FOR SUCCESS IN MATHEMATICS

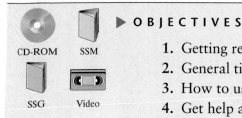

CD-ROM   SSM

SSG   Video

▶ **OBJECTIVES**

1. Getting ready for this course.
2. General tips for success.
3. How to use this text.
4. Get help as soon as you need it.
5. How to prepare for and take an exam.
6. Tips on time management.

Before reading this section, remember that your instructor is your best source for information. Please see your instructor for any additional help or information.

1   Now that you have decided to take this course, remember that a positive attitude will make all the difference in the world. Your belief that you can succeed is just as important as your commitment to this course. Make sure that you are ready for this course by having the time and positive attitude that it takes to succeed.

Next make sure that you have scheduled your math course at a time that will give you the best chance for success. For example, if you are also working, you may want to check with your employer to make sure that your work hours will not conflict with your course schedule.

Now you are ready for your first class period. Double-check your schedule and allow yourself extra time to arrive in case of traffic or in case you have trouble locating your classroom. Make sure that you bring at least your textbook, paper, and a writing instrument with you. Are you required to have a lab manual, graph paper, calculator, or some other supply besides this text? If so, bring this material with you also.

2   Below are some general tips that will increase your chance for success in a mathematics class. Many of these tips will also help you in other courses you may be registered for.

Exchange names and phone numbers with at least one other person in class. This contact person can be a great help in case you miss the class assignment or want to discuss math concepts or exercises that you find difficult.

Choose to attend all class periods. If possible, sit near the front of the classroom. This way, you will see and hear the presentation better. It may also be easier for you to participate in classroom activities.

Do your homework. You've probably heard the phrase "practice makes perfect" in relation to music and sports. It also applies to mathematics. You will find that the more time you spend solving mathematics problems, the easier the process becomes. Be sure to schedule enough time to complete your assignments before the next class period.

Check your work. Review the steps you made while working a problem. Learn to check your answers in the original problems. You may also compare your answers to the answers to selected exercises listed in the back of the book. If you have made a mistake, figure out what went wrong. Then correct your mistake. If you can't find your mistake, don't erase your work or throw it away. Bring your work to your instructor, a tutor in a math lab, or a classmate. Someone can help you find where you had trouble only if they have your work to look at.

Learn from your mistakes. Everyone, even your instructor, makes mistakes. (That definitely includes me—Elayn Martin-Gay. You usually don't see my mistakes because many other people double-check my work in this text. If I make a mistake on a videotape, it is edited out so that you are not confused by it.) Use your mistakes to learn and to become a better math student. The key is finding and understanding your mistakes. Was your mistake a careless mistake or did you make it because you can't read your own "math" writing? If so, try to work more slowly or write more neatly and make a conscious effort to carefully check your work. Did you make a mistake because you don't understand a concept? Take the time to review the concept or ask questions to better understand the concept.

Know how to get help if you need it. It's OK to ask for help. In fact, it's a good idea to ask for help whenever there is something that you don't understand. Make sure you know when your instructor has office hours and how to find his or her office. Find out if math tutoring services are available on your campus. Check out the hours, location, and requirements of the tutoring service. Know whether videotapes or software are available and how to access these resources.

Organize your class materials, including homework assignments, graded quizzes and tests, and notes from your class or lab. All of these items will make valuable references throughout your course and as you study for upcoming tests and your final exam. Make sure that you can locate any of these materials when you need them.

Read your textbook before class. Reading a mathematics textbook is unlike entertainment reading such as reading a newspaper. Your pace will be much slower. It is helpful to have a pencil and paper with you when you read. Try to work out examples on your own as you encounter them in your text. You may also write down any questions that you want to ask in class. I know that when you read a mathematics textbook, sometimes some of the information in a section will still be unclear. But once you hear a lecture or watch a video on that section, you will understand it much more easily than if you had not read your text.

Don't be afraid to ask questions. From experience, I can tell you that you are not the only person in class with questions. Other students are normally grateful that someone has spoken up.

Hand in assignments on time. This way you can be sure that you will not lose points needlessly for being late. Show every step of a problem and be neat and organized. Also be sure that you understand which problems are assigned for homework. You can always double-check this assignment with another student in your class.

3 There are many helpful resources that are available to you in this text. It is important that you become familiar with and use these resources. This should increase your chances for success in this course. For example:

- If you need help in a particular section, check at the beginning of the section to see what videotapes or software is available. These resources are usually available to you in a tutorial lab, resource center, or library.

- Many of the exercises in this text are referenced by an example(s). Use this referencing in case you have trouble completing an assignment from the exercise set.

- Make sure that you understand the meaning of the icons that are beside many exercises. The video icon ✎ tells you that the corresponding exercise may be viewed on the videotape that corresponds to that section. The pencil icon ╲ tells you that this exercise is a writing exercise in which you should answer in complete sentences. The calculator icons are placed by exercises that can be worked more efficiently with the use of a scientific calculator 📟 or a graphing calculator 📟 .

- There are many opportunities at the end of each chapter to help you understand the concepts of the chapter.

  Vocabulary Check provides a vocabulary self-check to make sure that you know the vocabulary in that chapter.

  Highlights contain chapter summaries with examples.

  Chapter Review contains additional exercises that are keyed to sections of the chapter.

  Chapter Test is a sample test to help you prepare for an exam.

  Cumulative Review is a review consisting of material from the beginning of the book to the end of the particular chapter.

4

If you have trouble completing assignments or understanding the mathematics, get help as soon as you need it! This tip is presented as an objective on its own because it is *so* important. In mathematics, usually the material presented in one section builds on your understanding of the previous section. What does this mean? It means that if you don't understand the concepts covered during a class period, there is a good chance that you will not understand the concepts covered during the next class period. If this happens to you, get help as soon as you can.

Where can you get help? Many suggestions have been made in this section on where to get help, and now it is up to you to do it. Try your instructor, a tutoring center, or math lab, or you may want to form a study group with fellow classmates. If you do decide to see your instructor or go to a tutoring center, make sure that you have a neat notebook and be ready with your questions.

5

Make sure that you allow yourself plenty of time to prepare for a test. If you think that you are a little "math anxious," it may be that you are not preparing for a test in a way that will insure success. The way that you prepare for a test in mathematics is important. To prepare for a test,

1. Review your previous homework assignments.
2. Review any notes from class and section level quizzes you may have taken. (If this is a final exam, also review chapter tests you have taken.)
3. Review concepts and definitions by reading the Highlights at the end of each chapter.
4. Practice working exercises by completing the Chapter Review found at the end of each chapter. (If this is a final exam, work a Cumulative Review. There is one found at the end of each chapter (except Chapter 1). Choose the review found at the end of the latest chapter that you have covered in your course.) **Don't stop here!**
5. It is important that you place yourself in conditions similar to test conditions to see how you will perform. In other words, once you feel that you know the material, get out a few blank sheets of paper and take a sample test. There is a Chapter Test available at the end of each chapter, or you can work selected problems from the Chapter Review, or your instructor may provide you with a review sheet. During this sample test, do not use your notes or your textbook. Then check your sample test. If you are not satisfied with the results, study the areas that you are weak in and try again.

6. On the day of the test, allow yourself plenty of time to arrive to where you will be taking your exam.

When taking your test,

1. Read the directions on the test carefully.

2. Read each problem carefully as you take your test. Make sure that you answer the question asked.

3. Watch your time and pace yourself so that you may attempt each problem on your test.

4. If you have time, check your work and answers.

5. Do not turn your test in early. If you have extra time, spend it double-checking your work.

6. As a college student, you know the demands that classes, homework, work, and family place on your time. Some days you probably wonder how you'll ever get everything done. One key to managing your time is developing a schedule. Here are some hints for making a schedule:

1. Make a list of all of your weekly commitments for the term. Include classes, work, regular meetings, extracurricular activities, etc. You may also find it helpful to list such things as doing laundry, regular workouts, grocery shopping, etc.

2. Next, estimate the time needed for each item on the list. Also make a note of how often you will need to do each item. Don't forget to include time estimates for reading, studying, and homework you do outside of your classes. You may want to ask your instructor for help estimating the time needed for this item.

3. In the exercise set below, you are asked to block out a typical week on the schedule grid given. Start with items with fixed time slots, like classes and work.

4. Next, include the items on your list with flexible time slots. Think carefully about how best to schedule some items such as study time.

5. Don't fill up every time slot on the schedule. Remember that you need to allow time for eating, sleeping, and relaxing! You should also allow a little extra time in case things take longer than planned.

6. If you find that your weekly schedule is too full for you to handle, you may need to make some changes in your workload, class load, or in other areas of your life. You may want to talk to your advisor, manager or supervisor at work, or someone in your college's academic counseling center for help with such decisions.

Exercise Set 1.1

1. What is your instructor's name?

2. What are your instructor's office location and office hours?

3. What is the best way to contact your instructor?

4. What does this icon ⟍ mean?

5. What does this icon ◈ mean?

6. Do you have the name and contact information of at least one other student in class?

7. Will your instructor allow you to use a calculator in this class?

8. Are videotapes and/or tutorial software available to you?
9. Is there a tutoring service available? If so, what are its hours?
10. Have you attempted this course before? If so, write down ways that you may improve your chances of success during this attempt.
11. List some steps that you may take in case you begin having trouble understanding the material or completing an assignment.
12. Read or reread objective **6** and fill out the schedule grid below.

	Monday	Tuesday	Wednesday	Thursday	Friday	Saturday	Sunday
7:00 a.m.							
8:00 a.m.							
9:00 a.m.							
10:00 a.m.							
11:00 a.m.							
12:00 p.m.							
1:00 p.m.							
2:00 p.m.							
3:00 p.m.							
4:00 p.m.							
5:00 p.m.							
6:00 p.m.							
7:00 p.m.							
8:00 p.m.							
9:00 p.m.							

1.2 ALGEBRAIC EXPRESSIONS AND SETS OF NUMBERS

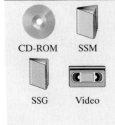

CD-ROM   SSM

SSG   Video

▶ **OBJECTIVES**

1. Identify and evaluate algebraic expressions.
2. Identify natural numbers, whole numbers, integers, and rational and irrational real numbers.
3. Find the absolute value of a number.
4. Find the opposite of a number.
5. Write phrases as algebraic expressions.

1   Recall that letters that represent numbers are called **variables.** An **algebraic expression** is formed by numbers and variables connected by the operations of addition, subtraction, multiplication, division, raising to powers, and/or taking roots. For example,

$$2x + 3, \quad \frac{x + 5}{6} - \frac{z^2}{y^2}, \quad \text{and} \quad \sqrt{y} - 1.6$$

are algebraic expressions or, more simply, expressions.

Algebraic expressions occur often during problem solving. For example, suppose that a television commercial for a watch is being filmed on the Golden Gate Bridge. A portion of this commercial consists of dropping a watch from the bridge. In order to determine the best camera angles and also whether the watch will survive the fall, it is important to know the speed of the watch at 1-second intervals. The algebraic expression

$$32t$$

gives the speed of the watch in feet per second for time t.

To find the speed of the watch at 1 second, for example, we replace the variable t with 1 and perform the indicated multiplication. This process is called **evaluating** an expression, and the result is called the **value** of the expression for the given replacement value.

> **HELPFUL HINT**
> Recall that $32t$ means $32 \cdot t$.

When $t = 1$ second, $32t = 32 \cdot 1 = 32$ feet per second.

When $t = 2$ seconds, $32t = 32 \cdot 2 = 64$ feet per second.

When $t = 3$ seconds, $32t = 32 \cdot 3 = 96$ feet per second.

△ Example 1   FINDING THE AREA OF A TILE

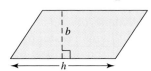

The research department of a flooring company is considering a new flooring design that contains parallelograms. The area of a parallelogram with base b and height h is bh. Find the area of a parallelogram with base 10 centimeters and height 8.2 centimeters.

Solution   We replace b with 10 and h with 8.2 in the algebraic expression bh.

$$bh = 10 \cdot 8.2 = 82$$

The area is 82 square centimeters.

Example 2   Evaluate: $3x - y$ when $x = 15$ and $y = 4$.

Solution   We replace x with 15 and y with 4 in the expression.

$$3x - y = 3 \cdot 15 - 4 = 45 - 4 = 41$$

When evaluating an expression to solve a problem, we often need to think about the kind of number that is appropriate for the solution. For example, if we are asked to determine the maximum number of parking spaces for a parking lot to be constructed, an answer of $98\frac{1}{10}$ is not appropriate because $\frac{1}{10}$ of a parking space is not realistic.

2   Let's review some common sets of numbers and their graphs on a number line. To construct a number line, we draw a line and label a point 0 with which we associate the number 0. This point is called the **origin**. Choose a point to the right of 0 and label it 1. The distance from 0 to 1 is called the **unit distance** and can be used to locate more points. The **positive numbers** lie to the right of the origin, and the **negative numbers** lie to the left of the origin. The number 0 is neither positive nor negative.

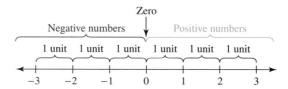

A number is **graphed** on a number line by shading the point on the number line that corresponds to the number. Some common sets of numbers and their graphs include:

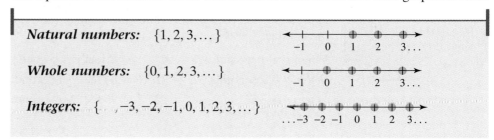

Natural numbers: $\{1, 2, 3, \ldots\}$

Whole numbers: $\{0, 1, 2, 3, \ldots\}$

Integers: $\{\ldots, -3, -2, -1, 0, 1, 2, 3, \ldots\}$

Each listing of three dots above, $\ldots$, is called an **ellipsis** and means to continue in the same pattern.

The members of a set are called its **elements**. When the elements of a set are listed, such as those displayed in the previous paragraph, the set is written in **roster** form. A set can also be written in **set builder notation**, which describes the members of a set but does not list them. The following set is written in set builder notation.

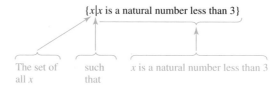

This same set written in roster form is $\{1, 2\}$.

A set that contains *no* elements is called the **empty set**, symbolized by $\{\ \}$, or the **null set**, symbolized by $\varnothing$.

$$\{x \mid x \text{ is a month with 32 days}\} \text{ is } \varnothing \text{ or } \{\ \}$$

because no month has 32 days. The set has no elements.

HELPFUL HINT
Use $\{\ \}$ or $\varnothing$ to write the empty set. $\{\varnothing\}$ is **not** the empty set because it has one element: $\varnothing$.

Example 3   List the elements in each set.

   a. $\{x \mid x \text{ is a whole number between 1 and 6}\}$
   b. $\{x \mid x \text{ is a natural number greater than 100}\}$

Solution   **a.** $\{2, 3, 4, 5\}$ **b.** $\{101, 102, 103, \ldots\}$

The symbol ∈ is used to denote that an element is in a particular set. The symbol ∈ is read as "is an element of." For example, the true statement

3 is an element of {1, 2, 3, 4, 5}

can be written in symbols as

$$3 \in \{1, 2, 3, 4, 5\}$$

The symbol ∉ is read as "is not an element of." In symbols, we write the true statement "p is not an element of $\{a, 5, g, j, q\}$" as

$$p \notin \{a, 5, g, j, q\}$$

Example 4 Determine whether each statement is true or false.

a. $3 \in \{x \mid x \text{ is a natural number}\}$ **b.** $7 \notin \{1, 2, 3\}$

Solution **a.** True, since 3 is a natural number and therefore an element of the set.
b. True, since 7 is not an element of the set $\{1, 2, 3\}$.

We can use set builder notation to describe three other common sets of numbers.

Real numbers: $\{x \mid x \text{ corresponds to a point on the number line}\}$

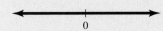

Rational numbers: $\left\{ \dfrac{a}{b} \;\middle|\; a \text{ and } b \text{ are integers and } b \neq 0 \right\}$

Irrational numbers: $\{x \mid x \text{ is a real number and } x \text{ is not a rational number}\}$

HELPFUL HINT
Notice from the definition that all real numbers are either rational or irrational.

Also notice that every integer is also a rational number since each integer can be written as the quotient of itself and 1:

$$3 = \frac{3}{1}, \quad 0 = \frac{0}{1}, \quad -8 = \frac{-8}{1}$$

Not every rational number, however, is an integer. The rational number $\frac{2}{3}$, for example, is not an integer. Some square roots are rational numbers and some are irrational numbers. For example, $\sqrt{2}$, $\sqrt{3}$ and $\sqrt{7}$ are irrational numbers while $\sqrt{25}$ is a rational number because $\sqrt{25} = 5 = \frac{5}{1}$. The number π is an irrational number. To help you make the distinction between rational and irrational numbers, here are a few examples of each.

Rational Numbers		Irrational Numbers
Numbers	**Equivalent Quotient of Integers, $\dfrac{a}{b}$**	
$-\dfrac{2}{3}$	$\dfrac{-2}{3}$ or $\dfrac{2}{-3}$	$\sqrt{5}$
$\sqrt{36}$	$\dfrac{6}{1}$	$\dfrac{\sqrt{6}}{7}$
5	$\dfrac{5}{1}$	$-\sqrt{13}$
0	$\dfrac{0}{1}$	π
1.2	$\dfrac{12}{10}$	$\dfrac{2}{\sqrt{3}}$
$3\dfrac{7}{8}$	$\dfrac{31}{8}$	

Every rational number can be written as a decimal that either repeats or terminates. For example,

$$\frac{1}{2} = 0.5 \qquad\qquad \frac{5}{4} = 1.25$$

$$\frac{2}{3} = 0.6666666\ldots \; = 0.\overline{6} \quad \frac{1}{11} = 0.090909\ldots \; = 0.\overline{09}$$

An irrational number written as a decimal neither terminates nor repeats. When we perform calculations with irrational numbers, we often use decimal approximations that have been rounded. For example, consider the following irrational numbers along with a 4-decimal-place approximations of each:

$$\pi \approx 3.1416 \qquad \sqrt{2} \approx 1.4142$$

Earlier we mentioned that every integer is also a rational number. In other words, all the elements of the set of integers are also elements of the set of rational numbers. When this happens, we say that the set of integers, set Z, is a subset of the set of rational numbers, set I. In symbols,

$$Z \subseteq I$$

is a subset of

The natural numbers, whole numbers, integers, rational numbers, and irrational numbers are each a subset of the set of real numbers. The relationships among these sets of numbers are shown in the following diagram.

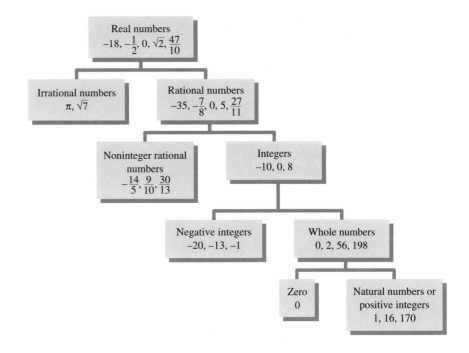

Example 5 Determine whether the following statements are true or false.

a. 3 is a real number.

b. $\frac{1}{5}$ is an irrational number.

c. Every rational number is an integer.

d. $\{1, 5\} \subseteq \{2, 3, 4, 5\}$

Solution **a.** True. Every whole number is a real number.

b. False. The number $\frac{1}{5}$ is a rational number, since it is in the form $\frac{a}{b}$ with a and b integers and $b \neq 0$.

c. False. The number $\frac{2}{3}$, for example, is a rational number, but it is not an integer.

d. False since the element 1 in the first set is not an element of the second set. ■

3 The number line can also be used to visualize distance, which leads to the concept of absolute value. The **absolute value** of a real number a, written as $|a|$, is the distance between a and 0 on the number line. Since distance is always positive or zero, $|a|$ is always positive or zero.

Using the number line, we see that

$$|4| = 4 \quad \text{and also} \quad |-4| = 4.$$

Why? Because both 4 and −4 are a distance of 4 units from 0.

An equivalent definition of the absolute value of a real number a is given next.

ABSOLUTE VALUE

The absolute value of a, written as $|a|$, is

$$|a| = \begin{cases} a \text{ if } a \text{ is 0 or a positive number} \\ -a \text{ if } a \text{ is a negative number} \end{cases}$$

Example 6   Find each absolute value.

a. $|3|$ **b.** $|-5|$ **c.** $-|2|$ **d.** $-|-8|$ **e.** $|0|$

Solution   **a.** $|3| = 3$ since 3 is located 3 units from 0 on the number line.

b. $|-5| = 5$ since -5 is 5 units from 0 on the number line.

c. $-|2| = -2$. The negative sign outside the absolute value bars means to take the opposite of the absolute value of 2.

d. $-|-8| = -8$. Since $|-8|$ is 8, $-|-8| = -8$.

e. $|0| = 0$ since 0 is located 0 units from 0 on the number line.

4   The number line can also help us visualize opposites. Two numbers that are the same distance from 0 on the number line but are on opposite sides of 0 are called **opposites**.

See the definition illustrated on the number lines below.

The opposite of 6 is -6

The opposite of $\dfrac{2}{3}$ is $-\dfrac{2}{3}$.

The opposite of -4 is 4.

OPPOSITE

The opposite of a number a is the number $-a$.

Above we state that the opposite of a number a is $-a$. This means that the opposite of -4 is $-(-4)$. But from the number line above, the opposite of -4 is 4. This means that $-(-4) = 4$, and in general, we have the following property.

HELPFUL HINT
The opposite of 0 is 0.

DOUBLE NEGATIVE PROPERTY

For every real number a, $-(-a) = a$.

Example 7   Write the opposite of each.

      a. 8   **b.** $\dfrac{1}{5}$ **c.** -9.6

Solution   **a.** The opposite of 8 is -8.

      b. The opposite of $\dfrac{1}{5}$ is $-\dfrac{1}{5}$.

      c. The opposite of -9.6 is $-(-9.6) = 9.6$.

---

5   Often, solving problems involves translating a phrase to an algebraic expression. The following is a list of key words and phrases and their translations.

Addition	*Subtraction*	*Multiplication*	*Division*
sum	difference of	product	quotient
plus	minus	times	divide
added to	subtracted from	multiply	into
more than	less than	twice	ratio
increased by	decreased by	of	
total	less		

Example 8   Translate each phrase to an algebraic expression. Use the variable x to represent each unknown number.

      a. Eight times a number

      b. Three more than eight times a number

      c. The quotient of a number and -7

      d. One and six-tenths subtracted from twice a number

Solution   **a.** $8 \cdot x$ or $8x$

      b. $8x + 3$

      c. $x \div -7$ or $\dfrac{x}{-7}$

      d. $2x - 1.6$

SPOTLIGHT ON DECISION MAKING

Suppose you work for an auto insurance company. Your company has just announced a new partnership with an automobile club that will allow club members to receive a 5% discount on their auto insurance. In addition, any auto club members who are safe drivers (rated 1 or 2 on the safety scale) will receive an additional 10% safe-driver discount. Your supervisor has asked you to compile a master mailing list of all current insurance clients who already belong to the auto club so they may be notified of their eligibility for the 5% discount. You must also identify the subset of auto club members who should receive a separate mailing about the additional 10% discount.

   Using the given list of current insurance clients, decide who should be included in the master mailing list for notification of the 5% discount. Which of these clients should also be sent information about the 10% safe-driver discount?

CURRENT CLIENT DATABASE

Client Name	Age (years)	Safety Rating (1-5)	Airbags (0 = no, 1 = yes)	Annual Mileage (miles)	Auto Club (0 = no, 1 = yes)
Alvarez, Wendy	29	1	1	5000	1
Brown, Keisha	19	2	0	5000	0
Cardoni, Anthony	43	1	0	10,000	0
Darden, Clay	35	3	1	7500	1
Evans, Gabriella	26	2	1	5000	1
Fonteneau, Monique	38	4	1	7500	0
Greenberg, Ira	49	1	0	5000	1
Hakkinen, Mika	31	1	1	15,000	0
Issacson, Maude	55	2	0	2000	1
Jones, Harold	47	1	0	7500	1
Khalosef, Avi	52	3	1	5000	1
Lee, Feng	33	2	1	10,000	0
Martinez, Ricardo	25	4	0	5000	1
Nunn, Destiny	21	4	1	5000	0

Exercise Set 1.2

Find the value of each algebraic expression at the given replacement values. See Examples 1 and 2.

1. $5x$ when $x = 7$

2. $3y$ when $y = 45$

3. $9.8z$ when $z = 3.1$

4. $7.1a$ when $a = 1.5$

5. ab when $a = \dfrac{1}{2}$ and $b = \dfrac{3}{4}$

6. yz when $y = \dfrac{2}{3}$ and $z = \dfrac{1}{5}$

7. $3x + y$ when $x = 6$ and $y = 4$

8. $2a - b$ when $a = 12$ and $b = 7$

9. The aircraft B737-400 flies an average speed of 400 miles per hour.

The expression

$$400t$$

gives the distance traveled by the aircraft in t hours. Find the distance traveled by the B737-400 in 5 hours.

10. The algebraic expression $1.5x$ gives the total length of shelf space needed in inches for x encyclopedias. Find the length of shelf space needed for a set of 30 encyclopedias.

△ **11.** Employees at Wal-Mart constantly reorganize and reshelve merchandise. In doing so, they calculate floor space needed for displays. The algebraic expression $l \cdot w$ gives the floor space needed in square units for a display that measures length l units and width w units. Calculate the floor space needed for a display whose length is 5.1 feet and whose width is 4 feet.

12. The algebraic expression $\frac{x}{5}$ can be used to calculate the distance in miles that you are from a flash of lightning, where x is the number of seconds between the time you see a flash of lightning and the time you hear the thunder. Calculate the distance that you are from the flash of lightning if you hear the thunder 2 seconds after you see the lightning.

13. The B747-400 aircraft costs $7098 dollars per hour to operate. The algebraic expression

$$7098t$$

gives the total cost to operate the aircraft for t hours. Find the total cost to operate the B747-400 for 5.2 hours.

14. Flying the SR-71A jet, Capt. Elden W. Joersz, USAF, set a record speed of 2193.16 miles per hour. At this speed, the algebraic expression $2193.16t$ gives the total distance flown in t hours. Find the distance flown by the SR-71A in 1.7 hours.

List the elements in each set. See Example 3.

15. $\{x \mid x$ is a natural number less than 6$\}$

16. $\{x \mid x$ is a natural number greater than 6$\}$

17. $\{x \mid x$ is a natural number between 10 and 17$\}$

18. $\{x \mid x$ is an odd natural number$\}$

19. $\{x \mid x$ is a whole number that is not a natural number$\}$

20. $\{x \mid x$ is a natural number less than 1$\}$

21. $\{x \mid x$ is an even whole number less than 9$\}$

22. $\{x \mid x$ is an odd whole number less than 9$\}$

Graph each set on a number line.

23. $\{0, 2, 4, 6\}$

24. $\{-1, -2, -3\}$

25. $\left\{\dfrac{1}{2}, \dfrac{2}{3}\right\}$

26. $\{1, 3, 5, 7\}$

27. $\{-2, -6, -10\}$

28. $\left\{\dfrac{1}{4}, \dfrac{1}{3}\right\}$

29. In your own words, explain why the empty set is a subset of every set.

30. In your own words, explain why every set is a subset of itself.

List the elements of the set $\left\{3, 0, \sqrt{7}, \sqrt{36}, \dfrac{2}{5}, -134\right\}$ that are also elements of the given set. See Example 4.

31. Whole numbers   **32.** Integers

33. Natural numbers   **34.** Rational numbers

35. Irrational numbers   **36.** Real numbers

Place $\in$ or $\notin$ in the space provided to make each statement true. See Example 4.

37. -11 ___ $\{x \mid x$ is an integer$\}$ **38.** -6 ___ $\{2, 4, 6, \ldots\}$

39. 0 ___ $\{x \mid x$ is a positive integer$\}$

40. 12 ___ $\{1, 2, 3, \ldots\}$ **41.** 12 ___ $\{1, 3, 5, \ldots\}$

42. $\dfrac{1}{2}$ ___ $\{x \mid x$ is an irrational number$\}$

43. 0 ___ $\{1, 2, 3, \ldots\}$

44. 0 ___ $\{x \mid x$ is a natural number$\}$

Determine whether each statement is true or false. See Examples 4 and 5. Use the following sets of numbers.

$$N = \text{set of natural numbers}$$
$$Z = \text{set of integers}$$
$$I = \text{set of irrational numbers}$$
$$Q = \text{set of rational numbers}$$
$$\mathbb{R} = \text{set of real numbers}$$

45. $Z \subseteq \mathbb{R}$

46. $\mathbb{R} \subseteq N$

47. $-1 \in Z$

48. $\frac{1}{2} \in Q$

49. $0 \in N$

50. $Z \subseteq Q$

51. $\sqrt{5} \notin I$

52. $\pi \notin \mathbb{R}$

53. $N \subseteq Z$

54. $I \subseteq N$

55. $\mathbb{R} \subseteq Q$

56. $N \subseteq Q$

57. In your own words, explain why every natural number is also a rational number but not every rational number is a natural number.

58. In your own words, explain why every irrational number is a real number but not every real number is an irrational number.

Find each absolute value. See Example 6.

59. $-|2|$

60. $|8|$

61. $|-4|$

62. $|-6|$

63. $|0|$

64. $|-1|$

65. $-|-3|$

66. $-|-11|$

67. Explain why $-(-2)$ and $-|-2|$ simplify to different numbers.

68. The boxed definition of absolute value states that $|a| = -a$ if a is a negative number. Explain why $|a|$ is always nonnegative, even though $|a| = -a$ for negative values of a.

Write the opposite of each number. See Example 7.

69. -6.2

70. -7.8

71. $\frac{4}{7}$

72. $\frac{9}{5}$

73. $-\frac{2}{3}$

74. $-\frac{14}{3}$

75. 0

76. 10.3

Write each phrase as an algebraic expression. Use the variable x to represent each unknown number. See Example 8.

77. Twice a number.

78. Six times a number.

79. Five more than twice a number.

80. One more than six times a number.

81. Ten less than a number.

82. A number minus seven.

83. The sum of a number and two.

84. The difference of twenty-five and a number.

85. A number divided by eleven.

86. The quotient of twice a number and thirteen.

87. Twelve added to three times a number.

88. Four subtracted from a number.

89. Seventeen subtracted from a number.

90. Four subtracted from three times a number.

91. Twice the sum of a number and three.

92. The quotient of four and the sum of a number and one.

93. The quotient of five and the difference of four and a number.

94. Eight times the difference of a number and 9.

95. The following bar graph shows the top five countries with the projected number of tourists visiting in 2020.

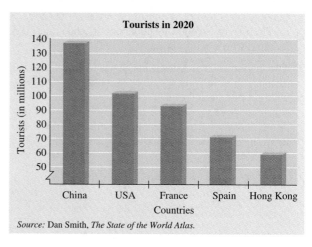

Source: Dan Smith, *The State of the World Atlas.*

Use the height of each bar to estimate the millions of tourists for each country.

China	
USA	
France	
Spain	
Hong Kong	

1.3 OPERATIONS ON REAL NUMBERS

CD-ROM SSM

SSG Video

▶ **OBJECTIVES**

1. Add and subtract real numbers.
2. Multiply and divide real numbers.
3. Simplify expressions containing exponents.
4. Find roots of numbers.
5. Use the order of operations.
6. Evaluate algebraic expressions.

1 When solving problems, we often have to add real numbers. For example, if the New Orleans Saints lose 5 yards in one play, then lose another 7 yards in the next play, their total loss may be described by $-5 + (-7)$.

The addition of two real numbers may be summarized by the following.

ADDING REAL NUMBERS

1. To add two numbers with the *same sign*, add their absolute values and attach their common sign.
2. To add two numbers with *different signs*, subtract the smaller absolute value from the larger absolute value and attach the sign of the number with the larger absolute value.

For example, to add $-5 + (-7)$, first add their absolute values.

$$|-5| = 5, |-7| = 7, \quad \text{and} \quad 5 + 7 = 12$$

Next, attach their common negative sign.

$$-5 + (-7) = -12$$

(This represents a total loss of 12 yards for the New Orleans Saints in the example above.)

To find $(-4) + 3$, first subtract their absolute values.

$$|-4| = 4, |3| = 3, \quad \text{and} \quad 4 - 3 = 1$$

Next, attach the sign of the number with the larger absolute value.

$$(-4) + 3 = -1$$

Example 1 Add.

a. $-3 + (-11)$ **b.** $3 + (-7)$ **c.** $-10 + 15$

d. $-8.3 + (-1.9)$ **e.** $-\dfrac{2}{3} + \dfrac{3}{7}$

Solution   **a.** $-3 + (-11) = -(3 + 11) = -14$ **b.** $3 + (-7) = -4$
c. $-10 + 15 = 5$ **d.** $-8.3 + (-1.9) = -10.2$
e. $-\dfrac{2}{3} + \dfrac{3}{7} = -\dfrac{14}{21} + \dfrac{9}{21} = -\dfrac{5}{21}$

Subtraction of two real numbers may be defined in terms of addition.

SUBTRACTING REAL NUMBERS

If a and b are real numbers,

$$a - b = a + (-b)$$

In other words, to subtract a real number, we add its opposite.

Example 2   Subtract.

a. $2 - 8$ **b.** $-8 - (-1)$ **c.** $-11 - 5$ **d.** $10.7 - (-9.8)$

e. $\dfrac{2}{3} - \dfrac{1}{2}$ **f.** $1 - 0.06$ **g.** Subtract 7 from 4.

Solution   Add the opposite   Add the opposite

a. $2 - 8 = 2 + (-8) = -6$ **b.** $-8 - (-1) = -8 + (1) = -7$
c. $-11 - 5 = -11 + (-5) = -16$ **d.** $10.7 - (-9.8) = 10.7 + 9.8 = 20.5$
e. $\dfrac{2}{3} - \dfrac{1}{2} = \dfrac{2 \cdot 2}{3 \cdot 2} - \dfrac{1 \cdot 3}{2 \cdot 3} = \dfrac{4}{6} + \left(-\dfrac{3}{6}\right) = \dfrac{1}{6}$
f. $1 - 0.06 = 1 + (-0.06) = 0.94$ **g.** $4 - 7 = 4 + (-7) = -3$

To add or subtract three or more real numbers, add or subtract from left to right.

Example 3   Simplify the following expressions.

a. $11 + 2 - 7$ **b.** $-5 - 4 + 2$

Solution   **a.** $11 + 2 - 7 = 13 - 7 = 6$ **b.** $-5 - 4 + 2 = -9 + 2 = -7$

2   In order to discover sign patterns when you multiply real numbers, recall that multiplication by a positive integer is the same as repeated addition. For example,

$$3(2) = 2 + 2 + 2 = 6$$
$$3(-2) = (-2) + (-2) + (-2) = -6$$

Notice here that $3(-2) = -6$. This illustrates that the product of two numbers with different signs is negative. We summarize sign patterns for multiplying any two real numbers as follows.

MULTIPLYING TWO REAL NUMBERS

The product of two numbers with the same sign is positive.
The product of two numbers with different signs is negative.

Also recall that the product of zero and any real number is zero.

$$0 \cdot a = 0$$

Example 4 Multiply.

a. $(-8)(-1)$ **b.** $(-2)\dfrac{1}{6}$ **c.** $3(-3)$ **d.** $0(11)$

e. $\left(\dfrac{1}{5}\right)\left(-\dfrac{10}{11}\right)$ **f.** $(7)(1)(-2)(-3)$ **g.** $8(-2)(0)$

Solution **a.** Since the signs of the two numbers are the same, the product is positive. Thus $(-8)(-1) = +8$, or 8.

b. Since the signs of the two numbers are different or unlike, the product is negative. Thus $(-2)\dfrac{1}{6} = -\dfrac{2}{6} = -\dfrac{1}{3}$.

c. $3(-3) = -9$

d. $0(11) = 0$

e. $\left(\dfrac{1}{5}\right)\left(-\dfrac{10}{11}\right) = -\dfrac{10}{55} = -\dfrac{2}{11}$

f. To multiply three or more real numbers, multiply from left to right.

$$\begin{aligned}
(7)(1)(-2)(-3) &= 7(-2)(-3) \\
&= -14(-3) \\
&= 42
\end{aligned}$$

g. Since zero is a factor, the product is zero.

$$(8)(-2)(0) = 0$$

> **HELPFUL HINT**
> The following sign patterns may be helpful when we are multiplying.
>
> 1. An odd number of negative factors gives a negative product.
> 2. An even number of negative factors gives a positive product.

Recall that $\frac{8}{4} = 2$ because $2 \cdot 4 = 8$. Likewise, $\frac{8}{-4} = -2$ because $(-2)(-4) = 8$. Also, $\frac{-8}{4} = -2$ because $(-2)4 = -8$, and $\frac{-8}{-4} = 2$ because $2(-4) = -8$. From these examples, we can see that the sign patterns for division are the same as for multiplication.

DIVIDING TWO REAL NUMBERS

The quotient of two numbers with the same sign is positive.
The quotient of two numbers with different signs is negative.

Also recall that division by a nonzero real number b is the same as multiplication by $\frac{1}{b}$. In other words,

$$\frac{a}{b} = a \cdot \frac{1}{b}$$

This means that to simplify $\frac{a}{b}$, we can divide by b or multiply by $\frac{1}{b}$. The nonzero numbers b and $\frac{1}{b}$ are called **reciprocals**. Notice that b *must* be a nonzero number. We do not define division by 0. For example, $5 \div 0$, or $\frac{5}{0}$, is undefined. To see why, recall that if $5 \div 0 = n$, a number, then $n \cdot 0 = 5$. This is not possible since $n \cdot 0 = 0$ for any number n, and never 5. Thus far we have learned that we cannot divide 5 or any other nonzero number by 0.

Can we divide 0 by 0? By the same reasoning, if $0 \div 0 = n$, a number, then $n \cdot 0 = 0$. This is true for any number n so that the quotient $0 \div 0$ would not be a single number. To avoid this, we say that

Division by 0 is undefined.

Example 5   Divide.

a. $\dfrac{20}{-4}$ **b.** $\dfrac{-9}{-3}$ **c.** $-\dfrac{3}{8} \div 3$ **d.** $\dfrac{-40}{10}$ **e.** $\dfrac{-1}{10} \div \dfrac{-2}{5}$ **f.** $\dfrac{8}{0}$

Solution   **a.** Since the signs are different or unlike, the quotient is negative and $\dfrac{20}{-4} = -5$.

b. Since the signs are the same, the quotient is positive and $\dfrac{-9}{-3} = 3$.

c. $-\dfrac{3}{8} \div 3 = -\dfrac{3}{8} \cdot \dfrac{1}{3} = -\dfrac{1}{8}$ **d.** $\dfrac{-40}{10} = -4$

e. $\dfrac{-1}{10} \div \dfrac{-2}{5} = -\dfrac{1}{10} \cdot \dfrac{5}{2} = \dfrac{1}{4}$ **f.** $\dfrac{8}{0}$ is undefined.   ∎

With sign rules for division, we can understand why the positioning of the negative sign in a fraction does not change the value of the fraction. For example,

$$\frac{-12}{3} = -4, \quad \frac{12}{-3} = -4, \quad \text{and} \quad -\frac{12}{3} = -4$$

Since all the fractions equal -4, we can say that

$$\frac{-12}{3} = \frac{12}{-3} = -\frac{12}{3}$$

In general, the following holds true.

> If a and b are real numbers and $b \neq 0$, then $\dfrac{a}{-b} = \dfrac{-a}{b} = -\dfrac{a}{b}$.

3 Recall that when two numbers are multiplied, they are called **factors**. For example, in $3 \cdot 5 = 15$, the 3 and 5 are called factors.

A natural number *exponent* is a shorthand notation for repeated multiplication of the same factor. This repeated factor is called the **base**, and the number of times it is used as a factor is indicated by the **exponent**. For example,

$$\overset{\text{exponent}}{\underset{\text{base}}{} 4^3 = \underbrace{4 \cdot 4 \cdot 4}_{4 \text{ is a factor 3 times}} = 64}$$

Also,

$$\overset{\text{exponent}}{\underset{\text{base}}{} 2^5 = \underbrace{2 \cdot 2 \cdot 2 \cdot 2 \cdot 2}_{2 \text{ is a factor 5 times}} = 32}$$

EXPONENTS

If a is a real number and n is a natural number, then the **nth power of a**, or **a raised to the nth power**, written as a^n, is the product of n factors, each of which is a.

$$\overset{\text{exponent}}{\underset{\text{base}}{} a^n = \underbrace{a \cdot a \cdot a \cdot a \cdot \ldots \cdot a}_{a \text{ is a factor } n \text{ times}}}$$

It is not necessary to write an exponent of 1. For example, 3 is assumed to be 3^1.

Example 6 Simplify each expression.

    a. 3^2 **b.** $\left(\dfrac{1}{2}\right)^4$ **c.** -5^2

    d. $(-5)^2$ **e.** -5^3 **f.** $(-5)^3$

Solution **a.** $3^2 = 3 \cdot 3 = 9$

    b. $\left(\dfrac{1}{2}\right)^4 = \left(\dfrac{1}{2}\right)\left(\dfrac{1}{2}\right)\left(\dfrac{1}{2}\right)\left(\dfrac{1}{2}\right) = \dfrac{1}{16}$ **c.** $-5^2 = -(5 \cdot 5) = -25$

    d. $(-5)^2 = (-5)(-5) = 25$ **e.** $-5^3 = -(5 \cdot 5 \cdot 5) = -125$

    f. $(-5)^3 = (-5)(-5)(-5) = -125$

> ▼ **HELPFUL HINT**
> Be very careful when simplifying expressions such as -5^2 and $(-5)^2$.
> $$-5^2 = -(5 \cdot 5) = -25 \quad \text{and} \quad (-5)^2 = (-5)(-5) = 25$$
> Without parentheses, the base to square is 5, not -5.

4

The opposite of squaring a number is taking the **square root** of a number. For example, since the square of 4, or 4^2, is 16, we say that a square root of 16 is 4. The notation $\sqrt{a}$ is used to denote the **positive**, or **principal, square root** of a nonnegative number a. We then have in symbols that

$$\sqrt{16} = 4$$

Example 7 Find the square roots.

    a. $\sqrt{9}$ **b.** $\sqrt{25}$ **c.** $\sqrt{\dfrac{1}{4}}$

Solution   **a.** $\sqrt{9} = 3$ since 3 is positive and $3^2 = 9$.

            b. $\sqrt{25} = 5$ since $5^2 = 25$.

            c. $\sqrt{\dfrac{1}{4}} = \dfrac{1}{2}$ since $\left(\dfrac{1}{2}\right)^2 = \dfrac{1}{4}$.

We can find roots other than square roots. Since 2 cubed, written as 2^3, is 8, we say that the **cube root** of 8 is 2. This is written as

$$\sqrt[3]{8} = 2.$$

Also, since $3^4 = 81$ and 3 is positive,

$$\sqrt[4]{81} = 3.$$

Example 8 Find the roots.

    a. $\sqrt[3]{27}$ **b.** $\sqrt[5]{1}$ **c.** $\sqrt[4]{16}$

Solution   **a.** $\sqrt[3]{27} = 3$ since $3^3 = 27$.

            b. $\sqrt[5]{1} = 1$ since $1^5 = 1$.

            c. $\sqrt[4]{16} = 2$ since 2 is positive and $2^4 = 16$.

Of course, as mentioned in Section 1.2, not all roots simplify to rational numbers. We study radicals further in Chapter 7.

5

Expressions containing more than one operation are written to follow a particular agreed-upon **order of operations**. For example, when we write $3 + 2 \cdot 10$, we mean to multiply first, and then add.

ORDER OF OPERATIONS

Simplify expressions using the order that follows. If grouping symbols such as parentheses are present, simplify expressions within those first, starting with the innermost set. If fraction bars are present, simplify the numerator and denominator separately.

1. Raise to powers or take roots in order from left to right.
2. Multiply or divide in order from left to right.
3. Add or subtract in order from left to right.

Example 9   Simplify.

a. $3 + 2 \cdot 10$ b. $2(1 - 4)^2$ c. $\dfrac{|-2|^3 + 1}{-7 - \sqrt{4}}$ d. $\dfrac{(6 + 2) - (-4)}{2 - (-3)}$

Solution   a. First multiply; then add.

$$3 + 2 \cdot 10 = 3 + 20 = 23$$

b. $2(1 - 4)^2 = 2(-3)^2$ Simplify inside grouping symbols first.

$$= 2(9)$$ Write $(-3)^2$ as 9.

$$= 18$$ Multiply.

c. Simplify the numerator and the denominator separately; then divide.

$$\frac{|-2|^3 + 1}{-7 - \sqrt{4}} = \frac{2^3 + 1}{-7 - 2}$$ Write $|-2|$ as 2 and $\sqrt{4}$ as 2.

$$= \frac{8 + 1}{-9}$$ Write 2^3 as 8.

$$= \frac{9}{-9} = -1$$ Simplify the numerator, then divide.

d. $\dfrac{(6 + 2) - (-4)}{2 - (-3)} = \dfrac{8 - (-4)}{2 - (-3)}$ Simplify inside grouping symbols first.

$$= \frac{8 + 4}{2 + 3}$$ Write subtractions as equivalent additions.

$$= \frac{12}{5}$$ Add in both the numerator and denominator.   ■

6   Recall from Section 1.2 that an algebraic expression is formed by numbers and variables connected by the operations of addition, subtraction, multiplication, division, raising to powers, and/or taking roots. Also, if numbers are substituted for the variables in an algebraic expression and the operations performed, the result is called **the value of the expression** for the given replacement values. This entire process is called **evaluating an expression**.

Example 10   Evaluate each algebraic expression when $x = 2$, $y = -1$, and $z = -3$.

    a. $z - y$ **b.** z^2 **c.** $\dfrac{2x + y}{z}$

Solution   **a.** $z - y = -3 - (-1) = -3 + 1 = -2$

       b. $z^2 = (-3)^2 = 9$

       c. $\dfrac{2x + y}{z} = \dfrac{2(2) + (-1)}{-3} = \dfrac{4 + (-1)}{-3} = \dfrac{3}{-3} = -1$

Sometimes variables such as x_1 and x_2 will be used in this book. The small 1 and 2 are called **subscripts.** The variable x_1 can be read as "x sub 1," and the variable x_2 can be read as "x sub 2." The important thing to remember is that they are two different variables. For example, if $x_1 = -5$ and $x_2 = 7$, then

$$x_1 - x_2 = -5 - 7 = -12.$$

Example 11   The algebraic expression $\dfrac{5(x - 32)}{9}$ represents the equivalent temperature in degrees Celsius when x is the temperature in degrees Fahrenheit. Complete the following table by evaluating this expression at the given values of x.

Degrees Fahrenheit	x	-4	10	32
Degrees Celsius	$\dfrac{5(x - 32)}{9}$			

Solution   To complete the table, evaluate $\dfrac{5(x - 32)}{9}$ at each given replacement value.

When $x = -4$,

$$\frac{5(x - 32)}{9} = \frac{5(-4 - 32)}{9} = \frac{5(-36)}{9} = -20$$

When $x = 10$,

$$\frac{5(x - 32)}{9} = \frac{5(10 - 32)}{9} = \frac{5(-22)}{9} = -\frac{110}{9}$$

When $x = 32$,

$$\frac{5(x - 32)}{9} = \frac{5(32 - 32)}{9} = \frac{5 \cdot 0}{9} = 0$$

The completed table is

Degrees Fahrenheit	x	-4	10	32
Degrees Celsius	$\dfrac{5(x - 32)}{9}$	-20	$-\dfrac{110}{9}$	0

Thus, $-4°$F is equivalent to $-20°$C, $10°$F is equivalent to $-\frac{110}{9}°$C, and $32°$F is equivalent to $0°$C.

SPOTLIGHT ON DECISION MAKING

Suppose you are a travel agent. A tour company is offering bonuses to travel agents booking clients on selected tour packages for a limited time. However, prior to participating in this bonus program, you must select only one type of tour package for which you will receive the bonus. Information about the selected tour packages is shown in the table.

Based on client inquiries during the past week, you estimate that you could probably interest 30 clients in a cruise to Alaska, 60 in a Bermuda package, 50 in a trip to Cancun, and 40 in a Hawaii package. However, you also estimate that in each case, only half of the clients would book the trip if it cost over $1000 per person.

Which one of the tour packages would you choose for participating in the tour company's bonus program? Why?

SELECTED TOUR PACKAGES

Destination	Cost per person	Bonus per person booked
Alaska cruise	$2029	$100
Bermuda	$ 699	$ 25
Cancun, Mexico	$1349	$ 75
Hawaii	$ 840	$ 50

Exercise Set 1.3

Find each sum or difference. See Examples 1 through 3.

1. $-3 + 8$

2. $-5 + (-9)$

3. $-14 + (-10)$

4. $12 + (-7)$

5. $-4.3 - 6.7$

6. $-8.2 - (-6.6)$

7. $13 - 17$

8. $15 - (-1)$

9. $\dfrac{11}{15} - \left(-\dfrac{3}{5}\right)$

10. $\dfrac{7}{10} - \dfrac{4}{5}$

11. $19 - 10 - 11$

12. $-13 - 4 + 9$

Find each product or quotient. See Examples 4 and 5.

13. $(-5)(12)$

14. $6(-3)$

15. $(-8)(-10)$

16. $7(0)$

17. $\dfrac{-12}{-4}$

18. $\dfrac{60}{-6}$

19. $\dfrac{0}{-2}$

20. $\dfrac{-2}{0}$

21. $(-4)(-2)(-1)$

22. $5(-3)(-2)$

23. $\dfrac{-6}{7} \div 2$

24. $\dfrac{-9}{13} \div (-3)$

25. $\left(-\dfrac{2}{7}\right)\left(-\dfrac{1}{6}\right)$

26. $\dfrac{5}{9}\left(-\dfrac{3}{5}\right)$

Evaluate. See Example 6.

27. -7^2

28. $(-7)^2$

29. $(-6)^2$

30. -6^2

31. $(-2)^3$

32. -2^3

33. Explain why -3^2 and $(-3)^2$ simplify to different numbers.

34. Explain why -3^3 and $(-3)^3$ simplify to the same number.

Find the following roots. See Examples 7 and 8.

35. $\sqrt{49}$

36. $\sqrt{81}$

37. $\sqrt{\dfrac{1}{9}}$

38. $\sqrt{\dfrac{1}{25}}$

39. $\sqrt[3]{64}$

40. $\sqrt[5]{32}$

41. $\sqrt[4]{81}$

42. $\sqrt[3]{1}$

Simplify each expression. Round Exercises 61 and 62 to the nearest ten thousandth. See Example 9.

43. $3(5 - 7)^4$

44. $7(3 - 8)^2$

45. $-3^2 + 2^3$

46. $-5^2 - 2^4$

47. $\dfrac{3 - (-12)}{-5}$

48. $\dfrac{-4 - (-8)}{-4}$

49. $|3.6 - 7.2| + |3.6 + 7.2|$

50. $|8.6 - 1.9| - |2.1 + 5.3|$

51. $\dfrac{(3 - \sqrt{9}) - (-5 - 1.3)}{-3}$

52. $\dfrac{-\sqrt{16} - (6 - 2.4)}{-2}$

53. $\dfrac{|3 - 9| - |-5|}{-3}$

54. $\dfrac{|-14| - |2 - 7|}{-15}$

55. $(-3)^2 + 2^3$

56. $(-15)^2 - 2^4$

57. $\dfrac{3(-2 + 1)}{5} - \dfrac{-7(2 - 4)}{1 - (-2)}$

58. $\dfrac{-1 - 2}{2(-3) + 10} - \dfrac{2(-5)}{-1(8) + 1}$

59. $\dfrac{\frac{-3}{10}}{\frac{42}{50}}$

60. $\dfrac{\frac{-5}{21}}{\frac{-6}{42}}$

61. $\dfrac{-1.682 - 17.895}{(-7.102)(-4.691)}$

62. $\dfrac{(-5.161)(3.222)}{7.955 - 19.676}$

Find the value of each expression when $x = -2$, $y = -5$, and $z = 3$. See Example 10.

63. $x^2 + z^2$

64. $y^2 - z^2$

65. $-5(-x + 3y)$

66. $-7(-y - 4z)$

67. $\dfrac{3z - y}{2x - z}$

68. $\dfrac{5x - z}{-2y + z}$

Find the value of the expression when $x_1 = 2$, $x_2 = 4$, $y_1 = -3$, $y_2 = 2$. See Example 10.

69. $\dfrac{y_2 - y_1}{x_2 - x_1}$

70. $\sqrt{(x_2 - x_1)^2 + (y_2 - y_1)^2}$

See Example 11.

△ **71.** The algebraic expression $8 + 2y$ represents the perimeter of a rectangle with width 4 and length y.

a. Complete the table that follows by evaluating this expression at the given values of y.

Length	y	5	7	10	100
Perimeter	$8 + 2y$				

b. Use the results of the table in **a** to answer the following question. As the width of a rectangle remains the same and the length increases, does the perimeter increase or decrease? Explain how you arrived at your answer.

△ **72.** The algebraic expression πr^2 represents the area of a circle with radius r.

a. Complete the table below by evaluating this expression at given values of r. (Use 3.14 for π.)

Radius	r	2	3	7	10
Area	πr^2				

b. As the radius of a circle increases, does its area increase or decrease? Explain your answer.

73. The algebraic expression $\dfrac{100x + 5000}{x}$ represents the cost per bookshelf (in dollars) of producing x bookshelves.

a. Complete the table below.

Number of Bookshelves	x	10	100	1000
Cost per Bookshelf	$\dfrac{100x + 5000}{x}$			

b. As the number of bookshelves manufactured increases, does the cost per bookshelf increase or decrease? Why do you think that this is so?

74. If c is degrees Celsius, the algebraic expression $1.8c + 32$ represents the equivalent temperature in degrees Fahrenheit.

a. Complete the table below.

Degrees Celsius	c	-10	0	50
Degrees Fahrenheit	$1.8c + 32$			

b. As degrees Celsius increase, do degrees Fahrenheit increase or decrease?

Each circle below represents a whole, or 1. Determine the unknown fractional part of each circle.

75.

76.

77. Most of Mount Kea, a volcano on Hawaii, lies below sea level. If this volcano begins at 5998 meters below sea level and then rises 10,203 meters, find the height of the volcano above sea level.

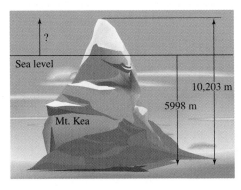

78. The highest point on land on Earth is the top of Mt. Everest in the Himalayas, at an elevation of 29,028 feet above sea level. The lowest point on land is the Dead Sea, between Israel and Jordan, at 1319 feet below sea level. Find the difference in elevations.

A fair game is one in which each team or player has the same chance of winning. Suppose that a game consists of three players taking turns spinning a spinner. If the spinner lands on yellow, player 1 gets a point. If the spinner lands on red, player 2 gets a point, and if the spinner lands on blue, player 3 gets a point. After 12 spins, the player with the most points wins.

a.

b.

c.

d.

79. Which spinner would lead to a fair game?
80. If you are player 2 and want to win the game, which spinner would you choose?
81. If you are player 1 and want to lose the game, which spinner would you choose?

82. Is it possible for the game to end in a three-way tie? If so, list the possible ending scores.

83. Is it possible for the game to end in a two-way tie? If so, list the possible ending scores.

Use a calculator to approximate each square root. Round to four decimal places.

84. $\sqrt{10}$

85. $\sqrt{273}$

86. $\sqrt{7.9}$

87. $\sqrt{19.6}$

Investment firms often advertise their gains and losses in the form of bar graphs such as the one that follows. This graph shows investment risk over time for the S&P 500 Index by showing average annual compound returns for 1 year, 5 years, 15 years, and 25 years. For example, after one year, the annual compound return in percent for an investor is anywhere from a gain of 181.5% to a loss of 64%. Use this graph to answer the questions below.

88. A person investing in the S&P 500 Index may expect at most an average annual gain of what percent after 15 years?

89. A person investing in the S&P 500 Index may expect to lose at most an average per year of what percent after 5 years?

90. Find the difference in percent of the highest average annual return and the lowest average annual return after 15 years.

91. Find the difference in percent of the highest average annual return and the lowest average annual return after 25 years.

92. Do you think that the type of investment shown in the figure is recommended for short-term investments or long-term investments? Explain your answer.

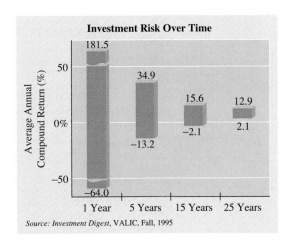

1.4 PROPERTIES OF REAL NUMBERS

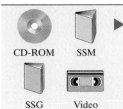

CD-ROM   SSM

SSG   Video

▶ **OBJECTIVES**

1. Use operation and order symbols to write mathematical sentences.
2. Identify identity numbers and inverses.
3. Identify and use the commutative, associative, and distributive properties.
4. Write algebraic expressions.
5. Simplify algebraic expressions.

1

In Section 1.2, we used the symbol $=$ to mean "is equal to." All of the following key words and phrases also imply equality.

> **EQUALITY**
>
> | | | | |
> |---|---|---|---|
> | equals | is/was | represents | is the same as |
> | gives | yields | amounts to | is equal to |

Example 1   Write each sentence using mathematical symbols.

a. The sum of x and 5 is 20.
b. Two times the sum of 3 and y amounts to 4.
c. Subtract 8 from x, and the difference is the same as the product of 2 and x.
d. The quotient of z and 9 is 3 times the difference of z and 5.

Solution   **a.** The sum of x and 5 can be written as "$x + 5$," and the word "is" means "is equal to" in this sentence, so we write $x + 5 = 20$.

b. $2(3 + y) = 4$

c. $x - 8 = 2x$

d. $\dfrac{z}{9} = 3(z - 5)$

If we want to write in symbols that two numbers are not equal, we can use the symbol $\neq$, which means "**is not equal to.**" For example,

$$3 \neq 2$$

Graphing two numbers on a number line gives us a way to compare two numbers. For two real numbers a and b, we say **a is less than b** if on the number line a lies to the left of b. Also, if b is to the right of a on the number line, then **b is greater than a.**

The symbol $>$ means "**is greater than.**" Since b is greater than a, we write

$$b > a$$

Example 2   Insert $<$, $>$, or $=$ between each pair of numbers to form a true statement.

   a. -1 -2 **b.** $\dfrac{12}{4}$ 3   **c.** -5 0   **d.** -3.5 -3.05

Solution   **a.** $-1 > -2$ since -1 lies to the right of -2 on the number line.

   b. $\dfrac{12}{4} = 3$.

   c. $-5 < 0$ since -5 lies to the left of 0 on the number line.

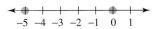

   d. $-3.5 < -3.05$ since -3.5 lies to the left of -3.05 on the number line.

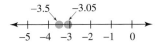

HELPFUL HINT
When inserting the $>$ or $<$ symbol, think of the symbols as arrowheads that "point" toward the smaller number when the statement is true.

In addition to $<$ and $>$, there are the inequality symbols $\le$ and $\ge$. The symbol

$\le$ means **"is less than or equal to"**

and the symbol

$\ge$ means **"is greater than or equal to"**

For example, the following are true statements.

$10 \le 10$	since	$10 = 10$
$-8 \le 13$	since	$-8 < 13$
$-5 \ge -5$	since	$-5 = -5$
$-7 \ge -9$	since	$-7 > -9$

Example 3   Write each sentence using mathematical symbols.

   a. The sum of 5 and y is greater than or equal to 7.
   b. 11 is not equal to z.
   c. 20 is less than the difference of 5 and twice x.

Solution   **a.** $5 + y \ge 7$ **b.** $11 \ne z$ **c.** $20 < 5 - 2x$

2 Of all the real numbers, two of them stand out as extraordinary: 0 and 1. Zero is the only number that when *added* to any real number, the result is the same real number. Zero is thus called the **additive identity.** Also, one is the only number that when *multiplied* by any real number, the result is the same real number. One is thus called the **multiplicative identity.**

	Addition	*Multiplication*
Identity Properties	The additive identity is 0. $a + 0 = 0 + a = a$	The multiplicative identity is 1. $a \cdot 1 = 1 \cdot a = a$

In section 1.2, we learned that a and $-a$ are opposites.

Another name for opposites is **additive inverse.** For example, the additive inverse of 3 is -3. Notice that the sum of a number and its opposite is always 0.

In section 1.3, we learned that, for a nonzero number, b and $\dfrac{1}{b}$ are reciprocals.

Another name for reciprocal is **multiplicative inverse.** For example, the multiplicative inverse of $-\dfrac{2}{3}$ is $-\dfrac{3}{2}$. Notice that the product of a number and its reciprocal is always 1.

Inverse Properties	For each number a, there is a unique number $-a$ called the **additive inverse** or **opposite** of a such that $$a + (-a) = (-a) + a = 0$$	For each nonzero a, there is a unique number $\dfrac{1}{a}$ called the **multiplicative inverse** or **reciprocal** of a such that $$a \cdot \frac{1}{a} = \frac{1}{a} \cdot a = 1$$

◆ **Example 4**   Write the additive inverse, or opposite, of each.

    a. 8   **b.** $\dfrac{1}{5}$ **c.** -9.6

Solution **a.** The opposite of 8 is -8.   **b.** The opposite of $\dfrac{1}{5}$ is $-\dfrac{1}{5}$.

        c. The opposite of -9.6 is $-(-9.6) = 9.6$.

◆ **Example 5**   Write the multiplicative inverse, or reciprocal, of each.

    a. 11   **b.** -9 **c.** $\dfrac{7}{4}$

Solution **a.** The reciprocal of 11 is $\dfrac{1}{11}$.

b. The reciprocal of -9 is $-\dfrac{1}{9}$.

c. The reciprocal of $\dfrac{7}{4}$ is $\dfrac{4}{7}$ because $\dfrac{7}{4} \cdot \dfrac{4}{7} = 1$.

3 In addition to these special real numbers, all real numbers have certain properties that allow us to write equivalent expressions—that is, expressions that have the same value. These properties will be especially useful in Chapter 2 when we solve equations.

The **commutative properties** state that the order in which two real numbers are added or multiplied does not affect their sum or product.

COMMUTATIVE PROPERTIES

For real numbers a and b,

$$\textbf{\textit{Addition}} \quad a + b = b + a$$

$$\textbf{\textit{Multiplication}} \quad a \cdot b = b \cdot a$$

The **associative properties** state that regrouping numbers that are added or multiplied does not affect their sum or product.

ASSOCIATIVE PROPERTIES

For real numbers a, b, and c,

$$\textbf{\textit{Addition}} \quad (a + b) + c = a + (b + c)$$

$$\textbf{\textit{Multiplication}} \quad (a \cdot b) \cdot c = a \cdot (b \cdot c)$$

Example 6 Use the commutative property of addition to write an expression equivalent to $7x + 5$.

Solution $7x + 5 = 5 + 7x$.

Example 7 Use the associative property of multiplication to write an expression equivalent to $4 \cdot (9y)$. Then simplify this equivalent expression.

Solution $4 \cdot (9y) = (4 \cdot 9)y = 36y$.

The **distributive property** states that multiplication distributes over addition.

> **DISTRIBUTIVE PROPERTY**
>
> For real numbers a, b, and c,
>
> $$a(b + c) = ab + ac$$

Example 8 Use the distributive property to multiply.

　a. $3(2x + y)$　　　　　　　　　**b.** $-(3x - 1)$

Solution **a.** $3(2x + y) = 3 \cdot 2x + 3 \cdot y$　　Apply the distributive property.

　　　　　　　　$= 6x + 3y$　　　Apply the associative property of multiplication.

b. Recall that $-(3x - 1)$ means $-1(3x - 1)$.

$$-1(3x - 1) = -1(3x) + (-1)(-1)$$

$$= -3x + 1$$

4　As mentioned earlier, an important step in problem solving is to be able to write algebraic expressions from word phrases. Sometimes this involves a direct translation, but often an indicated operation is not directly stated but rather implied.

Example 9 Write each as an algebraic expression.

　a. A vending machine contains x quarters. Write an expression for the *value* of the quarters.
　b. The number of grams of fat in x pieces of bread if each piece of bread contains 2 grams of fat.
　c. The cost of x desks if each desk costs $156.
　d. Sales tax on a purchase of x dollars if the tax rate is 9%.

Solution Each of these examples implies finding a product.

　a. The value of the quarters is found by multiplying the value of a quarter (0.25 dollar) by the number of quarters.

In words:	Value of a quarter	·	Number of quarters	
Translate:	0.25	·	x,	or $0.25x$

　b.

In words:	Number of grams of fat in one piece of bread	·	Number of pieces of bread	
Translate:	2	·	x,	or $2x$

　c.

In words:	Cost of a desk	·	Number of desks	
Translate:	156	·	x,	or $156x$

d. In words:

| Sales tax rate | · | purchase price |

Translate: 0.09   · x,   or $0.09x$

(Here, we wrote 9% as a decimal, 0.09.)

Two or more unknown numbers in a problem may sometimes be related. If so, try letting a variable represent one unknown number and then represent the other unknown number or numbers as expressions containing the same variable.

Example 10   Write each as an algebraic expression.

a. Two numbers have a sum of 20. If one number is x, represent the other number as an expression in x.

b. The older sister is 8 years older than her younger sister. If the age of the younger sister is x, represent the age of the older sister as an expression in x.

△ **c.** Two angles are complementary if the sum of their measures is 90°. If the measure of one angle is x degrees, represent the measure of the other angle as an expression in x.

d. If x is the first of two consecutive integers, represent the second integer as an expression in x.

Solution   **a.** If two numbers have a sum of 20 and one number is x, the other number is "the rest of 20."

In words:

| Twenty | minus | x |

Translate: 20   − x

b. The older sister's age is

In words:

| Eight years | added to | younger sister's age |

Translate: 8   + x

c. In words:

| Ninety | minus | x |

Translate: 90   − x

d. The next consecutive integer is always one more than the previous integer.

In words:

| The first integer | plus | one |

Translate: x +   1

5   Often, an expression may be **simplified** by removing grouping symbols and combining any like terms. The **terms** of an expression are the addends of the expression. For example, in the expression $3x^2 + 4x$, the terms are $3x^2$ and $4x$.

Expression	*Terms*
$-2x + y$	$-2x, y$
$3x^2 - \dfrac{y}{5} + 7$	$3x^2, -\dfrac{y}{5}, 7$

Terms with the same variable(s) raised to the same power are called **like terms.** We can add or subtract like terms by using the distributive property. This process is called **combining like terms.**

Example 11   Use the distributive property to simplify each expression.

    a. $3x - 5x + 4$ **b.** $7yz + yz$ **c.** $4z + 6.1$

Solution   **a.** $3x - 5x + 4 = (3 - 5)x + 4$ Apply the distributive property.

                             $= -2x + 4$

    b. $7yz + yz = (7 + 1)yz = 8yz$

    c. $4z + 6.1$ cannot be simplified further since $4z$ and 6.1 are not like terms.   ◼

Let's continue to use properties of real numbers to simplify expressions. Recall that the distributive property can also be used to multiply. For example,

$$-2(x + 3) = -2(x) + (-2)(3) = -2x - 6$$

The associative and commutative properties may sometimes be needed to rearrange and group like terms when we simplify expressions.

$$-7x^2 + 5 + 3x^2 - 2 = -7x^2 + 3x^2 + 5 - 2$$

$$= (-7 + 3)x^2 + (5 - 2)$$

$$= -4x^2 + 3$$

Example 12   Simplify each expression.

    a. $3xy - 2xy + 5 - 7 + xy$ **b.** $7x^2 + 3 - 5(x^2 - 4)$

    c. $(2.1x - 5.6) - (-x - 5.3)$

Solution   **a.** $3xy - 2xy + 5 - 7 + xy = 3xy - 2xy + xy + 5 - 7$ Apply the commutative property.

                                     $= (3 - 2 + 1)xy + (5 - 7)$ Apply the distributive property.

                                     $= 2xy - 2$ Simplify.

    b. $7x^2 + 3 - 5(x^2 - 4) = 7x^2 + 3 - 5x^2 + 20$ Apply the distributive property.

                               $= 2x^2 + 23$ Simplify.

    c. Think of $-(-x - 5.3)$ as $-1(-x - 5.3)$ and use the distributive property.

$$(2.1x - 5.6) - 1(-x - 5.3) = 2.1x - 5.6 + 1x + 5.3$$

$$= 3.1x - 0.3 \quad \text{Combine like terms.} \quad ◼$$

SPOTLIGHT ON DECISION MAKING

Suppose you are a geologist studying Hawaiian volcanoes. When lava from a volcano flows into the ocean, it heats the water around it. You are color-coding a map of ocean water temperatures around a lava flow. If the water temperature is less than or equal to 22°C, the map will be colored dark blue. If the water temperature is greater than 29°C, the map will be colored tan. Otherwise, the map will be colored green. Decide what color on the map should be used for the following temperatures.

    a. 25°C

    b. 18°C

    c. 29°C

    d. 22°C

    e. 31°C

Exercise Set 1.4

Write each statement using mathematical symbols. See Example 1.

1. The product of 4 and c is 7.

2. The sum of 10 and x is -12.

3. 3 times the sum of x and 1 amounts to 7.

4. 9 times the difference of 4 and m amounts to 1.

5. The quotient of n and 5 is 4 times n.

6. The quotient of 8 and y is 3 more than y.

7. The difference of z and 2 is the same as the product of z and 2.

8. Five added to twice q is the same as 4 more than q.

Insert $<$, $>$, or $=$ in the space provided to form a true statement. See Example 2.

9. 0 -2

10. -5 0

11. $\dfrac{12}{3}$ $\dfrac{8}{2}$

12. $\dfrac{20}{5}$ $\dfrac{20}{4}$

13. -7.9 -7.09

14. -13.07 -13.7

Write each sentence using mathematical symbols. See Example 3.

15. The product of 7 and x is less than or equal to -21.

16. 10 subtracted from x is greater than 0.

17. The sum of -2 and x is not equal to 10.

18. The quotient of y and 3 is less than or equal to y.

19. Twice the difference of x and 6 is greater than the reciprocal of 11.

20. Four times the sum of 5 and x is not equal to the opposite of 15.

21. 7 subtracted from y is 6.

22. The sum of z and w is 12.

23. Twice the difference of x and 6 is -27.

24. 5 times the sum of 6 and y is -35.

Write the opposite (additive inverse) of each number. Then write the reciprocal (multiplicative inverse) of each number if one exists. See Examples 4 and 5.

25. 5

26. 9

27. -8

28. -4

29. $-\dfrac{1}{4}$

30. $\dfrac{1}{9}$

31. 0

32. $\dfrac{0}{6}$

33. $\dfrac{7}{8}$

34. $-\dfrac{23}{5}$

35. Name the only real number that has no reciprocal, and explain why this is so.

36. Name the only real number that is its own opposite, and explain why this is so.

Use a commutative property to write an equivalent expression. See Example 6.

37. $7x + y$

38. $3a + 2b$

39. $z \cdot w$

40. $r \cdot s$

41. $\dfrac{1}{3} \cdot \dfrac{x}{5}$

42. $\dfrac{x}{2} \cdot \dfrac{9}{10}$

43. Is subtraction commutative? Explain why or why not.

44. Is division commutative? Explain why or why not.

Use an associative property to write an equivalent expression. See Example 7

45. $5 \cdot (7x)$

46. $3 \cdot (10z)$

47. $(x + 1.2) + y$

48. $5q + (2r + s)$

49. $(14z) \cdot y$

50. $(9.2x) \cdot y$

51. Evaluate $12 - (5 - 3)$ and $(12 - 5) - 3$. Use these two expressions and discuss whether subtraction is associative.

52. Evaluate $24 \div (6 \div 3)$ and $(24 \div 6) \div 3$. Use these two expressions and discuss whether division is associative.

Use the distributive property to find the product. See Example 8.

53. $3(x + 5)$

54. $7(y + 2)$

55. $-(2a + b)$

56. $-(c + 7d)$

57. $2(6x + 5y + 2z)$

58. $5(3a + b + 9c)$

Write each sentence using mathematical symbols.

59. 6 subtracted from twice y is the reciprocal of 8.

60. 7 subtracted from the product of 5 and n is the opposite of n.

61. The sum of n and 5, divided by 2, is greater than twice n.

62. The product of 8 and x, divided by 5, is less than 3 more than x.

Complete the statement to illustrate the given property.

63. $3x + 6 = $ _____ Commutative property of addition

64. $8 + 0 = $ ___ Additive identity property

65. $\dfrac{2}{3} + \left(-\dfrac{2}{3}\right) = $ ___ Additive inverse property

66. $4(x + 3) = $ _____ Distributive property

67. $7 \cdot 1 = $ ___ Multiplicative identity property

68. $0 \cdot (-5.4) = $ ___ Multiplication property of zero

69. $10(2y) = $ _____ Associative property

70. $9y + (x + 3z) = $ _____ Associative property

71. To demonstrate the distributive property geometrically, represent the area of the larger rectangle in two ways: First as length a times width $b + c$, and second as the sum of the areas of the smaller rectangles.

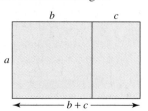

Write each of the following as an algebraic expression. See Examples 9 and 10.

72. Write an expression for the amount of money (in dollars) in n nickels.

73. Write an expression for the amount of money (in dollars) in d dimes.

74. Two numbers have a sum of 25. If one number is x, represent the other number as an expression in x.

75. Two numbers have a sum of 112. If one number is x, represent the other number as an expression in x.

76. Two angles are supplementary if the sum of their measures is 180°. If the measure of one angle is x degrees, represent the measure of the other angle as an expression in x.

77. If the measure of an angle is $5x$ degrees, represent the measure of its complement as an expression in x.

78. The cost of x compact discs if each compact disc costs $6.49.

79. The cost of y books if each book costs $35.61.

80. If x is an odd integer, represent the next odd integer as an expression in x.

81. If $2x$ is an even integer, represent the next even integer as an expression in x.

Simplify each expression. See Examples 11 and 12.

82. $-9 + 4x + 18 - 10x$

83. $5y - 14 + 7y - 20y$

84. $5k - (3k - 10)$

85. $-11c - (4 - 2c)$

86. $(3x + 4) - (6x - 1)$

87. $(8 - 5y) - (4 + 3y)$

88. $3(x - 2) + x + 15$

89. $-4(y + 3) - 7y + 1$

90. $-(n + 5) + (5n - 3)$

91. $-(8 - t) + (2t - 6)$

92. $4(6n - 3) - 3(8n + 4)$

93. $5(2z - 6) + 10(3 - z)$

94. $3x - 2(x - 5) + x$

95. $7n + 3(2n - 6) - 2$

96. $-1.2(5.7x - 3.6) + 8.75x$

97. $5.8(-9.6 - 31.2y) - 18.65$

98. $8.1z + 7.3(z + 5.2) - 6.85$

99. $6.5y - 4.4(1.8x - 3.3) + 10.95$

100. Do figures with the same surface area always have the same volume? To see, take two $8\frac{1}{2}$-by-11-inch sheets of paper and construct two cylinders using the following figures as a guide. Working with a partner, measure the height and the radius of each resulting cylinder and use the expression $\pi r^2 h$ to approximate each volume to the nearest tenth of a cubic inch. Explain your results.

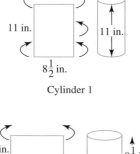

Cylinder 1

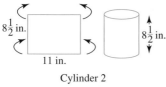

Cylinder 2

101. Use the same idea as in Exercise 100, work with a partner, and discover whether two rectangles with the same perimeter always have the same area. Explain your results.

The following graph is called a broken-line graph, or simply a line graph. This particular graph shows past, present, and future predicted population over 65. Just as with a bar graph, to find the population over 65 for a particular year, read the height of the corresponding point. To read the height, follow the point horizontally to the left until you reach the vertical axis.

102. Estimate the population over 65 in the year 1940.

103. Estimate the predicted population over 65 in the year 2030.

104. Estimate the predicted population over 65 in the year 2010.

105. Estimate the population over 65 in the year 1993.

106. Is the population over 65 increasing as time passes or decreasing? Explain how you arrived at your answer.

107. The percent of Americans over 65 approximately tripled from 1900 to 1993. If this percent in 1900 was 4.1 %, estimate the percent of Americans over 65 in the year 1993.

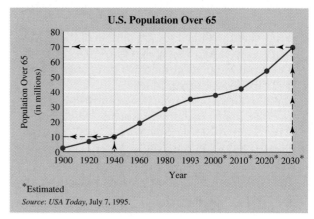

*Estimated
Source: USA Today, July 7, 1995.*

For additional Chapter Projects, visit the Real World Activities Website by going to http://www.prenhall.com/martin-gay.

CHAPTER PROJECT

Analyzing Newspaper Circulation

The number of daily newspapers in business in the United States has declined steadily recently, continuing a trend that started in the mid-1970s. In 1900, there were roughly 2300 daily newspapers in operation. However, by 1998, that number had dropped to only 1509 newspapers in existence. Average overall daily newspaper circulation also continues to decline, from 60.2 million in 1992 to 56.7 million in 1997.

The table below gives data about daily newspaper circulation for New York City–based newspapers for the years 1997 and 1998. In this project, you will have the opportunity to analyze this data. This project may be completed by working in groups or individually.

New York–based Newspaper	1997 Daily Circulation	1998 Daily Circulation	Daily Edition Newsstand Price
Wall Street Journal	1,774,880	1,740,450	$0.75
New York Times	1,074,741	1,066,658	$1.00
New York Daily News	721,256	723,143	$0.50
New York Newsday	568,914	572,444	$0.50
New York Post	436,226	437,467	$0.35

1. Find the change in circulation from 1997 to 1998 for each newspaper. Did any newspaper gain circulation? If so, which one(s) and by how much?
2. Construct a bar graph showing the change in circulation from 1997 to 1998 for each newspaper. Which newspaper experienced the largest change in circulation?
3. What was the total daily circulation of these New York City–based newspapers in 1997? In 1998? Did total circulation increase or decrease from 1997 to 1998? By how much?
4. Discuss factors that may have contributed to the overall change in daily newspaper circulation.
5. The population of New York City is approximately 7,381,000. Find the number of New York City–based newspapers sold per person in 1998 for New York City. (*Source:* U.S. Bureau of the Census)

6. The population of the New York City metropolitan area is approximately 16,332,000. Find the number of New York City–based newspapers sold per person in 1998 for the New York City metropolitan area. (*Source:* The United Nations)
7. Which of the figures found in Questions 5 and 6 do you think is more meaningful? Why? Why might neither of these figures be capable of describing the full circulation situation?
8. Assuming that each copy was sold from a newsstand in the New York City metropolitan area, use the daily edition newspaper prices given in the table to find the total amount spent each day on these New York City–based newspapers in 1998. Find the total amount spent annually on these daily newspapers in 1998. (Remember: Daily editions are published only on weekdays.)
9. How accurate do you think the figures you found in Question 8 are? Explain your reasoning.

CHAPTER 1 VOCABULARY CHECK

Fill in each blank with one of the words or phrases listed below.

distributive   absolute value   inequality   algebraic expression
real   opposite   commutative   exponent
reciprocals   associative   whole   variable

1. A(n) _____ is formed by numbers and variables connected by the operations of addition, subtraction, multiplication, division, raising to powers, and/or taking roots.
2. The _____ of a number a is $-a$.
3. $3(x - 6) = 3x - 18$ by the _____ property.
4. The _____ of a number is the distance between that number and 0 on the number line.
5. A(n) _____ is a shorthand notation for repeated multiplication of the same factor.
6. A letter that represents a number is called a _____.
7. The symbols $<$ and $>$ are called _____ symbols.
8. If a is not 0, then a and $1/a$ are called _____.
9. $A + B = B + A$ by the _____ property.
10. $(A + B) + C = A + (B + C)$ by the _____ property.
11. The numbers $0, 1, 2, 3, \ldots$ are called _____ numbers.
12. If a number corresponds to a point on the number line, we know that number is a _____ number.

CHAPTER 1 HIGHLIGHTS

DEFINITIONS AND CONCEPTS	EXAMPLES

Section 1.2 Algebraic Expressions and Sets of Numbers

Letters that represent numbers are called **variables.**

Examples of variables are
$$x, a, m, y$$

An **algebraic expression** is formed by numbers and variables connected by the operations of addition, subtraction, multiplication, division, raising to powers, and/or taking roots.

Examples of algebraic expressions are
$$7y, -3, \frac{x^2 - 9}{-2} + 14x, \sqrt{3} + \sqrt{m}$$

To **evaluate** an algebraic expression containing variables, substitute the given numbers for the variables and simplify. The result is called the **value** of the expression.

Evaluate $2.7x$ if $x = 3$.
$$2.7x = 2.7(3)$$
$$= 8.1$$

Natural numbers: $\{1, 2, 3, \ldots\}$
Whole numbers: $\{0, 1, 2, 3, \ldots\}$
Integers: $\{\ldots, -3, -2, -1, 0, 1, 2, 3, \ldots\}$
Each listing of three dots above is called an **ellipsis.**
The members of a set are called its **elements.**
Set builder notation describes the elements of a set but does not list them.
Real numbers: $\{x \mid x$ corresponds to a point on the number line.$\}$
Rational numbers: $\left\{\frac{a}{b} \mid a \text{ and } b \text{ are intergers and } b \neq 0\right\}$.
Irrational numbers: $\{x \mid x$ is a real number and x is not a rational number$\}$.
If all the elements of set A are also in set B, we say that set A is a **subset** of set B, and we write $A \subseteq B$.

Given the set $\left\{-9.6, -5, -\sqrt{2}, 0, \frac{2}{5}, 101\right\}$ list the elements that belong to the set of
Natural numbers   101
Whole numbers   0, 101
Integers $-5, 0, 101$
Real numbers $-9.6, -5, -\sqrt{2}, 0, \frac{2}{5}, 101$
Rational numbers $-9.6, -5, 0, \frac{2}{5}, 101$
Irrational numbers $-\sqrt{2}$

List the elements in the set $\{x \mid x$ is an integer between -2 and $5\}$.
$$\{-1, 0, 1, 2, 3, 4\}$$
$$\{1, 2, 4\} \subseteq \{1, 2, 3, 4\}.$$

Absolute value:
$$|a| = \begin{cases} a \text{ if } a \text{ is } 0 \text{ or a positive number} \\ -a \text{ if } a \text{ is a negative number} \end{cases}$$

$$|3| = 3, |0| = 0, |-7.2| = 7.2$$

The opposite of a number a is the number $-a$.

The opposite of 5 is -5. The opposite of -11 is 11.

Section 1.3 Operations on Real Numbers

Adding real numbers:
1. To add two numbers with the same sign, add their absolute values and attach their common sign.
2. To add two numbers with different signs, subtract the smaller absolute value from the larger absolute value and attach the sign of the number with the larger absolute value.

Subtracting real numbers:
$$a - b = a + (-b)$$

Multiplying and dividing real numbers:
The product or quotient of two numbers with the same sign is positive.
The product or quotient of two numbers with different signs is negative.

$$\frac{2}{7} + \frac{1}{7} = \frac{3}{7}$$
$$-5 + (-2.6) = -7.6$$
$$-18 + 6 = -12$$
$$20.8 + (-10.2) = 10.6$$
$$18 - 21 = 18 + (-21) = -3$$

$$(-8)(-4) = 32 \qquad \frac{-8}{-4} = 2$$

$$8 \cdot 4 = 32 \qquad \frac{8}{4} = 2$$

$$-17 \cdot 2 = -34 \qquad \frac{-14}{2} = -7$$

$$4(-1.6) = -6.4 \qquad \frac{22}{-2} = -11$$

(continued)

DEFINITIONS AND CONCEPTS	EXAMPLES

Section 1.3 Operations on Real Numbers, continued

A natural number **exponent** is a shorthand notation for repeated multiplication of the same factor.

The notation $\sqrt{a}$ is used to denote the **positive**, or **principal, square root** of a nonnegative number a.

$$\sqrt{a} = b \text{ if } b^2 = a \text{ and } b \text{ is positive.}$$

Also,

$$\sqrt[3]{a} = b \text{ if } b^3 = a$$

$$\sqrt[4]{a} = b \text{ if } b^4 = a \text{ and } b \text{ is positive}$$

$3^4 = 3 \cdot 3 \cdot 3 \cdot 3 = 81$

$\sqrt{49} = 7$

$\sqrt[3]{64} = 4$

$\sqrt[4]{16} = 2$

Order of Operations

Simplify expressions using the order that follows. If grouping symbols such as parentheses are present, simplify expressions within those first, starting with the innermost set. If fraction bars are present, simplify the numerator and denominator separately.

1. Raise to powers or take roots in order from left to right.
2. Multiply or divide in order from left to right.
3. Add or subtract in order from left to right.

Simplifly $\dfrac{42 - 2(3^2 - \sqrt{16})}{-8}$.

$$\frac{42 - 2(3^2 - \sqrt{16})}{-8} = \frac{42 - 2(9 - 4)}{-8}$$

$$= \frac{42 - 2(5)}{-8}$$

$$= \frac{42 - 10}{-8}$$

$$= \frac{32}{-8} = -4$$

Section 1.4 Properties of Real Numbers

Symbols:
$=$ is equal to
$\neq$ is not equal to
$>$ is greater than
$<$ is less than
$\geq$ is greater than or equal to
$\leq$ is less than or equal to

$-5 = -5$
$-5 \neq -3$
$1.7 > 1.2$
$-1.7 < -1.2$
$\dfrac{5}{3} \geq \dfrac{5}{3}$
$-\dfrac{1}{2} \leq \dfrac{1}{2}$

Identity:
$a + 0 = a \qquad 0 + a = a$
$a \cdot 1 = a \qquad 1 \cdot a = a$

Inverse:
$a + (-a) = 0 \qquad -a + a = 0$
$a \cdot \dfrac{1}{a} = 1 \qquad \dfrac{1}{a} \cdot a = 1, a \neq 0$

Commutative:
$a + b = b + a$
$a \cdot b = b \cdot a$

Associative:
$(a + b) + c = a + (b + c)$
$(a \cdot b) \cdot c = a \cdot (b \cdot c)$

Distributive:
$a(b + c) = ab + ac$

$3 + 0 = 3 \qquad 0 + 3 = 3$
$-1.8 \cdot 1 = -1.8 \qquad 1 \cdot -1.8 = -1.8$

$7 + (-7) = 0 \qquad -7 + 7 = 0$
$5 \cdot \dfrac{1}{5} = 1 \qquad \dfrac{1}{5} \cdot 5 = 1$

$x + 7 = 7 + x$
$9 \cdot y = y \cdot 9$

$(3 + 1) + 10 = 3 + (1 + 10)$
$(3 \cdot 1) \cdot 10 = 3(1 \cdot 10)$

$6(x + 5) = 6 \cdot x + 6 \cdot 5$
$\qquad\qquad = 6x + 30$

CHAPTER 1 REVIEW

(1.2) *Find the value of each algebraic expression at the given replacement values.*

1. $7x$ when $x = 3$

2. st when $s = 1.6$ and $t = 5$

3. The humming bird has an average wing speed of 90 beats per second. The expression $90t$ gives the number of wing beats in t seconds. Calculate the number of wing beats in *1 hour* for the hummingbird.

List the elements in each set.

4. $\{x \mid x$ is an odd integer between -2 and $4\}$

5. $\{x \mid x$ is an even integer between -3 and $7\}$

6. $\{x \mid x$ is a negative whole number$\}$

7. $\{x \mid x$ is a natural number that is not a rational number$\}$

8. $\{x \mid x$ is a whole number greater than 5$\}$

9. $\{x \mid x$ is an integer less than 3$\}$

Determine whether each statement is true or false if $A = \{6, 10, 12\}$, $B = \{5, 9, 11\}$, $C = \{\ldots, -3, -2, -1, 0, 1, 2, 3, \ldots\}$, $D = \{2, 4, 6, \ldots, 16\}$, $E = \{x \mid x$ is a rational number$\}$, $F = \{\ \}$, $G = \{x \mid x$ is an irrational number$\}$, and $H = \{x \mid x$ is a real number$\}$.

10. $10 \in D$
11. $B \in 9$
12. $\sqrt{169} \notin G$
13. $0 \notin F$
14. $\pi \in E$
15. $\pi \in H$
16. $\sqrt{4} \in G$
17. $-9 \in E$
18. $A \subseteq D$
19. $C \nsubseteq B$
20. $C \nsubseteq E$
21. $F \subseteq H$
22. $B \subseteq B$
23. $D \subseteq C$
24. $C \subseteq H$
25. $G \subseteq H$
26. $\{5\} \in B$
27. $\{5\} \subseteq B$

List the elements of the set $\left\{5, -\dfrac{2}{3}, \dfrac{8}{2}, \sqrt{9}, 0.3, \sqrt{7}, 1\dfrac{5}{8}, -1, \pi\right\}$ *that are also elements of each given set.*

28. Whole numbers
29. Natural numbers
30. Rational numbers
31. Irrational numbers
32. Real numbers
33. Integers

Find the opposite.

34. $-\dfrac{3}{4}$
35. 0.6
36. 0
37. 1

Find the reciprocal.

38. $-\dfrac{3}{4}$
39. 0.6
40. 0
41. 1

(1.3) *Simplify.*

42. $-7 + 3$
43. $-10 + (-25)$
44. $5(-0.4)$
45. $(-3.1)(-0.1)$
46. $-7 - (-15)$
47. $9 - (-4.3)$
48. $(-6)(-4)(0)(-3)$
49. $(-12)(0)(-1)(-5)$
50. $(-24) \div 0$
51. $0 \div (-45)$
52. $(-36) \div (-9)$
53. $60 \div (-12)$
54. $\left(-\dfrac{4}{5}\right) - \left(-\dfrac{2}{3}\right)$
55. $\left(\dfrac{5}{4}\right) - \left(-2\dfrac{3}{4}\right)$

56. Determine the unknown fractional part.

Simplify.

57. $-5 + 7 - 3 - (-10)$
58. $8 - (-3) + (-4) + 6$
59. $3(4 - 5)^4$
60. $6(7 - 10)^2$
61. $\left(-\dfrac{8}{15}\right) \cdot \left(-\dfrac{2}{3}\right)^2$
62. $\left(-\dfrac{3}{4}\right)^2 \cdot \left(-\dfrac{10}{21}\right)$
63. $\dfrac{-\dfrac{6}{15}}{\dfrac{8}{25}}$
64. $\dfrac{\dfrac{4}{9}}{-\dfrac{8}{45}}$
65. $-\dfrac{3}{8} + 3(2) \div 6$
66. $5(-2) - (-3) - \dfrac{1}{6} + \dfrac{2}{3}$
67. $|2^3 - 3^2| - |5 - 7|$
68. $|5^2 - 2^2| + |9 \div (-3)|$
69. $(2^3 - 3^2) - (5 - 7)$
70. $(5^2 - 2^4) + [9 \div (-3)]$
71. $\dfrac{(8 - 10)^3 - (-4)^2}{2 + 8(2) \div 4}$
72. $\dfrac{(2 + 4)^2 + (-1)^5}{12 \div 2 \cdot 3 - 3}$
73. $\dfrac{(4 - 9) + 4 - 9}{10 - 12 \div 4 \cdot 8}$
74. $\dfrac{3 - 7 - (7 - 3)}{15 + 30 \div 6 \cdot 2}$
75. $\dfrac{\sqrt{25}}{4 + 3 \cdot 7}$
76. $\dfrac{\sqrt{64}}{24 - 8 \cdot 2}$

Find the value of each expression when $x = 0$, $y = 3$, and $z = -2$.

77. $x^2 - y^2 + z^2$

78. $\dfrac{5x + z}{2y}$

79. $\dfrac{-7y - 3z}{-3}$

80. $(x - y + z)^2$

△ **81.** The algebraic expression $2\pi r$ represents the circumference of (distance around) a circle of radius r.

a. Complete the table below by evaluating the expression at given values of r. (Use 3.14 for π)

Radius	r	1	10	100
Circumference	$2\pi r$			

b. As the radius of a circle increases, does the circumference of the circle increase or decrease?

(1.4) Simplify each expression.

82. $5xy - 7xy + 3 - 2 + xy$

83. $4x + 10x - 19x + 10 - 19$

84. $6x^2 + 2 - 4(x^2 + 1)$ **85.** $-7(2x^2 - 1) - x^2 - 1$

86. $(3.2x - 1.5) - (4.3x - 1.2)$

87. $(7.6x + 4.7) - (1.9x + 3.6)$

Write each statement using mathematical symbols.

88. Twelve is the product of x and negative 4.

89. The sum of n and twice n is negative fifteen.

90. Four times the sum of y and three is -1.

91. The difference of t and five, multiplied by six is four.

92. Seven subtracted from z is six.

93. Ten less than the product of x and nine is five.

94. The difference of x and 5 is at least 12.

95. The opposite of four is less than the product of y and seven.

96. Two-thirds is not equal to twice the sum of n and one-fourth.

97. The sum of t and six is not more than negative twelve.

Name the property illustrated.

98. $(M + 5) + P = M + (5 + P)$

99. $5(3x - 4) = 15x - 20$ **100.** $(-4) + 4 = 0$

101. $(3 + x) + 7 = 7 + (3 + x)$

102. $(XY)Z = (YZ)X$ **103.** $\left(-\dfrac{3}{5}\right) \cdot \left(-\dfrac{5}{3}\right) = 1$

104. $T \cdot 0 = 0$ **105.** $(ab)c = a(bc)$

106. $A + 0 = A$ **107.** $8 \cdot 1 = 8$

Complete the equation using the given property.

108. $5x - 15z = $ _____ Distributive property

109. $(7 + y) + (3 + x) = $ _____ Commutative property

110. $0 = $ _____ Additive inverse property

111. $1 = $ _____ Multiplicative inverse property

112. $[(3.4)(0.7)]5 = $ _____ Associative property

113. $7 = $ _____ Additive identity property

Insert $<$, $>$, or $=$ to make each statement true.

114. -9 ___ -12 **115.** 0 ___ -6

116. -3 ___ -1 **117.** 7 ___ $|-7|$

118. -5 ___ $-(-5)$ **119.** $-(-2)$ ___ -2

CHAPTER 1 TEST

Determine whether each statement is true or false.

1. $-2.3 > -2.33$ **2.** $-6^2 = (-6)^2$

3. $-5 - 8 = -(5 - 8)$ **4.** $(-2)(-3)(0) = \dfrac{-4}{0}$

5. All natural numbers are integers.

6. All rational numbers are integers.

Simplify.

7. $5 - 12 \div 3(2)$ **8.** $|4 - 6|^3 - (1 - 6^2)$

9. $(4 - 9)^3 - |-4 - 6|^2$ **10.** $[3|4 - 5|^5 - (-9)] \div (-6)$

11. $\dfrac{6(7 - 9)^3 + (-2)}{(-2)(-5)(-5)}$

Evaluate each expression when $q = 4$, $r = -2$, and $t = 1$.

12. $q^2 - r^2$ **13.** $\dfrac{5t - 3q}{3r - 1}$

14. The algebraic expression $5.75x$ represents the total cost for x adults to attend the theater.

a. Complete the table that follows.

b. As the number of adults increases does the total cost increase or decrease?

Adults	x	1	3	10	20
Total Cost	$5.75x$				

Write each statement using mathematical symbols..

15. Twice the absolute value of the sum of x and five is 30.

16. The square of the difference of six and y, divided by seven, is less than -2.

17. The product of nine and z, divided by the absolute value of -12, is not equal to 10.

18. Three times the quotient of n and five is the opposite of n.

19. Twenty is equal to 6 subtracted from twice x.

20. Negative two is equal to x divided by the sum of x and five.

Name each property illustrated.

21. $6(x - 4) = 6x - 24$

22. $(4 + x) + z = 4 + (x + z)$

23. $(-7) + 7 = 0$

24. $(-18)(0) = 0$

25. Write an expression for the total amount of money (in dollars) in n nickels and d dimes.

Simplify each expression.

26. $4y^2 + 10 - 2(y^2 + 10)$

27. $(8.3x - 2.9) - (9.6x - 4.8)$

Keeping Us Informed

The field of journalism includes newspaper, radio, and television reporters, as well as photographers, graphic artists, copy editors, and other communications specialists. In the United States, the news media are responsible for keeping us informed about current national and international events.

Excellent communication skills are the top requirement for journalists. However, journalists also must be informed about a wide variety of subjects so they can report effectively on their news assignments. A liberal-arts education, including courses in economics, statistics, and sciences, can be a huge asset for journalists. Journalists must be able to do research, conduct interviews, study documents, and interpret numerical data and statistics.

 For more information about careers in journalism, visit the American Society of Newspaper Editors Website by first going to www.prenhall.com/martin-gay.

In the Spotlight on Decision Making feature on page 63, you will have the opportunity to use percents to make a decision about how to approach a story as a reporter.

EQUATIONS, INEQUALITIES, AND PROBLEM SOLVING

2

Mathematics is a tool for solving problems in such diverse fields as transportation, engineering, economics, medicine, business, and biology. We solve problems using mathematics by modeling real-world phenomena with mathematical equations or inequalities. Our ability to solve problems using mathematics, then, depends in part on our ability to solve equations and inequalities. In this chapter, we solve linear equations and inequalities in one variable and graph their solutions on number lines.

2.1 LINEAR EQUATIONS IN ONE VARIABLE

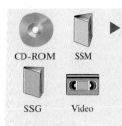

CD-ROM   SSM

SSG   Video

▶ **OBJECTIVES**

1. Solve linear equations using properties of equality.
2. Solve linear equations that can be simplified by combining like terms.
3. Solve linear equations containing fractions.
4. Recognize when an equation is an identity and when it has no solution.

1   Linear equations model many real-life problems. For example, we can use a linear equation to calculate the increase in digital camera sales.

With the help of your computer, digital cameras allow you to see your pictures and make copies immediately, send them in e-mail or use them on a Web page. Current sales and projected sales of these cameras are shown in the graph below.

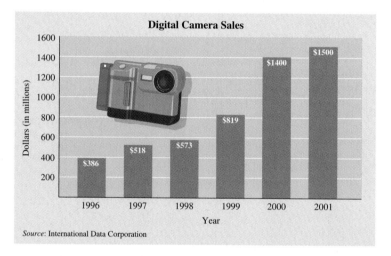

Digital Camera Sales

Source: International Data Corporation

To find the increase in sales from 1999 to 2000, for example, we can use the equation below.

In words:

Increase in sales	is	sales in 2000	minus	sales in 1999

Translate: x $=$ 1400 $-$ 819

Since our variable x (increase in sales) is by itself on one side of the equation, we can find the value of x by simplifying the right side.

$$x = 581$$

The increase in sales of digital cameras from 1999 to 2000 is $581 million.

The **equation**, $x = 1400 - 819$, like every other equation, is a statement that two expressions are equal. Oftentimes, the unknown variable is not by itself on one side of the equation. In these cases, we will use properties of equality to write equivalent equations so that a solution many be found. This is called **solving the equation**. In this section, we concentrate on solving equations such as this one, called **linear equations** in one variable. Linear equations are also called **first-degree equations** since the exponent on the variable is 1.

Linear Equations in One Variable

$$3x = -15 \qquad 7 - y = 3y \qquad 4n - 9n + 6 = 0 \qquad z = -2$$

LINEAR EQUATIONS IN ONE VARIABLE

A linear equation in one variable is an equation that can be written in the form

$$ax + b = c$$

where a, b, and c are real numbers and $a \neq 0$.

When a variable in an equation is replaced by a number and the resulting equation is true, then that number is called a **solution** of the equation. For example, 1 is a solution of the equation $3x + 4 = 7$, since $3(1) + 4 = 7$ is a true statement. But 2 is not a solution of this equation, since $3(2) + 4 = 7$ is not a true statement. The **solution set** of an equation is the set of solutions of the equation. For example, the solution set of $3x + 4 = 7$ is $\{1\}$.

To **solve an equation** is to find the solution set of an equation. Equations with the same solution set are called **equivalent equations**. For example,

$$3x + 4 = 7 \qquad 3x = 3 \qquad x = 1$$

are equivalent equations because they all have the same solution set, namely $\{1\}$. To solve an equation in x, we start with the given equation and write a series of simpler equivalent equations until we obtain an equation of the form

$$x = \textbf{number}$$

Two important properties are used to write equivalent equations.

THE ADDITION AND MULTIPLICATION PROPERTIES OF EQUALITY

If a, b, and c, are real numbers, then

$$a = b \quad \text{and} \quad a + c = b + c \text{ are equivalent equations.}$$

Also, $a = b$ and $ac = bc$ are equivalent equations as long as $c \neq 0$.

The **addition property of equality** guarantees that the same number may be added to (or subtracted from) both sides of an equation, and the result is an equivalent equation. The **multiplication property of equality** guarantees that both sides of an equation may be multiplied by (or divided by) the same nonzero number, and the result is an equivalent equation.

For example, to solve $2x + 5 = 9$, use the addition and multiplication properties of equality to isolate x—that is, to write an equivalent equation of the form

$$x = \text{number}$$

Example 1   Solve for x: $2x + 5 = 9$.

Solution   First, use the addition property of equality and subtract 5 from both sides. We do this so that our only variable term, $2x$, is by itself on one side of the equation.

$$\begin{aligned} 2x + 5 &= 9 \\ 2x + 5 - 5 &= 9 - 5 \qquad \text{Subtract 5 from both sides.} \\ 2x &= 4 \qquad\qquad \text{Simplify.} \end{aligned}$$

Now that the variable term is isolated, we can finish solving for x by using the multiplication property of equality and dividing both sides by 2.

$$\frac{2x}{2} = \frac{4}{2} \qquad \text{Divide both sides by 2.}$$

$$x = 2 \qquad \text{Simplify.}$$

Check   To see that 2 is the solution, replace x in the original equation with 2.

$$2x + 5 = 9 \qquad \text{Original equation.}$$
$$2(2) + 5 \stackrel{?}{=} 9 \qquad \text{Let } x = 2.$$
$$4 + 5 \stackrel{?}{=} 9$$
$$9 = 9 \qquad \text{True.}$$

Since we arrive at a true statement, 2 is the solution or the solution set is $\{2\}$. ▬

Example 2   Solve: $0.6 - 2$ $3.5c$.

Solution   We use both the addition property and the multiplication property of equality.

> **HELPFUL HINT**
>
> Don't forget that
>
> $0.4 = c$ and $c = 0.4$ are equivalent equations.
>
> We may solve an equation so that the variable is alone on either side of the equation.

$$0.6 = 2 - 3.5c$$
$$0.6 - 2 = 2 - 3.5c - 2 \qquad \text{Subtract 2 from both sides.}$$
$$-1.4 = -3.5c \qquad \text{Simplify. The variable term is now isolated.}$$
$$\frac{-1.4}{-3.5} = \frac{-3.5c}{-3.5} \qquad \text{Divide both sides by } -3.5.$$
$$0.4 = c \qquad \text{Simplify } \frac{-1.4}{-3.5}.$$

Check

$$0.6 = 2 - 3.5c$$
$$0.6 \stackrel{?}{=} 2 - 3.5(0.4) \qquad \text{Replace } c \text{ with 0.4.}$$
$$0.6 \stackrel{?}{=} 2 - 1.4 \qquad \text{Multiply.}$$
$$0.6 = 0.6 \qquad \text{True.}$$

The solution is 0.4. ▬

2   Often, an equation can be simplified by removing any grouping symbols and combining any like terms.

Example 3   Solve: $-6x - 1 + 5x = 3$.

Solution   First, the left side of this equation can be simplified by combining like terms $-6x$ and $5x$. Then use the addition property of equality and add 1 to both sides of the equation.

$$-6x - 1 + 5x = 3$$
$$-x - 1 = 3 \qquad \text{Combine like terms.}$$
$$-x - 1 + 1 = 3 + 1 \qquad \text{Add 1 to both sides of the equation.}$$
$$-x = 4 \qquad \text{Simplify.}$$

Notice that this equation is not solved for x since we have $-x$ or $-1x$, not x. To solve for x, divide both sides by -1.

$$\frac{-x}{-1} = \frac{4}{-1} \qquad \text{Divide both sides by } -1.$$

$$x = -4 \qquad \text{Simplify.}$$

Check to see that the solution is -4.

If an equation contains parentheses, use the distributive property to remove them.

Example 4   Solve: $2(x - 3) = 5x - 9$.

Solution   First, use the distributive property.

$$2(x - 3) = 5x - 9$$

$$2x - 6 = 5x - 9 \qquad \text{Use the distributive property.}$$

Next, get variable terms on the same side of the equation by subtracting $5x$ from both sides.

$$2x - 6 - 5x = 5x - 9 - 5x \qquad \text{Subtract } 5x \text{ from both sides.}$$

$$-3x - 6 = -9 \qquad \text{Simplify.}$$

$$-3x - 6 + 6 = -9 + 6 \qquad \text{Add 6 to both sides.}$$

$$-3x = -3 \qquad \text{Simplify.}$$

$$\frac{-3x}{-3} = \frac{-3}{-3} \qquad \text{Divide both sides by } -3.$$

$$x = 1$$

Let $x = 1$ in the original equation to see that 1 is the solution.

---

3   If an equation contains fractions, we first clear the equation of fractions by multiplying both sides of the equation by the *least common denominator* (LCD) of all fractions in the equation.

Example 5   Solve for y: $\dfrac{y}{3} - \dfrac{y}{4} = \dfrac{1}{6}$.

Solution   First, clear the equation of fractions by multiplying both sides of the equation by 12, the LCD of denominators 3, 4, and 6.

$$\frac{y}{3} - \frac{y}{4} = \frac{1}{6}$$

$$12\left(\frac{y}{3} - \frac{y}{4}\right) = 12\left(\frac{1}{6}\right) \qquad \text{Multiply both sides by the LCD 12.}$$

$$12\left(\frac{y}{3}\right) - 12\left(\frac{y}{4}\right) = 2 \qquad \text{Apply the distributive property.}$$

$$4y - 3y = 2 \qquad \text{Simplify.}$$

$$y = 2 \qquad \text{Simplify.}$$

Check: To check, let $y = 2$ in the original equation.

$$\frac{y}{3} - \frac{y}{4} = \frac{1}{6} \qquad \text{Original equation.}$$

$$\frac{2}{3} - \frac{2}{4} \stackrel{?}{=} \frac{1}{6} \qquad \text{Let } y = 2.$$

$$\frac{8}{12} - \frac{6}{12} \stackrel{?}{=} \frac{1}{6} \qquad \text{Write fractions with the LCD.}$$

$$\frac{2}{12} \stackrel{?}{=} \frac{1}{6} \qquad \text{Subtract.}$$

$$\frac{1}{6} = \frac{1}{6} \qquad \text{Simplify.}$$

This is a true statement, so the solution is 2.

As a general guideline, the following steps may be used to solve a linear equation in one variable.

SOLVING A LINEAR EQUATION IN ONE VARIABLE

Step 1: Clear the equation of fractions by multiplying both sides of the equation by the least common denominator (LCD) of all denominators in the equation.

Step 2: Use the distributive property to remove grouping symbols such as parentheses.

Step 3: Combine like terms on each side of the equation.

Step 4: Use the addition property of equality to rewrite the equation as an equivalent equation with variable terms on one side and numbers on the other side.

Step 5: Use the multiplication property of equality to isolate the variable.

Step 6: Check the proposed solution in the original equation.

Example 6 Solve for x: $\dfrac{x + 5}{2} + \dfrac{1}{2} = 2x - \dfrac{x - 3}{8}$.

Solution Multiply both sides of the equation by 8, the LCD of 2 and 8.

$$8\left(\frac{x + 5}{2} + \frac{1}{2}\right) = 8\left(2x - \frac{x - 3}{8}\right) \qquad \text{Multiply both sides by 8.}$$

$$8\left(\frac{x + 5}{2}\right) + 8 \cdot \frac{1}{2} = 8 \cdot 2x - 8\left(\frac{x - 3}{8}\right) \qquad \text{Apply the distributive property.}$$

$$4(x + 5) + 4 = 16x - (x - 3) \qquad \text{Simplify.}$$

$$\text{Use the distributive property to remove parentheses.}$$

$$4x + 20 + 4 = 16x - x + 3 \qquad \text{}$$

$$4x + 24 = 15x + 3 \qquad \text{Combine like terms.}$$

$$-11x + 24 = 3 \qquad \text{Subtract } 15x \text{ from both sides.}$$

$$-11x = -21 \qquad \text{Subtract 24 from both sides.}$$

$$\frac{-11x}{-11} = \frac{-21}{-11} \qquad \text{Divide both sides by } -11.$$

$$x = \frac{21}{11} \qquad \text{Simplify.}$$

To check, verify that replacing x with $\frac{21}{11}$ makes the original equation true. The solution is $\frac{21}{11}$.

If an equation contains decimals, you may want to first clear the equation of decimals.

Example 7   Solve: $0.3x + 0.1 = 0.27x - 0.02$.

Solution   To clear this equation of decimals, we multiply both sides of the equation by 100. Recall that multiplying a number by 100 moves its decimal point two places to the right.

$$100(0.3x + 0.1) = 100(0.27x - 0.02)$$
$$100(0.3x) + 100(0.1) = 100(0.27x) - 100(0.02) \qquad \text{Use the distributive property.}$$
$$30x + 10 = 27x - 2 \qquad \text{Multiply.}$$
$$30x - 27x = -2 - 10 \qquad \text{Subtract 27x and 10 from both sides.}$$
$$3x = -12 \qquad \text{Simplify.}$$
$$\frac{3x}{3} = \frac{-12}{3} \qquad \text{Divide both sides by 3.}$$
$$x = -4 \qquad \text{Simplify.}$$

Check to see that the solution is -4.

---

4   So far, each linear equation that we have solved has had a single solution. A linear equation in one variable that has exactly one solution is called a **conditional equation**. We will now look at two other types of equations: contradictions and identities.

An equation in one variable that has no solution is called a **contradiction**, and an equation in one variable that has every number (for which the equation is defined) as a solution is called an **identity**. The next examples show how to recognize contradictions and identities.

Example 8   Solve for x: $3x + 5 = 3(x + 2)$.

Solution   First, use the distributive property and remove parentheses.

$$3x + 5 = 3(x + 2)$$
$$3x + 5 = 3x + 6 \qquad \text{Apply the distributive property.}$$
$$3x + 5 - 3x = 3x + 6 - 3x \qquad \text{Subtract 3x from both sides.}$$
$$5 = 6$$

The equation $5 = 6$ is a false statement no matter what value the variable x might have. Thus, the original equation has no solution. Its solution set is written either as $\{\ \}$ or $\varnothing$. This equation is a contradiction.

Example 9   Solve for x: $6x - 4 = 2 + 6(x - 1)$.

Solution   First, use the distributive property and remove parentheses.

$$6x - 4 = 2 + 6(x - 1)$$
$$6x - 4 = 2 + 6x - 6 \qquad \text{Apply the distributive property.}$$
$$6x - 4 = 6x - 4 \qquad \text{Combine like terms.}$$

At this point we might notice that both sides of the equation are the same, so replacing x by any real number gives a true statement. Thus the solution set of this equation is the set of real numbers, and the equation is an identity. Continuing to "solve" $6x - 4 = 6x - 4$, we eventually arrive at the same conclusion.

$$6x - 4 + 4 = 6x - 4 + 4 \qquad \text{Add 4 to both sides.}$$
$$6x = 6x \qquad \text{Simplify.}$$
$$6x - 6x = 6x - 6x \qquad \text{Subtract 6x from both sides.}$$
$$0 = 0 \qquad \text{Simplify.}$$

Since $0 = 0$ is a true statement for every value of x, all real numbers are solutions. The solution set is the set of all real numbers or, $\mathbb{R}$, $\{x \mid x \text{ is a real number}\}$, and the equation is called an identity.

> **HELPFUL HINT**
> For linear equations, *any* false statement such as $5 = 6, 0 = 1$, or $-2 = 2$ informs us that the original equation has no solution. Also, *any* true statement such as $0 = 0, 2 = 2$, or $-5 = -5$ informs us that the original equation is an identity.

MENTAL MATH

Simplify each expression by combining like terms.

1. $3x + 5x + 6 + 15$
2. $8y + 3y + 7 + 11$
3. $5n + n + 3 - 10$
4. $m + 2m + 4 - 8$
5. $8x - 12x + 5 - 6$
6. $4x - 10x + 13 - 16$

Exercise Set 2.1

Solve for the variable. See Examples 1 and 2.

1. $-3x = 36$
2. $8x = -40$
3. $x + 2.8 = 1.9$
4. $y - 8.6 = -6.3$
5. $5x - 4 = 26$
6. $2y - 3 = 11$
7. $-4 = 3x + 11$
8. $-9 = 5x + 11$
9. $-4.1 - 7z = 3.6$
10. $10.3 - 6x = -2.3$
11. $5y + 12 = 2y - 3$
12. $4x + 14 = 6x + 8$

Solve for the variable. See Examples 3 and 4.

13. $8x - 5x + 3 = x - 7 + 10$
14. $6 + 3x + x = -x + 2 - 26$
15. $5x + 12 = 2(2x + 7)$
16. $2(x + 3) = x + 5$

17. $3(x - 6) = 5x$
18. $6x = 4(5 + x)$
19. $-2(5y - 1) - y = -4(y - 3)$
20. $-3(2w - 7) - 10 = 9 - 2(5w + 4)$
21. a. Simplify the expression $4(x + 1) + 1$.
   b. Solve the equation $4(x + 1) + 1 = -7$.
   c. Explain the difference between solving an equation for a variable and simplifying an expression.
22. Explain why the multiplication property of equality does not include multiplying both sides of an equation by 0. (*Hint:* Write down a false statement and then multiply both sides by 0. Is the result true or false? What does this mean?)

Solve for the variable. See Examples 5 through 7.

23. $\dfrac{x}{2} + \dfrac{2}{3} = \dfrac{3}{4}$ **24.** $\dfrac{x}{2} + \dfrac{x}{3} = \dfrac{5}{2}$

25. $\dfrac{3t}{4} - \dfrac{t}{2} = 1$ **26.** $\dfrac{4r}{5} - 7 = \dfrac{r}{10}$

27. $\dfrac{n-3}{4} + \dfrac{n+5}{7} = \dfrac{5}{14}$ **28.** $\dfrac{2+h}{9} + \dfrac{h-1}{3} = \dfrac{1}{3}$

29. $0.6x - 10 = 1.4x - 14$ **30.** $0.3x + 2.4 = 0.1x + 4$

Solve the following. See Examples 8 and 9.

31. $4(n + 3) = 2(6 + 2n)$

32. $6(4n + 4) = 8(3 + 3n)$

33. $3(x - 1) + 5 = 3x + 7$

34. $5x - (x + 4) = 5 + 4(x - 2)$

35. In your own words, explain why the equation $x + 7 = x + 6$ has no solution while the solution set of the equation $x + 7 = x + 7$ contains all real numbers.

36. In your own words, explain why the equation $x = -x$ has one solution, namely 0, while the solution set of the equation $x = x$ is all real numbers.

Solve the following.

37. $-9x = -72$ **38.** $-7x = 56$

39. $x - 1.7 = -7.6$ **40.** $y - 9.3 = -12.6$

41. $6x + 9 = 51$ **42.** $4x + 11 = 47$

43. $-5x + 1.5 = -19.5$ **44.** $-3x - 4.7 = 11.8$

45. $x - 10 = -6x + 4$ **46.** $4x - 7 = 2x - 7$

47. $3x - 4 - 5x = x + 4 + x$

48. $13x - 15x + 8 = 4x + 2 - 24$

49. $5(y + 4) = 4(y + 5)$ **50.** $6(y - 4) = 3(y - 8)$

51. $0.6x - 10 = 1.4x - 14$ **52.** $0.3x + 2.4 = 0.1x + 4$

53. $6x - 2(x - 3) = 4(x + 1) + 4$

54. $10x - 2(x + 4) = 8(x - 2) + 6$

55. $\dfrac{3}{8} + \dfrac{b}{3} = \dfrac{5}{12}$ **56.** $\dfrac{a}{2} + \dfrac{7}{4} = 5$

57. $z + 3(2 + 4z) = 6(z + 1) + 5z$

58. $4(m - 6) - m = 8(m - 3) - 5m$

59. $\dfrac{3t+1}{8} = \dfrac{5+2t}{7} + 2$ **60.** $4 - \dfrac{2z+7}{9} = \dfrac{7-z}{12}$

61. $\dfrac{m-4}{3} - \dfrac{3m-1}{5} = 1$ **62.** $\dfrac{n+1}{8} - \dfrac{2-n}{3} = \dfrac{5}{6}$

63. $5(x - 2) + 2x = 7(x + 4) - 38$

64. $3x + 2(x + 4) = 5(x + 1) + 3$

65. $y + 0.2 = 0.6(y + 3)$

66. $-(w + 0.2) = 0.3(4 - w)$

67. $2y + 5(y - 4) = 4y - 2(y - 10)$

68. $9c - 3(6 - 5c) = c - 2(3c + 9)$

69. $2(x - 8) + x = 3(x - 6) + 2$

70. $4(x + 5) = 3(x - 4) + x$

71. $\dfrac{3x-1}{9} + x = \dfrac{3x+1}{3} + 4$

72. $\dfrac{2z+7}{8} - 2 = z + \dfrac{z-1}{2}$

73. $1.5(4 - x) = 1.3(2 - x)$

74. $2.4(2x + 3) = -0.1(2x + 3)$

75. $-2(b - 4) - (3b - 1) = 5b + 3$

76. $4(t - 3) - 3(t - 2) = 2t + 8$

77. $\dfrac{1}{4}(a + 2) = \dfrac{1}{6}(5 - a)$

78. $\dfrac{1}{3}(8 + 2c) = \dfrac{1}{5}(3c - 5)$

Find the value of K such that the equations are equivalent.

79. $3.2x + 4 = 5.4x - 7$
$3.2x = 5.4x + K$

80. $-7.6y - 10 = -1.1y + 12$
$-7.6y = -1.1y + K$

81. $\dfrac{x}{6} + 4 = \dfrac{x}{3}$
$x + K = 2x$

82. $\dfrac{5x}{4} + \dfrac{1}{2} = \dfrac{x}{2}$
$5x + K = 2x$

Solve and check.

83. $2.569x = -12.48534$

84. $-9.112y = -47.537304$

85. $2.86z - 8.1258 = -3.75$

86. $1.25x - 20.175 = -8.15$

87. Recall from Section 1.3 that a game is fair if each team or player has an equal chance of winning. Cut or tear a sheet of paper into 10 pieces, numbering each piece from 1 to 10. Place the pieces into a bag. Draw 2 pieces from the bag, record their sum, and then return them to the bag. If the sum is 10 or less, player 1 gets a point. If their sum is more than 10, player 2 gets a point. Is this a fair game? Try it and see.

REVIEW EXERCISES

Translate each phrase into an expression. Use the variable x to represent each unknown number. See Section 1.2.

88. the quotient of 8 and a number

89. the sum of 8 and a number

90. the product of 8 and a number

91. the difference of 8 and a number

92. 2 more than three times a number

93. 5 subtracted from twice a number

A Look Ahead

Example
Solve for x: $5x(x - 1) + 14 = x(4x - 3) + x^2$.

Solution
$$5x^2 - 5x + 14 = 4x^2 - 3x + x^2$$
$$5x^2 - 5x + 14 = 5x^2 - 3x$$
$$-5x + 14 = -3x$$
$$14 = 2x$$
$$7 = x$$

Solve the following. See example.

94. $x(x - 6) + 7 = x(x + 1)$
95. $7x^2 + 2x - 3 = 6x(x + 4) + x^2$
96. $3x(x + 5) - 12 = 3x^2 + 10x + 3$
97. $x(x + 1) + 16 = x(x + 5)$

2.2 AN INTRODUCTION TO PROBLEM SOLVING

CD-ROM   SSM

SSG   Video

▶ **OBJECTIVES**

1. Write algebraic expressions that can be simplified.
2. Apply the steps for problem solving.

1

In order to prepare for problem solving, we practice writing algebraic expressions that can be simplified.

Our first example involves consecutive integers and perimeter. Recall that *consecutive integers* are integers that follow one another in order. Study the examples of consecutive, even, and odd integers and their representations.

Consecutive Integers:

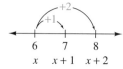

Consecutive Even Integers:

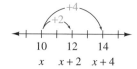

Consecutive Odd Integers:

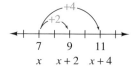

Example 1 Write the following as algebraic expressions. Then simplify.

    a. The sum of two consecutive integers, if x is the first consecutive integer.
△**b.** The perimeter of the triangle with sides of length $x, 5x,$ and $6x - 3$.

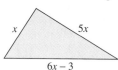

Solution   **a.** Recall that if x is the first integer, then the next consecutive integer is 1 more, or $x + 1$.

In words: | first integer | plus | next consecutive integer |

Translate: x $+$ $(x + 1)$
Then $x + (x + 1) = x + x + 1$
                    $= 2x + 1$ Simplify by combining like terms.

b. The perimeter of a triangle is the sum of the lengths of the sides.

In words: side   +   side   +   side

Translate: x + $5x$ + $(6x - 3)$

Then $x + 5x + (6x - 3) = x + 5x + 6x - 3$

$$= 12x - 3 \quad \text{Simplify.}$$

Example 2   The three busiest airports in the United States are in the cities of Chicago, Atlanta, and Dallas/Ft. Worth. The airport in Atlanta has 7.7 million more arrivals and departures than the Dallas/Ft. Worth airport. The Chicago airport has 9.8 million more arrivals and departures than the Dallas/Ft Worth airport. Write the sum of the arrivals and departures from these three cities as a simplified algebraic expression. Let x be the number of arrivals and departures from the Dallas/Ft. Worth airport.

Solution   If x = millions of arrivals and departures at the Dallas/Ft. Worth airport, then
$x + 7.7$ = millions of arrivals and departures at the Atlanta airport and
$x + 9.8$ = millions of arrivals and departures at the Chicago airport
Since we want their sum, we have

In words:

arrivals and departures at Dallas/Ft. Worth	+	arrivals and departures at Atlanta	+	arrivals and departures at Chicago.

Translate: x + $(x + 7.7)$ + $(x + 9.8)$

Then $x + (x + 7.7) + (x + 9.8) = x + x + 7.7 + x + 9.8$

$$= 3x + 17.5 \quad \text{Combine like terms.}$$

In Exercise 25, we will find the actual number of arrivals and departures at these airports.

2   Our main purpose for studying algebra is to solve problems. The following problem-solving strategy will be used throughout this text and may also be used to solve real-life problems that occur outside the mathematics classroom.

GENERAL STRATEGY FOR PROBLEM SOLVING

1. UNDERSTAND the problem. During this step, become comfortable with the problem. Some ways of doing this are:

   Read and reread the problem.

   Choose a variable to represent the unknown.

   Construct a drawing.

   Propose a solution and check. Pay careful attention to how you check your proposed solution. This will help when writing an equation to model the problem.

2. TRANSLATE the problem into an equation.

3. SOLVE the equation.

4. INTERPRET the results: *Check* the proposed solution in the stated problem and *state* your conclusion.

Let's review this strategy by solving a problem involving unknown numbers.

Example 3   FINDING UNKNOWN NUMBERS

Find two numbers such that the second number is 3 more than twice the first number and the sum of the two numbers is 72.

Solution   1. UNDERSTAND the problem. First let's read and reread the problem and then propose a solution. For example, if the first number is 25, then the second number is 3 more than twice 25, or 53. The sum of 25 and 53 is 78, not the required sum, but we have gained some valuable information about the problem. First, we know that the first number is less than 25 since our guess led to a sum greater than the required sum. Also, we have gained some information as to how to model the problem with an equation.

Next let's assign a variable and use this variable to represent any other unknown quantities. If we let

the first number $= x$, then

the second number $= \underbrace{2x}\ \overset{\uparrow}{+\ 3}$

$\uparrow$ 3 more than

twice the second number

2. TRANSLATE the problem into an equation. To do so, we use the fact that the sum of the numbers is 72. First let's write this relationship in words and then translate to an equation.

In words:

first number	added to	second number	is	72
↓	↓	↓	↓	↓

Translate: x $+$ $(2x + 3)$ $=$ 72

3. SOLVE the equation.

$$x + (2x + 3) = 72$$

$$x + 2x + 3 = 72 \qquad \text{Remove parentheses.}$$

$$3x + 3 = 72 \qquad \text{Combine like terms.}$$

$$3x = 69 \qquad \text{Subtract 3 from both sides.}$$

$$x = 23 \qquad \text{Divide both sides by 3.}$$

4. INTERPRET. Here, *we check* our work and *state* the solution. Recall that if the first number $x = 23$, then the second number $2x + 3 = 2 \cdot 23 + 3 = 49$.

Check: Is the second number 3 more than twice the first number? Yes, since 3 more than twice 23 is $46 + 3$, or 49. Also, their sum, $23 + 49 = 72$, is the required sum.

State: The two numbers are 23 and 49.   ▬

Many of today's rates and statistics are given as percents. Interest rates, tax rates, nutrition labeling, and percent of households in a given category are just a few examples. Before we practice solving problems containing percents, let's take a moment and review the meaning of percent and how to find a percent of a number.

The word *percent* means "per hundred," and the symbol % is used to denote percent. This means that 23% is 23 per hundred, or $\dfrac{23}{100}$. Also,

$$41\% = \frac{41}{100} = 0.41$$

To find a percent of a number, we multiply.

Example 4   Find 16% of 25.

Solution   To find 16% of 25, we find the product of 16% (written as a decimal) and 25.

$$16\% \cdot 25 = 0.16 \cdot 25$$

$$= 4$$

Thus, 16% of 25 is 4.   ▬

Next, we solve a problem containing percent.

Example 5   **FINDING THE ORIGINAL PRICE OF A COMPUTER**

Suppose that The Digital Store just announced an 8% decrease in the price of their Compaq Presario computers. If one particular computer model sells for $2162 after the decrease, find the original price of this computer.

Solution   1. UNDERSTAND. Read and reread the problem. Recall that a percent decrease means a percent of the original price. Let's guess that the original price of the computer is $2500. The amount of decrease is then 8% of $2500, or $(0.08)(\$2500) = \$200$. This means that the new price of the computer is the original price minus the decrease, or $2500 − \$200 = \$2300$. Our guess is incorrect, but we now have an idea of how to model this problem. In our model, we will let x = the original price of the computer.

2. TRANSLATE.

In words:	original price of computer	minus	8% of original price	is	new price
	↓	↓	↓	↓	↓
Translate:	x	−	$0.08x$	=	2162

3. SOLVE the equation.

$$x - 0.08x = 2162$$
$$0.92x = 2162 \qquad \text{Combine like terms.}$$
$$x = \frac{2162}{0.92} = 2350 \qquad \text{Divide both sides by 0.92.}$$

4. INTERPRET.

Check: If the original price of the computer was $2350, the new price is

$$\$2350 - (0.08)(\$2350) = \$2350 - \$188$$
$$= \$2162 \qquad \text{The given new price.}$$

State: The original price of the computer was $2350.

△ **Example 6**   **FINDING THE LENGTHS OF A TRIANGLE'S SIDES**

A pennant in the shape of an isosceles triangle is to be constructed for the Slidell High School Athletic Club and sold at a fund-raiser. The company manufacturing the pennant charges according to perimeter, and the athletic club has determined that a perimeter of 149 centimeters should make a nice profit. If each equal side of the triangle is twice the length of the third side, increased by 12 centimeters, find the lengths of the sides of the triangular pennant.

Solution   1. UNDERSTAND. Read and reread the problem. Recall that the perimeter of a triangle is the distance around. Let's guess that the third side of the triangular pennant is 20 centimeters. This means that each equal side is twice 20 centimeters, increased by 12 centimeters, or $2(20) + 12 = 52$ centimeters.

This gives a perimeter of $20 + 52 + 52 = 124$ centimeters. Our guess is incorrect, but we now have a better understanding of how to model this problem.

Now we let the third side of the triangle $= x$

the first side $=$	twice	the third side	increased by 12
	↓	↓	↓
$=$	2	x	$+$ 12,

or $2x + 12$

the second side $= 2x + 12$

2. TRANSLATE.

In words:

first side	$+$	second side	$+$	third side	$=$	149
↓		↓		↓		↓

Translate: $(2x + 12)$ $+$ $(2x + 12)$ $+$ x $=$ 149

3. SOLVE the equation.

$$(2x + 12) + (2x + 12) + x = 149$$
$$2x + 12 + 2x + 12 + x = 149 \quad \text{Remove parentheses.}$$
$$5x + 24 = 149 \quad \text{Combine like terms.}$$
$$5x = 125 \quad \text{Subtract 24 from both sides.}$$
$$x = 25 \quad \text{Divide both sides by 5.}$$

4. INTERPRET. If the third side is 25 centimeters, then the first side is $2(25) + 12 = 62$ centimeters and the second side is 62 centimeters also.

Check: The first and second sides are each twice 25 centimeters increased by 12 centimeters or 62 centimeters. Also, the perimeter is $25 + 62 + 62 = 149$ centimeters, the required perimeter.

State: The lengths of the sides of the triangle are 25 centimeters, 62 centimeters, and 62 centimeters.

Example 7 Kelsey Ohleger was helping her friend Benji Burnstine study for an algebra exam. Kelsey told Benji that her two latest art history quiz scores are two consecutive even integers whose sum is 174. Help Benji find the scores.

Solution
1. **UNDERSTAND.** Read and reread the problem. Since we are looking for consecutive even integers, let

$$x = \text{the first integer. Then}$$
$$x + 2 = \text{the next consecutive even integer.}$$

2. **TRANSLATE.**

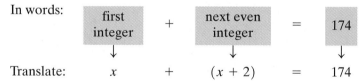

In words:
| first integer | + | next even integer | = | 174 |

Translate: x + $(x + 2)$ = 174

3. **SOLVE.**

$$x + (x + 2) = 174$$
$$2x + 2 = 174 \qquad \text{Combine like terms.}$$
$$2x = 172 \qquad \text{Subtract 2 from both sides.}$$
$$x = 86 \qquad \text{Divide both sides by 2.}$$

4. **INTERPRET.** If $x = 86$, then $x + 2 = 86 + 2$ or 88.

Check: The numbers 86 and 88 are two consecutive even integers. Their sum is 174, the required sum.

State: Kelsey's art history quiz scores are 86 and 88.

SPOTLIGHT ON DECISION MAKING

Suppose you are a reporter for the *Marston Gazette*, a daily newspaper serving the medium-sized industrial city of Marston. Your editor has assigned you to a feature story about food pantries, soup kitchens, and other efforts to alleviate hunger among the city's homeless, poor, and working poor.

While researching your story assignment, you find that, according to the U.S. Department of Agriculture, 10.2% of all households in the United States do not have access to enough food to meet their basic needs. A survey conducted by Marston Social Services reveals that approximately 4950 of the es-timated 39,400 Marston households must cope with hunger.

Armed with these basic facts, you now need to decide what angle to take with your story. Which of the following approaches would you choose? Why? What other information would you want to consider?

a. Marston lags behind nation in fight against hunger.

b. Marston mirrors national hunger picture.

c. Marston makes progress against hunger.

Exercise Set 2.2

Write the following as algebraic expressions. Then simplify. See Examples 1 and 2.

△ **1.** The perimeter of the square with side length y.

△ **2.** The perimeter of the rectangle with length x and width $x - 5$.

3. The sum of three consecutive integers if the first integer is z.

4. The sum of three consecutive odd integers if the first integer is x.

5. The total amount of money (in cents) in x nickels and $(x + 3)$ dimes. (*Hint:* the value of a nickel is 5 cents and the value of a dime is 10 cents.)

6. The total amount of money (in cents) in y quarters and $(2y - 1)$ nickels. (Use the hint for Exercise 5.)

△ **7.** A piece of land along Bayou Liberty is to be fenced and subdivided as shown so that each rectangle has the same dimensions. Express the total amount of fencing needed as an algebraic expression in x.

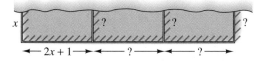

△ **8.** Write the perimeter of the floor plan shown as an algebraic expression in x.

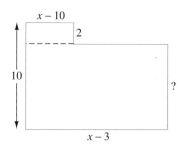

Solve. See Example 3.

9. Four times the difference of a number and 2 is the same as 6 times the number, increased by 2. Find the number.

10. Twice the sum of a number and 3 is the same as 1 subtracted from the number. Find the number.

11. One number is 5 times another number. If the sum of the two numbers is 270, find the numbers.

12. One number is 6 less than another number. If the sum of the two numbers is 150, find the numbers.

Solve. See Example 4.

13. Find 30% of 260.

14. Find 70% of 180.

15. Find 12% of 16.

16. Find 22% of 12.

17. The United States consists of 2271 million acres of land. Approximately 29% of this land is federally owned. Find the number of acres that are federally owned. (*Source:* U.S. General Services Administration)

18. The state of Nevada contains the most federally owned acres of land in the United States. If 90% of the state's 70 million acres of land is federally owned, find the number of federally owned acres. (*Source:* U.S. General Services Administration)

Nevada

19. Recently, 47% of homes in the United States contained computers. If Charlotte, North Carolina, contains 110,000 homes, how many of these homes would you expect to have computers? (*Source:* Telecommunication Research survey)

20. Recently, 26% of homes in the United States contained online services. If Abilene, Texas, contains 40,000 homes, how many of these homes would you expect to have online services? (*Source:* TelecommunicationResearch survey)

The following graph is called a circle graph or a pie chart. The circle represents a whole, or in this case, 100%. This particular graph shows the kind of loans that customers get from credit unions. Use this graph to answer Exercises 21–24.

Credit Union Loans

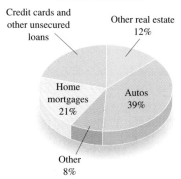

Credit cards and other unsecured loans

Other real estate 12%

Home mortgages 21%

Autos 39%

Other 8%

Source: National Credit Union Administration.

21. What percent of credit union loans are for credit cards and other unsecured loans?

22. What types of loans make up most credit union loans?

23. If the University of New Orleans Credit Union processed 300 loans last year, how many of these might we expect to be automobile loans?

24. If Homestead's Credit Union processed 537 loans last year, how many of these do you expect to be either home mortgages or other real estate? (Round to the nearest whole.)

Solve. See Examples 5 through 7.

25. The airports in Chicago, Atlanta, and Dallas/Ft. Worth have a total of 199 million annual arrivals and departures. Use this information and Example 2 in this section to find the number from each individual airport.

26. The perimeter of the triangle in Example 1b is 483 feet. Find the length of each side.

27. The B767-300ER aircraft has 104 more seats than the B737-200 aircraft. If their total number of seats is 328, find the number of seats for each aircraft. (*Source:* Air Transport Association of America)

28. The governor of Connecticut makes $29,000 less per year than the governor of Delaware. If the total of these salaries is $185,000, find the salary of each governor. (*Source: 2000 World Almanac*)

29. A new fax machine was recently purchased for an office in Hopedale for $464.40 including tax. If the tax rate in Hopedale is 8%, find the price of the fax machine before taxes.

30. A premedical student at a local university was complaining that she had just paid $86.11 for her human anatomy book, including tax. Find the price of the book before taxes if the tax rate at this university is 9%.

31. According to government statistics, the number of telephone company operators in the United States is expected to decrease to 26,000 by the year 2006. This represents a decrease of 47% from the number of telephone operators in 1996. (*Source:* U.S. Bureau of Labor Statistics)

a. Find the number of telephone company operators in 1996. Round to the nearest whole number.

b. In your own words, explain why you think that the need for telephone company operators is decreasing.

32. The number of deaths by tornadoes from the 1940s to the 1980s has decreased by 70.86%. There were 521 deaths from tornadoes in the 1980s. (*Source:* National Weather Service)

a. Find the number of deaths by tornadoes in the 1940s. Round to the nearest whole number.

b. In your own words, explain why you think that the number of deaths by tornadoes has decreased so much since the 1940s.

33. Manufacturers claim that a CD-ROM disc will last 20 years. Recently, statements made by the U.S. National Archives and Records Administration suggest that 20 years decreased by 75% is a more realistic lifespan because the aluminum substratum on which the data is recorded can be affected by oxidation. Find the lifespan of a CD-ROM according to the U.S. National Archives and Records Administration.

CD-ROM disc

34. In one year, 2.7% of India's forest was lost to deforestation. This percent represents 10,000 square kilometers of forest. Find the total square kilometers of forest in India before this decrease. (Round to the nearest whole square kilometer.)

35. Americans used computers to electronically file 21.1 million federal income tax returns in 1999. This represented a 24% increase over the previous year. How many federal income tax returns were filed electronically in 1998? Round to the nearest million. (*Source: Associated Press*, April, 1999)

36. HDPE (high-density polyethylene) plastics are used to make milk and water jugs, as well as bottles for juices and laundry detergents. When these types of bottles are recycled, they can be used to make bags, recycling bins, motor oil bottles, and agricultural pipe. HDPE bottle recycling increased 7% to 704 million pounds from 1996 to 1997. How many pounds of HDPE bottles were recycled in 1996? Round to the nearest million. (*Source:* American Plastics Council)

37. Two frames are needed with the same outside perimeter: one frame in the shape of a square and one in the shape of an equilateral triangle. Each side of the triangle is 6 centimeters longer than each side of the square. Find the dimensions of each frame.

38. The length of a rectangular sign is 2 feet less than three times its width. Find the dimensions if the perimeter is 28 feet.

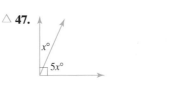

x feet

39. In a blueprint of a rectangular room, the length is to be 2 centimeters greater than twice its width. Find the dimensions if the perimeter is to be 40 centimeters.

40. A plant food solution contains 5 cups of water for every 1 cup of concentrate. If the solution contains 78 cups of these two ingredients, find the number of cups of concentrate in the solution.

41. The external tank of a NASA space shuttle contains the propellants used for the first 8.5 minutes after launch. Its height is 5 times the sum of its width and 1. If the sum of the height and width is 55.4 meters, find the dimensions of this tank.

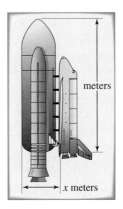

meters

x meters

42. The blue whale is the largest of the whales. Its average weight is 3 times the difference of the average weight of a humpback whale and 5 tons. If the total of the average weights is 117 tons, find the average weight of each type of whale.

Recall that the sum of the angle measures of a triangle is 180°.

43. Find the measures of the angles of a triangle if the measure of one angle is twice the measure of a second angle and the third angle measures 3 times the second angle decreased by 12.

44. Find the angles of a triangle whose two base angles are equal and whose third angle is 10° less than three times a base angle.

Recall that two angles are complements of each other if their sum is 90°. Two angles are supplements of each other if their sum is 180°. Find the measure of each angle.

45.

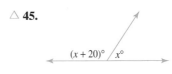

46.

47.

△ **48.**

△ **49.** One angle is three times its supplement increased by 20°. Find the measures of the two supplementary angles.

△ **50.** One angle is twice its complement increased by 30°. Find the measures of the two complementary angles.

Solve. Exercises 51–56 involve consecutive integers.

51. The sum of three consecutive integers is 228. Find the integers.

52. The sum of three consecutive odd integers is 327. Find the integers.

53. The zip codes of three Nevada locations—Fallon, Fernley, and Gardnerville Ranchos—are three consecutive even integers. If twice the first integer added to the third is 268,222, find each zip code.

54. During a recent year, the average SAT scores in math for the states of Alabama, Louisiana, and Michigan were 3 consecutive integers. If the sum of the first integer, second integer, and three times the third integer is 2637, find each score.

55. Determine whether there are three consecutive integers such that their sum is three times the second integer.

56. Determine whether there are two consecutive odd integers such that 7 times the first exceeds 5 times the second by 54.

To break even in a manufacturing business, income or revenue R must equal the cost of production C. Use this information for Exercises 57 through 62.

57. The cost C to produce x number of skateboards is $C = 100 + 20x$. The skateboards are sold wholesale for $24 each, so revenue R is given by $R = 24x$. Find how many skateboards the manufacturer needs to produce and sell to break even. (*Hint:* Set the cost expression equal to the revenue expression and solve for x.)

58. The revenue R from selling x number of computer boards is given by $R = 60x$, and the cost C of producing them is given by $C = 50x + 5000$. Find how many boards must be sold to break even. Find how much money is needed to produce the break-even number of boards.

59. The cost C of producing x number of paperback books is given by $C = 4.50x + 2400$. Income R from these books is given by $R = 7.50x$. Find how many books should be produced and sold to break even.

60. Find the break-even quantity for a company that makes x number of computer monitors at a cost C given by $C = 875 + 70x$ and receives revenue R given by $R = 105x$.

61. In your own words, explain what happens if a company makes and sells fewer products than the break-even point.

62. In your own words, explain what happens if more products than the break-even point are made and sold.

△ **63.** Newsprint is either discarded or recycled. Americans recycle about 27% of all newsprint, but an amount of newsprint equivalent to 30 million trees is discarded every year. About how many trees' worth of newsprint is *recycled* in the United States each year? (*Source:* The Earth Works Group)

△ **64.** Find an angle such that its supplement is equal to twice its complement increased by 50°.

REVIEW EXERCISES

Find the value of the following expressions for the given values. See Section 1.3.

65. $2a + b - c$; $a = 5$, $b = -1$, and $c = 3$

66. $-3a + 2c - b$; $a = -2$; $b = 6$, and $c = -7$

67. $4ab - 3bc$; $a = -5$, $b = -8$, and $c = 2$

68. $ab + 6bc$; $a = 0$, $b = -1$ and $c = 9$

69. $n^2 - m^2$; $n = -3$ and $m = -8$

70. $2n^2 + 3m^2$; $n = -2$ and $m = 7$

Use a calculator to find the value of the following expressions for the given values. See Section 1.3.

71. $P + Prt$; $P = 3000$, $r = 0.0325$, $t = 2$

72. $\frac{1}{3}lwh$; $l = 37.8$, $w = 5.6$, $h = 7.9$

73. $\frac{1}{3}Bh$; $B = 53.04$, $h = 6.89$

74. $\left(1 + \dfrac{r}{n}\right)^{nt}$; $r = 0.06$, $n = 3$, $t = 1$

2.3 FORMULAS AND PROBLEM SOLVING

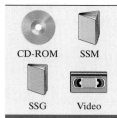

CD-ROM SSM

SSG Video

▶ **OBJECTIVES**

1. Solve a formula for a specified variable.
2. Use formulas to solve problems.

1 Solving problems that we encounter in the real world sometimes requires us to express relationships among measured quantities. A **formula** is an equation that describes a known relationship among quantities such as time, area, and gravity. Some examples of formulas are

Formula	*Meaning*
$I = PRT$	Interest = principal · rate · time
$A = lw$	Area of a rectangle = length · width
$d = rt$	Distance = rate · time
$C = 2\pi r$	Circumference of a circle = $2 \cdot \pi \cdot$ radius
$V = lwh$	Volume of a rectangular solid = length · width · height

Other formulas are listed in the front cover of this text. Notice that the formula for the volume of a rectangular solid $V = lwh$ is solved for V since V is by itself on one side of the equation with no V's on the other side of the equation. Suppose that the volume of a rectangular solid is known as well as its width and its length, and we wish to find its height. One way to find its height is to begin by solving the formula $V = lwh$ for h.

△ **Example 1** Solve $V = lwh$ for h.

Solution To solve $V = lwh$ for h, isolate h on one side of the equation. To do so, divide both sides of the equation by lw.

$$V = lwh$$

$$\frac{V}{lw} = \frac{lwh}{lw} \qquad \text{Divide both sides by } lw.$$

$$\frac{V}{lw} = h \qquad \text{Simplify.}$$

Then to find the height of a rectangular solid, divide the volume by the product of its length and its width. ■

The following steps may be used to solve formulas and equations in general for a specified variable.

SOLVING EQUATIONS FOR A SPECIFIED VARIABLE

Step 1: Clear the equation of fractions by multiplying each side of the equation by the least common denominator.

Step 2: Use the distributive property to remove grouping symbols such as parentheses.

Step 3: Combine like terms on each side of the equation.

Step 4: Use the addition property of equality to rewrite the equation as an equivalent equation with terms containing the specified variable on one side and all other terms on the other side.

Step 5: Use the distributive property and the multiplication property of equality to isolate the specified variable.

Example 2 Solve $3y - 2x = 7$ for y.

Solution This is a linear equation in two variables. Often an equation such as this is solved for y in order to reveal some properties about the graph of this equation, which we will learn more about in Chapter 3. Since there are no fractions or grouping symbols, we begin with Step 4 and isolate the term containing the specified variable y by adding $2x$ to both sides of the equation.

$$3y - 2x = 7$$

$$3y - 2x + 2x = 7 + 2x \qquad \text{Add } 2x \text{ to both sides.}$$

$$3y = 7 + 2x$$

To solve for y, divide both sides by 3.

$$\frac{3y}{3} = \frac{7 + 2x}{3} \qquad \text{Divide both sides by 3.}$$

$$y = \frac{2x + 7}{3} \quad \text{or} \quad y = \frac{2x}{3} + \frac{7}{3}$$

△ **Example 3** Solve $A = \dfrac{1}{2}(B + b)h$ for b.

Solution Since this formula for finding the area of a trapezoid contains fractions, we begin by multiplying both sides of the equation by the LCD 2.

$$A = \frac{1}{2}(B + b)h$$

$$2 \cdot A = 2 \cdot \frac{1}{2}(B + b)h \qquad \text{Multiply both sides by 2.}$$

$$2A = (B + b)h \qquad \text{Simplify.}$$

Next, use the distributive property and remove parentheses.

$$2A = (B + b)h$$

$$2A = Bh + bh \qquad \text{Apply the distributive property.}$$

$$2A - Bh = bh \qquad \begin{array}{l}\text{Isolate the term containing } b \text{ by} \\ \text{subtracting } Bh \text{ from both sides.}\end{array}$$

$$\frac{2A - Bh}{h} = \frac{bh}{h} \qquad \text{Divide both sides by } h.$$

$$\frac{2A - Bh}{h} = b, \quad \text{or} \quad b = \frac{2A - Bh}{h}$$

HELPFUL HINT

Remember that we may isolate the specified variable on either side of the equation.

2

In this section, we also solve problems that can be modeled by known formulas. We use the same problem-solving steps that were introduced in the previous section.

Formulas are very useful in problem solving. For example, the compound interest formula

$$A = P\left(1 + \frac{r}{n}\right)^{nt}$$

is used by banks to compute the amount A in an account that pays compound interest. The variable P represents the principal or amount invested in the account, r is the annual rate of interest, t is the time in years, and n is the number of times compounded per year.

Example 4   **FINDING THE AMOUNT IN A SAVINGS ACCOUNT**

Marial Callier just received an inheritance of $10,000 and plans to place all the money in a savings account that pays 5% compounded quarterly to help her son go to college in 3 years. How much money will be in the account in 3 years?

Solution   1. UNDERSTAND. Read and reread the problem. The appropriate formula needed to solve this problem is the compound interest formula

$$A = P\left(1 + \frac{r}{n}\right)^{nt}$$

Make sure that you understand the meaning of all the variables in this formula.

$$A = \text{amount in the account after } t \text{ years}$$
$$P = \text{principal or amount invested}$$
$$t = \text{time in years}$$
$$r = \text{annual rate of interest}$$
$$n = \text{number of times compounded per year}$$

2. TRANSLATE. Use the compound interest formula and let $P = \$10{,}000$, $r = 5\% = 0.05$, $t = 3$ years, and $n = 4$ since the account is compounded quarterly, or 4 times a year.

Formula: $A = P\left(1 + \dfrac{r}{n}\right)^{nt}$

Substitute: $A = 10{,}000\left(1 + \dfrac{0.05}{4}\right)^{4 \cdot 3}$

3. SOLVE. We simplify the right side of the equation.

$$A = 10{,}000\left(1 + \dfrac{0.05}{4}\right)^{4 \cdot 3}$$

$$A = 10{,}000(1.0125)^{12} \qquad \text{Simplify } 1 + \dfrac{0.05}{4} \text{ and write } 4 \cdot 3 \text{ as } 12.$$

$$A \approx 10{,}000(1.160754518) \qquad \text{Approximate } (1.0125)^{12}.$$
$$A \approx 11{,}607.55 \qquad \text{Multiply and round to two decimal places.}$$

4. INTERPRET.

Check: Repeat your calculations to make sure that no error was made. Notice that $\$11{,}607.55$ is a reasonable amount to have in the account after 3 years.

State: In 3 years, the account will contain $\$11{,}607.55$.   ▬

Example 5   FINDING CYCLING TIME

The fastest average speed by a cyclist across the continental United States is 15.4 mph, by Pete Penseyres. If he traveled a total distance of about 3107.5 miles at this speed, find his time cycling. Write the time in days, hours, and minutes. *(Source: The Guinness Book of World Records, 1998)*

Solution   1. UNDERSTAND. Read and reread the problem. The appropriate formula needed is the distance formula

$$d = rt \qquad \text{where}$$
$$d = \text{distance traveled} \quad r = \text{rate} \quad \text{and} \quad t = \text{time}$$

2. TRANSLATE. Use the distance formula and let $d = 3107.5$ miles and $r = 15.4$ mph.

Formula: $d = rt$

Substitute: $3107.5 = 15.4t$

3. SOLVE.

$$\frac{3107.5}{15.4} = \frac{15.4t}{15.4} \qquad \text{Divide both sides by 15.4.}$$
$$201.79 \approx t$$

The time is approximately 201.79 hours. Since there are 24 hours in a day, we divide 201.79 by 24 and find that the time is approximately 8.41 days. Now, let's convert the decimal part of 8.41 days back to hours. To do this, multiply 0.41 by 24 and the result is 9.84 hours. Next, we convert the decimal part of 9.84 hours to minutes by multiplying by 60 since there an 60 minutes in an hour. We have $0.84 \cdot 60 \approx 50$ minutes rounded to the nearest whole. The time is then approximately

8 days, 9 hours, 50 minutes.

4. INTERPRET.

Check: Repeat your calculations to make sure that an error was not made.

State: Pete Penseyres's cycling time was approximately 8 days, 9 hours, 50 minutes.

SPOTLIGHT ON DECISION MAKING

Suppose you are a dentist. Although fluoride can play an important part in a treatment plan to prevent tooth decay, you know that large doses of fluoride can be lethal. The formula $F = 10qpr$ can be used to calculate the number of milligrams (mg) of fluoride F ingested by a patient who receives q milliliters of a fluoride solution with p percent concentration and molecular weight ratio r. The molecular weight ratios for common fluoride compounds are given in Table 1. Table 2 shows the maximum safe doses of fluoride for children, along with certainly lethal doses.

    Decide whether or not a fluoride treatment of 5 milliliters of an 8 percent SnF_2 solution is safe for a 50-pound child.

MOLECULAR WEIGHT RATIOS

Fluoride Compound	Ratio
NaF	$\dfrac{1}{2.2}$
Na_2FPO_3	$\dfrac{1}{7.6}$
SnF_2	$\dfrac{1}{4.1}$

FLUORIDE DOSES FOR CHILDREN

Weight (pounds)	Maximum Safe Dose (mg)	Certainly Lethal Dose (mg)
20	73	291
30	109	436
40	146	582
50	182	727
60	218	873
70	255	1018
80	291	1163
90	327	1309
100	363	1454

(*Source*: Based on data from S.B. Heifetz and H.S Horowitz. "The Amounts of Fluoride in Current Fluoride Therapies: Safety Considerations for Children," *ASDC J. Dent. Child.*, July–Aug. 1984.)

MENTAL MATH

Solve each equation for the specified variable. See Examples 1 through 3.

1. $2x + y = 5$; for y

2. $7x - y = 3$; for y

3. $a - 5b = 8$; for a

4. $7r + s = 10$; for s

5. $5j + k - h = 6$; for k

6. $w - 4y + z = 0$; for z

Exercise Set 2.3

Solve each equation for the specified variable. See Examples 1–3.

1. $D = rt$; for t

2. $W = gh$; for g

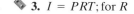 **3.** $I = PRT$; for R

△ **4.** $V = lwh$; for l

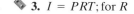 **5.** $9x - 4y = 16$; for y

6. $2x + 3y = 17$; for y

△ **7.** $P = 2L + 2W$; for W

8. $A = 3M - 2N$; for N

9. $J = AC - 3$; for A

10. $y = mx + b$; for x

11. $W = gh - 3gt^2$; for g

12. $A = Prt + P$; for P

13. $T = C(2 + AB)$; for B

14. $A = 5H(b + B)$; for b

△ **15.** $C = 2\pi r$; for r

△ **16.** $S = 2\pi r^2 + 2\pi rh$; for h

17. $E = I(r + R)$; for r

18. $A = P(1 + rt)$; for t

19. $s = \dfrac{n}{2}(a + L)$; for L

20. $\dfrac{3}{4}(b - 2c) = a$; for b

21. $N = 3st^4 - 5sv$; for v

22. $L = a + (n - 1)d$; for d

△ **23.** $S = 2LW + 2LH + 2WH$; for H

24. $T = 3vs - 4ws + 5vw$; for v

In this exercise set, round all dollar amounts to two decimal places. Solve. See Example 4.

 25. Complete the table and find the balance A if \$3500 is invested at an annual percentage rate of 3% for 10 years and compounded n times a year.

n	1	2	4	12	365
A					

 26. Complete the table and find the balance A if \$5000 is invested at an annual percentage rate of 6% for 15 years and compounded n times a year.

n	1	2	4	12	365
A					

27. If you are investing money in a savings account paying a rate of r, which account should you choose—an account compounded 4 times a year or 12 times a year? Explain your choice.

28. To borrow money at a rate of r, which bank should you choose—one compounding 4 times a year or 12 times a year? Explain your choice.

 29. A principal of \$6000 is invested in an account paying an annual percentage rate of 4%. Find the amount in the account after 5 years if the account is compounded
   a. semiannually
   b. quarterly
   c. monthly

30. A principal of \$25,000 is invested in an account paying an annual percentage rate of 5%. Find the amount in the account after 2 years if the account is compounded
   a. semiannually
   b. quarterly
   c. monthly

Solve. See Examples 4 and 5.

31. The day's high temperature in Phoenix, Arizona, was recorded as 104°F. Write 104°F as degrees Celsius.

32. The annual low temperature in Nome, Alaska, was recorded as −15°C. Write −15°C as degrees Fahrenheit.

33. Omaha, Nebraska, is about 90 miles from Lincoln, Nebraska. Irania must go to the law library in Lincoln to get a document for the law firm she works for. Find how long it takes her to drive round-trip if she averages 50 mph.

34. It took the Selby family $5\frac{1}{2}$ hours round-trip to drive from their house to their beach house 154 miles away. Find their average speed.

△ **35.** A package of floor tiles contains 24 one-foot-square tiles. Find how many packages should be bought to cover a square ballroom floor whose side measures 64 feet.

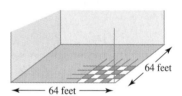

64 feet

64 feet

△ **36.** One-foot-square ceiling tiles are sold in packages of 50. Find how many packages must be bought for a rectangular ceiling 18 feet by 12 feet.

△ **37.** The deepest hole in the ocean floor is beneath the Pacific Ocean and is called Hole 504B. It is located off the coast of Ecuador. Scientists are drilling it to learn more about the Earth's history. Currently, the hole is in the shape of a cylinder whose volume is approximately 3800 cubic feet and whose length is 1.3 miles. Find the radius of the hole to the nearest hundredth of a foot. (*Hint:* Make sure the same units of measurement are used.)

38. The deepest man-made hole is called the Kola Superdeep Borehole. It is approximately 8 miles deep and is located near a small Russian town in the Arctic Circle. If it takes 7.5 hours to remove the drill from the bottom of the hole, find the rate that the drill can be retrieved in feet per second. Round to the nearest tenth. (*Hint:* Write 8 miles as feet, 7.5 hours as seconds, then use the formula $d = rt$.)

39. On April 1, 1985, *Sports Illustrated* published an April Fool's story by writer George Plimpton. He wrote that the New York Mets had discovered a man who could throw a 168-miles-per-hour fast ball. If the distance from the pitcher's mound to the plate is 60.5 feet, how long would it take for a ball thrown at that rate to travel that distance? (*Hint:* Write the rate 168 miles per hour in feet per second.

$$168 \text{ miles per hour} = \frac{168 \text{ miles}}{1 \text{ hour}}$$

$$= \frac{\_\_ \text{ feet}}{\_\_ \text{ seconds}}$$

$$= \frac{\_\_ \text{ feet}}{1 \text{ second}}$$

$$= \_\_ \text{ feet per second.}$$

Then use the formula $d = r \cdot t$.)

40. In 1945, Arthur C. Clarke, a scientist and science-fiction writer, predicted that an artificial satellite placed at a height of 22,248 miles directly above the equator would orbit the globe at the same speed with which the Earth was rotating. This belt along the equator is known as the Clarke belt. Use the formula for circumference of a circle and find the "length" of the Clarke belt. (*Hint:* Recall that the radius of the Earth is approximately 4000 miles. Round to the nearest whole mile.)

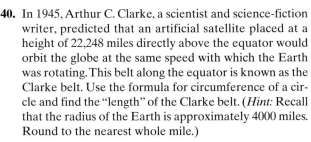

22,248 miles

41. Eartha is the world's largest globe. It is located at the headquarters of DeLorme, a mapmaking company in Yarmouth, Maine. Eartha is 41.125 feet in diameter. Find its exact circumference (distance around) and then approximate its circumference using 3.14 for π. (*Source:* DeLorme)

42. Eartha is in the shape of a sphere. Its radius is about 20.6 feet. Approximate its volume to the nearest cubic foot. (*Source:* DeLorme)

43. How much do you think it costs each American to build a space shuttle? Write down your estimate. The space shuttle *Endeavour* was completed in 1992 and cost approximately $1.7 billion. If the population of the United States in 1992 was 250 million, find the cost per person to build the *Endeavour*. How close was your estimate?

44. An orbit such as Clarke's belt in Exercise 40 is called a geostationary orbit. In your own words, why do you think that communications satellites are placed in geostationary orbits?

45. Find *how much interest* $10,000 earns in 2 years in a certificate of deposit paying 8.5% interest compounded quarterly.

46. Bryan, Eric, Mandy, and Melissa would like to go to Disneyland in 3 years. Their total cost should be $4500. If each invests $1000 in a savings account paying 5.5% interest, compounded semiannually, will they have enough in 3 years?

47. A gallon of latex paint can cover 500 square feet. Find how many gallon containers of paint should be bought to paint two coats on each wall of a rectangular room whose dimensions are 14 feet by 16 feet (assume 8-foot ceilings).

48. A gallon of enamel paint can cover 300 square feet. Find how many gallon containers of paint should be bought to paint three coats on a wall measuring 21 feet by 8 feet.

49. A portion of the external tank of the Space Shuttle *Endeavour* is a liquid hydrogen tank. If the ends of the tank are hemispheres, find the volume of the tank. To do so, answer parts a through c.

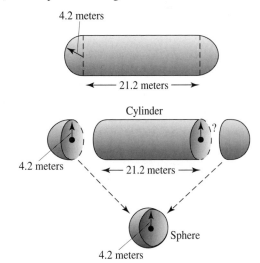

4.2 meters

21.2 meters

Cylinder

4.2 meters

21.2 meters

Sphere

4.2 meters

a. Find the volume of the cylinder shown. Round to 2 decimal places.

b. Find the volume of the sphere shown. Round to 2 decimal places.

c. Add the results of parts a and b. This sum is the approximate volume of the tank.

50. The space probe *Pioneer 10* traveled from Mars to Jupiter, a distance of 619 million miles, in 21 months. Find the average speed of the probe in miles per hour. (*Hint:* Convert 21 months to hours [using 1 month = 30 days] and then use the formula $d = rt$.)

51. Find how long it takes Mark to drive 135 miles on I-10 if he merges onto I-10 at 10 A.M. and drives nonstop with his cruise control set on 60 mph.

52. If the area of a triangular kite is 18 square feet and its base is 4 feet, find the height of the kite.

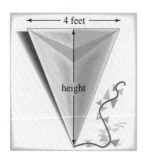

53. The Cassini spacecraft mission to Saturn was launched October 15, 1997. It will take more than six and a half years to reach Saturn, arriving in July 2004. During its mission, Cassini will travel a total distance of 2 billion miles in 80.5 months. Find the average speed of the spacecraft in miles per hour. (*Hint:* Convert 80.5 months to hours using 1 month = 30 days and then use the formula $d = rt$.) (*Source:* NASA Jet Propulsion Laboratory)

54. The Space Shuttle *Endeavour* has a cargo bay that is in the shape of a cylinder whose length is 18.3 meters and whose diameter is 4.6 meters. Find its volume.

55. Solar system distances are so great that units other than miles or kilometers are often used. For example, the astronomical unit (AU) is the average distance between the Earth and the Sun, or 92,900,000 miles. Use this information to convert each planet's distance in miles from the Sun to astronomical units. Round to three decimal places.

	Miles from the Sun	AU from the Sun
Mercury	36 million	
Venus	67.2 million	
Earth	92.9 million	
Mars	141.5 million	
Jupiter	483.3 million	
Saturn	886.1 million	
Uranus	1783 million	
Neptune	2793 million	
Pluto	3670 million	

*The measure of the chance or likelihood of an event occurring is its **probability**. A formula basic to the study of probability is the formula for the probability of an event when all the outcomes are equally likely. This formula is*

$$Probability\ of\ an\ event = \frac{number\ of\ ways\ that\ the\ event\ can\ occur}{number\ of\ possible\ outcomes}$$

For example, to find the probability that a single spin on the spinner will result in red, notice first that the spinner is divided into 8 parts, so there are 8 possible outcomes. Next, notice that there is only one sector of the spinner colored red, so the number of ways that the spinner can land on red is 1. Then this probability denoted by P(red) is

$$P(red) = \frac{1}{8}$$

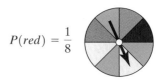

Find each probability in simplest form.

56. P(green)

57. P(yellow)

58. P(black)

59. P(blue)

60. P(green or blue)

61. P(black or yellow)

62. P(red, green, or black)

63. P(yellow, blue, or black)

64. P(white)

65. P(red, yellow, green, blue, or black)

66. From the previous probability formula, what do you think is always the probability of an event that is impossible occuring?

67. What do you think is always the probability of an event that is sure to occur?

REVIEW EXERCISES

Determine which numbers in the set $\{-3, -2, -1, 0, 1, 2, 3\}$ are solutions of each inequality.

68. $x < 0$ **69.** $x > 1$

70. $x + 5 \leq 6$ **71.** $x - 3 \geq -7$

72. In your own words, explain what real numbers are solutions of $x < 0$.

73. In your own words, explain what real numbers are solutions of $x > 1$.

2.4 LINEAR INEQUALITIES AND PROBLEM SOLVING

CD-ROM   SSM

SSG   Video

▶ **OBJECTIVES**

1. Use interval notation.
2. Solve linear inequalities using the addition property of inequality.
3. Solve linear inequalities using the multiplication property of inequality.
4. Solve problems that can be modeled by linear inequalities.

1

Relationships among measureable quantities are not always described by equations. For example, suppose that a salesperson earns a base of $600 per month plus a commission of 20% of sales. Find the minimum amount of sales needed to receive a total income of *at least* $1500 per month. Here, the phrase "at least" implies that an income of $1500 *or more* is acceptable. In symbols, we can write

$$\text{income} \geq 1500$$

This is an example of an inequality, and we will solve this problem in Example 8.

A **linear inequality** is similar to a linear equation except that the equality symbol is replaced with an inequality symbol, such as $<, >, \leq,$ or $\geq$.

Linear Inequalities in One Variable

$3x + 5 \geq 4$	$2y < 0$	$3(x - 4) > 5x$	$\dfrac{x}{3} \leq 5$
↑	↑	↑	↑
is greater than or equal to	is less than	is greater than	is less than or equal to

LINEAR INEQUALITY IN ONE VARIABLE

A linear inequality in one variable is an inequality that can be written in the form

$$ax + b < c$$

where a, b, and c are real numbers and $a \neq 0$.

In this section, when we make definitions, state properties, or list steps about an inequality containing the symbol $<$, we mean that the definition, property, or steps apply to inequalities containing the symbols $>$, $\leq$ and $\geq$ also.

A **solution** of an inequality is a value of the variable that makes the inequality a true statement. The **solution set** of an inequality is the set of all solutions. Notice that the solution set of the inequality $x > 2$, for example, contains all numbers greater than 2. Its graph is an interval on the number line since an infinite number of values satisfy the variable. If we use open/closed-circle notation, the graph of $\{x \mid x > 2\}$ looks like the following.

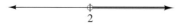

2

In this text, a convenient notation, called **interval notation**, will be used to write solution sets of inequalities. To help us understand this notation, a different graphing notation will be used. Instead of an open circle, we use a parenthesis; instead of a closed circle, we use a bracket. With this new notation, the graph of $\{x \mid x > 2\}$ now looks like

2

and can be represented in interval notation as $(2, \infty)$. The symbol ∞ is read "infinity" and indicates that the interval includes *all* numbers greater than 2. The left parenthesis indicates that 2 *is not* included in the interval. Using a left bracket, [, would indicate that 2 *is* included in the interval. The following table shows three equivalent ways to describe an interval: in set notation, as a graph, and in interval notation.

Set Notation	*Graph*	*Interval Notation*
$\{x \mid x < a\}$	⟵———)———⟶ a	$(-\infty, a)$
$\{x \mid x > a\}$	⟵———(———⟶ a	(a, ∞)
$\{x \mid x \leq a\}$	⟵———]———⟶ a	$(-\infty, a]$
$\{x \mid x \geq a\}$	⟵———[———⟶ a	$[a, \infty)$
$\{x \mid a < x < b\}$	⟵——(——)——⟶ a b	(a, b)
$\{x \mid a \leq x \leq b\}$	⟵——[——]——⟶ a b	$[a, b]$
$\{x \mid a < x \leq b\}$	⟵——(——]——⟶ a b	$(a, b]$
$\{x \mid a \leq x < b\}$	⟵——[——)——⟶ a b	$[a, b)$

> ▼
> **HELPFUL HINT**
> Notice that a parenthesis is always used to enclose ∞ and −∞.

Example 1 Graph each set on a number line and then write in interval notation.

a. $\{x \mid x \geq 2\}$ **b.** $\{x \mid x < -1\}$ **c.** $\{x \mid 0.5 < x \leq 3\}$

Solution **a.**

$[2, \infty)$

b.

$(-\infty, -1)$

c.

$(0.5, 3]$

2 Interval notation can be used to write solutions of linear inequalities. To solve a linear inequality, we use a process similar to the one used to solve a linear equation. We use properties of inequalities to write equivalent inequalities until the variable is isolated.

ADDITION PROPERTY OF INEQUALITY

If a, b, and c are real numbers, then

$$a < b \quad \text{and} \quad a + c < b + c$$

are equivalent inequalities.

In other words, we may add the same real number to both sides of an inequality and the resulting inequality will have the same solution set. This property also allows us to subtract the same real number from both sides.

Example 2 Solve $x - 2 < 5$. Graph the solution set.

Solution
$$x - 2 < 5$$
$$x - 2 + 2 < 5 + 2 \qquad \text{Add 2 to both sides.}$$
$$x < 7 \qquad \text{Simplify.}$$

The solution set is $\{x \mid x < 7\}$, which in interval notation is $(-\infty, 7)$. The graph of the solution set is

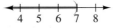

> **HELPFUL HINT**
> In Example 2, the solution set is $\{x \mid x < 7\}$. This means that *all* numbers less than 7 are solutions. For example, $6.9, 0, -\pi, 1$, and -56.7 are solutions, just to name a few. To see this, replace x in $x - 2 < 5$ with each of these numbers and see that the result is a true inequality.

Example 3   Solve $3x + 4 \geq 2x - 6$. Graph the solution set.

Solution

$$3x + 4 \geq 2x - 6$$
$$3x + 4 - 2x \geq 2x - 6 - 2x \qquad \text{Subtract } 2x \text{ from both sides.}$$
$$x + 4 \geq -6 \qquad \text{Combine like terms.}$$
$$x + 4 - 4 \geq -6 - 4 \qquad \text{Subtract 4 from both sides.}$$
$$x \geq -10 \qquad \text{Simplify.}$$

The solution set is $\{x \mid x \geq -10\}$, which in interval notation is $[-10, \infty)$. The graph of the solution set is

$$-11 \quad -10 \quad -9 \quad -8 \quad -7 \quad -6$$

3   Next, we introduce and use the multiplication property of inequality to solve linear inequalities. To understand this property, let's start with the true statement $-3 < 7$ and multiply both sides by 2.

$$-3 < 7$$
$$-3(2) < 7(2) \qquad \text{Multiply by 2.}$$
$$-6 < 14 \qquad \text{True.}$$

The statement remains true.

   Notice what happens if both sides of $-3 < 7$ are multiplied by -2.

$$-3 < 7$$
$$-3(-2) < 7(-2) \qquad \text{Multiply by } -2.$$
$$6 < -14 \qquad \textbf{False.}$$

The inequality $6 < -14$ is a false statement. However, **if the direction of the inequality sign is reversed**, the result is

$$6 > -14 \qquad \text{True.}$$

These examples suggest the following property.

MULTIPLICATION PROPERTY OF INEQUALITY

If a, b, and c are real numbers and c is **positive**, then
$a < b$ and $ac < bc$ are equivalent inequalities.
If a, b, and c are real numbers and c is **negative**, then
$a < b$ and $ac > bc$ are equivalent inequalities.

In other words, we may multiply both sides of an inequality by the same positive real number and the result is an equivalent inequality.

We may also multiply both sides of an inequality by the same **negative number** and **reverse the direction of the inequality symbol**, and the result is an equivalent inequality. The multiplication property holds for division also, since division is defined in terms of multiplication.

> **HELPFUL HINT**
> Whenever both sides of an inequality are multiplied or divided by a negative number, the direction of the inequality symbol **must be** reversed to form an equivalent inequality.

Example 4   Solve and graph the solution set.

a. $\dfrac{1}{4}x \leq \dfrac{3}{8}$ **b.** $-2.3x < 6.9$

Solution   **a.**

$$\frac{1}{4}x \leq \frac{3}{8}$$

> **HELPFUL HINT**
> The inequality symbol is the same since we are multiplying by a *positive* number.

$$4 \cdot \frac{1}{4}x \leq 4 \cdot \frac{3}{8} \qquad \text{Multiply both sides by 4.}$$

$$x \leq \frac{3}{2} \qquad \text{Simplify.}$$

The solution set is $\left\{ x \mid x \leq \dfrac{3}{2} \right\}$, which in interval notation is $\left(-\infty, \dfrac{3}{2} \right]$. The graph of the solution set is

b.

$$-2.3x < 6.9$$

> **HELPFUL HINT**
> The inequality symbol is *reversed* since we divided by a *negative* number.

$$\frac{-2.3x}{-2.3} > \frac{6.9}{-2.3} \qquad \begin{array}{l} \text{Divide both sides by } -2.3 \text{ and} \\ \text{reverse the inequality symbol.} \end{array}$$

$$x > -3 \qquad \text{Simplify.}$$

The solution set is $\{x \mid x > -3\}$, which is $(-3, \infty)$ in interval notation. The graph of the solution set is

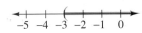

To solve linear inequalities in general, we follow steps similar to those for solving linear equations.

SOLVING A LINEAR INEQUALITY IN ONE VARIABLE

Step 1: Clear the equation of fractions by multiplying both sides of the inequality by the least common denominator (LCD) of all fractions in the inequality.

Step 2: Use the distributive property to remove grouping symbols such as parentheses.

Step 3: Combine like terms on each side of the inequality.

Step 4: Use the addition property of inequality to write the inequality as an equivalent inequality with variable terms on one side and numbers on the other side.

Step 5: Use the multiplication property of inequality to isolate the variable.

Example 5   Solve $-(x - 3) + 2 \le 3(2x - 5) + x$.

Solution

$$-(x - 3) + 2 \le 3(2x - 5) + x$$

$$-x + 3 + 2 \le 6x - 15 + x \qquad \text{Apply the distributive property.}$$

$$5 - x \le 7x - 15 \qquad \text{Combine like terms.}$$

$$5 - x + x \le 7x - 15 + x \qquad \text{Add } x \text{ to both sides.}$$

$$5 \le 8x - 15 \qquad \text{Combine like terms.}$$

$$5 + 15 \le 8x - 15 + 15 \qquad \text{Add 15 to both sides.}$$

$$20 \le 8x \qquad \text{Combine like terms.}$$

$$\frac{20}{8} \le \frac{8x}{8} \qquad \text{Divide both sides by 8.}$$

$$\frac{5}{2} \le x, \quad \text{or } x \ge \frac{5}{2} \qquad \text{Simplify.}$$

> ▼ **HELPFUL HINT**
>
> Don't forget that $\frac{5}{2} \le x$ means the same as $x \ge \frac{5}{2}$.

The solution set written in interval notation is $\left[\frac{5}{2}, \infty \right)$, and its graph is

Example 6   Solve $\frac{2}{5}(x - 6) \ge x - 1$

Solution

$$\frac{2}{5}(x - 6) \geq x - 1$$

$$5\left[\frac{2}{5}(x - 6)\right] \geq 5(x - 1) \qquad \text{Multiply both sides by 5 to eliminate fractions.}$$

$$2x - 12 \geq 5x - 5 \qquad \text{Apply the distributive property.}$$

$$-3x - 12 \geq -5 \qquad \text{Subtract } 5x \text{ from both sides.}$$

$$-3x \geq 7 \qquad \text{Add 12 to both sides.}$$

$$\frac{-3x}{-3} \leq \frac{7}{-3} \qquad \text{Divide both sides by } -3 \text{ and reverse the inequality symbol.}$$

$$x \leq -\frac{7}{3} \qquad \text{Simplify.}$$

The solution set written in interval notation is $\left(-\infty, -\frac{7}{3}\right]$, and its graph is

Example 7   Solve $2(x + 3) > 2x + 1$.

Solution

$$2(x + 3) > 2x + 1$$
$$2x + 6 > 2x + 1 \qquad \text{Distribute on the left side.}$$
$$2x + 6 - 2x > 2x + 1 - 2x \qquad \text{Subtract } 2x \text{ from both sides.}$$
$$6 > 1 \qquad \text{Simplify.}$$

$6 > 1$ is a true statement for all values of x, so this inequality and the original inequality are true for all numbers. The solution set is $\{x \mid x \text{ is a real number}\}$, or $(-\infty, \infty)$ in interval notation, and its graph is

4   Application problems containing words such as "at least," "at most," "between," "no more than," and "no less than" usually indicate that an inequality be solved instead of an equation. In solving applications involving linear inequalities, we use the same procedure as when we solved applications involving linear equations.

Example 8   **CALCULATING INCOME WITH COMMISSION**

A salesperson earns \$600 per month plus a commission of 20% of sales. Find the minimum amount of sales needed to receive a total income of at least \$1500 per month.

Solution   1. UNDERSTAND. Read and reread the problem. Let x = amount of sales

2. **TRANSLATE.** As stated in the beginning of this section, we want the income to be greater than or equal to $1500. To write an inequality, notice that the sales person's income consists of $600 plus a commission (20% of sales).

In words:

600	+	commission (20% of sales)	≥	1500
↓		↓		↓

Translate: 600   + $0.20x$ ≥   1500

3. **SOLVE** the inequality for x.

$$600 + 0.20x \geq 1500$$
$$600 + 0.20x - 600 \geq 1500 - 600$$
$$0.20x \geq 900$$
$$x \geq 4500$$

4. **INTERPRET.**

   Check: The income for sales of $4500 is

$$600 + 0.20(4500), \text{ or } 1500.$$

   Thus, if sales are greater than or equal to $4500, income is greater than or equal to $1500.

   State: The minimum amount of sales needed for the salesperson to earn at least $1500 per month is $4500 per month.

Example 9   **FINDING THE ANNUAL CONSUMPTION**

In the United States, the annual consumption of cigarettes is declining. The consumption c in billions of cigarettes per year since the year 1985 can be approximated by the formula

$$c = -14.25t + 598.69$$

where t is the number of years after 1985. Use this formula to predict the years that the consumption of cigarettes will be less than 200 billion per year.

Solution   1. **UNDERSTAND.** Read and reread the problem. To become familiar with the given formula, let's find the cigarette consumption after 20 years, which would be the year 1985 + 20, or 2005. To do so, we substitute 20 for t in the given formula.

$$c = -14.25(20) + 598.69 = 313.69$$

Thus, in 2005, we predict cigarette consumption to be about 313.69 billion.

Variables have already been assigned in the given formula. For review, they are

c = the annual consumption of cigarettes in the United States in billions of cigarettes

t = the number of years after 1985

2. **TRANSLATE.** We are looking for the years that the consumption of cigarettes c is less than 200. Since we are finding years t, we substitute the expression in the formula given for c, or

$$-14.25t + 598.69 < 200$$

3. SOLVE the inequality.

$$-14.25t + 598.69 < 200$$ Subtract 598.69 from both sides.
$$-14.25t < -398.69$$ Divide both sides by −14.25 and round the result.

$$t > 27.98$$

4. INTERPRET.

Check: We substitute a number greater than 27.98 and see that c is less than 200.

State: The annual consumption of cigarettes will be less than 200 billion for the years more than 27.98 years after 1985, or after approximately $28 + 1985 = 2013$.

SPOTLIGHT ON DECISION MAKING

Suppose you are the superintendent of Copley Public Schools. You are aware that the general population of Copley is increasing and that enrollment at the schools is steadily rising. The high school can house a maximum of 1200 students. Once this maximum has been exceeded, temporary classrooms must be erected to handle the overflow.

You have been studying the changes in population and conclude that the equation $y = 30x + 1025$ models the high school enrollment x years from now. As you prepare a long-term planning report, you must decide whether temporary classrooms will be needed in the next 10 years. If so, when is the latest that funding for temporary classrooms could be added to the annual budget?

MENTAL MATH

Solve each inequality mentally and write it in set notation.

1. $x - 2 < 4$
2. $x - 1 > 6$
3. $x + 5 \geq 15$
4. $x + 1 \leq 8$
5. $3x > 12$
6. $5x < 20$
7. $\dfrac{x}{2} \leq 1$
8. $\dfrac{x}{4} \geq 2$

Exercise Set 2.4

Graph the solution set of each inequality and write it in interval notation. See Example 1.

1. $\{x \mid x < -3\}$
2. $\{x \mid x \geq -7\}$
3. $\{x \mid x \geq 0.3\}$
4. $\{x \mid x < -0.2\}$
5. $\{x \mid 5 < x\}$
6. $\{x \mid -7 \geq x\}$
7. $\{x \mid -2 < x < 5\}$
8. $\{x \mid -5 \leq x \leq -1\}$
9. $\{x \mid 5 > x > -1\}$
10. $\{x \mid -3 \geq x \geq -7\}$

11. When graphing the solution set of an inequality, explain how you know whether to use a parenthesis or a bracket.

12. Explain what is wrong with the interval notation $(-6, -\infty)$

Determine which number(s) listed below are solutions to each inequality. A number may be used more than once.

$$0, 5, -5, \tfrac{3}{4}, -\tfrac{3}{4}, \pi, 100, -1,000,000$$

13. $x > 5$
14. $x < 5$
15. $y \leq -1$
16. $y \geq -\dfrac{1}{2}$

Solve. Graph the solution set and write it in interval notation. See Examples 2 through 4.

17. $x - 7 \geq -9$

18. $x + 2 \leq -1$

19. $7x < 6x + 1$

20. $11x < 10x + 5$

21. $8x - 7 \leq 7x - 5$

22. $7x - 1 \geq 6x - 1$

23. $2 + 4x > 5x + 6$

24. $7 + 8x > 9x + 12$

25. $\dfrac{3}{4} x \geq 2$

26. $\dfrac{5}{6} x \geq -8$

27. $5x < -23.5$

28. $4x > -11.2$

29. $-3x \geq 9$

30. $-4x \geq 15$

31. $-x < -4$

32. $-x > -2$

Solve. Write the solution set using interval notation. See Examples 5 through 7.

33. $-2x + 7 \geq 9$

34. $8 - 5x \leq 23$

35. $15 + 2x \geq 4x - 7$

36. $10 + x < 6x - 10$

37. $3(x - 5) < 2(2x - 1)$

38. $5(x + 4) \leq 4(2x + 3)$

39. $\dfrac{1}{2} + \dfrac{2}{3} \geq \dfrac{x}{6}$

40. $\dfrac{3}{4} - \dfrac{2}{3} > -\dfrac{x}{6}$

41. $4(x - 1) \geq 4x - 8$

42. $3x + 1 < 3(x - 2)$

43. $7x < 7(x - 2)$

44. $8(x + 3) \leq 7(x + 5) + x$

45. $4(2x + 1) > 4$

46. $6(2 - x) \geq 12$

47. $\dfrac{x + 7}{5} > 1$

48. $\dfrac{2x - 4}{3} \leq 2$

49. $\dfrac{-5x + 11}{2} \leq 7$

50. $\dfrac{4x - 8}{7} < 0$

51. $8x - 16.4 \leq 10x + 2.8$

52. $18x - 25.6 < 10x + 60.8$

53. $2(x - 3) > 70$

54. $3(5x + 6) \geq -12$

55. Explain how solving a linear inequality is similar to solving a linear equation.

56. Explain how solving a linear inequality is different from solving a linear equation.

Solve. Write the solution set using interval notation.

57. $-5x + 4 \leq -4(x - 1)$

58. $-6x + 2 < -3(x + 4)$

59. $\dfrac{1}{4} (x - 7) \geq x + 2$

60. $\dfrac{3}{5} (x + 1) \leq x + 1$

61. $\dfrac{2}{3} (x + 2) < \dfrac{1}{5} (2x + 7)$

62. $\dfrac{1}{6} (3x + 10) > \dfrac{5}{12} (x - 1)$

63. $4(x - 6) + 2x - 4 \geq 3(x - 7) + 10x$

64. $7(2x + 3) + 4x \leq 7 + 5(3x - 4)$

65. $\dfrac{5x + 1}{7} - \dfrac{2x - 6}{4} \geq -4$

66. $\dfrac{1 - 2x}{3} + \dfrac{3x + 7}{7} > 1$

67. $\dfrac{-x + 2}{2} - \dfrac{1 - 5x}{8} < -1$

68. $\dfrac{3 - 4x}{6} - \dfrac{1 - 2x}{12} \leq -2$

69. $0.8x + 0.6x \geq 4.2$

70. $0.7x - x > 0.45$

71. $\dfrac{x + 5}{5} - \dfrac{3 + x}{8} \geq -\dfrac{3}{10}$

72. $\dfrac{x - 4}{2} - \dfrac{x - 2}{3} > \dfrac{5}{6}$

73. $\dfrac{x + 3}{12} + \dfrac{x - 5}{15} < \dfrac{2}{3}$

74. $\dfrac{3x + 2}{18} - \dfrac{1 + 2x}{6} \leq -\dfrac{1}{2}$

Solve. See Examples 8 and 9

75. Shureka has scores of 72, 67, 82, and 79 on her algebra tests. Use an inequality to find the minimum score she can make on the final exam to pass the course with an average of 60 or higher, given that the final exam counts as two tests.

76. In a Winter Olympics speed-skating event, Hans scored times of 3.52, 4.04, and 3.87 minutes on his first three trials. Use an inequality to find the maximum time he can score on his last trial so that his average time is under 4.0 minutes.

77. A small plane's maximum takeoff weight is 2000 pounds. Six passengers weigh an average of 160 pounds each. Use an inequality to find the maximum weight of luggage and cargo the plane can carry.

78. A clerk must use the elevator to move boxes of paper. The elevator's weight limit is 1500 pounds. If each box of paper weighs 66 pounds and the clerk weighs 147 pounds, use an inequality to find the maximum number of boxes she can move on the elevator at one time.

79. To mail an envelope first class, the U.S. Post Office charges 33 cents for the first ounce and 22 cents per ounce for each additional ounce. Use an inequality to find the maximum number of whole ounces that can be mailed for $4.00

80. A shopping mall parking garage charges $2 for the first half hour and $1.20 for each additional half hour or a portion of a half hour. Use an inequality to find how long you can park if you have $8.00 in cash.

81. Northeast Telephone Company offers two billing plans for local calls. Plan 1 charges $25 per month for unlimited calls, and plan 2 charges $13 per month plus 6 cents per call. Use an inequality to find the number of monthly calls for which plan 1 is more economical than plan 2.

82. A car rental company offers two subcompact rental plans. Plan A charges $32 per day for unlimited mileage, and plan B charges $24 per day plus 15 cents per mile. Use an inequality to find the number of daily miles for which plan A is more economical than plan B.

83. At room temperature, glass used in windows actually has some properties of a liquid. It has a very slow, viscous flow. (Viscosity is the property of a fluid that resists internal flow. For example, lemonade flows more easily than fudge syrup. Fudge syrup has a higher viscosity than lemonade.) Glass does not become a true liquid until temperatures are greater than or equal to 500°C. Find the Fahrenheit temperatures for which glass is a liquid. (Use the formula $F = \frac{9}{5}C + 32$.)

84. Stibnite is a silvery white mineral with a metallic luster. It is one of the few minerals that melts easily in match flame or at temperatures of approximately 977°F or greater. Find the Celsius temperatures for which stibnite melts. (Use the formula $C = \frac{5}{9}[F - 32]$.)

85. Although beginning salaries vary greatly according to your field of study, the equation $s = 2806.6t + 32,558$ can be used to approximate and to predict average beginning salaries for candidates for bachelor's degrees. The variable s is the starting salary and t is the number of years after 1995.

   a. Approximate when beginning salaries for candidates will be greater than $50,000.

   b. Determine the year you plan to graduate from college. Use this year to find the corresponding value of t and approximate your beginning salary.

86. Use the formula in Example 9 to estimate the years that the consumption of cigarettes will be less than 50 billion per year.

The average consumption per person per year of whole milk w in gallons can be approximated by the equation

$$w = -0.18t + 8.72$$

where t is the number of years after 1994. The average consumption of skim milk s per person per year can be approximated by the equation

$$s = 0.26t + 5.86$$

where t is the number of years after 1994. The consumption of whole milk is shown on the graph in blue and the consumption of skim milk is shown on the graph in red. Use this information to answer Exercises 87–95.

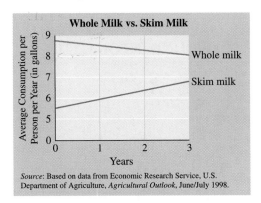

Source: Based on data from Economic Research Service, U.S. Department of Agriculture, *Agricultural Outlook*, June/July 1998.

87. Is the consumption of whole milk increasing or decreasing over time? Explain how you arrived at your answer.

88. Is the consumption of skim milk increasing or decreasing over time? Explain how you arrived at your answer.

89. Predict the consumption of whole milk in the year 2005 (*Hint:* Find the value of t that corresponds to the year 2005.)

90. Predict the consumption of skim milk in the year 2005 (*Hint:* Find the value of t that corresponds to the year 2005.)

91. Determine when the consumption of whole milk will be less than 7 gallons per person per year.

92. Determine when the consumption of skim milk will be greater than 8 gallons per person per year.

93. For 1994 through 1997 the consumption of whole milk was greater than the consumption of skim milk. Explain how this can be determined from the graph.

94. How will the two lines in the graph appear when the consumption of whole milk is the same as the consumption of skim milk?

95. The consumption of whole milk will be the same as the consumption of skim milk when $w = s$. Find when this will occur, by substituting the given equivalent expression for w and the given equivalent expression for s and solving for t. Round the value of t to the nearest whole and estimate the year when this will occur.

REVIEW EXERCISES

List or describe the integers that make both inequalities true.

96. $x < 5$ and $x > 1$

97. $x \geq 0$ and $x \leq 7$

98. $x \geq -2$ and $x \geq 2$

99. $x < 6$ and $x < -5$

Graph each set on a number line and write it in interval notation. See Section 2.4.

100. $\{x \mid 0 \leq x \leq 5\}$

101. $\{x \mid -7 < x \leq 1\}$

102. $\left\{x \mid -\dfrac{1}{2} < x < \dfrac{3}{2}\right\}$

103. $\{x \mid -2.5 \leq x < 5.3\}$

2.5 COMPOUND INEQUALITIES

CD-ROM   SSM

SSG   Video

▶ **OBJECTIVES**

1. Find the intersection of two sets.
2. Solve compound inequalities containing **and**.
3. Find the union of two sets.
4. Solve compound inequalities containing **or**.

Two inequalities joined by the words **and** or **or** are called **compound inequalities.**

Compound Inequalities

$$x + 3 < 8 \text{ and } x > 2$$

$$\frac{2x}{3} \geq 5 \text{ or } -x + 10 < 7$$

1   The solution set of a compound inequality formed by the word **and** is the **intersection** of the solution sets of the two inequalities.

INTERSECTION OF TWO SETS

The intersection of two sets, A and B, is the set of all elements common to both sets. A intersect B is denoted by

$$A \cap B$$

Example 1   Find the intersection: $\{2, 4, 6, 8\} \cap \{3, 4, 5, 6\}$

Solution   The numbers 4 and 6 are in both sets. The intersection is $\{4, 6\}$.

2   A value is a solution of a compound inequality formed by the word **and** if it is a solution of *both* inequalities. For example, the solution set of the compound inequality $x \leq 5$ and $x \geq 3$ contains all values of x that make the inequality $x \leq 5$ a true statement **and** the inequality $x \geq 3$ a true statement. The first graph shown below is the graph of $x \leq 5$, the second graph is the graph of $x \geq 3$, and the third graph shows the intersection of the two graphs. The third graph is the graph of $x \leq 5$ **and** $x \geq 3$.

$\{x \mid x \leq 5\}$ $(-\infty, 5]$

$\{x \mid x \geq 3\}$ $[3, \infty)$

$\{x \mid x \leq 5 \text{ and } x \geq 3\}$ $[3, 5]$

The compound inequality $x \leq 5$ and $x \geq 3$ can be written in a more compact form as $3 \leq x \leq 5$. The solution set $\{x \mid 3 \leq x \leq 5\}$ includes all numbers that are less than or equal to 5 and at the same time greater than or equal to 3. In interval notation, the solution set is $[3, 5]$.

Example 2   Solve $x - 7 < 2$ and $2x + 1 < 9$.

Solution   First we solve each inequality separately.

$$
\begin{array}{ccc}
x - 7 < 2 & \text{and} & 2x + 1 < 9 \\
x < 9 & \text{and} & 2x < 8 \\
x < 9 & \text{and} & x < 4
\end{array}
$$

Now we can graph the two intervals on two number lines and find their intersection. Their intersection is shown on the third number line.

$\{x \mid x < 9\}$ $(-\infty, 9)$

$\{x \mid x < 4\}$ $(-\infty, 4)$

$\{x \mid x < 9 \text{ and } x < 4\}$ $(-\infty, 4)$

$= \{x \mid x < 4\}$

The solution set is $(-\infty, 4)$.

Example 3   Solve $2x \geq 0$ and $4x - 1 \leq -9$.

Solution   First we solve each inequality separately.

$$
\begin{array}{ccc}
2x \geq 0 & \text{and} & 4x - 1 \leq -9 \\
x \geq 0 & \text{and} & 4x \leq -8 \\
x \geq 0 & \text{and} & x \leq -2
\end{array}
$$

Now we can graph the two intervals and find their intersection.

$\{x \mid x \geq 0\}$ $[0, \infty)$

$\{x \mid x \leq -2\}$ $(-\infty, -2]$

$\{x \mid x \geq 0 \text{ and } x \leq -2\} = \varnothing$ $\varnothing$

There is no number that is greater than or equal to 0 *and* less than or equal to -2. The solution set is $\varnothing$.

> **HELPFUL HINT**
> Example 3 shows that some compound inequalities have no solution. Also, some have all real numbers as solutions.

To solve a compound inequality written in a compact form, such as $2 < 4 - x < 7$, we get x alone in the "middle part." Since a compound inequality is really two inequalities in one statement, we must perform the same operations on all three parts of the inequality.

Example 4   Solve $2 < 4 - x < 7$.

Solution   To get x alone, we first subtract 4 from all three parts.

$$2 < 4 - x < 7$$

$$2 - 4 < 4 - x - 4 < 7 - 4 \qquad \text{Subtract 4 from all three parts.}$$

$$-2 < -x < 3 \qquad \text{Simplify.}$$

> **HELPFUL HINT**
> Don't forget to reverse both inequality symbols.

$$\frac{-2}{-1} > \frac{-x}{-1} > \frac{3}{-1} \qquad \text{Divide all three parts by } -1 \text{ and reverse the inequality symbols.}$$

$$2 > x > -3$$

This is equivalent to $-3 < x < 2$.
The solution set in interval notation is $(-3, 2)$, and its graph is shown.

Example 5   Solve $-1 \le \dfrac{2x}{3} + 5 \le 2$.

Solution   First, clear the inequality of fractions by multiplying all three parts by the LCD of 3.

$$-1 \le \frac{2x}{3} + 5 \le 2$$

$$3(-1) \le 3\left(\frac{2x}{3} + 5\right) \le 3(2) \qquad \text{Multiply all three parts by the LCD of 3.}$$

$$-3 \le 2x + 15 \le 6 \qquad \text{Use the distributive property and multiply.}$$

$$-3 - 15 \le 2x + 15 - 15 \le 6 - 15 \qquad \text{Subtract 15 from all three parts.}$$

$$-18 \le 2x \le -9 \qquad \text{Simplify.}$$

$$\frac{-18}{2} \le \frac{2x}{2} \le \frac{-9}{2} \qquad \text{Divide all three parts by 2.}$$

$$-9 \le x \le -\frac{9}{2} \qquad \text{Simplify.}$$

The graph of the solution is shown.

$$-\frac{9}{2}$$

```
◄──+──┤├─+──+──+──+──┤├─+──+──►
   -10 -9 -8 -7 -6 -5 -4 -3
```

The solution set in interval notation is $\left[-9, -\frac{9}{2}\right]$.

3　The solution set of a compound inequality formed by the word **or** is the **union** of the solution sets of the two inequalities.

UNION OF TWO SETS

The union of two sets, A and B, is the set of elements that belong to *either* of the sets. A union B is denoted by

$$A \cup B$$

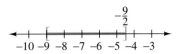

$A \cup B$

Example 6　Find the union: $\{2, 4, 6, 8\} \cup \{3, 4, 5, 6\}$

Solution　The numbers that are in either set or both sets are $\{2, 3, 4, 5, 6, 8\}$. This set is the union.

4　A value is a solution of a compound inequality formed by the word **or** if it is a solution of **either** inequality. For example, the solution set of the compound inequality $x \le 1$ **or** $x \ge 3$ contains all numbers that make the inequality $x \le 1$ a true statement **or** the inequality $x \ge 3$ a true statement.

$\{x \mid x \le 1\}$

```
◄──+──+──┤─+──+──+──+──+──►
  -1  0  1  2  3  4  5  6
```

$(-\infty, 1]$

$\{x \mid x \ge 3\}$

```
◄──+──+──+──+──├─+──+──+──►
  -1  0  1  2  3  4  5  6
```

$[3, \infty)$

$\{x \mid x \le 1 \text{ or } x \ge 3\}$

```
◄──+──+──┤─+──├─+──+──+──►
  -1  0  1  2  3  4  5  6
```

$(-\infty, 1] \cup [3, \infty)$

In interval notation, the set $\{x \mid x \le 1 \text{ or } x \ge 3\}$ is written as $(-\infty, 1] \cup [3, \infty)$.

Example 7　Solve $5x - 3 \le 10$ or $x + 1 \ge 5$.

Solution　First we solve each inequality separately.

$$
\begin{aligned}
5x - 3 &\le 10 & \text{or} & & x + 1 &\ge 5 \\
5x &\le 13 & \text{or} & & x &\ge 4 \\
x &\le \frac{13}{5} & \text{or} & & x &\ge 4
\end{aligned}
$$

Now we can graph each interval and find their union.

$$\left\{x \mid x \le \frac{13}{5}\right\}$$

$$\left(-\infty, \frac{13}{5}\right]$$

$$\{x \mid x \ge 4\}$$

$$[4, \infty)$$

$$\left\{x \mid x \le \frac{13}{5} \text{ or } x \ge 4\right\}$$

$$\left(-\infty, \frac{13}{5}\right] \cup [4, \infty)$$

The solution set is $\left(-\infty, \frac{13}{5}\right] \cup [4, \infty)$.

Example 8

Solve: $-2x - 5 < -3$ or $6x < 0$.

Solution   First we solve each inequality separately.

$$\begin{array}{ccc} -2x - 5 < -3 & \text{or} & 6x < 0 \\ -2x < 2 & \text{or} & x < 0 \\ x > -1 & \text{or} & x < 0 \end{array}$$

Now we can graph each interval and find their union.

$$\{x \mid x > -1\}$$

$$(-1, \infty)$$

$$\{x \mid x < 0\}$$

$$(-\infty, 0)$$

$$\{x \mid x > -1 \text{ or } x < 0\}$$
$$= \text{all real numbers}$$

$$(-\infty, \infty)$$

The solution set is $(-\infty, \infty)$.

Exercise Set 2.5

If $A = \{x \mid x \text{ is an even integer}\}$, $B = \{x \mid x \text{ is an odd integer}\}$, $C = \{2, 3, 4, 5\}$, and $D = \{4, 5, 6, 7\}$, list the elements of each set. See Examples 1 and 6.

1. $C \cup D$ **2.** $C \cap D$

3. $A \cap D$ **4.** $A \cup D$

5. $A \cup B$ **6.** $A \cap B$

7. $B \cap D$ **8.** $B \cup D$

9. $B \cup C$ **10.** $B \cap C$

11. $A \cap C$ **12.** $A \cup C$

Solve each compound inequality. Graph the solution set and write it in interval notation. See Examples 2 and 3.

13. $x < 5$ and $x > -2$

14. $x \le 7$ and $x \le 1$

15. $x + 1 \ge 7$ and $3x - 1 \ge 5$

16. $-2x < -8$ and $x - 5 < 5$

17. $4x + 2 \le -10$ and $2x \le 0$

18. $x + 4 > 0$ and $4x > 0$

Solve each compound inequality. Graph the solution set and write it in interval notation. See Examples 4 and 5.

19. $5 < x - 6 < 11$

20. $-2 \le x + 3 \le 0$

21. $-2 \le 3x - 5 \le 7$

22. $1 < 4 + 2x < 7$

23. $1 \le \dfrac{2}{3}x + 3 \le 4$

24. $-2 < \dfrac{1}{2}x - 5 < 1$

25. $-5 \le \dfrac{x + 1}{4} \le -2$

26. $-4 \le \dfrac{2x + 5}{3} \le 1$

Solve each compound inequality. Graph the solution set and write it in interval notation. See Examples 7 and 8.

27. $x < -1$ or $x > 0$

28. $x \le 1$ or $x \le -3$

29. $-2x \le -4$ or $5x - 20 \ge 5$

30. $x + 4 < 0$ or $6x > -12$

31. $3(x - 1) < 12$ or $x + 7 > 10$

32. $5(x - 1) \ge -5$ or $5 - x \le 11$

33. Explain how solving an and-compound inequality is similar to finding the intersection of two sets.

34. Explain how solving an or-compound inequality is similar to finding the union of two sets.

Solve each compound inequality. Graph the solution set and write it in interval notation.

35. $x < 2$ and $x > -1$

36. $x < 5$ and $x < 1$

37. $x < 2$ or $x > -1$

38. $x < 5$ or $x < 1$

39. $x \ge -5$ and $x \ge -1$

40. $x \le 0$ or $x \ge -3$

41. $x \ge -5$ or $x \ge -1$

42. $x \le 0$ and $x \ge -3$

43. $0 \le 2x - 3 \le 9$

44. $3 < 5x + 1 < 11$

45. $\dfrac{1}{2} < x - \dfrac{3}{4} < 2$

46. $\dfrac{2}{3} < x + \dfrac{1}{2} < 4$

47. $x + 3 \ge 3$ and $x + 3 \le 2$

48. $2x - 1 \ge 3$ and $-x > 2$

49. $3x \ge 5$ or $-x - 6 < 1$

50. $\dfrac{3}{8}x + 1 \le 0$ or $-2x < -4$

51. $0 < \dfrac{5 - 2x}{3} < 5$

52. $-2 < \dfrac{-2x - 1}{3} < 2$

53. $-6 < 3(x - 2) \le 8$

54. $-5 < 2(x + 4) < 8$

55. $-x + 5 > 6$ and $1 + 2x \le -5$

56. $5x \le 0$ and $-x + 5 < 8$

57. $3x + 2 \leq 5$ or $7x > 29$

58. $-x < 7$ or $3x + 1 < -20$

59. $5 - x > 7$ and $2x + 3 \geq 13$

60. $-2x < -6$ or $1 - x > -2$

61. $-\dfrac{1}{2} \leq \dfrac{4x - 1}{6} < \dfrac{5}{6}$

62. $-\dfrac{1}{2} \leq \dfrac{3x - 1}{10} < \dfrac{1}{2}$

63. $\dfrac{1}{15} < \dfrac{8 - 3x}{15} < \dfrac{4}{5}$

64. $-\dfrac{1}{4} < \dfrac{6 - x}{12} < -\dfrac{1}{6}$

65. $0.3 < 0.2x - 0.9 < 1.5$

66. $-0.7 \leq 0.4x + 0.8 < 0.5$

The formula for converting Fahrenheit temperatures to Celsius temperatures is $C = \frac{5}{9}(F - 32)$. Use this formula for Exercises 67 and 68.

67. During a recent year, the temperatures in Chicago ranged from $-29°$ to $35°$C. Use a compound inequality to convert these temperatures to Fahrenheit temperatures.

68. In Oslo, the average temperature ranges from $-10°$ to $18°$ Celsius. Use a compound inequality to convert these temperatures to the Fahrenheit scale.

Solve.

69. Christian D'Angelo has scores of 68, 65, 75, and 78 on his algebra tests. Use a compound inequality to find the scores he can make on his final exam to receive a C in the course. The final exam counts as two tests, and a C is received if the final course average is from 70 to 79.

70. Wendy Wood has scores of 80, 90, 82, and 75 on her chemistry tests. Use a compound inequality to find the range of scores she can make on her final exam to receive a B in the course. The final exam counts as two tests, and a B is received if the final course average is from 80 to 89.

Use the graph to answer Exercises 71 and 72.

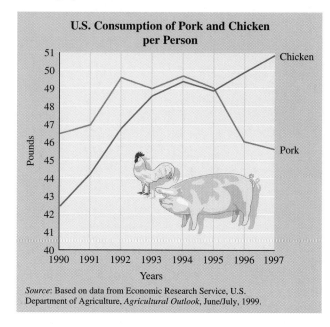

U.S. Consumption of Pork and Chicken per Person

Source: Based on data from Economic Research Service, U.S. Department of Agriculture, *Agricultural Outlook*, June/July, 1999.

71. For what years was the consumption of pork greater than 48 pounds per person *and* the consumption of chicken greater than 48 pounds per person?

72. For what years was the consumption of pork less than 48 pounds per person *or* the consumption of chicken greater than 49 pounds per person?

REVIEW EXERCISES

Evaluate the following. See Sections 1.2 and 1.3.

73. $|-7| - |19|$

74. $|-7 - 19|$

75. $-(-6) - |-10|$

76. $|-4| - (-4) + |-20|$

Find by inspection all values for x that make each equation true.

77. $|x| = 7$

78. $|x| = 5$

79. $|x| = 0$

80. $|x| = -2$

A Look Ahead

Example
Solve $x - 6 < 3x < 2x + 5$.

Solution:
Notice that this inequality contains a variable not only in the middle, but also on the left and the right. When this occurs, we solve by rewriting the inequality using the word ***and***.

$$x - 6 < 3x \quad \text{and} \quad 3x < 2x + 5$$
$$-6 < 2x \quad \text{and} \quad x < 5$$
$$-3 < x$$
$$x > -3 \quad \text{and} \quad x < 5$$

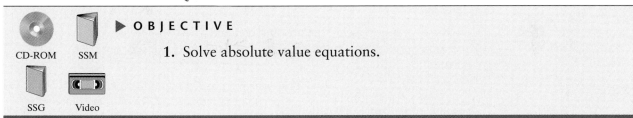

$$x > -3$$

$$x < 5$$

$$-3 < x < 5, \text{ or } (-3, 5)$$

Solve each compound inequality for x. See the example.

81. $2x - 3 < 3x + 1 < 4x - 5$

82. $x + 3 < 2x + 1 < 4x + 6$

83. $-3(x - 2) \le 3 - 2x \le 10 - 3x$

84. $7x - 1 \le 7 + 5x \le 3(1 + 2x)$

85. $5x - 8 < 2(2 + x) < -2(1 + 2x)$

86. $1 + 2x < 3(2 + x) < 1 + 4x$

2.6 ABSOLUTE VALUE EQUATIONS

CD-ROM SSM SSG Video

▶ **OBJECTIVE**

1. Solve absolute value equations.

1 In Chapter 1, we defined the absolute value of a number as its distance from 0 on a number line.

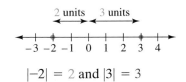

$$|-2| = 2 \text{ and } |3| = 3$$

In this section, we concentrate on solving equations containing the absolute value of a variable or a variable expression. Examples of absolute value equations are

$$|x| = 3 \qquad -5 = |2y + 7| \qquad |z - 6.7| = |3z + 1.2|$$

Since distance and absolute value are so closely related, absolute value equations and inequalities (see Section 2.7) are extremely useful in solving distance-type problems, such as calculating the possible error in a measurement. For the absolute value equation $|x| = 3$, its solution set will contain all numbers whose distance from 0 is 3 units. Two numbers are 3 units away from 0 on the number line: 3 and -3.

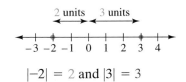

Thus, the solution set of the equation $|x| = 3$ is $\{3, -3\}$. This suggests the following:

SOLVING EQUATIONS OF THE FORM $|x| = a$

If a is a positive number, then $|x| = a$ is equivalent to $x = a$ or $x = -a$.

Example 1   Solve $|p| = 2$.

Solution   Since 2 is positive, $|p| = 2$ is equivalent to $p = 2$ or $p = -2$.
To check, let $p = 2$ and then $p = -2$ in the original equation.

$|p| = 2$	*Original equation.*	$|p| = 2$	*Original equation.*
$|2| = 2$	*Let $p = 2$.*	$|-2| = 2$	*Let $p = -2$.*
$2 = 2$	*True.*	$2 = 2$	*True.*

The solutions are 2 and -2 or the solution set is $\{2, -2\}$.

If the expression inside the absolute value bars is more complicated than a single variable x, we can still apply the absolute value property.

Example 2   Solve $|5w + 3| = 7$.

Solution   Here the expression inside the absolute value bars is $5w + 3$. If we think of the expression $5w + 3$ as x in the absolute value property, we see that $|x| = 7$ is equivalent to

$$x = 7 \quad \text{or} \quad x = -7$$

Then substitute $5w + 3$ for x, and we have

$$5w + 3 = 7 \quad \text{or} \quad 5w + 3 = -7$$

Solve these two equations for w.

$$5w + 3 = 7 \quad \text{or} \quad 5w + 3 = -7$$
$$5w = 4 \quad \text{or} \quad 5w = -10$$
$$w = \frac{4}{5} \quad \text{or} \quad w = -2$$

Check   To check, let $w = -2$ and then $w = \frac{4}{5}$ in the original equation.

Let $w = -2$ 　　　　　　Let $w = \frac{4}{5}$

$$|5(-2) + 3| = 7 \qquad \left|5\left(\frac{4}{5}\right) + 3\right| = 7$$
$$|-10 + 3| = 7 \qquad |4 + 3| = 7$$
$$|-7| = 7 \qquad |7| = 7$$
$$7 = 7 \quad \text{True.} \qquad 7 = 7 \quad \text{True.}$$

Both solutions check, and the solutions are -2 and $\frac{4}{5}$.

Example 3   Solve $\left|\dfrac{x}{2} - 1\right| = 11$.

Solution $\left|\dfrac{x}{2} - 1\right| = 11$ is equivalent to

$$\frac{x}{2} - 1 = 11 \qquad \text{or} \qquad \frac{x}{2} - 1 = -11$$

$$2\left(\frac{x}{2} - 1\right) = 2(11) \quad \text{or} \quad 2\left(\frac{x}{2} - 1\right) = 2(-11) \qquad \textit{Clear fractions.}$$

$$x - 2 = 22 \qquad \text{or} \qquad x - 2 = -22 \qquad \textit{Apply the distributive property.}$$

$$x = 24 \qquad \text{or} \qquad x = -20$$

The solutions are 24 and −20.

To apply the absolute value rule, first make sure that the absolute value expression is isolated.

HELPFUL HINT

If the equation has a single absolute value expression containing variables, isolate the absolute value expression first.

Example 4 Solve $|2x| + 5 = 7$.

Solution We want the absolute value expression alone on one side of the equation, so begin by subtracting 5 from both sides. Then apply the absolute value property.

$$|2x| + 5 = 7$$
$$|2x| = 2 \qquad \textit{Subtract 5 from both sides.}$$
$$2x = 2 \quad \text{or} \quad 2x = -2$$
$$x = 1 \quad \text{or} \quad x = -1$$

The solutions are −1 and 1.

Example 5 Solve $|y| = 0$.

Solution We are looking for all numbers whose distance from 0 is zero units. The only number is 0. The solution is 0.

The next two examples illustrate a special case for absolute value equations. This special case occurs when an isolated absolute value is equal to a negative number.

Example 6 Solve $2|x| + 25 = 23$.

Solution First, isolate the absolute value.

$$2|x| + 25 = 23$$
$$2|x| = -2 \qquad \textit{Subtract 25 from both sides.}$$
$$|x| = -1 \qquad \textit{Divide both sides by 2.}$$

The absolute value of a number is never negative, so this equation has no solution. The solution set is { } or $\varnothing$.

Example 7   Solve $\left|\dfrac{3x + 1}{2}\right| = -2$.

Solution   Again, the absolute value of any expression is never negative, so no solution exists. The solution set is { } or ∅.

Given two absolute value expressions, we might ask, when are the absolute values of two expressions equal? To see the answer, notice that

$$|2| = |2|, \quad |-2| = |-2|, \quad |-2| = |2|, \quad \text{and} \quad |2| = |-2|$$

same   same   opposites   opposites

Two absolute value expressions are equal when the expressions inside the absolute value bars are equal to or are opposites of each other.

Example 8   Solve $|3x + 2| = |5x - 8|$.

Solution   This equation is true if the expressions inside the absolute value bars are equal to or are opposites of each other.

$$3x + 2 = 5x - 8 \quad \text{or} \quad 3x + 2 = -(5x - 8)$$

Next, solve each equation.

$$3x + 2 = 5x - 8 \quad \text{or} \quad 3x + 2 = -5x + 8$$
$$-2x + 2 = -8 \quad \text{or} \quad 8x + 2 = 8$$
$$-2x = -10 \quad \text{or} \quad 8x = 6$$
$$x = 5 \quad \text{or} \quad x = \frac{3}{4}$$

The solutions are $\dfrac{3}{4}$ and 5.

Example 9   Solve $|x - 3| = |5 - x|$.

Solution

$$x - 3 = 5 - x \quad \text{or} \quad x - 3 = -(5 - x)$$
$$2x - 3 = 5 \quad \text{or} \quad x - 3 = -5 + x$$
$$2x = 8 \quad \text{or} \quad x - 3 - x = -5 + x - x$$
$$x = 4 \quad \text{or} \quad -3 = -5 \qquad \text{False.}$$

Recall from Section 2.1 that when an equation simplifies to a false statement, the equation has no solution. Thus, the only solution for the original absolute value equation is 4.

The following box summarizes the methods shown for solving absolute value equations.

ABSOLUTE VALUE EQUATIONS

$|x| = a$
- If a is positive, then solve $x = a$ or $x = -a$.
- If a is 0, solve $x = 0$.
- If a is negative, the equation $|x| = a$ has no solution.

$|x| = |y|$ Solve $x = y$ or $x = -y$.

MENTAL MATH

Simplify each expression.

1. $|-7|$ **2.** $|-8|$ **3.** $-|5|$

4. $-|10|$ **5.** $-|-6|$ **6.** $-|-3|$

7. $|-3| + |-2| + |-7|$ **8.** $|-1| + |-6| + |-8|$

Exercise Set 2.6

Solve each absolute value equation. See Examples 1 through 7.

1. $|x| = 7$ **2.** $|y| = 15$

3. $|3x| = 12.6$ **4.** $|6n| = 12.6$

5. $|2x - 5| = 9$ **6.** $|6 + 2n| = 4$

7. $\left|\dfrac{x}{2} - 3\right| = 1$ **8.** $\left|\dfrac{n}{3} + 2\right| = 4$

9. $|z| + 4 = 9$ **10.** $|x| + 1 = 3$

11. $|3x| + 5 = 14$ **12.** $|2x| - 6 = 4$

13. $|2x| = 0$ **14.** $|7z| = 0$

15. $|4n + 1| + 10 = 4$ **16.** $|3z - 2| + 8 = 1$

17. $|5x - 1| = 0$ **18.** $|3y + 2| = 0$

19. Write an absolute value equation representing all numbers x whose distance from 0 is 5 units.

20. Write an absolute value equation representing all numbers x whose distance from 0 is 2 units.

Solve. See Examples 8 and 9.

21. $|5x - 7| = |3x + 11|$ **22.** $|9y + 1| = |6y + 4|$

23. $|z + 8| = |z - 3|$ **24.** $|2x - 5| = |2x + 5|$

25. Describe how solving an absolute value equation such as $|2x - 1| = 3$ is similar to solving an absolute value equation such as $|2x - 1| = |x - 5|$.

26. Describe how solving an absolute value equation such as $|2x - 1| = 3$ is different from solving an absolute value equation such as $|2x - 1| = |x - 5|$.

Solve each absolute value equation.

27. $|x| = 4$ **28.** $|x| = 1$

29. $|y| = 0$ **30.** $|y| = 8$

31. $|z| = -2$ **32.** $|y| = -9$

33. $|7 - 3x| = 7$ **34.** $|4m + 5| = 5$

35. $|6x| - 1 = 11$ **36.** $|7z| + 1 = 22$

37. $|4p| = -8$ **38.** $|5m| = -10$

39. $|x - 3| + 3 = 7$ **40.** $|x + 4| - 4 = 1$

41. $\left|\dfrac{z}{4} + 5\right| = -7$ **42.** $\left|\dfrac{c}{5} - 1\right| = -2$

43. $|9v - 3| = -8$ **44.** $|1 - 3b| = -7$

45. $|8n + 1| = 0$ **46.** $|5x - 2| = 0$

47. $|1 + 6c| - 7 = -3$ **48.** $|2 + 3m| - 9 = -7$

49. $|5x + 1| = 11$ **50.** $|8 - 6c| = 1$

51. $|4x - 2| = |-10|$ **52.** $|3x + 5| = |-4|$

53. $|5x + 1| = |4x - 7|$

54. $|3 + 6n| = |4n + 11|$

55. $|6 + 2x| = -|-7|$

56. $|4 - 5y| = -|-3|$

57. $|2x - 6| = |10 - 2x|$

58. $|4n + 5| = |4n + 3|$

59. $\left|\dfrac{2x - 5}{3}\right| = 7$

60. $\left|\dfrac{1 + 3n}{4}\right| = 4$

61. $2 + |5n| = 17$

62. $8 + |4m| = 24$

63. $\left|\dfrac{2x - 1}{3}\right| = |-5|$

64. $\left|\dfrac{5x + 2}{2}\right| = |-6|$

65. $|2y - 3| = |9 - 4y|$

66. $|5z - 1| = |7 - z|$

67. $\left|\dfrac{3n + 2}{8}\right| = |-1|$

68. $\left|\dfrac{2r - 6}{5}\right| = |-?|$

69. $|x + 4| = |7 - x|$

70. $|8 - y| = |y + 2|$

71. $\left|\dfrac{8c - 7}{3}\right| = -|-5|$

72. $\left|\dfrac{5d + 1}{6}\right| = -|-9|$

73. Explain why some absolute value equations have two solutions.

74. Explain why some absolute value equations have one solution.

REVIEW EXERCISES

The circle graph shows the sources of Walt Disney Company's operating income for 1999. Use this graph to answer Exercises 75–77. See Section 2.2.

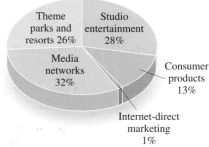

Walt Disney Company
Operating Income 1999

Theme parks and resorts 26%
Studio entertainment 28%
Media networks 32%
Consumer products 13%
Internet-direct marketing 1%

Source: Walt Disney Company.

75. What percent of Disney's operating income came from the consumer products?

△ **76.** A circle contains 360°. Find the number of degrees found in the 26% sector for theme parks and resorts.

77. If Disney's operating income for all of 1999 was $3.4 billion, find the amount of income expected from the media networks segment.

List five integer solutions of each inequality.

78. $|x| \le 3$

79. $|x| \ge -2$

80. $|y| > -10$

81. $|y| < 0$

2.7 ABSOLUTE VALUE INEQUALITIES

CD-ROM   SSM

SSG   Video

▶ **OBJECTIVES**

1. Solve absolute value inequalities of the form $|x| < a$.

2. Solve absolute value inequalities of the form $|x| > a$.

<u>**1**</u>   The solution set of an absolute value inequality such as $|x| < 2$ contains all numbers whose distance from 0 is less than 2 units, as shown below.

Distance from 0: less than 2 units

Distance from 0: less than 2 units

$$-3 \quad -2 \quad -1 \quad 0 \quad 1 \quad 2 \quad 3$$

The solution set is $\{x|-2 < x < 2\}$, or $(-2, 2)$ in interval notation.

Example 1 Solve $|x| \le 3$.

Solution The solution set of this inequality contains all numbers whose distance from 0 is less than or equal to 3. Thus 3, −3, and all numbers between 3 and −3 are in the solution set.

$$\xleftarrow{\quad} \underset{-4\ -3\ -2\ -1\ \ 0\ \ 1\ \ 2\ \ 3\ \ 4\ \ 5}{\big[\quad\quad\quad\big]} \xrightarrow{\quad}$$

The solution set is $[-3, 3]$.

In general, we have the following.

SOLVING ABSOLUTE VALUE INEQUALITIES OF THE FORM $|x| < a$

If a is a positive number, then $|x| < a$ is equivalent to $-a < x < a$.

This property also holds true for the inequality symbol $\le$.

Example 2 Solve for m: $|m - 6| < 2$.

Solution Replace x with $m - 6$ and a with 2 in the preceding property, and we see that

$$|m - 6| < 2 \quad \text{is equivalent to} \quad -2 < m - 6 < 2$$

Solve this compound inequality for m by adding 6 to all three parts.

$$-2 < m - 6 < 2$$
$$-2 + 6 < m - 6 + 6 < 2 + 6 \qquad \text{Add 6 to all three parts.}$$
$$4 < m < 8 \qquad \text{Simplify.}$$

The solution set is $(4, 8)$, and its graph is shown.

$$\xleftarrow{\quad} \underset{3\ \ 4\ \ 5\ \ 6\ \ 7\ \ 8\ \ 9}{(\quad\quad\quad)} \xrightarrow{\quad}$$

HELPFUL HINT
Before using an absolute value inequality property, isolate the absolute value expression on one side of the inequality.

Example 3 Solve for x: $|5x + 1| + 1 \le 10$.

Solution First, isolate the absolute value expression by subtracting 1 from both sides.

$$|5x + 1| + 1 \le 10$$
$$|5x + 1| \le 10 - 1 \qquad \text{Subtract 1 from both sides.}$$
$$|5x + 1| \le 9 \qquad \text{Simplify.}$$

Since 9 is positive, we apply the absolute value property for $|x| \le a$.

$$-9 \le 5x + 1 \le 9$$

$$-9 - 1 \le 5x + 1 - 1 \le 9 - 1 \qquad \text{Subtract 1 from all three parts.}$$

$$-10 \le 5x \le 8 \qquad \text{Simplify.}$$

$$-2 \le x \le \frac{8}{5} \qquad \text{Divide all three parts by 5.}$$

The solution set is $\left[-2, \dfrac{8}{5} \right]$, and the graph is shown above.

Example 4   Solve for x: $\left| 2x - \dfrac{1}{10} \right| < -13$.

Solution   The absolute value of a number is always nonnegative and can never be less than -13. Thus this absolute value inequality has no solution. The solution set is $\{\ \}$ or $\varnothing$.

2   Let us now solve an absolute value inequality of the form $|x| > a$, such as $|x| \ge 3$. The solution set contains all numbers whose distance from 0 is 3 or more units. Thus the graph of the solution set contains 3 and all points to the right of 3 on the number line or -3 and all points to the left of -3 on the number line.

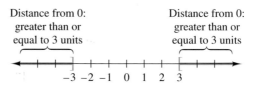

This solution set is written as $\{x \mid x \le -3 \text{ or } x \ge 3\}$. In interval notation, the solution is $(-\infty, -3] \cup [3, \infty)$, since "or" means "union." In general, we have the following.

> ### SOLVING ABSOLUTE VALUE INEQUALITIES OF THE FORM $|x| > a$
>
> If a is a positive number, then $|x| > a$ is equivalent to $x < -a$ or $x > a$.

This property also holds true for the inequality symbol $\ge$.

Example 5   Solve for y: $|y - 3| > 7$.

Solution   Since 7 is positive, we apply the property for $|x| > a$.

$$|y - 3| > 7 \text{ is equivalent to } y - 3 < -7 \text{ or } y - 3 > 7$$

Next, solve the compound inequality.

$$
\begin{array}{lll}
y - 3 < -7 & \text{or} & y - 3 > 7 \\
y - 3 + 3 < -7 + 3 & \text{or} & y - 3 + 3 > 7 + 3 \qquad \text{Add 3 to both sides.} \\
y < -4 & \text{or} & y > 10 \qquad \text{Simplify.}
\end{array}
$$

The solution set is $(-\infty, -4) \cup (10, \infty)$, and its graph is shown.

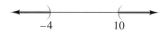

Examples 6 and 8 illustrate special cases of absolute value inequalities. These special cases occur when an isolated absolute value expression is less than, less than or equal to, greater than, or greater than or equal to a negative number or 0.

Example 6   Solve $|2x + 9| + 5 > 3$.

Solution   First isolate the absolute value expression by subtracting 5 from both sides.

$$|2x + 9| + 5 > 3$$
$$|2x + 9| + 5 - 5 > 3 - 5 \qquad \text{Subtract 5 from both sides.}$$
$$|2x + 9| > -2 \qquad \text{Simplify.}$$

The absolute value of any number is always nonnegative and thus is always greater than -2. This inequality and the original inequality are true for all values of x. The solution set is $\{x \mid x \text{ is a real number}\}$ or $(-\infty, \infty)$ and its graph is shown.

Example 7   Solve $\left| \dfrac{x}{3} - 1 \right| - 7 \geq -5$.

Solution   First, isolate the absolute value expression by adding 7 to both sides.

$$\left| \frac{x}{3} - 1 \right| - 7 \geq -5$$
$$\left| \frac{x}{3} - 1 \right| - 7 + 7 \geq -5 + 7 \qquad \text{Add 7 to both sides.}$$
$$\left| \frac{x}{3} - 1 \right| \geq 2 \qquad \text{Simplify.}$$

Next, write the absolute value inequality as an equivalent compound inequality and solve.

$$\frac{x}{3} - 1 \leq -2 \qquad \text{or} \qquad \frac{x}{3} - 1 \geq 2$$
$$3\left(\frac{x}{3} - 1 \right) \leq 3(-2) \quad \text{or} \quad 3\left(\frac{x}{3} - 1 \right) \geq 3(2) \qquad \text{Clear the inequalities of fractions.}$$
$$x - 3 \leq -6 \qquad \text{or} \qquad x - 3 \geq 6 \qquad \text{Apply the distributive property.}$$
$$x \leq -3 \qquad \text{or} \qquad x \geq 9 \qquad \text{Add 3 to both sides.}$$

The solution set is $(-\infty, -3] \cup [9, \infty)$, and its graph is shown.

83. $|9 + 4x| = 0$

84. $|9 + 4x| \geq 0$

85. $|2x + 1| + 4 < 7$

86. $8 + |5x - 3| \geq 11$

87. $|3x - 5| + 4 = 5$

88. $|8x| = -5$

89. $|x + 11| = -1$

90. $|4x - 4| = -3$

91. $\left|\dfrac{2x - 1}{3}\right| = 6$

92. $\left|\dfrac{6 - x}{4}\right| = 5$

93. $\left|\dfrac{3x - 5}{6}\right| > 5$

94. $\left|\dfrac{4x - 7}{5}\right| < 2$

95. Describe how solving $|x - 3| = 5$ is different from solving $|x - 3| < 5$.

96. Describe how solving $|x + 4| = 0$ is similar to solving $|x + 4| \leq 0$.

The expression $|x_T - x|$ is defined to be the absolute error in x, where x_T is the true value of a quantity and x is the measured value or value as stored in a computer.

97. If the true value of a quantity is 3.5 and the absolute error must be less than 0.05, find the acceptable measured values.

98. If the true value of a quantity is 0.2 and the approximate value stored in a computer is $\dfrac{51}{256}$, find the absolute error.

REVIEW EXERCISES

Recall the formula:

$$\text{Probability of an event} = \frac{\substack{\text{number of ways that} \\ \text{the event can occur}}}{\substack{\text{number of possible} \\ \text{outcomes}}}$$

Find the probability of rolling each number on a single toss of a die. (Recall that a die is a cube with each of its six sides containing 1, 2, 3, 4, 5, and 6 black dots, respectively.) See Section 2.3.

99. $P(\text{rolling a 2})$

100. $P(\text{rolling a 5})$

101. $P(\text{rolling a 7})$

102. $P(\text{rolling a 0})$

103. $P(\text{rolling a 1 or 3})$

104. $P(\text{rolling a 1, 2, 3, 4, 5, or 6})$

Consider the equation $3x - 4y = 12$. For each value of x or y given, find the corresponding value of the other variable that makes the statement true. See Section 2.3.

105. If $x = 2$, find y.

106. If $y = -1$, find x.

107. If $y = -3$, find x

108. If $x = 4$, find y

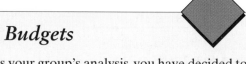

For additional Chapter Projects, visit the Real World Activities Website by going to http://www.prenhall.com/martin-gay.

CHAPTER PROJECT

Analyzing Municipal Budgets

Nearly all cities, towns, and villages operate with an annual budget. Budget items might include expenses for fire and police protection as well as for street maintenance and parks. No matter how big or small the budget, city officials need to know if municipal spending is over or under budget. In this project, you will have the opportunity to analyze a municipal budget and make budgetary recommendations. This project may be completed by working in groups or individually.

Suppose that each year your town creates a municipal budget. The next year's annual municipal budget is submitted for approval by the town's citizens at the annual town meeting. This year's budget was printed in the town newspaper earlier in the year.

  You have joined a group of citizens who are concerned about your town's budgeting and spending processes. Your group plans to analyze this year's budget along with what was actually spent by the town this year. You hope to present your findings at the annual town meeting and make some budgetary recommendations for next year's budget. The municipal budget contains many different areas of spending. To

help focus your group's analysis, you have decided to research spending habits only for categories in which the actual expenses differ from the budgeted amount by more than 12% of the budgeted amount.

1. For each category in the budget, write a specific absolute value inequality that describes the condition that must be met before your group will research spending habits for that category. In each case, let the variable x represent the actual expense for a budget category.

2. For each category in the budget, write an equivalent compound inequality for the condition described in Question 1. Again, let the variable x represent the actual expense for a budget category.

3. Below is a listing of the actual expenditures made this year for each budget category. Use the inequalities from either Question 1 or Question 2 to complete the Budget Worksheet given at the end of this project. (The first category has been filled in.) From the Budget Worksheet, decide which categories must be researched.

	Department/Program	Actual Expenditure
I.	**Board of Health**	
	Immunization Programs	$14,800
	Inspections	$41,900
II.	**Fire Department**	
	Equipment	$375,000
	Salaries	$268,500
III.	**Libraries**	
	Book/Periodical Purchases	$107,300
	Equipment	$29,000
	Salaries	$118,400
IV.	**Parks and Recreation**	
	Maintenance	$82,500
	Playground Equipment	$45,000
	Salaries	$118,000
	Summer Programs	$96,200
V.	**Police Department**	
	Equipment	$328,000
	Salaries	$405,000
VI.	**Public Works**	
	Recycling	$48,100
	Sewage	$92,500
	Snow Removal & Road Salt	$268,300
	Street Maintenance	$284,000
	Water Treatment	$94,100
	TOTAL	$2,816,600

THE TOWN CRIER
Annual Budget Set at Town Meeting
ANYTOWN, USA (MG)—This year's annual budget is as follows:

	Amount Budgeted
BOARD OF HEALTH	
Immunization Programs	$15,000
Inspections	$50,000
FIRE DEPARTMENT	
Equipment	$450,000
Salaries	$275,000
LIBRARIES	
Book/Periodical Purchases	$90,000
Equipment	$30,000
Salaries	$120,000
PARKS AND RECREATION	
Maintenance	$70,000
Playground Equipment	$50,000
Salaries	$140,000
Summer Programs	$80,000
POLICE DEPARTMENT	
Equipment	$300,000
Salaries	$400,000
PUBLIC WORKS	
Recycling	$50,000
Sewage	$100,000
Snow Removal & Road Salt	$200,000
Street Maintenance	$250,000
Water Treatment	$100,000
TOTAL	**$2,770,000**

4. Can you think of possible reasons why spending in the categories that must be researched were over or under budget?

5. Based on this year's municipal budget and actual expenses, what recommendations would you make for next year's budget? Explain your reasoning.

6. (Optional) Research the annual budget used by your own town or your college or university. Conduct a similar analysis of the budget with respect to actual expenses. What can you conclude?

BUDGET WORKSHEET

Budget category	Budgeted amount	Minimum allowed	Actual expense	Maximum allowed	Within budget?	Amt over/ under budget
Immunization Programs	$15,000	$13,200	$14,800	$16,800	Yes	Under $200

CHAPTER 2 VOCABULARY CHECK

Fill in each blank with one of the words or phrases listed below.

contradiction   formula   consecutive integers   linear equation in one variable   identity   solution
absolute value   linear inequality in one variable   compound inequality   intersection   union

1. The statement "$x < 5$ or $x > 7$" *is called a(n)* _____.

2. An equation in one variable that has no solution is called a(n) _____.

3. The _____ of two sets is the set of all elements common to both sets.

4. The _____ of two sets is the set of all elements that belong to either of the sets.

5. An equation in one variable that has every number (for which the equation is defined) as a solution is called a(n) _____.

6. The equation $d = rt$ is also called a(n) _____.

7. A number's distance from 0 is called its _____.

8. When a variable in an equation is replaced by a number and the resulting equation is true, then that number is called a(n) _____ of the equation.

9. The integers 17, 18, 19 are examples of _____.

10. The statement $5x - 0.2 < 7$ is an example of a(n) _____.

11. The statement $5x - 0.2 = 7$ is an example of a(n) _____.

CHAPTER 2 HIGHLIGHTS

DEFINITIONS AND CONCEPTS	EXAMPLES

Section 2.1 Linear Equations in One Variable

An **equation** is a statement that two expressions are equal.	Equations: $5 = 5$ $7x + 2 = -14$ $3(x - 1)^2 = 9x^2 - 6$
A **linear equation in one variable** is an equation that can be written in the form $ax + b = c$, where a, b, and c are real numbers and a is not 0.	Linear equations: $7x + 2 = -14$ $x = -3$ $5(2y - 7) = -2(8y - 1)$
A **solution** of an equation is a value for the variable that makes the equation a true statement.	Check to see that -1 is a solution of $3(x - 1) = 4x - 2.$ $3(-1 - 1) = 4(-1) - 2$ $3(-2) = -4 - 2$ $-6 = -6$ True. Thus, -1 is a solution.
Equivalent equations have the same solution.	$x - 12 = 14$ and $x = 26$ are equivalent equations.
The **addition property of equality** guarantees that the same number may be added to (or subtracted from) both sides of an equation, and the result is an equivalent equation. The **multiplication property of equality** guarantees that both sides of an equation may be multiplied by (or divided by) the same nonzero number, and the result is an equivalent equation. To solve linear equations in one variable:	Solve for x: $-3x - 2 = 10$. $-3x - 2 + 2 = 10 + 2$ Add 2 to both sides. $-3x = 12$ $\dfrac{-3x}{-3} = \dfrac{12}{-3}$ Divide both sides by -3. $x = -4$ Solve for x: $x - \dfrac{x - 2}{6} = \dfrac{x - 7}{3} + \dfrac{2}{3}$

(continued)

| **DEFINITIONS AND CONCEPTS** | **EXAMPLES** |

Section 2.1 Linear Equations in One Variable

1. Clear the equation of fractions.

1. $6\left(x - \dfrac{x-2}{6}\right) = 6\left(\dfrac{x-7}{3} + \dfrac{2}{3}\right)$ Multiply both sides by 6.

$6x - (x-2) = 2(x-7) + 2(2)$

2. Remove grouping symbols such as parentheses.

2. $6x - x + 2 = 2x - 14 + 4$ Remove grouping symbols.

3. Simplify by combining like terms.

3. $5x + 2 = 2x - 10$

4. Write variable terms on one side and numbers on the other side using the addition property of equality.

4. $5x + 2 - 2 = 2x - 10 - 2$ Subtract 2.

$5x = 2x - 12$

$5x - 2x = 2x - 12 - 2x$ Subtract $2x$.

$3x = -12$

5. Isolate the variable using the multiplication property of equality.

5. $\dfrac{3x}{3} = \dfrac{-12}{3}$ Divide by 3.

$x = -4$

6. Check the proposed solution in the original equation.

6. $-4 - \dfrac{-4-2}{6} \overset{?}{=} \dfrac{-4-7}{3} + \dfrac{2}{3}$ Replace x with -4 in the original equation.

$-4 - \dfrac{-6}{6} \overset{?}{=} \dfrac{-11}{3} + \dfrac{2}{3}$

$-4 - (-1) \overset{?}{=} \dfrac{-9}{3}$

$-3 = -3$ True.

Section 2.2 An Introduction to Problem Solving

Problem-Solving Strategy

Colorado is shaped like a rectangle whose length is about 1.3 times its width. If the perimeter of Colorado is 2070 kilometers, find its dimensions.

1. UNDERSTAND the problem.

1. Read and reread the problem. Guess a solution and check your guess.
Let x = width of Colorado in kilometers. Then $1.3x$ = length of Colorado in kilometers

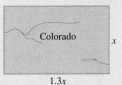
1.3x

2. TRANSLATE the problem.

2. In words:

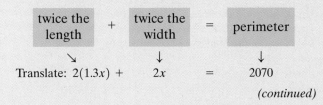

Translate: $2(1.3x)$ + $2x$ = 2070

(continued)

DEFINITIONS AND CONCEPTS	EXAMPLES

Section 2.2 An Introduction to Problem Solving

3. SOLVE the equation.

3. $2.6x + 2x = 2070$
$4.6x = 2070$
$x = 450$

4. INTERPRET the results.

4. If $x = 450$ kilometers, then $1.3x = 1.3(450) = 585$ kilometers. *Check:* The perimeter of a rectangle whose width is 450 kilometers and length is 585 kilometers is $2(450) + 2(585) = 2070$ kilometers, the required perimeter. *State:* The dimensions of Colorado are 450 kilometers by 585 kilometers

Section 2.3 Formulas and Problem Solving

An equation that describes a known relationship among quantities is called a **formula.**

Formulas:

$$A = \pi r^2 \text{ (area of a circle)}$$

$$I = PRT \qquad \text{(interest = principal · rate · time)}$$

To solve a formula for a specified variable, use the steps for solving an equation. Treat the specified variable as the only variable of the equation.

Solve $A = 2HW + 2LW + 2LH$ for H

$A - 2LW = 2HW + 2LH$ Subtract $2LW$.

$A - 2LW = H(2W + 2L)$ Factor out H.

$\dfrac{A - 2LW}{2W + 2L} = \dfrac{H(2W + 2L)}{2W + 2L}$ Divide by $2W + 2L$.

$\dfrac{A - 2LW}{2W + 2L} = H$ Simplify.

Section 2.4 Linear Inequalities and Problem Solving

A **linear inequality in one variable** is an inequality that can be written in the form $ax + b < c$, where a, b, and c are real numbers and $a \neq 0$. (The inequality symbols $\leq$, $>$, and $\geq$ also apply here.)

Linear inequalities:

$$5x - 2 \leq -7 \qquad 3y > 1 \qquad \frac{z}{7} < -9(z - 3)$$

The **addition property of inequality** guarantees that the same number may be added to (or subtracted from) both sides of an inequality, and the resulting inequality will have the same solution set.

$$x - 9 \leq -16$$
$$x - 9 + 9 \leq -16 + 9 \qquad \text{Add 9.}$$
$$x \leq -7$$

The **multiplication property of inequality** guarantees that both sides of an inequality may be multiplied by (or divided by) the same **positive** number, and the resulting inequality will have the same solution set. We may also multiply (or divide) both sides of an inequality by the same **negative** number and **reverse the direction of the inequality symbol**, and the result is an inequality with the same solution set.

$$6x < -66$$
$$\frac{6x}{6} < \frac{-66}{6} \qquad \text{Divide by 6. Do not reverse direction of inequality symbol.}$$
$$x < -11$$

$$-6x < -66$$
$$\frac{-6x}{-6} > \frac{-66}{-6} \qquad \text{Divide by } -6. \text{ Reverse direction of inequality symbol.}$$
$$x > 11$$

(continued)

DEFINITIONS AND CONCEPTS	EXAMPLES

Section 2.4 Linear Inequalities and Problem Solving

To solve a linear inequality in one variable:

Solve for x:

$$\frac{3}{7}(x - 4) \geq x + 2$$

1. Clear the equation of fractions.

1. $7\left[\frac{3}{7}(x - 4)\right] \geq 7(x + 2)$ Multiply by 7.

$$3(x - 4) \geq 7(x + 2)$$

2. Remove grouping symbols such as parentheses.
3. Simplify by combining like terms.

2. $3x - 12 \geq 7x + 14$ Apply the distributive property.

4. Write variable terms on one side and numbers on the other side using the addition property of inequality.

4. $-4x - 12 \geq 14$ Subtract $7x$.

$$-4x \geq 26$$ Add 12.

$$\frac{-4x}{-4} \leq \frac{26}{-4}$$ Divide by -4. Reverse direction of inequality symbol.

5. Isolate the variable using the multiplication property of inequality.

$$x \leq -\frac{13}{2}$$

Section 2.5 Compound Inequalities

Two inequalities joined by the words **and** or **or** are called **compound inequalities.**

Compound inequalities:

$$x - 7 \leq 4 \quad \text{and} \quad x \geq -21$$

$$2x + 7 > x - 3 \quad \text{or} \quad 5x + 2 > -3$$

The solution set of a compound inequality formed by the word **and** is the **intersection** $\cap$ of the solution sets of the two inequalities.

Solve for x:
   $x < 5$ and $x < 3$

$\{x | x < 5\}$ $(-\infty, 5)$

$\{x | x < 3\}$ $(-\infty, 3)$

$\{x | x < 3$ and $x < 5\}$ $(-\infty, 3)$

The solution set of a compound inequality formed by the word **or** is the **union,** $\cup$, of the solution sets of the two inequalities.

Solve for x:

$$x - 2 \geq -3 \quad \text{or} \quad 2x \leq -4$$

$$x \geq -1 \quad \text{or} \quad x \leq -2$$

$\{x | x \geq -1\}$ $[-1, \infty)$

$\{x | x \leq -2\}$ $(-\infty, -2]$

$\{x | x \leq -2$ or $x \geq -1\}$ $(-\infty, -2]$ $\cup [-1, \infty)$

(continued)

DEFINITIONS AND CONCEPTS	EXAMPLES

Section 2.6 Absolute Value Equations

If a is a positive number, then $|x| = a$ is equivalent to $x = a$ or $x = -a$.

Solve for y:

$$|5y - 1| - 7 = 4$$

$\|5y - 1\| = 11$	Add 7.
$5y - 1 = 11$ or $5y - 1 = -11$	
$5y = 12$ or $\quad 5y = -10$	Add 1.
$y = \dfrac{12}{5}$ or $\quad y = -2$	Divide by 5.

The solutions are -2 and $\frac{12}{5}$.

If a is negative, then $|x| = a$ has no solution.

Solve for x:

$$\left|\frac{x}{2} - 7\right| = -1$$

The solution set is { } or $\varnothing$.

If an absolute value equation is of the form $|x| = |y|$, solve $x = y$ or $x = -y$.

Solve for x:

$$|x - 7| = |2x + 1|$$

$x - 7 = 2x + 1$ or $x - 7 = -(2x + 1)$

$x = 2x + 8 \qquad\qquad x - 7 = -2x - 1$

$-x = 8 \qquad\qquad\qquad\quad x = -2x + 6$

$x = -8 \qquad$ or $\qquad 3x = 6$

$\qquad\qquad\qquad\qquad\qquad x = 2$

The solutions are -8 and 2.

Section 2.7 Absolute Value Inequalities

If a is a positive number, then $|x| < a$ is equivalent to $-a < x < a$.

Solve for y:

$$|y - 5| \le 3$$

$$-3 \le y - 5 \le 3$$

$$-3 + 5 \le y - 5 + 5 \le 3 + 5 \qquad \text{Add 5.}$$

$$2 \le y \le 8$$

The solution set is $[2, 8]$.

If a is a positive number, then $|x| > a$ is equivalent to $x < -a$ or $x > a$.

Solve for x:

$$\left|\frac{x}{2} - 3\right| > 7$$

$$\frac{x}{2} - 3 < -7 \quad \text{or} \quad \frac{x}{2} - 3 > 7$$

$$x - 6 < -14 \quad \text{or} \quad x - 6 > 14 \qquad \text{Multiply by 2.}$$

$$x < -8 \quad \text{or} \quad x > 20 \qquad \text{Add 6.}$$

The solution set is $(-\infty, -8) \cup (20, \infty)$.

CHAPTER 2 REVIEW

(2.1) *Solve each linear equation.*

1. $4(x - 5) = 2x - 14$

2. $x + 7 = -2(x + 8)$

3. $3(2y - 1) = -8(6 + y)$

4. $-(z + 12) = 5(2z - 1)$

5. $n - (8 + 4n) = 2(3n - 4)$

6. $4(9v + 2) = 6(1 + 6v) - 10$

7. $0.3(x - 2) = 1.2$

8. $1.5 = 0.2(c - 0.3)$

9. $-4(2 - 3h) = 2(3h - 4) + 6h$

10. $6(m - 1) + 3(2 - m) = 0$

11. $6 - 3(2g + 4) - 4g = 5(1 - 2g)$

12. $20 - 5(p + 1) + 3p = -(2p - 15)$

13. $\dfrac{x}{3} - 4 = x - 2$

14. $\dfrac{9}{4}y = \dfrac{2}{3}y$

15. $\dfrac{3n}{8} - 1 = 3 + \dfrac{n}{6}$

16. $\dfrac{z}{6} + 1 = \dfrac{z}{2} + 2$

17. $\dfrac{y}{4} - \dfrac{y}{2} = -8$

18. $\dfrac{2x}{3} - \dfrac{8}{3} = x$

19. $\dfrac{b - 2}{3} = \dfrac{b + 2}{5}$

20. $\dfrac{2t - 1}{3} = \dfrac{3t + 2}{15}$

21. $\dfrac{2(t + 1)}{3} = \dfrac{2(t - 1)}{3}$

22. $\dfrac{3a - 3}{6} = \dfrac{4a + 1}{15} + 2$

23. $\dfrac{x - 2}{5} + \dfrac{x + 2}{2} = \dfrac{x + 4}{3}$

24. $\dfrac{2z - 3}{4} - \dfrac{4 - z}{2} = \dfrac{z + 1}{3}$

(2.2) *Solve.*

25. Twice the difference of a number and 3 is the same as 1 added to three times the number. Find the number.

26. One number is 5 more than another number. If the sum of the numbers is 285, find the numbers.

27. Find 40% of 130.

28. Find 1.5% of 8.

29. In 1998, the average annual earnings for a worker with an associate's degree was $29,872. This represents a 30.47% increase over the average annual earnings for a high school graduate in 1998. Find the average annual earnings for a high school graduate in 1998. Round to the nearest whole dollar. (*Source:* U.S. Bureau of the Census)

30. Find four consecutive integers such that twice the first subtracted from the sum of the other three integers is sixteen.

31. Determine whether there are two consecutive odd integers such that 5 times the first exceeds 3 times the second by 54.

△ **32.** The length of a rectangular playing field is 5 meters less than twice its width. If 230 meters of fencing goes around the field, find the dimensions of the field.

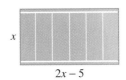

x

$2x - 5$

33. A car rental company charges $29.95 per day for a compact car plus 15 cents per mile for every mile over 100 miles driven per day. If Mr. Woo's bill for 2 days' use is $83.60 before taxes, find how many miles to the nearest whole mile he drove.

34. The cost C of producing x number of scientific calculators is given by $C = 4.50x + 3000$, and the revenue R from selling them is given by $R = 16.50x$. Find the number of calculators that must be sold to break even. (To break even, revenue = cost.)

35. An entrepreneur can sell her musically vibrating plants for $40 each, while her cost C to produce x number of plants is given by $C = 20x + 100$. Find her break-even point. Find her revenue if she sells exactly that number of plants.

Solve each equation for the specified variable.

△ **36.** $V = lwh; w$

△ **37.** $C = 2\pi r; r$

38. $5x - 4y = -12; y$

39. $5x - 4y = -12; x$

40. $y - y_1 = m(x - x_1); m$

41. $y - y_1 = m(x - x_1); x$

42. $E = I(R + r); r$

43. $S = vt + gt^2; g$

44. $T = gr + gvt; g$

45. $I = Prt + P; P$

△ **46.** $A = \dfrac{h}{2}(B + b); B$

△ **47.** $V = \dfrac{1}{3}\pi r^2 h; h$

48. $R = \dfrac{r_1 + r_2}{2}; r_1$

49. $\dfrac{V_1}{T_1} = \dfrac{V_2}{T_2}; T_2$

Solve.

50. A principal of $3000 is invested in an account paying an annual percentage rate of 3%. Find the amount in the account after 7 years if the amount is compounded

   a. semiannually

   b. weekly

   (Approximate to the nearest cent.)

51. The high temperature in Slidell, Louisiana, one day was 90° Fahrenheit. Convert this temperature to degrees Celsius.

△ **52.** Angie Applegate has a photograph in which the length is 2 inches longer than the width. If she increases each dimension by 4 inches, the area is increased by 88 square inches. Find the original dimensions.

△ **53.** One-square-foot floor tiles come 24 to a package. Find how many packages are needed to cover a rectangular floor 18 feet by 21 feet.

△ **54.** Determine which container holds more ice cream, an 8 inch by 5 inch by 3 inch box or a cylinder with radius of 3 inches and height of 6 inches.

55. Erasmos Gonzales left Los Angeles at 11 A.M. and drove nonstop to San Diego, 130 miles away. If she arrived at 1:15 P.M., find her average speed, rounded to the nearest mile per hour.

(2.4) Solve each linear inequality.

56. $3(x - 5) > -(x + 3)$

57. $-2(x + 7) \geq 3(x + 2)$

58. $4x - (5 + 2x) < 3x - 1$

59. $3(x - 8) < 7x + 2(5 - x)$

60. $24 \geq 6x - 2(3x - 5) + 2x$

61. $48 + x \geq 5(2x + 4) - 2x$

62. $\dfrac{x}{3} + \dfrac{1}{2} > \dfrac{2}{3}$

63. $x + \dfrac{3}{4} < -\dfrac{x}{2} + \dfrac{9}{4}$

64. $\dfrac{x - 5}{2} \leq \dfrac{3}{8}(2x + 6)$

65. $\dfrac{3(x - 2)}{5} > \dfrac{-5(x - 2)}{3}$

Solve.

66. George Boros can pay his housekeeper $25 per week to do his laundry, or he can have the laundromat do it at a cost of 90 cents per pound for the first 10 pounds and 80 cents for each additional pound. Use an inequality to find the weight at which it is more economical to use the housekeeper than the laundromat.

67. Ceramic firing temperatures usually range from 500° to 1000° Fahrenheit. Use a compound inequality to convert this range to the Celsius scale. Round to the nearest degree.

68. In the Olympic gymnastics competition, Nana must average a score of 9.65 to win the silver medal. Seven of the eight judges have reported scores of 9.5, 9.7, 9.9, 9.7, 9.7, 9.6, and 9.5. Use an inequality to find the minimum score that the last judge can give so that Nana wins the silver medal.

69. Carol would like to pay cash for a car when she graduates from college and estimates that she can afford a car that costs between $4000 and $8000. She has saved $500 so far and plans to earn the rest of the money by working the next two summers. If Carol plans to save the same amount each summer, use a compound inequality to find the range of money she must save each summer to buy the car.

(2.5) Solve each inequality.

70. $1 \leq 4x - 7 \leq 3$

71. $-2 \leq 8 + 5x < -1$

72. $-3 < 4(2x - 1) < 12$

73. $-6 < x - (3 - 4x) < -3$

74. $\dfrac{1}{6} < \dfrac{4x - 3}{3} \leq \dfrac{4}{5}$

75. $0 \leq \dfrac{2(3x + 4)}{5} \leq 3$

76. $x \leq 2$ and $x > -5$

77. $x \leq 2$ or $x > -5$

78. $3x - 5 > 6$ or $-x < -5$

79. $-2x \leq 6$ and $-2x + 3 < -7$

(2.6) Solve each absolute value equation.

80. $|x - 7| = 9$

81. $|8 - x| = 3$

82. $|2x + 9| = 9$

83. $|-3x + 4| = 7$

84. $|3x - 2| + 6 = 10$

85. $5 + |6x + 1| = 5$

86. $-5 = |4x - 3|$

87. $|5 - 6x| + 8 = 3$

88. $|7x| - 26 = -5$

89. $-8 = |x - 3| - 10$

90. $\left|\dfrac{3x - 7}{4}\right| = 2$

91. $\left|\dfrac{9 - 2x}{5}\right| = -3$

92. $|6x + 1| = |15 + 4x|$

93. $|x - 3| = |7 + 2x|$

97. $9 + |5x| < 24$

98. $|6x - 5| \le -1$

99. $|6x - 5| \ge -1$

100. $\left|3x + \dfrac{2}{5}\right| \ge 4$

(2.7) *Solve each absolute value inequality. Graph the solution set and write in interval notation.*

94. $|5x - 1| < 9$

95. $|6 + 4x| \ge 10$

96. $|3x| - 8 > 1$

101. $\left|\dfrac{4x - 3}{5}\right| < 1$

102. $\left|\dfrac{x}{3} + 6\right| - 8 > -5$

103. $\left|\dfrac{4(x - 1)}{7}\right| + 10 < 2$

CHAPTER 2 TEST

Solve each equation.

1. $8x + 14 = 5x + 44$

2. $3(x + 2) = 11 - 2(2 - x)$

3. $3(y - 4) + y = 2(6 + 2y)$

4. $7n - 6 + n = 2(4n - 3)$

5. $\dfrac{z}{2} + \dfrac{z}{3} = 10$

6. $\dfrac{7w}{4} + 5 = \dfrac{3w}{10} + 1$

7. $|6x - 5| = 1$

8. $|8 - 2t| = -6$

Solve each equation for the specified variable.

9. $3x - 4y = 8; y$

10. $4(2n - 3m) - 3(5n - 7m) = 0; n$

11. $S = gt^2 + gvt; g$

12. $F = \dfrac{9}{5}C + 32; C$

Solve each inequality.

13. $3(2x - 7) - 4x > -(x + 6)$

14. $8 - \dfrac{x}{2} \le 7$

15. $-3 < 2(x - 3) \le 4$

16. $|3x + 1| > 5$

17. $x \ge 5 \text{ and } x \ge 4$

18. $x \ge 5 \text{ or } x \ge 4$

19. $-x > 1 \text{ and } 3x + 3 \ge x - 3$

20. $6x + 1 > 5x + 4 \text{ or } 1 - x > -4$

21. Find 12% of 80.

Solve.

22. In 2006, the number of people employed as database administrators, computer support specialists, and all other computer scientists is expected to be 461,000 in the United States. This represents a 118% increase over the number of people employed in these occupations in 1996. Find the number of database administrators, computer support specialists, and all other computer scientists employed in 1996. (*Source:* U.S. Bureau of Labor Statistics)

△ **23.** A circular dog pen has a circumference of 78.5 feet. Approximate π by 3.14 and estimate how many hunting dogs could be safely kept in the pen if each dog needs at least 60 square feet of room.

24. The company that makes Photoray sunglasses figures that the cost C to make x number of sunglasses weekly is given by $C = 3910 + 2.8x$, and the weekly revenue R is given by $R = 7.4x$. Use an inequality to find the number of sunglasses that must be made and sold to make a profit. (Revenue must exceed cost in order to make a profit.)

25. Find the amount of money in an account after 10 years if a principal of $2500 is invested at 3.5% interest compounded quarterly. (Round to the nearest cent.)

26. The average fresh market price for broccoli in 1998 was $1.10 per pound. A renewed demand for broccoli had caused the price to jump 27% to this level from 1995 market prices. What was the average fresh market price for broccoli in 1995? Round to the nearest cent. *(Source: Associated Press,* April, 1999)

27. The formula for the power generated by a wind turbine generator is $P = 0.5rAV^3$, where P is the power generated in watts, r is the density of air (1.225 kilograms per cubic meter at sea level), A is the area swept by the wind turbine rotor in square meters, and V is the wind speed in meters per second. Find the power generated by a wind turbine generator, at sea level, whose rotor sweeps an area of 3.14 square meters, when the wind is blowing

at a speed of 9 meters per second. Round to the nearest whole watt. (Note: A wind speed of 9 meters per second is roughly equivalent to 20 mph.)

CHAPTER 2 CUMULATIVE REVIEW

1. List the elements in each set.

a. $\{x \mid x \text{ is a whole number between 1 and 6}\}$

b. $\{x \mid x \text{ is a natural number greater than 100}\}$

2. Find each absolute value.

a. $|3|$ **b.** $|-5|$

c. $-|2|$ **d.** $-|-8|$

e. $|0|$

3. Add.

a. $-3 + (-11)$ **b.** $3 + (-7)$

c. $-10 + 15$ **d.** $-8.3 + (-1.9)$

e. $-\dfrac{2}{3} + \dfrac{3}{7}$

4. Find the square roots.

a. $\sqrt{9}$ **b.** $\sqrt{25}$

c. $\sqrt{\dfrac{1}{4}}$

5. Evaluate each algebraic expression when $x = 2$, $y = -1$, and $z = -3$.

a. $z - y$ **b.** z^2

c. $\dfrac{2x + y}{z}$

6. Write each sentence using mathematical symbols.

a. The sum of x and 5 is 20.

b. Two times the sum of 3 and y amounts to 4.

c. Subtract 8 from x, and the difference is the same as the product of 2 and x.

d. The quotient of z and 9 is 3 times the difference of z and 5.

7. Use the commutative property of addition to write an expression equivalent to $7x + 5$.

Solve for x.

8. $2x + 5 = 9$

9. $6x - 4 = 2 + 6(x - 1)$

10. Write the following as algebraic expressions. Then simplify.

a. The sum of two consecutive integers, if x is the first consecutive integer.

b. The perimeter of the triangle with sides of length x, $5x$, and $6x - 3$.

11. Find two numbers such that the second number is 3 more than twice the first number and the sum of the two numbers is 72.

12. Solve $3y - 2x = 7$ for y.

13. Solve $A = \dfrac{1}{2}(B + b)h$ for b.

14. Graph each set on a number line and then write in interval notation.

a. $\{x \mid x \geq 2\}$ **b.** $\{x \mid x < -1\}$

c. $\{x \mid 0.5 < x \leq 3\}$

Solve.

15. $-(x - 3) + 2 \leq 3(2x - 5) + x$

16. $2(x + 3) > 2x + 1$

17. Find the intersection: $\{2, 4, 6, 8\} \cap \{3, 4, 5, 6\}$

18. Solve: $x - 7 < 2$ and $2x + 1 < 9$

19. Find the union: $\{2, 4, 6, 8\} \cup \{3, 4, 5, 6\}$

20. Solve: $-2x - 5 < -3$ or $6x < 0$

Solve:

21. $|p| = 2$

22. $\left| \dfrac{x}{2} - 1 \right| = 11$

23. $|x - 3| = |5 - x|$

24. $|x| \leq 3$

25. $|2x + 9| + 5 > 3$

Helping Prepare for Possible Dangerous Situations

Weather affects many aspects of our daily lives. An afternoon thunderstorm can put the damper on picnic plans or yard work. A cold snap can drive up our heating bills or affect the price of orange juice. Heavy rains can cause dangerous driving conditions or catastrophic flooding. High winds can damage roofs or bring down power lines. Accurately predicting the weather can allow people to prepare for possible damage or avoid dangerous weather situations.

Meteorology is the study of the atmosphere, including the science of weather forecasting. Meteorologists must be able to collect and interpret data, read maps and graphs, plot coordinates, make mathematical computations, use mathematical and physical models, and understand basic statistics. They should also have a solid background in chemistry, physics, earth science, and geography, as well as good computer and communication skills. Meteorologists often work as part of a team.

 For more information about careers in meteorology and the atmospheric sciences, visit the National Weather Association Website by first going to www.prenhall.com/martin-gay.

In the Spotlight on Decision Making feature on page 125, you will have the opportunity to make a decision about keeping track of a hurricane as a meteorologist.

GRAPHS AND FUNCTIONS

The linear equations and inequalities we explored in Chapter 2 are statements about a single variable. This chapter examines statements about two variables: linear equations and inequalities in two variables. We focus particularly on graphs of those equations and inequalities which lead to the notion of relation and to the notion of function, perhaps the single most important and useful concept in all of mathematics.

3.1 GRAPHING EQUATIONS

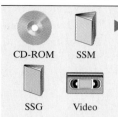

CD-ROM   SSM

SSG   Video

▶ **OBJECTIVES**

1. Plot ordered pairs.
2. Determine whether an ordered pair of numbers is a solution to an equation in two variables.
3. Graph linear equations.
4. Graph nonlinear equations.

1

When two varying quantities are measured simultaneously and repeatedly, we can record the pairs of measurements and try to detect a pattern. If we recognize a pattern, we may be able to express the pattern as a two-variable equation. For example, suppose that the two quantities, products sold x and monthly salary y, are measured simultaneously and repeatedly for an employee and recorded in the following table.

PRODUCTS SOLD	x	0	100	200	300	400	1000
MONTHLY SALARY	y	1500	1510	1520	1530	1540	1600

After studying the measurements, you may notice that there is a pattern in the quantities. Notice that the monthly salary y is always equal to $1500 + \frac{1}{10}x$. We can use this information to write the equation $y = 1500 + \frac{1}{10}x$. This equation is called a **linear equation in two variables**. Before we discuss such equations further, let's first review the rectangular coordinate system.

In order to visualize the data in the table, the data pairs can be listed as ordered pairs of numbers. These ordered pairs of numbers can then be plotted on a **rectangular coordinate system**, which is also called a **Cartesian coordinate system** after its inventor, Rene Descartes (1596–1650).

The Cartesian coordinate system consists of two number lines that intersect at right angles at their 0 coordinates. We position these axes on paper such that one number line is horizontal and the other number line is then vertical. The horizontal number line is called the **x-axis** (or the axis of the **abscissa**), and the vertical number line is called the **y-axis** (or the axis of the **ordinate**). The point of intersection of these axes is named the **origin.**

Notice in the left figure below that the axes divide the plane into four regions. These regions are called **quadrants.** The top-right region is quadrant I. Quadrants II, III, and IV are numbered counterclockwise from the first quadrant as shown. The x-axis and the y-axis are not in any quadrant.

Each point in the plane can be located, or **plotted**, or graphed by describing its position in terms of distances along each axis from the origin. An **ordered pair**, represented by the notation (x, y), records these distances.

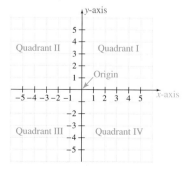

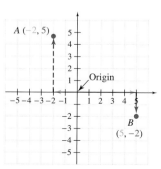

For example, the location of point A in the figure on the right on page 118 is described as 2 units to the left of the origin along the x-axis and 5 units upward parallel to the y-axis. Thus, we identify point A with the ordered pair $(-2, 5)$. Notice that the order of these numbers is critical. The x-value -2 is called the **x-coordinate** and is associated with the x-axis. The y-value 5 is called the **y-coordinate** and is associated with the y-axis. Compare the location of point A with the location of point B, which corresponds to the ordered pair $(5, -2)$.

Keep in mind that **each ordered pair corresponds to exactly one point in the real plane and that each point in the plane corresponds to exactly one ordered pair.** Thus, we may refer to the ordered pair (x, y) as the point (x, y).

Example 1   Plot each ordered pair on a Cartesian coordinate system and name the quadrant in which the point is located.

a. $(2, -1)$ **b.** $(0, 5)$ **c.** $(-3, 5)$ **d.** $(-2, 0)$ **e.** $\left(-\dfrac{1}{2}, -4\right)$ **f.** $(1.5, 1.5)$

Solution   The six points are graphed as shown.

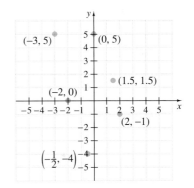

a. $(2, -1)$ lies in quadrant IV.

b. $(0, 5)$ is not in any quadrant.

c. $(-3, 5)$ lies in quadrant II.

d. $(-2, 0)$ is not in any quadrant.

e. $\left(-\dfrac{1}{2}, -4\right)$ is in quadrant III.

f. $(1.5, 1.5)$ is in quadrant I.

Notice that the y-coordinate of any point on the x-axis is 0. For example, the point with coordinates $(-2, 0)$ lies on the x-axis. Also, the x-coordinate of any point on the y-axis is 0. For example, the point with coordinates $(0, 5)$ lies on the y-axis. These points that lie on the axes do not lie in any quadrants.

2   **Solutions** of equations in two variables consist of two numbers that form a true statement when substituted into the equation. A convenient notation for writing these numbers is as ordered pairs. For example, we say that the ordered pair $(100, 1510)$ is a solution of the equation $y = 1500 + \frac{1}{10}x$ because when x is replaced with 100 and y is replaced with 1510, a true statement results.

$$y = 1500 + \frac{1}{10}x$$

$$1510 \stackrel{?}{=} 1500 + \frac{1}{10}(100) \qquad \text{Let } x = 100 \text{ and } y = 1510.$$

$$1510 \stackrel{?}{=} 1500 + 10$$

$$1510 = 1510 \qquad\qquad \text{True.}$$

Example 2   Determine whether $(0, -12)$, $(1, 9)$, and $(2, -6)$ are solutions of the equation $3x - y = 12$.

Solution   To check each ordered pair, replace x with the x-coordinate and y with the y-coordinate and see whether a true statement results.

Let $x = 0$ and $y = -12$.　　Let $x = 1$ and $y = 9$.　　Let $x = 2$ and $y = -6$.

$$3x - y = 12 \qquad\qquad 3x - y = 12 \qquad\qquad 3x - y = 12$$
$$3(0) - (-12) \stackrel{?}{=} 12 \qquad 3(1) - 9 \stackrel{?}{=} 12 \qquad 3(2) - (-6) \stackrel{?}{=} 12$$
$$0 + 12 \stackrel{?}{=} 12 \qquad\quad 3 - 9 \stackrel{?}{=} 12 \qquad\qquad 6 + 6 \stackrel{?}{=} 12$$
$$12 = 12 \quad \text{True.} \qquad -6 = 12 \quad \text{False.} \qquad 12 = 12 \quad \text{True.}$$

Thus, $(1, 9)$ is not a solution but both $(0, -12)$ and $(2, -6)$ are solutions.

3   In fact, the equation $3x - y = 12$ has an infinite number of ordered pair solutions. Since it is impossible to list all solutions, we visualize them by graphing them.

A few more ordered pairs that satisfy $3x - y = 12$ are $(4, 0)$, $(3, -3)$, $(5, 3)$, and $(1, -9)$. These ordered pair solutions along with the ordered pair solutions from Example 2 are plotted on the following graph. The graph of $3x - y = 12$ is the single line containing these points. Every ordered pair solution of the equation corresponds to a point on this line, and every point on this line corresponds to an ordered pair solution.

x	y	$3x - y = 12$
5	3	$3 \cdot 5 - 3 = 12$
4	0	$3 \cdot 4 - 0 = 12$
3	-3	$3 \cdot 3 - (-3) = 12$
2	-6	$3 \cdot 2 - (-6) = 12$
1	-9	$3 \cdot 1 - (-9) = 12$
0	-12	$3 \cdot 0 - (-12) = 12$

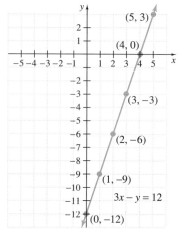

The equation $3x - y = 12$ is called a linear equation in two variables, and **the graph of every linear equation in two variables is a line.**

LINEAR EQUATION IN TWO VARIABLES

A linear equation in two variables is an equation that can be written in the form

$$Ax + By = C$$

where A and B are not both 0. This form is called **standard form.**

As we mentioned earlier, the equation $y = 1500 + \frac{1}{10}x$ is also a linear equation in two variables. This means that the equation $y = 1500 + \frac{1}{10}x$ can be written in standard form $Ax + By = C$ and that its graph is a line. Its solutions in ordered pair form are shown in the next example along with a portion of its graph. Recall that x is products sold and y is monthly salary. Since we assume that the smallest amount of product sold is none, or 0, then x must be greater than or equal to 0. Therefore, only the part of the graph that lies in Quadrant I is shown. Notice that the graph gives a visual picture of the correspondence between products sold and salary.

> ### HELPFUL HINT
> A line contains an infinite number of points and each ordered pair is a solution of its corresponding equation.

Example 3   Use the graph of $y = 1500 + \frac{1}{10}x$ to answer the following questions.

   a. If the salesperson has $800 of products sold for a particular month, what is the salary for that month?
   b. If the salesperson wants to make more than $1600 per month, what must be the total amount of products sold?

Solution   **a.** Since x is products sold, find 800 along the x-axis and move vertically up until you reach a point on the line. From this point on the line, move horizontally to the left until you reach the y-axis. Its value on the y-axis is 1580, which means if $800 worth of products is sold, the salary for the month is $1580.

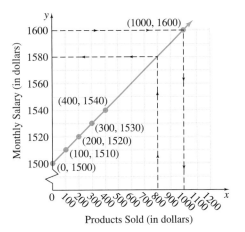

Products Sold (in dollars)

   b. Since y is monthly salary, find 1600 along the y-axis and move horizontally to the right until you reach a point on the line. Either read the corresponding x-value from the labeled ordered pair, or move vertically downward until you reach the x-axis. The corresponding x-value is 1000. This means that $1000 worth of products sold gives a salary of $1600 for the month. For the salary to be greater than $1600, products sold must be greater that $1000.

   Recall from geometry that a line is determined by two points. This means that to graph a linear equation in two variables, just two solutions are needed. We will find a third solution, just to check our work. To find ordered pair solutions of linear equations in two variables, we can choose an x-value and find its corresponding y-value, or we can choose a y-value and find its corresponding x-value. The number 0 is often a convenient value to choose for x and also for y.

Example 4 Graph the equation $y = -2x + 3$.

Solution Find three ordered pair solutions, and plot the ordered pairs. The line through the plotted points is the graph. Since the equation is solved for y, let's choose three x-values. Let's let x be 0, 2, and then -1 to find our three ordered pair solutions.

Let $x = 0$	Let $x = 2$	Let $x = -1$
$y = -2x + 3$	$y = -2x + 3$	$y = -2x + 3$
$y = -2 \cdot 0 + 3$	$y = -2 \cdot 2 + 3$	$y = -2(-1) + 3$
$y = 3$ Simplify.	$y = -1$ Simplify.	$y = 5$ Simplify.

The three ordered pairs $(0, 3)$, $(2, -1)$ and $(-1, 5)$ are listed in the table and the graph is shown.

x	y
0	3
2	-1
-1	5

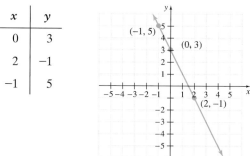

Notice that the graph crosses the y-axis at the point $(0, 3)$. This point is called the **y-intercept**. (You may sometimes see just the number 3 called the y-intercept.) This graph also crosses the x-axis at the point $\left(\frac{3}{2}, 0\right)$. This point is called the **x-intercept**. (You may also see just the number $\frac{3}{2}$ called the x-intercept.)

Example 5 Graph the linear equation $y = \frac{1}{3}x$.

Solution To graph, we find ordered pair solutions, graph the solutions, and draw a line through the solutions. We will choose x-values and substitute in the equation. To avoid fractions, we choose x-values that are multiples of 3.

> ▼
> **HELPFUL HINT**
> Notice that by using multiples of 3, we avoid fractions.

$$y = \frac{1}{3}x$$
$$\downarrow$$

If $x = 6$, then $y = \frac{1}{3}(6)$, or 2.

$$\downarrow$$

If $x = 0$, then $y = \frac{1}{3}(0)$, or 0.

$$\searrow$$

If $x = -3$, then $y = \frac{1}{3}(-3)$, or -1.

x	y
6	2
0	0
-3	-1

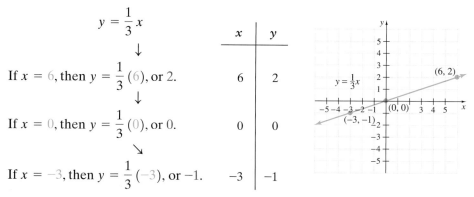

> ▼
> **HELPFUL HINT**
> Since the equation $y = \frac{1}{3}x$ is solved for y, we choose x-values for finding points. This way, we simply need to evaluate an expression to find the x-value, as shown.

This graph crosses the x-axis at $(0, 0)$ and the y-axis at $(0, 0)$. This means that the x-intercept is $(0, 0)$ and that the y-intercept is $(0, 0)$. ▬

4

Not all equations in two variables are linear equations, and not all graphs of equations in two variables are lines.

◆ **Example 6**   Graph $y = x^2$.

Solution   This equation is not linear, and its graph is not a line. We begin by finding ordered pair solutions. Because this graph is solved for y, we choose x-values and find corresponding y-values.

x	y
-3	9
-2	4
-1	1
0	0
1	1
2	4
3	9

If $x = -3$, then $y = (-3)^2$, or 9.

If $x = -2$, then $y = (-2)^2$, or 4.

If $x = -1$, then $y = (-1)^2$, or 1.

If $x = 0$, then $y = 0^2$, or 0.

If $x = 1$, then $y = 1^2$, or 1.

If $x = 2$, then $y = 2^2$, or 4.

If $x = 3$, then $y = 3^2$, or 9.

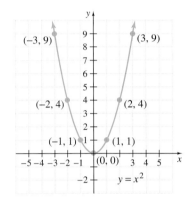

Study the table a moment and look for patterns. Notice that the ordered pair solution $(0, 0)$ contains the smallest y-value because any other x-value squared will give a positive result. This means that the point $(0, 0)$ will be the lowest point on the graph. Also notice that all other y-values correspond to two different x-values. For example, $3^2 = 9$ and also $(-3)^2 = 9$. This means that the graph will be a mirror image of itself across the y-axis. Connect the plotted points with a smooth curve to sketch its graph.

This curve is given a special name, a parabola. We will study more about parabolas in later chapters. ▬

Example 7   Graph the equation $y = |x|$.

Solution   This is not a linear equation, and its graph is not a line. Because we do not know the shape of this graph, we find many ordered pair solutions. We will choose x-values and substitute to find corresponding y-values.

x	y
-3	3
-2	2
-1	1
0	0
1	1
2	2
3	3

If $x = -3$, then $y = |-3|$, or 3.

If $x = -2$, then $y = |-2|$, or 2.

If $x = -1$, then $y = |-1|$, or 1.

If $x = 0$, then $y = |0|$, or 0.

If $x = 1$, then $y = |1|$, or 1.

If $x = 2$, then $y = |2|$, or 2.

If $x = 3$, then $y = |3|$, or 3.

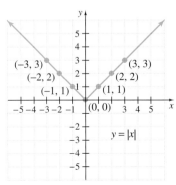

Again, study the table of values for a moment and notice any patterns.

From the plotted ordered pairs, we see that the graph of this absolute value equation is V-shaped.

GRAPHING CALCULATOR EXPLORATIONS

In this section, we begin a study of graphing calculators and graphing software packages for computers. These graphers use the same point plotting technique that we introduced in this section. The advantage of this graphing technology is, of course, that graphing calculators and computers can find and plot ordered pair solutions much faster than we can. Note, however, that the features described in these boxes may not be available on all graphing calculators.

The rectangular screen where a portion of the rectangular coordinate system is displayed is called a **window**. We call it a **standard window** for graphing when both the x- and y-axes display coordinates between -10 and 10. This information is often displayed in the window menu on a graphing calculator as

$$\text{Xmin} = -10$$
$$\text{Xmax} = 10$$
$$\text{Xscl} = 1 \qquad \text{The scale on the } x\text{-axis is one unit per tick mark.}$$
$$\text{Ymin} = -10$$
$$\text{Ymax} = 10$$
$$\text{Yscl} = 1 \qquad \text{The scale on the } y\text{-axis is one unit per tick mark.}$$

To use a graphing calculator to graph the equation $y = -5x + 4$, press the $\boxed{Y=}$ key and enter the keystrokes

(Check your owner's manual to make sure the "negative" key is pressed here and not the "subtraction" key.)

The top row should now read $Y_1 = -5x + 4$. Next press the $\boxed{\text{GRAPH}}$ key, and the display should look like this:

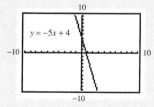

Use a standard window and graph the following equations. (Unless otherwise stated, we will use a standard window when graphing.)

1. $y = -3.2x + 7.9$

2. $y = -x + 5.85$

3. $y = \dfrac{1}{4}x - \dfrac{2}{3}$

4. $y = \dfrac{2}{3}x - \dfrac{1}{5}$

5. $y = |x - 3| + 2$

6. $y = |x + 1| - 1$

7. $y = x^2 + 3$

8. $y = (x + 3)^2$

SPOTLIGHT ON DECISION MAKING

Suppose you are a meteorologist. You are tracking Hurricane Felix. Hurricane position information is is-sued every 6 hours. The table lists Felix's most recent positions, given in latitude (vertical scale on the hur-ricane tracking chart) and longitude (horizontal scale on the hurricane tracking chart). Plot the position of the hurricane on the tracking chart and decide whether Felix is a threat to the United States. If so, what part?

NATIONAL HURRICANE CENTER
RECONNAISSANCE REPORT

Felix Coordinates			
Date	Time	Latitude	Longitude
9/7	4 PM	23.2	88.0
9/7	10 PM	23.7	88.6
9/8	4 AM	23.4	89.1
9/8	10 AM	22.8	89.9
9/8	4 PM	22.2	91.2
9/8	10 PM	21.7	91.8
9/9	4 AM	21.5	92.4
9/9	10 AM	21.2	93.1

Hurricane Tracking Chart

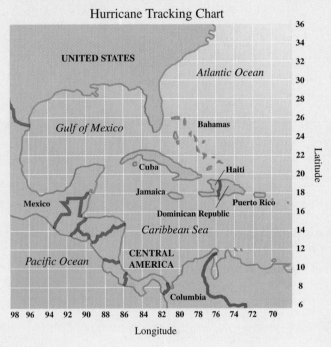

MENTAL MATH

Determine the coordinates of each point on the graph.

1. Point *A*   **2.** Point *B*
3. Point *C*   **4.** Point *D*
5. Point *E*   **6.** Point *F*
7. Point *G*   **8.** Point *H*

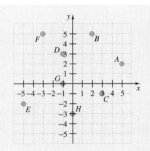

Exercise Set 3.1

Plot each point and name the quadrant or axis in which the point lies. See Example 1.

1. $(3, 2)$ **2.** $(2, -1)$
3. $(-5, 3)$ **4.** $(-3, -1)$
5. $\left(5\frac{1}{2}, -4\right)$ **6.** $\left(-2, 6\frac{1}{3}\right)$
7. $(0, 3.5)$ **8.** $(-2, 4)$

9. $(-2, -4)$ **10.** $(-4.2, 0)$

Given that x is a positive number and that y is a positive num-ber, determine the quadrant or axis in which each point lies.

11. $(x, -y)$ **12.** $(-x, y)$
13. $(x, 0)$ **14.** $(0, -y)$
15. $(-x, -y)$ **16.** $(0, 0)$

Determine whether each ordered pair is a solution of the given equation. See Example 2.

17. $y = 3x - 5$; $(0, 5)$, $(-1, -8)$

18. $y = -2x + 7$; $(1, 5)$, $(-2, 3)$

19. $-6x + 5y = -6$; $(1, 0)$, $\left(2, \dfrac{6}{5}\right)$

20. $5x - 3y = 9$; $(0, 3)$, $\left(\dfrac{12}{5}, -1\right)$

21. $y = 2x^2$; $(1, 2)$, $(3, 18)$

22. $y = 2|x|$; $(-1, 2)$, $(0, 2)$

23. $y = x^3$; $(2, 8)$, $(3, 9)$

24. $y = x^4$; $(-1, 1)$, $(2, 16)$

25. $y = \sqrt{x} + 2$; $(1, 3)$, $(4, 4)$

26. $y = \sqrt[3]{x} - 4$; $(1, -3)$, $(8, 6)$

Determine whether each equation is linear or not. Then graph the equation. See Examples 3 through 7.

27. $x + y = 3$

28. $y - x = 8$

29. $y = 4x$

30. $y = 6x$

31. $y = 4x - 2$

32. $y = 6x - 5$

33. $y = |x| + 3$

34. $y = |x| + 2$

35. $2x - y = 5$

36. $4x - y = 7$

37. $y = 2x^2$

38. $y = 3x^2$

39. $y = x^2 - 3$

40. $y = x^2 + 3$

41. $y = -2x$

42. $y = -3x$

43. $y = -2x + 3$

44. $y = -3x + 2$

45. $y = |x + 2|$

46. $y = |x - 1|$

47. $y = x^3$

   Hint: Let $x = -3, -2, -1, 0, 1, 2$.

48. $y = x^3 - 2$

   Hint: Let $x = -3, -2, -1, 0, 1, 2$.

49. $y = -|x|$

50. $y = -x^2$

51. $y = \dfrac{1}{3}x - 1$

52. $y = \dfrac{1}{2}x - 3$

53. $y = -\dfrac{3}{2}x + 1$

54. $y = -\dfrac{2}{3}x + 1$

55. Graph $y = x^2 - 4x + 7$. Let $x = 0, 1, 2, 3, 4$ to generate ordered pair solutions.

56. Graph $y = x^2 + 2x + 3$. Let $x = -3, -2, -1, 0, 1$ to generate ordered pair solutions.

△ **57.** The perimeter y of a rectangle whose width is a constant 3 inches and whose length is x inches is given by the equation

$$y = 2x + 6$$

   a. Draw a graph of this equation.

   b. Read from the graph the perimeter y of a rectangle whose length x is 4 inches.

58. The distance y traveled in a train moving at a constant speed of 50 miles per hour is given by the equation

$$y = 50x$$

   where x is the time in hours traveled.

   a. Draw a graph of this equation.

   b. Read from the graph the distance y traveled after 6 hours.

This graph shows hourly minimum wages and the years it increased. Use this graph for Exercises 59 through 62.

59. What was the first year that the minimum hourly wage rose above \$4.00?

60. What was the first year that the minimum hourly wage rose above \$5.00?

61. Why do you think that this graph is shaped the way it is?

62. The federal hourly minimum wage started in 1938 at \$0.25. How much will it have increased by in 2002?

For income tax purposes, Jason Verges, owner of Copy Services, uses a method called **straight-line depreciation** to show the loss in value of a copy machine he recently purchased. Jason assumes that he can use the machine for 7 years. The following graph shows the value of the machine over the years. Use this graph to answer the following questions.

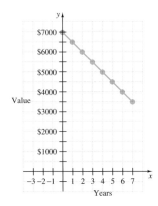

63. What was the purchase price of the copy machine?

64. What is the depreciated value of the machine in 7 years?

65. What loss in value occurred during the first year?

66. What loss in value occurred during the second year?

67. Why do you think that this method of depreciating is called straight-line depreciation?

68. Why is the line tilted downward?

For exercises 69 through 72, match each description with the graph that best illustrates it.

69. Moe worked 40 hours per week until the fall semester started. He quit and didn't work again until he worked 60 hours a week during the Christmas break.

70. Kawana worked 40 hours a week for her father during the summer. She slowly cut back her hours to not working at all during the fall semester. During the Christmas break, she started working again and increased her hours to 60 hours per week.

71. Wendy worked from July through February, never quitting. She worked between 10 and 30 hours per week.

72. Bartholomew worked from July through February, never quitting. He worked between 10 and 30 hours per week except during Christmas. At that time, he worked 40 hours per week.

A.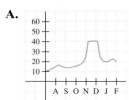

B.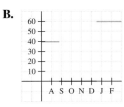

C.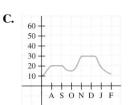

D.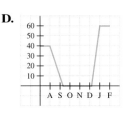

73. On the same set of axes, graph $y = 2x$, $y = 2x - 5$, and $y = 2x + 5$. What patterns do you see in these graphs?

74. On the same set of axes, graph $y = 2x$, $y = x$, and $y = -2x$. Describe the differences and similarities in these graphs.

75. Explain why we generally use three points to graph a line, when only two points are needed.

Write each statement as an equation in two variables. Then graph each equation.

76. The y-value is 5 more than three times the x-value.

77. The y-value is -3 decreased by twice the x-value.

78. The y-value is 2 more than the square of the x-value.

79. The y-value is 5 decreased by the square of the x-value.

Use a graphing calculator to verify the graphs of the following exercises.

80. Exercise 39 **81.** Exercise 40

82. Exercise 47 **83.** Exercise 48

REVIEW EXERCISES

Solve the following equations. See Section 2.1.

84. $3(x - 2) + 5x = 6x - 16$

85. $5 + 7(x + 1) = 12 + 10x$

86. $3x + \dfrac{2}{5} = \dfrac{1}{10}$

87. $\dfrac{1}{6} + 2x = \dfrac{2}{3}$

Solve the following inequalities. See Section 2.4.

88. $3x \le -15$

89. $-3x > 18$

90. $2x - 5 > 4x + 3$

91. $9x + 8 \le 6x - 4$

3.2 INTRODUCTION TO FUNCTIONS

CD-ROM   SSM

SSG   Video

▶ **OBJECTIVES**

1. Define relation, domain, and range.
2. Identify functions.
3. Use the vertical line test for functions.
4. Find the domain and range of a function.
5. Use function notation.

1

Equations in two variables, such as $y = 2x + 1$, describe **relations** between x-values and y-values. For example, if $x = 1$, then this equation describes how to find the y-value related to $x = 1$. In words, the equation $y = 2x + 1$ says that twice the x-value increased by 1 gives the corresponding y-value. The x-value of 1 corresponds to the y-value of $2(1) + 1 = 3$ for this equation, and we have the ordered pair $(1, 3)$.

There are other ways of describing relations or correspondences between two numbers or, in general, a first set (sometimes called the set of *inputs*) and a second set (sometimes called the set of *outputs*). For example.

First Set: Input	*Correspondence*	*Second Set: Output*
People in a certain city	Each person's age	The set of nonnegative integers

A few examples of ordered pairs from this relation might be (Ana, 4); (Bob, 36); (Trey, 21); and so on.

Below are just a few other ways of describing relations between two sets and the ordered pairs that they generate.

First Set: *Second Set:*
Input   **Output**

Correspondence

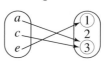

Ordered Pairs
$(a, 3), (c, 3), (e, 1)$

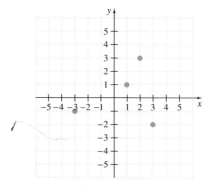

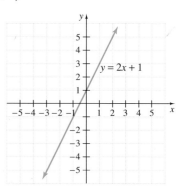

Ordered Pairs
$(-3, -1), (1, 1), (2, 3), (3, -2)$

Some Ordered Pairs
$(1, 3), (0, 1)$ and so on

RELATION, DOMAIN, AND RANGE

A **relation** is a set of ordered pairs.
The **domain** of the relation is the set of all first components of the ordered pairs.
The **range** of the relation is the set of all second components of the ordered pairs.

For example, the domain for our relation in the middle of the previous page is $\{a, c, e\}$ and the range is $\{1, 3\}$. Notice that the range does not include the element 2 of the second set. This is because no element of the first set is assigned to this element. If a relation is defined in terms of x- and y-values, we will agree that the domain corresponds to x-values and that the range corresponds to y-values.

◆**Example 1**   Determine the domain and range of each relation.

a. $\{(2, 3), (2, 4), (0, -1), (3, -1)\}$

b.

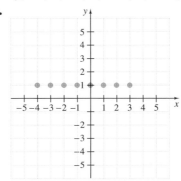

c.   Input: Output:

Cities   Population
(in thousands)

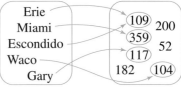

Solution   **a.** The domain is the set of all first coordinates of the ordered pairs, $\{2, 0, 3\}$. The range is the set of all second coordinates, $\{3, 4, -1\}$.
   b. Ordered pairs are not listed here, but are given in graph form. The relation is $\{(-4, 1), (-3, 1), (-2, 1), (-1, 1), (0, 1), (1, 1), (2, 1), (3, 1)\}$. The domain is $\{-4, -3, -2, -1, 0, 1, 2, 3\}$.
   The range is $\{1\}$.
   c. The domain is the first set, {Erie, Escondido, Gary, Miami, Waco}.
   The range is the numbers in the second set that correspond to elements in the first set $\{104, 109, 117, 359\}$.

2   Now we consider a special kind of relation called a function.

FUNCTION

A **function** is a relation in which <u>each</u> first component in the ordered pairs corresponds to *exactly* one second component.

> ▼ **HELPFUL HINT**
> A function is a special type of relation, so all functions are relations, but not all relations are functions.

Example 2   Which of the following relations are also functions?

a. $\{(-2, 5), (2, 7), (-3, 5), (9, 9)\}$

b.

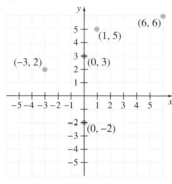

c.

Input	Correspondence	Output
People in a certain city	Each person's age	The set of nonnegative integers

Solution   **a.** Although the ordered pairs $(-2, 5)$ and $(-3, 5)$ have the same y-value, each x-value is assigned to only one y-value, so this set of ordered pairs is a function.

b. The x-value 0 is assigned to two y-values, -2 and 3, in this graph so this relation does not define a function.

c. This relation is a function because although two different people may have the same age, each person has only one age. This means that each element in the first set is assigned to only one element in the second set.   ■

We will call an equation such as $y = 2x + 1$ a **relation** since this equation defines a set of ordered pair solutions.

Example 3   Is the relation $y = 2x + 1$ also a function?

Solution   The relation $y = 2x + 1$ is a function if each x-value corresponds to just one y-value. For each x-value substituted in the equation $y = 2x + 1$, the multiplication and addition performed on each gives a single result, so only one y-value will be associated with each x-value. Thus, $y = 2x + 1$ is a function.   ■

◆**Example 4**   Is the relation $x = y^2$ also a function?

Solution   In $x = y^2$, if $y = 3$, then $x = 9$. Also, if $y = -3$, then $x = 9$. In other words, the x-value 9 corresponds to two y-values, 3 and -3. Thus, $x = y^2$ is not a function.   ■

3   As we have seen so far, not all relations are functions. Consider the graphs of $y = 2x + 1$ and $x = y^2$ shown next. On the graph of $y = 2x + 1$, notice that each *x*-value corresponds to only one *y*-value. Recall from Example 3 that $y = 2x + 1$ is a function.

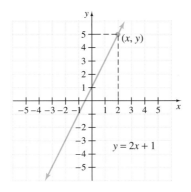

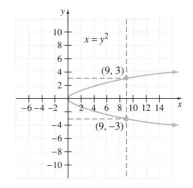

On the graph of $x = y^2$ the *x*-value 9, for example, corresponds to two *y*-values, 3 and −3, as shown by the vertical line. Recall from Example 4 that $x = y^2$ is not a function.

Graphs can be used to help determine whether a relation is also a function by the following vertical line test.

VERTICAL LINE TEST

If no vertical line can be drawn so that it intersects a graph more than once, the graph is the graph of a function.

Example 5 Which of the following graphs are graphs of functions?

a.

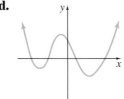

b.

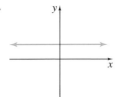

c.

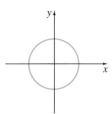

d.

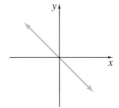

e.

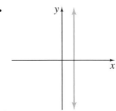

Solution **a.** This graph is the graph of a function since no vertical line will intersect this graph more than once.

b. This graph is also the graph of a function.

c. This graph is not the graph of a function. Note that vertical lines can be drawn that intersect the graph in two points.

d. This graph is the graph of a function.

e. This graph is not the graph of a function. A vertical line can be drawn that intersects this line at every point.

     Recall that the graph of a linear equation in two variables is a line, and a line that is not vertical will pass the vertical line test. Thus, **all linear equations are functions except those whose graph is a vertical line.**

4   Next, we practice finding the domain and range of a relation from its graph.

Example 6 Find the domain and range of each relation. Determine whether the relation is also a function.

a.

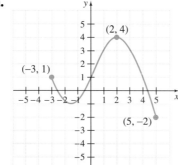

b.

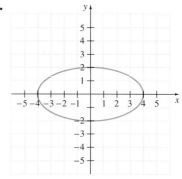

c.

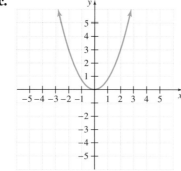

d.

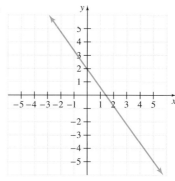

▼ **HELPFUL HINT**
In Example 6, Part **a**, notice that the graph contains the endpoints $(-3, 1)$ and $(5, -2)$ whereas the graphs in Parts **c** and **d** contain arrows that indicate that they continue forever.

Solution   By the vertical line test, graphs **a**, **c**, and **d** are graphs of functions. The domain is the set of values of x and the range is the set of values of y. We read these values from each graph.

a.

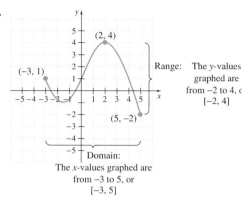

Range: The y-values graphed are from −2 to 4, or [−2, 4]

Domain: The x-values graphed are from −3 to 5, or [−3, 5]

b.

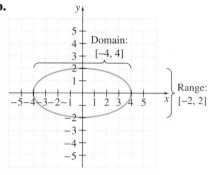

Domain: [−4, 4]

Range: [−2, 2]

c.

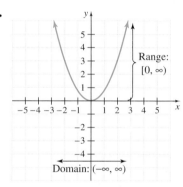

Range: [0, ∞)

Domain: (−∞, ∞)

d.

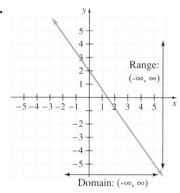

Range: (-∞, ∞)

Domain: (-∞, ∞)

5   Many times letters such as f, g, and h are used to name functions. To denote that y is a function of x, we can write

$$y = f(x)$$

This means that **y is a function of x** or that y *depends on* x. For this reason, y is called the **dependent variable** and x the **independent variable**. The notation $f(x)$ is read "f of x" and is called **function notation**.

For example, to use function notation with the function $y = 4x + 3$, we write $f(x) = 4x + 3$. The notation $f(1)$ means to replace x with 1 and find the resulting y or function value. Since

$$f(x) = 4x + 3$$

then

$$f(1) = 4(1) + 3 = 7$$

This means that when $x = 1$, y or $f(x) = 7$. The corresponding ordered pair is $(1, 7)$. Here, the input is 1 and the output is $f(1)$ or 7. Now let's find $f(2)$, $f(0)$, and $f(-1)$.

$$f(x) = 4x + 3 \qquad\qquad f(x) = 4x + 3 \qquad\qquad f(x) = 4x + 3$$
$$f(2) = 4(2) + 3 \qquad\qquad f(0) = 4(0) + 3 \qquad\qquad f(-1) = 4(-1) + 3$$
$$= 8 + 3 \qquad\qquad\qquad = 0 + 3 \qquad\qquad\qquad = -4 + 3$$
$$= 11 \qquad\qquad\qquad\qquad = 3 \qquad\qquad\qquad\qquad = -1$$

Ordered Pairs:
$$(2, 11) \qquad\qquad\qquad (0, 3) \qquad\qquad\qquad (-1, -1)$$

> **HELPFUL HINT**
> Note that $f(x)$ is a special symbol in mathematics used to denote a function.
> The symbol $f(x)$ is read "f of x." It does *not* mean $f \cdot x$ (f times x).

Example 7   If $f(x) = 7x^2 - 3x + 1$ and $g(x) = 3x - 2$, find the following.

a. $f(1)$ **b.** $g(1)$ **c.** $f(-2)$ **d.** $g(0)$

Solution   **a.** Substitute 1 for x in $f(x) = 7x^2 - 3x + 1$ and simplify.

$$f(x) = 7x^2 - 3x + 1$$
$$f(1) = 7(1)^2 - 3(1) + 1 = 5$$

b. $g(x) = 3x - 2$
$$g(1) = 3(1) - 2 = 1$$

c. $f(x) = 7x^2 - 3x + 1$
$$f(-2) = 7(-2)^2 - 3(-2) + 1 = 35$$

d. $g(x) = 3x - 2$
$$g(0) = 3(0) - 2 = -2$$

If it helps, think of a function, f, as a machine that has been programmed with a certain correspondence or rule. An input value (a member of the domain) is then fed into the machine, the machine does the correspondence or rule and the result is the output (a member of the range).

Many types of real-world paired data form functions. The broken-line graph on the next page shows the research and development spending by the Pharmaceutical Manufacturers Association.

Example 8   The following graph shows the research and development expenditures by the Pharmaceutical Manufacturers Association as a function of time.

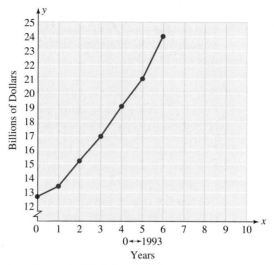

Source: Pharmaceutical Manufacturers Association
*The notation 0 ◄─► 1993 means that year 0 corresponds to
the year 1993, 1 corresponds to 1994, and so on.

    a. Approximate the money spent on research and development in 1997.
    b. In 1958, research and development expenditures were $200 million. Find the increase in expenditures from 1958 to 1999.

Solution   **a.** On the graph, since 0 corresponds to the year 1993, then 4 (0 + 4) corresponds to the year 1997 (1993 + 4). In 1997, approximately $19 billion was spent.
    b. In 1999, approximately $24 billion, or $24,000 million, was spent. The increase in spending from 1958 to 1999 is $24,000 − $200 = $23,800 million.   ■

    Notice that the graph in Example 8 is the graph of a function since each year there is only one total amount of money spent by the Pharmaceutical Manufacturers Association on research and development. Also notice that the graph resembles the graph of a line. Often, businesses depend on equations that "closely fit" data-defined functions like this one in order to model the data and predict future trends. For example, by a method called **least squares**, the function $f(x) = 1.882x + 11.79$ approximates the data shown. Its graph and the actual data function are shown next.

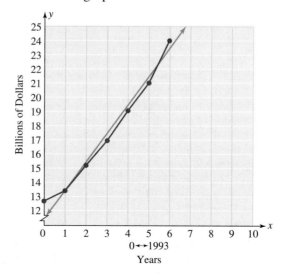

Example 9   Use the function $f(x) = 1.882x + 11.79$ to predict the amount of money that will be spent by the Pharmaceutical Manufacturers Association on research and development in 2006.

Solution   To predict the amount of money that will be spent in the year 2006 we use $f(x) = 1.882x + 11.79$ and find $f(13)$. (Notice that year 0 on the graph corresponds to the year 1993, so year 13 corresponds to the year 2006.)

$$f(x) = 1.882x + 11.79$$
$$f(13) = 1.882(13) + 11.79$$
$$= 36.256$$

We predict that in the year 2006, $36.256 billion dollars will be spent on research and development by the Pharmaceutical Manufacturers Association.

GRAPHING CALCULATOR EXPLORATIONS

It is possible to use a graphing calculator to sketch the graph of more than one equation on the same set of axes. For example, graph the functions $f(x) = x^2$ and $g(x) = x^2 + 4$ on the same set of axes.

To graph on the same set of axes, press the $\boxed{Y =}$ key and enter the equations on the first two lines.

$$Y_1 = x^2$$

$$Y_2 = x^2 + 4$$

Then press the $\boxed{\text{GRAPH}}$ key as usual. The screen should look like this.

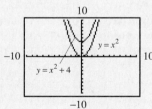

Notice that the graph of y or $g(x) = x^2 + 4$ is the graph of $y = x^2$ moved 4 units upward.

Graph each pair of functions on the same set of axes. Describe the similarities and differences in their graphs.

1. $f(x) = |x|$
$g(x) = |x| + 1$

2. $f(x) = x^2$
$h(x) = x^2 - 5$

3. $f(x) = x$
$H(x) = x - 6$

4. $f(x) = |x|$
$G(x) = |x| + 3$

5. $f(x) = -x^2$
$F(x) = -x^2 + 7$

6. $f(x) = x$
$F(x) = x + 2$

Exercise Set 3.2

Find the domain and the range of each relation. Also deter-mine whether the relation is a function. See Examples 1 and 2.

1. $\{(-1, 7), (0, 6), (-2, 2), (5, 6)\}$

2. $\{(4, 9), (-4, 9), (2, 3), (10, -5)\}$

3. $\{(-2, 4), (6, 4), (-2, -3), (-7, -8)\}$

4. $\{(6, 6), (5, 6), (5, -2), (7, 6)\}$

5. $\{(1, 1), (1, 2), (1, 3), (1, 4)\}$

6. $\{(1, 1), (2, 1), (3, 1), (4, 1)\}$

7. $\left\{\left(\frac{3}{2}, \frac{1}{2}\right), \left(1\frac{1}{2}, -7\right), \left(0, \frac{4}{5}\right)\right\}$

8. $\{(\pi, 0), (0, \pi), (-2, 4), (4, -2)\}$

9. $\{(-3, -3), (0, 0), (3, 3)\}$

10. $\left\{\left(\frac{1}{2}, \frac{1}{4}\right), \left(0, \frac{7}{8}\right), (0.5, \pi)\right\}$

11.

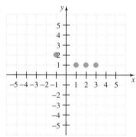

12.

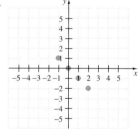

13.

Input: Output:

State   Number of Congressional
          Representatives

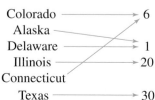

14.

Input: Output:

Animal   Average Life Span
           (in years)

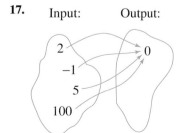

Polar Bear ──────→ 20
    Cow ──────→ 15
Chimpanzee
   Giraffe ──────→ 10
   Gorilla
 Kangaroo ──────→ 7
  Red Fox

15.

Input: Output:

Degrees   Degrees
Fahrenheit   Celsius

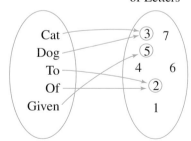

16.

Input: Output:

Words   Number
             of Letters

Cat   3   7
Dog   5
To   4   6
Of   2
Given   1

17.

Input: Output:

2   0
  −1
   5
 100

18.

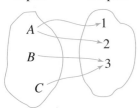

Input: Output:

In Exercises 19 and 20, determine whether the relation is a function.

19.

First set: Input	Correspondence	Second set: Output
Class of algebra students	Grade average	Set of nonnegative numbers

20.

First set: Input	Correspondence	Second set: Output
People in New Orleans (population 500,000)	Birthdate	Days of the year

21. Describe a function whose domain is the set of people in your hometown.

22. Describe a function whose domain is the set of people in your algebra class.

Use the vertical line test to determine whether each graph is the graph of a function. See Example 5.

23.

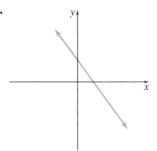

24.

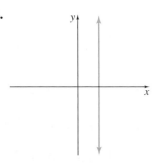

25.

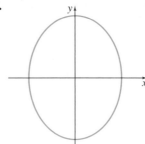

26.

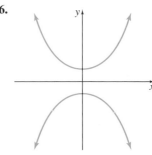

27.

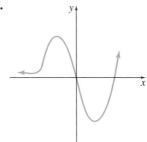

28.

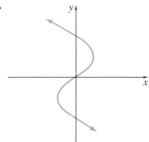

Find the domain and the range of each relation. Use the vertical line test to determine whether each graph is the graph of a function. See Example 6.

29.

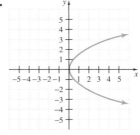

30.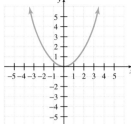

31.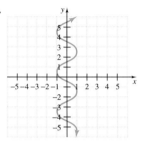

32.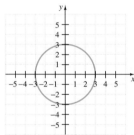

33.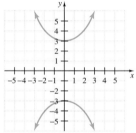

34.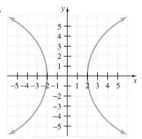

35.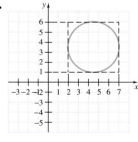

36.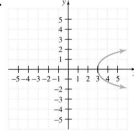

37.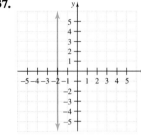

38.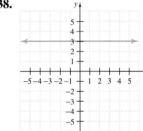

39.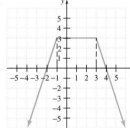

40.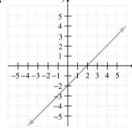

41. In your own words define **(a)** function; **(b)** domain; **(c)** range.

42. Explain the vertical line test and how it is used.

Decide whether each is a function. See Examples 3 and 4.

43. $y = x + 1$

44. $y = x - 1$

45. $x = 2y^2$

46. $y = x^2$

47. $y - x = 7$

48. $2x - 3y = 9$

49. $y = \dfrac{1}{x}$

50. $y = \dfrac{1}{x - 3}$

51. $y = 5x - 12$

52. $y = \dfrac{1}{2}x + 4$

53. $x = y^2$

54. $x = |y|$

If $f(x) = 3x + 3$, $g(x) = 4x^2 - 6x + 3$, and $h(x) = 5x^2 - 7$, find the following. See Example 7.

55. $f(4)$

56. $f(-1)$

57. $h(-3)$

58. $h(0)$

59. $g(2)$

60. $g(1)$

61. $g(0)$

62. $h(-2)$

Given the following functions, find the indicated values. See Example 7.

63. $f(x) = \dfrac{1}{2}x;$

    a. $f(0)$

    b. $f(2)$

    c. $f(-2)$

64. $g(x) = -\dfrac{1}{3}x;$

    a. $g(0)$

    b. $g(-1)$

    c. $g(3)$

65. $g(x) = 2x^2 + 4;$

    a. $g(-11)$

    b. $g(-1)$

    c. $g\left(\dfrac{1}{2}\right)$

66. $h(x) = -x^2;$

    a. $h(-5)$

    b. $h\left(-\dfrac{1}{3}\right)$

    c. $h\left(\dfrac{1}{3}\right)$

67. $f(x) = -5;$

    a. $f(2)$

    b. $f(0)$

    c. $f(606)$

68. $h(x) = 7;$

    a. $h(7)$

    b. $h(542)$

    c. $h\left(-\dfrac{3}{4}\right)$

69. $f(x) = 1.3x^2 - 2.6x + 5.1$ **a.** $f(2)$

    b. $f(-2)$ **c.** $f(3.1)$

70. $g(x) = 2.7x^2 + 6.8x - 10.2$

    a. $g(1)$ **b.** $g(-5)$

    c. $g(7.2)$

Use the graph of the function below to answer Exercises 71 through 78.

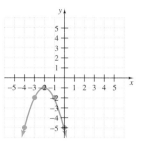

71. If $f(1) = -10$ write the corresponding ordered pair.

72. If $f(-5) = -10$, write the corresponding ordered pair.

73. Find $f(-1)$.   **74.** Find $f(-2)$.

75. Find all values of x such that $f(x) = -5$.

76. Find all values of x such that $f(x) = -2$.

77. What is the greatest number of x-intercepts that a function may have? Explain your answer.

78. What is the greatest number of y-intercepts that a function may have? Explain your answer.

Use the graph in Example 8 to answer the following.

79. a. Use the graph to approximate the money spent on research and development in 1994.

    b. Recall that the function $f(x) = 1.882x + 11.79$ approximates the graph of Example 8. Use this equation to approximate the money spent on research and development in 1994. [*Hint:* Find $f(1)$.]

80. a. Use the graph to approximate the money spent on research and development in 1998.

    b. Use the function $f(x) = 1.882x + 11.79$ to approximate the money spent on research and development in 1998. [*Hint:* Find $f(5)$.]

81. Use the function $f(x) = 1.882x + 11.79$ to predict the money that will be spent on research and development in 2005.

82. Use the function $f(x) = 1.882x + 11.79$ to predict the money that will be spent on research and development in 2010.

83. Since $y = x + 7$ describes a function, rewrite the equation using function notation.

84. In your own words, explain how to find the domain of a function given its graph.

The function $A(r) = \pi r^2$ may be used to find the area of a circle if we are given its radius.

△ **85.** Find the area of a circle whose radius is 5 centimeters. (Do not approximate π.)

△ **86.** Find the area of a circular garden whose radius is 8 feet. (Do not approximate π.)

The function $V(x) = x^3$ may be used to find the volume of a cube if we are given the length x of a side.

 87. Find the volume of a cube whose side is 14 inches.

 88. Find the volume of a die whose side is 1.7 centimeters.

Forensic scientists use the following functions to find the height of a woman if they are given the height of her femur bone f or her tibia bone t in centimeters.

$$H(f) = 2.59f + 47.24$$
$$H(t) = 2.72t + 61.28$$

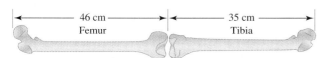

 89. Find the height of a woman whose femur measures 46 centimeters.

90. Find the height of a woman whose tibia measures 35 centimeters.

The dosage in milligrams D of Ivermectin, a heartworm preventive, for a dog who weighs x pounds is given by

$$D(x) = \frac{136}{25}x;$$

91. Find the proper dosage for a dog that weighs 30 pounds.

92. Find the proper dosage for a dog that weighs 50 pounds.

93. The per capita consumption (in pounds) of all poultry in the United States is given by the function $C(x) = 1.7x + 88$, where x is the number of years since 1995. (*Source:* Based on actual and estimated data from the Economic Research Service, U.S. Department of Agriculture, 1995–1999)

   a. Find and interpret $C(2)$.

   b. Predict the per capita consumption of all poultry in the United States in 2006.

94. The number of passengers (in millions) aboard airline flights in the United States is given by the function $P(x) = 25.4x + 448.4$, where x is the number of years since 1991. (*Source:* Based on data from the Air Transport Association of America, 1991–1997)

   a. Find and interpret $P(4)$.

   b. Predict the number of airline passengers in 2005.

REVIEW EXERCISES

Complete the given table and use the table to graph the linear equation. See Section 3.1.

95. $x - y = -5$

x	0		1
y		0	

96. $2x + 3y = 10$

x	0		
y		0	2

97. $7x + 4y = 8$

x	0		
y		0	-1

98. $5y - x = -15$

x	0		-2
y		0	

99. $y = 6x$

x	0		-1
y		0	

100. $y = -2x$

x	0		-2
y		0	

△ **101.** Is it possible to find the perimeter of the following geometric figure? If so, find the perimeter.

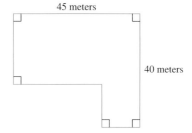

45 meters

40 meters

A Look Ahead

Example

If $f(x) = x^2 + 2x + 1$, find the following.

   a. $f(\pi)$ **b.** $f(c)$

Solution

   a. $f(x) = x^2 + 2x + 1$
   $f(\pi) = \pi^2 + 2\pi + 1$

   b. $f(x) = x^2 + 2x + 1$
   $f(c) = (c)^2 + 2(c) + 1$
   $= c^2 + 2c + 1$

Given the following functions, find the indicated values. See the previous example.

102. $f(x) = 2x + 7$;

   a. $f(2)$ **b.** $f(a)$

103. $g(x) = -3x + 12$;

   a. $g(s)$ **b.** $g(r)$

104. $h(x) = x^2 + 7$;

   a. $h(3)$ **b.** $h(a)$

105. $f(x) = x^2 - 12$;

   a. $f(12)$ **b.** $f(a)$

3.3 GRAPHING LINEAR FUNCTIONS

▶ O B J E C T I V E S

CD-ROM   SSM

SSG   Video

1. Graph linear functions.
2. Graph linear functions by finding intercepts.
3. Graph vertical and horizontal lines.

1   In this section, we identify and graph linear functions. By the vertical line test, we know that all linear equations except those whose graphs are vertical lines are functions. For example, we know from Section 3.1 that $y = 2x$ is a linear equation in two variables. Its graph is shown.

x	$y = 2x$
1	2
0	0
−1	−2

Because this graph passes the vertical line test, we know that $y = 2x$ is a function. If we want to emphasize that this equation describes a function, we may write $y = 2x$ as $f(x) = 2x$.

Example 1   Graph $g(x) = 2x + 1$. Compare this graph with the graph of $f(x) = 2x$.

Solution   To graph $g(x) = 2x + 1$, find three ordered pair solutions.

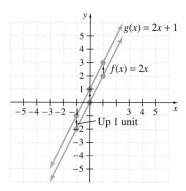

x	$f(x) = 2x$	$g(x) = 2x + 1$
0	0	1
−1	−2	−1
1	2	3

Notice that y-values for the graph of $g(x) = 2x + 1$ are obtained by adding 1 to each y-value of each corresponding point of the graph of $f(x) = 2x$. The graph of $g(x) = 2x + 1$ is the same as the graph of $f(x) = 2x$ shifted upward 1 unit.   ■

In general, a **linear function** is a function that can be written in the form $f(x) = mx + b$. For example, $g(x) = 2x + 1$ is in this form, with $m = 2$ and $b = 1$.

Example 2   Graph the linear functions $f(x) = -3x$ and $g(x) = -3x - 6$ on the same set of axes.

Solution   To graph $f(x)$ and $g(x)$, find ordered pair solutions.

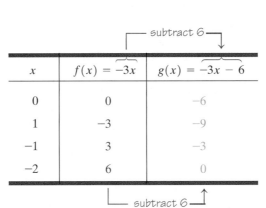

— subtract 6 —↓

x	$f(x) = -3x$	$g(x) = -3x - 6$
0	0	-6
1	-3	-9
-1	3	-3
-2	6	0

└— subtract 6 —↑

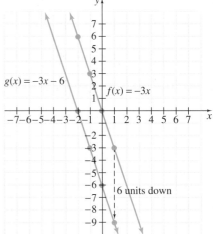

Each y-value for the graph of $g(x) = -3x - 6$ is obtained by subtracting 6 from the y-value of the corresponding point of the graph of $f(x) = -3x$. The graph of $g(x) = -3x - 6$ is the same as the graph of $f(x) = -3x$ shifted down 6 units.   ■

2   Notice that the y-intercept of the graph of $g(x) = -3x - 6$ in the preceding figure is $(0, -6)$. In general, if *a linear function is written in the form* $f(x) = mx + b$ *or* $y = mx + b$, *the* y-*intercept is* $(0, b)$. This is because if x is 0, then $f(x) = mx + b$ becomes $f(0) = m \cdot 0 + b = b$, and we have the ordered pair solution $(0, b)$. We will study this form more in the next section.

Example 3   Find the y-intercept of the graph of each equation.

a. $f(x) = \dfrac{1}{2}x + \dfrac{3}{7}$ **b.** $y = -2.5x - 3.2$

Solution   **a.** The y-intercept of $f(x) = \dfrac{1}{2}x + \dfrac{3}{7}$ is $\left(0, \dfrac{3}{7}\right)$.

b. The y-intercept of $y = -2.5x - 3.2$ is $(0, -3.2)$.   ■

In general, to find the y-intercept of the graph of an equation not in the form $y = mx + b$, let $x = 0$ since any point on the y-axis has an x-coordinate of 0. To find the x-intercept of a line, let $y = 0$ or $f(x) = 0$ since any point on the x-axis has a y-coordinate of 0.

FINDING x- AND y-INTERCEPTS

To find an x-intercept, let $y = 0$ or $f(x) = 0$ and solve for x.
To find a y-intercept, let $x = 0$ and solve for y.

Intercepts are usually easy to find and plot since one coordinate is 0.

Example 4   Graph $x - 3y = 6$ by plotting intercepts.

Solution   Let $y = 0$ to find the x-intercept and $x = 0$ to find the y-intercept.

$$\text{If } y = 0 \quad \text{then} \qquad\qquad \text{If } x = 0 \quad \text{then}$$
$$x - 3(0) = 6 \qquad\qquad\qquad 0 - 3y = 6$$
$$x - 0 = 6 \qquad\qquad\qquad\quad -3y = 6$$
$$x = 6 \qquad\qquad\qquad\quad\ y = -2$$

The x-intercept is $(6, 0)$ and the y-intercept is $(0, -2)$. We find a third ordered pair solution to check our work. If we let $y = -1$, then $x = 3$. Plot the points $(6, 0)$, $(0, -2)$, and $(3, -1)$. The graph of $x - 3y = 6$ is the line drawn through these points, as shown.

x	y
6	0
0	-2
3	-1

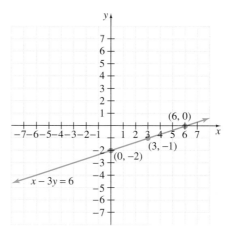

Notice that the equation $x - 3y = 6$ describes a linear function—"linear" because its graph is a line and "function" because the graph passes the vertical line test.

If we want to emphasize that the equation $x - 3y = 6$ from Example 4 describes a function, first solve the equation for y.

$$x - 3y = 6$$
$$-3y = -x + 6 \qquad \text{Subtract } x \text{ from both sides.}$$
$$\frac{-3y}{-3} = \frac{-x}{-3} + \frac{6}{-3} \qquad \text{Divide both sides by } -3.$$
$$y = \frac{1}{3}x - 2 \qquad \text{Simplify.}$$

Next, let
$$y = f(x).$$
$$f(x) = \frac{1}{3}x - 2$$

▼
HELPFUL HINT
Any linear equation that describes a function can be written using function notation. To do so, solve the equation for y and then replace y with $f(x)$, as we did above.

Example 5   Graph $x = -2y$ by plotting intercepts.

Solution   Let $y = 0$ to find the x-intercept and $x = 0$ to find the y-intercept.

If $y = 0$	then	If $x = 0$	then
$x = -2(0)$	or	$0 = -2y$	or
$x = 0$		$0 = y$	

Ordered pairs $(0, 0)$ $\qquad\qquad\qquad$ $(0, 0)$

Both the x-intercept and y-intercept are $(0, 0)$. This happens when the graph passes through the origin. Since two points are needed to determine a line, we must find at least one more ordered pair that satisfies $x = -2y$. Let $y = -1$ to find a second ordered pair solution and let $y = 1$ as a check point.

If $y = -1$	then	If $y = 1$	then
$x = -2(-1)$	or	$x = -2(1)$	or
$x = 2$		$x = -2$	

The ordered pairs are $(0, 0)$, $(2, -1)$, and $(-2, 1)$. Plot these points to graph $x = -2y$.

x	y
0	0
2	−1
−2	1

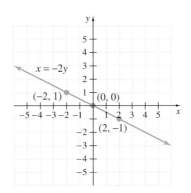

3   The equations $x = c$ and $y = c$, where c is a real number constant, are both linear equations in two variables. Why? Because $x = c$ can be written as $x + 0y = c$ and $y = c$ can be written as $0x + y = c$. We graph these two special linear equations below.

Example 6   Graph $x = 2$.

Solution   The equation $x = 2$ can be written as $x + 0y = 2$. For any y-value chosen, notice that x is 2. No other value for x satisfies $x + 0y = 2$. Any ordered pair whose x-coordinate is 2 is a solution to $x + 0y = 2$ because 2 added to 0 times any value of y is $2 + 0$, or 2. We will use the ordered pairs $(2, 3)$, $(2, 0)$ and $(2, -3)$ to graph $x = 2$.

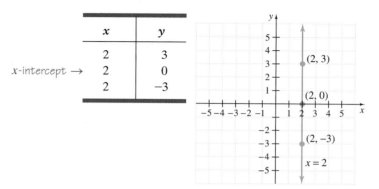

x	y
2	3
x-intercept → 2	0
2	-3

The graph is a vertical line with x-intercept $(2, 0)$. Notice that this graph is not the graph of a function, and it has no y-intercept because x is never 0.

Example 7   Graph $y = -3$.

Solution   The equation $y = -3$ can be written as $0x + y = -3$. For any x-value chosen, y is -3. If we choose 4, 0, and -2 as x-values, the ordered pair solutions are $(4, -3)$, $(0, -3)$, and $(-2, -3)$. We will use these ordered pairs to graph $y = -3$.

x	y	
4	-3	
0	-3	← y-intercept
-2	-3	

The graph is a horizontal line with y-intercept $(0, -3)$ and no x-intercept. Notice that this graph is the graph of a function.

From Examples 6 and 7, we have the following generalization.

GRAPHING VERTICAL AND HORIZONTAL LINES

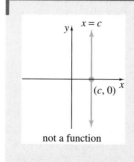

not a function

The graph of $x = c$, where c is a real number, is a vertical line with x-intercept $(c, 0)$.
The graph of $y = c$, where c is a real number, is a horizontal line with y-intercept $(0, c)$.

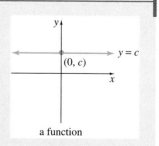

a function

GRAPHING CALCULATOR EXPLORATIONS

You may have noticed by now that to use the $\boxed{Y=}$ key on a graphing calculator to graph an equation, the equation must be solved for y.

Graph each function by first solving the function for y.

1. $x = 3.5y$ **2.** $-2.7y = x$

3. $5.78x + 2.31y = 10.98$ **4.** $-7.22x + 3.89y = 12.57$

5. $y - |x| = 3.78$ **6.** $3y - 5x^2 = 6x - 4$

7. $y - 5.6x^2 = 7.7x + 1.5$ **8.** $y + 2.6|x| = -3.2$

Exercise Set 3.3

Graph each linear function. See Examples 1 and 2.

1. $f(x) = -2x$ **2.** $f(x) = 2x$

3. $f(x) = -2x + 3$ **4.** $f(x) = 2x + 6$

5. $f(x) = \frac{1}{2}x$ **6.** $f(x) = \frac{1}{3}x$

7. $f(x) = \frac{1}{2}x - 4$ **8.** $f(x) = \frac{1}{3}x - 2$

The graph of $f(x) = 5x$ follows. Use this graph to match each linear function with its graph. See Examples 1 through 3.

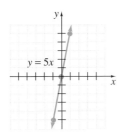

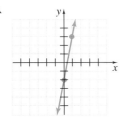

A   B

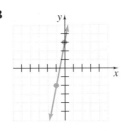

C   D

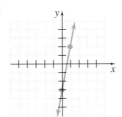

9. $f(x) = 5x - 3$ **10.** $f(x) = 5x - 2$
11. $f(x) = 5x + 1$ **12.** $f(x) = 5x + 3$

Graph each linear function by finding x-and y-intercepts. See Examples 4 and 5.

13. $x - y = 3$ **14.** $x - y = -4$
15. $x = 5y$ **16.** $2x = y$
17. $-x + 2y = 6$ **18.** $x - 2y = -8$
19. $2x - 4y = 8$ **20.** $2x + 3y = 6$

21. In your own words, explain how to find x- and y-intercepts.

22. Explain why it is a good idea to use three points to graph a linear equation.

Graph each linear equation. See Examples 6 and 7.

23. $x = -1$ **24.** $y = 5$
25. $y = 0$ **26.** $x = 0$
27. $y + 7 = 0$ **28.** $x - 3 = 0$

Match each equation with its graph.

A
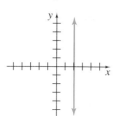

B
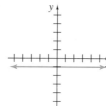

C
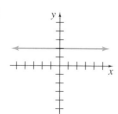

D
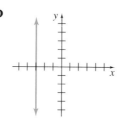

29. $y = 2$

30. $x = -3$

31. $x - 2 = 0$

32. $y + 1 = 0$

33. Discuss whether a vertical line ever has a y-intercept.

34. Discuss whether a horizontal line ever has an x-intercept.

Graph each linear equation.

35. $x + 2y = 8$

36. $x - 3y = 3$

37. $f(x) = \dfrac{3}{4}x + 2$

38. $f(x) = \dfrac{4}{3}x + 2$

39. $x = -3$

40. $f(x) = 3$

41. $3x + 5y = 7$

42. $3x - 2y = 5$

43. $f(x) = x$

44. $f(x) = -x$

45. $x + 8y = 8$

46. $x - 3y = 9$

47. $5 = 6x - y$

48. $4 = x - 3y$

49. $-x + 10y = 11$

50. $-x + 9 = -y$

51. $y = 1$

52. $x = 1$

53. $f(x) = \dfrac{1}{2}x$

54. $f(x) = -2x$

55. $x + 3 = 0$

56. $y - 6 = 0$

57. $f(x) = 4x - \dfrac{1}{3}$

58. $f(x) = -3x + \dfrac{3}{4}$

59. $2x + 3y = 6$

60. $4x + y = 5$

Solve.

61. Broyhill Furniture found that it takes 2 hours to manufacture each table for one of its special dining room sets. Each chair takes 3 hours to manufacture. A total of 1500 hours is available to produce tables and chairs of this style. The linear equation that models this situation is $2x + 3y = 1500$, where x represents the number of tables produced and y the number of chairs produced.

a. Complete the ordered pair solution $(0, \ )$ of this equation. Describe the manufacturing situation this solution corresponds to.

b. Complete the ordered pair solution $(\ , 0)$ for this equation. Describe the manufacturing situation this solution corresponds to.

c. If 50 tables are produced, find the greatest number of chairs the company can make.

62. While manufacturing two different camera models, Kodak found that the basic model costs $55 to produce, whereas the deluxe model costs $75. The weekly budget for these two models is limited to $33,000 in production costs. The linear equation that models this situation is $55x + 75y = 33,000$, where x represents the number of basic models and y the number of deluxe models.

a. Complete the ordered pair solution $(0, \ )$ of this equation. Describe the manufacturing situation this solution corresponds to.

b. Complete the ordered pair solution $(\ , 0)$ of this equation. Describe the manufacturing situation this solution corresponds to.

c. If 350 deluxe models are produced, find the greatest number of basic models that can be made in one week.

63. The cost of renting a car for a day is given by the linear function $C(x) = 0.2x + 24$, where $C(x)$ is in dollars and x is the number of miles driven.

a. Find the cost of driving the car 200 miles.

b. Graph $C(x) = 0.2x + 24$.

c. How can you tell from the graph of $C(x)$ that as the number of miles driven increases, the total cost increases also?

64. The cost of renting a piece of machinery is given by the linear function $C(x) = 4x + 10$, where $C(x)$ is in dollars and x is given in hours.

a. Find the cost of renting the piece of machinery for 8 hours.

b. Graph $C(x) = 4x + 10$.

c. How can you tell from the graph of $C(x)$ that as the number of hours increases, the total cost increases also?

65. The yearly cost of tuition and required fees for attending a public two-year college full time can be estimated by the linear function $f(x) = 72.9x + 785.2$, where x is the number of years after 1990 and $f(x)$ is the total cost. (*Source:* U.S. National Center for Education Statistics)

a. Use this function to approximate the yearly cost of attending a two-year college in the year 2010. [*Hint:* Find $f(20)$.]

b. Use the given function to predict in what year the yearly cost of tuition and required fees will exceed $2000. [*Hint:* Let $f(x) = 2000$ and solve for x.]

c. Use this function to approximate the yearly cost of attending a two-year college in the present year. If you attend a two-year college, is this amount greater than or less than the amount that is currently charged by the college that you attend?

66. The yearly cost of tuition and required fees for attending a public four-year college can be estimated by the linear function $f(x) = 186.1x + 2030$, where x is the number of years after 1990 and $f(x)$ is the total cost in dollars. (*Source:* U.S. National Center for Education Statistics)

  a. Use this function to approximate the yearly cost of attending a four-year college in the year 2010. [*Hint:* Find $f(20)$.]

  b. Use the given function to predict in what year the yearly cost of tuition and required fees will exceed \$5000. [*Hint:* Let $f(x) = 5000$ and solve for x.]

  c. Use this function to approximate the yearly cost of attending a four-year college in the present year. If you attend a four-year college, is this amount greater than or less than the amount that is currently charged by the college that you attend?

Use a graphing calculator to verify the results of each exercise.

67. Exercise 9   **68.** Exercise 10

69. Exercise 17   **70.** Exercise 18

REVIEW EXERCISES

Solve the following. See Sections 2.6 and 2.7.

71. $|x - 3| = 6$ **72.** $|x + 2| < 4$

73. $|2x + 5| > 3$ **74.** $|5x| = 10$

75. $|3x - 4| \le 2$ **76.** $|7x - 2| \ge 5$

Simplify.

77. $\dfrac{-6 - 3}{2 - 8}$ **78.** $\dfrac{4 - 5}{-1 - 0}$

79. $\dfrac{-8 - (-2)}{-3 - (-2)}$ **80.** $\dfrac{12 - 3}{10 - 9}$

81. $\dfrac{0 - 6}{5 - 0}$ **82.** $\dfrac{2 - 2}{3 - 5}$

3.4 THE SLOPE OF A LINE

CD-ROM   SSM

SSG   Video

▶ **OBJECTIVES**

1. Find the slope of a line given two points on the line.
2. Find the slope of a line given the equation of a line.
3. Interpret the slope–intercept form in an application.
4. Find the slopes of horizontal and vertical lines.
5. Compare the slopes of parallel and perpendicular lines.

1

You may have noticed by now that different lines often tilt differently. It is very important in many fields to be able to measure and compare the tilt, or **slope**, of lines. For example, a wheelchair ramp with a slope of $\frac{1}{12}$ means that the ramp rises 1 foot for every 12 horizontal feet. A road with a slope or grade of 11% (or $\frac{11}{100}$) means that the road rises 11 feet for every 100 horizontal feet.

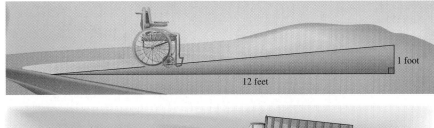

1 foot

12 feet

11 feet

100 feet

We measure the slope of a line as a ratio of **vertical change** to **horizontal change**. Slope is usually designated by the letter m.

Suppose that we want to measure the slope of the following line.

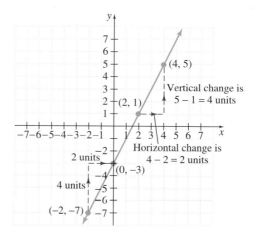

The vertical change between both pairs of points on the line is 4 units per horizontal change of 2 units. Then

$$\text{slope } m = \frac{\text{change in } y \text{ (vertical change)}}{\text{change in } x \text{ (horizontal change)}} = \frac{4}{2} = 2$$

Notice that slope is a rate of change between points. A slope of 2 or $\frac{2}{1}$ means that between pairs of points on the line, the rate of change is a vertical change of 2 units per horizontal change of 1 unit.

Consider the line below, which passes through the points (x_1, y_1) and (x_2, y_2). (The notation x_1 is read "x-sub-one.") The vertical change, or *rise*, between these points is the difference in the y-coordinates: $y_2 - y_1$. The horizontal change, or *run*, between the points is the difference of the x-coordinates: $x_2 - x_1$.

SLOPE OF A LINE

Given a line passing through points (x_1, y_1) and (x_2, y_2) the **slope** m of the line is

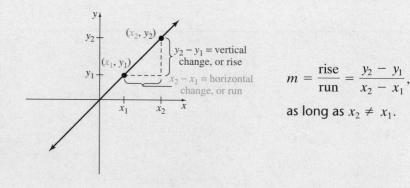

$$m = \frac{\text{rise}}{\text{run}} = \frac{y_2 - y_1}{x_2 - x_1},$$

as long as $x_2 \neq x_1$.

Example 1   Find the slope of the line containing the points $(0, 3)$ and $(2, 5)$. Graph the line.

Solution   We use the slope formula. It does not matter which point we call (x_1, y_1) and which point we call (x_2, y_2). We'll let $(x_1, y_1) = (0, 3)$ and $(x_2, y_2) = (2, 5)$.

$$m = \frac{y_2 - y_1}{x_2 - x_1}$$

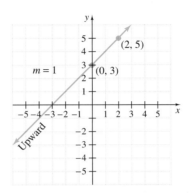

$$= \frac{5 - 3}{2 - 0} = \frac{2}{2} = 1$$

Notice in this example that the slope is positive and that the graph of the line containing $(0, 3)$ and $(2, 5)$ moves upward, or increases, as we go from left to right.

> **HELPFUL HINT**
> When we are trying to find the slope of a line through two given points, it makes no difference which given point is called (x_1, y_1) and which is called (x_2, y_2). Once an x-coordinate is called x_1, however, make sure its corresponding y-coordinate is called y_1.

Example 2   Find the slope of the line containing the points $(5, -4)$ and $(-3, 3)$. Graph the line.

Solution   We use the slope formula, and let $(x_1, y_1) = (5, -4)$ and $(x_2, y_2) = (-3, 3)$.

$$m = \frac{y_2 - y_1}{x_2 - x_1}$$

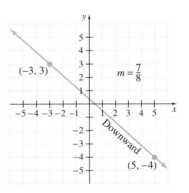

$$= \frac{3 - (-4)}{-3 - 5} = \frac{7}{-8} = -\frac{7}{8}$$

Notice in this example that the slope is negative and that the graph of the line through $(5, -4)$ and $(-3, 3)$ moves downward, or decreases, as we go from left to right.

2   As we have seen, the slope of a line is defined by two points on the line. Thus, if we know the equation of a line, we can find its slope.

Example 3   Find the slope of the line whose equation is $f(x) = \dfrac{2}{3}x + 4$.

Solution   Two points are needed on the line defined by $f(x) = \dfrac{2}{3}x + 4$ or $y = \dfrac{2}{3}x + 4$ to find its slope. We will use intercepts as our two points.

$$\text{If } x = 0, \text{ then} \qquad\qquad \text{If } y = 0, \text{ then}$$

$$y = \frac{2}{3} \cdot 0 + 4 \qquad\qquad 0 = \frac{2}{3}x + 4$$

$$y = 4 \qquad\qquad\qquad -4 = \frac{2}{3}x \qquad\qquad \text{Subtract 4.}$$

$$\frac{3}{2}(-4) = \frac{3}{2} \cdot \frac{2}{3}x \qquad\qquad \text{Multiply by } \frac{3}{2}.$$

$$-6 = x$$

Use the points $(0, 4)$ and $(-6, 0)$ to find the slope. Let (x_1, y_1) be $(0, 4)$ and (x_2, y_2) be $(-6, 0)$. Then

$$m = \frac{y_2 - y_1}{x_2 - x_1} = \frac{0 - 4}{-6 - 0} = \frac{-4}{-6} = \frac{2}{3}$$

Analyzing the results of Example 3, you may notice a striking pattern:

The slope of $y = \dfrac{2}{3}x + 4$ is $\dfrac{2}{3}$, the same as the coefficient of x.

Also, the y-intercept is $(0, 4)$, as expected.

When a linear equation is written in the form $f(x) = mx + b$ or $y = mx + b, m$ is the slope of the line and $(0, b)$ is its y-intercept. The form $y = mx + b$ is appropriately called the **slope–intercept form**.

SLOPE–INTERCEPT FORM

When a linear equation in two variables is written in slope–intercept form,

$$\overset{\text{slope}}{\downarrow} \quad \overset{y\text{-intercept is } (0,\, b)}{\downarrow}$$

$$y = mx + b$$

then m is the slope of the line and $(0, b)$ is the y-intercept of the line.

Example 4   Find the slope and the y-intercept of the line $3x - 4y = 4$.

Solution   We write the equation in slope–intercept form by solving for y.

$$3x - 4y = 4$$

$$-4y = -3x + 4 \qquad\qquad \text{Subtract 3x from both sides.}$$

$$\frac{-4y}{-4} = \frac{-3x}{-4} + \frac{4}{-4} \qquad\qquad \text{Divide both sides by } -4.$$

$$y = \frac{3}{4}x - 1 \qquad\qquad \text{Simplify.}$$

The coefficient of x, $\dfrac{3}{4}$, is the slope, and the y-intercept is $(0, -1)$.

3

Below is the graph of one-day ticket prices at Disney World for the years shown.

Notice that the graph resembles the graph of a line. Recall that businesses often depend on equations that "closely fit" graphs like this one to model the data and predict future trends. By the **least squares** method, the linear function $f(x) = 1.505x + 32.56$ approximates the data shown, where x is the number of years since 1990 and y is the ticket price for that year.

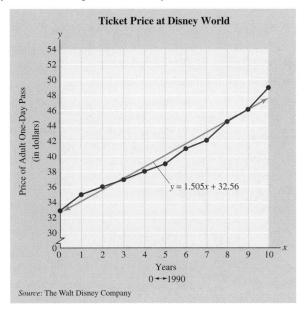

Source: The Walt Disney Company

Example 5 PREDICTING FUTURE PRICES

The adult one-day pass price $f(x)$ for Disney World is given by

$$f(x) = 1.505x + 32.56$$

where x is the number of years since 1990

a. Use this equation to predict the ticket price for the year 2004.
b. What does the slope of this equation mean?
c. What does the y-intercept of this equation mean?

Solution **a.** To predict the price of a pass in 2004, we need to find $f(14)$. (Since year 1990 corresponds to $x = 0$, year 2004 corresponds to $x = 14$.)

$$f(x) = 1.505x + 32.56$$
$$f(14) = 1.505(14) + 32.56 \qquad \text{Let } x = 14.$$
$$= 53.63$$

We predict that in the year 2004 the price of an adult one-day pass to Disney World will be about $53.63.

b. The slope of $f(x) = 1.505x + 32.56$ is 1.505. We can think of this number as $\dfrac{\text{rise}}{\text{run}}$ or $\dfrac{1.505}{1}$. This means that the ticket price increases on the average by $1.505 every 1 year.

c. The y-intercept of $y = 1.505 + 32.56$ is $(0, 32.56)$.

↑   ↖

year   price

This means that at year $x = 0$ or 1990, the ticket price was about \$32.56.   ▪

4   Next we find the slopes of two special types of lines: vertical lines and horizontal lines.

Example 6   Find the slope of the line $x = -5$.

Solution   Recall that the graph of $x = -5$ is a vertical line with x-intercept $(-5, 0)$. To find the slope, we find two ordered pair solutions of $x = -5$. Of course, solutions of $x = -5$ must have an x-value of -5. We will let $(x_1, y_1) = (-5, 0)$ and $(x_2, y_2) = (-5, 4)$. Then

$$m = \frac{y_2 - y_1}{x_2 - x_1}$$

$$= \frac{4 - 0}{-5 - (-5)}$$

$$= \frac{4}{0}$$

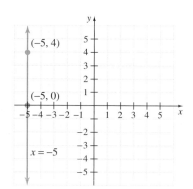

Since $\dfrac{4}{0}$ is undefined, we say that the slope of the vertical line $x = -5$ is undefined.   ▪

Example 7   Find the slope of the line $y = 2$.

Solution   Recall that the graph of $y = 2$ is a horizontal line with y-intercept $(0, 2)$. To find the slope, we find two points on the line, such as $(0, 2)$ and $(1, 2)$, and use these points to find the slope.

$$m = \frac{2 - 2}{1 - 0}$$

$$= \frac{0}{1}$$

$$= 0$$

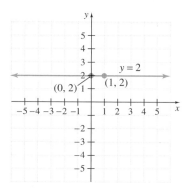

The slope of the horizontal line $y = 2$ is 0.   ▪

From the previous two examples, we have the following generalization.

> The slope of any vertical line is undefined.
> The slope of any horizontal line is 0.

▼ HELPFUL HINT
Slope of 0 and undefined slope are not the same. Vertical lines have undefined slope, whereas horizontal lines have slope of 0.

The following four graphs summarize the overall appearance of lines with positive, negative, zero, or undefined slopes.

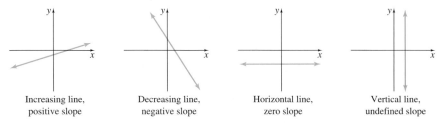

| Increasing line, positive slope | Decreasing line, negative slope | Horizontal line, zero slope | Vertical line, undefined slope |

The appearance of a line can give us further information about its slope.

The graphs of $y = \frac{1}{2}x + 1$

and $y = 5x + 1$ are shown to the right. Recall that the graph of $y = \frac{1}{2}x + 1$ has a slope of $\frac{1}{2}$ and that the graph of $y = 5x + 1$ has a slope of 5.

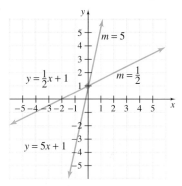

Notice that the line with the slope of 5 is steeper than the line with the slope of $\frac{1}{2}$. This is true in general for positive slopes.

> For a line with positive slope m, as m increases, the line becomes steeper.

5 Slopes of lines can help us determine whether lines are parallel. Parallel lines are distinct lines with the same steepness, so it follows that they have the same slope.

PARALLEL LINES

> Two nonvertical lines are parallel if they have the same slope and different y-intercepts.

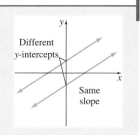

How do the slopes of perpendicular lines compare? (Two lines intersecting at right angles are called **perpendicular lines**.) Suppose that a line has a slope of $\frac{a}{b}$. If the line is rotated 90°, the rise and run are now switched, except that the run is now negative. This means that the new slope is $-\frac{b}{a}$. Notice that

$$\left(\frac{a}{b}\right) \cdot \left(-\frac{b}{a}\right) = -1$$

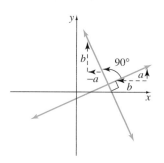

This is how we tell whether two lines are perpendicular.

PERPENDICULAR LINES

Two nonvertical lines are perpendicular if the product of their slopes is −1.

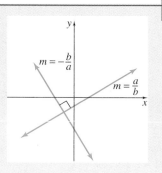

In other words, two nonvertical lines are perpendicular if the slope of one is the negative reciprocal of the slope of the other.

▲ Example 8

Are the following pairs of lines parallel, perpendicular, or neither?

a. $3x + 7y = 4$
$6x + 14y = 7$

b. $-x + 3y = 2$
$2x + 6y = 5$

Solution Find the slope of each line by solving each equation for y.

a. $3x + 7y = 4$ $6x + 14y = 7$

$7y = -3x + 4$ $14y = -6x + 7$

$\dfrac{7y}{7} = \dfrac{-3x}{7} + \dfrac{4}{7}$ $\dfrac{14y}{14} = \dfrac{-6x}{14} + \dfrac{7}{14}$

$y = -\dfrac{3}{7}x + \dfrac{4}{7}$ $y = -\dfrac{3}{7}x + \dfrac{1}{2}$

$\uparrow\nwarrow$ $\uparrow\uparrow$

slope y-intercept slope y-intercept

$\left(0, \dfrac{4}{7}\right)$ $\left(0, \dfrac{1}{2}\right)$

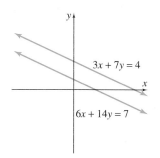

The slopes of both lines are $-\dfrac{3}{7}$.

The y-intercepts are different.
Therefore, the lines are parallel.

b. $-x + 3y = 2$ $2x + 6y = 5$

$$3y = x + 2 \qquad\qquad 6y = -2x + 5$$

$$\frac{3y}{3} = \frac{x}{3} + \frac{2}{3} \qquad \frac{6y}{6} = \frac{-2x}{6} + \frac{5}{6}$$

$$y = \frac{1}{3}x + \frac{2}{3} \qquad y = -\frac{1}{3}x + \frac{5}{6}$$

   ↑ ↖   ↑ ↖

  slope y-intercept slope y-intercept

     $\left(0, \dfrac{2}{3}\right)$ $\left(0, \dfrac{5}{6}\right)$

The slopes are not the same and their product is not -1. $\left[\left(\dfrac{1}{3}\right) \cdot \left(-\dfrac{1}{3}\right) = -\dfrac{1}{9}\right]$

Therefore, the lines are neither parallel nor perpendicular.

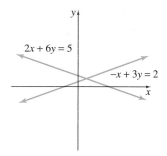

GRAPHING CALCULATOR EXPLORATIONS

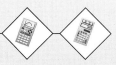

Many graphing calculators have a TRACE feature. This feature allows you to trace along a graph and see the corresponding x- and y-coordinates appear on the screen. Use this feature for the following exercises.

 Graph each function and then use the TRACE feature to complete each ordered pair solution. (Many times the tracer will not show an exact x- or y-value asked for. In each case, trace as closely as you can to the given x- or y-coordinate and approximate the other, unknown coordinate to one decimal place.)

1. $y = 2.3x + 6.7$
$x = 5.1, y = ?$

2. $y = -4.8x + 2.9$
$x = -1.8, y = ?$

3. $y = -5.9x - 1.6$
$x = ?, y = 7.2$

4. $y = 0.4x - 8.6$
$x = ?, y = -4.4$

5. $y = x^2 + 5.2x - 3.3$
$x = 2.3, y = ?$
$x = ?, y = 36$
(There will be two answers here.)

6. $y = 5x^2 - 6.2x - 8.3$
$x = 3.2, y = ?$
$x = ?, y = 12$
(There will be two answers here.)

SPOTLIGHT ON DECISION MAKING

Suppose you are the manager of an apartment complex. You have just notified residents of a rent increase. Some residents think that the increase may be unjustified and out of line with recent increases. A group of concerned residents asks you to hold an open meeting to answer questions about the increase. You are preparing a set of overheads to use during the meeting to show the history of rent increases at the apartment complex. Which overhead would you use and why?

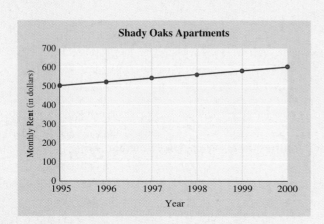

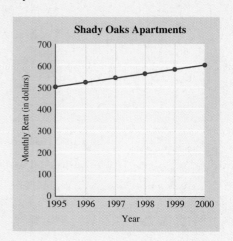

MENTAL MATH

Decide whether a line with the given slope slants upward, downward, horizontally, or vertically from left to right.

1. $m = \dfrac{7}{6}$

2. $m = -3$

3. $m = 0$

4. m is undefined

Exercise Set 3.4

Find the slope of the line that goes through the given points. See Examples 1 and 2.

1. $(3, 2), (8, 11)$ **2.** $(1, 6), (7, 11)$

3. $(3, 1), (1, 8)$ **4.** $(2, 9), (6, 4)$

5. $(-2, 8), (4, 3)$ **6.** $(3, 7), (-2, 11)$

7. $(-2, -6), (4, -4)$ **8.** $(-3, -4), (-1, 6)$

9. $(-3, -1), (-12, 11)$ **10.** $(3, -1), (-6, 5)$

11. $(-2, 5), (3, 5)$ **12.** $(4, 2), (4, 0)$

13. $(-1, 1), (-1, -5)$ **14.** $(-2, -5), (3, -5)$

15. $(0, 6), (-3, 0)$ **16.** $(5, 2), (0, 5)$

17. $(-1, 2), (-3, 4)$ **18.** $(3, -2), (-1, -6)$

Two lines are graphed on each set of axes. Decide whether l_1 or l_2 has the greater slope.

19.

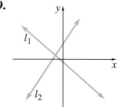

20.

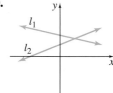

21.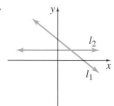

22.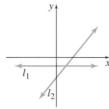

23.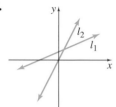

24.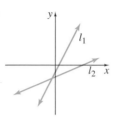

C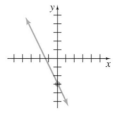

D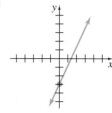

34. $f(x) = 2x + 3$

36. $f(x) = -2x + 3$

35. $f(x) = 2x - 3$

37. $f(x) = -2x - 3$

Find the slope of each line. See Examples 6 and 7.

38. $x = 1$

39. $y = -2$

40. $y = -3$

41. $x = 4$

42. $x + 2 = 0$

43. $y - 7 = 0$

44. Explain how merely looking at a line can tell us whether its slope is negative, positive, undefined, or zero.

45. Explain why the graph of $y = b$ is a horizontal line.

25. Each line below has negative slope.

   a. Find the slope of each line.

   b. Use the result of Part **a** to fill in the blank. For lines with negative slopes, the steeper line has the ____ (greater/lesser) slope.

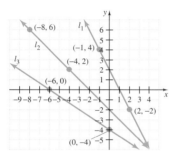

Find the slope and the y-intercept of each line. See Examples 3 and 4.

26. $f(x) = 5x - 2$

27. $f(x) = -2x + 6$

28. $2x + y = 7$

29. $-5x + y = 10$

30. $2x - 3y = 10$

31. $-3x - 4y = 6$

32. $f(x) = \dfrac{1}{2}x$

33. $f(x) = -\dfrac{1}{4}x$

Find the slope and the y-intercept of each line.

46. $f(x) = -x + 5$

47. $f(x) = x + 2$

48. $-6x + 5y = 30$

49. $4x - 7y = 28$

50. $3x + 9 = y$

51. $2y - 7 = x$

52. $y = 4$

53. $x = 7$

54. $f(x) = 7x$

55. $f(x) = \dfrac{1}{7}x$

56. $6 + y = 0$

57. $x - 7 = 0$

58. $2 - x = 3$

59. $2y + 4 = -7$

Determine whether the lines are parallel, perpendicular, or neither. See Example 8.

△ **60.** $f(x) = -3x + 6$
     $g(x) = 3x + 5$

△ **61.** $f(x) = 5x - 6$
     $g(x) = 5x + 2$

△ **62.** $-4x + 2y = 5$
     $2x - y = 7$

△ **63.** $2x - y = -10$
     $2x + 4y = 2$

△ **64.** $-2x + 3y = 1$
     $3x + 2y = 12$

△ **65.** $x + 4y = 7$
     $2x - 5y = 0$

66. Explain whether two lines, both with positive slopes, can be perpendicular.

67. Explain why it is reasonable that nonvertical parallel lines have the same slope.

Match each graph with its equation.

A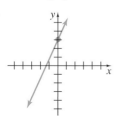

B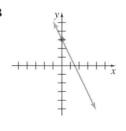

Determine the slope of each line.

68.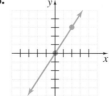

69.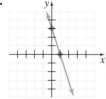

70.

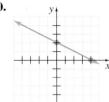

71.

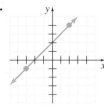

Find each slope.

72. Find the pitch, or slope, of the roof shown.

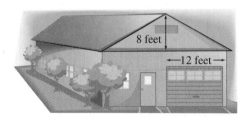

8 feet

←12 feet→

73. Upon takeoff, a Delta Airlines jet climbs to 3 miles as it passes over 25 miles of land below it. Find the slope of its climb.

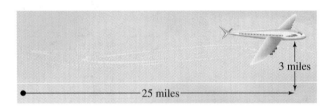

3 miles

25 miles

74. Driving down Bald Mountain in Wyoming, Bob Dean finds that he descends 1600 feet in elevation by the time he is 2.5 miles (horizontally) away from the high point on the mountain road. Find the slope of his descent rounded to two decimal places (1 mile = 5280 feet).

75. Find the grade, or slope, of the road shown.

15 feet

100 feet

Solve. See Example 5.

76. The annual average income y of an American man with an associate's degree is given by the linear equation $y = 1431.5x + 31{,}775.2$, where x is the number of years after 1992. (*Source:* Based on data from the U.S. Bureau of the Census, 1992–1996)

a. Find the average income of an American man with an associate's degree in 1996.

b. Find and interpret the slope of the equation.

c. Find and interpret the y-intercept of the equation.

77. The annual income of an American woman with a bachelor's degree is given by the linear equation $y = 1054.7x + 23{,}285.9$, where x is the number of years after 1991. (*Source:* Based on data from the U.S. Bureau of the Census, 1991–1996)

a. Find the average income of an American woman with a bachelor's degree in 1996.

b. Find and interpret the slope of the equation.

c. Find and interpret the y-intercept of the equation.

78. One of the top ten occupations in terms of job growth in the next few years is expected to be home health aide. The number of people y in thousands employed as home health aides in the United States can be estimated by the linear equation

$$378x - 10y = -4950,$$

where x is the number of years after 1996. (*Source:* Based on projections from the U.S. Bureau of Labor Statistics, 1996–2006)

a. Find the slope and y-intercept of the linear equation.

b. What does the slope mean in this context?

c. What does the y-intercept mean in this context?

79. One of the faster growing occupations over the next few years is expected to be paralegal. The number of people y in thousands employed as paralegals in the United States can be estimated by the linear equation $-76x + 10y = 1130$, where x is the number of years after 1996. (*Source:* Based on projections from the U.S. Bureau of Labor Statistics, 1996–2006)

a. Find the slope and y-intercept of the linear equation.

b. What does the slope mean in this context?

c. What does the y-intercept mean in this context?

80. In an earlier section, it was given that the yearly cost of tuition and required fees for attending a public four-year college full-time can be estimated by the linear function

$$f(x) = 186.1x + 2030$$

where x is the number of years after 1990 and $f(x)$ is the total cost. (*Source:* U.S. National Center for Education Statistics)

a. Find and interpret the slope of this equation.

b. Find and interpret the y-intercept of this equation.

81. If an earlier section, it was given that the yearly cost of tuition and required fees for attending a public two-year college full-time can be estimated by the linear function

$$f(x) = 72.9x + 785.2$$

where x is the number of years after 1990 and $f(x)$ is the total cost. (*Source:* U.S. National Center for Education Statistics)

a. Find and interpret the slope of this equation.

b. Find and interpret the y-intercept of this equation.

Solve.

△ **82.** Find the slope of a line parallel to the line

$$f(x) = -\frac{7}{2}x - 6.$$

△ **83.** Find the slope of a line parallel to the line $f(x) = x$.

△ **84.** Find the slope of a line perpendicular to the line

$$f(x) = -\frac{7}{2}x - 6.$$

△ **85.** Find the slope of a line perpendicular to the line $f(x) = x$.

△ **86.** Find the slope of a line parallel to the line $5x - 2y = 6$.

△ **87.** Find the slope of a line parallel to the line $-3x + 4y = 10$.

△ **88.** Find the slope of a line perpendicular to the line $5x - 2y = 6$.

89. The following graph shows the altitude of a seagull in flight over a time period of 30 seconds.

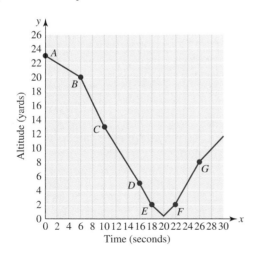

a. Find the coordinates of point B.

b. Find the coordinates of point C.

c. Find the rate of change of altitude between points B and C. (Recall that the rate of change between points is the slope between points. This rate of change will be in yards per second.)

d. Find the rate of change of altitude (in yards per second) between points F and G.

90. Professional plumbers suggest that a sewer pipe should be sloped 0.25 inch for every foot. Find the recommended slope for a sewer pipe. (*Source: Rules of Thumb* by Tom Parker, 1983, Houghton Mifflin Company)

91. Support the result of Exercise 62 by graphing the pair of equations on a graphing calculator.

92. Support the result of Exercise 63 by graphing the pair of equations on a graphing calculator. (*Hint:* Use the window showing $[-15, 15]$ on the x-axis and $[-10, 10]$ on the y-axis.)

93. **a.** On a single screen, graph $y = \frac{1}{2}x + 1$, $y = x + 1$ and $y = 2x + 1$. Notice the change in slope for each graph.

b. On a single screen, graph $y = -\frac{1}{2}x + 1$, $y = -x + 1$ and $y = -2x + 1$. Notice the change in slope for each graph.

c. Determine whether the following statement is true or false for slope m of a given line. As $|m|$ becomes greater, the line becomes steeper.

REVIEW EXERCISES

Recall the formula

$$\text{Probability of an event} = \frac{\text{number of ways that the event can occur}}{\text{number of possible outcomes}}$$

Suppose these cards are shuffled and one card is turned up. Find the possibility of selecting each letter.

P R O B A B I L I T Y

94. $P(\text{R})$

95. $P(\text{B})$

96. $P(\text{E})$

97. $P(\text{I or T})$

98. $P(\text{selecting a letter of the alphabet})$

99. $P(\text{vowel})$

Simplify and solve for y. See Section 2.3.

100. $y - 2 = 5(x + 6)$

101. $y - 0 = -3[x - (-10)]$

102. $y - (-1) = 2(x - 0)$

103. $y - 9 = -8[x - (-4)]$

3.5 EQUATIONS OF LINES

CD-ROM   SSM

SSG   Video

▶ **OBJECTIVES**

1. Use the slope–intercept form to write the equation of a line.
2. Graph a line using its slope and y-intercept.
3. Use the point–slope form to write the equation of a line.
4. Write equations of vertical and horizontal lines.
5. Find equations of parallel and perpendicular lines.

1

In the last section, we learned that the slope–intercept form of a linear equation is $y = mx + b$. When an equation is written in this form, the slope of the line is the same as the coefficient m of x. Also, the y-intercept of the line is the same as the constant term b. For example, the slope of the line defined by $y = 2x + 3$ is, 2, and its y-intercept is 3.

We may also use the slope–intercept form to write the equation of a line given its slope and y-intercept.

Example 1   Write an equation of the line with y-intercept $(0, -3)$ and slope of $\frac{1}{4}$.

Solution   We are given the slope and the y-intercept. Let $m = \frac{1}{4}$ and $b = -3$, and write the equation in slope–intercept form, $y = mx + b$.

$$y = mx + b$$

$$y = \frac{1}{4}x + (-3) \qquad \text{Let } m = \frac{1}{4} \text{ and } b = -3.$$

$$y = \frac{1}{4}x - 3 \qquad \text{Simplify.}$$

2

Given the slope and y-intercept of a line, we may graph the line as well as write its equation. Let's graph the line from Example 1.

Example 2   Graph $y = \frac{1}{4}x - 3$.

Solution   Recall that the slope of the graph of $y = \frac{1}{4}x - 3$ is $\frac{1}{4}$ and the y-intercept is $(0, -3)$.

To graph the line, we first plot the y-intercept $(0, -3)$. To find another point on the line, we recall that slope is $\dfrac{\text{rise}}{\text{run}} = \dfrac{1}{4}$. Another point may then be plotted by starting at $(0, -3)$, rising 1 unit up, and then running 4 units to the right. We are now at the point $(4, -2)$. The graph is the line through these two points.

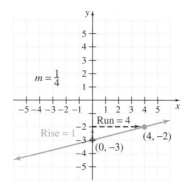

Example 3   Graph $2x + 3y = 12$.

Solution   First, we solve the equation for y to write it in slope–intercept form. In slope–intercept form, the equation is $y = -\dfrac{2}{3}x + 4$. Next we plot the y-intercept $(0, 4)$. To find another point on the line, we use the slope $-\dfrac{2}{3}$, which can be written as $\dfrac{\text{rise}}{\text{run}} = \dfrac{-2}{3}$. We start at $(0, 4)$ and move down 2 units since the numerator of the slope is -2; then we move 3 units to the right since the denominator of the slope is 3. We arrive at the point $(3, 2)$. The line through these points is the graph.

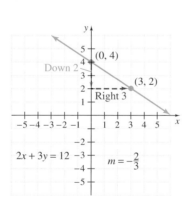

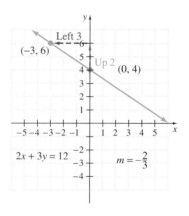

The slope $\dfrac{-2}{3}$ can also be written as $\dfrac{2}{-3}$, so to find another point in Example 3 we could start at $(0, 4)$ and move up 2 units and then 3 units to the left. We would stop at the point $(-3, 6)$. The line through $(-3, 6)$ and $(0, 4)$ is the same line as shown previously through $(3, 2)$ and $(0, 4)$.

---

3   When the slope of a line and a point on the line are known, the equation of the line can also be found. To do this, use the slope formula to write the slope of a line that passes through points (x_1, y_1) and (x, y). We have

$$m = \frac{y - y_1}{x - x_1}$$

Multiply both sides of this equation by $x - x_1$ to obtain

$$y - y_1 = m(x - x_1)$$

This form is called the **point–slope form** of the equation of a line.

POINT–SLOPE FORM OF THE EQUATION OF A LINE

The point–slope form of the equation of a line is $y - y_1 = m(x - x_1)$, where m is the slope of the line and (x_1, y_1) is a point on the line.

Example 4   Find an equation of the line with slope -3 containing the point $(1, -5)$. Write the equation in slope–intercept form $y = mx + b$.

Solution   Because we know the slope and a point of the line, we use the point–slope form with $m = -3$ and $(x_1, y_1) = (1, -5)$.

$$
\begin{aligned}
y - y_1 &= m(x - x_1) && \text{Point–slope form.} \\
y - (-5) &= -3(x - 1) && \text{Let } m = -3 \text{ and } (x_1, y_1) = (1, -5). \\
y + 5 &= -3x + 3 && \text{Apply the distributive property.} \\
y &= -3x - 2 && \text{Write in slope–intercept form.}
\end{aligned}
$$

In slope–intercept form, the equation is $y = -3x - 2$.

Example 5   Find an equation of the line through points $(4, 0)$ and $(-4, -5)$. Write the equation using function notation.

Solution   First, find the slope of the line.

$$m = \frac{-5 - 0}{-4 - 4} = \frac{-5}{-8} = \frac{5}{8}$$

Next, make use of the point–slope form. Replace (x_1, y_1) by either $(4, 0)$ or $(-4, -5)$ in the point–slope equation. We will choose the point $(4, 0)$. The line through $(4, 0)$ with slope $\frac{5}{8}$ is

$$
\begin{aligned}
y - y_1 &= m(x - x_1) && \text{Point–slope form.} \\
y - 0 &= \frac{5}{8}(x - 4) && \text{Let } m = \frac{5}{8} \text{ and } (x_1, y_1) = (4, 0). \\
8y &= 5(x - 4) && \text{Multiply both sides by 8.} \\
8y &= 5x - 20 && \text{Apply the distributive property.}
\end{aligned}
$$

To write the equation using function notation, we solve for y.

$$
\begin{aligned}
8y &= 5x - 20 \\
y &= \frac{5}{8}x - \frac{20}{8} && \text{Divide both sides by 8.} \\
f(x) &= \frac{5}{8}x - \frac{5}{2} && \text{Write using function notation.}
\end{aligned}
$$

The point–slope form of an equation is very useful for solving real-world problems.

Example 6 PREDICTING SALES

Southern Star Realty is an established real estate company that has enjoyed constant growth in sales since 1990. In 1992 the company sold 200 houses, and in 1997 the company sold 275 houses. Use these figures to predict the number of houses this company will sell in the year 2006.

Solution
1. UNDERSTAND. Read and reread the problem. Then let

x = the number of years after 1990 and
y = the number of houses sold in the year corresponding to x.
The information provided then gives the ordered pairs $(2, 200)$ and $(7, 275)$. To better visualize the sales of Southern Star Realty, we graph the linear equation that passes through the points $(2, 200)$ and $(7, 275)$.

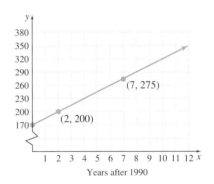

Years after 1990

2. TRANSLATE. We write a linear equation that passes through the points $(2, 200)$ and $(7, 275)$. To do so, we first find the slope of the line.

$$m = \frac{275 - 200}{7 - 2} = \frac{75}{5} = 15$$

Then, using the point–slope form to write the equation, we have

$$y - y_1 = m(x - x_1)$$
$$y - 200 = 15(x - 2) \qquad \text{Let } m = 15 \text{ and } (x_1, y_1) = (2, 200).$$
$$y - 200 = 15x - 30 \qquad \text{Multiply.}$$
$$y = 15x + 170 \qquad \text{Add 200 to both sides.}$$

3. SOLVE. To predict the number of houses sold in the year 2006, we use $y = 15x + 170$ and complete the ordered pair $(16, \ \ )$, since $2006 - 1990 = 16$.

$$y = 15(16) + 170 \qquad \text{Let } x = 16.$$
$$y = 410$$

4. INTERPRET.

Check: Verify that the point $(16, 410)$ is a point on the line graphed in step 1.
State: Southern Star Realty should expect to sell 410 houses in the year 2006.

4   A few special types of linear equations are linear equations whose graphs are vertical and horizontal lines.

Example 7   Find the equation of the horizontal line containing the point $(2, 3)$.

Solution   Recall that a horizontal line has an equation of the form $y = b$. Since the line contains the point $(2, 3)$, the equation is $y = 3$.   ▬

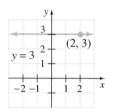

Example 8   Find the equation of the line containing the point $(2, 3)$ with undefined slope.

Solution   Since the line has undefined slope, the line must be vertical. A vertical line has an equation of the form $x = c$, and since the line contains the point $(2, 3)$, the equation is $x = 2$.   ▬

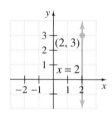

5   Next, we find equations of parallel and perpendicular lines.

△ **Example 9**   Find an equation of the line containing the point $(4, 4)$ and parallel to the line $2x + 3y = -6$. Write the equation in standard form.

Solution   Because the line we want to find is *parallel* to the line $2x + 3y = -6$, the two lines must have equal slopes. Find the slope of $2x + 3y = -6$ by writing it in the form $y = mx + b$.

$$2x + 3y = -6$$

$$3y = -2x - 6 \qquad \text{Subtract } 2x \text{ from both sides.}$$

$$y = \frac{-2x}{3} - \frac{6}{3} \qquad \text{Divide by 3.}$$

$$y = -\frac{2}{3}x - 2 \qquad \text{Write in slope–intercept form.}$$

The slope of this line is $-\dfrac{2}{3}$. Thus, a line parallel to this line will also have a slope of $-\dfrac{2}{3}$. The equation we are asked to find describes a line containing the point $(4, 4)$ with a slope of $-\dfrac{2}{3}$. We use the point–slope form.

$$y - y_1 = m(x - x_1)$$

$$y - 4 = -\dfrac{2}{3}(x - 4) \qquad \text{Let } m = -\dfrac{2}{3}, x_1 = 4, \text{ and } y_1 = 4.$$

$$3(y - 4) = -2(x - 4) \qquad \text{Multiply both sides by 3.}$$

$$3y - 12 = -2x + 8 \qquad \text{Apply the distributive property.}$$

$$2x + 3y = 20 \qquad \text{Write in standard form.} \qquad \blacksquare$$

HELPFUL HINT

Multiply both sides of the equation $2x + 3y = 20$ by -1, and it becomes $-2x - 3y = -20$. Both equations are in standard form, and their graphs are the same line.

△ **Example 10** Write a function that describes the line containing the point $(4, 4)$ and is perpendicular to the line $2x + 3y = -6$.

Solution In the previous example, we found that the slope of the line $2x + 3y = -6$ is $-\dfrac{2}{3}$. A line perpendicular to this line will have a slope that is the negative reciprocal of $-\dfrac{2}{3}$, or $\dfrac{3}{2}$. From the point–slope equation, we have

$$y - y_1 = m(x - x_1)$$

$$y - 4 = \dfrac{3}{2}(x - 4) \qquad \text{Let } x_1 = 4, y_1 = 4 \text{ and } m = \dfrac{3}{2}.$$

$$2(y - 4) = 3(x - 4) \qquad \text{Multiply both sides by 2.}$$

$$2y - 8 = 3x - 12 \qquad \text{Apply the distributive property.}$$

$$2y = 3x - 4 \qquad \text{Add 8 to both sides.}$$

$$y = \dfrac{3}{2}x - 2 \qquad \text{Divide both sides by 2.}$$

$$f(x) = \dfrac{3}{2}x - 2 \qquad \text{Write using function notation.} \qquad \blacksquare$$

FORMS OF LINEAR EQUATIONS

$Ax + By = C$	**Standard form** of a linear equation
	A and B are not both 0.
$y = mx + b$	**Slope–intercept form** of a linear equation
	The slope is m, and the y-intercept is $(0, b)$.
$y - y_1 = m(x - x_1)$	**Point–slope form** of a linear equation
	The slope is m, and (x_1, y_1) is a point on the line.
$y = c$	**Horizontal line**
	The slope is 0, and the y-intercept is $(0, c)$.
$x = c$	**Vertical line**
	The slope is undefined and the x-intercept is $(c, 0)$.

PARALLEL AND PERPENDICULAR LINES

Nonvertical parallel lines have the same slope. The product of the slopes of two nonvertical perpendicular lines is -1.

SPOTLIGHT ON DECISION MAKING

Suppose you are a public health official. In 1993, the International Task Force for Disease Eradication (ITFDE) identified mumps as one of six infectious diseases that could probably be eradicated worldwide with current technology. The ITFDE defined "eradication" as reducing the incidence of a disease to zero. Does the graph of reported mumps cases in the United States support the possibility of U.S. mumps eradication? Explain.

Suppose U.S. officials would like to see mumps eradicated by 2010. If this goal does not currently seem possible, your department will increase eradication efforts with the launch of a new public awareness campaign. Will the new public awareness campaign be necessary? (*Hint:* Use the data for the years 1996 and 1997 to help you decide.)

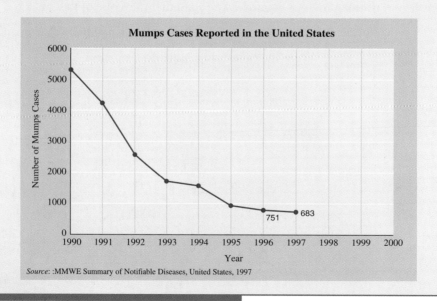

Source: :MMWE Summary of Notifiable Diseases, United States, 1997

MENTAL MATH

State the slope and the y-intercept of each line with the given equation.

1. $y = -4x + 12$

2. $y = \dfrac{2}{3}x - \dfrac{7}{2}$

3. $y = 5x$

4. $y = -x$

5. $y = \dfrac{1}{2}x + 6$

6. $y = -\dfrac{2}{3}x + 5$

Decide whether the lines are parallel, perpendicular, or neither.

7. $y = 12x + 6$
$y = 12x - 2$

8. $y = -5x + 8$
$y = -5x - 8$

9. $y = -9x + 3$
$y = \dfrac{3}{2}x - 7$

10. $y = 2x - 12$
$y = \dfrac{1}{2}x - 6$

Exercise Set 3.5

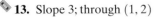

Use the slope–intercept form of the linear equation to write the equation of each line with the given slope and y-intercept. See Example 1.

1. Slope -1; y-intercept $(0, 1)$

2. Slope $\dfrac{1}{2}$; y-intercept $(0, -6)$

3. Slope 2; y-intercept $\left(0, \dfrac{3}{4}\right)$

4. Slope -3; y-intercept $\left(0, -\dfrac{1}{5}\right)$

5. Slope $\dfrac{2}{7}$; y-intercept $(0, 0)$

6. Slope $-\dfrac{4}{5}$; y-intercept $(0, 0)$

Graph each linear equation. See Examples 2 and 3.

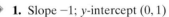

7. $y = 5x$

8. $y = 2x + 12$

9. $x + y = 7$

10. $3x + y = 9$

11. $-3x + 2y = 3$

12. $-2x + 5y = -16$

Find an equation of the line with the given slope and containing the given point. Write the equation in slope–intercept form. See Example 4.

13. Slope 3; through $(1, 2)$

14. Slope 4; through $(5, 1)$

15. Slope -2; through $(1, -3)$

16. Slope -4; through $(2, -4)$

17. Slope $\dfrac{1}{2}$; through $(-6, 2)$

18. Slope $\dfrac{2}{3}$; through $(-9, 4)$

19. Slope $-\dfrac{9}{10}$; through $(-3, 0)$

20. Slope $-\dfrac{1}{5}$; through $(4, -6)$

Find an equation of each line graphed. Write the equation in standard form.

21.

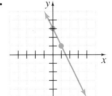

22.

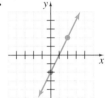

23.

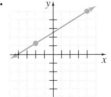

24.

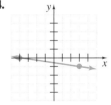

Find an equation of the line passing through the given points. Use function notation to write the equation. See Example 5.

25. $(2, 0), (4, 6)$

26. $(3, 0), (7, 8)$

27. $(-2, 5), (-6, 13)$

28. $(7, -4), (2, 6)$

29. $(-2, -4), (-4, -3)$

30. $(-9, -2), (-3, 10)$

31. $(-3, -8), (-6, -9)$

32. $(8, -3), (4, -8)$

33. Describe how to check to see if the graph of $2x - 4y = 7$ passes through the points $(1.4, -1.05)$ and $(0, -1.75)$. Then follow your directions and check these points.

Use the graph of the following function $f(x)$ to find each value.

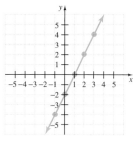

34. $f(1)$ **35.** $f(0)$

36. $f(-1)$ **37.** $f(2)$

38. Find x such that $f(x) = 4$.

39. Find x such that $f(x) = -6$.

Write an equation of each line. See Examples 7 and 8.

40. Vertical; through $(2, 6)$

41. Slope 0; through $(-2, -4)$

42. Horizontal; through $(-3, 1)$

43. Vertical; through $(4, 7)$

44. Undefined slope; through $(0, 5)$

45. Horizontal; through $(0, 5)$

△ 46. Answer the following true or false. A vertical line is always perpendicular to a horizontal line.

Find an equation of each line. Write the equation using function notation. See Examples 9 and 10.

△ 47. Through $(3, 8)$; parallel to $f(x) = 4x - 2$

△ 48. Through $(1, 5)$; parallel to $f(x) = 3x - 4$

✎ 49. Through $(2, -5)$; perpendicular to $3y = x - 6$

△ 50. Through $(-4, 8)$; perpendicular to $2x - 3y = 1$

△ 51. Through $(-2, -3)$; parallel to $3x + 2y = 5$

△ 52. Through $(-2, -3)$; perpendicular to $3x + 2y = 5$

Find the equation of each line. Write the equation in standard form unless indicated otherwise.

53. Slope 2; through $(-2, 3)$

54. Slope 3; through $(-4, 2)$

55. Through $(1, 6)$ and $(5, 2)$; use function notation.

56. Through $(2, 9)$ and $(8, 6)$

57. With slope $-\dfrac{1}{2}$; y-intercept 11

58. With slope -4; y-intercept $\dfrac{2}{9}$; use function notation.

59. Through $(-7, -4)$ and $(0, -6)$

60. Through $(2, -8)$ and $(-4, -3)$

61. Slope $-\dfrac{4}{3}$; through $(-5, 0)$

62. Slope $-\dfrac{3}{5}$; through $(4, -1)$

63. Vertical line; through $(-2, -10)$

64. Horizontal line; through $(1, 0)$

△ 65. Through $(6, -2)$; parallel to the line $2x + 4y = 9$

△ 66. Through $(8, -3)$; parallel to the line $6x + 2y = 5$

67. Slope 0; through $(-9, 12)$

68. Undefined slope; through $(10, -8)$

△ 69. Through $(6, 1)$; parallel to the line $8x - y = 9$

△ 70. Through $(3, 5)$; perpendicular to the line $2x - y = 8$

△ 71. Through $(5, -6)$; perpendicular to $y = 9$

△ 72. Through $(-3, -5)$; parallel to $y = 9$

73. Through $(2, -8)$ and $(-6, -5)$; use function notation.

74. Through $(-4, -2)$ and $(-6, 5)$; use function notation.

75. Del Monte Fruit Company recently released a new applesauce. By the end of its first year, profits on this product amounted to $30,000. The anticipated profit for the end of the fourth year is $66,000. The ratio of change in time to change in profit is constant. Let x be years and P be profit.

   a. Write a linear function $P(x)$ that expresses profit as a function of time.

   b. Use this function to predict the company's profit at the end of the seventh year.

   c. Predict when the profit should reach $126,000.

76. The value of a computer bought in 1996 depreciates, or decreases, as time passes. Two years after the computer was bought, it was worth $2600; 4 years after it was bought, it was worth $1000.

   a. If this relationship between number of years past 1996 and value of computer is linear, write an equation describing this relationship. [Use ordered pairs of the form (years past 1996, value of computer).]

   b. Use this equation to estimate the value of the computer in the year 2001.

77. The Pool Fun Company has learned that, by pricing a newly released Fun Noodle at $3, sales will reach 10,000 Fun Noodles per day during the summer. Raising the price to $5 will cause the sales to fall to 8000 Fun Noodles per day.

   a. Assume that the relationship between sales price and number of Fun Noodles sold is linear and write an equation describing this relationship.

   b. Predict the daily sales of Fun Noodles if the price is $3.50.

78. The value of a building bought in 1980 appreciates, or increases, as time passes. Seven years after the building was bought, it was worth $165,000; 12 years after it was bought, it was worth $180,000.

   a. If this relationship between number of years past 1980 and value of building is linear, write an equation describing this relationship. [Use ordered pairs of the form (years past 1980, value of building).]

   b. Use this equation to estimate the value of the building in the year 2000.

79. In 1994, the median price of an existing home in the United States was $109,900. In 1998, the median price of an existing home was $128,400. Let y be the median price of an existing home in the year x, where $x = 0$ represents 1994. (*Source:* National Association of REALTORS®)

a. Write a linear equation that models the median existing home price in terms of the year x. [*Hint:* The line must pass through the points $(0, 109,900)$ and $(4, 128,400)$]

b. Use this equation to predict the median existing home price for the year 2008.

80. The number of births (in thousands) in the United States in 1997 was 3895. The number of births (in thousands) in the United States in 1991 was 4111. Let y be the number of births (in thousands) in the year x, where $x = 0$ represents 1991. (*Source:* National Center for Health Statistics)

a. Write a linear equation that models the number of births (in thousands) in terms of the year x. (See hint for Exercise 79**a.**)

b. Use this equation to predict the number of births in the United States for the year 2010.

81. The number of people employed in the United States as medical assistants was 225 thousand in 1996. By the year 2006, this number is expected to rise to 391 thousand. Let y be the number of medical assistants (in thousands) employed in the United States in the year x, where $x = 0$ represents 1996. (*Source:* Bureau of Labor Statistics)

a. Write a linear equation that models the number of people (in thousands) employed as medical assistants in the year x. (See hint for Exercise 79**a.**)

b. Use this equation to estimate the number of people who will be employed as medical assistants in the year 2004.

82. The number of people employed in the United States as systems analysts was 506 thousand in 1996. By the year 2006, this number is expected to rise to 1025 thousand. Let y be the number of systems analysts (in thousands) employed in the United States in the year x, where $x = 0$ represents 1996. (*Source:* Bureau of Labor Statistics)

a. Write a linear equation that models the number of people (in thousands) employed as systems analysts in the year x. (See hint for Exercise 79**a.**)

b. Use this equation to estimate the number of people who will be employed as systems analysts in the year 2002.

Use a graphing calculator with a TRACE feature to see the results of each exercise.

83. Exercise 55; graph the function and verify that it passes through $(1, 6)$ and $(5, 2)$.

84. Exercise 56; graph the equation and verify that it passes through $(2, 9)$ and $(8, 6)$.

85. Exercise 61; graph the equation. See that it has a negative slope and passes through $(-5, 0)$.

86. Exercise 62; graph the equation. See that it has a negative slope and passes through $(4, -1)$.

REVIEW EXERCISES

Solve and graph the solution. See Section 2.4.

87. $2x - 7 \leq 21$ **88.** $-3x + 1 > 0$

89. $5(x - 2) \geq 3(x - 1)$ **90.** $-2(x + 1) \leq -x + 10$

91. $\dfrac{x}{2} + \dfrac{1}{4} < \dfrac{1}{8}$ **92.** $\dfrac{x}{5} - \dfrac{3}{10} \geq \dfrac{x}{2} - 1$

A Look Ahead

Example
Find an equation of the perpendicular bisector of the line segment whose endpoints are $(2, 6)$ and $(0, -2)$.

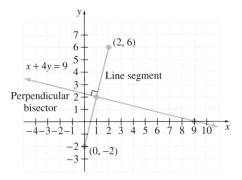

Solution
A perpendicular bisector is a line that contains the midpoint of the given segment and is perpendicular to the segment.

Step 1: The midpoint of the segment with endpoints $(2, 6)$ and $(0, -2)$ is $(1, 2)$.

Step 2: The slope of the segment containing points $(2, 6)$ and $(0, -2)$ is 4.

Step 3: A line perpendicular to this line segment will have slope of $-\frac{1}{4}$.

Step 4: The equation of the line through the midpoint $(1, 2)$ with a slope of $-\frac{1}{4}$ will be the equation of the perpendicular bisector. This equation in standard form is $x + 4y = 9$.

Find an equation of the perpendicular bisector of the line segment whose endpoints are given. See the previous example.

△ **93.** $(3, -1); (-5, 1)$ △ **94.** $(-6, -3); (-8, -1)$

△ **95.** $(-2, 6); (-22, -4)$ △ **96.** $(5, 8); (7, 2)$

△ **97.** $(2, 3); (-4, 7)$ △ **98.** $(-6, 8); (-4, -2)$

3.6 GRAPHING LINEAR INEQUALITIES

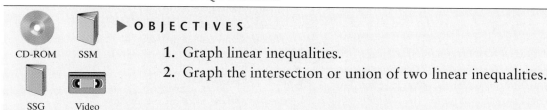

CD-ROM   SSM

SSG   Video

▶ **OBJECTIVES**

1. Graph linear inequalities.
2. Graph the intersection or union of two linear inequalities.

1 Recall that the graph of a linear equation in two variables is the graph of all ordered pairs that satisfy the equation, and we determined that the graph is a line. Here we graph **linear inequalities** in two variables; that is, we graph all the ordered pairs that satisfy the inequality.

If the equal sign in a linear equation in two variables is replaced with an inequality symbol, the result is a linear inequality in two variables.

Examples of Linear Inequalities in Two Variables

$$3x + 5y \geq 6 \qquad 2x - 4y < -3$$

$$4x > 2 \qquad y \leq 5$$

To graph the linear inequality $x + y < 3$, for example, we first graph the related **boundary** equation $x + y = 3$. The resulting boundary line contains all ordered pairs the sum of whose coordinates is 3. This line separates the plane into two **half-planes**. All points "above" the boundary line $x + y = 3$ have coordinates that satisfy the inequality $x + y > 3$, and all points "below" the line have coordinates that satisfy the inequality $x + y < 3$.

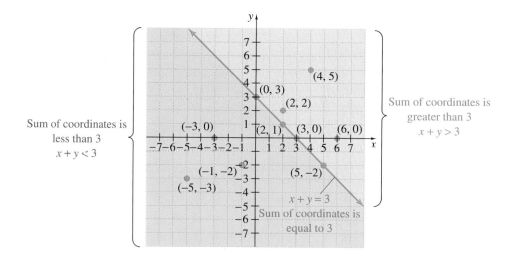

The graph, or **solution region**, for $x + y < 3$, then, is the half-plane below the boundary line and is shown shaded on page 173. The boundary line is shown dashed since it is not a part of the solution region. These ordered pairs on this line satisfy $x + y = 3$ and not $x + y < 3$.

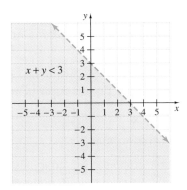

The following steps may be used to graph linear inequalities in two variables.

GRAPHING A LINEAR INEQUALITY IN TWO VARIABLES

Step 1: Graph the boundary line found by replacing the inequality sign with an equal sign. If the inequality sign is < or >, graph a dashed line indicating that points on the line are not solutions of the inequality. If the inequality sign is ≤ or ≥, graph a solid line indicating that points on the line are solutions of the inequality.

Step 2: Choose a **test point not on the boundary line** and substitute the coordinates of this test point into the **original inequality**.

Step 3: If a true statement is obtained in Step 2, shade the half-plane that contains the test point. If a false statement is obtained, shade the half-plane that does not contain the test point.

Example 1   Graph $2x - y < 6$.

Solution   First, the boundary line for this inequality is the graph of $2x - y = 6$. Graph a dashed boundary line because the inequality symbol is <. Next, choose a test point on either side of the boundary line. The point $(0, 0)$ is not on the boundary line, so we use this point. Replacing x with 0 and y with 0 in the *original inequality* $2x - y < 6$ leads to the following:

$$2x - y < 6$$
$$2(0) - 0 < 6 \qquad \text{Let } x = 0 \text{ and } y = 0.$$
$$0 < 6 \qquad \text{True.}$$

Because $(0, 0)$ satisfies the inequality, so does every point on the same side of the boundary line as $(0, 0)$. Shade the half-plane that contains $(0, 0)$. The half-plane graph of the inequality is shown.

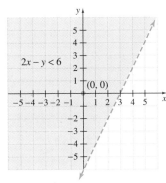

Every point in the shaded half-plane satisfies the original inequality. Notice that the inequality $2x - y < 6$ does not describe a function since its graph does not pass the vertical line test.

In general, linear inequalities of the form $Ax + By \leq C$, when A and B are not both 0, do not describe functions.

Example 2   Graph $3x \geq y$.

Solution   First, graph the boundary line $3x = y$. Graph a solid boundary line because the inequality symbol is $\geq$. Test a point not on the boundary line to determine which half-plane contains points that satisfy the inequality. We choose $(0, 1)$ as our test point.

$$3x \geq y$$
$$3(0) \geq 1 \qquad \text{Let } x = 0 \text{ and } y = 1.$$
$$0 \geq 1 \qquad \text{False.}$$

This point does not satisfy the inequality, so the correct half-plane is on the opposite side of the boundary line from $(0, 1)$. The graph of $3x \geq y$ is the boundary line together with the shaded region shown.

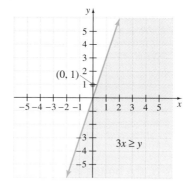

2   The intersection and the union of linear inequalities can also be graphed, as shown in the next two examples.

Example 3   Graph the intersection of $x \geq 1$ and $y \geq 2x - 1$.

Solution   Graph each inequality. The intersection of the two graphs is all points common to both regions, as shown by the heaviest shading in the third graph.

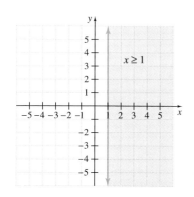
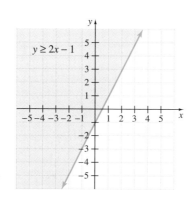
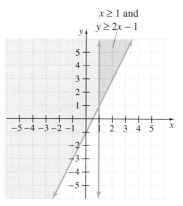

Example 4   Graph the union of $x + \dfrac{1}{2}y \geq -4$ or $y \leq -2$.

Solution   Graph each inequality. The union of the two inequalities is both shaded regions, including the solid boundary lines shown in the third graph.

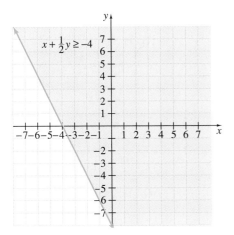

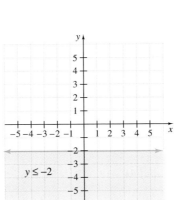

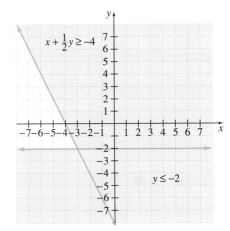

SPOTLIGHT ON DECISION MAKING

Suppose you are a customer service representative for a mail-order medical supply company that sells support stockings. A customer, whose weight is 160 pounds and whose height is 5 feet 9 inches, places an order for support stockings and has asked your assistance in selecting the correct size. What size would you recommend that this customer order? Explain.

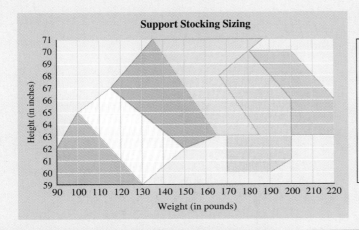

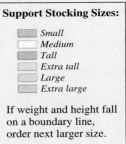

Support Stocking Sizes:

■ *Small*
□ *Medium*
■ *Tall*
▨ *Extra tall*
□ *Large*
■ *Extra large*

If weight and height fall on a boundary line, order next larger size.

Exercise Set 3.6

Graph each inequality. See Examples 1 and 2.

1. $x < 2$

2. $x > -3$

3. $x - y \geq 7$

4. $3x + y \leq 1$

5. $3x + y > 6$

6. $2x + y > 2$

7. $y \leq -2x$

8. $y \leq 3x$

9. $2x + 4y \geq 8$

10. $2x + 6y \leq 12$

11. $5x + 3y > -15$

12. $2x + 5y < -20$

13. Explain when a dashed boundary line should be used in the graph of an inequality.

14. Explain why, after the boundary line is sketched, we test a point on either side of this boundary in the original inequality.

Graph each union or intersection. See Examples 3 and 4.

15. The intersection of $x \geq 3$ and $y \leq -2$

16. The union of $x \geq 3$ or $y \leq -2$

17. The union of $x \leq -2$ or $y \geq 4$

18. The intersection of $x \leq -2$ and $y \geq 4$

19. The intersection of $x - y < 3$ and $x > 4$

20. The intersection of $2x > y$ and $y > x + 2$

21. The union of $x + y \leq 3$ or $x - y \geq 5$

22. The union of $x - y \leq 3$ or $x + y > -1$

Graph each inequality.

23. $y \geq -2$

24. $y \leq 4$

25. $x - 6y < 12$

26. $x - 4y < 8$

27. $x > 5$

28. $y \geq -2$

29. $-2x + y \leq 4$

30. $-3x + y \leq 9$

31. $x - 3y < 0$

32. $x + 2y > 0$

33. $3x - 2y \leq 12$

34. $2x - 3y \leq 9$

35. The union of $x - y \geq 2$ or $y < 5$

36. The union of $x - y < 3$ or $x > 4$

37. The intersection of $x + y \leq 1$ and $y \leq -1$

38. The intersection of $y \geq x$ and $2x - 4y \geq 6$

39. The union of $2x + y > 4$ or $x \geq 1$

40. The union of $3x + y < 9$ or $y \leq 2$

41. The intersection of $x \geq -2$ and $x \leq 1$

42. The intersection of $x \geq -4$ and $x \leq 3$

43. The union of $x + y \leq 0$ or $3x - 6y \geq 12$

44. The intersection of $x + y \leq 0$ and $3x - 6y \geq 12$

45. The intersection of $2x - y > 3$ and $x \geq 0$

46. The union of $2x - y > 3$ or $x \geq 0$

Match each inequality with its graph.

A

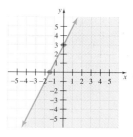

B

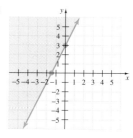

C

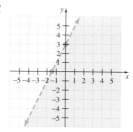

D

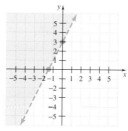

47. $y \leq 2x + 3$

48. $y < 2x + 3$

49. $y > 2x + 3$

50. $y \geq 2x + 3$

Write the inequality whose graph is given.

51.

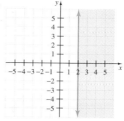

52.

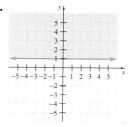

53.

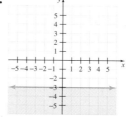

54.

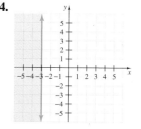

55.

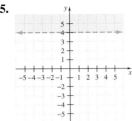

56.

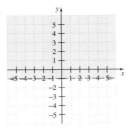

57.

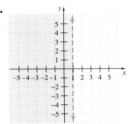

58.

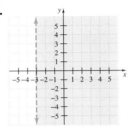

Solve.

59. Rheem Abo-Zahrah decides that she will study at most 20 hours every week and that she must work at least 10 hours every week. Let x represent the hours studying and y represent the hours working. Write two inequalities that model this situation and graph their intersection.

60. The movie and TV critic for the *New York Times* spends between 2 and 6 hours daily reviewing movies and fewer than 5 hours reviewing TV shows. Let x represent the hours watching movies and y represent the time spent watching TV. Write two inequalities that model this situation and graph their intersection.

61. Chris-Craft manufactures boats out of Fiberglas and wood. Fiberglas hulls require 2 hours work, whereas wood hulls require 4 hours work. Employees work at most 40 hours a week. The following inequalities model these restrictions, where x represents the number of Fiberglas hulls produced and y represents the number of wood hulls produced.

$$\begin{cases} x \geq 0 \\ y \geq 0 \\ 2x + 4y \leq 40 \end{cases}$$

Graph the intersection of these inequalities.

REVIEW EXERCISES

Evaluate each expression. See Sections 1.3 and 1.4.

62. 2^3

63. 3^2

64. -5^2

65. $(-5)^2$

66. $(-2)^4$

67. -2^4

68. $\left(\dfrac{3}{5}\right)^3$

69. $\left(\dfrac{2}{7}\right)^2$

Find the domain and the range of each relation. Determine whether the relation is also a function. See Section 3.2.

70.

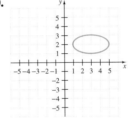

71.

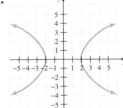

For additional Chapter Projects, visit the Real World Activities Website by going to http://www.prenhall.com/martin-gay.

CHAPTER PROJECT

Modeling Real Data

The number of children who live with only one parent has been steadily increasing in the United States since the 1960s. According to the U.S. Bureau of the Census, the percent of children living with one parent varies widely by race/ethnic background. The trend since the 1960s also varies widely, with the data for white families being the most linear. The following table shows the percent of white children (under age 18) living with *both* parents during selected years from 1970 to 1998. In this project, you will have the opportunity to use the data in the table to find a linear function $f(x)$ that represents the data, reflecting the change in living arrangements for children. This project may be completed by working in groups or individually.

PERCENT OF U.S. CHILDREN (WHITE) WHO LIVE WITH BOTH PARENTS

Year	1970	1980	1990	1995	1996	1997	1998
x	0	10	20	25	26	27	28
PERCENT, y	90	83	79	76	75	75	74

Source: U.S. Bureau of the Census

1. Plot the data given in the table as ordered pairs.
2. Use a straight edge to draw on your graph what appears to be the line that "best fits" the data you plotted.
3. Estimate the coordinates of two points that fall on your best-fitting line. Use these points to find a linear function $f(x)$ for the line.
4. What is the slope of your line? Interpret its meaning. Does it make sense in the context of this situation?
5. Find the value of $f(50)$. Write a sentence interpreting its meaning in context.

6. Compare your linear function with that of another student or group. Are they different? If so, explain why.

(Optional) Enter the data from the table into a graphing calculator. Use the linear regression feature of the calculator to find a linear function for the data. Compare this function to the one you found in Question 3. How are they alike or different? Find the value of $f(50)$ using the model you found with the graphing calculator. Compare it to the value of $f(50)$ you found in Question 5.

CHAPTER 3 VOCABULARY CHECK

Fill in each blank with one of the words or phrases listed below.

relation	line	function	standard	slope	domain
slope–intercept	x	y	range	parallel	linear function
point–slope	perpendicular	linear inequality			

1. A _____ is a set of ordered pairs.
2. The graph of every linear equation in two variables is a _____.
3. The statement $-x + 2y > 0$ is called a _____ in two variables.
4. _____ form of linear equation in two variables is $Ax + By = C$.
5. The _____ of a relation is the set of all second components of the ordered pairs of the relation.
6. _____ lines have the same slope and different y-intercepts.
7. _____ form of a linear equation in two variables is $y = mx + b$.
8. A _____ is a relation in which each first component in the ordered pairs corresponds to exactly one second component.
9. In the equation $y = 4x - 2$, the coefficient of x is the _____ of its corresponding graph.
10. Two lines are _____ if the product of their slopes is −1.
11. To find the x-intercept of a linear equation, let ____ = 0 and solve for the other variable.
12. The _____ of a relation is the set of all first components of the ordered pairs of the relation.
13. A _____ is a function that can be written in the form $f(x) = mx + b$.
14. To find the y-intercept of a linear equation, let ___ = 0 and solve for the other variable.
15. The equation $y - 8 = -5(x + 1)$ is written in _____ form.

CHAPTER 3 HIGHLIGHTS

DEFINITIONS AND CONCEPTS	EXAMPLES

Section 3.1 Graphing Equations

The **rectangular coordinate system,** or **Cartesian coordinate system,** consists of a vertical and a horizontal number line intersecting at their 0 coordinate. The vertical number line is called the **y-axis,** and the horizontal number line is called the **x-axis.** The point of intersection of the axes is called the **origin.** The axes divide the plane into four regions called **quadrants.**

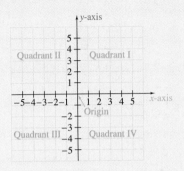

To **plot** or **graph** an ordered pair means to find its corresponding point on a rectangular coordinate system.

To plot or graph the ordered pair $(-2, 5)$, start at the origin. Move 2 units to the left along the x-axis, then 5 units upward parallel to the y-axis.

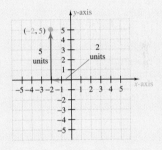

An ordered pair is a **solution** of an equation in two variables if replacing the variables by the corresponding coordinates results in a true statement.

Determine whether $(-2, 3)$ is a solution of
$3x + 2y = 0$

$$3(-2) + 2(3) = 0$$
$$-6 + 6 = 0$$
$$0 = 0 \quad \text{True.}$$

$(-2, 3)$ is a solution.

A **linear equation in two variables** is an equation that can be written in the form $Ax + By = C$, where A, B, and C are real numbers and A and B are not both 0. The form $Ax + By = C$ is called **standard form.**

Linear Equations in Two Variables

$$y = -2x + 5, \quad x = 7$$

$$y - 3 = 0, \quad 6x - 4y = 10$$

$6x - 4y = 10$ is in standard form.

The graph of a linear equation in two variables is a line. To graph a linear equation in two variables, find three ordered pair solutions. Plot the solution points, and draw the line connecting the points.

Graph $3x + y = -6$.

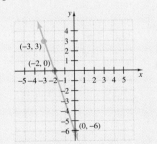

x	y
0	-6
-2	0
-3	3

(continued)

| DEFINITIONS AND CONCEPTS | EXAMPLES |

Section 3.1 Graphing Equations

To graph an equation that is not linear, find a sufficient number of ordered pair solutions so that a pattern may be discovered.

Graph $y = x^3 + 2$.

x	y
-2	-6
-1	1
0	2
1	3
2	10

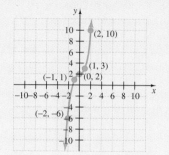

Section 3.2 Introduction to Functions

A **relation** is a set of ordered pairs. The **domain** of the relation is the set of all first components of the ordered pairs. The **range** of the relation is the set of all second components of the ordered pairs.

Relation

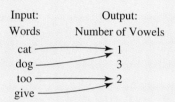

Domain: {cat, dog, too, give}
Range: {1, 2}

A **function** is a relation in which each element of the first set corresponds to exactly one element of the second set.

The previous relation is a function. Each word contains exactly one number of vowels.

Vertical Line Test

If no vertical line can be drawn so that it intersects a graph more than once, the graph is the graph of a function.

Find the domain and the range of the relation. Also determine whether the relation is a function.

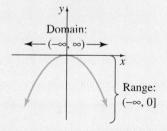

By the vertical line test, this graph is the graph of a function.

The symbol $f(x)$ means **function of x** and is called **function notation.**

If $f(x) = 2x^2 - 5$, find $f(-3)$.

$$f(-3) = 2(-3)^2 - 5 = 2(9) - 5 = 13$$

(continued)

DEFINITIONS AND CONCEPTS	EXAMPLES

Section 3.3 Graphing Linear Functions

A **linear function** is a function that can be written in the form $f(x) = mx + b$.

Linear Functions

$f(x) = -3, g(x) = 5x, h(x) = -\dfrac{1}{3}x - 7$

To graph a linear function, find three ordered pair solutions. Graph the solutions and draw a line through the plotted points.

Graph $f(x) = -2x$.

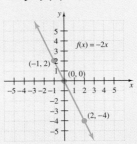

x	y or $f(x)$
-1	2
0	0
2	-4

For any function $f(x)$, the graph of $y = f(x) + K$ is the same as the graph of $y = f(x)$ shifted K units up if K is positive and $|K|$ units down if K is negative.

Graph $g(x) = -2x + 3$.
This is the same as the graph of $f(x) = -2x$ shifted 3 units up.

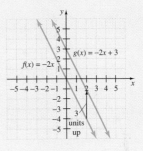

The x-coordinate of a point where a graph crosses the x-axis is called an **x-intercept**. The y-coordinate of a point where a graph crosses the y-axis is called a **y-intercept.**

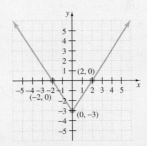

The x-intercepts of the graph are $(-2, 0)$ and $(2, 0)$.
The y-intercept is $(0, -3)$.

To find an x-intercept, let $y = 0$ or $f(x) = 0$ and solve for x.
To find a y-intercept, let $x = 0$ and solve for y.

Graph $5x - y = -5$ by finding intercepts.

If $x = 0$, then	If $y = 0$, then
$5x - y = -5$	$5x - y = -5$
$5 \cdot 0 - y = -5$	$5x - 0 = -5$
$-y = -5$	$5x = -5$
$y = 5$	$x = -1$
$(0, 5)$	$(-1, 0)$

(continued)

DEFINITIONS AND CONCEPTS	EXAMPLES

Section 3.3 Graphing Linear Functions

Ordered pairs are $(0, 5)$ and $(-1, 0)$.

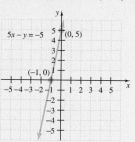

The graph of $x = c$ is a vertical line with x-intercept $(c, 0)$.

The graph of $y = c$ is a horizontal line with y-intercept $(0, c)$.

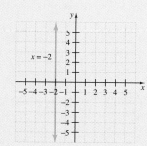 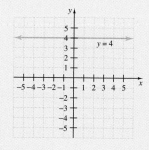

Section 3.4 The Slope of a Line

The **slope** m of the line through (x_1, y_1) and (x_2, y_2) is given by

$$m = \frac{y_2 - y_1}{x_2 - x_1} \text{ as long } x_2 \neq x_1$$

Find the slope of the line through $(-1, 7)$ and $(-2, -3)$.

$$m = \frac{y_2 - y_1}{x_2 - x_1} = \frac{-3 - 7}{-2 - (-1)} = \frac{-10}{-1} = 10$$

The **slope–intercept form** of a linear equation is $y = mx + b$, where m is the slope of the line and b is the y-intercept.

Find the slope and y-intercept of $-3x + 2y = -8$.

$$2y = 3x - 8$$

$$\frac{2y}{2} = \frac{3x}{2} - \frac{8}{2}$$

$$y = \frac{3}{2}x - 4$$

The slope the line is $\frac{3}{2}$, and the y-intercept is $(0, -4)$.

Nonvertical parallel lines have the same slope.

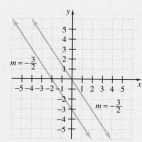

(continued)

DEFINITIONS AND CONCEPTS	EXAMPLES

Section 3.4 The Slope of a Line

If the product of the slopes of two lines is -1, then the lines are perpendicular.

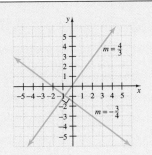

The slope of a horizontal line is 0.
The slope of a vertical line is undefined.

The slope of $y = -2$ is 0.
The slope of $x = 5$ is undefined.

Section 3.5 Equations of Lines

We can use the slope–intercept form to write an equation of a line given its slope and y-intercept.

Write an equation of the line with y-intercept $(0, -1)$ and slope $\dfrac{2}{3}$.

$$y = mx + b$$

$$y = \frac{2}{3}x - 1$$

The point–slope form of the equation of a line is $y - y_1 = m(x - x_1)$, where m is the slope of the line and (x_1, y_1) is a point on the line.

Find an equation of the line with slope 2 containing the point $(1, -4)$. Write the equation in standard form: $Ax + By = C$.

$$y - y_1 = m(x - x_1)$$

$$y - (-4) = 2(x - 1)$$

$$y + 4 = 2x - 2$$

$$-2x + y = -6 \qquad \text{Standard form.}$$

Section 3.6 Graphing Linear Inequalities

If the equal sign in a linear equation in two variables is replaced with an inequality symbol, the result is a **linear inequality in two variables.**

Linear Inequalities in Two Variables

$$x \le -5 \qquad y \ge 2$$

$$3x - 2y > 7 \qquad x < -5$$

To graph a linear inequality

1. Graph the boundary line by graphing the related equation. Draw the line solid if the inequality symbol is $\le$ or $\ge$. Draw the line dashed if the inequality symbol is $<$ or $>$.
2. Choose a test point not on the line. Substitute its coordinates into the original inequality.

Graph $2x - 4y > 4$.

1. Graph $2x - 4y = 4$. Draw a dashed line because the inequality symbol is $>$.

2. Check the test point $(0, 0)$ in the inequality $2x - 4y > 4$.

$$2 \cdot 0 - 4 \cdot 0 > 4 \qquad \text{Let } x = 0 \text{ and } y = 0.$$

$$0 > 4 \qquad \text{False.}$$

(continued)

DEFINITIONS AND CONCEPTS	EXAMPLES

Section 3.6 Graphing Linear Inequalities

3. If the resulting inequality is true, shade the **half-plane** that contains the test point. If the inequality is not true, shade the half-plane that does not contain the test point.

3. The inequality is false, so we shade the half-plane that does not contain $(0, 0)$.

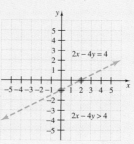

CHAPTER 3 REVIEW

(3.1) *Plot the points and name the quadrant or axis in which each point lies.*

1. $A(2, -1), B(-2, 1), C(0, 3), D(-3, -5)$

2. $A(-3, 4), B(4, -3), C(-2, 0), D(-4, 1)$

Determine whether each ordered pair is a solution to the given equation.

3. $7x - 8y = 56; (0, 56), (8, 0)$

4. $-2x + 5y = 10; (-5, 0), (1, 1)$

5. $x = 13; (13, 5), (13, 13)$

6. $y = 2; (7, 2), (2, 7)$

Determine whether each equation is linear or not. Then graph the equation already written below.

7. $y = 3x$

8. $y = 5x$

9. $3x - y = 4$

10. $x - 3y = 2$

11. $y = |x| + 4$

12. $y = x^2 + 4$

13. $y = -\dfrac{1}{2}x + 2$

14. $y = -x + 5$

15. $y = 2x - 1$

16. $y = \dfrac{1}{3}x + 1$

17. $y = -1.36x$

18. $y = 2.1x + 5.9$

(3.2) *Find the domain and range of each relation. Also determine whether the relation is a function.*

19. $\left\{ \left(-\dfrac{1}{2}, \dfrac{3}{4} \right), (6, 0.75), (0, -12), (25, 25) \right\}$

20. $\left\{ \left(\dfrac{3}{4}, -\dfrac{1}{2} \right), (0.75, 6), (-12, 0), (25, 25) \right\}$

21.

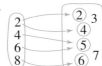

22.

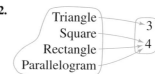

23.

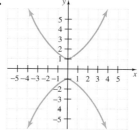

24.

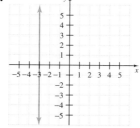

25.

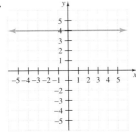

26.

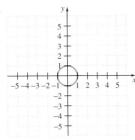

If $f(x) = x - 5$, $g(x) = -3x$, and $h(x) = 2x^2 - 6x + 1$, find the following.

27. $f(2)$
28. $g(0)$
29. $g(-6)$
30. $h(-1)$
31. $h(1)$
32. $f(5)$

The function $J(x) = 2.54x$ may be used to calculate the weight of an object on Jupiter J given its weight on Earth x.

33. If a person weighs 150 pounds on Earth, find the equivalent weight on Jupiter.

34. A 2000-pound probe on Earth weighs how many pounds on Jupiter?

Use the graph of the function below to answer Exercises 35 through 38.

35. Find $f(-1)$.
36. Find $f(1)$.
37. Find all values of x such that $f(x) = 1$.
38. Find all values of x such that $f(x) = -1$.

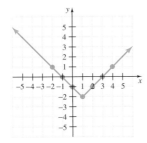

(3.3) *Graph each linear function.*

39. $f(x) = x$
40. $f(x) = -\dfrac{1}{3}x$
41. $g(x) = 4x - 1$

The graph of $f(x) = 3x$ is sketched below. Use this graph to match each linear function with its graph.

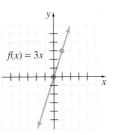

$f(x) = 3x$

A

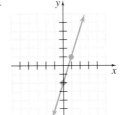

B

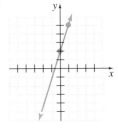

C

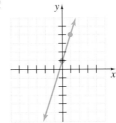

D

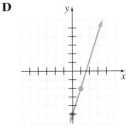

42. $f(x) = 3x + 1$
43. $f(x) = 3x - 2$
44. $f(x) = 3x + 2$
45. $f(x) = 3x - 5$

Graph each linear equation by finding intercepts if possible.

46. $4x + 5y = 20$
47. $3x - 2y = -9$
48. $4x - y = 3$
49. $2x + 6y = 9$
50. $y = 5$
51. $x = -2$

Graph each linear equation.

52. $x - 2 = 0$
53. $y + 3 = 0$

54. The cost C, in dollars, of renting a minivan for a day is given by the linear function $C(x) = 0.3x + 42$, where x is number of miles driven.
   a. Find the cost of renting the minivan for a day and driving it 150 miles.
   b. Graph $C(x) = 0.3x + 42$.

(3.4) *Find the slope of the line through each pair of points.*

55. $(2, 8)$ and $(6, -4)$
56. $(-3, 9)$ and $(5, 13)$
57. $(-7, -4)$ and $(-3, 6)$
58. $(7, -2)$ and $(-5, 7)$

Find the slope and y-intercept of each line.

59. $6x - 15y = 20$

60. $4x + 14y = 21$

Find the slope of each line.

61. $y - 3 = 0$

62. $x = -5$

Two lines are graphed on each set of axes. Decide whether l_1 or l_2 has the greater slope.

63.

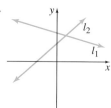

64.

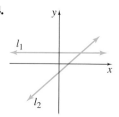

65.

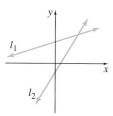

66.

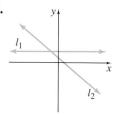

67. Recall from Exercise 54, that the cost C, in dollars, of renting a minivan for a day is given by the linear equation $y = 0.3x + 42$, where x is number of miles driven.

   a. Find and interpret the slope of this equation.

   b. Find and interpret the y-intercept of this equation.

Decide whether the lines are parallel, perpendicular, or neither.

△ **68.** $f(x) = -2x + 6$
     $g(x) = 2x - 1$

△ **69.** $-x + 3y = 2$
     $6x - 18y = 3$

(3.5) Graph each linear equation using the slope and y-intercept.

70. $y = -x + 1$

71. $y = 4x - 3$

72. $3x - y = 6$

73. $y = -5x$

Find an equation of the line satisfying the conditions given.

74. Horizontal; through $(3, -1)$

75. Vertical; through $(-2, -4)$

△ **76.** Parallel to the line $x = 6$; through $(-4, -3)$

77. Slope 0; through $(2, 5)$

Find the standard form equation of each line satisfying the conditions given.

78. Through $(-3, 5)$; slope 3

79. Slope 2; through $(5, -2)$

80. Through $(-6, -1)$ and $(-4, -2)$

81. Through $(-5, 3)$ and $(-4, -8)$

△ **82.** Through $(-2, 3)$; perpendicular to $x = 4$

△ **83.** Through $(-2, -5)$; parallel to $y = 8$

Find the equation of each line satisfying the given conditions. Write each equation using function notation.

84. Slope $-\dfrac{2}{3}$; y-intercept $(0, 4)$

85. Slope -1; y-intercept $(0, -2)$

△ **86.** Through $(2, -6)$; parallel to $6x + 3y = 5$

△ **87.** Through $(-4, -2)$; parallel to $3x + 2y = 8$

△ **88.** Through $(-6, -1)$; perpendicular to $4x + 3y = 5$

△ **89.** Through $(-4, 5)$; perpendicular to $2x - 3y = 6$

90. In 1996, the number of U.S. paging subscribers (in millions) was 42. The number of subscribers in 1999 (in millions) was 58. Let y be the number of subscribers (in millions) in the year x, where $x = 0$ represents 1996. (*Source:* Strategis Group for Personal Communications Asso.)

   a. Write a linear equation that models the number of U.S. paging subscribers (in millions) in terms of the year x. [*Hint:* Write 2 ordered pairs of the form (years past 1996, number of subscribers).]

   b. Use this equation to predict the number of U.S. paging subscribers in the year 2007. (Round to the nearest million.)

91. In 1998, the number of people (in millions) reporting arthritis was 43. The number of people (in millions) predicted to be reporting arthritis in 2020 is 60. Let y be the number of people (in millions) reporting arthritis in the year x, where $x = 0$ represents 1998. (*Source:* Arthritis Foundation)

   a. Write a linear equation that models the number of people (in millions) reporting arthritis in terms of the year x (See the hint for Exercise 90.)

   b. Use this equation to predict the number of people reporting arthritis in 2010. (Round to the nearest million.)

(3.6) Graph each linear inequality.

92. $3x + y > 4$

93. $\frac{1}{2}x - y < 2$

94. $5x - 2y \le 9$

95. $3y \ge x$

96. $y < 1$

97. $x > -2$

98. Graph the union of $y > 2x + 3$ or $x \le -3$.

99. Graph the intersection of $2x < 3y + 8$ and $y \ge -2$.

CHAPTER 3 TEST

1. Plot the points, and name the quadrant in which each is located: $A(6, -2)$, $B(4, 0)$, $C(-1, 6)$.

2. Complete the ordered pair solution $(-6, \quad)$ of the equation $2y - 3x = 12$.

Graph each line.

3. $2x - 3y = -6$

4. $4x + 6y = 7$

5. $f(x) = \dfrac{2}{3}x$

6. $y = -3$

7. Find the slope of the line that passes through $(5, -8)$ and $(-7, 10)$.

8. Find the slope and the y-intercept of the line $3x + 12y = 8$.

Graph each nonlinear function. Suggested x-values have been given for ordered pair solutions.

9. $f(x) = (x - 1)^2$

   Let $x = -2, -1, 0, 1, 2, 3, 4$

10. $g(x) = |x| + 2$

   Let $x = -3, -2, -1, 0, 1, 2, 3$

Find an equation of each line satisfying the conditions given. Write Exercises 11–15 in standard form. Write Exercises 16–18 using function notation.

11. Horizontal; through $(2, -8)$

12. Vertical; through $(-4, -3)$

△ **13.** Perpendicular to $x = 5$; through $(3, -2)$

14. Through $(4, -1)$; slope -3

15. Through $(0, -2)$; slope 5

16. Through $(4, -2)$ and $(6, -3)$

△ **17.** Through $(-1, 2)$; perpendicular to $3x - y = 4$

△ **18.** Parallel to $2y + x = 3$; through $(3, -2)$

△ **19.** Line L_1 has the equation $2x - 5y = 8$. Line L_2 passes through the points $(1, 4)$ and $(-1, -1)$. Determine whether these lines are parallel lines, perpendicular lines, or neither.

Graph each inequality.

20. $x \le -4$

21. $y > -2$

22. $2x - y > 5$

23. The intersection of $2x + 4y < 6$ and $y \le -4$

Find the domain and range of each relation. Also determine whether the relation is a function.

24.

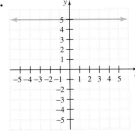

25.

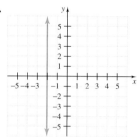

26.

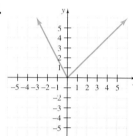

27.

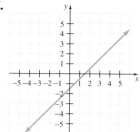

28. The average yearly earnings for high school graduates age 18 and older is given by the linear function

$$f(x) = 732x + 21{,}428$$

where x is the number of years since 1996 that a person graduated. (*Source:* U.S. Census Bureau)

a. Find the average earnings in 1998 for high school graduates.

b. Predict the average earnings for high school graduates in the year 2005.

c. Predict the first year that the average earnings for high school graduates will be greater than $30,000.

d. Find and interpret the slope of this equation.

e. Find and interpret the y-intercept of this equation.

CHAPTER 3 CUMULATIVE REVIEW

1. Evaluate: $3x - y$ when $x = 15$ and $y = 4$.

2. Determine whether the following statements are true or false.

a. 3 is a real number.

b. $\dfrac{1}{5}$ is an irrational number.

c. Every rational number is an integer.

d. $\{1, 5\} \subseteq \{2, 3, 4, 5\}$

3. Subtract.

a. $2 - 8$ b. $-8 - (-1)$
c. $-11 - 5$ d. $10.7 - (-9.8)$
e. $\dfrac{2}{3} - \dfrac{1}{2}$ f. $1 - 0.06$
g. Subtract 7 from 4.

4. Simplify each expression.

a. 3^2 b. $\left(\dfrac{1}{2}\right)^4$

c. -5^2 d. $(-5)^2$
e. -5^3 f. $(-5)^3$

5. Insert $<, >,$ or $=$ between each pair of numbers to form a true statement.

a. $-1 \quad -2$ b. $\dfrac{12}{4} \quad 3$

c. $-5 \quad 0$ d. $-3.5 \quad -3.05$

6. Write the multiplicative inverse, or reciprocal, of each.

a. 11   b. -9

c. $\dfrac{7}{4}$

7. Solve: $0.6 = 2 - 3.5c$

8. Solve for x: $3x + 5 = 3(x + 2)$

9. Find 16% of 25.

10. Kelsey Ohleger was helping her friend Benji Burnstine study for an algebra exam. Kelsey told Benji that her two latest art history quiz scores are two consecutive even integers whose sum is 174. Help Benji find the scores.

11. Solve $V = lwh$ for h.

12. Solve: $x - 2 < 5$. Graph the solution set.

13. Solve: $\dfrac{2}{5}(x - 6) \geq x - 1$

14. Solve: $2x \geq 0$ and $4x - 1 \leq -9$

15. Solve: $5x - 3 \leq 10$ or $x + 1 \geq 5$

16. Solve: $|5w + 3| = 7$

17. Solve: $|3x + 2| = |5x - 8|$

18. Solve for x: $|5x + 1| + 1 \leq 10$

19. Solve for y: $|y - 3| > 7$

20. Determine whether $(0, -12)$, $(1, 9)$, and $(2, -6)$ are solutions of the equation $3x - y = 12$.

21. Is the relation $y = 2x + 1$ also a function?

22. Find the y-intercept of the graph of each equation.

a. $f(x) = \dfrac{1}{2}x + \dfrac{3}{7}$

b. $y = -2.5x - 3.2$

23. Find the slope of the line whose equation is $f(x) = \dfrac{2}{3}x + 4$.

24. Write an equation of the line with y-intercept $(0, -3)$ and slope of $\dfrac{1}{4}$.

25. Graph: $2x - y < 6$.

Planning for Growth

Development affects our lives and our environment in many ways. According to the Sierra Club Foundation, increased highway congestion lowered the average vehicle speed on the Washington D.C. beltway from 47 mph in 1981 to 23 mph in 1991. The American Farmland Trust reports that 50 acres of farmland are lost to development each hour. According to the Institute of Transportation Studies, at least half of the parking spaces in most American shopping malls are vacant at least 40% of the time.

Urban or regional planners tackle problems like these. They build or improve communities and cities and their environments. Planners analyze issues like population growth, housing needs, land use, urban or suburban sprawl, parks and recreation space, public transportation, and highways. They decide if current resources are adequate and, if not, propose ways to improve them. If their plans are approved by the community, planners then help with plan implementation. Planners must be problem solvers, understand how governments work, listen and communicate well, work well as part of a team, understand the principles of city design, and analyze and interpret data, as well as be able to identify trends in data.

 For more information about careers in urban and regional planning, visit the American Planning Association Website by first going to www.prenhall.com/martin-gay.

In the Spotlight on Decision Making feature on page 223, you will have the opportunity to make a decision about city bus routes as an urban planner.

SYSTEMS OF EQUATIONS

In this chapter, two or more equations in two or more variables are solved simultaneously. Such a collection of equations is called a **system of equations**. Systems of equations are good mathematical models for many real-world problems because these problems may involve several related patterns.

4.1 SOLVING SYSTEMS OF LINEAR EQUATIONS IN TWO VARIABLES

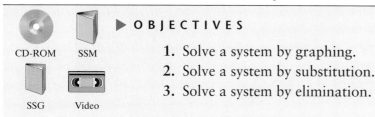

▶ OBJECTIVES

1. Solve a system by graphing.
2. Solve a system by substitution.
3. Solve a system by elimination.

1

An important problem that often occurs in the fields of business and economics concerns the concepts of revenue and cost. For example, suppose that a small manufacturing company begins to manufacture and sell compact disc storage units. The revenue of a company is the company's income from selling these units, and the cost is the amount of money that a company spends to manufacture these units. The following coordinate system shows the graphs of revenue and cost for the storage units.

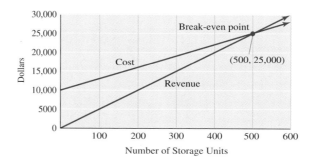

These lines intersect at the point $(500, 25,000)$. This means that when 500 storage units are manufactured and sold, both cost and revenue are $25,000. In business, this point of intersection is called the **break-even point.** Notice that for x-values (units sold) less than 500, the cost graph is above the revenue graph, meaning that cost of manufacturing is greater than revenue, and so the company is losing money. For x-values (units sold) greater than 500, the revenue graph is above the cost graph, meaning that revenue is greater than cost, and so the company is making money.

Recall from Chapter 3 that each line is a graph of some linear equation in two variables. Both equations together form a **system of equations.** The common point of intersection is called the **solution of the system.** Some examples of systems of linear equations in two variables are

Systems of Linear Equations in Two Variables

$$\begin{cases} x - 2y = -7 \\ 3x + y = 0 \end{cases} \qquad \begin{cases} x = 5 \\ x + \dfrac{y}{2} = 9 \end{cases} \qquad \begin{cases} x - 3 = 2y + 6 \\ y = 1 \end{cases}$$

Recall that a solution of an equation in two variables is an ordered pair (x, y) that makes the equation true. A **solution of a system** of two equations in two variables is an ordered pair (x, y) that makes both equations true.

Example 1 Determine whether the given ordered pair is a solution of the system.

a. $\begin{cases} -x + y = 2 \\ 2x - y = -3 \end{cases}$

$(-1, 1)$

b. $\begin{cases} 5x + 3y = -1 \\ x - y = 1 \end{cases}$

$(-2, 3)$

Solution **a.** We replace x with -1 and y with 1 in each equation.

$-x + y = 2$ First equation

$-(-1) + (1) \overset{?}{=} 2$ Let $x = -1$ and $y = 1$.

$1 + 1 \overset{?}{=} 2$

$2 = 2$ True.

$2x - y = -3$ Second equation

$2(-1) - (1) \overset{?}{=} -3$ Let $x = -1$ and $y = 1$.

$-2 - 1 \overset{?}{=} -3$

$-3 = -3$ True.

Since $(-1, 1)$ makes *both* equations true, it is a solution.

b. We replace x with -2 and y with 3 in each equation.

$5x + 3y = -1$ First equation

$5(-2) + 3(3) \overset{?}{=} -1$ Let $x = -2$ and $y = 3$.

$-10 + 9 \overset{?}{=} -1$

$-1 = -1$ True.

$x - y = 1$ Second equation

$(-2) - (3) \overset{?}{=} 1$ Let $x = -2$ and $y = 3$.

$-5 = 1$ False.

Since the ordered pair $(-2, 3)$ does not make *both* equations true, it is not a solution of the system.

We can estimate the solutions of a system by graphing each equation on the same coordinate system and estimating the coordinates of any point of intersection.

Example 2 Solve each system by graphing. If the system has just one solution, estimate the solution.

a. $\begin{cases} x + y = 2 \\ 3x - y = -2 \end{cases}$

b. $\begin{cases} x - 2y = 4 \\ x = 2y \end{cases}$

c. $\begin{cases} 2x + 4y = 10 \\ x + 2y = 5 \end{cases}$

Solution Since the graph of a linear equation in two variables is a line, graphing two such equations yields two lines in a plane.

a. $\begin{cases} x + y = 2 \\ 3x - y = -2 \end{cases}$

These lines intersect at one point as shown. The coordinates of the point of intersection appear to be $(0, 2)$. Check this estimated solution by replacing x with 0 and y with 2 in **both** equations.

$x + y = 2$ First equation.

$0 + 2 \overset{?}{=} 2$ Let $x = 0$ and $y = 2$.

$2 = 2$ True.

$3x - y = -2$ Second equation.

$3 \cdot 0 - 2 \overset{?}{=} -2$ Let $x = 0$ and $y = 2$.

$-2 = -2$ True.

The ordered pair $(0, 2)$ does satisfy both equations. We conclude therefore that $(0, 2)$ is the solution of the system. A system that has at least one solution, such as this one, is said to be **consistent.**

b. $\begin{cases} x - 2y = 4 \\ x = 2y \end{cases}$

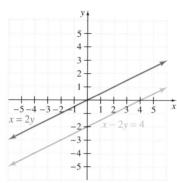
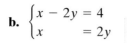

The lines appear to be parallel. To be sure, write each equation in point–slope form, $y = mx + b$.

$x - 2y = 4$	First equation.	$x = 2y$	Second equation.
$-2y = -x + 4$	Subtract x from both sides.	$\dfrac{1}{2}x = y$	Divide both sides by 2.
$y = \dfrac{1}{2}x - 2$	Divide both sides by -2.	$y = \dfrac{1}{2}x$	

The graphs of these equations have the same slope, $\dfrac{1}{2}$, but different y-intercepts, so we have confirmed that these lines are parallel. Therefore, the system has no solution since the equations have no common solution (there are no intersection points). A system that has no solution is said to be **inconsistent.**

c. $\begin{cases} 2x + 4y = 10 \\ x + 2y = 5 \end{cases}$

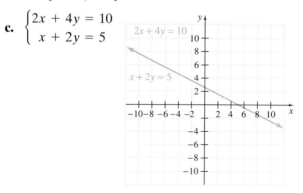

The graph of each equation is the same line. To confirm this, notice that if both sides of the second equation are multiplied by 2, the result is the first equation. This means that the equations have identical solutions. Any ordered pair solution of one equation satisfies the other equation also. Thus, these equations are said to be **dependent equations.** The solution set of the system is $\{(x, y) \mid x + 2y = 5\}$ or, equivalently, $\{(x, y) \mid 2x + 4y = 10\}$ since the lines describe identical ordered pairs. Written this way, the solution set is read "the set of all ordered pairs (x, y), such that $2x + 4y = 10$." There are therefore an infinite number of solutions to this system.

We can summarize the information discovered in Example 2 as follows.

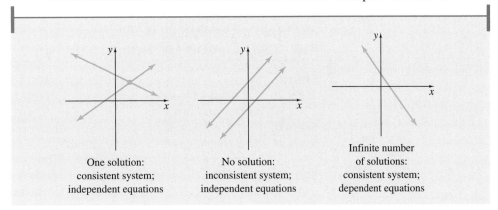

One solution:
consistent system;
independent equations

No solution:
inconsistent system;
independent equations

Infinite number
of solutions:
consistent system;
dependent equations

2 Graphing the equations of a system by hand is often a good method of finding approximate solutions of a system, but it is not a reliable method of finding exact solutions of a system. We turn instead to two algebraic methods of solving systems. We use the first method, the **substitution method,** to solve the system

$$\begin{cases} 2x + 4y = -6 & \text{First equation} \\ x = 2y - 5 & \text{Second equation} \end{cases}$$

Example 3 Use the substitution method to solve the system.

$$\begin{cases} 2x + 4y = -6 & \text{First equation} \\ x = 2y - 5 & \text{Second equation} \end{cases}$$

Solution In the second equation, we are told that x is equal to $2y - 5$. Since they are equal, we can *substitute* $2y - 5$ for x in the first equation. This will give us an equation in one variable, which we can solve for y.

$$2x + 4y = -6 \qquad \text{First equation}$$

$$2(2y - 5) + 4y = -6 \qquad \text{Substitute } 2y - 5 \text{ for } x.$$

$$4y - 10 + 4y = -6$$

$$8y = 4$$

$$y = \frac{4}{8} = \frac{1}{2} \qquad \text{Solve for } y.$$

The y-coordinate of the solution is $\frac{1}{2}$. To find the x-coordinate, we replace y with $\frac{1}{2}$ in the second equation,

$$x = 2y - 5.$$

$$x = 2y - 5$$

$$x = 2\left(\frac{1}{2}\right) - 5 = 1 - 5 = -4$$

The ordered pair solution is $\left(-4, \frac{1}{2}\right)$. Check to see that $\left(-4, \frac{1}{2}\right)$ satisfies both equations of the system.

The steps below summarize the substitution method.

SOLVING A SYSTEM OF TWO EQUATIONS USING THE SUBSTITUTION METHOD

Step 1: Solve one of the equations for one of its variables.
Step 2: Substitute the expression for the variable found in Step 1 into the other equation.
Step 3: Find the value of one variable by solving the equation from Step 2.
Step 4: Find the value of the other variable by substituting the value found in Step 3 into the equation from Step 1.
Step 5: Check the ordered pair solution in *both* original equations.

Example 4   Use the substitution method to solve the system.

$$\begin{cases} -\dfrac{x}{6} + \dfrac{y}{2} = \dfrac{1}{2} \\[2mm] \dfrac{x}{3} - \dfrac{y}{6} = -\dfrac{3}{4} \end{cases}$$

Solution   First we multiply each equation by its least common denominator to clear the system of fractions. We multiply the first equation by 6 and the second equation by 12.

$$\begin{cases} 6\left(-\dfrac{x}{6} + \dfrac{y}{2}\right) = 6\left(\dfrac{1}{2}\right) \\[2mm] 12\left(\dfrac{x}{3} - \dfrac{y}{6}\right) = 12\left(-\dfrac{3}{4}\right) \end{cases}$$ simplifies to $$\begin{cases} -x + 3y = 3 & \text{First equation} \\ 4x - 2y = -9 & \text{Second equation} \end{cases}$$

> **HELPFUL HINT**
> To avoid tedious fractions, solve for a variable whose coefficient is 1 or −1, if possible.

To use the substitution method, we now solve the first equation for x.

$$-x + 3y = 3 \qquad \text{First equation}$$
$$3y - 3 = x \qquad \text{Solve for } x.$$

Next we replace x with $3y - 3$ in the second equation.

$$4x - 2y = -9 \qquad \text{Second equation}$$

$$4(3y - 3) - 2y = -9$$
$$12y - 12 - 2y = -9$$
$$10y = 3$$
$$y = \frac{3}{10} \qquad \text{Solve for } y.$$

To find the corresponding x-coordinate, we replace y with $\dfrac{3}{10}$ in the equation $x = 3y - 3$. Then

$$x = 3\left(\frac{3}{10}\right) - 3 = \frac{9}{10} - 3 = \frac{9}{10} - \frac{30}{10} = -\frac{21}{10}$$

The ordered pair solution is $\left(-\dfrac{21}{10}, \dfrac{3}{10}\right)$. Check to see that this solution satisfies both original equations. ▬

> **HELPFUL HINT**
> If a system of equations contains equations with fractions, first clear the equations of fractions.

3 The **elimination method,** or **addition method,** is a second algebraic technique for solving systems of equations. For this method, we rely on a version of the addition property of equality, which states that "equals added to equals are equal."

If $A = B$ and $C = D$ then $A + C = B + D$.

Example 5 Use the elimination method to solve the system.

$$\begin{cases} x - 5y = -12 & \text{First equation} \\ -x + y = 4 & \text{Second equation} \end{cases}$$

Solution Since the left side of each equation is equal to the right side, we add equal quantities by adding the left sides of the equations and the right sides of the equations. This sum gives us an equation in one variable, y, which we can solve for y.

$$\begin{array}{ll} x - 5y = -12 & \text{First equation} \\ \underline{-x + y = 4} & \text{Second equation} \\ -4y = -8 & \text{Add.} \\ y = 2 & \text{Solve for } y. \end{array}$$

The y-coordinate of the solution is 2. To find the corresponding x-coordinate, we replace y with 2 in either original equation of the system. Let's use the second equation.

$$\begin{array}{ll} -x + y = 4 & \text{Second equation} \\ -x + 2 = 4 & \text{Let } y = 2. \\ -x = 2 \\ x = -2 \end{array}$$

The ordered pair solution is $(-2, 2)$. Check to see that $(-2, 2)$ satisfies both equations of the system. ▬

The steps below summarize the elimination method.

SOLVING A SYSTEM OF TWO LINEAR EQUATIONS USING THE ELIMINATION METHOD

Step 1: Rewrite each equation in standard form, $Ax + By = C$.

Step 2: If necessary, multiply one or both equations by some nonzero number so that the coefficient of one variable in one equation is the opposite of its coefficient in the other equation.

Step 3: Add the equations.

Step 4: Find the value of one variable by solving the equation from Step 3.

Step 5: Find the value of the second variable by substituting the value found in Step 4 into either original equation.

Step 6: Check the proposed ordered pair solution in *both* original equations.

Example 6 Use the elimination method to solve the system.

$$\begin{cases} 3x - 2y = 10 \\ 4x - 3y = 15 \end{cases}$$

Solution If we add the two equations, the sum will still be an equation in two variables. Notice, however, that we can eliminate y when the equations are added if we multiply both sides of the first equation by 3 and both sides of the second equation by -2. Then

$$\begin{cases} 3(3x - 2y) = 3(10) \\ -2(4x - 3y) = -2(15) \end{cases} \quad \text{simplifies to} \quad \begin{cases} 9x - 6y = 30 \\ -8x + 6y = -30 \end{cases}$$

Next we add the left sides and add the right sides.

$$\begin{array}{r} 9x - 6y = 30 \\ -8x + 6y = -30 \\ \hline x \qquad\quad = 0 \end{array}$$

To find y, we let $x = 0$ in either equation of the system.

$$\begin{aligned} 3x - 2y &= 10 & &\text{First equation} \\ 3(0) - 2y &= 10 & &\text{Let } x = 0. \\ -2y &= 10 \\ y &= -5 \end{aligned}$$

The ordered pair solution is $(0, -5)$. Check to see that $(0, -5)$ satisfies both equations.

Example 7 Use the elimination method to solve the system.

$$\begin{cases} 3x + \dfrac{y}{2} = 2 \\ 6x + y = 5 \end{cases}$$

Solution If we multiply both sides of the first equation by -2, the coefficients of x in the two equations will be opposites. Then

$$\begin{cases} -2\left(3x + \dfrac{y}{2}\right) = -2(2) \\ 6x + y \quad = 5 \end{cases} \quad \text{simplifies to} \quad \begin{cases} -6x - y - -4 \\ 6x + y = 5 \end{cases}$$

Now we can add the left sides and add the right sides.

$$\begin{array}{r} -6x - y = -4 \\ 6x + y = 5 \\ \hline 0 = 1 \end{array} \quad \text{False.}$$

The resulting equation, $0 = 1$, is false for all values of y or x. Thus, the system has no solution. The solution set is $\{\ \}$ or $\varnothing$. This system is inconsistent, and the graphs of the equations are parallel lines.

Example 8   Use the elimination method to solve the system.

$$\begin{cases} -5x - 3y = 9 \\ 10x + 6y = -18 \end{cases}$$

Solution   To eliminate x when the equations are added, we multiply both sides of the first equation by 2. Then

$$\begin{cases} 2(-5x - 3y) = 2(9) \\ 10x + 6y = -18 \end{cases} \quad \text{simplifies to} \quad \begin{cases} -10x - 6y = 18 \\ 10x + 6y = -18 \end{cases}$$

Next we add the equations.

$$\begin{array}{r} -10x - 6y = 18 \\ 10x + 6y = -18 \\ \hline 0 = 0 \end{array}$$

The resulting equation, $0 = 0$, is true for all possible values of y or x. Notice in the original system that if both sides of the first equation are multiplied by -2, the result is the second equation. This means that the two equations are equivalent. They have the same solution set and there are an infinite number of solutions. Thus, the equations of this system are dependent, and the solution set of the system is

$$\{(x, y) \mid -5x - 3y = 9\} \quad \text{or, equivalently,} \quad \{(x, y) \mid 10x + 6y = -18\}.$$

SPOTLIGHT ON DECISION MAKING

Suppose you have just signed a 12-month lease for an apartment. After moving in, you find that the tap water tastes terrible. You have two options: (a) buy bottled water or (b) buy a reusable water filter pitcher and filters to filter the tap water. You estimate that you use 10 gallons of drinking water each week. Buying bottled water costs $0.50 per gallon. Using a water filter pitcher involves the following costs:

- A reusable water filter pitcher costs $50.
- A water filter costs $10 each. Each water filter lasts for 40 gallons, or 4 weeks in your situation. The cost of a water filter is $2.50 per week.
- Tap water costs $0.005 per gallon

An equation for the cumulative cost y of the bottled water option after x weeks is

$y = $ (cost per gallon of bottled water)(number of gallons used per week)x

An equation for the cumulative cost y of filtered water option after x weeks is
$y = $ (cost of reusable pitcher) + (cost of water filter per week)x + (cost per gallon of tap water)(number of gallons used per week)x

Which option would you choose? Why?

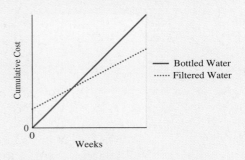

GRAPHING CALCULATOR EXPLORATIONS

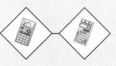

A graphing calculator may be used to approximate solutions of systems of equations by graphing each equation on the same set of axes and approximating any points of intersection. For example, approximate the solution of the system

$$\begin{cases} y = -2.6x + 5.6 \\ y = 4.3x - 4.9 \end{cases}$$

First use a standard window and graph both equations on a single screen.

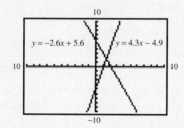

The two lines intersect. To approximate the point of intersection, trace to the point of intersection and use an Intersect feature of the graphing calculator or a Zoom In feature. Using either method, we find that the approximate point of intersection is $(1.52, 1.64)$.

Solve each system of equations. Approximate the solutions to two decimal places.

1. $y = -1.65x + 3.65$
$y = 4.56x - 9.44$

2. $y = 7.61x + 3.48$
$y = -1.26x - 6.43$

3. $2.33x - 4.72y = 10.61$
$5.86x + 6.22y = -8.89$

4. $-7.89x - 5.68y = 3.26$
$-3.65x + 4.98y = 11.77$

MENTAL MATH

Match each graph with the solution of the corresponding system.

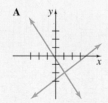

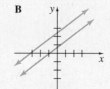

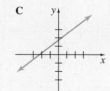

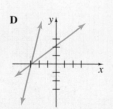

1. no solution

2. Infinite number of solutions

3. $(1, -2)$

4. $(-3, 0)$

Exercise Set 4.1

Determine whether each given ordered pair is a solution of each system. See Example 1.

1. $\begin{cases} x - y = 3 \\ 2x - 4y = 8 \end{cases}$ $(2, -1)$

2. $\begin{cases} x - y = -4 \\ 2x + 10y = 4 \end{cases}$ $(-3, 1)$

3. $\begin{cases} 2x - 3y = -9 \\ 4x + 2y = -2 \end{cases}$ $(3, 5)$

4. $\begin{cases} 2x - 5y = -2 \\ 3x + 4y = 4 \end{cases}$ $(4, 2)$

5. $\begin{cases} y = -5x \\ x = -2 \end{cases}$ $(-2, 10)$

6. $\begin{cases} y = 6 \\ x = -2y \end{cases}$ $(-12, 6)$

Solve each system by graphing. See Example 2.

7. $\begin{cases} x + y = 1 \\ x - 2y = 4 \end{cases}$

8. $\begin{cases} 2x - y = 8 \\ x + 3y = 11 \end{cases}$

9. $\begin{cases} 2y - 4 = 0 \\ x + 2y = 5 \end{cases}$

10. $\begin{cases} 4x - y = 6 \\ x - y = 0 \end{cases}$

11. $\begin{cases} 3x - y = 4 \\ 6x - 2y = 4 \end{cases}$

12. $\begin{cases} -x + 3y = 6 \\ 3x - 9y = 9 \end{cases}$

13. Can a system consisting of two linear equations have exactly two solutions? Explain why or why not.

14. Suppose the graph of the equations in a system of two equations in two variables consists of a circle and a line. Discuss the possible number of solutions for this system.

Solve each system of equations by the substitution method. See Examples 3 and 4.

15. $\begin{cases} x + y = 10 \\ y = 4x \end{cases}$

16. $\begin{cases} 5x + 2y = -17 \\ x = 3y \end{cases}$

17. $\begin{cases} 4x - y = 9 \\ 2x + 3y = -27 \end{cases}$

18. $\begin{cases} 3x - y = 6 \\ -4x + 2y = -8 \end{cases}$

19. $\begin{cases} \dfrac{1}{2}x + \dfrac{3}{4}y = -\dfrac{1}{4} \\ \dfrac{3}{4}x - \dfrac{1}{4}y = 1 \end{cases}$

20. $\begin{cases} \dfrac{2}{5}x + \dfrac{1}{5}y = -1 \\ x + \dfrac{2}{5}y = -\dfrac{8}{5} \end{cases}$

21. $\begin{cases} \dfrac{x}{3} + y = \dfrac{4}{3} \\ -x + 2y = 11 \end{cases}$

22. $\begin{cases} \dfrac{x}{8} - \dfrac{y}{2} = 1 \\ \dfrac{x}{3} - y = 2 \end{cases}$

Solve each system of equations by the elimination method. See Examples 5–8.

23. $\begin{cases} 2x - 4y = 0 \\ x + 2y = 5 \end{cases}$

24. $\begin{cases} 2x - 3y = 0 \\ 2x + 6y = 3 \end{cases}$

25. $\begin{cases} 5x + 2y = 1 \\ x - 3y = 7 \end{cases}$

26. $\begin{cases} 6x - y = -5 \\ 4x - 2y = 6 \end{cases}$

27. $\begin{cases} 5x - 2y = 27 \\ -3x + 5y = 18 \end{cases}$

28. $\begin{cases} 3x + 4y = 2 \\ 2x + 5y = -1 \end{cases}$

29. $\begin{cases} 3x - 5y = 11 \\ 2x - 6y = 2 \end{cases}$

30. $\begin{cases} 6x - 3y = -3 \\ 4x + 5y = -9 \end{cases}$

31. $\begin{cases} x - 2y = 4 \\ 2x - 4y = 4 \end{cases}$

32. $\begin{cases} -x + 3y = 6 \\ 3x - 9y = 9 \end{cases}$

33. $\begin{cases} 3x + y = 1 \\ 2y = 2 - 6x \end{cases}$

34. $\begin{cases} y = 2x - 5 \\ 8x - 4y = 20 \end{cases}$

35. Write a system of two linear equations in x and y that has the ordered pair solution $(2, 5)$.

36. Which method would you use to solve the system
$$\begin{cases} 5x - 2y = 6 \\ 2x + 3y = 5 \end{cases}$$
Explain your choice.

Solve each system of equations.

37. $\begin{cases} 2x + 5y = 8 \\ 6x + y = 10 \end{cases}$

38. $\begin{cases} x - 4y = -5 \\ -3x - 8y = 0 \end{cases}$

39. $\begin{cases} x + y = 1 \\ x - 2y = 4 \end{cases}$

40. $\begin{cases} 2x - y = 8 \\ x + 3y = 11 \end{cases}$

41. $\begin{cases} \dfrac{1}{3}x + y = \dfrac{4}{3} \\ -\dfrac{1}{4}x - \dfrac{1}{2}y = -\dfrac{1}{4} \end{cases}$

42. $\begin{cases} \dfrac{3}{4}x - \dfrac{1}{2}y = -\dfrac{1}{2} \\ x + y = -\dfrac{3}{2} \end{cases}$

43. $\begin{cases} 2x + 6y = 8 \\ 3x + 9y = 12 \end{cases}$

44. $\begin{cases} x = 3y - 1 \\ 2x - 6y = -2 \end{cases}$

45. $\begin{cases} 4x + 2y = 5 \\ 2x + y = -1 \end{cases}$

46. $\begin{cases} 3x + 6y = 15 \\ 2x + 4y = 3 \end{cases}$

47. $\begin{cases} 10y - 2x = 1 \\ 5y = 4 - 6x \end{cases}$

48. $\begin{cases} 3x + 4y = 0 \\ 7x = 3y \end{cases}$

49. $\begin{cases} \dfrac{3}{4}x + \dfrac{5}{2}y = 11 \\ \dfrac{1}{16}x - \dfrac{3}{4}y = -1 \end{cases}$

50. $\begin{cases} \dfrac{2}{3}x + \dfrac{1}{4}y = -\dfrac{3}{2} \\ \dfrac{1}{2}x - \dfrac{1}{4}y = -2 \end{cases}$

51. $\begin{cases} x = 3y + 2 \\ 5x - 15y = 10 \end{cases}$

52. $\begin{cases} y = \dfrac{1}{7}x + 3 \\ x - 7y = -21 \end{cases}$

53. $\begin{cases} 2x - y = -1 \\ y = -2x \end{cases}$

54. $\begin{cases} x = \dfrac{1}{5}y \\ x - y = -4 \end{cases}$

55. $\begin{cases} 2x = 6 \\ y = 5 - x \end{cases}$

56. $\begin{cases} x = 3y + 4 \\ -y = 5 \end{cases}$

57. $\begin{cases} \dfrac{x + 5}{2} = \dfrac{6 - 4y}{3} \\ \dfrac{3x}{5} = \dfrac{21 - 7y}{10} \end{cases}$

58. $\begin{cases} \dfrac{y}{5} = \dfrac{8 - x}{2} \\ x = \dfrac{2y - 8}{3} \end{cases}$

59. $\begin{cases} 4x - 7y = 7 \\ 12x - 21y = 24 \end{cases}$

60. $\begin{cases} 2x - 5y = 12 \\ 4x + 10y = 20 \end{cases}$

61. $\begin{cases} \dfrac{2}{3}x - \dfrac{3}{4}y = -1 \\ -\dfrac{1}{6}x + \dfrac{3}{8}y = 1 \end{cases}$

62. $\begin{cases} \dfrac{1}{2}x - \dfrac{1}{3}y = -3 \\ \dfrac{1}{8}x + \dfrac{1}{6}y = 0 \end{cases}$

63. $\begin{cases} 0.7x - 0.2y = -1.6 \\ 0.2x - y = -1.4 \end{cases}$

64. $\begin{cases} -0.7x + 0.6y = 1.3 \\ 0.5x - 0.3y = -0.8 \end{cases}$

65. $\begin{cases} 4x - 1.5y = 10.2 \\ 2x + 7.8y = -25.68 \end{cases}$

66. $\begin{cases} x - 3y = -5.3 \\ 6.3x + 6y = 3.96 \end{cases}$

The concept of supply and demand is used often in business. In general, as the unit price of a commodity increases, the demand for that commodity decreases. Also, as a commodity's unit price increases, the manufacturer normally increases the supply. The point where supply is equal to demand is called the equilibrium point. The following graph shows the graph of a demand equation and a supply equation for ties. The x-axis represents number of ties in thousands, and the y-axis represents the cost of a tie. Use this graph for Exercises 67–70.

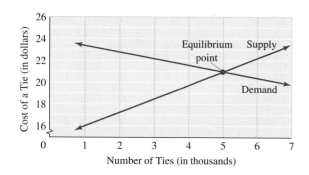

67. Find the number of ties and the price per tie when supply equals demand.

68. When x is between 3 and 4, is supply greater than demand or is demand greater than supply?

69. When x is greater than 7, is supply greater than demand or is demand greater than supply?

70. For what x-values are the y-values corresponding to the supply equation greater than the y-values corresponding to the demand equation?

The revenue equation for a certain brand of toothpaste is $y = 2.5x$, where x is the number of tubes of toothpaste sold and y is the total income for selling x tubes. The cost equation is $y = 0.9x + 3000$, where x is the number of tubes of toothpaste manufactured and y is the cost of producing x tubes. The following set of axes shows the graph of the cost and revenue equations. Use this graph for Exercises 71–76.

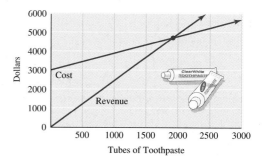

71. Find the coordinates of the point of intersection by solving the system

$$\begin{cases} y = 2.5x \\ y = 0.9x + 3000 \end{cases}$$

72. Explain the meaning of the ordered pair point of intersection.

73. If the company sells 2000 tubes of toothpaste, does the company make money or lose money?

74. If the company sells 1000 tubes of toothpaste, does the company make money or lose money?

75. For what x-values will the company make a profit? (*Hint:* For what x-values is the revenue graph "higher" than the cost graph?)

76. For what x-values will the company lose money? (*Hint:* For what x-values is the revenue graph "lower" than the cost graph?)

77. The amount y of red meat consumed per person in the United States (in pounds) in the year x can be modeled by the linear equation $y = -0.6x + 121.2$. The amount y of all poultry consumed per person in the United States (in pounds) in the year x can be modeled by the linear equation $y = 1.7x + 88$. In both models, $x = 0$ represents the year 1995. (*Source:* Based on data and forecasts from the Economic Research Service, U.S. Department of Agriculture, 1995–1999)

a. What does the slope of each equation tell you about the patterns of red meat and poultry consumption in the United States?

b. Solve this system of equations. (Round your final results to the nearest whole numbers.)

c. Explain the meaning of your answer to Part **b**.

 78. The amount of U.S. federal government income y (in billions of dollars) for the fiscal year x, from 1996 through 1999 ($x = 0$ represents 1996), can be modeled by the linear equation $y = 126.4x + 1455.4$. The amount of U.S. federal government expenditures (in billions of dollars) for the same period can be modeled by the linear equation $y = 48.6x + 1556.6$. Did expenses ever equal income during this period? If so, in what year? (*Source:* Financial Management Service, U.S. Dept. of the Treasury)

 79. The number of milk cows y (in thousands) on farms in the United States for the year x, from 1980 through 1995 ($x = 0$ represents 1980), can be modeled by the linear equation $107x + y = 11{,}096$. The number of sheep (in thousands) on farms in the United States for the same period can be modeled by the linear equation $y = -399x + 15{,}149$. In which year were there the same number of milk cows as sheep? (*Source:* National Agricultural Statistics Service)

REVIEW EXERCISES

Determine whether the given replacement values make each equation true or false. See Section 1.3.

80. $3x - 4y + 2z = 5$; $x = 1$, $y = 2$, and $z = 5$

81. $x + 2y - z = 7$; $x = 2$, $y = -3$, and $z = 3$

82. $-x - 5y + 3z = 15$; $x = 0$, $y = -1$, and $z = 5$

83. $-4x + y - 8z = 4$; $x = 1$, $y = 0$, and $z = -1$

Add the equations. See Section 4.1.

84. $3x + 2y - 5z = 10$
$-3x + 4y + z = 15$

85. $x + 4y - 5z = 20$
$2x - 4y - 2z = -17$

86. $10x + 5y + 6z = 14$
$-9x + 5y - 6z = -12$

87. $-9x - 8y - z = 31$
$9x + 4y - z = 12$

A Look Ahead

Example

Solve the system $\begin{cases} -\dfrac{4}{x} - \dfrac{4}{y} = -11 \\ \dfrac{1}{x} + \dfrac{1}{y} = 1 \end{cases}$

Solution

First, make the following substitution. Let $a = \dfrac{1}{x}$ and $b = \dfrac{1}{y}$ in both equations. Then

$$\begin{cases} -4\left(\dfrac{1}{x}\right) - 4\left(\dfrac{1}{y}\right) = -11 \\ \dfrac{1}{x} + \dfrac{1}{y} = 1 \end{cases}$$

is equivalent to $\begin{cases} -4a - 4b = -11 \\ a + b = 1 \end{cases}$

We solve by the elimination method. Multiplying both sides of the second equation by 4 and adding the left sides and the right sides of the equations,

$$\begin{cases} -4a - 4b = -11 \\ 4(a + b) = 4(1) \end{cases}$$

simplifies to $\begin{cases} -4a - 4b = -11 \\ 4a + 4b = 4 \end{cases}$

$$0 = -7 \quad \text{false}$$

The equation $0 = -7$ is false. Therefore, this system in a and b has no solution and hence the original system in x and y has no solution.

Solve each system. See the preceding example.

88. $\begin{cases} \dfrac{1}{x} + y = 12 \\ \dfrac{3}{x} - y = 4 \end{cases}$

89. $\begin{cases} x + \dfrac{2}{y} = 7 \\ 3x + \dfrac{3}{y} = 6 \end{cases}$

90. $\begin{cases} \dfrac{1}{x} + \dfrac{1}{y} = 5 \\ \dfrac{1}{x} - \dfrac{1}{y} = 1 \end{cases}$

91. $\begin{cases} \dfrac{2}{x} + \dfrac{3}{y} = 5 \\ \dfrac{5}{x} - \dfrac{3}{y} = 2 \end{cases}$

92. $\begin{cases} \dfrac{2}{x} + \dfrac{3}{y} = -1 \\ \dfrac{3}{x} - \dfrac{2}{y} = 18 \end{cases}$

93. $\begin{cases} \dfrac{3}{x} - \dfrac{2}{y} = -18 \\ \dfrac{2}{x} + \dfrac{3}{y} = 1 \end{cases}$

94. $\begin{cases} \dfrac{2}{x} - \dfrac{4}{y} = 5 \\ \dfrac{1}{x} - \dfrac{2}{y} = \dfrac{3}{2} \end{cases}$

95. $\begin{cases} \dfrac{5}{x} + \dfrac{7}{y} = 1 \\ -\dfrac{10}{x} - \dfrac{14}{y} = 0 \end{cases}$

4.2 SOLVING SYSTEMS OF LINEAR EQUATIONS IN THREE VARIABLES

CD-ROM SSM

SSG Video

▶ **OBJECTIVE**

1. Solve a system of three linear equations in three variables.

In this section, the algebraic methods of solving systems of two linear equations in two variables are extended to systems of three linear equations in three variables. We call the equation $3x - y + z = -15$, for example, a **linear equation in three variables** since there are three variables and each variable is raised only to the power 1. A solution of this equation is an **ordered triple (x, y, z)** that makes the equation a true statement. For example, the ordered triple $(2, 0, -21)$ is a solution of $3x - y + z = -15$ since replacing x with 2, y with 0, and z with -21 yields the true statement $3(2) - 0 + (-21) = -15$. The graph of this equation is a plane in three-dimensional space, just as the graph of a linear equation in two variables is a line in two-dimensional space.

Although we will not discuss the techniques for graphing equations in three variables, visualizing the possible patterns of intersecting planes gives us insight into the possible patterns of solutions of a system of three three-variable linear equations. There are four possible patterns.

1. Three planes have a single point in common. This point represents the single solution of the system. This system is **consistent**.

2. Three planes intersect at no point common to all three. This system has no solution. A few ways that this can occur are shown. This system is **inconsistent**.

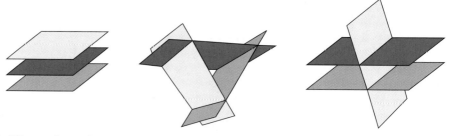

3. Three planes intersect at all the points of a single line. The system has infinitely many solutions. This system is **consistent**.

4. Three planes coincide at all points on the plane. The system is consistent, and the equations are **dependent**.

1 To use the elimination method to solve a system in three variables, we eliminate a variable and obtain a system in two variables.

Example 1 Solve the system.

$$\begin{cases} 3x - y + z = -15 & \text{Equation (1)} \\ x + 2y - z = 1 & \text{Equation (2)} \\ 2x + 3y - 2z = 0 & \text{Equation (3)} \end{cases}$$

Solution Add equations (1) and (2) to eliminate z.

$$\begin{array}{r} 3x - y + z = -15 \\ x + 2y - z = 1 \\ \hline 4x + y \quad\quad = -14 \quad \text{Equation (4)} \end{array}$$

HELPFUL HINT
Don't forget to add two other equations besides equations (1) and (2) *and* to eliminate the same variable.

Next, add two *other* equations and *eliminate z again.* To do so, multiply both sides of equation (1) by 2 and add this resulting equation to equation (3). Then

$$\begin{cases} 2(3x - y + z) = 2(-15) \\ 2x + 3y - 2z = 0 \end{cases} \quad \begin{array}{l} \text{simplifies} \\ \text{to} \end{array} \quad \begin{cases} 6x - 2y + 2z = -30 \\ 2x + 3y - 2z = 0 \\ \hline 8x + y \quad\quad = -30 \quad \text{Equation (5)} \end{cases}$$

Now solve equations (4) and (5) for x and y. To solve by elimination, multiply both sides of equation (4) by -1 and add this resulting equation to equation (5). Then

$$\begin{cases} -1(4x + y) = -1(-14) \\ 8x + y = -30 \end{cases} \quad \begin{array}{l} \text{simplifies} \\ \text{to} \end{array} \quad \begin{cases} -4x - y = 14 \\ 8x + y = -30 \\ \hline 4x \quad\quad = -16 \quad \text{Add the equations.} \\ x = -4 \quad \text{Solve for } x. \end{cases}$$

Replace x with -4 in equation (4) or (5).

$$\begin{array}{rl} 4x + y = -14 & \text{Equation (4)} \\ 4(-4) + y = -14 & \text{Let } x = -4. \\ y = 2 & \text{Solve for } y. \end{array}$$

Finally, replace x with -4 and y with 2 in equation (1), (2), or (3).

$$\begin{array}{rl} x + 2y - z = 1 & \text{Equation (2)} \\ -4 + 2(2) - z = 1 & \text{Let } x = -4 \text{ and } y = 2. \\ -4 + 4 - z = 1 & \\ -z = 1 & \\ z = -1 & \end{array}$$

The solution is $(-4, 2, -1)$. To check, let $x = -4$, $y = 2$, and $z = -1$ in all three original equations of the system.

Equation (1)	Equation (2)	Equation (3)

$$3x - y + z = -15$$
$$3(-4) - 2 + (-1) = -15$$
$$-12 - 2 - 1 = -15$$
$$-15 = -15$$
True.

$$x + 2y - z = 1$$
$$-4 + 2(2) - (-1) = 1$$
$$-4 + 4 + 1 = 1$$
$$1 = 1$$
True.

$$2x + 3y - 2z = 0$$
$$2(-4) + 3(2) - 2(-1) = 0$$
$$-8 + 6 + 2 = 0$$
$$0 = 0$$
True.

All three statements are true, so the solution is $(-4, 2, -1)$.

Example 2   Solve the system.

$$\begin{cases} 2x - 4y + 8z = 2 & (1) \\ -x - 3y + z = 11 & (2) \\ x - 2y + 4z = 0 & (3) \end{cases}$$

Solution   Add equations (2) and (3) to eliminate x, and the new equation is

$$-5y + 5z = 11 \quad (4)$$

To eliminate x again, multiply both sides of equation (2) by 2, and add the resulting equation to equation (1). Then

$$\begin{cases} 2x - 4y + 8z = 2 \\ 2(-x - 3y + z) = 2(11) \end{cases} \quad \begin{matrix} \text{simplifies} \\ \text{to} \end{matrix} \quad \begin{cases} 2x - 4y + 8z = 2 \\ -2x - 6y + 2z = 22 \\ \hline -10y + 10z = 24 \quad (5) \end{cases}$$

Next, solve for y and z using equations (4) and (5). Multiply both sides of equation (4) by -2, and add the resulting equation to equation (5).

$$\begin{cases} -2(-5y + 5z) = -2(11) \\ -10y + 10z = 24 \end{cases} \quad \begin{matrix} \text{simplifies} \\ \text{to} \end{matrix} \quad \begin{cases} 10y - 10z = -22 \\ -10y + 10z = 24 \\ \hline 0 = 2 \quad \text{False.} \end{cases}$$

Since the statement is false, this system is inconsistent and has no solution. The solution set is the empty set $\{\ \}$ or $\varnothing$.

The elimination method is summarized next.

SOLVING A SYSTEM OF THREE LINEAR EQUATIONS BY THE ELIMINATION METHOD

Step 1: Write each equation in standard form $Ax + By + Cz = D$.

Step 2: Choose a pair of equations and use the equations to eliminate a variable.

Step 3: Choose any other pair of equations and eliminate the **same variable** as in Step 2.

Step 4: Two equations in two variables should be obtained from Step 2 and Step 3. Use methods from Section 4.1 to solve this system for both variables.

Step 5: To solve for the third variable, substitute the values of the variables found in Step 4 into any of the original equations containing the third variable.

Example 3 Solve the system.

$$\begin{cases} 2x + 4y & = 1 & (1) \\ 4x & - 4z = -1 & (2) \\ & y - 4z = -3 & (3) \end{cases}$$

Solution Notice that equation (2) has no term containing the variable y. Let us eliminate y using equations (1) and (3). Multiply both sides of equation (3) by -4, and add the resulting equation to equation (1). Then

$$\begin{cases} 2x + 4y & = 1 \\ -4(y - 4z) = -4(-3) \end{cases} \quad \begin{matrix} \text{simplifies} \\ \text{to} \end{matrix} \quad \begin{cases} 2x + 4y & = 1 \\ \underline{- 4y + 16z = 12} \\ 2x \quad + 16z = 13 & (4) \end{cases}$$

Next, solve for z using equations (4) and (2). Multiply both sides of equation (4) by -2 and add the resulting equation to equation (2).

$$\begin{cases} -2(2x + 16z) = -2(13) \\ 4x - 4z = -1 \end{cases} \quad \begin{matrix} \text{simplifies} \\ \text{to} \end{matrix} \quad \begin{cases} -4x - 32z = -26 \\ \underline{4x - 4z = -1} \\ -36z = -27 \end{cases}$$

$$z = \frac{3}{4}$$

Replace z with $\frac{3}{4}$ in equation (3) and solve for y.

$$y - 4\left(\frac{3}{4}\right) = -3 \qquad \text{Let } z = \frac{3}{4} \text{ in equation (3).}$$
$$y - 3 = -3$$
$$y = 0$$

Replace y with 0 in equation (1) and solve for x.

$$2x + 4(0) = 1$$
$$2x = 1$$
$$x = \frac{1}{2}$$

The solution is $\left(\frac{1}{2}, 0, \frac{3}{4}\right)$. Check to see that this solution satisfies all three equations of the system.

Example 4 Solve the system.

$$\begin{cases} x - 5y - 2z = 6 & (1) \\ -2x + 10y + 4z = -12 & (2) \\ \frac{1}{2}x - \frac{5}{2}y - z = 3 & (3) \end{cases}$$

Solution   Multiply both sides of equation (3) by 2 to eliminate fractions, and multiply both sides

of equation (2) by $-\dfrac{1}{2}$ so that the coefficient of x is 1. The resulting system is then

$$\begin{cases} x - 5y - 2z = 6 & \text{(1)} \\ x - 5y - 2z = 6 & \text{Multiply (2) by } -\dfrac{1}{2}. \\ x - 5y - 2z = 6 & \text{Multiply (3) by 2.} \end{cases}$$

All three equations are identical, and therefore equations (1), (2), and (3) are all equivalent. There are infinitely many solutions of this system. The equations are dependent. The solution set can be written as $\{(x, y, z) \mid x - 5y - 2z = 6\}$.   ▬

Exercise Set 4.2

Solve each system. See Examples 1 and 3.

1. $\begin{cases} x + y = 3 \\ 2y = 10 \\ 3x + 2y - 3z = 1 \end{cases}$

2. $\begin{cases} 5x = 5 \\ 2x + y = 4 \\ 3x + y - 4z = -15 \end{cases}$

3. $\begin{cases} 2x + 2y + z = 1 \\ -x + y + 2z = 3 \\ x + 2y + 4z = 0 \end{cases}$

4. $\begin{cases} 2x - 3y + z = 5 \\ x + y + z = 0 \\ 4x + 2y + 4z = 4 \end{cases}$

Solve each system. See Examples 2 and 4.

5. $\begin{cases} x - 2y + z = -5 \\ -3x + 6y - 3z = 15 \\ 2x - 4y + 2z = -10 \end{cases}$

6. $\begin{cases} 3x + y - 2z = 2 \\ -6x - 2y + 4z = -2 \\ 9x + 3y - 6z = 6 \end{cases}$

7. $\begin{cases} 4x - y + 2z = 5 \\ 2y + z = 4 \\ 4x + y + 3z = 10 \end{cases}$

8. $\begin{cases} 5y - 7z = 14 \\ 2x + y + 4z = 10 \\ 2x + 6y - 3z = 30 \end{cases}$

9. Write a system of linear equations in three variables that has $(-1, 2, -4)$ as a solution. (There are many possibilities.)

10. Write a system of three linear equations in three variables that has $(2, 1, 5)$ as a solution. (There are many possibilities.)

Solve each system.

11. $\begin{cases} x + 5z = 0 \\ 5x + y = 0 \\ y - 3z = 0 \end{cases}$

12. $\begin{cases} x - 5y = 0 \\ x - z = 0 \\ -x + 5z = 0 \end{cases}$

13. $\begin{cases} 6x - 5z = 17 \\ 5x - y + 3z = -1 \\ 2x + y = -41 \end{cases}$

14. $\begin{cases} x + 2y = 6 \\ 7x + 3y + z = -33 \\ x - z = 16 \end{cases}$

15. $\begin{cases} x + y + z = 8 \\ 2x - y - z = 10 \\ x - 2y - 3z = 22 \end{cases}$

16. $\begin{cases} 5x + y + 3z = 1 \\ x - y + 3z = -7 \\ -x + y = 1 \end{cases}$

17. $\begin{cases} x + 2y - z = 5 \\ 6x + y + z = 7 \\ 2x + 4y - 2z = 5 \end{cases}$

18. $\begin{cases} 4x - y + 3z = 10 \\ x + y - z = 5 \\ 8x - 2y + 6z = 10 \end{cases}$

19. $\begin{cases} 2x - 3y + z = 2 \\ x - 5y + 5z = 3 \\ 3x + y - 3z = 5 \end{cases}$

20. $\begin{cases} 4x + y - z = 8 \\ x - y + 2z = 3 \\ 3x - y + z = 6 \end{cases}$

21. $\begin{cases} -2x - 4y + 6z = -8 \\ x + 2y - 3z = 4 \\ 4x + 8y - 12z = 16 \end{cases}$

22. $\begin{cases} -6x + 12y + 3z = -6 \\ 2x - 4y - z = 2 \\ -x + 2y + \dfrac{z}{2} = -1 \end{cases}$

23. $\begin{cases} 2x + 2y - 3z = 1 \\ y + 2z = -14 \\ 3x - 2y = -1 \end{cases}$

24. $\begin{cases} 7x + 4y = 10 \\ x - 4y + 2z = 6 \\ y - 2z = -1 \end{cases}$

25. $\begin{cases} \dfrac{3}{4}x - \dfrac{1}{3}y + \dfrac{1}{2}z = 9 \\ \dfrac{1}{6}x + \dfrac{1}{3}y - \dfrac{1}{2}z = 2 \\ \dfrac{1}{2}x - y + \dfrac{1}{2}z = 2 \end{cases}$

26. $\begin{cases} \dfrac{1}{3}x - \dfrac{1}{4}y + z = -9 \\ \dfrac{1}{2}x - \dfrac{1}{3}y - \dfrac{1}{4}z = -6 \\ x - \dfrac{1}{2}y - z = -8 \end{cases}$

27. The fraction $\frac{1}{24}$ can be written as the following sum:

$$\frac{1}{24} = \frac{x}{8} + \frac{y}{4} + \frac{z}{3}$$

where the numbers x, y, and z are solutions of

$$\begin{cases} x + y + z = 1 \\ 2x - y + z = 0 \\ -x + 2y + 2z = -1 \end{cases}$$

Solve the system and see that the sum of the fractions is $\frac{1}{24}$.

28. The fraction $\frac{1}{18}$ can be written as the following sum.

$$\frac{1}{18} = \frac{x}{2} + \frac{y}{3} + \frac{z}{9}$$

where the numbers x, y, and z are solutions of

$$\begin{cases} x + 3y + z = -3 \\ -x + y + 2z = -14 \\ 3x + 2y - z = 12 \end{cases}$$

Solve the system and see that the sum of the fractions is $\frac{1}{18}$.

REVIEW EXERCISES

Solve. See Section 2.2.

29. The sum of two numbers is 45 and one number is twice the other. Find the numbers.

30. The difference between two numbers is 5. Twice the smaller number added to five times the larger number is 53. Find the numbers.

Solve. See Section 2.1.

31. $2(x - 1) - 3x = x - 12$

32. $7(2x - 1) + 4 = 11(3x - 2)$

33. $-y - 5(y + 5) = 3y - 10$

34. $z - 3(z + 7) = 6(2z + 1)$

A Look Ahead

Solve each system.

35. $\begin{cases} x + y \quad - w = 0 \\ y + 2z + w = 3 \\ x \quad - z = 1 \\ 2x - y \quad - w = -1 \end{cases}$

36. $\begin{cases} 5x + 4y = 29 \\ y + z - w = -2 \\ 5x + z = 23 \\ y - z + w = 4 \end{cases}$

37. $\begin{cases} x + y + z + w = 5 \\ 2x + y + z + w = 6 \\ x + y + z = 2 \\ x + y = 0 \end{cases}$

38. $\begin{cases} 2x - z = -1 \\ y + z + w = 9 \\ y - 2w = -6 \\ x + y = 3 \end{cases}$

4.3 SYSTEMS OF LINEAR EQUATIONS AND PROBLEM SOLVING

CD-ROM   SSM   SSG   Video

▶ **OBJECTIVES**

1. Solve problems that can be modeled by a system of two linear equations.
2. Solve problems with cost and revenue functions.
3. Solve problems that can be modeled by a system of three linear equations.

1 Thus far, we have solved problems by writing one-variable equations and solving for the variable. Some of these problems can be solved, perhaps more easily, by writing a system of equations, as illustrated in this section. We begin with a problem about numbers.

Example 1 **FINDING UNKNOWN NUMBERS**

A first number is 4 less than a second number. Four times the first number is 6 more than twice the second. Find the numbers.

Solution

1. UNDERSTAND. Read and reread the problem and guess a solution. If one number is 10 and this is 4 less than a second number, the second number is 14. Four times the first number is 4(10), or 40. This is not equal to 6 more than twice the second number, which is 2(14) + 6 or 34. Although we guessed incorrectly, we now have a better understanding of the problem.

   Since we are looking for two numbers, we will let

$$x = \text{first number}$$
$$y = \text{second number}$$

2. TRANSLATE. Since we have assigned two variables to this problem, we will translate the given facts into two equations. For the first statement we have

In words:

the first number	is	4 less than the second number
↓	↓	↓

Translate: x $=$ $y - 4$

Next we translate the second statement into an equation.

In words:

four times the first number	is	6 more than twice the second number
↓	↓	↓

Translate: $4x$ $=$ $2y + 6$

3. SOLVE. Here we solve the system

$$\begin{cases} x = y - 4 \\ 4x = 2y + 6 \end{cases}$$

Since the first equation expresses x in terms of y, we will use substitution. We substitute $y - 4$ for x in the second equation and solve for y.

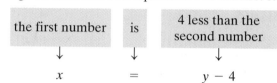

$$4x = 2y + 6 \quad \textit{Second equation}$$

$$4(y - 4) = 2y + 6 \quad \textit{Let } x = y - 4.$$

$$4y - 16 = 2y + 6$$

$$2y = 22$$

$$y = 11$$

Now we replace y with 11 in the equation $x = y - 4$ and solve for x. Then $x = y - 4$ becomes $x = 11 - 4 = 7$. The ordered pair solution of the system is $(7, 11)$.

4. INTERPRET. Since the solution of the system is $(7, 11)$, then the first number we are looking for is 7 and the second number is 11.

   Check: Notice that 7 *is* 4 less than 11, and 4 times 7 *is* 6 more than twice 11. The proposed numbers, 7 and 11, are correct.

   State: The numbers are 7 and 11.

Example 2   **FINDING THE RATE OF SPEED**

Two cars leave Indianapolis, one traveling east and the other west. After 3 hours they are 297 miles apart. If one car is traveling 5 mph faster than the other, what is the speed of each?

Solution
1. UNDERSTAND. Read and reread the problem. Let's guess a solution and use the formula $d = rt$ to check. Suppose that one car is traveling at a rate of 55 miles per hour. This means that the other car is traveling at a rate of 50 miles per hour since we are told that one car is traveling 5 mph faster than the other. To find the distance apart after 3 hours, we will first find the distance traveled by each car. One car's distance is rate · time = 55(3) = 165 miles. The other car's distance is rate · time = 50(3) = 150 miles. Since one car is traveling east and the other west, their distance apart is the sum of their distances, or 165 miles + 150 miles = 315 miles. Although this distance apart is not the required distance of 297 miles, we now have a better understanding of the problem.

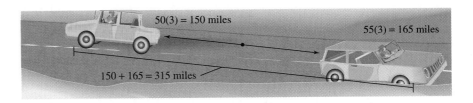

Let's model the problem with a system of equations. We will let

$$x = \text{speed of one car}$$

$$y = \text{speed of the other car}$$

We summarize the information on the following chart. Both cars have traveled 3 hours. Since distance = rate · time, their distances are $3x$ and $3y$ miles, respectively.

	Rate ·	*Time* =	*Distance*
ONE CAR	x	3	$3x$
OTHER CAR	y	3	$3y$

2. TRANSLATE. We can now translate the stated conditions into two equations.

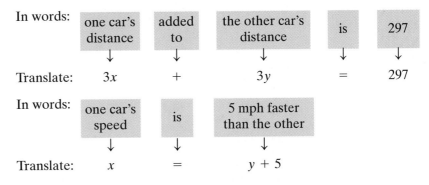

3. SOLVE. Here we solve the system

$$\begin{cases} 3x + 3y = 297 \\ x = y + 5 \end{cases}$$

Again, the substitution method is appropriate. We replace x with $y + 5$ in the first equation and solve for y.

$$3x + 3y = 297 \qquad \textit{First equation}$$

$$3(\overbrace{y + 5}) + 3y = 297 \qquad \textit{Let } x = y + 5.$$

$$3y + 15 + 3y = 297$$

$$6y = 282$$

$$y = 47$$

To find x, we replace y with 47 in the equation $x = y + 5$. Then $x = 47 + 5 = 52$. The ordered pair solution of the system is $(52, 47)$.

4. INTERPRET. The solution $(52, 47)$ means that the cars are traveling at 52 mph and 47 mph, respectively.

HELPFUL HINT
Don't forget to attach units, if appropriate.

Check: Notice that one car is traveling 5 mph faster than the other. Also, if one car travels 52 mph for 3 hours, the distance is $3(52) = 156$ miles. The other car traveling for 3 hours at 47 mph travels a distance of $3(47) = 141$ miles. The sum of the distances $156 + 141$ is 297 miles, the required distance.

State: The cars are traveling at 52 mph and 47 mph.

Example 3   MIXING SOLUTIONS

Lynn Pike, a pharmacist, needs 70 liters of a 50% alcohol solution. She has available a 30% alcohol solution and an 80% alcohol solution. How many liters of each solution should she mix to obtain 70 liters of a 50% alcohol solution?

Solution   1. UNDERSTAND. Read and reread the problem. Next, guess the solution. Suppose that we need 20 liters of the 30% solution. Then we need $70 - 20 = 50$ liters of the 80% solution. To see if this gives us 70 liters of a 50% alcohol solution, let's find the amount of pure alcohol in each solution.

number of liters	×	alcohol strength	=	amount of pure alcohol
↓		↓		↓
20 liters	×	0.30	=	6 liters
50 liters	×	0.80	=	40 liters
70 liters	×	0.50	=	35 liters

Since 6 liters + 40 liters = 46 liters and not 35 liters, our guess is incorrect, but we have gained some insight as to how to model and check this problem. We will let

$$x = \text{amount of 30\% solution, in liters}$$

$$y = \text{amount of 80\% solution, in liters}$$

and use a table to organize the given data.

	Number of Liters	Alcohol Strength	Amount of Pure Alcohol
30% SOLUTION	x	30%	$0.30x$
80% SOLUTION	y	80%	$0.80y$
50% SOLUTION NEEDED	70	50%	$(0.50)(70)$

2. TRANSLATE. We translate the stated conditions into two equations.

In words: amount of 30% solution $+$ amount of 80% solution $=$ 70

Translate: x $+$ y $=$ 70

In words: amount of pure alcohol in 30% solution $+$ amount of pure alcohol in 80% solution $=$ amount of pure alcohol in 50% solution

Translate: $0.30x$ $+$ $0.80y$ $=$ $(0.50)(70)$

3. SOLVE. Here we solve the system

$$\begin{cases} x + y = 70 \\ 0.30x + 0.80y = (0.50)(70) \end{cases}$$

To solve this system, we use the elimination method. We multiply both sides of the first equation by -3 and both sides of the second equation by 10. Then

$$\begin{cases} -3(x + y) = -3(70) \\ 10(0.30x + 0.80y) = 10(0.50)(70) \end{cases} \quad \begin{matrix} \text{simplifies} \\ \text{to} \end{matrix} \quad \begin{cases} -3x - 3y = -210 \\ 3x + 8y = 350 \\ \hline \phantom{3x + {}} 5y = 140 \\ y = 28 \end{cases}$$

Now we replace y with 28 in the equation $x + y = 70$ and find that $x + 28 = 70$, or $x = 42$.

The ordered pair solution of the system is $(42, 28)$.

4. INTERPRET.

Check: Check the solution in the same way that we checked our guess.

State: The pharmacist needs to mix 42 liters of 30% solution and 28 liters of 80% solution to obtain 70 liters of 50% solution.

2

Recall that businesses are often computing cost and revenue functions or equations to predict sales, to determine whether prices need to be adjusted, and to see whether the company is making or losing money. Recall also that the value at which revenue equals cost is called the break-even point. When revenue is less than cost, the company is losing money; when revenue is greater than cost, the company is making money.

Example 4   FINDING A BREAK-EVEN POINT

A manufacturing company recently purchased $3000 worth of new equipment to offer new personalized stationery to its customers. The cost of producing a package of personalized stationery is $3.00, and it is sold for $5.50. Find the number of packages that must be sold for the company to break even.

Solution   1. UNDERSTAND. Read and reread the problem. Notice that the cost to the company will include a one-time cost of $3000 for the equipment and then $3.00 per package produced. The revenue will be $5.50 per package sold. To model this problem, we will let

$$x = \text{number of packages of personalized stationery}$$
$$C(x) = \text{total cost for producing } x \text{ packages of stationery}$$
$$R(x) = \text{total revenue for selling } x \text{ packages of stationery}$$

2. TRANSLATE. The revenue equation is

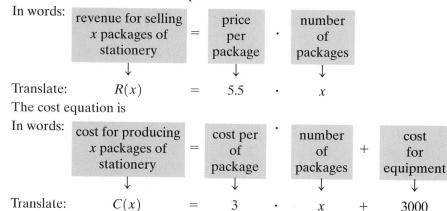

Translate: $R(x)$ =   5.5   · x

The cost equation is

Translate: $C(x)$ =   3   · x +   3000

Since the break-even point is when $R(x) = C(x)$, we solve the equation

$$5.5x = 3x + 3000$$

3. SOLVE.

$$5.5x = 3x + 3000$$
$$2.5x = 3000 \qquad \text{Subtract } 3x \text{ from both sides.}$$
$$x = 1200 \qquad \text{Divide both sides by 2.5.}$$

4. INTERPRET.

Check: To see whether the break-even point occurs when 1200 packages are produced and sold, see if revenue equals cost when $x = 1200$. When $x = 1200$, $R(x) = 5.5x = 5.5(1200) = 6600$ and $C(x) = 3x + 3000 = 3(1200) + 3000 = 6600$. Since $R(1200) = C(1200) = 6600$, the break-even point is 1200.

State: The company must sell 1200 packages of stationery to break even. The graph of this system is shown.

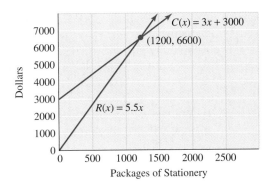

3   To introduce problem solving by writing a system of three linear equations in three variables, we solve a problem about triangles.

◈ **Example 5**   **FINDING ANGLE MEASURES**

The measure of the largest angle of a triangle is 80° more than the measure of the smallest angle, and the measure of the remaining angle is 10° more than the measure of the smallest angle. Find the measure of each angle.

Solution   1. UNDERSTAND. Read and reread the problem. Recall that the sum of the measures of the angles of a triangle is 180°. Then guess a solution. If the smallest angle measures 20°, the measure of the largest angle is 80° more, or 20° + 80° = 100°. The measure of the remaining angle is 10° more than the measure of the smallest angle, or 20° + 10° = 30°. The sum of these three angles is 20° + 100° + 30° = 150°, not the required 180°. We now know that the measure of the smallest angle is greater than 20°.

To model this problem we will let

$$x = \text{degree measure of the smallest angle}$$
$$y = \text{degree measure of the largest angle}$$
$$z = \text{degree measure of the remaining angle}$$

2. TRANSLATE. We translate the given information into three equations.

In words:

the sum of the measures	=	180

↓   ↓

Translate: $x + y + z$ =   180

In words:

the largest angle	is	80 more than the smallest angle

↓ ↓ ↓

Translate: y $=$ $x + 80$

In words:

the remaining angle	is	10 more than the smallest angle

↓ ↓ ↓

Translate: z $=$ $x + 10$

3. SOLVE. We solve the system

$$\begin{cases} x + y + z = 180 \\ y = x + 80 \\ z = x + 10 \end{cases}$$

Since y and z are both expressed in terms of x, we will solve using the subsitution method. We substitute $y = x + 80$ and $z = x + 10$ in the first equation. Then

$$x + y + z = 180 \quad \text{First equation}$$

$$x + (x + 80) + (x + 10) = 180 \quad \text{Let } y = x + 80 \text{ and } z = x + 10.$$

$$3x + 90 = 180$$

$$3x = 90$$

$$x = 30$$

Then $y = x + 80 = 30 + 80 = 110$, and $z = x + 10 = 30 + 10 = 40$. The ordered triple solution is $(30, 110, 40)$.

4. INTERPRET.

Check: Notice that $30° + 40° + 110° = 180°$. Also, the measure of the largest angle, $110°$, is $80°$ more than the measure of the smallest angle, $30°$. The measure of the remaining angle, $40°$, is $10°$ more than the measure of the smallest angle, $30°$.

State: The angles measure $30°$, $110°$, and $40°$.

SPOTLIGHT ON DECISION MAKING

Suppose you are choosing a long-distance telephone plan. You have narrowed your choices to the One Rate® 7¢ Plan offered by AT&T and the Qwest Communicator plan offered by Qwest Communications International, Inc. Under the AT&T One Rate® 7¢ Plan, calls made any time cost $0.07 per minute and users are charged a $5.95 monthly fee. Under the Qwest Communicator plan, calls made any time cost $0.05 per minute and users are charged a $9.95 monthly fee. Which long-distance plan would you choose? Why? What other factors would you want to consider? Would you change your choice if you knew that your long-distance calls averaged 4 hours per month? Explain your reasoning.

Exercise Set 4.3

Solve. See Examples 1–3 and 5.

1. One number is two more than a second number. Twice the first is 4 less than 3 times the second. Find the numbers.

2. Three times one number minus a second is 8, and the sum of the numbers is 12. Find the numbers.

3. A Delta 727 traveled 560 mph with the wind and 480 mph against the wind. Find the speed of the plane in still air and the speed of the wind.

4. Terry Watkins can row about 10.6 kilometers in 1 hour downstream and 6.8 kilometers upstream in 1 hour. Find how fast he can row in still water, and find the speed of the current.

5. Find how many quarts of 4% butterfat milk and 1% butterfat milk should be mixed to yield 60 quarts of 2% butterfat milk.

6. A pharmacist needs 500 milliliters of a 20% phenobarbital solution but has only 5% and 25% phenobarbital solutions available. Find how many milliliters of each he should mix to get the desired solution.

7. Karen Karlin bought some large frames for $15 each and some small frames for $8 each at a closeout sale. If she bought 22 frames for $239, find how many of each type she bought.

8. Hilton University Drama Club sold 311 tickets for a play. Student tickets cost 50 cents each; nonstudent tickets cost $1.50. If total receipts were $385.50, find how many tickets of each type were sold.

9. One number is two less than a second number. Twice the first is 4 more than 3 times the second. Find the numbers.

10. Twice one number plus a second number is 42, and the one number minus the second number is −6. Find the numbers.

11. An office supply store in San Diego sells seven tablets and 4 pens for $6.40. Also, two tablets and 19 pens cost $5.40. Find the price of each.

12. A Candy Barrel shop manager mixes M&M's worth $2.00 per pound with trail mix worth $1.50 per pound. Find how many pounds of each she should use to get 50 pounds of a party mix worth $1.80 per pound.

13. An airplane takes 3 hours to travel a distance of 2160 miles with the wind. The return trip takes 4 hours against the wind. Find the speed of the plane in still air and the speed of the wind.

14. Two cyclists start at the same point and travel in opposite directions. One travels 4 mph faster than the other. In 4 hours they are 112 miles apart. Find how fast each is traveling.

△ 15. The perimeter of a quadrilateral (four-sided polygon) is 29 inches. The longest side is twice as long as the shortest side. The other two sides are equally long and are 2 inches longer than the shortest side. Find the lengths of all four sides.

△ 16. The perimeter of a triangle is 93 centimeters. If two sides are equally long and the third side is 9 centimeters longer than the others, find the lengths of the three sides.

17. The sum of three numbers is 40. One number is five more than a second and twice the third. Find the numbers.

18. The sum of the digits of a three-digit number is 15. The tens-place digit is twice the hundreds-place digit, and the ones-place digit is 1 less than the hundreds-place digit. Find the three-digit number.

19. Jack Reinholt, a car salesman, has a choice of two pay arrangements: a weekly salary of $200 plus 5% commission on sales, or a straight 15% commission. Find the amount of sales for which Jack's earnings are the same regardless of the pay arrangement.

20. Hertz car rental agency charges $25 daily plus 10¢ per mile. Budget charges $20 daily plus 25¢ per mile. Find the daily mileage for which the Budget charge for the day is twice that of the Hertz charge for the day.

21. Carroll Blakemore, a drafting student, bought 3 templates and a pencil one day for $6.45. Another day he bought 2 pads of paper and 4 pencils for $7.50. If the price of a pad of paper is three times the price of a pencil, find the price of each type of item.

Given the cost function $C(x)$ and the revenue function $R(x)$, find the number of units x that must be sold to break even. See Example 4.

22. $C(x) = 30x + 10,000$
    $R(x) = 46x$

23. $C(x) = 12x + 15,000$
    $R(x) = 32x$

24. $C(x) = 1.2x + 1500$
    $R(x) = 1.7x$

25. $C(x) = 0.8x + 900$
    $R(x) = 2x$

26. $C(x) = 75x + 160,000$
    $R(x) = 200x$

27. $C(x) = 105x + 70,000$
    $R(x) = 245x$

28. The planning department of Abstract Office Supplies has been asked to determine whether the company should introduce a new computer desk next year. The department estimates that $6000 of new equipment will need to be purchased and that the cost of manufacturing each desk will be $200. The department also estimates that the revenue from each desk will be $450.

    a. Determine the revenue function $R(x)$ from the sale of x desks.

    b. Determine the cost function $C(x)$ for manufacturing x desks.

    c. Find the break-even point.

29. Baskets, Inc., is planning to introduce a new woven basket. The company estimates that $500 worth of new equipment will be needed to manufacture this new type of basket and that it will cost $15 per basket to manufacture. The company also estimates that the revenue from each basket will be $31.

   a. Determine the revenue function $R(x)$ from the sale of x baskets.

   b. Determine the cost function $C(x)$ for manufacturing x baskets.

   c. Find the break-even point.

Solve.

△ **30.** Line l and line m are parallel lines cut by transversal t. Find the values of x and y.

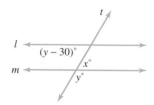

△ **31.** Find the values of x and y in the following isosceles triangle.

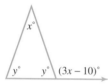

32. Two trains leave Tulsa, one traveling north and the other south. After 4 hours, they are 376 miles apart. If one train is traveling 10 mph faster than the other, what is the speed of each?

33. One solution contains 20% acid and a second solution contains 50% acid. How many ounces of each solution should be mixed in order to have 60 ounces of a 30% acid solution?

Solve. See Example 5.

34. Rabbits in a lab are to be kept on a strict daily diet to include 30 grams of protein, 16 grams of fat, and 24 grams of carbohydrates. The scientist has only three food mixes available with the following grams of nutrients per unit.

	Protein	Fat	Carbohydrate
Mix A	4	6	3
Mix B	6	1	2
Mix C	4	1	12

Find how many units of each mix are needed daily to meet each rabbit's dietary needs.

35. Gary Gundersen mixes different solutions with concentrations of 25%, 40%, and 50% to get 200 liters of a 32% solution. If he uses twice as much of the 25% solution as of the 40% solution, find how many liters of each kind he uses.

36. In 1999 the WNBA's top scorer was Cynthia Cooper of the Houston Comets. She scored a total of 686 points during the regular season. The number of two-point field goals Cooper made was 20 less than three times the number of three-point field goals she made. She also made 50 more free throws (each worth one point) than two-point field goals. Find how many free throws, two-point field goals, and three-point field goals Cynthia Cooper made during the 1999 season. (*Source:* Women's National Basketball Association)

37. During the 2000 NBA All-Star Game, the top-scoring player was Allen Iverson of the Philadelphia 76ers. Iverson, playing for the Eastern Conference All-Star Team, scored a total of 26 points during the All-Star Game. The number of free throws (each worth 1 point) he made was 2 more than the number of three-point field goals he made. Iverson also made 4 more two-point field goals than free throws. How many free throws, two-point field goals, and three-point field goals did Allen Iverson make during the 2000 NBA All-Star Game? (*Source:* National Basketball Association)

△ **38.** The measure of the largest angle of a triangle is 90° more than the measure of the smallest angle, and the measure of the remaining angle is 30° more than the measure of the smallest angle. Find the measure of each angle.

39. Suppose you mix an amount of 25% acid solution with an amount of 60% acid solution. You then calculate the acid strength of the resulting acid mixture. For which of the following results should you suspect an error in your calculation? Why?

a. 14%   **b.** 32%   **c.** 55%

40. Find the values of a, b, and c such that the equation $y = ax^2 + bx + c$ has ordered pair solutions $(1, 6)$, $(-1, -2)$, and $(0, -1)$. To do so, substitute each ordered pair solution into the equation. Each time, the result is an equation in three unknowns: a, b, and c. Then solve the resulting system of three linear equations in three unknowns, a, b, and c.

41. Find the values of a, b, and c such that the equation $y = ax^2 + bx + c$ has ordered pair solutions $(1, 2)$, $(2, 3)$ and $(-1, 6)$. (*Hint:* See Exercise 40.)

△ **42.** Find the values of x, y, and z in the following triangle.

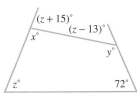

△ **43.** The sum of the measures of the angles of a quadrilateral is 360°. Find the values of x, y, and z in the following quadrilateral.

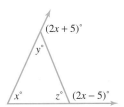

44. Data (x, y) for the total number y (in thousands) of college-bound students who took the ACT assessment in the year x are $(5, 945)$, $(6, 925)$, and $(9, 1019)$, where $x = 5$ represents 1995 and $x = 9$ represents 1999. Find the values of a, b, and c such that the equation $y = ax^2 + bx + c$ models this data. According to your model, how many students will take the ACT in 2005? (*Source:* ACT, Inc.)

45. Monthly normal rainfall data (x, y) for Portland, Oregon, are $(4, 2.47)$, $(7, 0.6)$, $(8, 1.1)$, where x represents time in months (with $x = 1$ representing January) and y represents rainfall in inches. Find the values of a, b, and c rounded to 2 decimal places such that the equation $y = ax^2 + bx + c$ models this data. According to your model, how much rain should Portland expect during September? (*Source:* National Climatic Data Center)

REVIEW EXERCISES

Multiply both sides of equation (1) by 2, and add the resulting equation to equation (2). See Section 4.2.

46. $3x - y + z = 2$ (1)
   $-x + 2y + 3z = 6$ (2)

47. $2x + y + 3z = 7$ (1)
   $-4x + y + 2z = 4$ (2)

Multiply both sides of equation (1) by -3, and add the resulting equation to equation (2). See Section 4.2.

48. $x + 2y - z = 0$ (1)
   $3x + y - z = 2$ (2)

49. $2x - 3y + 2z = 5$ (1)
   $x - 9y + z = -1$ (2)

Given the spinner below, find the probability of the spinner landing on the indicated color in one spin. See Section 2.3 Exercise set.

50. $P(\text{red})$

51. $P(\text{green})$

52. $P(\text{white})$

53. $P(\text{red or blue})$

4.4 SOLVING SYSTEMS OF EQUATIONS BY MATRICES

CD-ROM   SSM

SSG   Video

▶ **OBJECTIVES**

1. Use matrices to solve a system of two equations.
2. Use matrices to solve a system of three equations.

By now, you may have noticed that the solution of a system of equations depends on the coefficients of the equations in the system and not on the variables. In this section, we introduce solving a system of equations by a **matrix.**

1 A matrix (plural: **matrices**) is a rectangular array of numbers. The following are examples of matrices.

$$\begin{bmatrix} 1 & 0 \\ 0 & 1 \end{bmatrix} \qquad \begin{bmatrix} 2 & 1 & 3 & -1 \\ 0 & -1 & 4 & 5 \\ -6 & 2 & 1 & 0 \end{bmatrix} \qquad \begin{bmatrix} a & b & c \\ d & e & f \end{bmatrix}$$

The numbers aligned horizontally in a matrix are in the same **row**. The numbers aligned vertically are in the same **column**.

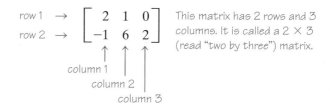

To see the relationship between systems of equations and matrices, study the example below.

System of Equations	***Corresponding Matrix***

$$\begin{cases} 2x - 3y = 6 \quad \text{Equation 1} \\ x + y = 0 \quad \text{Equation 2} \end{cases} \qquad \begin{bmatrix} 2 & -3 & \vdots & 6 \\ 1 & 1 & \vdots & 0 \end{bmatrix} \begin{matrix} \text{Row 1} \\ \text{Row 2} \end{matrix}$$

Notice that the rows of the matrix correspond to the equations in the system. The coefficients of each variable are placed to the left of a vertical dashed line. The constants are placed to the right. Each of these numbers in the matrix is called an **element**.

The method of solving systems by matrices is to write this matrix as an equivalent matrix from which we easily identify the solution. Two matrices are equivalent if they represent systems that have the same solution set. The following **row operations** can be performed on matrices, and the result is an equivalent matrix.

ELEMENTARY ROW OPERATIONS

1. Any two rows in a matrix may be interchanged.
2. The elements of any row may be multiplied (or divided) by the same nonzero number.
3. The elements of any row may be multiplied (or divided) by a nonzero number and added to their corresponding elements in any other row.

HELPFUL HINT
Notice that these *row* operations are the same operations that we can perform on *equations* in a system.

Example 1 Use matrices to solve the system.

$$\begin{cases} x + 3y = 5 \\ 2x - y = -4 \end{cases}$$

Solution The corresponding matrix is $\begin{bmatrix} 1 & 3 & \vdots & 5 \\ 2 & -1 & \vdots & -4 \end{bmatrix}$. We use elementary row operations to write an equivalent matrix that looks like $\begin{bmatrix} 1 & a & \vdots & b \\ 0 & 1 & \vdots & c \end{bmatrix}$.

For the matrix given, the element in the first row, first column is already 1, as desired. Next we write an equivalent matrix with a 0 below the 1. To do this, we multiply row 1 by -2 and add to row 2. *We will change only row 2.*

$$\begin{bmatrix} 1 & 3 & \vdots & 5 \\ -2(1) + 2 & -2(3) + (-1) & \vdots & -2(5) + (-4) \end{bmatrix}$$ simplifies to $\begin{bmatrix} 1 & 3 & \vdots & 5 \\ 0 & -7 & \vdots & -14 \end{bmatrix}$

row 1   row 2   row 1   row 2   row 1   row 2
element element element element element element

Now we change the -7 to a 1 by use of an elementary row operation. We divide row 2 by -7, then

$$\begin{bmatrix} 1 & 3 & \vdots & 5 \\ \dfrac{0}{-7} & \dfrac{-7}{-7} & \vdots & \dfrac{-14}{-7} \end{bmatrix}$$ simplifies to $\begin{bmatrix} 1 & 3 & \vdots & 5 \\ 0 & 1 & \vdots & 2 \end{bmatrix}$

This last matrix corresponds to the system

$$\begin{cases} x + 3y = 5 \\ y = 2 \end{cases}$$

To find x, we let $y = 2$ in the first equation, $x + 3y = 5$.

$$x + 3y = 5 \qquad \text{First equation}$$
$$x + 3(2) = 5 \qquad \text{Let } y = 2.$$
$$x = -1$$

The ordered pair solution is $(-1, 2)$. Check to see that this ordered pair satisfies both equations.

Example 2 Use matrices to solve the system.

$$\begin{cases} 2x - y = 3 \\ 4x - 2y = 5 \end{cases}$$

Solution The corresponding matrix is $\begin{bmatrix} 2 & -1 & \vdots & 3 \\ 4 & -2 & \vdots & 5 \end{bmatrix}$. To get 1 in the row 1, column 1 position, we divide the elements of row 1 by 2.

$$\begin{bmatrix} \dfrac{2}{2} & -\dfrac{1}{2} & \vdots & \dfrac{3}{2} \\ 4 & -2 & \vdots & 5 \end{bmatrix}$$ simplifies to $\begin{bmatrix} 1 & -\dfrac{1}{2} & \vdots & \dfrac{3}{2} \\ 4 & -2 & \vdots & 5 \end{bmatrix}$

To get 0 under the 1, we multiply the elements of row 1 by -4 and add the new elements to the elements of row 2.

$$\begin{bmatrix} 1 & -\dfrac{1}{2} & \vdots & \dfrac{3}{2} \\ -4(1)+4 & -4\left(-\dfrac{1}{2}\right)-2 & \vdots & -4\left(\dfrac{3}{2}\right)+5 \end{bmatrix}$$ simplifies to $$\begin{bmatrix} 1 & -\dfrac{1}{2} & \vdots & \dfrac{3}{2} \\ 0 & 0 & \vdots & -1 \end{bmatrix}$$

The corresponding system is $\begin{cases} x - \dfrac{1}{2}y = \dfrac{3}{2} \\ 0 = -1 \end{cases}$. The equation $0 = -1$ is false for all y

or x values; hence the system is inconsistent and has no solution.

2 To solve a system of three equations in three variables using matrices, we will write the corresponding matrix in the form

$$\begin{bmatrix} 1 & a & b & \vdots & d \\ 0 & 1 & c & \vdots & e \\ 0 & 0 & 1 & \vdots & f \end{bmatrix}$$

Example 3 Use matrices to solve the system.

$$\begin{cases} x + 2y + z = 2 \\ -2x - y + 2z = 5 \\ x + 3y - 2z = -8 \end{cases}$$

Solution The corresponding matrix is $\begin{bmatrix} 1 & 2 & 1 & \vdots & 2 \\ -2 & -1 & 2 & \vdots & 5 \\ 1 & 3 & -2 & \vdots & -8 \end{bmatrix}$. Our goal is to write an

equivalent matrix with 1's along the diagonal (see the numbers in red) and 0's below the 1's. The element in row 1, column 1 is already 1. Next we get 0's for each element in the rest of column 1. To do this, first we multiply the elements of row 1 by 2 and add the new elements to row 2. Also, we multiply the elements of row 1 by -1 and add the new elements to the elements of row 3. We *do not change row 1.* Then

$$\begin{bmatrix} 1 & 2 & 1 & \vdots & 2 \\ 2(1)-2 & 2(2)-1 & 2(1)+2 & \vdots & 2(2)+5 \\ -1(1)+1 & -1(2)+3 & -1(1)-2 & \vdots & -1(2)-8 \end{bmatrix}$$ simplifies to $$\begin{bmatrix} 1 & 2 & 1 & \vdots & 2 \\ 0 & 3 & 4 & \vdots & 9 \\ 0 & 1 & -3 & \vdots & -10 \end{bmatrix}$$

We continue down the diagonal and use elementary row operations to get 1 where the element 3 is now. To do this, we interchange rows 2 and 3.

$$\begin{bmatrix} 1 & 2 & 1 & \vdots & 2 \\ 0 & 3 & 4 & \vdots & 9 \\ 0 & 1 & -3 & \vdots & -10 \end{bmatrix}$$ is equivalent to $$\begin{bmatrix} 1 & 2 & 1 & \vdots & 2 \\ 0 & 1 & -3 & \vdots & -10 \\ 0 & 3 & 4 & \vdots & 9 \end{bmatrix}$$

Next we want the new row 3, column 2 element to be 0. We multiply the elements of row 2 by -3 and add the result to the elements of row 3.

$$\begin{bmatrix} 1 & 2 & 1 & \vdots & 2 \\ 0 & 1 & -3 & \vdots & -10 \\ -3(0)+0 & -3(1)+3 & -3(-3)+4 & \vdots & -3(-10)+9 \end{bmatrix} \quad \text{simplifies to} \quad \begin{bmatrix} 1 & 2 & 1 & \vdots & 2 \\ 0 & 1 & -3 & \vdots & -10 \\ 0 & 0 & 13 & \vdots & 39 \end{bmatrix}$$

Finally, we divide the elements of row 3 by 13 so that the final diagonal element is 1.

$$\begin{bmatrix} 1 & 2 & 1 & \vdots & 2 \\ 0 & 1 & -3 & \vdots & -10 \\ \dfrac{0}{13} & \dfrac{0}{13} & \dfrac{13}{13} & \vdots & \dfrac{39}{13} \end{bmatrix} \quad \text{simplifies to} \quad \begin{bmatrix} 1 & 2 & 1 & \vdots & 2 \\ 0 & 1 & -3 & \vdots & -10 \\ 0 & 0 & 1 & \vdots & 3 \end{bmatrix}$$

This matrix corresponds to the system

$$\begin{cases} x + 2y + z = 2 \\ y - 3z = -10 \\ z = 3 \end{cases}$$

We identify the z-coordinate of the solution as 3. Next we replace z with 3 in the second equation and solve for y.

$$\begin{aligned} y - 3z &= -10 && \text{\textit{Second equation}} \\ y - 3(3) &= -10 && \text{\textit{Let } z = 3.} \\ y &= -1 \end{aligned}$$

To find x, we let $z = 3$ and $y = -1$ in the first equation.

$$\begin{aligned} x + 2y + z &= 2 && \text{\textit{First equation}} \\ x + 2(-1) + 3 &= 2 && \text{\textit{Let } z = 3 \text{ and } y = -1.} \\ x &= 1 \end{aligned}$$

The ordered triple solution is $(1, -1, 3)$. Check to see that it satisfies all three equations in the original system.

SPOTLIGHT ON DECISION MAKING

Suppose you are an urban planner working for the public transportation authority of a large city. Currently, more commuters travel into the downtown area during the morning rush hour than travel out of it. However, a strong economy is creating new jobs in the suburbs. As suburban job growth continues, more city dwellers will travel out of the downtown area during the morning rush hour. You have been assigned to study the situation, focusing on how the trend will impact existing bus routes and schedules and how soon.

After a detailed study of public transportation utilization, you find that the number of commuters into downtown each morning can be described by the equation $y = 40{,}000 + 200x$, where x is the number of months from now. The number of commuters out of downtown each morning can be described by the equation $y = 20{,}000 + 1000x$, where x is the number of months from now. In the short term, as the numbers of commuters in each direction increase, additional buses can be put on the existing routes to handle the load. But once the number of commuters leaving downtown exceeds the number of commuters traveling into downtown, the bus routes must be totally revamped.

It usually takes the public transportation authority $1\frac{1}{2}$ years to plan major changes to bus routes. If changes are needed more quickly than that, a consulting firm can be hired to speed up the process. Decide whether a consulting firm will be needed to help revamp the bus routes.

Exercise Set 4.4

Solve each system of linear equations using matrices. See Example 1.

1. $\begin{cases} x + y = 1 \\ x - 2y = 4 \end{cases}$

2. $\begin{cases} 2x - y = 8 \\ x + 3y = 11 \end{cases}$

3. $\begin{cases} x + 3y = 2 \\ x + 2y = 0 \end{cases}$

4. $\begin{cases} 4x - y = 5 \\ 3x - 3y = 0 \end{cases}$

Solve each system of linear equations using matrices. See Example 2.

5. $\begin{cases} x - 2y = 4 \\ 2x - 4y = 4 \end{cases}$

6. $\begin{cases} -x + 3y = 6 \\ 3x - 9y = 9 \end{cases}$

7. $\begin{cases} 3x - 3y = 9 \\ 2x - 2y = 6 \end{cases}$

8. $\begin{cases} 9x - 3y = 6 \\ -18x + 6y = -12 \end{cases}$

Solve each system of linear equations using matrices. See Example 3.

9. $\begin{cases} x + y = 3 \\ 2y = 10 \\ 3x + 2y - 4z = 12 \end{cases}$

10. $\begin{cases} 5x = 5 \\ 2x + y = 4 \\ 3x + y - 5z = -15 \end{cases}$

11. $\begin{cases} 2y - z = -7 \\ x + 4y + z = -4 \\ 5x - y + 2z = 13 \end{cases}$

12. $\begin{cases} 4y + 3z = -2 \\ 5x - 4y = 1 \\ -5x + 4y + z = -3 \end{cases}$

Solve each system of linear equations using matrices.

13. $\begin{cases} x - 4 = 0 \\ x + y = 1 \end{cases}$

14. $\begin{cases} 3y = 6 \\ x + y = 7 \end{cases}$

15. $\begin{cases} x + y + z = 2 \\ 2x - z = 5 \\ 3y + z = 2 \end{cases}$

16. $\begin{cases} x + 2y + z = 5 \\ x - y - z = 3 \\ y + z = 2 \end{cases}$

17. $\begin{cases} 5x - 2y = 27 \\ -3x + 5y = 18 \end{cases}$

18. $\begin{cases} 4x - y = 9 \\ 2x + 3y = -27 \end{cases}$

19. $\begin{cases} 4x - 7y = 7 \\ 12x - 21y = 24 \end{cases}$

20. $\begin{cases} 2x = 5y - 12 \\ -4x + 10y = 20 \end{cases}$

21. $\begin{cases} 4x - y + 2z = 5 \\ 2y + z = 4 \\ 4x + y + 3z = 10 \end{cases}$

22. $\begin{cases} 5y - 7z = 14 \\ 2x + y + 4z = 10 \\ 2x + 6y - 3z = 30 \end{cases}$

23. $\begin{cases} 4x + y + z = 3 \\ -x + y - 2z = -11 \\ x + 2y + 2z = -1 \end{cases}$

24. $\begin{cases} x + y + z = 9 \\ 3x - y + z = -1 \\ -2x + 2y - 3z = -2 \end{cases}$

25. Consider the system
$\begin{cases} 2x - 3y = 8 \\ x + 5y = -3 \end{cases}$

What is wrong with its corresponding matrix shown below?

$$\begin{bmatrix} 2 & 3 & | & 8 \\ 0 & 5 & | & 3 \end{bmatrix}$$

26. The percent y of U.S. households that owned a black-and-white television set between the years 1980 and 1993 can be modeled by the linear equation $2.3x + y = 52$, where x represents the number of years after 1980. Similarly, the percent y of U.S. households that owned a microwave oven during this same period can be modeled by the linear equation $-5.4x + y = 14$. (*Source:* Based on data from the Energy Information Administration, U.S. Department of Energy)

a. The data used to form these two models was incomplete. It is impossible to tell from the data the year in which the percent of households owning black-and-white television sets was the same as the percent of households owning microwave ovens. Use matrix methods to estimate the year in which this occurred.

b. Did more households own black-and-white television sets or microwave ovens in 1980? In 1993? What trends do these models show? Does this seem to make sense? Why or why not?

c. According to the models, when will the percent of households owning black-and-white television sets reach 0%?

REVIEW EXERCISES

Determine whether each graph is the graph of a function. See Section 3.2.

27.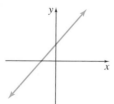

28.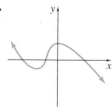

29.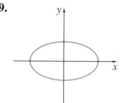

30.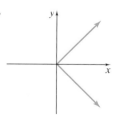

Evaluate. See Section 1.3.

31. $(-1)(-5) - (6)(3)$

32. $(2)(-8) - (-4)(1)$

33. $(4)(-10) - (2)(-2)$

34. $(-7)(3) - (-2)(-6)$

35. $(-3)(-3) - (-1)(-9)$

36. $(5)(6) - (10)(10)$

4.5 SOLVING SYSTEMS OF EQUATIONS BY DETERMINANTS

CD-ROM   SSM

SSG   Video

▶ **O B J E C T I V E S**

1. Define and evaluate a 2 × 2 determinant.
2. Use Cramer's rule to solve a system of two linear equations in two variables.
3. Define and evaluate a 3 × 3 determinant.
4. Use Cramer's rule to solve a linear system of three equations in three variables.

1

We have solved systems of two linear equations in two variables in four different ways: graphically, by substitution, by elimination, and by matrices. Now we analyze another method called **Cramer's rule**.

Recall that a matrix is a rectangular array of numbers. If a matrix has the same number of rows and columns, it is called a **square matrix**. Examples of square matrices are

$$\begin{bmatrix} 1 & 6 \\ 5 & 2 \end{bmatrix} \qquad \begin{bmatrix} 2 & 4 & 1 \\ 0 & 5 & 2 \\ 3 & 6 & 9 \end{bmatrix}.$$

A **determinant** is a real number associated with a square matrix. The determinant of a square matrix is denoted by placing vertical bars about the array of numbers. Thus,

The determinant of the square matrix $\begin{bmatrix} 1 & 6 \\ 5 & 2 \end{bmatrix}$ is $\begin{vmatrix} 1 & 6 \\ 5 & 2 \end{vmatrix}.$

The determinant of the square matrix $\begin{bmatrix} 2 & 4 & 1 \\ 0 & 5 & 2 \\ 3 & 6 & 9 \end{bmatrix}$ is $\begin{vmatrix} 2 & 4 & 1 \\ 0 & 5 & 2 \\ 3 & 6 & 9 \end{vmatrix}.$

We define the determinant of a 2 × 2 matrix first. (Recall that 2 × 2 is read "two by two." It means that the matrix has 2 rows and 2 columns.)

DETERMINANT OF A 2 × 2 MATRIX

$$\begin{vmatrix} a & b \\ c & d \end{vmatrix} = ad - bc$$

Example 1 Evaluate each determinant.

a. $\begin{vmatrix} -1 & 2 \\ 3 & -4 \end{vmatrix}$ **b.** $\begin{vmatrix} 2 & 0 \\ 7 & -5 \end{vmatrix}$

Solution First we identify the values of $a, b, c,$ and $d.$ Then we perform the evaluation.

a. Here $a = -1, b = 2, c = 3,$ and $d = -4.$

$$\begin{vmatrix} -1 & 2 \\ 3 & -4 \end{vmatrix} = ad - bc = (-1)(-4) - (2)(3) = -2$$

b. In this example, $a = 2, b = 0, c = 7$, and $d = -5$.

$$\begin{vmatrix} 2 & 0 \\ 7 & -5 \end{vmatrix} = ad - bc = 2(-5) - (0)(7) = -10$$

2   To develop Cramer's rule, we solve the system $\begin{cases} ax + by = h \\ cx + dy = k \end{cases}$ using elimination.

First, we eliminate y by multiplying both sides of the first equation by d and both sides of the second equation by $-b$ so that the coefficients of y are opposites. The result is that

$$\begin{cases} d(ax + by) = d \cdot h \\ -b(cx + dy) = -b \cdot k \end{cases} \quad \text{simplifies to} \quad \begin{cases} adx + bdy = hd \\ -bcx - bdy = -kb \end{cases}$$

We now add the two equations and solve for x.

$$\begin{array}{rl} adx + bdy & = hd \\ -bcx - bdy & = -kb \\ \hline adx - bcx & = hd - kb \qquad \text{Add the equations.} \\ (ad - bc)x & = hd - kb \\ x & = \dfrac{hd - kb}{ad - bc} \qquad \text{Solve for } x. \end{array}$$

When we replace x with $\dfrac{hd - kb}{ad - bc}$ in the equation $ax + by = h$ and solve for y, we find that $y = \dfrac{ak - ch}{ad - bc}$.

Notice that the numerator of the value of x is the determinant of

$$\begin{vmatrix} h & b \\ k & d \end{vmatrix} = hd - kb$$

Also, the numerator of the value of y is the determinant of

$$\begin{vmatrix} a & h \\ c & k \end{vmatrix} = ak - hc$$

Finally, the denominators of the values of x and y are the same and are the determinant of

$$\begin{vmatrix} a & b \\ c & d \end{vmatrix} = ad - bc$$

This means that the values of x and y can be written in determinant notation.

$$x = \frac{\begin{vmatrix} h & b \\ k & d \end{vmatrix}}{\begin{vmatrix} a & b \\ c & d \end{vmatrix}} \quad \text{and} \quad y = \frac{\begin{vmatrix} a & h \\ c & k \end{vmatrix}}{\begin{vmatrix} a & b \\ c & d \end{vmatrix}}$$

For convenience, we label the determinants D, D_x, and D_y.

x-coefficients
y-coefficients

$$\begin{vmatrix} a & b \\ c & d \end{vmatrix} = D \qquad \begin{vmatrix} h & b \\ k & d \end{vmatrix} = D_x \qquad \begin{vmatrix} a & h \\ c & k \end{vmatrix} = D_y$$

x-column replaced by constants

y-column replaced by constants

These determinant formulas for the coordinates of the solution of a system are known as **Cramer's rule**.

CRAMER'S RULE FOR TWO LINEAR EQUATIONS IN TWO VARIABLES

The solution of the system $\begin{cases} ax + by = h \\ cx + dy = k \end{cases}$ is given by

$$x = \frac{\begin{vmatrix} h & b \\ k & d \end{vmatrix}}{\begin{vmatrix} a & b \\ c & d \end{vmatrix}} = \frac{D_x}{D} \qquad y = \frac{\begin{vmatrix} a & h \\ c & k \end{vmatrix}}{\begin{vmatrix} a & b \\ c & d \end{vmatrix}} = \frac{D_y}{D}$$

as long as $D = ad - bc$ is not 0.

When $D = 0$, the system is either inconsistent or the equations are dependent. When this happens, we need to use another method to see which is the case.

Example 2   Use Cramer's rule to solve each system.

a. $\begin{cases} 3x + 4y = -7 \\ x - 2y = -9 \end{cases}$ b. $\begin{cases} 5x + y = 5 \\ -7x - 2y = -7 \end{cases}$

Solution   **a.** First we find D, D_x, and D_y.

$$\begin{cases} \overset{a}{\downarrow} \; 3x + \overset{b}{\downarrow} \; 4y = \overset{h}{\downarrow} \; -7 \\ \underset{c}{\uparrow} \; x - \underset{d}{\uparrow} \; 2y = \underset{k}{\uparrow} \; -9 \end{cases}$$

$$D = \begin{vmatrix} a & b \\ c & d \end{vmatrix} = \begin{vmatrix} 3 & 4 \\ 1 & -2 \end{vmatrix} = 3(-2) - 4(1) = -10$$

$$D_x = \begin{vmatrix} h & b \\ k & d \end{vmatrix} = \begin{vmatrix} -7 & 4 \\ -9 & -2 \end{vmatrix} = (-7)(-2) - 4(-9) = 50$$

$$D_y = \begin{vmatrix} a & h \\ c & k \end{vmatrix} = \begin{vmatrix} 3 & -7 \\ 1 & -9 \end{vmatrix} = 3(-9) - (-7)(1) = -20$$

Then $x = \dfrac{D_x}{D} = \dfrac{50}{-10} = -5$ and $y = \dfrac{D_y}{D} = \dfrac{-20}{-10} = 2$. The ordered pair solution is $(-5, 2)$.

As always, check the solution in both original equations.

b. Find $D, D_x,$ and D_y for $\begin{cases} 5x + y = 5 \\ -7x - 2y = -7 \end{cases}$.

$$D = \begin{vmatrix} 5 & 1 \\ -7 & -2 \end{vmatrix} = 5(-2) - (1)(-7) = -3$$

$$D_x = \begin{vmatrix} 5 & 1 \\ -7 & -2 \end{vmatrix} = 5(-2) - (1)(-7) = -3$$

$$D_y = \begin{vmatrix} 5 & 5 \\ -7 & -7 \end{vmatrix} = 5(-7) - 5(-7) = 0$$

Then $x = \dfrac{D_x}{D} = \dfrac{-3}{-3} = 1$ and $y = \dfrac{D_y}{D} = \dfrac{0}{-3} = 0.$

The ordered pair solution is $(1, 0)$. Check this solution in both original equations.

3   A 3×3 determinant can be used to solve a system of three equations in three variables. The determinant of a 3×3 matrix, however, is considerably more complex than a 2×2 one.

DETERMINANT OF A 3 × 3 MATRIX

$$\begin{vmatrix} a_1 & b_1 & c_1 \\ a_2 & b_2 & c_2 \\ a_3 & b_3 & c_3 \end{vmatrix} = a_1 \cdot \begin{vmatrix} b_2 & c_2 \\ b_3 & c_3 \end{vmatrix} - a_2 \cdot \begin{vmatrix} b_1 & c_1 \\ b_3 & c_3 \end{vmatrix} + a_3 \cdot \begin{vmatrix} b_1 & c_1 \\ b_2 & c_2 \end{vmatrix}$$

Notice that the determinant of a 3×3 matrix is related to the determinants of three 2×2 matrices. Each determinant of these 2×2 matrices is called a **minor**, and every element of a 3×3 matrix has a minor associated with it. For example, the minor of c_2 is the determinant of the 2×2 matrix found by deleting the row and column containing c_2.

$$\begin{array}{ccc} a_1 & b_1 & c_1 \\ a_2 & b_2 & c_2 \\ a_3 & b_3 & c_3 \end{array} \qquad \text{The minor of } c_2 \text{ is} \qquad \begin{vmatrix} a_1 & b_1 \\ a_3 & b_3 \end{vmatrix}$$

Also, the minor of element a_1 is the determinant of the 2×2 matrix that has no row or column containing a_1.

$$\begin{array}{ccc} a_1 & b_1 & c_1 \\ a_2 & b_2 & c_2 \\ a_3 & b_3 & c_3 \end{array} \qquad \text{The minor of } a_1 \text{ is} \qquad \begin{vmatrix} b_2 & c_2 \\ b_3 & c_3 \end{vmatrix}$$

So the determinant of a 3×3 matrix can be written as

$$a_1 \cdot (\text{minor of } a_1) - a_2 \cdot (\text{minor of } a_2) + a_3 \cdot (\text{minor of } a_3)$$

Finding the determinant by using minors of elements in the first column is called **expanding** by the minors of the first column. *The value of a determinant can be found by expanding by the minors of any row or column.* The following **array of signs** is helpful in determining whether to add or subtract the product of an element and its minor.

$$
\begin{array}{ccc}
+ & - & + \\
- & + & - \\
+ & - & +
\end{array}
$$

If an element is in a position marked $+$, we add. If marked $-$, we subtract.

Example 3   Evaluate by expanding by the minors of the given row or column.

$$
\begin{vmatrix}
0 & 5 & 1 \\
1 & 3 & -1 \\
-2 & 2 & 4
\end{vmatrix}
$$

a. First column   **b.** Second row

Solution   **a.** The elements of the first column are $0, 1$, and -2. The first column of the array of signs is $+$, $-$, $+$.

$$
\begin{vmatrix}
0 & 5 & 1 \\
1 & 3 & -1 \\
-2 & 2 & 4
\end{vmatrix}
= 0 \cdot \begin{vmatrix} 3 & -1 \\ 2 & 4 \end{vmatrix} - 1 \cdot \begin{vmatrix} 5 & 1 \\ 2 & 4 \end{vmatrix} + (-2) \cdot \begin{vmatrix} 5 & 1 \\ 3 & -1 \end{vmatrix}
$$

$$
= 0(12 - (-2)) - 1(20 - 2) + (-2)(-5 - 3)
$$

$$
= 0 - 18 + 16 = -2
$$

b. The elements of the second row are $1, 3$, and -1. This time, the signs begin with $-$ and again alternate.

$$
\begin{vmatrix}
0 & 5 & 1 \\
1 & 3 & -1 \\
-2 & 2 & 4
\end{vmatrix}
= -1 \cdot \begin{vmatrix} 5 & 1 \\ 2 & 4 \end{vmatrix} + 3 \cdot \begin{vmatrix} 0 & 1 \\ -2 & 4 \end{vmatrix} - (-1) \cdot \begin{vmatrix} 0 & 5 \\ -2 & 2 \end{vmatrix}
$$

$$
= -1(20 - 2) + 3(0 - (-2)) - (-1)(0 - (-10))
$$

$$
= -18 + 6 + 10 = -2
$$

Notice that the determinant of the 3×3 matrix is the same regardless of the row or column you select to expand by.

4   A system of three equations in three variables may be solved with Cramer's rule also. Using the elimination process to solve a system with unknown constants as coefficients leads to the following.

> **CRAMER'S RULE FOR THREE EQUATIONS IN THREE VARIABLES**
>
> The solution of the system $\begin{cases} a_1 x + b_1 y + c_1 z = k_1 \\ a_2 x + b_2 y + c_2 z = k_2 \\ a_3 x + b_3 y + c_3 z = k_3 \end{cases}$ is given by
>
> $$ x = \frac{D_x}{D} \qquad y = \frac{D_y}{D} \qquad \text{and} \qquad z = \frac{D_z}{D} $$
>
> *(continued)*

where

$$D = \begin{vmatrix} a_1 & b_1 & c_1 \\ a_2 & b_2 & c_2 \\ a_3 & b_3 & c_3 \end{vmatrix} \qquad D_x = \begin{vmatrix} k_1 & b_1 & c_1 \\ k_2 & b_2 & c_2 \\ k_3 & b_3 & c_3 \end{vmatrix}$$

$$D_y = \begin{vmatrix} a_1 & k_1 & c_1 \\ a_2 & k_2 & c_2 \\ a_3 & k_3 & c_3 \end{vmatrix} \qquad D_z = \begin{vmatrix} a_1 & b_1 & k_1 \\ a_2 & b_2 & k_2 \\ a_3 & b_3 & k_3 \end{vmatrix}$$

as long as D is not 0.

Example 4 Use Cramer's rule to solve the system.

$$\begin{cases} x - 2y + z = 4 \\ 3x + y - 2z = 3 \\ 5x + 5y + 3z = -8 \end{cases}$$

Solution First we find $D, D_x, D_y,$ and D_z. Beginning with D, we expand by the minors of the first column.

$$D = \begin{vmatrix} 1 & -2 & 1 \\ 3 & 1 & -2 \\ 5 & 5 & 3 \end{vmatrix} = 1 \cdot \begin{vmatrix} 1 & -2 \\ 5 & 3 \end{vmatrix} - 3 \cdot \begin{vmatrix} -2 & 1 \\ 5 & 3 \end{vmatrix} + 5 \cdot \begin{vmatrix} -2 & 1 \\ 1 & -2 \end{vmatrix}$$

$$= 1(3 - (-10)) - 3(-6 - 5) + 5(4 - 1)$$

$$= 13 + 33 + 15 = 61$$

$$D_x = \begin{vmatrix} 4 & -2 & 1 \\ 3 & 1 & -2 \\ -8 & 5 & 3 \end{vmatrix} = 4 \cdot \begin{vmatrix} 1 & -2 \\ 5 & 3 \end{vmatrix} - 3 \cdot \begin{vmatrix} -2 & 1 \\ 5 & 3 \end{vmatrix} + (-8) \cdot \begin{vmatrix} -2 & 1 \\ 1 & -2 \end{vmatrix}$$

$$= 4(3 - (-10)) - 3(-6 - 5) + (-8)(4 - 1)$$

$$= 52 + 33 - 24 = 61$$

$$D_y = \begin{vmatrix} 1 & 4 & 1 \\ 3 & 3 & -2 \\ 5 & -8 & 3 \end{vmatrix} = 1 \cdot \begin{vmatrix} 3 & -2 \\ -8 & 3 \end{vmatrix} - 3 \cdot \begin{vmatrix} 4 & 1 \\ -8 & 3 \end{vmatrix} + 5 \cdot \begin{vmatrix} 4 & 1 \\ 3 & -2 \end{vmatrix}$$

$$= 1(9 - 16) - 3(12 - (-8)) + 5(-8 - 3)$$

$$= -7 - 60 - 55 = -122$$

$$D_z = \begin{vmatrix} 1 & -2 & 4 \\ 3 & 1 & 3 \\ 5 & 5 & -8 \end{vmatrix} = 1 \cdot \begin{vmatrix} 1 & 3 \\ 5 & -8 \end{vmatrix} - 3 \cdot \begin{vmatrix} -2 & 4 \\ 5 & -8 \end{vmatrix} + 5 \cdot \begin{vmatrix} -2 & 4 \\ 1 & 3 \end{vmatrix}$$

$$= 1(-8 - 15) - 3(16 - 20) + 5(-6 - 4)$$

$$= -23 + 12 - 50 = -61$$

From these determinants, we calculate the solution.

$$x = \frac{D_x}{D} = \frac{61}{61} = 1 \qquad y = \frac{D_y}{D} = \frac{-122}{61} = -2 \qquad z = \frac{D_z}{D} = \frac{-61}{61} = -1$$

The ordered triple solution is $(1, -2, -1)$. Check this solution by verifying that it satisfies each equation of the system.

Exercise Set 4.5

Evaluate. See Example 1.

1. $\begin{vmatrix} 3 & 5 \\ -1 & 7 \end{vmatrix}$

2. $\begin{vmatrix} -5 & 1 \\ 0 & -4 \end{vmatrix}$

3. $\begin{vmatrix} 9 & -2 \\ 4 & -3 \end{vmatrix}$

4. $\begin{vmatrix} 4 & 0 \\ 9 & 8 \end{vmatrix}$

5. $\begin{vmatrix} -2 & 9 \\ 4 & -18 \end{vmatrix}$

6. $\begin{vmatrix} -40 & 8 \\ 70 & -14 \end{vmatrix}$

Use Cramer's rule, if possible, to solve each system of linear equations. See Example 2.

7. $\begin{cases} 2y - 4 = 0 \\ x + 2y = 5 \end{cases}$

8. $\begin{cases} 4x - y = 5 \\ 3x - 3 = 0 \end{cases}$

9. $\begin{cases} 3x + y = 1 \\ 2y = 2 - 6x \end{cases}$

10. $\begin{cases} y = 2x - 5 \\ 8x - 4y = 20 \end{cases}$

11. $\begin{cases} 5x - 2y = 27 \\ -3x + 5y = 18 \end{cases}$

12. $\begin{cases} 4x - y = 9 \\ 2x + 3y = -27 \end{cases}$

Evaluate. See Example 3.

13. $\begin{vmatrix} 2 & 1 & 0 \\ 0 & 5 & -3 \\ 4 & 0 & 2 \end{vmatrix}$

14. $\begin{vmatrix} -6 & 4 & 2 \\ 1 & 0 & 5 \\ 0 & 3 & 1 \end{vmatrix}$

15. $\begin{vmatrix} 4 & -6 & 0 \\ -2 & 3 & 0 \\ 4 & -6 & 1 \end{vmatrix}$

16. $\begin{vmatrix} 5 & 2 & 1 \\ 3 & -6 & 0 \\ -2 & 8 & 0 \end{vmatrix}$

17. $\begin{vmatrix} 3 & 6 & -3 \\ -1 & -2 & 3 \\ 4 & -1 & 6 \end{vmatrix}$

18. $\begin{vmatrix} 2 & -2 & 1 \\ 4 & 1 & 3 \\ 3 & 1 & 2 \end{vmatrix}$

Use Cramer's rule, if possible, to solve each system of linear equations. See Example 4.

19. $\begin{cases} 3x + z = -1 \\ -x - 3y + z = 7 \\ 3y + z = 5 \end{cases}$

20. $\begin{cases} 4y - 3z = -2 \\ 8x - 4y = 4 \\ -8x + 4y + z = -2 \end{cases}$

21. $\begin{cases} x + y + z = 8 \\ 2x - y - z = 10 \\ x - 2y + 3z = 22 \end{cases}$

22. $\begin{cases} 5x + y + 3z = 1 \\ x - y - 3z = -7 \\ -x + y = 1 \end{cases}$

Evaluate.

23. $\begin{vmatrix} 10 & -1 \\ -4 & 2 \end{vmatrix}$

24. $\begin{vmatrix} -6 & 2 \\ 5 & -1 \end{vmatrix}$

25. $\begin{vmatrix} 1 & 0 & 4 \\ 1 & -1 & 2 \\ 3 & 2 & 1 \end{vmatrix}$

26. $\begin{vmatrix} 0 & 1 & 2 \\ 3 & -1 & 2 \\ 3 & 2 & -2 \end{vmatrix}$

27. $\begin{vmatrix} \frac{3}{4} & \frac{5}{2} \\ -\frac{1}{6} & \frac{7}{3} \end{vmatrix}$

28. $\begin{vmatrix} \frac{5}{7} & \frac{1}{3} \\ \frac{6}{7} & \frac{2}{3} \end{vmatrix}$

29. $\begin{vmatrix} 4 & -2 & 2 \\ 6 & -1 & 3 \\ 2 & 1 & 1 \end{vmatrix}$

30. $\begin{vmatrix} 1 & 5 & 0 \\ 7 & 9 & -4 \\ 3 & 2 & -2 \end{vmatrix}$

31. $\begin{vmatrix} -2 & 5 & 4 \\ 5 & -1 & 3 \\ 4 & 1 & 2 \end{vmatrix}$

32. $\begin{vmatrix} 5 & -2 & 4 \\ -1 & 5 & 3 \\ 1 & 4 & 2 \end{vmatrix}$

33. If all the elements in a single row of a determinant are zero, to what does the determinant evaluate? Explain your answer.

34. If all the elements in a single column of a determinant are 0, to what does the determinant evaluate? Explain your answer.

Find the value of x such that each is a true statement.

35. $\begin{vmatrix} 1 & x \\ 2 & 7 \end{vmatrix} = -3$

36. $\begin{vmatrix} 6 & 1 \\ -2 & x \end{vmatrix} = 26$

Use Cramer's rule, if possible, to solve each system of linear equations.

37. $\begin{cases} 2x - 5y = 4 \\ x + 2y = -7 \end{cases}$

38. $\begin{cases} 3x - y = 2 \\ -5x + 2y = 0 \end{cases}$

39. $\begin{cases} 4x + 2y = 5 \\ 2x + y = -1 \end{cases}$

40. $\begin{cases} 3x + 6y = 15 \\ 2x + 4y = 3 \end{cases}$

41. $\begin{cases} 2x + 2y + z = 1 \\ -x + y + 2z = 3 \\ x + 2y + 4z = 0 \end{cases}$

42. $\begin{cases} 2x - 3y + z = 5 \\ x + y + z = 0 \\ 4x + 2y + 4z = 4 \end{cases}$

43. $\begin{cases} \dfrac{2}{3}x - \dfrac{3}{4}y = -1 \\ -\dfrac{1}{6}x + \dfrac{3}{4}y = \dfrac{5}{2} \end{cases}$

44. $\begin{cases} \dfrac{1}{2}x - \dfrac{1}{3}y = -3 \\ \dfrac{1}{8}x + \dfrac{1}{6}y = 0 \end{cases}$

45. $\begin{cases} 0.7x - 0.2y = -1.6 \\ 0.2x - y = -1.4 \end{cases}$

46. $\begin{cases} -0.7x + 0.6y = 1.3 \\ 0.5x - 0.3y = -0.8 \end{cases}$

47. $\begin{cases} -2x + 4y - 2z = 6 \\ x - 2y + z = -3 \\ 3x - 6y + 3z = -9 \end{cases}$

48. $\begin{cases} -x - y + 3z = 2 \\ 4x + 4y - 12z = -8 \\ -3x - 3y + 9z = 6 \end{cases}$

49. $\begin{cases} x - 2y + z = -5 \\ 3y + 2z = 4 \\ 3x - y = -2 \end{cases}$ **50.** $\begin{cases} 4x + 5y = 10 \\ 3y + 2z = -6 \\ x + y + z = 3 \end{cases}$

51. Suppose you are interested in finding the determinant of a 4 × 4 matrix. Study the pattern shown in the array of signs for a 3 × 3 matrix. Use the pattern to expand the array of signs for use with a 4 × 4 matrix.

52. Why would expanding by minors of the second row be a good choice for the determinant $\begin{vmatrix} 3 & 4 & -2 \\ 5 & 0 & 0 \\ 6 & -3 & 7 \end{vmatrix}$?

REVIEW EXERCISES

Simplify each expression. See Section 1.4.

53. $5x - 6 + x - 12$ **54.** $4y + 3 - 15y$ 1

55. $2(3x - 6) + 3(x - 1)$

56. $-3(2y - 7) - 1(11 + 12y)$

Graph each function. See Section 3.3.

57. $f(x) = 5x - 6$ **58.** $g(x) = -x + 1$

59. $h(x) = 3$ **60.** $f(x) = -3$

A Look Ahead

Example
Evaluate the determinant.
$$\begin{vmatrix} 2 & 0 & -1 & 3 \\ 0 & 5 & -2 & -1 \\ 3 & 1 & 0 & 1 \\ 4 & 2 & -2 & 0 \end{vmatrix}$$

Solution
To evaluate a 4 × 4 determinant, select any row or column and expand by the minors. The array of signs for a 4 × 4 determinant is the same as for a 3 × 3 determinant except expanded. We expand using the fourth row.

$$\begin{vmatrix} 2 & 0 & -1 & 3 \\ 0 & 5 & -2 & -1 \\ 3 & 1 & 0 & 1 \\ \rightarrow 4 & 2 & -2 & 0 \end{vmatrix}$$

$$= -4 \cdot \begin{vmatrix} 0 & -1 & 3 \\ 5 & -2 & -1 \\ 1 & 0 & 1 \end{vmatrix} + 2 \cdot \begin{vmatrix} 2 & -1 & 3 \\ 0 & -2 & -1 \\ 3 & 0 & 1 \end{vmatrix}$$

$$-(-2) \cdot \begin{vmatrix} 2 & 0 & 3 \\ 0 & 5 & -1 \\ 3 & 1 & 1 \end{vmatrix} + 0 \cdot \begin{vmatrix} 2 & 0 & -1 \\ 0 & 5 & -2 \\ 3 & 1 & 0 \end{vmatrix}$$

Now find the value of each 3 × 3 determinant. The value of the 4 × 4 determinant is

$$-4(12) + 2(17) + 2(-33) + 0 = -80$$

Find the value of each determinant. See the preceding example.

61. $\begin{vmatrix} 5 & 0 & 0 & 0 \\ 0 & 4 & 2 & -1 \\ 1 & 3 & -2 & 0 \\ 0 & -3 & 1 & 2 \end{vmatrix}$ **62.** $\begin{vmatrix} 1 & 7 & 0 & -1 \\ 1 & 3 & -2 & 0 \\ 1 & 0 & -1 & 2 \\ 0 & -6 & 2 & 4 \end{vmatrix}$

63. $\begin{vmatrix} 4 & 0 & 2 & 5 \\ 0 & 3 & -1 & 1 \\ 0 & 0 & 2 & 0 \\ 0 & 0 & 0 & 1 \end{vmatrix}$ **64.** $\begin{vmatrix} 2 & 0 & -1 & 4 \\ 6 & 0 & 4 & 1 \\ 2 & 4 & 3 & -1 \\ 4 & 0 & 5 & -4 \end{vmatrix}$

4

For additional Chapter Projects, visit the Real World Activities
Website by going to http://www.prenhall.com/martin-gay.

CHAPTER PROJECT

Locating Lightning Strikes

Lightning, most often produced during thunderstorms, is a rapid discharge of high-current electricity into the atmosphere. Around the world, lightning occurs at a rate of approximately 100 flashes per second. Because of lightning's potentially destructive nature, meteorologists track lightning activity by recording and plotting the positions of lightning strikes. In this project, you will have the opportunity to pinpoint the location of a lightning strike. This project may be completed by working in groups or individually.

Weather recording stations use a directional antenna to detect and measure the electromagnetic field emitted by a lightning bolt. The antenna can determine the angle between a fixed point and the position of the lightning strike but cannot determine the distance to the lightning strike. However, the angle measured by the antenna can be used to find the slope of the line connecting the positions of the weather station and the lightning strike. From there, the equation of the line connecting these points may be found.

If two such lines may be found—that is, if another weather station's antenna detects the same lightning flash—the coordinates of the lightning strike's position may be pinpointed.

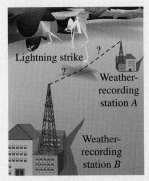

1. A weather recording station A is located at the coordinates (35, 28). A second weather recording station B is located at the coordinates (52, 12). Plot the positions of the two weather recording stations.

2. A lightning strike is detected by both stations. Station A uses a measured angle to find the slope of the line from the station to the lightning strike as $m = -1.732$. Station B computes a slope of $m = 0.577$ from the angle it measured. Use this information to find the equations of the lines connecting each station to the position of the lightning strike.

3. Solve the resulting system of equations in each of the following ways (or work with other students in your group so that each student solves the system in one of the following ways).

   (a) Using a graph. Graph the two equations on your plot of the positions of the two weather recording stations. Estimate the coordinates of their point of intersection.

   (b) Using either the method of substitution or of elimination (whichever you prefer)

   (c) Using matrices

   (d) Using Cramer's rule

   (e) (Optional) Using a graphing calculator to graph the lines and an intersect feature to estimate the coordinates of their point of intersection

4. Compare the results from each method. What are the coordinates of the lightning strike? Which method do you prefer? Why?

CHAPTER 4 VOCABULARY CHECK

Fill in each blank with one of the words or phrases listed below.

matrix   determinant   consistent   system of equations

solution   inconsistent   square

1. Two or more linear equations in two variables form a _____.

2. A _____ of a system of two equations in two variables is an ordered pair that makes both equations true.

3. A(n) _____ system of equations has at least one solution.

4. If a matrix has the same number of rows and columns, it is called a _____ matrix.

5. A real number associated with a square matrix is called its _____.

6. A(n) _____ system of equations has no solution.

7. A _____ is a rectangular array of numbers.

CHAPTER 4 HIGHLIGHTS

DEFINITIONS AND CONCEPTS	EXAMPLES

Section 4.1 Solving Systems of Linear Equations in Two Variables

A **system of linear equations** consists of two or more linear equations.

A **solution** of a system of two equations in two variables is an ordered pair (x, y) that makes both equations true.

Geometrically, a solution of a system in two variables is a point common to the graphs of the equations.

A system of equations with at least one solution is a **consistent system**. A system that has no solution is an **inconsistent system**.

If the graphs of two linear equations are identical, the equations are **dependent**.

If their graphs are different, the equations are **independent**.

One solution:
consistent and
independent

No solution:
inconsistent and
independent

Infinite number of
solutions; consistent
and dependent

To solve a system of linear equations by the **substitution method:**

Step 1: Solve one equation for a variable.

Step 2: Substitute the expression for the variable into the other equation.

Step 3: Solve the equation from *Step 2* to find the value of one variable.

Step 4: Substitute the value from *Step 3* in either original equation to find the value of the other variable.

Step 5: Check the solution in both equations.

Solve by substitution:

$$\begin{cases} y = x + 2 \\ 3x - 2y = -5 \end{cases}$$

Substitute $x + 2$ for y in the second equation.

$$3x - 2y = -5$$
$$3x - 2(x + 2) = -5$$
$$3x - 2x - 4 = -5$$
$$x - 4 = -5 \qquad \text{Simplify.}$$
$$x = -1 \qquad \text{Add 4.}$$

To find y, let $x = -1$ in $y = x + 2$, so $y = -1 + 2 = 1$. The solution $(-1, 1)$ checks.

To solve a system of linear equations by the **elimination method:**

Step 1: Rewrite each equation in standard form $Ax + By = C$.

Step 2: Multiply one or both equations by a nonzero number so that the coefficients of a variable are opposites.

Step 3: Add the equations.

Step 4: Find the value of one variable by solving the resulting equation.

Step 5: Substitute the value from *Step 4* into either original equation to find the value of the other variable.

Step 6: Check the solution in both equations.

Solve by elimination:

$$\begin{cases} x - 3y = -3 \\ -2x + y = 6 \end{cases}$$

Multiply both sides of the first equation by 2.

$$\begin{array}{r} 2x - 6y = -6 \\ -2x + y = 6 \\ \hline -5y = 0 \qquad \text{Add.} \\ y = 0 \qquad \text{Divide by } -5. \end{array}$$

To find x, let $y = 0$ in an original equation.
$$x - 3y = -3$$
$$x - 3 \cdot 0 = -3$$
$$x = -3$$

The solution $(-3, 0)$ checks.

DEFINITIONS AND CONCEPTS	EXAMPLES

Section 4.2 Solving Systems of Linear Equations in Three Variables

A **solution** of an equation in three variables x, y, and z is an **ordered triple** (x, y, z) that makes the equation a true statement.

Verify that $(-2, 1, 3)$ is a solution of $2x + 3y - 2z = -7$.

Replace x with -2, y with 1, and z with 3.

$$2(-2) + 3(1) - 2(3) = -7$$
$$-4 + 3 - 6 = -7$$
$$-7 = -7 \quad \text{True.}$$

$(-2, 1, 3)$ is a solution.

To solve a system of three linear equations by the elimination method:

Step 1: Write each equation in standard form, $Ax + By + Cz = D$.

Step 2: Choose a pair of equations and use the equations to eliminate a variable.

Step 3: Choose any other pair of equations and eliminate the same variable.

Step 4: Solve the system of two equations in two variables from Steps 1 and 2.

Step 5: Solve for the third variable by substituting the values of the variables from Step 4 into any of the original equations.

Solve

$$\begin{cases} 2x + y - z = 0 \ (1) \\ x - y - 2z = -6 \ (2) \\ -3x - 2y + 3z = -22 \ (3) \end{cases}$$

1. Each equation is written in standard form.

2.
$$\begin{array}{l} 2x + y - z = 0 \ (1) \\ \underline{x - y - 2z = -6 \ (2)} \\ 3x \qquad - 3z = -6 \ (4) \quad \text{Add.} \end{array}$$

3. Eliminate y from equations (1) and (3) also.

$$\begin{array}{l} 4x + 2y - 2z = 0 \qquad \text{Multiply equation} \\ \underline{-3x - 2y + 3z = -22 \ (3)} \quad \text{(1) by 2.} \\ x \qquad + z = -22 \ (5) \quad \text{Add.} \end{array}$$

4. Solve

$$\begin{cases} 3x - 3z = -6 \ (4) \\ x + z = -22 \ (5) \end{cases}$$

$$\begin{array}{l} x - z = -2 \qquad \text{Divide equation} \\ \underline{x + z = -22 \ (5)} \quad \text{(4) by 3.} \\ 2x \qquad = -24 \\ x = -12 \end{array}$$

To find z, use equation (5).

$$x + z = -22$$
$$-12 + z = -22$$
$$z = -10$$

5. To find y, use equation (1).
$$2x + y - z = 0$$
$$2(-12) + y - (-10) = 0$$
$$-24 + y + 10 = 0$$
$$y = 14$$

The solution is $(-12, 14, -10)$.

DEFINITIONS AND CONCEPTS	EXAMPLES

Section 4.3 Systems of Linear Equations and Problem Solving

1. UNDERSTAND the problem.

Two numbers have a sum of 11. Twice one number is 3 less than 3 times the other. Find the numbers.

1. Read and reread.

$$x = \text{one number}$$
$$y = \text{other number}$$

2. TRANSLATE.

2. In words:

sum of numbers	is	11
↓	↓	↓

Translate: $x + y$ = 11

In words:

twice one number	is	3 less than 3 times the other number
↓	↓	↓

Translate: $2x$ = $3y - 3$

3. SOLVE.

3. Solve the system: $\begin{cases} x + y = 11 \\ 2x = 3y - 3 \end{cases}$

In the first equation $x = 11 - y$. Substitute into the other equation.

$$2x = 3y - 3$$
$$2(11 - y) = 3y - 3$$
$$22 - 2y = 3y - 3$$
$$-5y = -25$$
$$y = 5$$

Replace y with 5 in the equation $x = 11 - y$. Then $x = 11 - 5 = 6$. The solution is $(6, 5)$.

4. INTERPRET.

4. *Check:* See that $6 + 5 = 11$ is the required sum and that twice 6 is 3 times 5 less 3. *State:* The numbers are 6 and 5.

Section 4.4 Solving Systems of Equations by Matrices

A **matrix** is a rectangular array of numbers.

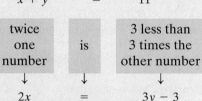

The **corresponding matrix of the system** is obtained by writing a matrix composed of the coefficients of the variables and the constants of the system.

The corresponding matrix of the system

$$\begin{cases} x - y = 1 \\ 2x + y = 11 \end{cases} \quad \text{is} \quad \left[\begin{array}{cc|c} 1 & -1 & 1 \\ 2 & 1 & 11 \end{array}\right]$$

(continued)

DEFINITIONS AND CONCEPTS	EXAMPLES

Section 4.4 Solving Systems of Equations by Matrices

The following **row operations** can be performed on matrices, and the result is an equivalent matrix.

Elementary row operations

1. Interchange any two rows.
2. Multiply (or divide) the elements of one row by the same nonzero number.
3. Multiply (or divide) the elements of one row by the same nonzero number and add to its corresponding elements in any other row.

Use matrices to solve: $\begin{cases} x - y = 1 \\ 2x + y = 11 \end{cases}$

The corresponding matrix is

$$\left[\begin{array}{cc|c} 1 & -1 & 1 \\ 2 & 1 & 11 \end{array}\right]$$

Use row operations to write an equivalent matrix with 1's along the diagonal and 0's below each 1 in the diagonal. Multiply row 1 by -2 and add to row 2. Change row 2 only.

$$\left[\begin{array}{cc|c} 1 & -1 & 1 \\ -2(1) + 2 & -2(-1) + 1 & -2(1) + 11 \end{array}\right]$$

simplifies to $\left[\begin{array}{cc|c} 1 & -1 & 1 \\ 0 & 3 & 9 \end{array}\right]$

Divide row 2 by 3.

$$\left[\begin{array}{cc|c} 1 & -1 & 1 \\ \dfrac{0}{3} & \dfrac{3}{3} & \dfrac{9}{3} \end{array}\right] \quad \text{simplifies to} \quad \left[\begin{array}{cc|c} 1 & -1 & 1 \\ 0 & 1 & 3 \end{array}\right]$$

This matrix corresponds to the system

$$\begin{cases} x - y = 1 \\ \quad\ \ y = 3 \end{cases}$$

Let $y = 3$ in the first equation.

$$x - 3 = 1$$
$$x = 4$$

The ordered pair solution is $(4, 3)$.

Section 4.5 Solving Systems of Equations by Determinants

A **square matrix** is a matrix with the same number of rows and columns.

$$\left[\begin{array}{cc} -2 & 1 \\ 6 & 8 \end{array}\right] \qquad \left[\begin{array}{ccc} 4 & -1 & 6 \\ 0 & 2 & 5 \\ 1 & 1 & 2 \end{array}\right]$$

A **determinant** is a real number associated with a square matrix. To denote the determinant, place vertical bars about the array of numbers.

The determinant of $\left[\begin{array}{cc} -2 & 1 \\ 6 & 8 \end{array}\right]$ is $\left|\begin{array}{cc} -2 & 1 \\ 6 & 8 \end{array}\right|$.

The determinant of a 2×2 matrix is

$$\left|\begin{array}{cc} a & b \\ c & d \end{array}\right| = ad - bc$$

$$\left|\begin{array}{cc} -2 & 1 \\ 6 & 8 \end{array}\right| = -2 \cdot 8 - 1 \cdot 6 = -22$$

(continued)

DEFINITIONS AND CONCEPTS	EXAMPLES

Section 4.5 Solving Systems of Equations by Determinants

Cramer's Rule for Two Linear Equations in Two Variables

The solution of the system $\begin{cases} ax + by = h \\ cx + dy = k \end{cases}$ is given by

$$x = \frac{\begin{vmatrix} h & b \\ k & d \end{vmatrix}}{\begin{vmatrix} a & b \\ c & d \end{vmatrix}} = \frac{D_x}{D} \qquad y = \frac{\begin{vmatrix} a & h \\ c & k \end{vmatrix}}{\begin{vmatrix} a & b \\ c & d \end{vmatrix}} = \frac{D_y}{D}$$

as long as $D = ad - bc$ is not 0.

Determinant of a 3 × 3 Matrix

$$\begin{vmatrix} a_1 & b_1 & c_1 \\ a_2 & b_2 & c_2 \\ a_3 & b_3 & c_3 \end{vmatrix} = a_1 \cdot \begin{vmatrix} b_2 & c_2 \\ b_3 & c_3 \end{vmatrix} - a_2 \cdot$$

$$\begin{vmatrix} b_1 & c_1 \\ b_3 & c_3 \end{vmatrix} + a_3 \cdot \begin{vmatrix} b_1 & c_1 \\ b_2 & c_2 \end{vmatrix}$$

Each 2 × 2 matrix above is called a **minor**.

Cramer's Rule for Three Equations in Three Variables

The solution of the system $\begin{cases} a_1 x + b_1 y + c_1 z = k_1 \\ a_2 x + b_2 y + c_2 z = k_2 \\ a_3 x + b_3 y + c_3 z = k_3 \end{cases}$
is given by

$$x = \frac{D_x}{D}, \qquad y = \frac{D_y}{D}, \qquad \text{and} \qquad z = \frac{D_z}{D}$$

where

$$D = \begin{vmatrix} a_1 & b_1 & c_1 \\ a_2 & b_2 & c_2 \\ a_3 & b_3 & c_3 \end{vmatrix} \qquad D_x = \begin{vmatrix} k_1 & b_1 & c_1 \\ k_2 & b_2 & c_2 \\ k_3 & b_3 & c_3 \end{vmatrix}$$

$$D_y = \begin{vmatrix} a_1 & k_1 & c_1 \\ a_2 & k_2 & c_2 \\ a_3 & k_3 & c_3 \end{vmatrix} \qquad D_z = \begin{vmatrix} a_1 & b_1 & k_1 \\ a_2 & b_2 & k_2 \\ a_3 & b_3 & k_3 \end{vmatrix}$$

as long as D is not 0.

Use Cramer's rule to solve

$$\begin{cases} 3x + 2y = 8 \\ 2x - y = -11 \end{cases}$$

$$D = \begin{vmatrix} 3 & 2 \\ 2 & -1 \end{vmatrix} = 3(-1) - 2(2) = -7$$

$$D_x = \begin{vmatrix} 8 & 2 \\ -11 & -1 \end{vmatrix} = 8(-1) - 2(-11) = 14$$

$$D_y = \begin{vmatrix} 3 & 8 \\ 2 & -11 \end{vmatrix} = 3(-11) - 8(2) = -49$$

$$x = \frac{D_x}{D} = \frac{14}{-7} = -2 \qquad y = \frac{D_y}{D} = \frac{-49}{-7} = 7$$

The ordered pair solution is $(-2, 7)$.

$$\begin{vmatrix} 0 & 2 & -1 \\ 5 & 3 & 0 \\ 2 & -2 & 4 \end{vmatrix} = 0\begin{vmatrix} 3 & 0 \\ -2 & 4 \end{vmatrix} - 2\begin{vmatrix} 5 & 0 \\ 2 & 4 \end{vmatrix} + (-1)\begin{vmatrix} 5 & 3 \\ 2 & -2 \end{vmatrix}$$

$$= 0(12 - 0) - 2(20 - 0) - 1(-10 - 6)$$

$$= 0 - 40 + 16 = -24$$

Use Cramer's rule to solve

$$\begin{cases} 3y + 2z = 8 \\ x + y + z = 3 \\ 2x - y + z = 2 \end{cases}$$

$$D = \begin{vmatrix} 0 & 3 & 2 \\ 1 & 1 & 1 \\ 2 & -1 & 1 \end{vmatrix} = -3$$

$$D_x = \begin{vmatrix} 8 & 3 & 2 \\ 3 & 1 & 1 \\ 2 & -1 & 1 \end{vmatrix} = 3$$

$$D_y = \begin{vmatrix} 0 & 8 & 2 \\ 1 & 3 & 1 \\ 2 & 2 & 1 \end{vmatrix} = 0$$

$$D_z = \begin{vmatrix} 0 & 3 & 8 \\ 1 & 1 & 3 \\ 2 & -1 & 2 \end{vmatrix} = -12$$

$$x = \frac{D_x}{D} = \frac{3}{-3} = -1 \qquad y = \frac{D_y}{D} = \frac{0}{-3} = 0$$

$$z = \frac{D_z}{D} = \frac{-12}{-3} = 4$$

The ordered triple solution is $(-1, 0, 4)$.

CHAPTER 4 REVIEW

(4.1) *Solve each system of equations in two variables by each of three methods: (1) graphing, (2) substitution, and (3) elimination.*

1. $\begin{cases} 3x + 10y = 1 \\ x + 2y = -1 \end{cases}$

2. $\begin{cases} y = \dfrac{1}{2}x + \dfrac{2}{3} \\ 4x + 6y = 4 \end{cases}$

3. $\begin{cases} 2x - 4y = 22 \\ 5x - 10y = 16 \end{cases}$

4. $\begin{cases} 3x - 6y = 12 \\ 2y = x - 4 \end{cases}$

5. $\begin{cases} \dfrac{1}{2}x - \dfrac{3}{4}y = -\dfrac{1}{2} \\ \dfrac{1}{8}x + \dfrac{3}{4}y = \dfrac{19}{8} \end{cases}$

6. The revenue equation for a certain style of backpack is
$$y = 32x$$
where x is the number of backpacks sold and y is the income in dollars for selling x backpacks. The cost equation for these units is
$$y = 15x + 25{,}500$$
where x is the number of backpacks manufactured and y is the cost in dollars for manufacturing x backpacks. Find the number of units to be sold for the company to break even.

(4.2) *Solve each system of equations in three variables.*

7. $\begin{cases} x \quad\; + z = 4 \\ 2x - y \quad\;\; = 4 \\ x + y - z = 0 \end{cases}$

8. $\begin{cases} 2x + 5y \quad\;\; = 4 \\ x - 5y + z = -1 \\ 4x \quad\quad - z = 11 \end{cases}$

9. $\begin{cases} 4y + 2z = 5 \\ 2x + 8y \quad\;\; = 5 \\ 6x + \quad\; 4z = 1 \end{cases}$

10. $\begin{cases} 5x + 7y \quad\;\; = 9 \\ 14y - z = 28 \\ 4x \quad\quad + 2z = -4 \end{cases}$

11. $\begin{cases} 3x - 2y + 2z = 5 \\ -x + 6y + z = 4 \\ 3x + 14y + 7z = 20 \end{cases}$

12. $\begin{cases} x + 2y + 3z = 11 \\ y + 2z = 3 \\ 2x \quad\quad + 2z = 10 \end{cases}$

13. $\begin{cases} 7x - 3y + 2z = 0 \\ 4x - 4y - z = 2 \\ 5x + 2y + 3z = 1 \end{cases}$

14. $\begin{cases} x - 3y - 5z = -5 \\ 4x - 2y + 3z = 13 \\ 5x + 3y + 4z = 22 \end{cases}$

(4.3) *Use systems of equations to solve the following applications.*

15. The sum of three numbers is 98. The sum of the first and second is two more than the third number, and the second is four times the first. Find the numbers.

16. One number is 3 times a second number, and twice the sum of the numbers is 168. Find the numbers.

17. Two cars leave Chicago, one traveling east and the other west. After 4 hours they are 492 miles apart. If one car is traveling 7 mph faster than the other, find the speed of each.

△ **18.** The foundation for a rectangular Hardware Warehouse has a length three times the width and is 296 feet around. Find the dimensions of the building.

19. James Callahan has available a 10% alcohol solution and a 60% alcohol solution. Find how many liters of each solution he should mix to make 50 liters of a 40% alcohol solution.

20. An employee at a See's Candy Store needs a special mixture of candy. She has creme-filled chocolates that sell for $3.00 per pound, chocolate-covered nuts that sell for $2.70 per pound, and chocolate-covered raisins that sell for $2.25 per pound. She wants to have twice as many raisins as nuts in the mixture. Find how many pounds of each she should use to make 45 pounds worth $2.80 per pound.

21. Chris Kringler has $2.77 in his coin jar—all in pennies, nickels, and dimes. If he has 53 coins in all and four more nickels than dimes, find how many of each type of coin he has.

22. If $10,000 and $4000 are invested such that $1250 is earned in one year, and if the rate of interest on the larger investment is 2% more than that of the smaller investment, find the rates of interest.

△ **23.** The perimeter of an isosceles (two sides equal) triangle is 73 centimeters. If two sides are of equal length and the third side is 7 centimeters longer than the others, find the lengths of the three sides.

24. The sum of three numbers is 295. One number is five more than a second and twice the third. Find the numbers.

(4.4) *Use matrices to solve each system.*

25. $\begin{cases} 3x + 10y = 1 \\ x + 2y = -1 \end{cases}$

26. $\begin{cases} 3x - 6y = 12 \\ 2y = x - 4 \end{cases}$

27. $\begin{cases} 3x - 2y = -8 \\ 6x + 5y = 11 \end{cases}$

28. $\begin{cases} 6x - 6y = -5 \\ 10x - 2y = 1 \end{cases}$

29. $\begin{cases} 3x - 6y = 0 \\ 2x + 4y = 5 \end{cases}$

30. $\begin{cases} 5x - 3y = 10 \\ -2x + y = -1 \end{cases}$

31. $\begin{cases} 0.2x - 0.3y = -0.7 \\ 0.5x + 0.3y = 1.4 \end{cases}$

32. $\begin{cases} 3x + 2y = 8 \\ 3x - y = 5 \end{cases}$

33. $\begin{cases} x \quad\; + z = 4 \\ 2x - y \quad\;\; = 0 \\ x + y - z = 0 \end{cases}$

34. $\begin{cases} 2x + 5y \quad\;\; = 4 \\ x - 5y + z = -1 \\ 4x \quad\quad - z = 11 \end{cases}$

35. $\begin{cases} 3x - y \quad\;\; = 11 \\ x \quad\; + 2z = 13 \\ y - z = -7 \end{cases}$

36. $\begin{cases} 5x + 7y + 3z = 9 \\ 14y - z = 28 \\ 4x \quad\quad + 2z = -4 \end{cases}$

37. $\begin{cases} 7x - 3y + 2z = 0 \\ 4x - 4y - z = 2 \\ 5x + 2y + 3z = 1 \end{cases}$ **38.** $\begin{cases} x + 2y + 3z = 14 \\ y + 2z = 3 \\ 2x - 2z = 10 \end{cases}$

46. $\begin{cases} y = \dfrac{1}{2}x + \dfrac{2}{3} \\ 4x + 6y = 4 \end{cases}$

(4.5) *Evaluate.*

39. $\begin{vmatrix} -1 & 3 \\ 5 & 2 \end{vmatrix}$ **40.** $\begin{vmatrix} 3 & -1 \\ 2 & 5 \end{vmatrix}$

41. $\begin{vmatrix} 2 & -1 & -3 \\ 1 & 2 & 0 \\ 3 & -2 & 2 \end{vmatrix}$ **42.** $\begin{vmatrix} -2 & 3 & 1 \\ 4 & 4 & 0 \\ 1 & -2 & 3 \end{vmatrix}$

Use Cramer's rule, if possible, to solve each system of equations.

43. $\begin{cases} 3x - 2y = -8 \\ 6x + 5y = 11 \end{cases}$ **44.** $\begin{cases} 6x - 6y = -5 \\ 10x - 2y = 1 \end{cases}$

45. $\begin{cases} 3x + 10y = 1 \\ x + 2y = -1 \end{cases}$

47. $\begin{cases} 2x - 4y = 22 \\ 5x - 10y = 16 \end{cases}$ **48.** $\begin{cases} 3x - 6y = 12 \\ 2y = x - 4 \end{cases}$

49. $\begin{cases} x + z = 4 \\ 2x - y = 0 \\ x + y - z = 0 \end{cases}$ **50.** $\begin{cases} 2x + 5y = 4 \\ x - 5y + z = -1 \\ 4x - z = 11 \end{cases}$

51. $\begin{cases} x + 3y - z = 5 \\ 2x - y - 2z = 3 \\ x + 2y + 3z = 4 \end{cases}$ **52.** $\begin{cases} 2x - z = 1 \\ 3x - y + 2z = 3 \\ x + y + 3z = -2 \end{cases}$

53. $\begin{cases} x + 2y + 3z = 14 \\ y + 2z = 3 \\ 2x - 2z = 10 \end{cases}$ **54.** $\begin{cases} 5x + 7y = 9 \\ 14y - z = 28 \\ 4x + 2z = -4 \end{cases}$

CHAPTER 4 TEST

Evaluate each determinant.

1. $\begin{vmatrix} 4 & -7 \\ 2 & 5 \end{vmatrix}$ **2.** $\begin{vmatrix} 4 & 0 & 2 \\ 1 & -3 & 5 \\ 0 & -1 & 2 \end{vmatrix}$

Solve each system of equations graphically and then solve by the elimination method or the substitution method.

3. $\begin{cases} 2x - y = -1 \\ 5x + 4y = 17 \end{cases}$ **4.** $\begin{cases} 7x - 14y = 5 \\ x = 2y \end{cases}$

Solve each system.

5. $\begin{cases} 4x - 7y = 29 \\ 2x + 5y = -11 \end{cases}$ **6.** $\begin{cases} 15x + 6y = 15 \\ 10x + 4y = 10 \end{cases}$

7. $\begin{cases} 2x - 3y = 4 \\ 3y + 2z = 2 \\ x - z = -5 \end{cases}$ **8.** $\begin{cases} 3x - 2y - z = -1 \\ 2x - 2y = 4 \\ 2x - 2z = -12 \end{cases}$

9. $\begin{cases} \dfrac{x}{2} + \dfrac{y}{4} = -\dfrac{3}{4} \\ x + \dfrac{3}{4}y = -4 \end{cases}$

Use Cramer's rule, if possible, to solve each system.

10. $\begin{cases} 3x - y = 7 \\ 2x + 5y = -1 \end{cases}$ **11.** $\begin{cases} 4x - 3y = -6 \\ -2x + y = 0 \end{cases}$

12. $\begin{cases} x + y + z = 4 \\ 2x + 5y = 1 \\ x - y - 2z = 0 \end{cases}$ **13.** $\begin{cases} 3x + 2y + 3z = 3 \\ x - z = 9 \\ 4y + z = -4 \end{cases}$

Use matrices to solve each system.

14. $\begin{cases} x - y = -2 \\ 3x - 3y = -6 \end{cases}$ **15.** $\begin{cases} x + 2y = -1 \\ 2x + 5y = -5 \end{cases}$

16. $\begin{cases} x - y - z = 0 \\ 3x - y - 5z = -2 \\ 2x + 3y = -5 \end{cases}$ **17.** $\begin{cases} 2x - y + 3z = 4 \\ 3x - 3z = -2 \\ -5x + y = 0 \end{cases}$

18. Frame Masters, Inc., recently purchased $5500 worth of new equipment in order to offer a new style of eyeglass frame. The marketing department of Frame Masters estimates that the cost of producing this new frame is $18 and that the frame will be sold to stores for $38. Find the number of frames that must be sold in order to break even.

19. A motel in New Orleans charges $90 per day for double occupancy and $80 per day for single occupancy. If 80 rooms are occupied for a total of $6930, how many rooms of each kind are there?

20. The research department of a company that manufactures children's fruit drinks is experimenting with a new flavor. A 17.5% fructose solution is needed, but only 10% and 20% solutions are available. How many gallons of a 10% fructose solution should be mixed with a 20% fructose solution in order to obtain 20 gallons of a 17.5% fructose solution?

21. A company that manufactures boxes recently purchased $2000 worth of new equipment to offer gift boxes to its customers. The cost of producing a package of gift boxes is $1.50 and it is sold for $4.00. Find the number of packages that must be sold for the company to break even.

CHAPTER 4 CUMULATIVE REVIEW

1. Determine whether each statement is true or false.

  a. $3 \in \{x \mid x \text{ is a natural number}\}$

  b. $7 \notin \{1, 2, 3\}$

2. Simplify the following expressions.

  a. $11 + 2 - 7$

  b. $-5 - 4 + 2$

3. Write the additive inverse, or opposite, of each.

  a. 8

  b. $\dfrac{1}{5}$

  c. -9.6

4. Use the distributive property to multiply.

  a. $3(2x + y)$ **b.** $-(3x - 1)$

5. Use the distributive property to simplify each expression.

  a. $3x - 5x + 4$

  b. $7yz + yz$

  c. $4z + 6.1$

Solve.

6. $-6x - 1 + 5x = 3$

7. $0.3x + 0.1 = 0.27x - 0.02$

8. A pennant in the shape of an isosceles triangle is to be constructed for the Slidell High School Athletic Club and sold at a fund-raiser. The company manufacturing the pennant charges according to perimeter, and the athletic club has determined that a perimeter of 149 centimeters should make a nice profit. If each equal side of the triangle is twice the length of the third side, increased by 12 centimeters, find the lengths of the sides of the triangular pennant.

9. Solve: $3x + 4 \geq 2x - 6$. Graph the solution set.

10. Solve: $2 < 4 - x < 7$

11. Solve: $|2x| + 5 = 7$

12. Solve for m: $|m - 6| < 2$

13. Plot each ordered pair on a Cartesian coordinate system and name the quadrant in which the point is located.

  a. $(2, -1)$ **b.** $(0, 5)$

  c. $(-3, 5)$ **d.** $(-2, 0)$

  e. $\left(-\dfrac{1}{2}, -4\right)$ **f.** $(1.5, 1.5)$

14. Use the graph of $y = 1500 + \dfrac{1}{10}x$ to answer the following questions:

  a. If the salesperson has $800 of products sold for a particular month, what is the salary for that month?

  b. If the salesperson wants to make more than $1600 per month, what must be the total amount of products sold?

15. If $f(x) = 7x^2 - 3x + 1$ and $g(x) = 3x - 2$, find the following.

  a. $f(1)$ **b.** $g(1)$

  c. $f(-2)$ **d.** $g(0)$

16. Graph $g(x) = 2x + 1$. Compare this graph with the graph of $f(x) = 2x$.

17. Find the slope and the y-intercept of the line $3x - 4y = 4$.

18. Are the following pairs of lines parallel, perpendicular, or neither?

  a. $3x + 7y = 4$
       $6x + 14y = 7$

  b. $-x + 3y = 2$
       $2x + 6y = 5$

19. Find an equation of the line through points $(4, 0)$ and $(-4, -5)$. Write the equation using function notation.

20. Graph $3x \geq y$.

21. Determine whether the given ordered pair is a solution of the system.

  a. $\begin{cases} -x + y = 2 \\ 2x - y = -3 \end{cases}$ $(-1, 1)$

  b. $\begin{cases} 5x + 3y = -1 \\ x - y = 1 \end{cases}$ $(-2, 3)$

22. Solve the system.
$$\begin{cases} 3x - y + z = -15 \\ x + 2y - z = 1 \\ 2x + 3y - 2z = 0 \end{cases}$$

23. Use matrices to solve the system.
$$\begin{cases} x + 3y = 5 \\ 2x - y = -4 \end{cases}$$

24. Evaluate each determinant.

  a. $\begin{vmatrix} -1 & 2 \\ 3 & -4 \end{vmatrix}$

  b. $\begin{vmatrix} 2 & 0 \\ 7 & -5 \end{vmatrix}$

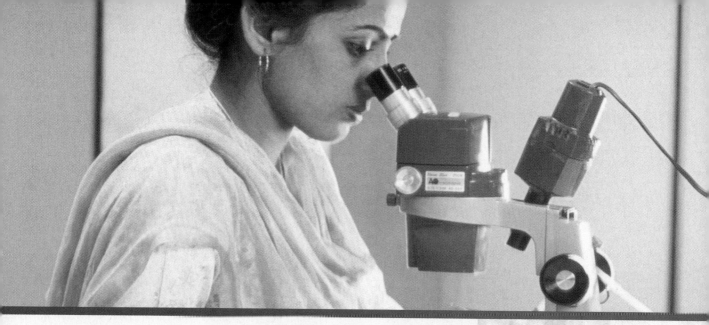

Too Small to be Seen with the Naked Eye

A microbe is a tiny living organism that is too small to be seen with the naked eye. Microbes are everywhere, both indoors and outdoors. Some scientists estimate that a single gram of ordinary soil may contain up to one billion microbes belonging to over 10,000 different species of microbes. In addition, a single milliliter of coastal ocean water may contain up to one million microbes. We even find microbes in our food: Bread, chocolate, yogurt, and cheese are produced with the help of certain microbes.

A microbiologist is a person who studies microbes. Microbiologists work in both the public and private sectors, identifying harmful microbes in food and water, developing vaccines or treatments for disease, increasing crop yields, protecting the environment, or conducting research. They need an understanding of the sciences, especially biology, chemistry, and physics, as well as mathematics. Microbiologists use mathematics in tasks such as writing grant proposals to obtain project funding, summarizing research results with percents or statistics, modeling bacterial growth, and taking measurements of microbes.

 For more information about a career in microbiology, visit the American Society for Microbiology Website by first going to www.prenhall. com/martin-gay.

In the Spotlight on Decision Making feature on page 250, you will have the opportunity to make a decision about microscope magnification as a microbiologist.

EXPONENTS, POLYNOMIALS, AND POLYNOMIAL FUNCTIONS

5

Linear equations are important for solving problems. They are not sufficient, however, to solve all problems. Many real-world phenomena are modeled by polynomials. We begin this chapter by reviewing exponents. We will then study operations on polynomials and how polynomials can be used in problem solving. We conclude with a study of graphs of polynomial functions.

5.1 EXPONENTS AND SCIENTIFIC NOTATION

▶ **OBJECTIVES**

1. Use the product rule for exponents.
2. Evaluate expressions raised to the 0 power.
3. Use the quotient rule for exponents.
4. Evaluate expressions raised to the negative nth power.
5. Convert between scientific notation and standard notation.

1 Recall that exponents may be used to write repeated factors in a more compact form. As we have seen in the previous chapters, exponents can be used when the repeated factor is a number or a variable. For example,

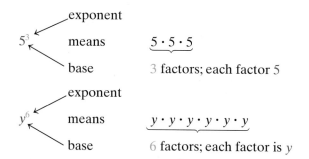

Expressions such as 5^3 and y^6 that contain exponents are called **exponential expressions.**

Exponential expressions can be multiplied, divided, added, subtracted, and themselves raised to powers. In this section, we review operations on exponential expressions.

We review multiplication first. To multiply x^2 by x^3, use the definition of a^n.

$$x^2 \cdot x^3 = \underbrace{(x \cdot x)(x \cdot x \cdot x)}_{x \text{ is a factor 5 times}}$$
$$= x^5$$

Notice that the result is exactly the same if we add the exponents.

$$x^2 \cdot x^3 = x^{2+3} = x^5$$

This suggests the following.

PRODUCT RULE FOR EXPONENTS

If m and n are positive integers and a is a real number, then

$$a^m \cdot a^n = a^{m+n}$$

In other words, the *product* of exponential expressions with a common base is the common base raised to a power equal to the *sum* of the exponents of the factors.

Example 1   Use the product rule to simplify.

   a. $2^2 \cdot 2^5$ **b.** $x^7 x^3$ **c.** $y \cdot y^2 \cdot y^4$

Solution   **a.** $2^2 \cdot 2^5 = 2^{2+5} = 2^7$
   b. $x^7 x^3 = x^{7+3} = x^{10}$
   c. $y \cdot y^2 \cdot y^4 = \left(y^1 \cdot y^2\right) \cdot y^4$
                   $= y^3 \cdot y^4$
                   $= y^7$

Example 2   Use the product rule to multiply.

   a. $\left(3x^6\right)\left(5x\right)$ **b.** $\left(-2x^3 p^2\right)\left(4xp^{10}\right)$

Solution   Here, we use properties of multiplication to group together like bases.

   a. $\left(3x^6\right)\left(5x\right) = 3(5)x^6 x^1 = 15x^7$
   b. $\left(-2x^3 p^2\right)\left(4xp^{10}\right) = -2(4)x^3 x^1 p^2 p^{10} = -8x^4 p^{12}$

2   The definition of a^n does not include the possibility that n might be 0. But if it did, then, by the product rule,

$$\underbrace{a^0 \cdot a^n}_{} = a^{0+n} = a^n = \underbrace{1 \cdot a^n}.$$

From this, we reasonably define that $a^0 = 1$, as long as a does not equal 0.

ZERO EXPONENT

If a does not equal 0, then $a^0 = 1$.

Example 3   Evaluate the following.

   a. 7^0 **b.** -7^0 **c.** $(2x + 5)^0$ **d.** $2x^0$

Solution   **a.** $7^0 = 1$
   b. Without parentheses, only 7 is raised to the 0 power.

$$-7^0 = -\left(7^0\right) = -(1) = -1$$

   c. $(2x + 5)^0 = 1$
   d. $2x^0 = 2(1) = 2$

3   To find quotients of exponential expressions, we again begin with the definition of a^n to simplify $\dfrac{x^9}{x^2}$. For example,

$$\frac{x^9}{x^2} = \frac{x \cdot x \cdot x \cdot x \cdot x \cdot x \cdot x \cdot x \cdot x}{x \cdot x} = x^7$$

(Assume for the next two sections that denominators containing variables are not 0.)

Notice that the result is exactly the same if we subtract the exponents.

$$\frac{x^9}{x^2} = x^{9-2} = x^7$$

This suggests the following.

QUOTIENT RULE FOR EXPONENTS

If a is a nonzero real number and n and m are integers, then

$$\frac{a^m}{a^n} = a^{m-n}$$

In other words, the *quotient* of exponential expressions with a common base is the common base raised to a power equal to the *difference* of the exponents.

Example 4   Use the quotient rule to simplify.

a. $\dfrac{x^7}{x^4}$ **b.** $\dfrac{5^8}{5^2}$ **c.** $\dfrac{20x^6}{4x^5}$ **d.** $\dfrac{12y^{10}z^7}{14y^8z^7}$

Solution   **a.** $\dfrac{x^7}{x^4} = x^{7-4} = x^3$

b. $\dfrac{5^8}{5^2} = 5^{8-2} = 5^6$

c. $\dfrac{20x^6}{4x^5} = 5x^{6-5} = 5x^1,$ or $5x$

d. $\dfrac{12y^{10}z^7}{14y^8z^7} = \dfrac{6}{7}y^{10-8} \cdot z^{7-7} = \dfrac{6}{7}y^2z^0 = \dfrac{6}{7}y^2,$ or $\dfrac{6y^2}{7}$

4   When the exponent of the denominator is larger than the exponent of the numerator, applying the quotient rule yields a negative exponent. For example,

$$\frac{x^3}{x^5} = x^{3-5} = x^{-2}$$

Using the definition of a^n, though, gives us

$$\frac{x^3}{x^5} = \frac{x \cdot x \cdot x}{x \cdot x \cdot x \cdot x \cdot x} = \frac{1}{x^2}$$

From this, we reasonably define $x^{-2} = \dfrac{1}{x^2}$ or, in general, $a^{-n} = \dfrac{1}{a^n}.$

NEGATIVE EXPONENTS

If a is a real number other than 0 and n is a positive integer, then

$$a^{-n} = \frac{1}{a^n}$$

Example 5   Use only positive exponents to write the following. Simplify if possible.

a. 5^{-2} **b.** $2x^{-3}$ **c.** $(3x)^{-1}$ **d.** $\dfrac{m^5}{m^{15}}$

e. $\dfrac{3^3}{3^6}$ **f.** $2^{-1} + 3^{-2}$ **g.** $\dfrac{1}{t^{-5}}$

Solution   **a.** $5^{-2} = \dfrac{1}{5^2} = \dfrac{1}{25}$

b. $2x^{-3} = 2 \cdot \dfrac{1}{x^3} = \dfrac{2}{x^3}$ Without parentheses, only x is raised to the -3 power.

c. $(3x)^{-1} = \dfrac{1}{(3x)^1} = \dfrac{1}{3x}$ With parentheses, both 3 and x are raised to the -1 power.

d. $\dfrac{m^5}{m^{15}} = m^{5-15} = m^{-10} = \dfrac{1}{m^{10}}$

e. $\dfrac{3^3}{3^6} = 3^{3-6} = 3^{-3} = \dfrac{1}{3^3} = \dfrac{1}{27}$

f. $2^{-1} + 3^{-2} = \dfrac{1}{2^1} + \dfrac{1}{3^2} = \dfrac{1}{2} + \dfrac{1}{9} = \dfrac{9}{18} + \dfrac{2}{18} = \dfrac{11}{18}$

g. $\dfrac{1}{t^{-5}} = \dfrac{1}{\dfrac{1}{t^5}} = 1 \div \dfrac{1}{t^5} = 1 \cdot \dfrac{t^5}{1} = t^5$

HELPFUL HINT

Notice that when a factor containing an exponent is moved from the numerator to the denominator or from the denominator to the numerator, the sign of its exponent changes.

$$x^{-3} = \dfrac{1}{x^3}, \qquad 5^{-2} = \dfrac{1}{5^2} = \dfrac{1}{25}$$

$$\dfrac{1}{y^{-4}} = y^4, \qquad \dfrac{1}{2^{-3}} = 2^3 = 8$$

Example 6   Simplify each expression. Use positive exponents to write the answers.

a. $\dfrac{x^{-9}}{x^2}$ **b.** $\dfrac{p^4}{p^{-3}}$ **c.** $\dfrac{2^{-3}}{2^{-1}}$ **d.** $\dfrac{2x^{-7}y^2}{10xy^{-5}}$ **e.** $\dfrac{(3x^{-3})(x^2)}{x^6}$

Solution   **a.** $\dfrac{x^{-9}}{x^2} = x^{-9-2} = x^{-11} = \dfrac{1}{x^{11}}$

b. $\dfrac{p^4}{p^{-3}} = p^{4-(-3)} = p^7$

c. $\dfrac{2^{-3}}{2^{-1}} = 2^{-3-(-1)} = 2^{-2} = \dfrac{1}{2^2} = \dfrac{1}{4}$

d. $\dfrac{2x^{-7}y^2}{10xy^{-5}} = \dfrac{x^{-7-1} \cdot y^{2-(-5)}}{5} = \dfrac{x^{-8}y^7}{5} = \dfrac{y^7}{5x^8}$

e. Simplify the numerator first.

$$\dfrac{(3x^{-3})(x^2)}{x^6} = \dfrac{3x^{-3+2}}{x^6} = \dfrac{3x^{-1}}{x^6} = 3x^{-1-6} = 3x^{-7} = \dfrac{3}{x^7}$$

Example 7   Simplify. Assume that a and t are nonzero integers and that x is not 0.

a. $x^{2a} \cdot x^3$ **b.** $\dfrac{x^{2t-1}}{x^{t-5}}$

Solution   **a.** $x^{2a} \cdot x^3 = x^{2a+3}$ Use the product rule.

b. $\dfrac{x^{2t-1}}{x^{t-5}} = x^{(2t-1)-(t-5)}$ Use the quotient rule.

$\phantom{\text{b.} \dfrac{x^{2t-1}}{x^{t-5}}} = x^{2t-1-t+5} = x^{t+4}$

---

5   Very large and very small numbers occur frequently in nature. For example, the distance between the Earth and the Sun is approximately 150,000,000 kilometers. A helium atom has a diameter of 0.000 000 022 centimeters. It can be tedious to write these very large and very small numbers in standard notation like this. **Scientific notation** is a convenient shorthand notation for writing very large and very small numbers.

Helium Atom

0.000 000 022
centimeters

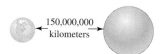

150,000,000
kilometers

SCIENTIFIC NOTATION

A positive number is written in **scientific notation** if it is written as the product of a number a, where $1 \le a < 10$ and an integer power r of 10:

$$a \times 10^r$$

The following are examples of numbers written in scientific notation.

diameter of helium atom $\rightarrow 2.2 \times 10^{-8}$ cm; 1.5×10^8 Km $\leftarrow$ approximate distance between Earth and Sun

WRITING A NUMBER IN SCIENTIFIC NOTATION

Step 1: Move the decimal point in the original number until the new number has a value between 1 and 10.

Step 2: Count the number of decimal places the decimal point was moved in Step 1. If the decimal point was moved to the left, the count is positive. If the decimal point was moved to the right, the count is negative.

Step 3: Write the product of the new number in Step 1 and 10 raised to an exponent equal to the count found in Step 2.

Example 8 Write each number in scientific notation.

   a. 730,000

   b. 0.00000104

Solution   **a. Step. 1:** Move the decimal point until the number is between 1 and 10.

$$730{,}000.$$

   Step 2: The decimal point is moved 5 places to the left, so the count is positive 5.

   Step 3: $730{,}000 = 7.3 \times 10^5$.

   b. Step 1: Move the decimal point until the number is between 1 and 10.

$$0.00000104$$

   Step 2: The decimal point is moved 6 places to the right, so the count is -6.

   Step 3: $0.00000104 = 1.04 \times 10^{-6}$.

To write a scientific notation number in standard form, we reverse the preceding steps.

WRITING A SCIENTIFIC NOTATION NUMBER IN STANDARD NOTATION

Move the decimal point in the number the same number of places as the exponent on 10. If the exponent is positive, move the decimal point to the right. If the exponent is negative, move the decimal point to the left.

Example 9 Write each number in standard notation.

   a. 7.7×10^8

   b. 1.025×10^{-3}

Solution   **a.** $7.7 \times 10^8 = 770{,}000{,}000$

Since the exponent is positive, move the decimal point 8 places to the right. Add zeros as needed.

   b. $1.025 \times 10^{-3} = 0.001025$

Since the exponent is negative, move the decimal point 3 places to the left. Add zeros as needed.

SCIENTIFIC CALCULATOR EXPLORATIONS

Multiply 5,000,000 by 700,000 on your calculator. The display should read $\boxed{3.5 \quad 12}$ or $\boxed{3.5 \text{ E } 12}$, which is the product written in scientific notation. Both these notations mean 3.5×10^{12}.

To enter a number written in scientific notation on a calculator, find the key marked $\boxed{\text{EE}}$. $\Big($On some calculators, this key may be marked $\boxed{\text{EXP}}$.$\Big)$

To enter 7.26×10^{13}, press the keys

$$\boxed{7.26} \quad \boxed{\text{EE}} \quad \boxed{13}$$

The display will read $\boxed{7.26 \quad 13}$ or $\boxed{7.26 \text{ E } 13}$.

Use your calculator to perform each operation indicated.

1. Multiply 3×10^{11} and 2×10^{32}.
2. Divide 6×10^{14} by 3×10^{9}.
3. Multiply 5.2×10^{23} and 7.3×10^{4}.
4. Divide 4.38×10^{41} by 3×10^{17}.

SPOTLIGHT ON DECISION MAKING

Suppose you are a microbiologist. You know that when an image is viewed through a microscope, its magnification is the number of times the image is enlarged. For example, if a 4-millimeter-long object is viewed at five times magnification (denoted $5\times$ magnification), it appears as an object that is $5 \times 4 = 20$ millimeters long.

Suppose you are studying the *Ebola Zaire* virus, which has an average length of 9.2×10^{-5} centimeters. You would like to view an Ebola virus with a microscope so that it appears to be 4 centimeters long. Decide what magnification setting (rounded to the nearest thousand) you will need to use on the microscope.

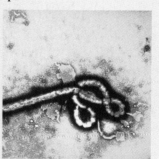

MENTAL MATH

Use positive exponents to state each expression.

1. $5x^{-1}y^{-2}$

2. $7xy^{-4}$

3. $a^2b^{-1}c^{-5}$

4. $a^{-4}b^2c^{-6}$

5. $\dfrac{y^{-2}}{x^{-4}}$

6. $\dfrac{x^{-7}}{z^{-3}}$

Exercise Set 5.1

Use the product rule to simplify each expression. See Examples 1 and 2.

1. $4^2 \cdot 4^3$ **2.** $3^3 \cdot 3^5$

3. $x^5 \cdot x^3$ **4.** $a^2 \cdot a^9$

5. $-7x^3 \cdot 20x^9$ **6.** $-3y \cdot -9y^4$

7. $(4xy)(-5x)$ **8.** $(7xy)(7aby)$

9. $(-4x^3p^2)(4y^3x^3)$ **10.** $(-6a^2b^3)(-3ab^3)$

Evaluate the following. See Example 3.

11. -8^0 **12.** $(-9)^0$

13. $(4x + 5)^0$ **14.** $8x^0 + 1$

15. $(5x)^0 + 5x^0$ **16.** $4y^0 - (4y)^0$

17. Explain why $(-5)^0$ simplifies to 1 but -5^0 simplifies to -1.

18. Explain why both $4x^0 - 3y^0$ and $(4x - 3y)^0$ simplify to 1.

Find each quotient. See Example 4.

19. $\dfrac{a^5}{a^2}$ **20.** $\dfrac{x^9}{x^4}$

21. $\dfrac{x^9 y^6}{x^8 y^6}$ **22.** $\dfrac{a^{12} b^2}{a^9 b}$

23. $-\dfrac{26z^{11}}{2z^7}$ **24.** $\dfrac{16x^5}{8x}$

25. $\dfrac{-36a^5 b^7 c^{10}}{6ab^3 c^4}$ **26.** $\dfrac{49a^3 bc^{14}}{-7abc^8}$

Simplify each expression. Write answers with positive exponents. See Examples 5 and 6.

27. 4^{-2} **28.** 2^{-3}

29. $\dfrac{x^7}{x^{15}}$ **30.** $\dfrac{z}{z^3}$

31. $5a^{-4}$ **32.** $10b^{-1}$

33. $\dfrac{x^{-2}}{x^5}$ **34.** $\dfrac{y^{-6}}{y^{-9}}$

35. $\dfrac{8r^4}{2r^{-4}}$ **36.** $\dfrac{3s^3}{15s^{-3}}$

37. $\dfrac{x^{-9} x^4}{x^{-5}}$ **38.** $\dfrac{y^{-7} y}{y^8}$

Simplify the following. Write answers with positive exponents.

39. $4^{-1} + 3^{-2}$ **40.** $1^{-3} - 4^{-2}$

41. $4x^0 + 5$ **42.** $-5x^0$

43. $x^7 \cdot x^8$ **44.** $y^6 \cdot y$

45. $2x^3 \cdot 5x^7$ **46.** $-3z^4 \cdot 10z^7$

47. $\dfrac{z^{12}}{z^{15}}$ **48.** $\dfrac{x^{11}}{x^{20}}$

49. $\dfrac{y^{-3}}{y^{-7}}$ **50.** $\dfrac{z^{-12}}{z^{10}}$

51. $3x^{-1}$ **52.** $(4x)^{-1}$

53. $3^0 - 3t^0$ **54.** $4^0 + 4x^0$

55. $\dfrac{r^4}{r^{-4}}$ **56.** $\dfrac{x^{-5}}{x^3}$

57. $\dfrac{x^{-7} y^{-2}}{x^2 y^2}$ **58.** $\dfrac{a^{-5} b^7}{a^{-2} b^{-3}}$

59. $\dfrac{2a^{-6} b^2}{18ab^{-5}}$ **60.** $\dfrac{18ab^{-6}}{3a^{-3} b^6}$

61. $\dfrac{(24x^8)(x)}{20x^{-7}}$ **62.** $\dfrac{(30z^2)(z^5)}{55z^{-4}}$

Write each number in scientific notation. See Example 8.

63. 31,250,000   **64.** 678,000

65. 0.016   **66.** 0.007613

67. 67,413   **68.** 36,800,000

69. 0.0125   **70.** 0.00084

71. 0.000053   **72.** 98,700,000,000

Write each number in standard notation, without exponents. See Example 9.

73. 3.6×10^{-9} **74.** 2.7×10^{-5}

75. 9.3×10^7 **76.** 6.378×10^8

77. 1.278×10^6 **78.** 7.6×10^4

79. 7.35×10^{12} **80.** 1.66×10^{-5}

81. 4.03×10^{-7} **82.** 8.007×10^8

83. Explain how to convert a number from standard notation to scientific notation.

84. Explain how to convert a number from scientific notation to standard notation.

85. Which numbers have values that are less than 1?
   a. 3.5×10^{-5} **b.** 3.5×10^5
   c. -3.5×10^5 **d.** -3.5×10^{-5}

86. Which numbers are equal to 36,000? Of these, which is written in scientific notation?
   a. 36×10^3 **b.** 360×10^2
   c. 0.36×10^5 **d.** 3.6×10^4

Write each number in scientific notation.

87. The approximate distance between Jupiter and the sun is 778,300,000 kilometers. (*Source:* National Space Data Center)

88. Total revenues for Wal-Mart in fiscal year 2000 were $166,808,000,000. (*Source:* Wal-Mart Stores, Inc.)

89. In February 2000, domestic airline flights carried a total of 43,141,000 passengers. (*Source:* Air Transport Association of America)

90. In 1998, the American toy industry had retail sales of $27,200,000. (*Source:* Toy Manufacturers of America, Inc.)

91. In 1997, the New York City subway system carried a total of 1,130,000,000 passengers. (*Source:* New York City Transit Authority)

92. The center of the sun is about 27,000,000°F.

93. A pulsar is a rotating neutron star that gives off sharp, regular pulses of radio waves. For one particular pulsar, the rate of pulses is every 0.001 second.

94. To convert from cubic inches to cubic meters, multiply by 0.0000164.

Simplify. Assume that variables in the exponent represent nonzero integers and that x, y, and z are not 0. See Example 7.

95. $x^5 \cdot x^{7a}$

96. $y^{2p} \cdot y^{9p}$

97. $\dfrac{x^{3t-1}}{x^t}$

98. $\dfrac{y^{4p-2}}{y^{3p}}$

99. $x^{4a} \cdot x^7$

100. $x^{9y} \cdot x^{-7y}$

101. $\dfrac{z^{6x}}{z^7}$

102. $\dfrac{y^6}{y^{4z}}$

103. $\dfrac{x^{3t} \cdot x^{4t-1}}{x^t}$

104. $\dfrac{z^{5x} \cdot z^{x-7}}{z^x}$

105. $x^{9+b} \cdot x^{3a-b}$

106. $z^{2a-b} \cdot z^{5a-b}$

Without calculating, determine which number is larger.

107. 7^{11} or 7^{13}

108. 5^{10} or 5^9

109. 7^{-11} or 7^{-13}

110. 5^{-10} or 5^{-9}

REVIEW EXERCISES

Evaluate. See Section 1.3.

111. $(5 \cdot 2)^2$

112. $5^2 \cdot 2^2$

113. $\left(\dfrac{3}{4}\right)^3$

114. $\dfrac{3^3}{4^3}$

115. $\left(2^3\right)^2$

116. $\left(2^2\right)^3$

117. $\left(2^{-1}\right)^4$

118. $\left(2^4\right)^{-1}$

5.2 MORE WORK WITH EXPONENTS AND SCIENTIFIC NOTATION

CD-ROM   SSM

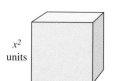

SSG   Video

▶ **OBJECTIVES**

1. Use the power rules for exponents.
2. Use exponent rules and definitions to simplify exponential expressions.
3. Compute, using scientific notation.

1　The volume of the cube shown whose side measures x^2 units is $\left(x^2\right)^3$ cubic units. To simplify an expression such as $\left(x^2\right)^3$, we use the definition of a^n. Then

$$\left(x^2\right)^3 = \underbrace{\left(x^2\right)\left(x^2\right)\left(x^2\right)}_{x^2 \text{ is a factor 3 times}} = x^{2+2+2} = x^6$$

x^2
units

Notice that the result is exactly the same if the exponents are multiplied.

$$\left(x^2\right)^3 = x^{2 \cdot 3} = x^6$$

This suggests that the power of an exponential expression raised to a power is the product of the exponents. Two additional rules for exponents are given in the following box.

THE POWER RULE AND POWER OF A PRODUCT OR QUOTIENT RULES FOR EXPONENTS

If a and b are real numbers and m and n are integers, then

$$(a^m)^n = a^{m \cdot n} \qquad \text{Power rule}$$

$$(ab)^m = a^m b^m \qquad \text{Power of a product}$$

$$\left(\frac{a}{b}\right)^n = \frac{a^n}{b^n} \ (b \neq 0) \qquad \text{Power of a quotient}$$

Example 1 Use the power rule to simplify the following expressions. Use positive exponents to write all results.

a. $\left(x^5\right)^7$ **b.** $\left(2^2\right)^3$ **c.** $\left(5^{-1}\right)^2$ **d.** $\left(y^{-3}\right)^{-4}$

Solution **a.** $\left(x^5\right)^7 = x^{5 \cdot 7} = x^{35}$

b. $\left(2^2\right)^3 = 2^{2 \cdot 3} = 2^6 = 64$

c. $\left(5^{-1}\right)^2 = 5^{-1 \cdot 2} = 5^{-2} = \dfrac{1}{5^2} = \dfrac{1}{25}$

d. $\left(y^{-3}\right)^{-4} = y^{-3(-4)} = y^{12}$

Example 2 Use the power rules to simplify the following. Use positive exponents to write all results.

a. $\left(5x^2\right)^3$ **b.** $\left(\dfrac{2}{3}\right)^3$ **c.** $\left(\dfrac{3p^4}{q^5}\right)^2$ **d.** $\left(\dfrac{2^{-3}}{y}\right)^{-2}$ **e.** $\left(x^{-5}y^2z^{-1}\right)^7$

Solution **a.** $\left(5x^2\right)^3 = 5^3 \cdot \left(x^2\right)^3 = 5^3 \cdot x^{2 \cdot 3} = 125x^6$

b. $\left(\dfrac{2}{3}\right)^3 = \dfrac{2^3}{3^3} = \dfrac{8}{27}$

c. $\left(\dfrac{3p^4}{q^5}\right)^2 = \dfrac{\left(3p^4\right)^2}{\left(q^5\right)^2} = \dfrac{3^2 \cdot \left(p^4\right)^2}{\left(q^5\right)^2} = \dfrac{9p^8}{q^{10}}$

d. $\left(\dfrac{2^{-3}}{y}\right)^{-2} = \dfrac{\left(2^{-3}\right)^{-2}}{y^{-2}}$

$= \dfrac{2^6}{y^{-2}} = 64y^2$ Use the negative exponent rule.

e. $\left(x^{-5}y^2z^{-1}\right)^7 = \left(x^{-5}\right)^7 \cdot \left(y^2\right)^7 \cdot \left(z^{-1}\right)^7$

$= x^{-35}y^{14}z^{-7} = \dfrac{y^{14}}{x^{35}z^7}$

2   In the next few examples, we practice the use of several of the rules and definitions for exponents. The following is a summary of these rules and definitions.

SUMMARY OF RULES FOR EXPONENTS

If a and b are real numbers and m and n are integers, then

Product rule	$a^m \cdot a^n = a^{m+n}$	
Zero exponent	$a^0 = 1$	$(a \neq 0)$
Negative exponent	$a^{-n} = \dfrac{1}{a^n}$	$(a \neq 0)$
Quotient rule	$\dfrac{a^m}{a^n} = a^{m-n}$	$(a \neq 0)$
Power rule	$\left(a^m\right)^n = a^{m \cdot n}$	
Power of a product	$(ab)^m = a^m \cdot b^m$	
Power of a quotient	$\left(\dfrac{a}{b}\right)^m = \dfrac{a^m}{b^m}$	$(b \neq 0)$

Example 3   Simplify each expression. Use positive exponents to write the answers.

a. $\left(2x^0 y^{-3}\right)^{-2}$ **b.** $\left(\dfrac{x^{-5}}{x^{-2}}\right)^{-3}$ **c.** $\left(\dfrac{2}{7}\right)^{-2}$ **d.** $\dfrac{5^{-2}x^{-3}y^{11}}{x^2 y^{-5}}$

Solution   **a.** $\left(2x^0 y^{-3}\right)^{-2} = 2^{-2}\left(x^0\right)^{-2}\left(y^{-3}\right)^{-2}$

$$= 2^{-2}x^0 y^6$$

$$= \frac{1\left(y^6\right)}{2^2} \qquad \text{Write } x^0 \text{ as 1.}$$

$$= \frac{y^6}{4}$$

b. $\left(\dfrac{x^{-5}}{x^{-2}}\right)^{-3} = \dfrac{\left(x^{-5}\right)^{-3}}{\left(x^{-2}\right)^{-3}} = \dfrac{x^{15}}{x^6} = x^{15-6} = x^9$

c. $\left(\dfrac{2}{7}\right)^{-2} = \dfrac{2^{-2}}{7^{-2}} = \dfrac{7^2}{2^2} = \dfrac{49}{4}$

d. $\dfrac{5^{-2}x^{-3}y^{11}}{x^2 y^{-5}} = \left(5^{-2}\right)\left(\dfrac{x^{-3}}{x^2}\right)\left(\dfrac{y^{11}}{y^{-5}}\right) = 5^{-2}x^{-3-2}y^{11-(-5)} = 5^{-2}x^{-5}y^{16}$

$$= \frac{y^{16}}{5^2 x^5} = \frac{y^{16}}{25x^5}$$

Example 4   Simplify each expression. Use positive exponents to write the answers.

a. $\left(\dfrac{3x^2 y}{y^{-9} z}\right)^{-2}$

b. $\left(\dfrac{3a^2}{2x^{-1}}\right)^3 \left(\dfrac{x^{-3}}{4a^{-2}}\right)^{-1}$

Solution   There is often more than one way to simplify exponential expressions. Here, we will simplify inside the parentheses if possible before we apply the power rules for exponents.

a. $\left(\dfrac{3x^2 y}{y^{-9} z}\right)^{-2} = \left(\dfrac{3x^2 y^{10}}{z}\right)^{-2} = \dfrac{3^{-2} x^{-4} y^{-20}}{z^{-2}} = \dfrac{z^2}{3^2 x^4 y^{20}} = \dfrac{z^2}{9x^4 y^{20}}$

b. $\left(\dfrac{3a^2}{2x^{-1}}\right)^3 \left(\dfrac{x^{-3}}{4a^{-2}}\right)^{-1} = \dfrac{27a^6}{8x^{-3}} \cdot \dfrac{x^3}{4^{-1} a^2}$

$= \dfrac{27 \cdot 4 \cdot a^6 x^3 x^3}{8 \cdot a^2} = \dfrac{27a^4 x^6}{2}$

Example 5   Simplify each expression. Assume that a and b are integers and that x and y are not 0.

a. $x^{-b}(2x^b)^2$

b. $\dfrac{(y^{3a})^2}{y^{a-6}}$

Solution   **a.** $x^{-b}(2x^b)^2 = x^{-b} 2^2 x^{2b} = 4x^{-b+2b} = 4x^b$

b. $\dfrac{(y^{3a})^2}{y^{a-6}} = \dfrac{y^{2(3a)}}{y^{a-6}} = \dfrac{y^{6a}}{y^{a-6}} = y^{6a-(a-6)} = y^{6a-a+6} = y^{5a+6}$

3   To perform operations on numbers written in scientific notation, we use properties of exponents.

Example 6   Perform the indicated operations. Write each result in scientific notation.

a. $(8.1 \times 10^5)(5 \times 10^{-7})$

b. $\dfrac{1.2 \times 10^4}{3 \times 10^{-2}}$

Solution   **a.** $(8.1 \times 10^5)(5 \times 10^{-7}) = 8.1 \times 5 \times 10^5 \times 10^{-7}$

$= 40.5 \times 10^{-2}$

$= (4.05 \times 10^1) \times 10^{-2}$

$= 4.05 \times 10^{-1}$

b. $\dfrac{1.2 \times 10^4}{3 \times 10^{-2}} = \left(\dfrac{1.2}{3}\right)\left(\dfrac{10^4}{10^{-2}}\right) = 0.4 \times 10^{4-(-2)}$

$= 0.4 \times 10^6 = (4 \times 10^{-1}) \times 10^6 = 4 \times 10^5$

Example 7   Use scientific notation to simplify $\dfrac{2000 \times 0.000021}{700}$.

Solution $\dfrac{2000 \times 0.000021}{700} = \dfrac{(2 \times 10^3)(2.1 \times 10^{-5})}{7 \times 10^2} = \dfrac{2(2.1)}{7} \cdot \dfrac{10^3 \cdot 10^{-5}}{10^2}$

$$= 0.6 \times 10^{-4}$$
$$= (6 \times 10^{-1}) \times 10^{-4}$$
$$= 6 \times 10^{-5}$$

MENTAL MATH

Simplify. See Example 1.

1. $(x^4)^5$
2. $(5^6)^2$
3. $x^4 \cdot x^5$
4. $x^7 \cdot x^8$
5. $(y^6)^7$
6. $(x^3)^4$
7. $(z^4)^5$
8. $(z^3)^7$
9. $(z^{-6})^{-3}$
10. $(y^{-4})^{-2}$

Exercise Set 5.2

Simplify. Use positive exponents to write each answer. See Examples 1 and 2.

1. $(3^{-1})^2$
2. $(2^{-2})^2$
3. $(x^4)^{-9}$
4. $(y^7)^{-3}$
5. $(y)^{-5}$
6. $(z^{-1})^{10}$
7. $(3x^2y^3)^2$
8. $(4x^3yz)^2$
9. $\left(\dfrac{2x^5}{y^{-3}}\right)^4$
10. $\left(\dfrac{3a^{-4}}{b^7}\right)^3$
11. $(a^2bc^{-3})^{-6}$
12. $(6x^{-6}y^7z^0)^{-2}$
13. $\left(\dfrac{x^7y^{-3}}{z^{-4}}\right)^{-5}$
14. $\left(\dfrac{a^{-2}b^{-5}}{c^{-11}}\right)^{-6}$

Simplify. Use positive exponents to write each answer. See Examples 3 and 4.

15. $\left(\dfrac{a^{-4}}{a^{-5}}\right)^{-2}$
16. $\left(\dfrac{x^{-9}}{x^{-4}}\right)^{-3}$
17. $\left(\dfrac{2a^{-2}b^5}{4a^2b^7}\right)^{-2}$
18. $\left(\dfrac{5x^7y^4}{10x^3y^{-2}}\right)^{-3}$
19. $\dfrac{4^{-1}x^2yz}{x^{-2}yz^3}$
20. $\dfrac{8^{-2}x^{-3}y^{11}}{x^2y^{-5}}$
21. Is there a number a such that $a^{-1} = a^1$? If so, give the value of a.
22. Is there a number a such that a^{-2} is a negative number? If so, give the value of a.

Simplify. Use positive exponents to write each answer.

23. $(5^{-1})^3$
24. $(8^2)^{-1}$
25. $(x^7)^{-9}$
26. $(y^{-4})^5$
27. $\left(\dfrac{7}{8}\right)^3$
28. $\left(\dfrac{4}{3}\right)^2$
29. $(4x^2)^2$
30. $(-8x^3)^2$
31. $(-2^{-2}y)^3$
32. $(-4^{-6}y^{-6})^{-4}$
33. $\left(\dfrac{4^{-4}}{y^3x}\right)^{-2}$
34. $\left(\dfrac{7^{-3}}{ab^2}\right)^{-2}$
35. $\left(\dfrac{6p^6}{p^{12}}\right)^2$
36. $\left(\dfrac{4p^6}{p^9}\right)^3$
37. $(-8y^3xa^{-2})^{-3}$
38. $(-xy^0x^2a^3)^{-3}$
39. $\left(\dfrac{x^{-2}y^{-2}}{a^{-3}}\right)^{-7}$
40. $\left(\dfrac{x^{-1}y^{-2}}{5^{-3}}\right)^{-5}$
41. $\left(\dfrac{3x^5}{6x^4}\right)^4$
42. $\left(\dfrac{8^{-3}}{y^2}\right)^{-2}$
43. $\left(\dfrac{1}{4}\right)^{-3}$
44. $\left(\dfrac{1}{8}\right)^{-2}$
45. $\dfrac{(y^3)^{-4}}{y^3}$
46. $\dfrac{2(y^3)^{-3}}{y^{-3}}$
47. $\dfrac{8p^7}{4p^9}$
48. $\left(\dfrac{2x^4}{x^2}\right)^3$

49. $(4x^6y^5)^{-2}(6x^4y^3)$

50. $(5xy)^3(z^{-2})^{-3}$

51. $x^6(x^6bc)^{-6}$

52. $2(y^2b)^{-4}$

53. $\dfrac{2^{-3}x^2y^{-5}}{5^{-2}x^7y^{-1}}$

54. $\dfrac{7^{-1}a^{-3}b^5}{a^2b^{-2}}$

55. $\left(\dfrac{2x^2}{y^4}\right)^3 \cdot \left(\dfrac{2x^5}{y}\right)^{-2}$

56. $\left(\dfrac{3z^{-2}}{y}\right)^2 \cdot \left(\dfrac{9y^{-4}}{z^{-3}}\right)^{-1}$

Perform indicated operations. Write each result in scientific notation. See Examples 6 and 7.

57. $(5 \times 10^{11})(2.9 \times 10^{-3})$

58. $(3.6 \times 10^{-12})(6 \times 10^9)$

59. $(2 \times 10^5)^3$

60. $(3 \times 10^{-7})^3$

61. $\dfrac{3.6 \times 10^{-4}}{9 \times 10^2}$

62. $\dfrac{1.2 \times 10^9}{2 \times 10^{-5}}$

63. $\dfrac{0.0069}{0.023}$

64. $\dfrac{0.00048}{0.0016}$

65. $\dfrac{18{,}200 \times 100}{91{,}000}$

66. $\dfrac{0.0003 \times 0.0024}{0.0006 \times 20}$

67. $\dfrac{6000 \times 0.006}{0.009 \times 400}$

68. $\dfrac{0.00016 \times 300}{0.064 \times 100}$

69. $\dfrac{0.00064 \times 2000}{16{,}000}$

70. $\dfrac{0.00072 \times 0.003}{0.00024}$

71. $\dfrac{66{,}000 \times 0.001}{0.002 \times 0.003}$

72. $\dfrac{0.0007 \times 11{,}000}{0.001 \times 0.0001}$

73. $\dfrac{8.25 \times 10^{15}}{(2.5 \times 10^{-2})(2.2 \times 10^{-5})}$

74. $\dfrac{(2.6 \times 10^{-3})(4.8 \times 10^{-4})}{1.3 \times 10^{-12}}$

Solve.

75. A computer can add two numbers in about 10^{-8} second. Express in scientific notation how long it would take this computer to do this task 200,000 times.

76. The density D of an object is equivalent to the quotient of its mass M and volume V. Thus, $D = \dfrac{M}{V}$. Express in scientific notation the density of an object whose mass is 500,000 pounds and whose volume is 250 cubic feet.

77. The density of ordinary water is 3.12×10^{-2} tons per cubic foot. The volume of water in the largest of the Great Lakes, Lake Superior, is 4.269×10^{14} cubic feet. Use the formula $D = \dfrac{M}{V}$ (see Exercise 76) to find the mass (in tons) of the water in Lake Superior. Express your answer in scientific notation. (*Source:* National Ocean Service)

78. The estimated population of the United States in 1999 was 2.73×10^8. The land area of the United States is 3.536×10^6 square miles. Find the population density (number of people per square mile) for the United States in 1999. Round to the nearest whole number. (*Source:* U.S. Bureau of the Census)

△ **79.** Each side of the cube shown is $\dfrac{2x^{-2}}{y}$ meters. Find its volume.

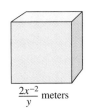

$\dfrac{2x^{-2}}{y}$ meters

△ **80.** The lot shown is in the shape of a parallelogram with base $\dfrac{3x^{-1}}{y^{-3}}$ feet and height $5x^{-7}$ feet. Find its area.

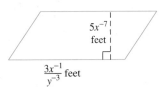

$5x^{-7}$ feet

$\dfrac{3x^{-1}}{y^{-3}}$ feet

81. To convert from square inches to square meters, multiply by 6.452×10^{-4}. The area of the following square is 4×10^{-2} square inches. Convert this area to square meters.

4×10^{-2}
square inches

82. To convert from cubic inches to cubic meters, multiply by 1.64×10^{-5}. A grain of salt is in the shape of a cube. If the average size of a grain of salt is 3.8×10^{-6} cubic inches, convert this volume to cubic meters.

83. Explain whether 0.4×10^{-5} is written in scientific notation.

84. The subway system with the largest passenger volume in the world in 1997 was the Moscow subway with 3.16×10^9 passengers. The tenth busiest subway system was São Paulo's with 7.01×10^8 passengers in 1997. How many times greater was the Moscow subway volume than the São Paulo volume? Round to the nearest tenth. (*Source:* New York City Transit Authority)

85. In 1997, China had the largest armed forces in the world. Its fighting force numbered 2.93×10^6 soldiers. Taiwan's fighting force numbered only 4.25×10^5. How many times greater was China's armed forces than Taiwan's? Round to the nearest whole number. (*Source:* Russell Ash, *The Top 10 of Everything 1997*)

Simplify the following. Assume that variables in the exponents represent integers and that all other variables are not 0. See Example 5.

86. $\left(x^{3a+6}\right)^3$

87. $\left(x^{2b+7}\right)^2$

88. $\dfrac{x^{4a}\left(x^{4a}\right)^3}{x^{4a-2}}$

89. $\dfrac{x^{-5y+2}x^{2y}}{x}$

90. $\left(b^{5x-2}\right)^{2x}$

91. $\left(c^{2a+3}\right)^3$

92. $\dfrac{\left(y^{2a}\right)^8}{y^{a-3}}$

93. $\dfrac{\left(y^{4a}\right)^7}{y^{2a-1}}$

94. $\left(\dfrac{2x^{3t}}{x^{2t-1}}\right)^4$

95. $\left(\dfrac{3y^{5a}}{y^{-a+1}}\right)^2$

96. $\dfrac{\left(z^{a+2}\right)^b}{\left(z^{b-1}\right)^a}$

97. $\dfrac{\left(y^{3-a}\right)^b}{\left(y^{1-b}\right)^a}$

98. $\dfrac{x^{2a+1}y^{a-1}}{x^{3a+1}y^{2a-3}}$

99. $\dfrac{x^{-5-3a}y^{-2a-b}}{x^{-5+3b}y^{-2b-a}}$

REVIEW EXERCISES

Simplify each expression. See Section 1.4.

100. $-5y + 4y - 18 - y$

101. $12m - 14 - 15m - 1$

102. $-3x - (4x - 2)$

103. $-9y - (5 - 6y)$

104. $3(z - 4) - 2(3z + 1)$

105. $5(x - 3) - 4(2x - 5)$

5.3 POLYNOMIALS AND POLYNOMIAL FUNCTIONS

CD-ROM

SSM

SSG   Video

▶ **OBJECTIVES**

1. Identify term, constant, polynomial, monomial, binomial, trinomial, and the degree of a term and of a polynomial.
2. Define polynomial functions.
3. Review combining like terms.
4. Add polynomials.
5. Subtract polynomials.
6. Recognize the graph of a polynomial function from the degree of the polynomial.

1

A **term** is a number or the product of a number and one or more variables raised to powers. The **numerical coefficient**, or simply the **coefficient**, is the numerical factor of a term.

Term	Numerical Coefficient
$-12x^5$	-12
x^3y	1
$-z$	-1
2	2

If a term contains only a number, it is called a **constant term**, or simply a **constant**.

A **polynomial** is a finite sum of terms in which all variables are raised to non-negative integer powers and no variables appear in any denominator.

Polynomials	*Not Polynomials*	
$4x^5y + 7xz$	$5x^{-3} + 2x$	Negative integer exponent
$-5x^3 + 2x + \dfrac{2}{3}$	$\dfrac{6}{x^2} - 5x + 1$	Variable in denominator

A polynomial that contains only one variable is called a **polynomial in one variable**. For example, $3x^2 - 2x + 7$ is a **polynomial in x**. This polynomial in x is written in *descending order* since the terms are listed in descending order of the variable's exponents. (The term 7 can be thought of as $7x^0$.) The following examples are polynomials in one variable written in **descending order**.

$$4x^3 - 7x^2 + 5 \qquad y^2 - 4 \qquad 8a^4 - 7a^2 + 4a$$

A **monomial** is a polynomial consisting of one term. A **binomial** is a polynomial consisting of two terms. A **trinomial** is a polynomial consisting of three terms.

Monomials	*Binomials*	*Trinomials*
ax^2	$x + y$	$x^2 + 4xy + y^2$
$-3x$	$6y^2 - 2$	$-x^4 + 3x^3 + 1$
4	$\dfrac{5}{7}z^3 - 2z$	$8y^2 - 2y - 10$

By definition, all monomials, binomials, and trinomials are also polynomials.
   Each term of a polynomial has a **degree**.

DEGREE OF A TERM

The **degree of a term** is the sum of the exponents on the *variables* contained in the term.

Example 1   Find the degree of each term.

   a. $3x^2$ **b.** -2^3x^5 **c.** y **d.** $12x^2yz^3$ **e.** 5

Solution   **a.** The exponent on x is 2, so the degree of the term is 2.
   b. The exponent on x is 5, so the degree of the term is 5. (Recall that the degree is the sum of the exponents on only the *variables*.)
   c. The degree of y, or y^1, is 1.
   d. The degree is the sum of the exponents on the variables, or $2 + 1 + 3 = 6$.
   c. The degree of 5, which can be written as $5x^0$, is 0.

From the preceding example, we can say that the degree of a constant is 0. Also, the term 0 has no degree.
   Each polynomial also has a degree.

DEGREE OF A POLYNOMIAL

The **degree of a polynomial** is the largest degree of all its terms.

Example 2   Find the degree of each polynomial and also indicate whether the polynomial is a monomial, binomial, or trinomial.

	Polynomial	*Degree*	*Classification*
a.	$7x^3 - 3x + 2$	3	Trinomial
b.	$-xyz$	$1 + 1 + 1 = 3$	Monomial
c.	$x^4 - 16$	4	Binomial

Example 3   Find the degree of the polynomial

$$3xy + x^2y^2 - 5x^2 - 6.$$

Solution   The degree of each term is

$$3xy + x^2y^2 - 5x^2 - 6$$

Degree: 2   4   2   0

The largest degree of any term is 4, so the degree of this polynomial is 4.

2   At times, it is convenient to use function notation to represent polynomials. For example, we may write $P(x)$ to represent the polynomial $3x^2 - 2x - 5$. In symbols, this is

$$P(x) = 3x^2 - 2x - 5$$

This function is called a **polynomial function** because the expression $3x^2 - 2x - 5$ is a polynomial.

> **HELPFUL HINT**
> Recall that the symbol $P(x)$ **does not mean** P times x. It is a special symbol used to denote a function.

Example 4   If $P(x) = 3x^2 - 2x - 5$, find the following.

a. $P(1)$ **b.** $P(-2)$

Solution   **a.** Substitute 1 for x in $P(x) = 3x^2 - 2x - 5$ and simplify.

$$P(x) = 3x^2 - 2x - 5$$
$$P(1) = 3(1)^2 - 2(1) - 5 = -4$$

b. Substitute -2 for x in $P(x) = 3x^2 - 2x - 5$ and simplify.

$$P(x) = 3x^2 - 2x - 5$$
$$P(-2) = 3(-2)^2 - 2(-2) - 5 = 11$$

Many real-world phenomena are modeled by polynomial functions. If the polynomial function model is given, we can often find the solution of a problem by evaluating the function at a certain value.

Example 5   FINDING THE HEIGHT OF AN OBJECT

The world's highest bridge, Royal Gorge suspension bridge in Colorado, is 1053 feet above the Arkansas River. An object is dropped from the top of this bridge. Neglecting air resistance, the height of the object at time t seconds is given by the polynomial function $P(t) = -16t^2 + 1053$. Find the height of the object when $t = 1$ second and when $t = 8$ seconds.

Solution   To find the height of the object at 1 second, we find $P(1)$.

$$P(t) = -16t^2 + 1053$$
$$P(1) = -16(1)^2 + 1053$$
$$P(1) = 1037$$

When $t = 1$ second, the height of the object is 1037 feet.
To find the height of the object at 8 seconds, we find $P(8)$.

$$P(t) = -16t^2 + 1053$$
$$P(8) = -16(8)^2 + 1053$$
$$P(8) = -1024 + 1053$$
$$P(8) = 29$$

When $t = 8$ seconds, the height of the object is 29 feet. Notice that as time t increases, the height of the object decreases.

3   Before we add polynomials, recall that terms are considered to be **like terms** if they contain exactly the same variables raised to exactly the same powers.

Like Terms	Unlike Terms
$-5x^2, -x^2$	$4x^2, 3x$
$7xy^3z, -2xzy^3$	$12x^2y^3, -2xy^3$

To simplify a polynomial, **combine like terms** by using the distributive property. For example, by the distributive property,

$$5x + 7x = (5 + 7)x = 12x$$

Example 6   Simplify by combining like terms.

a. $-12x^2 + 7x^2 - 6x$ 　　　　　　　　　**b.** $3xy - 2x + 5xy - x$

Solution   By the distributive property,

a. $-12x^2 + 7x^2 - 6x = (-12 + 7)x^2 - 6x = -5x^2 - 6x$
b. Use the associative and commutative properties to group together like terms; then combine.

$$3xy - 2x + 5xy - x = 3xy + 5xy - 2x - x$$
$$= (3 + 5)xy + (-2 - 1)x$$
$$= 8xy - 3x$$

4   Now we have reviewed the necessary skills to add polynomials.

ADDING POLYNOMIALS

Combine all like terms.

Example 7   Add.

   a. $\left(7x^3y - xy^3 + 11\right) + \left(6x^3y - 4\right)$ **b.** $\left(3a^3 - b + 2a - 5\right) + (a + b + 5)$

Solution   **a.** To add, remove the parentheses and group like terms.

$$\left(7x^3y - xy^3 + 11\right) + \left(6x^3y - 4\right)$$
$$= 7x^3y - xy^3 + 11 + 6x^3y - 4$$
$$= 7x^3y + 6x^3y - xy^3 + 11 - 4 \qquad \text{Group like terms.}$$
$$= 13x^3y - xy^3 + 7 \qquad\qquad \text{Combine like terms.}$$

   b. $\left(3a^3 - b + 2a - 5\right) + (a + b + 5)$

$$= 3a^3 - b + 2a - 5 + a + b + 5$$
$$= 3a^3 - b + b + 2a + a - 5 + 5 \qquad \text{Group like terms.}$$
$$= 3a^3 + 3a \qquad\qquad\qquad\qquad \text{Combine like terms.} \ \blacksquare$$

Example 8   Add $11x^3 - 12x^2 + x - 3$ and $x^3 - 10x + 5$.

Solution $\left(11x^3 - 12x^2 + x - 3\right) + \left(x^3 - 10x + 5\right)$

$$= 11x^3 + x^3 - 12x^2 + x - 10x - 3 + 5 \qquad \text{Group like terms.}$$
$$= 12x^3 - 12x^2 - 9x + 2 \qquad\qquad\qquad \text{Combine like terms.} \ \blacksquare$$

Sometimes it is more convenient to add polynomials vertically. To do this, line up like terms beneath one another and add like terms.

5   The definition of subtraction of real numbers can be extended to apply to polynomials. To subtract a number, we add its opposite.

$$a - b = a + (-b)$$

Likewise, to subtract a polynomial, we add its opposite. In other words, if P and Q are polynomials, then

$$P - Q = P + (-Q)$$

The polynomial $-Q$ is the **opposite**, or **additive inverse**, of the polynomial Q. We can find $-Q$ by writing the opposite of each term of Q.

SUBTRACTING POLYNOMIALS

To subtract a polynomial, add its opposite.

For example,

To subtract, add its opposite (found by writing the opposite of each term).

$$(3x^2 + 4x - 7) - (3x^2 - 2x - 5) = (3x^2 + 4x - 7) + (-3x^2 + 2x + 5)$$
$$= 3x^2 + 4x - 7 - 3x^2 + 2x + 5$$
$$= 6x - 2 \qquad \text{Combine like terms.}$$

Example 9   Subtract $(12z^5 - 12z^3 + z) - (-3z^4 + z^3 + 12z)$.

Solution   To subtract, add the opposite of the second polynomial to the first polynomial.

$$(12z^5 - 12z^3 + z) - (-3z^4 + z^3 + 12z)$$
$$= 12z^5 - 12z^3 + z + 3z^4 - z^3 - 12z) \qquad \text{Add the opposite of the polynomial being subtracted.}$$
$$= 12z^5 + 3z^4 - 12z^3 - z^3 + z - 12z \qquad \text{Group like terms.}$$
$$= 12z^5 + 3z^4 - 13z^3 - 11z \qquad \text{Combine like terms.} \qquad \blacksquare$$

Example 10   Subtract $4x^3y^2 - 3x^2y^2 + 2y^2$ from $10x^3y^2 - 7x^2y^2$.

Solution   If we subtract 2 from 8, the difference is $8 - 2 = 6$. Notice the order of the numbers, and then write "Subtract $4x^3y^2 - 3x^2y^2 + 2y^2$ from $10x^3y^2 - 7x^2y^2$" as a mathematical expression.

$$(10x^3y^2 - 7x^2y^2) - (4x^3y^2 - 3x^2y^2 + 2y^2)$$
$$= 10x^3y^2 - 7x^2y^2 - 4x^3y^2 + 3x^2y^2 - 2y^2 \qquad \text{Remove parentheses.}$$
$$= 6x^3y^2 - 4x^2y^2 - 2y^2 \qquad \text{Combine like terms.} \qquad \blacksquare$$

Polynomials can also be added or subtracted vertically. Just remember to line up like terms. For example, perform the subtraction $(10x^3y^2 - 7x^2y^2) - (4x^3y^2 - 3x^2y^2 + 2y^2)$ vertically.

Add the opposite of the second polynomial.

$$
\begin{array}{r}
10x^3y^2 - 7x^2y^2 \\
-(4x^3y^2 - 3x^2y^2 + 2y^2)
\end{array}
\quad \text{is equivalent to} \quad
\begin{array}{r}
10x^3y^2 - 7x^2y^2 \\
-4x^3y^2 + 3x^2y^2 - 2y^2 \\
\hline
6x^3y^2 - 4x^2y^2 - 2y^2
\end{array}
$$

Polynomial functions, like polynomials, can be added, subtracted, multiplied, and divided. For example, if

$$P(x) = x^2 + x + 1$$

then

$$2P(x) = 2(x^2 + x + 1) = 2x^2 + 2x + 2 \qquad \text{Use the distributive property.}$$

Also, if $Q(x) = 5x^2 - 1$, then $P(x) + Q(x) = (x^2 + x + 1) + (5x^2 - 1)$ $= 6x^2 + x$.

A useful business and economics application of subtracting polynomial functions is finding the profit function $P(x)$ when given a revenue function $R(x)$ and a cost function $C(x)$. In business, it is true that

$$\text{profit} = \text{revenue} - \text{cost, or}$$
$$P(x) = R(x) - C(x)$$

For example, if the revenue function is $R(x) = 7x$ and the cost function is $C(x) = 2x + 5000$, then the profit function is

$$P(x) = R(x) - C(x)$$

or

$$P(x) = 7x - (2x + 5000) \qquad \text{Substitute } R(x) = 7x$$
$$P(x) = 5x - 5000 \qquad\qquad\quad \text{and } C(x) = 2x + 5000.$$

Problem-solving exercises involving profit are in the exercise set.

6

In this section, we reviewed how to find the degree of a polynomial. Knowing the degree of a polynomial can help us recognize the graph of the related polynomial function. For example, we know from Section 3.1 that the graph of the polynomial function $f(x) = x^2$ is a parabola as shown to the left.

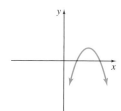

The polynomial x^2 has degree 2. The graphs of all polynomial functions of degree 2 will have this same general shape—opening upward, as shown, or downward. Graphs of polynomial functions of degree 2 or 3 will, in general, resemble one of the graphs shown next.

Degree 2

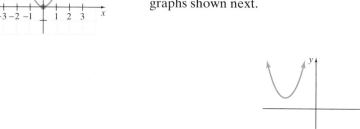

Coefficient of x^2
is a positive number.

Coefficient of x^2
is a negative number.

Degree 3

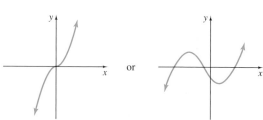   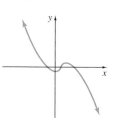

Coefficient of x^3
is a positive number.

Coefficient of x^3
is a negative number.

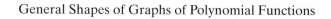

General Shapes of Graphs of Polynomial Functions

Example 11   Determine which of the following graphs is the graph of
$$f(x) = 5x^3 - 6x^2 + 2x + 3$$

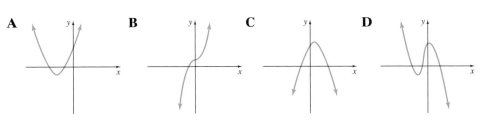

A   B   C   D

Solution   The degree of $f(x)$ is 3, which means that its graph has the shape of B or D. The coefficient of x^3 is 5, a positive number, so the graph has the shape of B.

GRAPHING CALCULATOR EXPLORATIONS

A graphing calculator may be used to visualize addition and subtraction of polynomials in one variable. For example, to visualize the following polynomial subtraction statement
$$(3x^2 - 6x + 9) - (x^2 - 5x + 6) = 2x^2 - x + 3$$
graph both
$$Y_1 = (3x^2 - 6x + 9) - (x^2 - 5x + 6) \qquad \text{Left side of equation}$$
and
$$Y_2 = 2x^2 - x + 3 \qquad \text{Right side of equation}$$
on the same screen and see that their graphs coincide. (*Note:* If the graphs do not coincide, we can be sure that a mistake has been made in combining polynomials or in calculator key-strokes. If the graphs appear to coincide, we cannot be sure that our work is correct. This is because it is possible for the graphs to differ so slightly that we do not notice it.)

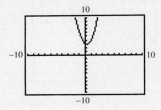

The graphs of Y_1 and Y_2 are shown. The graphs appear to coincide, so the subtraction statement
$$(3x^2 - 6x + 9) - (x^2 - 5x + 6) = 2x^2 - x + 3$$
appears to be correct.

Perform the indicated operations. Then visualize by using the procedure described above.

1. $(2x^2 + 7x + 6) + (x^3 - 6x^2 - 14)$
2. $(-14x^3 - x + 2) + (-x^3 + 3x^2 + 4x)$
3. $(1.8x^2 - 6.8x - 1.7) - (3.9x^2 - 3.6x)$
4. $(-4.8x^2 + 12.5x - 7.8) - (3.1x^2 - 7.8x)$
5. $(1.29x - 5.68) + (7.69x^2 - 2.55x + 10.98)$
6. $(-0.98x^2 - 1.56x + 5.57) + (4.36x - 3.71)$

Exercise Set 5.3

Find the degree of each term. See Example 1.

1. 4

2. 7

3. $5x^2$

4. $-z^3$

5. $-3xy^2$

6. $12x^3z$

Find the degree of each polynomial and indicate whether the polynomial is a monomial, binomial, trinomial, or none of these. See Examples 2 and 3.

7. $6x + 3$

8. $7x - 8$

9. $3x^2 - 2x + 5$

10. $5x^2 - 3x^2y - 2x^3$

11. $-xyz$

12. -9

13. $x^2y - 4xy^2 + 5x + y$

14. $-2x^2y - 3y^2 + 4x + y^5$

15. In your own words, describe how to find the degree of a term.

16. In your own words, describe how to find the degree of a polynomial.

If $P(x) = x^2 + x + 1$ and $Q(x) = 5x^2 - 1$, find the following. See Example 4.

17. $P(7)$

18. $Q(4)$

19. $Q(-10)$

20. $P(-4)$

21. $P(0)$

22. $Q(0)$

Refer to Example 5 for Exercises 23 through 26.

23. Find the height of the object at $t = 2$ seconds.

24. Find the height of the object at $t = 4$ seconds.

25. Find the height of the object at $t = 6$ seconds.

26. Approximate (to the nearest second) how long it takes before the object hits the ground. (*Hint:* The object hits the ground when $P(x) = 0$.)

Simplify by combining like terms. See Example 6.

27. $5y + y$

28. $-x + 3x$

29. $4x + 7x - 3$

30. $-8y + 9y + 4y^2$

31. $4xy + 2x - 3xy - 1$

32. $-8xy^2 + 4x - x + 2xy^2$

Perform the indicated operations. See Examples 7 through 10.

33. $(9y^2 - 8) + (9y^2 - 9)$

34. $(x^2 + 4x - 7) + (8x^2 + 9x - 7)$

35. Add $(x^2 + xy - y^2)$ and $(2x^2 - 4xy + 7y^2)$.

36. Add $(4x^3 - 6x^2 + 5x + 7)$ and $(2x^2 + 6x - 3)$.

37. $\begin{array}{r} x^2 - 6x + 3 \\ + \quad (2x + 5) \\ \hline \end{array}$

38. $\begin{array}{r} -2x^2 + 3x - 9 \\ + \quad (2x - 3) \\ \hline \end{array}$

39. $(9y^2 - 7y + 5) - (8y^2 - 7y + 2)$

40. $(2x^2 + 3x + 12) - (5x - 7)$

41. Subtract $(6x^2 - 3x)$ from $(4x^2 + 2x)$.

42. Subtract $(xy + x - y)$ from $(xy + x - 3)$.

43. $\begin{array}{r} 3x^2 - 4x + 8 \\ - \quad (5x^2 - 7) \\ \hline \end{array}$

44. $\begin{array}{r} -3x^2 - 4x + 8 \\ - \quad (5x + 12) \\ \hline \end{array}$

45. $(5x - 11) + (-x - 2)$

46. $(3x^2 - 2x) + (5x^2 - 9x)$

47. $(7x^2 + x + 1) - (6x^2 + x - 1)$

48. $(4x - 4) - (-x - 4)$

49. $(7x^3 - 4x + 8) + (5x^3 + 4x + 8x)$

50. $(9xyz + 4x - y) + (-9xyz - 3x + y + 2)$

51. $(9x^3 - 2x^2 + 4x - 7) - (2x^3 - 6x^2 - 4x + 3)$

52. $(3x^2 + 6xy + 3y^2) - (8x^2 - 6xy - y^2)$

53. Add $(y^2 + 4yx + 7)$ and $(-19y^2 + 7yx + 7)$.

54. Subtract $(x - 4)$ from $(3x^2 - 4x + 5)$.

55. $(3x^3 - b + 2a - 6) + (-4x^3 + b + 6a - 6)$

56. $(5x^2 - 6) + (2x^2 - 4x + 8)$

57. $(4x^2 - 6x + 2) - (-x^2 + 3x + 5)$

58. $(5x^2 + x + 9) - (2x^2 - 9)$

59. $(-3x + 8) + (-3x^2 + 3x - 5)$

60. $(5y^2 - 2y + 4) + (3y + 7)$

61. $(-3 + 4x^2 + 7xy^2) + (2x^3 - x^2 + xy^2)$

62. $(-3x^2y + 4) - (-7x^2y - 8y)$

63. $\begin{array}{r} 6y^2 - 6y + 4 \\ -(-y^2 - 6y + 7) \\ \hline \end{array}$

64. $\begin{array}{r} -4x^3 + 4x^2 - 4x \\ -(2x^3 - 2x^2 + 3x) \\ \hline \end{array}$

65. $\begin{array}{r} 3x^2 + 15x + 8 \\ +(2x^2 + 7x + 8) \\ \hline \end{array}$

66. $\begin{array}{r} 9x^2 + 9x - 4 \\ +(7x^2 - 3x - 4) \\ \hline \end{array}$

67. Find the sum of $(5q^4 - 2q^2 - 3q)$ and $(-6q^4 + 3q^2 + 5)$.

68. Find the sum of $(5y^4 - 7y^2 + x^2 - 3)$ and $(-3y^4 + 2y^2 + 4)$.

69. Subtract $(3x + 7)$ from the sum of $(7x^2 + 4x + 9)$ and $(8x^2 + 7x - 8)$.

70. Subtract $(9x + 8)$ from the sum of $(3x^2 - 2x - x^3 + 2)$ and $(5x^2 - 8x - x^3 + 4)$.

71. Find the sum of $(4x^4 - 7x^2 + 3)$ and $(2 - 3x^4)$.

72. Find the sum of $(8x^4 - 14x^2 + 6)$ and $(-12x^6 - 21x^4 - 9x^2)$.

73. $(8x^{2y} - 7x^y + 3) + (-4x^{2y} + 9x^y - 14)$

74. $\left(14z^{5x} + 3z^{2x} + z\right) - \left(2z^{5x} - 10z^{2x} + 3z\right)$

Solve.

75. The polynomial $P(t) = -32t + 500$ models the relationship between the length of time t in seconds a particle flies through space, beginning at a velocity of 500 feet per second, and its accrued velocity, $P(t)$. Find $P(3)$, the accrued velocity after 3 seconds.

76. The polynomial function $P(x) = 45x - 100,000$ models the relationship between the number of lamps x that Sherry's Lamp Shop sells and the profit the shop makes, $P(x)$. Find $P(4000)$, the profit from selling 4000 lamps.

77. The function $f(x) = 0.43x^2 + 164.6x + 949.3$ can be used to approximate spending for health care in the United States, where x is the number of years since 1980 and $f(x)$ is the amount of money spent per capita. (*Source:* U.S. Health Care Financing Administration)

   a. Approximate the amount of money spent on health care per capita in the year 1985.

   b. Approximate the amount of money spent on health care per capita in the year 1995.

   c. Use the given function to predict the amount of money that will be spent on health care per capita in the year 2010.

   d. From parts **a**, **b**, and **c**, is the amount of money spent rising at a steady rate? Why or why not?

78. An object is thrown upward with an initial velocity of 50 feet per second from the top of the 350-foot high City Hall in Milwaukee, Wisconsin. The height of the object at any time t can be described by the polynomial function $P(t) = -16t^2 + 50t + 350$. Find the height of the projectile when $t = 1$ second, $t = 2$ seconds, and $t = 3$ seconds. (*Source: World Almanac*)

79. The total cost (in dollars) for MCD, Inc., Manufacturing Company to produce x blank audiocassette tapes per week is given by the polynomial function $C(x) = 0.8x + 10,000$. Find the total cost in producing 20,000 tapes per week.

80. The total revenues (in dollars) for MCD, Inc., Manufacturing Company to sell x blank audiocassette tapes per week is given by the polynomial function $R(x) = 2x$. Find the total revenue in selling 20,000 tapes per week.

A projectile is fired upward from the ground with an initial velocity of 300 feet per second. Neglecting air resistance, the height of the projectile at any time t can be described by the polynomial function

$$P(t) = -16t^2 + 300t$$

Use this in Exercises 81.–83.

81. Find the height of the projectile at the given times.

   a. $t = 1$ second

   b. $t = 2$ seconds

   c. $t = 3$ seconds

   d. $t = 4$ seconds

82. Explain why the height increases and then decreases as time passes.

83. Approximate (to the nearest second) how long before the object hits the ground.

84. An object is thrown upward with an initial velocity of 25 feet per second from the top of the 984-foot-high Eiffel Tower in Paris, France. The height of the object at any time t can be described by the polynomial function $P(t) = -16t^2 + 25t + 984$. Find the height of the projectile when $t = 1$ second, $t = 3$ seconds, and $t = 5$ seconds. (*Source:* Council on Tall Buildings and Urban Habitat, Lehigh University)

85. The function $f(x) = -0.85x^3 + 14.28x^2 - 49.38x + 574.16$ can be used to approximate the number of health maintenance organizations (HMO's) in the United States x years after 1990. (Round each answer to the nearest whole.) (*Source:* Based on data from Interstudy, Minneapolis, MN)

   a. Approximate the number of HMO's in 1995.

   b. Approximate the number of HMO's in 1998.

   c. Use the given model to predict the number of HMO's in the United States in 2003.

86. The function $f(x) = -1869x^3 + 30,581x^2 - 169,111x + 384,559$ can be used to approximate the number of AIDS cases reported in the United States from 1993 to 1997, where x is the number of years since 1990. (*Source:* Based on data from the U.S. Centers for Disease Control and Prevention)

   a. Approximate the number of AIDS cases reported in the United States in 1993.

   b. Approximate the number of AIDS cases reported in the United States in 1995.

   c. Approximate the number of AIDS cases reported in the United States in 1997.

   d. Describe the trend in the number of AIDS cases reported during the period covered by the model.

If $P(x) = 3x + 3$, $Q(x) = 4x^2 - 6x + 3$, and $R(x) = 5x^2 - 7$, find the following.

87. $P(x) + Q(x)$ **88.** $R(x) + P(x)$

89. $Q(x) - R(x)$ **90.** $P(x) - Q(x)$

91. $2[Q(x)] - R(x)$ **92.** $-5[P(x)] - Q(x)$

93. $3[R(x)] + 4[P(x)]$ **94.** $2[Q(x)] + 7[R(x)]$

95. If the revenue function of a certain company is given by $R(x) = 5.5x$, where x is the number of packages of personalized stationery sold and the cost function is given by $C(x) = 3x + 3000$,

   a. Find the profit function. (Recall that revenue − cost = profit.)

   b. Find the profit when 2000 packages of stationery are sold.

Match each equation with its graph. See Example 11.

96. $f(x) = 3x^2 - 2$

97. $h(x) = 5x^3 - 6x + 2$

98. $g(x) = -2x^3 - 3x^2 + 3x - 2$

99. $g(x) = -2x^2 - 6x + 2$

A

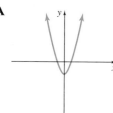

B

C

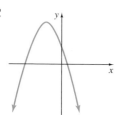

D

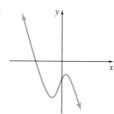

Find each perimeter.

△ **100.**

$(x + 5y)$ units

$(3x^2 - x + 2y)$ units

△ **101.**

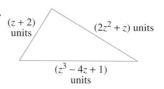

$(z + 2)$ units

$(2z^2 + z)$ units

$(z^3 - 4z + 1)$ units

REVIEW EXERCISES

Multiply. See Section 1.4.

102. $5(3x - 2)$

103. $-7(2z - 6y)$

104. $-2(x^2 - 5x + 6)$

105. $5(-3y^2 - 2y + 7)$

A Look Ahead

Example
If $P(x) = -3x + 5$, find the following.

    a. $P(a)$ **b.** $P(-x)$ **c.** $P(x + h)$

Solution:

    a. $P(x) = -3x + 5$

        $P(a) = -3a + 5$

    b. $P(x) = -3x + 5$

       $P(-x) = -3(-x) + 5$

            $= 3x + 5$

    c. $P(x) = -3x + 5$

      $P(x + h) = -3(x + h) + 5$

                $= -3x - 3h + 5$

If $P(x)$ is the polynomial given, find **a.** $P(a)$, **b.** $P(-x)$, *and* **c.** $P(x + h)$. *See the preceding example.*

106. $P(x) = 2x - 3$

107. $P(x) = 8x + 3$

108. $P(x) = 4x$

109. $P(x) = -4x$

110. $P(x) = 4x - 1$

111. $P(x) = 3x - 2$

5.4 MULTIPLYING POLYNOMIALS

CD-ROM   SSM

SSG   Video

▶ **OBJECTIVES**

    1. Multiply two polynomials.

    2. Multiply binomials.

    3. Square binomials.

    4. Multiply the sum and difference of two terms.

    5. Evaluate polynomial functions.

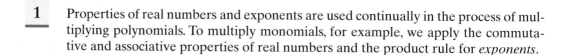

1   Properties of real numbers and exponents are used continually in the process of multiplying polynomials. To multiply monomials, for example, we apply the commutative and associative properties of real numbers and the product rule for *exponents*.

Example 1

Multiply.

a. $(2x^3)(5x^6)$

b. $(7y^4z^4)(-xy^{11}z^5)$

Solution Group like bases and apply the product rule for exponents.

a. $(2x^3)(5x^6) = 2(5)(x^3)(x^6) = 10x^9$

b. $(7y^4z^4)(-xy^{11}z^5) = 7(-1)x(y^4y^{11})(z^4z^5) = -7xy^{15}z^9$

> **HELPFUL HINT**
> See Sections 5.1 and 5.2 to review exponential expressions further.

To multiply a monomial by a polynomial other than a monomial, we use an expanded form of the distributive property.

$$a(b + c + d + \cdots + z) = ab + ac + ad + \cdots + az$$

Notice that the monomial a is multiplied by each term of the polynomial.

Example 2

Multiply.

a. $2x(5x - 4)$ **b.** $-3x^2(4x^2 - 6x + 1)$ **c.** $-xy(7x^2y + 3xy - 11)$

Solution Apply the distributive property.

a. $2x(5x - 4) = 2x(5x) + 2x(-4)$ Use the distributive property.

$= 10x^2 - 8x$ Multiply.

b. $-3x^2(4x^2 - 6x + 1) = -3x^2(4x^2) + (-3x^2)(-6x) + (-3x^2)(1)$

$= -12x^4 + 18x^3 - 3x^2$

c. $-xy(7x^2y + 3xy - 11) = -xy(7x^2y) + (-xy)(3xy) + (-xy)(-11)$

$= -7x^3y^2 - 3x^2y^2 + 11xy$

To multiply any two polynomials, we can use the following.

MULTIPLYING TWO POLYNOMIALS

To multiply any two polynomials, use the distributive property and multiply each term of one polynomial by each term of the other polynomial. Then combine any like terms.

Example 3

Multiply and simplify the product if possible.

a. $(x + 3)(2x + 5)$ **b.** $(2x - 3)(5x^2 - 6x + 7)$

Solution   **a.** Multiply each term of $(x + 3)$ by $(2x + 5)$.

$$(x + 3)(2x + 5) = x(2x + 5) + 3(2x + 5) \qquad \text{Apply the distributive property.}$$
$$= 2x^2 + 5x + 6x + 15 \qquad \text{Apply the distributive property again.}$$
$$= 2x^2 + 11x + 15 \qquad \text{Combine like terms.}$$

b. Multiply each term of $(2x - 3)$ by each term of $(5x^2 - 6x + 7)$.

$$(2x - 3)(5x^2 - 6x + 7) = 2x(5x^2 - 6x + 7) + (-3)(5x^2 - 6x + 7)$$
$$= 10x^3 - 12x^2 + 14x - 15x^2 + 18x - 21$$
$$= 10x^3 - 27x^2 + 32x - 21 \qquad \text{Combine like terms.} \quad \blacksquare$$

Sometimes polynomials are easier to multiply vertically, in the same way we multiply real numbers. When multiplying vertically, we line up like terms in the **partial products** vertically. This makes combining like terms easier.

Example 4   Multiply vertically $(4x^2 + 7)(x^2 + 2x + 8)$.

Solution

$$
\begin{array}{r}
x^2 + \ 2x + \ 8 \\
4x^2 + \ 7 \\
\hline
7x^2 + 14x \ + 56 \\
4x^4 + 8x^3 + 32x^2 \\
\hline
4x^4 + 8x^3 + 39x^2 + 14x \ + 56
\end{array}
$$

$7(x^2 + 2x + 8)$

$4x^2(x^2 + 2x + 8)$

Combine like terms.

$\blacksquare$

---

2   When multiplying a binomial by a binomial, we can use a special order of multiplying terms, called the **FOIL** order. The letters of FOIL stand for "**F**irst-**O**uter-**I**nner-**L**ast." To illustrate this method, let's multiply $(2x - 3)$ by $(3x + 1)$.

Multiply the **F**irst terms of each binomial. $(2x - 3)(3x + 1)$ **F** $2x(3x) = 6x^2$

Multiply the **O**uter terms of each binomial. $(2x - 3)(3x + 1)$ **O** $2x(1) = 2x$

Multiply the **I**nner terms of each binomial. $(2x - 3)(3x + 1)$ **I** $-3(3x) = -9x$

Multiply the **L**ast terms of each binomial. $(2x - 3)(3x + 1)$ **L** $-3(1) = -3$
Combine like terms.

$$6x^2 + 2x - 9x - 3 = 6x^2 - 7x - 3$$

Example 5   Use the FOIL order to multiply $(x - 1)(x + 2)$.

Solution

First   Outer   Inner   Last

$$(x - 1)(x + 2) = x \cdot x + 2 \cdot x + (-1)x + (-1)(2)$$
$$= x^2 + 2x - x - 2$$
$$= x^2 + x - 2 \quad \text{Combine like terms.}$$

Example 6   Multiply. **a.** $(2x - 7)(3x - 4)$ **b.** $(3x + y)(5x - 2y)$

Solution

First   Outer   Inner   Last

a. $(2x - 7)(3x - 4) = 2x(3x) + 2x(-4) + (-7)(3x) + (-7)(-4)$
$$= 6x^2 - 8x - 21x + 28$$
$$= 6x^2 - 29x + 28$$

F   O   I   L

b. $(3x + y)(5x - 2y) = 15x^2 - 6xy + 5xy - 2y^2$
$$= 15x^2 - xy + 2y^2$$

3   The **square of a binomial** is a special case of the product of two binomials. By the FOIL order for multiplying two binomials, we have

$$(a + b)^2 = (a + b)(a + b)$$

F   O   I   L

$$= a^2 + ab + ba + b^2$$
$$= a^2 + 2ab + b^2$$

This product can be visualized geometrically by analyzing areas.

Area of larger square: $(a + b)^2$

Sum of areas of smaller rectangles: $a^2 + 2ab + b^2$

Thus, $(a + b)^2 = a^2 + 2ab + b^2$

The same pattern occurs for the square of a difference. In general,

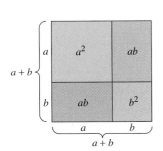

SQUARE OF A BINOMIAL

$$(a + b)^2 = a^2 + 2ab + b^2 \qquad (a - b)^2 = a^2 - 2ab + b^2$$

In other words, a binomial squared is the sum of the first term squared, twice the product of both terms, and the second term squared.

Example 7   Multiply.

   a. $(x + 5)^2$ **b.** $(x - 9)^2$ **c.** $(3x + 2z)^2$ **d.** $\left(4m^2 - 3n\right)^2$

$$(a + b)^2 = a^2 + 2 \cdot a \cdot b + b^2$$

Solution   **a.** $(x + 5)^2 = x^2 + 2 \cdot x \cdot 5 + 5^2 = x^2 + 10x + 25$

   b. $(x - 9)^2 = x^2 - 2 \cdot x \cdot 9 + 9^2 = x^2 - 18x + 81$

   c. $(3x + 2z)^2 = (3x)^2 + 2(3x)(2z) + (2z)^2 = 9x^2 + 12xz + 4z^2$

   d. $\left(4m^2 - 3n\right)^2 = \left(4m^2\right)^2 - 2\left(4m^2\right)(3n) + (3n)^2 = 16m^4 - 24m^2n + 9n^2$

> **HELPFUL HINT**
> Note that $(a + b)^2 = a^2 + 2ab + b^2$, **not** $a^2 + b^2$. Also, $(a - b)^2 = a^2 - 2ab + b^2$, **not** $a^2 - b^2$.

4   Another special product applies to the sum and difference of the same two terms. Multiply $(a + b)(a - b)$ to see a pattern.

$$(a + b)(a - b) = a^2 - ab + ba - b^2$$
$$= a^2 - b^2$$

PRODUCT OF THE SUM AND DIFFERENCE OF TWO TERMS

$$(a + b)(a - b) = a^2 - b^2$$

The product of the sum and difference of the same two terms is the difference of the first term squared and the second term squared.

Example 8   Multiply.

   a. $(x - 3)(x + 3)$ **b.** $(4y + 1)(4y - 1)$ **c.** $\left(3m^2 - \dfrac{1}{2}\right)\left(3m^2 + \dfrac{1}{2}\right)$

Solution

$$(a + b)\,(a - b) = a^2 - b^2$$

   a. $(x + 3)(x - 3) = x^2 - 3^2 = x^2 - 9$

   b. $(4y + 1)(4y - 1) = (4y)^2 - 1^2 = 16y^2 - 1$

   c. $\left(3m^2 - \dfrac{1}{2}\right)\left(3m^2 + \dfrac{1}{2}\right) = (3m^2)^2 - \left(\dfrac{1}{2}\right)^2 = 9m^4 - \dfrac{1}{4}$

Example 9   Multiply $\left[3 + (2a + b)\right]^2$.

Solution   Think of 3 as the first term and $(2a + b)$ as the second term, and apply the method for squaring a binomial.

$$[a + b]^2 = a^2 + 2\,(a) \cdot b + b^2$$

$$\left[3 + (2a + b)\right]^2 = 3^2 + 2(3)(2a + b) + (2a + b)^2$$
$$= 9 + 6(2a + b) + (2a + b)^2$$
$$= 9 + 12a + 6b + (2a)^2 + 2(2a)(b) + b^2 \qquad \text{Square } (2a + b).$$
$$= 9 + 12a + 6b + 4a^2 + 4ab + b^2$$

Example 10 Multiply $[(5x - 2y) - 1][(5x - 2y) + 1]$.

Solution Think of $(5x - 2y)$ as the first term and 1 as the second term, and apply the method for the product of the sum and difference of two terms.

$$\underbrace{(a \quad - b)}\ \underbrace{(a \quad + b)} = \underbrace{a^2 \quad - b^2}$$

$$[(5x - 2y) - 1][(5x - 2y) + 1] = (5x - 2y)^2 - 1^2$$
$$= (5x)^2 - 2(5x)(2y) + (2y)^2 - 1$$
$$= 25x^2 - 20xy + 4y^2 - 1$$

Square $(5x - 2y)$.

5 Our work in multiplying polynomials is often useful in evaluating polynomial functions.

Example 11 If $f(x) = x^2 + 5x - 2$, find $f(a + 1)$.

Solution To find $f(a + 1)$, replace x with the expression $a + 1$ in the polynomial function $f(x)$.

$$f(x) = x^2 + 5x - 2$$
$$f(a + 1) = (a + 1)^2 + 5(a + 1) - 2$$
$$= a^2 + 2a + 1 + 5a + 5 - 2$$
$$= a^2 + 7a + 4$$

GRAPHING CALCULATOR EXPLORATIONS

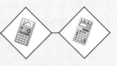

In the previous section, we used a graphing calculator to visualize addition and subtraction of polynomials in one variable. In this section, the same method is used to visualize multiplication of polynomials in one variable. For example, to see that

$$(x - 2)(x + 1) = x^2 - x - 2,$$

graph both $Y_1 = (x - 2)(x + 1)$ and $Y_2 = x^2 - x - 2$ on the same screen and see whether their graphs coincide.

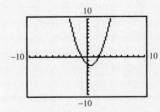

By tracing along both graphs, we see that the graphs of Y_1 and Y_2 appear to coincide, and thus $(x - 2)(x + 1) = x^2 - x - 2$ appears to be correct.

Multiply. Then use a graphing calculator to visualize the results.

1. $(x + 4)(x - 4)$ **2.** $(x + 3)(x + 3)$
3. $(3x - 7)^2$ **4.** $(5x - 2)^2$
5. $(5x + 1)(x^2 - 3x - 2)$ **6.** $(7x + 4)(2x^2 + 3x - 5)$

SPOTLIGHT ON DECISION MAKING

Suppose you would like to sign up for an online service and have received the following advertisements from internet service providers in the mail.

US Online

Try our Internet service FREE for 30 days! See why everyone is talking about us:
- Unlimited Internet access and e-mail for a low monthly fee of $21.95
- No set-up fee
- Your own 6 MB Web site
- Thousands of local access numbers across the nation
- Around-the-clock help with our toll-free 888 number

Give us a call to set up your service today!

Interconnect

When you sign up with Interconnect as your Internet service provider, you get:
- Unlimited access to the Internet and e-mail
- Local access numbers in major metropolitan areas
- Online expert help

all for just $11.95 per month*! And, for a limited time, you can try Interconnect for a full month for FREE!

*A one-time $20 set-up fee applies, however.

e-Link

The sky's the limit with e-Link! If you act now, you can get your first 60 days for FREE, as well as a waiver of the $25 set-up fee. For just $19.95 per month, you get:
- 150 hours of Internet access and e-mail*
- a personal 3 MB Web page
- toll-free help, 24 hours a day, 7 days a week
- local access numbers around the country

*Each additional hour costs $2.95.

You construct a decision grid to help make your choice. In the decision grid, give each of the decision criteria a rank reflecting its importance to you, with 1 being not important to 10 being very important. Then for each online service, decide how well the criteria are supported, assigning a 1 in the rating column for poor support to a rating of 10 for excellent support. For US Online, fill in the Score column by multiplying rank by rating for each criteria. Repeat for each online service. Finally, total the scores in each column for each online service. The service with the highest score is likely to be the best choice for you.

Based on your decision-grid analysis, which online service would you choose? Explain.

Criteria	Rank	US Online Rating	US Online Score	Interconnect Rating	Interconnect Score	e-Link Rating	e-Link Score
FREE TRIAL PERIOD							
MONTHLY FEE							
UNLIMITED ACCESS							
INCLUDES E-MAIL							
INCLUDES PERSONAL WEB PAGE							
SET-UP FEE							
TOLL-FREE HELP							
LOCAL ACCESS NUMBERS							
TOTAL							

Exercise Set 5.4

Multiply. See Examples 1 through 4.

1. $(-4x^3)(3x^2)$ **2.** $(-6a)(4a)$

3. $3x(4x + 7)$ **4.** $5x(6x - 4)$

5. $-6xy(4x + y)$ **6.** $-8y(6xy + 4x)$

7. $-4ab(xa^2 + ya^2 - 3)$ **8.** $-6b^2z(z^2a + baz - 3b)$

9. $(x - 3)(2x + 4)$ **10.** $(y + 5)(3y - 2)$

11. $(2x + 3)(x^3 - x + 2)$ **12.** $(a + 2)(3a^2 - a + 5)$

13. $\begin{aligned}3x - 2\\ \times\ \ 5x + 1\end{aligned}$ **14.** $\begin{aligned}2z - 4\\ \times\ \ 6z - 2\end{aligned}$

15. $\begin{aligned}3m^2 + 2m - 1\\ \times\ \ \ \ \ \ \ \ \ 5m + 2\end{aligned}$ **16.** $\begin{aligned}2x^2 - 3x - 4\\ \times\ \ \ \ \ \ \ \ x + 5\end{aligned}$

17. Explain how to multiply a polynomial by a polynomial.

18. Explain why $(3x + 2)^2$ does not equal $9x^2 + 4$.

Multiply the binomials. See Examples 5 and 6.

19. $(x - 3)(x + 4)$ **20.** $(c - 3)(c + 1)$

21. $(5x + 8y)(2x - y)$ **22.** $(2n - 9m)(n - 7m)$

23. $(3x - 1)(x + 3)$ **24.** $(5d - 3)(d + 6)$

25. $\left(3x + \dfrac{1}{2}\right)\left(3x - \dfrac{1}{2}\right)$ **26.** $\left(2x - \dfrac{1}{3}\right)\left(2x + \dfrac{1}{3}\right)$

Multiply, using special product methods. See Examples 7 and 8.

27. $(x + 4)^2$ **28.** $(x - 5)^2$

29. $(6y - 1)(6y + 1)$ **30.** $(x - 9)(x + 9)$

31. $(3x - y)^2$ **32.** $(4x - z)^2$

33. $(3b - 6y)(3b + 6y)$ **34.** $(2x - 4y)(2x + 4y)$

Multiply, using special product methods. See Examples 9 and 10.

35. $[3 + (4b + 1)]^2$ **36.** $[5 - (3b - 3)]^2$

37. $[(2s - 3) - 1][(2s - 3) + 1]$

38. $[(2y + 5) + 6][(2y + 5) - 6]$

39. $[(xy + 4) - 6]^2$ **40.** $[(2a^2 + 4a) + 1]^2$

41. Explain when the FOIL method can be used to multiply polynomials.

42. Explain why the product of $(a + b)$ and $(a - b)$ is not a trinomial.

Multiply.

43. $(3x + 1)(3x + 5)$ **44.** $(4x - 5)(5x + 6)$

45. $(2x^3 + 5)(5x^2 + 4x + 1)$

46. $(3y^3 - 1)(3y^3 - 6y + 1)$

47. $(7x - 3)(7x + 3)$ **48.** $(4x + 1)(4x - 1)$

49. $\begin{aligned}3x^2 + 4x - 4\\ \times\ \ \ \ \ \ \ \ 3x + 6\end{aligned}$ **50.** $\begin{aligned}6x^2 + 2x - 1\\ \times\ \ \ \ \ \ \ \ 3x - 6\end{aligned}$

51. $\left(4x + \dfrac{1}{3}\right)\left(4x - \dfrac{1}{2}\right)$ **52.** $\left(4y - \dfrac{1}{3}\right)\left(3y - \dfrac{1}{8}\right)$

53. $(6x + 1)^2$ **54.** $(4x + 7)^2$

55. $(x^2 + 2y)(x^2 - 2y)$ **56.** $(3x + 2y)(3x - 2y)$

57. $-6a^2b^2[5a^2b^2 - 6a - 6b]$

58. $7x^2y^3(-3ax - 4xy + z)$

59. $(a - 4)(2a - 4)$ **60.** $(2x - 3)(x + 1)$

61. $(7ab + 3c)(7ab - 3c)$ **62.** $(3xy - 2b)(3xy + 2b)$

63. $(m - 4)^2$ **64.** $(x + 2)^2$

65. $(3x + 1)^2$ **66.** $(4x + 6)^2$

67. $(y - 4)(y - 3)$ **68.** $(c - 8)(c + 2)$

69. $(x + y)(2x - 1)(x + 1)$

70. $(z + 2)(z - 3)(2z + 1)$

71. $(3x^2 + 2x - 1)^2$

72. $(4x^2 + 4x - 4)^2$

73. $(3x + 1)(4x^2 - 2x + 5)$

74. $(2x - 1)(5x^2 - x - 2)$

If $R(x) = x + 5$, $Q(x) = x^2 - 2$, and $P(x) = 5x$, find the following.

75. $P(x) \cdot R(x)$ **76.** $P(x) \cdot Q(x)$

77. $[Q(x)]^2$ **78.** $[R(x)]^2$

79. $R(x) \cdot Q(x)$

80. $P(x) \cdot R(x) \cdot Q(x)$

81. Perform the indicated operations. Explain the difference between the two problems.

    a. $(3x + 5) + (3x + 7)$

    b. $(3x + 5)(3x + 7)$

Explain where the error occurs.

82. $\begin{aligned}4x(x - 5) + 2x\\ = 4x(x) + 4x(-5) + 4x(2x)\\ = 4x^2 - 20x + 8x^2\\ = 12x^2 - 20x\end{aligned}$

83. Find the area of the circle. Do not approximate π.

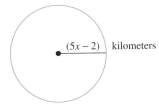

$(5x - 2)$ kilometers

△ **84.** Find the volume of the cylinder. Do not approximate π.

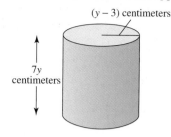

$(y - 3)$ centimeters

$7y$ centimeters

If $f(x) = x^2 - 3x$, find the following. See Example 11.

85. $f(a)$

86. $f(c)$

87. $f(a + h)$

88. $f(a + 5)$

89. $f(b - 2)$

90. $f(a - b)$

91. If $F(x) = x^2 + 3x + 2$, find

   a. $F(a + h)$

   b. $F(a)$

   c. $F(a + h) - F(a)$

92. If $g(x) = x^2 + 2x + 1$, find

   a. $g(a + h)$

   b. $g(a)$

   c. $g(a + h) - g(a)$

Multiply. Assume that variables represent positive integers.

93. $5x^2 y^n (6y^{n+1} - 2)$

94. $-3yz^n (2y^3 z^{2n} - 1)$

95. $(x^a + 5)(x^{2a} - 3)$

96. $(x^a + y^{2b})(x^a - y^{2b})$

REVIEW EXERCISES

Use the slope–intercept form of a line, $y = mx + b$, to find the slope of each line. See Section 3.4.

97. $y = -2x + 7$

98. $y = \dfrac{3}{2}x - 1$

99. $3x - 5y = 14$

100. $x + 7y = 2$

Use the vertical line test to determine which of the following are graphs of functions. See Section 3.2.

101.

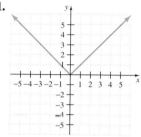

102.

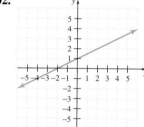

5.5 THE GREATEST COMMON FACTOR AND FACTORING BY GROUPING

CD-ROM   SSM

SSG   Video

▶ **OBJECTIVES**

1. Identify the GCF.
2. Factor out the GCF of a polynomial's terms.
3. Factor polynomials by grouping.

1

Factoring is the reverse process of multiplying. It is the process of writing a polynomial as a product.

$$\overset{\text{factoring}}{6x^2 + 13x - 5 = (3x - 1)(2x + 5)}$$

multiplying

In the next few sections, we review techniques for factoring polynomials. These techniques are used at the end of this chapter to solve polynomial equations and to graph polynomial functions.

To factor a polynomial, we first factor out the greatest common factor (GCF) of its terms, using the distributive property. The GCF of a list of terms or monomials is the product of the GCF of the numerical coefficients and each GCF of the powers of a common variable.

FINDING THE GCF OF A LIST OF MONOMIALS

Step 1: Find the GCF of the numerical coefficients.
Step 2: Find the GCF of the variable factors.
Step 3: The product of the factors found in Steps 1 and 2 is the GCF of the monomials.

Example 1   Find the GCF of $20x^3y$, $10x^2y^2$, and $35x^3$.

Solution   The GCF of the numerical coefficients 20, 10, and 35 is 5, the largest integer that is a factor of each integer. The GCF of the variable factors x^3, x^2, and x^3 is x^2 because x^2 is the largest factor common to all three powers of x. The variable y is not a common factor because it does not appear in all three monomials. The GCF is thus

$$5 \cdot x^2, \quad \text{or} \quad 5x^2$$

---

2   A first step in factoring polynomials is to use the distributive property and write the polynomial as a product of the GCF of its monomial terms and a simpler polynomial. This is called **factoring out** the GCF.

Example 2   Factor.

a. $8x^2 + 4$ **b.** $5y - 2z^4$ **c.** $6x^2 - 3x^3$

Solution   **a.** The GCF of terms $8x^2$ and 4 is 4.

$$8x^2 + 4 = 4 \cdot 2x^2 + 4 \cdot 1 \qquad \text{Factor out 4 from each term.}$$
$$= 4(2x^2 + 1) \qquad \text{Apply the distributive property.}$$

The factored form of $8x^2 + 4$ is $4(2x^2 + 1)$. To check, multiply $4(2x^2 + 1)$ to see that the product is $8x^2 + 4$.

b. There is no common factor of the terms $5y$ and $-2z^4$ other than 1 (or -1).
c. The greatest common factor of $6x^2$ and $-3x^3$ is $3x^2$. Thus,

$$6x^2 - 3x^3 = 3x^2 \cdot 2 - 3x^2 \cdot x$$
$$= 3x^2(2 - x)$$

HELPFUL HINT
To verity that the GCF has been factored out correctly, multiply the factors together and see that their product is the original polynomial.

Example 3 Factor $17x^3y^2 - 34x^4y^2$.

Solution The GCF of the two terms is $17x^3y^2$, which we factor out of each term.

$$17x^3y^2 - 34x^4y^2 = 17x^3y^2 \cdot 1 - 17x^3y^2 \cdot 2x$$
$$= 17x^3y^2(1 - 2x)$$

> **HELPFUL HINT**
> If the GCF happens to be one of the terms in the polynomial, a factor of 1 will remain for this term when the GCF is factored out. For example, in the polynomial $21x^2 + 7x$, the, GCF of $21x^2$ and $7x$ is $7x$, so
>
> $$21x^2 + 7x = 7x \cdot 3x + 7x \cdot 1 = 7x(3x + 1)$$

Example 4 Factor $-3x^3y + 2x^2y - 5xy$.

Solution Two possibilities are shown for factoring this polynomial. First, the common factor xy is factored out.

$$-3x^3y + 2x^2y - 5xy = xy(-3x^2 + 2x - 5)$$

Also, the common factor $-xy$ can be factored out as shown.

$$-3x^3y + 2x^2y - 5xy = -xy(3x^2) + (-xy)(-2x) + (-xy)(5)$$
$$= -xy(3x^2 - 2x + 5)$$

Both of these alternatives are correct.

Example 5 Factor $2(x - 5) + 3a(x - 5)$.

Solution The greatest common factor is the binomial factor $(x - 5)$.

$$2(x - 5) + 3a(x - 5) = (x - 5)(2 + 3a)$$

Example 6 Factor $7x(x^2 + 5y) - (x^2 + 5y)$.

Solution

$$7x(x^2 + 5y) - (x^2 + 5y) = 7x(x^2 + 5y) - 1(x^2 + 5y)$$
$$= (x^2 + 5y)(7x - 1)$$

> **HELPFUL HINT**
> Notice that we wrote $-(x^2 + 5y)$ as $-1(x^2 + 5y)$ to aid in factoring.

3 Sometimes it is possible to factor a polynomial by grouping the terms of the polynomial and looking for common factors in each group. This method of factoring is called **factoring by grouping**.

Example 7   Factor $ab - 6a + 2b - 12$.

Solution   First look for the GCF of all four terms. The GCF of all four terms is 1. Next group the first two terms and the last two terms and factor out common factors from each group.

$$ab - 6a + 2b - 12 = (ab - 6a) + (2b - 12)$$

Factor a from the first group and 2 from the second group.

$$= a(b - 6) + 2(b - 6)$$

Now we see a GCF of $(b - 6)$. Factor out $(b - 6)$ to get

$$a(b - 6) + 2(b - 6) = (b - 6)(a + 2)$$

Check: To check, multiply $(b - 6)$ and $(a + 2)$ to see that the product is $ab - 6a + 2b - 12$.   ∎

> **HELPFUL HINT**
> Notice that the polynomial $a(b - 6) + 2(b - 6)$ is *not* in factored form. It is a *sum*, not a *product*. The factored form is $(b - 6)(a + 2)$.

Example 8   Factor $x^3 + 5x^2 + 3x + 15$.

Solution
$$\begin{aligned} x^3 + 5x^2 + 3x + 15 &= (x^3 + 5x^2) + (3x + 15) && \text{Group pairs of terms.} \\ &= x^2(x + 5) + 3(x + 5) && \text{Factor each binomial.} \\ &= (x + 5)(x^2 + 3) && \text{Factor out the common factor, } (x + 5). \end{aligned}$$
   ∎

Example 9   Factor $m^2n^2 + m^2 - 2n^2 - 2$.

Solution
$$\begin{aligned} m^2n^2 + m^2 - 2n^2 - 2 &= (m^2n^2 + m^2) + (-2n^2 - 2) && \text{Group pairs of terms.} \\ &= m^2(n^2 + 1) - 2(n^2 + 1) && \text{Factor each binomial.} \\ &= (n^2 + 1)(m^2 - 2) && \text{Factor out the common factor,} \\ & && (n^2 + 1). \end{aligned}$$
   ∎

Example 10   Factor $xy + 2x - y - 2$.

Solution
$$\begin{aligned} xy + 2x - y - 2 &= (xy + 2x) + (-y - 2) && \text{Group pairs of terms.} \\ &= x(y + 2) - 1(y + 2) && \text{Factor each binomial.} \\ &= (y + 2)(x - 1) && \text{Factor out the common factor, } (y + 2). \end{aligned}$$
   ∎

MENTAL MATH

Find the GCF of each list of monomials.

1. $6, 12$
2. $9, 27$
3. $15x, 10$
4. $9x, 12$
5. $13x, 2x$
6. $4y, 5y$
7. $7x, 14x$
8. $8z, 4z$

Exercise Set 5.5

Find the GCF of each list of monomials. See Example 1.

1. a^8, a^5, a^3
2. b^9, b^2, b^5
3. $x^2y^3z^3, y^2z^3, xy^2z^2$
4. $xy^2z^3, x^2y^2z^2, x^2y^3$
5. $6x^3y, 9x^2y^2, 12x^2y$
6. $4xy^2, 16xy^3, 8x^2y^2$
7. $10x^3yz^3, 20x^2z^5, 45xz^3$
8. $12y^2z^4, 9xy^3z^4, 15x^2y^2z^3$

Factor out the GCF in each polynomial. See Examples 2 through 6.

9. $18x - 12$
10. $21x + 14$
11. $4y^2 - 16xy^3$
12. $3z - 21xz^4$
13. $6x^5 - 8x^4 + 2x^3$
14. $9x + 3x^2 - 6x^3$
15. $8a^3b^3 - 4a^2b^2 + 4ab + 16ab^2$
16. $12a^3b - 6ab + 18ab^2 - 18a^2b$
17. $6(x + 3) + 5a(x + 3)$
18. $2(x - 4) + 3y(x - 4)$
19. $2x(z + 7) + (z + 7)$
20. $x(y - 2) + (y - 2)$
21. $3x(x^2 + 5) - 2(x^2 + 5)$
22. $4x(2y + 3) - 5(2y + 3)$
23. When $3x^2 - 9x + 3$ is factored, the result is $3(x^2 - 3x + 1)$. Explain why it is necessary to include the term 1 in this factored form.
24. Construct a trinomial whose GCF is $5x^2y^3$.

Factor each polynomial by grouping. See Examples 7 through 10.

25. $ab + 3a + 2b + 6$
26. $ab + 2a + 5b + 10$
27. $ac + 4a - 2c - 8$
28. $bc + 8b - 3c - 24$
29. $2xy - 3x - 4y + 6$
30. $12xy - 18x - 10y + 15$
31. $12xy - 8x - 3y + 2$
32. $20xy - 15x - 4y + 3$

Factor each polynomial

33. $6x^3 + 9$
34. $6x^2 - 8$
35. $x^3 + 3x^2$
36. $x^4 - 4x^3$
37. $8a^3 - 4a$
38. $12b^4 + 3b^2$
39. $-20x^2y + 16xy^3$
40. $-18xy^3 + 27x^4y$

41. $10a^2b^3 + 5ab^2 - 15ab^3$
42. $10ef - 20e^2f^3 + 30e^3f$
43. $9abc^2 + 6a^2bc - 6ab + 3bc$
44. $4a^2b^2c - 6ab^2c - 4ac + 8a$
45. $4x(y - 2) - 3(y - 2)$
46. $8y(z + 8) - 3(z + 8)$
47. $6xy + 10x + 9y + 15$
48. $15xy + 20x + 6y + 8$
49. $xy + 3y - 5x - 15$
50. $xy + 4y - 3x - 12$
51. $6ab - 2a - 9b + 3$
52. $16ab - 8a - 6b + 3$
53. $12xy + 18x + 2y + 3$
54. $20xy + 8x + 5y + 2$
55. $2m(n - 8) - (n - 8)$
56. $3a(b - 4) - (b - 4)$
57. $15x^3y^2 - 18x^2y^2$
58. $12x^4y^2 - 16x^3y^3$
59. $2x^2 + 3xy + 4x + 6y$
60. $3x^2 + 12x + 4xy + 16y$
61. $5x^2 + 5xy - 3x - 3y$
62. $4x^2 + 2xy - 10x - 5y$
63. $x^3 + 3x^2 + 4x + 12$
64. $x^3 + 4x^2 + 3x + 12$
65. $x^3 - x^2 - 2x + 2$
66. $x^3 - 2x^2 - 3x + 6$

Solve.

△ **67.** The material needed to manufacture a tin can is given by the polynomial

$$2\pi r^2 + 2\pi rh$$

where the radius is r and height is h. Factor this expression.

68. The amount E of voltage in an electrical circuit is given by the formula

$$IR_1 + IR_2 = E$$

Write an equivalent equation by factoring the expression $IR_1 + IR_2$.

69. At the end of T years, the amount of money A in a savings account earning simple interest from an initial investment of P dollars at rate R is given by the formula
$$A = P + PRT$$
Write an equivalent equation by factoring the expression $P + PRT$.

△ **70.** An open-topped box has a square base and a height of 10 inches. If each of the bottom edges of the box has length x inches, find the amount of material needed to construct the box. Write the answer in factored form.

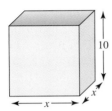

71. An object is thrown upward from the ground with an initial velocity of 64 feet per second. The height $h(t)$ of the object after t seconds is given by the polynomial function
$$h(t) = -16t^2 + 64t$$
　a. Write an equivalent factored expression for the function $h(t)$ by factoring $-16t^2 + 64t$.
　b. Find $h(1)$ by using $h(t) = -16t^2 + 64t$ and then by using the factored form of $h(t)$.
✎　**c.** Explain why the values found in part **b** are the same.
72. An object is dropped from the gondola of a hot-air balloon at a height of 224 feet. The height $h(t)$ of the object after t seconds is given by the polynomial function
$$h(t) = -16t^2 + 224$$

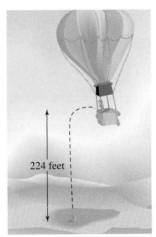

224 feet

　a. Write an equivalent factored expression for the function $h(t)$ by factoring $-16t^2 + 224$.
　b. Find $h(2)$ by using $h(t) = -16t^2 + 224$ and then by using the factored form of the function.
✎　**c.** Explain why the values found in part **b** are the same.

73. A factored polynomial can be in many forms. For example, a factored form of $xy - 3x - 2y + 6$ is $(x - 2)(y - 3)$. Which of the following is not a factored form of $xy - 3x - 2y + 6$?
　a. $(2 - x)(3 - y)$　　**b.** $(-2 + x)(-3 + y)$
　c. $(x - 2)(y - 3)$　　**d.** $(-x + 2)(-y + 3)$

✎ **74.** Consider the following sequence of algebraic steps:
$$x^3 - 6x^2 + 2x - 10 = (x^3 - 6x^2) + (2x - 10)$$
$$= x^2(x - 6) + 2(x - 5)$$
Explain whether the final result is the factored form of the original polynomial.

75. Which factorization of $12x^2 + 9x + 3$ is correct?
　a. $3(4x^2 + 3x + 1)$　　**b.** $3(4x^2 + 3x - 1)$
　c. $3(4x^2 + 3x - 3)$　　**d.** $3(4x^2 + 3x)$

REVIEW EXERCISES

Simplify the following. See Section 5.1.

76. $(5x^2)(11x^5)$　　　　**77.** $(7y)(-2y^3)$

78. $(5x^2)^3$　　　　　**79.** $(-2y^3)^4$

Find each product by using the FOIL order of multiplying binomials. See Section 5.4.

80. $(x + 2)(x - 5)$　　**81.** $(x - 7)(x - 1)$

82. $(x + 3)(x + 2)$　　**83.** $(x - 4)(x + 2)$

84. $(y - 3)(y - 1)$　　**85.** $(s + 8)(s + 10)$

A Look Ahead

Example
Factor $x^{5a} - x^{3a} + x^{7a}$.

Solution
The variable x is common to all three terms, and the power $3a$ is the smallest of the exponents. So factor out the common factor x^{3a}.
$$x^{5a} - x^{3a} + x^{7a} = x^{3a}(x^{2a}) - x^{3a}(1) + x^{3a}(x^{4a})$$
$$= x^{3a}(x^{2a} - 1 + x^{4a})$$

Factor. Assume that variables used as exponents represent positive integers.

86. $x^{3n} - 2x^{2n} + 5x^n$　　**87.** $3y^n + 3y^{2n} + 5y^{8n}$

88. $6x^{8a} - 2x^{5a} - 4x^{3a}$　　**89.** $3x^{5a} - 6x^{3a} + 9x^{2a}$

5.6 FACTORING TRINOMIALS

CD-ROM   SSM

SSG   Video

▶ **OBJECTIVES**

1. Factor trinomials of the form $x^2 + bx + c$.
2. Factor trinomials of the form $ax^2 + bx + c$.
3. Factor by substitution.
4. Factor trinomials by grouping.

1 In the previous section, we used factoring by grouping to factor four-term polynomials. In this section, we present techniques for factoring trinomials. Since $(x - 2)(x + 5) = x^2 + 3x - 10$, we say that $(x - 2)(x + 5)$ is a factored form of $x^2 + 3x - 10$. Taking a close look at how $(x - 2)$ and $(x + 5)$ are multiplied suggests a pattern for factoring trinomials of the form

$$x^2 + bx + c$$

$$(x - 2)(x + 5) = x^2 + 3x - 10$$

The pattern for factoring is summarized next.

FACTORING A TRINOMIAL OF THE FORM $x^2 + bx + c$

Find two numbers whose product is c and whose sum is b. The factored form of $x^2 + bx + c$ is

$$(x + \text{one number})(x + \text{other number})$$

Example 1   Factor $x^2 + 10x + 16$.

Solution   We look for two integers whose product is 16 and whose sum is 10. Since our integers must have a positive product and a positive sum, we look at only positive factors of 16.

Positive Factors of 16	Sum of Factors	
1, 16	$1 + 16 = 17$	
4, 4	$4 + 4 = 8$	
2, 8	$2 + 8 = 10$	Correct pair

The correct pair of numbers is 2 and 8 because their product is 16 and their sum is 10. Thus,

$$x^2 + 10x + 16 = (x + 2)(x + 8)$$

Check: To check, see that $(x + 2)(x + 8) = x^2 + 10x + 16$. ▬

Example 2   Factor $x^2 - 12x + 35$.

Solution   We need to find two integers whose product is 35 and whose sum is -12. Since our integers must have a positive product and a negative sum, we consider only negative factors of 35. The numbers are -5 and -7.

$$x^2 - 12x + 35 = [x + (-5)][x + (-7)]$$
$$= (x - 5)(x - 7)$$

Check: To check, see that $(x - 5)(x - 7) = x^2 - 12x + 35$.

Example 3   Factor $5x^3 - 30x^2 - 35x$.

Solution   First we factor out the greatest common factor, $5x$.

$$5x^3 - 30x^2 - 35x = 5x(x^2 - 6x - 7)$$

Next we factor $x^2 - 6x - 7$ by finding two numbers whose product is -7 and whose sum is -6. The numbers are 1 and -7.

$$5x^3 - 30x^2 - 35x = 5x(x^2 - 6x - 7)$$
$$= 5x(x + 1)(x - 7)$$

> ▼
> **HELPFUL HINT**
> If the polynomial to be factored contains a common factor that is factored out, don't forget to include that common factor in the final factored form of the original polynomial.

Example 4   Factor $2n^2 - 38n + 80$.

Solution   The terms of this polynomial have a greatest common factor of 2, which we factor out first.

$$2n^2 - 38n + 80 = 2(n^2 - 19n + 40)$$

Next we factor $n^2 - 19n + 40$ by finding two numbers whose product is 40 and whose sum is -19. Both numbers must be negative since their sum is -19. Possibilities are

$$-1 \text{ and } -40, \qquad -2 \text{ and } -20, \qquad -4 \text{ and } -10, \qquad -5 \text{ and } -8$$

None of the pairs has a sum of -19, so no further factoring with integers is possible. The factored form of $2n^2 - 38n + 80$ is

$$2n^2 - 38n + 80 = 2(n^2 - 19n + 40)$$

We call a polynomial such as $n^2 - 19n + 40$ that cannot be factored further, a **prime polynomial**.

2   Next, we factor trinomials of the form $ax^2 + bx + c$, where the coefficient a of x^2 is not 1. Don't forget that the first step in factoring any polynomial is to factor out the greatest common factor of its terms.

Example 5 Factor $2x^2 + 11x + 15$.

Solution Factors of $2x^2$ are $2x$ and x. Let's try these factors as first terms of the binomials.

$$2x^2 + 11x + 15 = (2x + \quad)(x + \quad)$$

Next we try combinations of factors of 15 until the correct middle term, $11x$, is obtained. We will try only positive factors of 15 since the coefficient of the middle term, 11, is positive. Positive factors of 15 are 1 and 15 and 3 and 5.

$(2x + 1)(x + 15)$ $(2x + 15)(x + 1)$

     $1x$ $15x$

   $\dfrac{30x}{31x}$ Incorrect middle term $\dfrac{2x}{17x}$ Incorrect middle term

$(2x + 3)(x + 5)$ $(2x + 5)(x + 3)$

     $3x$ $5x$

   $\dfrac{10x}{13x}$ Incorrect middle term $\dfrac{6x}{11x}$ Correct middle term

Thus, the factored form of $2x^2 + 11x + 15$ is $(2x + 5)(x + 3)$.

FACTORING A TRINOMIAL OF THE FORM $ax^2 + bx + c$

Step 1: Write all pairs of factors of ax^2.
Step 2: Write all pairs of factors of c, the constant term.
Step 3: Try various combinations of these factors until the correct middle term bx is found.
Step 4: If no combination exists, the polynomial is **prime**.

Example 6 Factor $3x^2 - x - 4$.

Solution Factors of $3x^2$: $3x \cdot x$
Factors of -4: $-1 \cdot 4$, $1 \cdot -4$, $-2 \cdot 2$, $2 \cdot -2$
Let's try possible combinations of these factors.

$(3x - 1)(x + 4)$ $(3x + 4)(x - 1)$

    $-1x$ $4x$

   $\dfrac{12x}{11x}$ Incorrect middle term $\dfrac{-3x}{1x}$ Incorrect middle term

$(3x - 4)(x + 1)$

    $-4x$

   $\dfrac{3x}{-1}$ Correct middle term

Thus, $3x^2 - x - 4 = (3x - 4)(x + 1)$.

> ### HELPFUL HINT—SIGN PATTERNS
>
> A positive constant in a trinomial tells us to look for two numbers with the same sign. The sign of the coefficient of the middle term tells us whether the signs are both positive or both negative.
>
> | both positive | same sign |
> |---|---|
>
> $\downarrow$ $\downarrow$
>
> | both negative | same sign |
> |---|---|
>
> $\downarrow$ $\downarrow$
>
> $$2x^2 + 7x + 3 = (2x + 1)(x + 3) \qquad 2x^2 - 7x + 3 = (2x - 1)(x - 3)$$
>
> A negative constant in a trinomial tells us to look for two numbers with opposite signs.
>
> | opposite signs |
> |---|
>
> $\downarrow$
>
> | opposite signs |
> |---|
>
> $\downarrow$
>
> $$2x^2 - 5x - 3 = (2x + 1)(x - 3) \qquad 2x^2 + 5x - 3 = (2x - 1)(x + 3)$$

Example 7   Factor $12x^3y - 22x^2y + 8xy$.

Solution   First we factor out the greatest common factor of the terms of this trinomial, $2xy$.

$$12x^3y - 22x^2y + 8xy = 2xy(6x^2 - 11x + 4)$$

Now we try to factor the trinomial $6x^2 - 11x + 4$.

Factors of $6x^2$: $2x \cdot 3x, \qquad 6x \cdot x$

Let's try $2x$ and $3x$.

$$2xy(6x^2 - 11x + 4) = 2xy(2x + \quad)(3x + \quad)$$

The constant term, 4, is positive and the coefficient of the middle term, -11, is negative, so we factor 4 into negative factors only.

Negative factors of 4: $-4(-1), \qquad -2(-2)$

Let's try -4 and -1.

$$2xy(2x - 4)(3x - 1)$$

$$-12x$$

$$-2x$$

$$\overline{-14x} \quad \text{Incorrect middle term}$$

This combination cannot be correct, because one of the factors, $(2x - 4)$, has a common factor of 2. This cannot happen if the polynomial $6x^2 - 11x + 4$ has no common factors.

Now let's try -1 and -4.

$$2xy(2x - 1)(3x - 4)$$

$$-3x$$

$$-8x$$

$$\overline{-11x} \quad \text{Correct middle term}$$

Thus,

$$12x^3y - 22x^2y + 8xy = 2xy(2x - 1)(3x - 4)$$

If this combination had not worked, we would have tried -2 and -2 as factors of 4 and then $6x$ and x as factors of $6x^2$.

> **HELPFUL HINT**
> If a trinomial has no common factor (other than 1), then none of its binomial factors will contain a common factor (other than 1).

Example 8 Factor $16x^2 + 24xy + 9y^2$.

Solution No greatest common factor can be factored out of this trinomial.

Factors of $16x^2$: $16x \cdot x$, $8x \cdot 2x$, $4x \cdot 4x$
Factors of $9y^2$: $y \cdot 9y$, $3y \cdot 3y$

We try possible combinations until the correct factorization is found.

$$16x^2 + 24xy + 9y^2 = (4x + 3y)(4x + 3y) \quad \text{or} \quad (4x + 3y)^2$$

The trinomial $16x^2 + 24xy + 9y^2$ in Example 8 is an example of a **perfect square trinomial** since its factors are two identical binomials. In the next section, we examine a special method for factoring perfect square trinomials.

3 A complicated looking polynomial may be a simpler trinomial "in disguise." Revealing the simpler trinomial is possible by substitution.

Example 9 Factor $2(a + 3)^2 - 5(a + 3) - 7$.

Solution The quantity $(a + 3)$ is in two of the terms of this polynomial. **Substitute** x for $(a + 3)$, and the result is the following simpler trinomial.

$$2(a + 3)^2 - 5(a + 3) - 7 \qquad \textit{Original trinomial.}$$
$$= 2(x)^2 - 5(x) - 7 \qquad \textit{Substitute } x \textit{ for } (a + 3).$$

Now factor $2x^2 - 5x - 7$.

$$2x^2 - 5x - 7 = (2x - 7)(x + 1)$$

But the quantity in the original polynomial was $(a + 3)$, not x. Thus, we need to reverse the substitution and replace x with $(a + 3)$.

$$(2x - 7)(x + 1) \qquad \textit{Factored expression.}$$
$$= [2(a + 3) - 7][(a + 3) + 1] \qquad \textit{Substitute } (a + 3) \textit{ for } x.$$
$$= (2a + 6 - 7)(a + 3 + 1) \qquad \textit{Remove inside parentheses.}$$
$$= (2a - 1)(a + 4) \qquad \textit{Simplify.}$$

Thus, $2(a + 3)^2 - 5(a + 3) - 7 = (2a - 1)(a + 4)$.

Example 10   Factor $5x^4 + 29x^2 - 42$.

Solution   Again, substitution may help us factor this polynomial more easily. Since this polynomial contains the variable x, we will choose a different substitution variable. Let $y = x^2$, so $y^2 = (x^2)^2$, or x^4. Then

$$5x^4 + 29x^2 - 42$$

becomes

$$5y^2 + 29y - 42$$

which factors as

$$5y^2 + 29y - 42 = (5y - 6)(y + 7)$$

Next, replace y with x^2 to get

$$(5x^2 - 6)(x^2 + 7)$$

4   There is another method we can use when factoring trinomials of the form $ax^2 + bx + c$: Write the trinomial as a four-term polynomial, and then factor by grouping.

FACTORING A TRINOMIAL OF THE FORM $ax^2 + bx + c$ BY GROUPING

Step 1: Find two numbers whose product is $a \cdot c$ and whose sum is b.
Step 2: Write the term bx as a sum by using the factors found in Step 1.
Step 3: Factor by grouping.

Example 11   Factor $6x^2 + 13x + 6$.

Solution   In this trinomial, $a = 6$, $b = 13$, and $c = 6$.

Step 1: Find two numbers whose product is $a \cdot c$, or $6 \cdot 6 = 36$, and whose sum is b, 13. The two numbers are 4 and 9.
Step 2: Write the middle term, $13x$, as the sum $4x + 9x$.

$$6x^2 + 13x + 6 = 6x^2 + 4x + 9x + 6$$

Step 3: Factor $6x^2 + 4x + 9x + 6$ by grouping.

$$(6x^2 + 4x) + (9x + 6) = 2x(3x + 2) + 3(3x + 2)$$
$$= (3x + 2)(2x + 3)$$

MENTAL MATH

1. Find two numbers whose product is 10 and whose sum is 7.
2. Find two numbers whose product is 12 and whose sum is 8.
3. Find two numbers whose product is 24 and whose sum is 11.
4. Find two numbers whose product is 30 and whose sum is 13.

Exercise Set 5.6

Factor each trinomial. See Examples 1 through 4.

1. $x^2 + 9x + 18$
2. $x^2 + 9x + 20$
3. $x^2 - 12x + 32$
4. $x^2 - 12x + 27$
5. $x^2 + 10x - 24$
6. $x^2 + 3x - 54$
7. $x^2 - 2x - 24$
8. $x^2 - 9x - 36$
9. $3x^2 - 18x + 24$
10. $x^2y^2 + 4xy^2 + 3y^2$
11. $4x^2z + 28xz + 40z$
12. $5x^2 - 45x + 70$
13. $2x^2 + 30x - 108$
14. $3x^2 + 12x - 96$

15. Find all positive and negative integers b such that $x^2 + bx + 6$ factors.

16. Find all positive and negative integers b such that $x^2 + bx - 10$ factors.

Factor each trinomial. See Examples 5 through 8 and 11.

17. $5x^2 + 16x + 3$
18. $3x^2 + 8x + 4$
19. $2x^2 - 11x + 12$
20. $3x^2 - 19x + 20$
21. $2x^2 + 25x - 20$
22. $6x^2 - 13x - 8$
23. $4x^2 - 12x + 9$
24. $25x^2 - 30x + 9$
25. $12x^2 + 10x - 50$
26. $12y^2 - 48y + 45$
27. $3y^4 - y^3 - 10y^2$
28. $2x^2z + 5xz - 12z$
29. $6x^3 + 8x^2 + 24x$
30. $18y^3 + 12y^2 + 2y$
31. $x^2 + 8xz + 7z^2$
32. $a^2 - 2ab - 15b^2$
33. $2x^2 - 5xy - 3y^2$
34. $6x^2 + 11xy + 4y^2$
35. $x^2 - x - 12$
36. $x^2 + 4x - 5$
37. $28y^2 + 22y + 4$
38. $24y^3 - 2y^2 - y$
39. $2x^2 + 15x - 27$
40. $3x^2 + 14x + 15$

41. Find all positive and negative integers b such that $3x^2 + bx + 5$ factors.

42. Find all positive and negative integers b such that $2x^2 + bx + 7$ factors.

Use substitution to factor each polynomial completely. See Examples 9 and 10.

43. $x^4 + x^2 - 6$
44. $x^4 - x^2 - 20$
45. $(5x + 1)^2 + 8(5x + 1) + 7$
46. $(3x - 1)^2 + 5(3x - 1) + 6$
47. $x^6 - 7x^3 + 12$
48. $x^6 - 4x^3 - 12$
49. $(a + 5)^2 - 5(a + 5) - 24$
50. $(3c + 6)^2 + 12(3c + 6) - 28$

Solve.

△ 51. The volume $V(x)$ of a box in terms of its height x is given by the function $V(x) = 3x^3 - 2x^2 - 8x$. Factor this expression for $V(x)$.

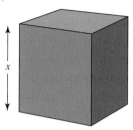

△ 52. Based on your results from Exercise 51, find the length and width of the box if the height is 5 inches and the dimensions of the box are whole numbers.

Factor each polynomial completely.

53. $x^2 - 24x - 81$
54. $x^2 - 48x - 100$
55. $x^2 - 15x - 54$
56. $x^2 - 15x + 54$
57. $3x^2 - 6x + 3$
58. $8x^2 - 8x + 2$
59. $3x^2 - 5x - 2$
60. $5x^2 - 14x - 3$
61. $8x^2 - 26x + 15$
62. $12x^2 - 17x + 6$
63. $18x^4 + 21x^3 + 6x^2$
64. $20x^5 + 54x^4 + 10x^3$
65. $3a^2 + 12ab + 12b^2$
66. $2x^2 + 16xy + 32y^2$
67. $x^2 + 4x + 5$
68. $x^2 + 6x + 8$
69. $2(x + 4)^2 + 3(x + 4) - 5$
70. $3(x + 3)^2 + 2(x + 3) - 5$
71. $6x^2 - 49x + 30$
72. $4x^2 - 39x + 27$
73. $x^4 - 5x^2 - 6$
74. $x^4 - 5x^2 + 6$
75. $6x^3 - x^2 - x$
76. $12x^3 + x^2 - x$
77. $12a^2 - 29ab + 15b^2$
78. $16y^2 + 6yx - 27x^2$
79. $9x^2 + 30x + 25$
80. $4x^2 + 6x + 9$
81. $3x^2y - 11xy + 8y$
82. $5xy^2 - 9xy + 4x$
83. $2x^2 + 2x - 12$
84. $3x^2 + 6x - 45$
85. $(x - 4)^2 + 3(x - 4) - 18$
86. $(x - 3)^2 - 2(x - 3) - 8$
87. $2x^6 + 3x^3 - 9$
88. $3x^6 - 14x^3 + 8$
89. $72xy^4 - 24xy^2z + 2xz^2$
90. $36xy^2 - 48xyz^2 + 16xz^4$

Recall that a graphing calculator may be used to visualize addition, subtraction, and multiplication of polynomials. In the same manner, a graphing calculator may be used to visualize factoring of polynomials in one variable. For example, to see that

$$2x^3 - 9x^2 - 5x = x(2x + 1)(x - 5)$$

graph $Y_1 = 2x^3 - 9x^2 - 5x$ and $Y_2 = x(2x + 1)(x - 5)$. Then trace along both graphs to see that they coincide. Factor the following and use this method to check your results.

91. $x^4 + 6x^3 + 5x^2$ **92.** $x^3 + 6x^2 + 8x$

93. $30x^3 + 9x^2 - 3x$ **94.** $-6x^4 + 10x^3 - 4x^2$

REVIEW EXERCISES

Multiply the following. See Section 5.4.

95. $(x - 2)(x^2 + 2x + 4)$

96. $(y + 1)(y^2 - y + 1)$

If $P(x) = 3x^2 + 2x - 9$, find the following. See Section 5.3.

97. $P(0)$ **98.** $P(1)$

99. $P(-1)$ **100.** $P(-2)$

A Look Ahead

Example
Factor $x^{2n} + 7x^n + 12$.

Solution
Factors of x^{2n} are x^n and x_n so $x^{2n} + 7x^n + 12 = (x^n + \text{one number})(x^n + \text{other number})$. Factors of 12 whose sum is 7 are 3 and 4. Thus

$$x^{2n} + 7x^n + 12 = (x^n + 4)(x^n + 3)$$

Factor. Assume that variables used as exponents represent positive integers. See the preceding example.

101. $x^{2n} + 10x^n + 16$ **102.** $x^{2n} - 7x^n + 12$

103. $x^{2n} - 3x^n - 18$ **104.** $x^{2n} + 7x^n - 18$

105. $2x^{2n} + 11x^n + 5$ **106.** $3x^{2n} - 8x^n + 4$

107. $4x^{2n} - 12x^n + 9$ **108.** $9x^{2n} + 24x^n + 16$

5.7 FACTORING BY SPECIAL PRODUCTS AND FACTORING STRATEGIES

CD-ROM   SSM

SSG   Video

▶ **OBJECTIVES**

1. Factor a perfect square trinomial.
2. Factor the difference of two squares.
3. Factor the sum or difference of two cubes.
4. Practice techniques for factoring polynomials.

1

In the previous section, we considered a variety of ways to factor trinomials of the form $ax^2 + bx + c$. In one particular example, we factored $16x^2 + 24xy + 9y^2$ as

$$16x^2 + 24xy + 9y^2 = (4x + 3y)^2$$

Recall that $16x^2 + 24xy + 9y^2$ is a perfect square trinomial because its factors are two identical binomials. A perfect square trinomial can be factored quickly if you recognize the trinomial as a perfect square.

A trinomial is a perfect square trinomial if it can be written so that its first term is the square of some quantity a, its last term is the square of some quantity b, and its middle term is twice the product of the quantities a and b. The following special formulas can be used to factor perfect square trinomials.

PERFECT SQUARE TRINOMIALS

$$a^2 + 2ab + b^2 = (a + b)^2$$
$$a^2 - 2ab + b^2 = (a - b)^2$$

Notice that these formulas above are the same special products from Section 5.4 for the square of a binomial.

From $a^2 + 2ab + b^2 = (a + b)^2$, we see that

$$16x^2 + 24xy + 9y^2 = (4x)^2 + 2(4x)(3y) + (3y)^2 = (4x + 3y)^2$$

Example 1   Factor $m^2 + 10m + 25$.

Solution   Notice that the first term is a square: $m^2 = (m)^2$, the last term is a square: $25 = 5^2$; and $10m = 2 \cdot 5 \cdot m$.
Thus,

$$m^2 + 10m + 25 = m^2 + 2(m)(5) + 5^2 = (m + 5)^2$$

Example 2   Factor $3a^2x - 12abx + 12b^2x$.

Solution   The terms of this trinomial have a GCF of $3x$, which we factor out first.

$$3a^2x - 12abx + 12b^2x = 3x(a^2 - 4ab + 4b^2)$$

Now, the polynomial $a^2 - 4ab + 4b^2$ is a perfect square trinomial. Notice that the first term is a square: $a^2 = (a)^2$; the last term is a square: $4b^2 = (2b)^2$; and $4ab = 2(a)(2b)$.
The factoring can now be completed as

$$3x(a^2 - 4ab + 4b^2) = 3x(a - 2b)^2$$

> **HELPFUL HINT**
> If you recognize a trinomial as a perfect square trinomial, use the special formulas to factor. However, methods for factoring trinomials in general from Section 5.6 will also result in the correct factored form.

2   We now factor special types of binomials, beginning with the **difference of two squares.** The special product pattern presented in Section 5.4 for the product of a sum and a difference of two terms is used again here. However, the emphasis is now on factoring rather than on multiplying.

DIFFERENCE OF TWO SQUARES

$$a^2 - b^2 = (a + b)(a - b)$$

Notice that a binomial is a difference of two squares when it is the difference of the square of some quantity a and the square of some quantity b.

Example 3 Factor the following.

   a. $x^2 - 9$ **b.** $16y^2 - 9$ **c.** $50 - 8y^2$ **d.** $x^2 - \dfrac{1}{4}$

Solution **a.** $\begin{aligned} x^2 - 9 &= x^2 - 3^2 \\ &= (x + 3)(x - 3) \end{aligned}$ **b.** $\begin{aligned} 16y^2 - 9 &= (4y)^2 - 3^2 \\ &= (4y + 3)(4y - 3) \end{aligned}$

   c. First factor out the common factor of 2.
   $$\begin{aligned} 50 - 8y^2 &= 2(25 - 4y^2) \\ &= 2(5 + 2y)(5 - 2y) \end{aligned}$$

   d. $x^2 - \dfrac{1}{4} = x^2 - \left(\dfrac{1}{2}\right)^2 = \left(x + \dfrac{1}{2}\right)\left(x - \dfrac{1}{2}\right)$

The binomial $x^2 + 9$ is a **sum of two squares** and cannot be factored by using real numbers. **In general, except for factoring out a GCF, the sum of two squares usually cannot be factored by using real numbers.**

> **HELPFUL HINT**
> The sum of two squares whose GCF is 1 usually cannot be factored by using real numbers.

Example 4 Factor the following.

   a. $p^4 - 16$ **b.** $(x + 3)^2 - 36$

Solution **a.** $\begin{aligned} p^4 - 16 &= (p^2)^2 - 4^2 \\ &= (p^2 + 4)(p^2 - 4) \end{aligned}$

   The binomial factor $p^2 + 4$ cannot be factored by using real numbers, but the binomial factor $p^2 - 4$ is a difference of squares.

   $$(p^2 + 4)(p^2 - 4) = (p^2 + 4)(p + 2)(p - 2)$$

   b. Factor $(x + 3)^2 - 36$ as the difference of squares.
   $$\begin{aligned} (x + 3)^2 - 36 &= (x + 3)^2 - 6^2 \\ &= [(x + 3) + 6][(x + 3) - 6] && \text{Factor.} \\ &= [x + 3 + 6][x + 3 - 6] && \text{Remove parentheses.} \\ &= (x + 9)(x - 3) && \text{Simplify.} \end{aligned}$$

Example 5 Factor $x^2 + 4x + 4 - y^2$.

Solution Factoring by grouping comes to mind since the sum of the first three terms of this polynomial is a perfect square trinomial.
   $$\begin{aligned} x^2 + 4x + 4 - y^2 &= (x^2 + 4x + 4) - y^2 && \text{Group the first three terms.} \\ &= (x + 2)^2 - y^2 && \text{Factor the perfect square trinomial.} \end{aligned}$$

This is not completely factored yet since we have a *difference*, not a *product*. Since $(x + 2)^2 - y^2$ is a difference of squares, we have

$$(x + 2)^2 - y^2 = [(x + 2) + y][(x + 2) - y]$$
$$= (x + 2 + y)(x + 2 - y)$$

3 Although the sum of two squares usually cannot be factored, the sum of two cubes, as well as the difference of two cubes, can be factored as follows.

SUM AND DIFFERENCE OF TWO CUBES

$$a^3 + b^3 = (a + b)(a^2 - ab + b^2)$$
$$a^3 - b^3 = (a - b)(a^2 + ab + b^2)$$

To check the first pattern, let's find the product of $(a + b)$ and $(a^2 - ab + b^2)$.

$$(a + b)(a^2 - ab + b^2) = a(a^2 - ab + b^2) + b(a^2 - ab + b^2)$$
$$= a^3 - a^2b + ab^2 + a^2b - ab^2 + b^3$$
$$= a^3 + b^3$$

Example 6 Factor $x^3 + 8$.

Solution First we write the binomial in the form $a^3 + b^3$. Then we use the formula

$$a^3 + b^3 = (a + b)(a^2 - a \cdot b + b^2), \quad \text{where } a \text{ is } x \text{ and } b \text{ is } 2.$$
$$\downarrow \quad \downarrow \quad \quad \downarrow \quad \downarrow \; \downarrow \quad \downarrow \; \downarrow \quad \downarrow$$
$$x^3 + 8 = x^3 + 2^3 = (x + 2)(x^2 - x \cdot 2 + 2^2)$$

Thus, $x^3 + 8 = (x + 2)(x^2 - 2x + 4)$

Example 7 Factor $p^3 + 27q^3$.

Solution $p^3 + 27q^3 = p^3 + (3q)^3$

$$= (p + 3q)[p^2 - (p)(3q) + (3q)^2]$$

$$= (p + 3q)(p^2 - 3pq + 9q^2)$$

Example 8 Factor $y^3 - 64$.

Solution This is a difference of cubes since $y^3 - 64 = y^3 - 4^3$.

$$\text{From} \quad a^3 - b^3 = (a - b)(a^2 + a \cdot b + b^2) \quad \text{we have that}$$
$$\downarrow \quad \downarrow \quad \quad \downarrow \quad \downarrow \; \downarrow \quad \downarrow \; \downarrow \quad \downarrow$$
$$y^3 - 4^3 = (y - 4)(y^2 + y \cdot 4 + 4^2)$$
$$= (y - 4)(y^2 + 4y + 16)$$

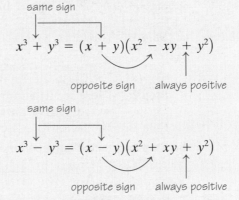

> **▼ HELPFUL HINT**
> When factoring sums or differences of cubes, be sure to notice the sign patterns.
>
> same sign
>
> $$x^3 + y^3 = (x + y)(x^2 - xy + y^2)$$
>
> opposite sign   always positive
>
> same sign
>
> $$x^3 - y^3 = (x - y)(x^2 + xy + y^2)$$
>
> opposite sign   always positive

Example 9   Factor $125q^2 - n^3q^2$

Solution   First we factor out a common factor of q^2.

$$125q^2 - n^3q^2 = q^2(125 - n^3)$$
$$= q^2(5^3 - n^3)$$

opposite sign   positive

$$= q^2(5 - n)[5^2 + (5)(n) + n^2]$$
$$= q^2(5 - n)(25 + 5n + n^2)$$

Thus, $125q^2 - n^3q^2 = q^2(5 - n)(25 + 5n + n^2)$. The trinomial $25 + 5n + n^2$ cannot be factored further.

4   The key to proficiency in factoring polynomials is to practice until you are comfortable with each technique. A strategy for factoring polynomials is given next.

FACTORING A POLYNOMIAL

Step 1:   Are there any common factors? If so, factor out the GCF.
Step 2:   How many terms are in the polynomial?
    a. If there are **two** terms, decide if one of the following formulas may be applied.
        i.   Difference of two squares: $a^2 - b^2 = (a + b)(a - b)$.
        ii.   Difference of two cubes: $a^3 - b^3 = (a - b)(a^2 + ab + b^2)$.
        iii. Sum of two cubes: $a^3 + b^3 = (a + b)(a^2 - ab + b^2)$.
    b. If there are **three** terms, try one of the following.
        i.   Perfect square trinomial: $a^2 + 2ab + b^2 = (a + b)^2$;
                           $a^2 - 2ab + b^2 = (a - b)^2$
        ii.   If not a perfect square trinomial, factor by using the methods presented in Section 5.6.
    c. If there are **four** or more terms, try factoring by grouping.
Step 3:   See if any factors in the factored polynomial can be factored further.

Example 10   Factor each polynomial completely.

a. $8a^2b - 4ab$ **b.** $36x^2 - 9$ **c.** $2x^2 - 5x - 7$

Solution   **a.** **Step 1:**   The terms have a common factor of $4ab$, which we factor out.

$$8a^2b - 4ab = 4ab(2a - 1)$$

Step 2:   There are two terms, but the binomial $2a - 1$ is not the difference of two squares or the sum or difference of two cubes.

Step 3:   The factor $2a - 1$ cannot be factored further.

b. **Step 1:**   Factor out a common factor of 9.

$$36x^2 - 9 = 9(4x^2 - 1)$$

Step 2:   The factor $4x^2 - 1$ has two terms, and it is the difference of two squares.

$$9(4x^2 - 1) = 9(2x + 1)(2x - 1)$$

Step 3:   No factor with more than one term can be factored further.

c. **Step 1:**   The terms of $2x^2 - 5x - 7$ contain no common factor other than 1 or -1.

Step 2.   There are three terms. The trinomial is not a perfect square, so we factor by methods from Section 5.6.

$$2x^2 - 5x - 7 = (2x - 7)(x + 1)$$

Step 3:   No factor with more than one term can be factored further.

Example 11   Factor each polynomial completely.

a. $5p^2 + 5 + qp^2 + q$ **b.** $9x^2 + 24x + 16$ **c.** $y^2 + 25$

Solution   **a.** **Step 1:**   There is no common factor of all terms of $5p^2 + 5 + qp^2 + q$.

Step 2:   The polynomial has four terms, so try factoring by grouping.

$$\begin{aligned} 5p^2 + 5 + qp^2 + q &= (5p^2 + 5) + (qp^2 + q) \quad \text{\small Group the terms.} \\ &= 5(p^2 + 1) + q(p^2 + 1) \\ &= (p^2 + 1)(5 + q) \end{aligned}$$

Step 3:   No factor can be factored further.

b. **Step 1:**   The terms of $9x^2 + 24x + 16$ contain no common factor other than 1 or -1.

Step 2:   The trinomial $9x^2 + 24x + 16$ is a perfect square trinomial, and $9x^2 + 24x + 16 = (3x + 4)^2$.

Step 3:   No factor can be factored further.

c. **Step 1:**   There is no common factor of $y^2 + 25$ other than 1.

Step 2:   This binomial is the sum of two squares and is prime.

Step 3:   The binomial $y^2 + 25$ cannot be factored further.

Example 12   Factor each completely.

a. $27a^3 - b^3$ **b.** $3n^2m^4 - 48m^6$ **c.** $2x^2 - 12x + 18 - 2z^2$

d. $8x^4y^2 + 125xy^2$ **e.** $(x - 5)^2 - 49y^2$

Solution   **a.**   This binomial is the difference of two cubes.

$$27a^3 - b^3 = (3a)^3 - b^3$$
$$= (3a - b)\big[(3a)^2 + (3a)(b) + b^2\big]$$
$$= (3a - b)(9a^2 + 3ab + b^2)$$

b. $3n^2m^4 - 48m^6 = 3m^4(n^2 - 16m^2)$ Factor out the GCF, $3m^4$.
$$= 3m^4(n + 4m)(n - 4m)$$ Factor the difference of squares.

c. $2x^2 - 12x + 18 - 2z^2 = 2(x^2 - 6x + 9 - z^2)$ The GCF is 2.
$$= 2\big[(x^2 - 6x + 9) - z^2\big]$$ Group the first three terms together.
$$= 2\big[(x - 3)^2 - z^2\big]$$ Factor the perfect square trinomial.
$$= 2\big[(x - 3) + z\big]\big[(x - 3) - z\big]$$ Factor the difference of squares.
$$= 2(x - 3 + z)(x - 3 - z)$$

d. $8x^4y^2 + 125xy^2 = xy^2(8x^3 + 125)$ The GCF is xy^2.
$$= xy^2\big[(2x)^3 + 5^3\big]$$
$$= xy^2(2x + 5)\big[(2x)^2 - (2x)(5) + 5^2\big]$$ Factor the sum of cubes.
$$= xy^2(2x + 5)(4x^2 - 10x + 25)$$

e.   This binomial is the difference of squares.

$$(x - 5)^2 - 49y^2 = (x - 5)^2 - (7y)^2$$
$$= \big[(x - 5) + 7y\big]\big[(x - 5) - 7y\big]$$
$$= (x - 5 + 7y)(x - 5 - 7y)$$

Exercise Set 5.7

Factor the following. See Examples 1 and 2.

1. $x^2 + 6x + 9$ **2.** $x^2 - 10x + 25$

3. $4x^2 - 12x + 9$ **4.** $25x^2 + 10x + 1$

5. $3x^2 - 24x + 48$ **6.** $x^3 + 14x^2 + 49x$

7. $9y^2x^2 + 12yx^2 + 4x^2$ **8.** $32x^2 - 16xy + 2y^2$

Factor the following. See Examples 3 through 5.

9. $x^2 - 25$ **10.** $y^2 - 100$

11. $9 - 4z^2$ **12.** $16x^2 - y^2$

13. $(y + 2)^2 - 49$ **14.** $(x - 1)^2 - z^2$

15. $64x^2 - 100$ **16.** $4x^2 - 36$

Factor the following. See Examples 6 through 8.

17. $x^3 + 27$ **18.** $y^3 + 1$

19. $z^3 - 1$ **20.** $x^3 - 8$

21. $m^3 + n^3$ **22.** $r^3 + 125$

23. $x^3y^2 - 27y^2$ **24.** $64 - p^3$

25. $a^3b + 8b^4$ **26.** $8ab^3 + 27a^4$

27. $125y^3 - 8x^3$ **28.** $54y^3 - 128$

Factor the following. See Example 9.

29. $x^2 + 6x + 9 - y^2$ **30.** $x^2 + 12x + 36 - y^2$

31. $x^2 - 10x + 25 - y^2$ **32.** $x^2 - 18x + 81 - y^2$

33. $4x^2 + 4x + 1 - z^2$ **34.** $9y^2 + 12y + 4 - x^2$

Factor each polynomial completely.

35. $9x^2 - 49$ **36.** $25x^2 - 4$

37. $x^2 - 12x + 36$ **38.** $x^2 - 18x + 81$

39. $x^4 - 81$ **40.** $x^4 - 256$

41. $x^2 + 8x + 16 - 4y^2$ **42.** $x^2 + 14x + 49 - 9y^2$

43. $(x + 2y)^2 - 9$ **44.** $(3x + y)^2 - 25$

45. $x^3 - 216$

46. $8 - a^3$

47. $x^3 + 125$

48. $x^3 + 216$

49. $4x^2 + 25$

50. $16x^2 + 25$

51. $4a^2 + 12a + 9$

52. $9a^2 - 30a + 25$

53. $18x^2y - 2y$

54. $12xy^2 - 108x$

55. $8x^3 + y^3$

56. $27x^3 - y^3$

57. $x^6 - y^3$

58. $x^3 - y^6$

59. $x^2 + 16x + 64 - x^4$

60. $x^2 + 20x + 100 - x^4$

61. $3x^6y^2 + 81y^2$

62. $x^2y^9 + x^2y^3$

63. $(x + y)^3 + 125$

64. $(x + y)^3 + 27$

65. $(2x + 3)^3 - 64$

66. $(4x + 2)^3 - 125$

Solve.

△ **67.** The manufacturer of Antonio's Metal Washers needs to determine the cross-sectional area of each washer. If the outer radius of the washer is R and the radius of the hole is r, express the area of the washer as a polynomial. Factor this polynomial completely.

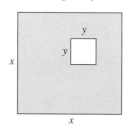

△ **68.** Express the area of the shaded region as a polynomial. Factor the polynomial completely.

△ **69.** The manufacturer of Tootsie Roll Pops plans to change the size of its candy. To compute the new cost, the company needs a formula for the volume of the candy coating without the Tootsie Roll center. Given the diagram, express the volume as a polynomial. Factor this polynomial completely.

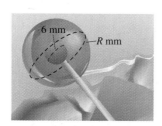

△ **70.** Express the area of the shaded region as a polynomial. Factor the polynomial completely.

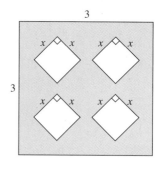

Factor completely. See Examples 10 through 12.

71. $1 - y^3$

72. $8 - a^3$

73. $9x^2 + 6x + 1$

74. $16y^2 - 24y + 9$

75. $x^2 - 8x + 16 - y^2$

76. $12x^2 - 22x - 20$

77. $x^4 - x$

78. $(2x + 1)^2 - 3(2x + 1) + 2$

79. $14x^2y - 2xy$

80. $24ab^2 - 6ab$

81. $4x^2 - 16$

82. $9x^2 - 81$

83. $128a^3 - 2b^3$

84. $32x^3 - 4y^3$

85. $3x^2 - 8x - 11$

86. $5x^2 - 2x - 3$

87. $4x^2 + 8x - 12$

88. $6x^2 - 6x - 12$

89. $4x^2 + 36x + 81$

90. $25x^2 + 40x + 16$

91. $8x^3 + 27y^3$

92. $125x^3 + 8y^3$

93. $64x^2y^3 - 8x^2$

94. $27x^5y^4 - 216x^2y$

95. $(x + 5)^3 + y^3$

96. $(y - 1)^3 + 27x^3$

97. $(5a - 3)^2 - 6(5a - 3) + 9$

98. $(4r + 1)^2 + 8(4r + 1) + 16$

Find a value of c that makes each trinomial a perfect square trinomial.

99. $x^2 + 6x + c$

100. $y^2 + 10y + c$

101. $m^2 - 14m + c$

102. $n^2 - 2n + c$

103. $x^2 + cx + 16$

104. $x^2 + cx + 36$

105. Factor $x^6 - 1$ completely, using the following methods from this chapter.

  a. Factor the expression by treating it as the difference of two squares, $(x^3)^2 - 1^2$.

  b. Factor the expression by treating it as the difference of two cubes, $(x^2)^3 - 1^3$.

  c. Are the answers to parts **a** and **b** the same? Why or why not?

REVIEW EXERCISES

Solve the following equations. See Section 2.1.

106. $x - 5 = 0$ **107.** $x + 7 = 0$
108. $3x + 1 = 0$ **109.** $5x - 15 = 0$
110. $-2x = 0$ **111.** $3x = 0$
112. $-5x + 25 = 0$ **113.** $-4x - 16 = 0$

A Look Ahead

Example
Factor $x^{2n} - 100$.

Solution
This binomial is the difference of squares.
$$x^{2n} - 100 = \left(x^n\right)^2 - 10^2$$
$$= \left(x^n + 10\right)\left(x^n - 10\right)$$

Factor each expression. Assume that variables used as exponents represent positive integers. See the preceding example.

114. $x^{2n} - 25$ **115.** $x^{2n} - 36$
116. $36x^{2n} - 49$ **117.** $25x^{2n} - 81$
118. $x^{4n} - 16$ **119.** $x^{4n} - 625$

5.8 SOLVING EQUATIONS BY FACTORING AND PROBLEM SOLVING

CD-ROM   SSM

SSG   Video

▶ **OBJECTIVES**

1. Solve polynomial equations by factoring.
2. Solve problems that can be modeled by polynomial equations.
3. Find the x-intercepts of a polynomial function.

1   In this section, your efforts to learn factoring start to pay off. We use factoring to solve polynomial equations, which in turn helps us solve problems that can be modeled by polynomial equations and also helps us sketch the graph of polynomial functions.

A **polynomial equation** is the result of setting two polynomials equal to each other. Examples of polynomial equations are

$$3x^3 - 2x^2 = x^2 + 2x - 1 \qquad 2.6x + 7 = -1.3 \qquad -5x^2 - 5 = -9x^2 - 2x + 1$$

A polynomial equation is in **standard form** if one side of the equation is 0. In standard form the polynomial equations above are

$$3x^3 - 3x^2 - 2x + 1 = 0 \qquad 2.6x + 8.3 = 0 \qquad 4x^2 + 2x - 6 = 0$$

The degree of a simplified polynomial equation in standard form is the same as the highest degree of any of its terms. A polynomial equation of degree 2 is also called a **quadratic equation.**

A solution of a polynomial equation in one variable is a value of the variable that makes the equation true. The method presented in this section for solving polynomial equations is called the **factoring method.** This method is based on the **zero-factor property.**

ZERO-FACTOR PROPERTY

If a and b are real numbers and $a \cdot b = 0$, then $a = 0$ or $b = 0$.
This property is true for three or more factors also.

In other words, if the product of two or more real numbers is zero, then at least one number must be zero.

Example 1   Solve $(x + 2)(x - 6) = 0$.

Solution   By the zero-factor property, $(x + 2)(x - 6) = 0$ only if $x + 2 = 0$ or $x - 6 = 0$.

$$x + 2 = 0 \quad \text{or} \quad x - 6 = 0 \qquad \text{Apply the zero-factor property.}$$
$$x = -2 \quad \text{or} \qquad x = 6 \qquad \text{Solve each linear equation.}$$

To check, let $x = -2$ and then let $x = 6$ in the original equation.

Let $x = -2$.	Let $x = 6$.
Then $(x + 2)(x - 6) = 0$	Then $(x + 2)(x - 6) = 0$
becomes $(-2 + 2)(-2 - 6) = 0$	becomes $(6 + 2)(6 - 6) = 0$
$(0)(-8) = 0$	$(8)(0) = 0$
$0 = 0$ True.	$0 = 0$ True.

Both -2 and 6 check, so they are both solutions.

Example 2   Solve $2x^2 + 9x - 5 = 0$.

Solution   To use the zero-factor property, one side of the equation must be 0, and the other side must be in factored form.

$$2x^2 + 9x - 5 = 0$$
$$(2x - 1)(x + 5) = 0 \qquad \text{Factor.}$$
$$2x - 1 = 0 \quad \text{or} \quad x + 5 = 0 \qquad \text{Set each factor equal to zero.}$$
$$2x = 1$$
$$x = \frac{1}{2} \quad \text{or} \qquad x = -5 \qquad \text{Solve each linear equation.}$$

The solutions are -5 and $\frac{1}{2}$. To check, let $x = \frac{1}{2}$ in the original equation; then let $x = -5$ in the original equation.

SOLVING POLYNOMIAL EQUATIONS BY FACTORING

Step 1: Write the equation in standard form so that one side of the equation is 0.
Step 2: Factor the polynomial completely.
Step 3: Set each factor containing a variable equal to 0.
Step 4: Solve the resulting equations.
Step 5: Check each solution in the original equation.

Since it is not always possible to factor a polynomial, not all polynomial equations can be solved by factoring. Other methods of solving polynomial equations are presented in Chapter 8.

Example 3   Solve $x(2x - 7) = 4$.

Solution   First write the equation in standard form; then factor.

$$x(2x - 7) = 4$$
$$2x^2 - 7x = 4 \qquad \text{Multiply.}$$
$$2x^2 - 7x - 4 = 0 \qquad \text{Write in standard form.}$$
$$(2x + 1)(x - 4) = 0 \qquad \text{Factor.}$$
$$2x + 1 = 0 \quad \text{or} \quad x - 4 = 0 \qquad \text{Set each factor equal to zero.}$$
$$2x = -1 \qquad \text{Solve.}$$
$$x = -\frac{1}{2} \quad \text{or} \qquad x = 4$$

The solutions are $-\dfrac{1}{2}$ and 4. Check both solutions in the original equation.

HELPFUL HINT
To apply the zero-factor property, one side of the equation must be 0, and the other side of the equation must be factored. To solve the equation $x(2x - 7) = 4$, for example, you may **not** set each factor equal to 4.

Example 4   Solve $3(x^2 + 4) + 5 = -6(x^2 + 2x) + 13$.

Solution   Rewrite the equation so that one side is 0.

$$3(x^2 + 4) + 5 = -6(x^2 + 2x) + 13$$
$$3x^2 + 12 + 5 = -6x^2 - 12x + 13 \qquad \text{Apply the distributive property.}$$
$$9x^2 + 12x + 4 = 0 \qquad \text{Rewrite the equation so that one side is 0.}$$
$$(3x + 2)(3x + 2) = 0 \qquad \text{Factor.}$$
$$3x + 2 = 0 \quad \text{or} \quad 3x + 2 = 0 \qquad \text{Set each factor equal to 0.}$$
$$3x = -2 \quad \text{or} \quad 3x = -2$$
$$x = -\frac{2}{3} \quad \text{or} \quad x = -\frac{2}{3} \qquad \text{Solve each equation.}$$

The solution is $-\dfrac{2}{3}$. Check by substituting $-\dfrac{2}{3}$ into the original equation.

If the equation contains fractions, we clear the equation of fractions as a first step.

Example 5   Solve $2x^2 = \dfrac{17}{3}x + 1$.

Solution

$$2x^2 = \frac{17}{3}x + 1$$

$$3(2x^2) = 3\left(\frac{17}{3}x + 1\right)$$ Clear the equation of fractions.

$$6x^2 = 17x + 3$$ Apply the distributive property.

$$6x^2 - 17x - 3 = 0$$ Rewrite the equation in standard form.

$$(6x + 1)(x - 3) = 0$$ Factor.

$$6x + 1 = 0 \quad \text{or} \quad x - 3 = 0$$ Set each factor equal to zero.

$$6x = -1$$

$$x = -\frac{1}{6} \quad \text{or} \quad x = 3$$ Solve each equation.

The solutions are $-\dfrac{1}{6}$ and 3.

Example 6   Solve $x^3 = 4x$.

Solution

$$x^3 = 4x$$

$$x^3 - 4x = 0$$ Rewrite the equation so that one side is 0.

$$x(x^2 - 4) = 0$$ Factor out the GCF, x.

$$x(x + 2)(x - 2) = 0$$ Factor the difference of squares.

$$x = 0 \quad \text{or} \quad x + 2 = 0 \quad \text{or} \quad x - 2 = 0$$ Set each factor equal to 0.

$$x = 0 \quad \text{or} \quad x = -2 \quad \text{or} \quad x = 2$$ Solve each equation.

The solutions are $-2, 0$, and 2. Check by substituting into the original equation.

Notice that the *third*-degree equation of Example 6 yielded *three* solutions.

Example 7   Solve $x^3 + 5x^2 = x + 5$.

Solution   First write the equation so that one side is 0.

$$x^3 + 5x^2 - x - 5 = 0$$

$$(x^3 - x) + (5x^2 - 5) = 0$$ Factor by grouping.

$$x(x^2 - 1) + 5(x^2 - 1) = 0$$

$$(x^2 - 1)(x + 5) = 0$$

$$(x + 1)(x - 1)(x + 5) = 0$$ Factor the difference of squares.

$$x + 1 = 0 \quad \text{or} \quad x - 1 = 0 \quad \text{or} \quad x + 5 = 0$$ Set each factor equal to 0.

$$x = -1 \quad \text{or} \quad x = 1 \quad \text{or} \quad x = -5$$ Solve each equation.

The solutions are $-5, -1$, and 1. Check in the original equation.

2   Some problems may be modeled by polynomial equations. To solve these problems, we use the same problem-solving steps that were introduced in Section 2.2. When solving these problems, keep in mind that a solution of an equation that models a problem is not always a solution to the problem. For example, a person's weight or the length of a side of a geometric figure is always a positive number. Discard solutions that do not make sense as solutions of the problem.

Example 8   FINDING THE RETURN TIME OF A ROCKET

An Alpha III model rocket is launched from the ground with an A8–3 engine. Without a parachute the height of the rocket h at time t seconds is approximated by the equation.

$$h = -16t^2 + 144t$$

Find how long it takes the rocket to return to the ground.

Solution

1. UNDERSTAND. Read and reread the problem. The equation $h = -16t^2 + 144t$ models the height of the rocket. Familiarize yourself with this equation by finding a few values.

   When $t = 1$ second, the height of the rocket is
   $$h = -16(1)^2 + 144(1) = 128 \text{ feet}$$
   When $t = 2$ seconds, the height of the rocket is
   $$h = -16(2)^2 + 144(2) = 224 \text{ feet}$$

2. TRANSLATE. To find how long it takes the rocket to return to the ground, we want to know what value of t makes the height h equal to 0. That is, we want to solve $h = 0$.
   $$-16t^2 + 144t = 0$$

3. SOLVE the quadratic equation by factoring.
   $$-16t^2 + 144t = 0$$
   $$-16t(t - 9) = 0$$
   $$-16t = 0 \quad \text{or} \quad t - 9 = 0$$
   $$t = 0 \qquad\qquad\quad t = 9$$

4. INTERPRET. The height h is 0 feet at time 0 seconds (when the rocket is launched) and at time 9 seconds.

   Check: See that the height of the rocket at 9 seconds equals 0.
   $$h = -16(9)^2 + 144(9) = -1296 + 1296 = 0$$

   State: The rocket returns to the ground 9 seconds after it is launched.

Some of the exercises at the end of this section make use of the **Pythagorean theorem.** Before we review this theorem, recall that a **right triangle** is a triangle that contains a 90° angle, or right angle. The **hypotenuse** of a right triangle is the side opposite the right angle and is the longest side of the triangle. The **legs** of a right triangle are the other sides of the triangle.

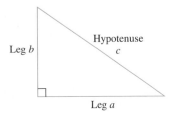

Leg b Hypotenuse c Leg a

PYTHAGOREAN THEOREM

In a right triangle, the sum of the squares of the lengths of the two legs is equal to the square of the length of the hypotenuse.

$$(\text{leg})^2 + (\text{leg})^2 = (\text{hypotenuse})^2 \quad \text{or} \quad a^2 + b^2 = c^2$$

△ Example 9   USING THE PYTHAGOREAN THEOREM

While framing an addition to an existing home, Kim Menzies, a carpenter, used the Pythagorean theorem to determine whether a wall was "square"—that is, whether the wall formed a right angle with the floor. He used a triangle whose sides are three consecutive integers. Find a right triangle whose sides are three consecutive integers.

Solution 1. UNDERSTAND. Read and reread the problem.

Let x, $x + 1$, and $x + 2$ be three consecutive integers. Since these integers represent lengths of the sides of a right triangle, we have

$$x = \text{one leg}$$
$$x + 1 = \text{other leg}$$
$$x + 2 = \text{hypotenuse (longest side)}$$

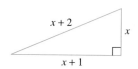

2. TRANSLATE. By the Pythagorean theorem, we have

In words: | $(\text{leg})^2$ | $+$ | $(\text{leg})^2$ | $=$ | $(\text{hypotenuse})^2$ |

Translate: $(x)^2 \quad + \quad (x + 1)^2 \quad = \quad (x + 2)^2$

3. SOLVE the equation.

$$x^2 + (x + 1)^2 = (x + 2)^2$$
$$x^2 + x^2 + 2x + 1 = x^2 + 4x + 4 \quad \text{Multiply.}$$
$$2x^2 + 2x + 1 = x^2 + 4x + 4$$
$$x^2 - 2x - 3 = 0 \quad\quad \text{Write in standard form.}$$
$$(x - 3)(x + 1) = 0$$
$$x - 3 = 0 \quad \text{or} \quad x + 1 = 0$$
$$x = 3 \quad\quad\quad x = -1$$

4. **INTERPRET.** Discard $x = -1$ since length cannot be negative. If $x = 3$, then $x + 1 = 4$ and $x + 2 = 5$.

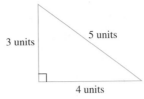

3 units

5 units

4 units

Check: To check, see that $(\text{leg})^2 + (\text{leg})^2 = (\text{hypotenuse})^2$

$$3^2 + 4^2 = 5^2$$
$$9 + 16 = 25 \quad \text{True.}$$

State: The lengths of the sides of the right triangle are 3, 4, and 5 units. Kim used this information, for example, by marking off lengths of 3 and 4 feet on the floor and framing respectively. If the diagonal length between these marks was 5 feet, the wall was "square." If not, adjustments were made.

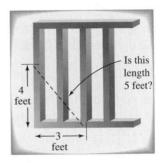

Is this length 5 feet?

4 feet

3 feet

3

Recall that to find the x-intercepts of the graph of a function, let $f(x) = 0$, or $y = 0$, and solve for x. This fact gives us a visual interpretation of the results of this section.

From Example 1, we know that the solutions of the equation $(x + 2)(x - 6) = 0$ are -2 and 6. These solutions give us important information about the related polynomial function $p(x) = (x + 2)(x - 6)$. We know that when x is -2 or when x is 6, the value of $p(x)$ is 0.

$$p(x) = (x + 2)(x - 6)$$
$$p(-2) = (-2 + 2)(-2 - 6) = (0)(-8) = 0$$
$$p(6) = (6 + 2)(6 - 6) = (8)(0) = 0$$

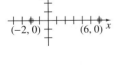

(-2, 0)   (6, 0)

Thus, we know that $(-2, 0)$ and $(6, 0)$ are the x-intercepts of the graph of $p(x)$.

We also know that the graph of $p(x)$ does not cross the x-axis at any other point. For this reason, and the fact that $p(x) = (x + 2)(x - 6) = x^2 - 4x - 12$ has degree 2, we conclude that the graph of p must look something like one of these two graphs:

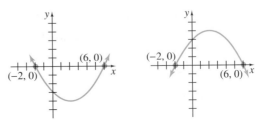

In the following section and in a later chapter, we explore these graphs more fully. For the moment, know that the solutions of a polynomial equation are the x-intercepts of the graph of the related function and that the x-intercepts of the graph of a polynomial function are the solutions of the related polynomial equation. These values are also called **roots**, or **zeros**, of a polynomial function.

Example 10   Match each function with its graph.

$$f(x) = (x - 3)(x + 2) \qquad g(x) = x(x + 2)(x - 2) \qquad h(x) = (x - 2)(x + 2)(x - 1)$$

A 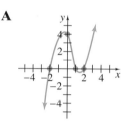   **B** 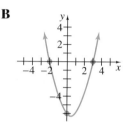   **C**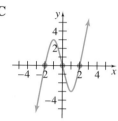

Solution   The graph of the function $f(x) = (x - 3)(x + 2)$ has two x-intercepts, $(3, 0)$ and $(-2, 0)$, because the equation $0 = (x - 3)(x + 2)$ has two solutions, 3 and -2.

The graph of $f(x)$ is graph B.

The graph of the function $g(x) = x(x + 2)(x - 2)$ has three x-intercepts $(0, 0)$, $(-2, 0)$, and $(2, 0)$, because the equation $0 = x(x + 2)(x - 2)$ has three solutions, 0, -2, and 2.

The graph of $g(x)$ is graph C.

The graph of the function $h(x) = (x - 2)(x + 2)(x - 1)$ has three x-intercepts, $(-2, 0)$, $(1, 0)$, and $(2, 0)$, because the equation $0 = (x - 2)(x + 2)(x - 1)$ has three solutions, -2, 1, and 2.

The graph of $h(x)$ is graph A.

GRAPHING CALCULATOR EXPLORATIONS

We can use a graphing calculator to approximate real number solutions of any quadratic equation in standard form, whether the associated polynomial is factorable or not. For example, let's solve the quadratic equation $x^2 - 2x - 4 = 0$. The solutions of this equation will be the x-intercepts of the graph of the function $f(x) = x^2 - 2x - 4$. (Recall that to find x-intercepts, we let $f(x) = 0$, or $y = 0$.) When we use a standard window, the graph of this function looks like this.

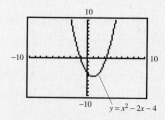

The graph appears to have one x-intercept between -2 and -1 and one between 3 and 4. To find the x-intercept between 3 and 4 to the nearest hundredth, we can use a zero feature, a Zoom feature, which magnifies a portion of the graph around the cursor, or we can redefine our window. If we redefine our window to

Xmin = 2	Ymin = -1
Xmax = 5	Ymax = 1
Xscl = 1	Yscl = 1

the resulting screen is

By using the Trace feature, we can now see that one of the intercepts is between 3.21 and 3.25. To approximate to the nearest hundredth, Zoom again or redefine the window to

Xmin = 3.2	Ymin = -0.1
Xmax = 3.3	Ymax = 0.1
Xscl = 1	Yscl = 1

If we use the Trace feature again, we see that, to the nearest hundredth, the x-intercept is 3.24. By repeating this process, we can approximate the other x-intercept to be -1.24.

To check, find $f(3.24)$ and $f(-1.24)$. Both of these values should be close to 0. (They will not be exactly 0 since we approximated these solutions.)

$$f(3.24) = 0.0176 \quad \text{and} \quad f(-1.24) = 0.0176$$

Solve each of these quadratic equations by graphing a related function and approximating the x-intercepts to the nearest thousandth.

1. $x^2 + 3x - 2 = 0$

2. $5x^2 - 7x + 1 = 0$

3. $2.3x^2 - 4.4x - 5.6 = 0$

4. $0.2x^2 + 6.2x + 2.1 = 0$

5. $0.09x^2 - 0.13x - 0.08 = 0$

6. $x^2 + 0.08x - 0.01 = 0$

MENTAL MATH

Solve each equation for the variable. See Example 1.

1. $(x - 3)(x + 5) = 0$

2. $(y + 5)(y + 3) = 0$

3. $(z - 3)(z + 7) = 0$

4. $(c - 2)(c - 4) = 0$

5. $x(x - 9) = 0$

6. $w(w + 7) = 0$

Exercise Set 5.8

Solve each equation. See Example 1.

1. $(x + 3)(3x - 4) = 0$

3. $3(2x - 5)(4x + 3) = 0$

2. $(5x + 1)(x - 2) = 0$

4. $8(3x - 4)(2x - 7) = 0$

Solve each equation. See Examples 2 through 5.

5. $x^2 + 11x + 24 = 0$

6. $y^2 - 10y + 24 = 0$

7. $12x^2 + 5x - 2 = 0$

8. $3y^2 - y - 14 = 0$

9. $z^2 + 9 = 10z$

10. $n^2 + n = 72$

11. $x(5x + 2) = 3$

12. $n(2n - 3) = 2$

13. $x^2 - 6x = x(8 + x)$

14. $n(3 + n) = n^2 + 4n$

15. $\dfrac{z^2}{6} - \dfrac{z}{2} - 3 = 0$

16. $\dfrac{c^2}{20} - \dfrac{c}{4} + \dfrac{1}{5} = 0$

17. $\dfrac{x^2}{2} + \dfrac{x}{20} = \dfrac{1}{10}$

18. $\dfrac{y^2}{30} = \dfrac{y}{15} + \dfrac{1}{2}$

19. $\dfrac{4t^2}{5} = \dfrac{t}{5} + \dfrac{3}{10}$

20. $\dfrac{5x^2}{6} - \dfrac{7x}{2} + \dfrac{2}{3} = 0$

Solve each equation. See Examples 6 and 7.

21. $(x + 2)(x - 7)(3x - 8) = 0$

22. $(4x + 9)(x - 4)(x + 1) = 0$

23. $y^3 = 9y$

24. $n^3 = 16n$

25. $x^3 - x = 2x^2 - 2$

26. $m^3 = m^2 + 12m$

27. Explain how solving $2(x - 3)(x - 1) = 0$ differs from solving $2x(x - 3)(x - 1) = 0$.

28. Explain why the zero-factor property works for more than two numbers whose product is 0.

Solve each equation.

29. $(2x + 7)(x - 10) = 0$

30. $(x + 4)(5x - 1) = 0$

31. $3x(x - 5) = 0$

32. $4x(2x + 3) = 0$

33. $x^2 - 2x - 15 = 0$

34. $x^2 + 6x - 7 = 0$

35. $12x^2 + 2x - 2 = 0$

36. $8x^2 + 13x + 5 = 0$

37. $w^2 - 5w = 36$

38. $x^2 + 32 = 12x$

39. $25x^2 - 40x + 16 = 0$

40. $9n^2 + 30n + 25 = 0$

41. $2r^3 + 6r^2 = 20r$

42. $-2t^3 - 108t - 30t^2$

43. $z(5z - 4)(z + 3) = 0$

44. $2r(r + 3)(5r - 4) = 0$

45. $2z(z + 6) = 2z^2 + 12z - 8$

46. $3c^2 - 8c + 2 = c(3c - 8)$

47. $(x - 1)(x + 4) = 24$

48. $(2x - 1)(x + 2) = -3$

49. $\dfrac{x^2}{4} - \dfrac{5}{2}x + 6 = 0$

50. $\dfrac{x^2}{18} + \dfrac{x}{2} + 1 = 0$

51. $y^2 + \dfrac{1}{4} = -y$

52. $\dfrac{x^2}{10} + \dfrac{5}{2} = x$

53. $y^3 + 4y^2 = 9y + 36$

54. $x^3 + 5x^2 = x + 5$

55. $2x^3 = 50x$

56. $m^5 = 36m^3$

57. $x^2 + (x + 1)^2 = 61$

58. $y^2 + (y + 2)^2 = 34$

59. $m^2(3m - 2) = m$

60. $x^2(5x + 3) = 26x$

61. $3x^2 = -x$

62. $y^2 = -5y$

63. $x(x - 3) = x^2 + 5x + 7$

64. $z^2 - 4z + 10 = z(z - 5)$

65. $3(t - 8) + 2t = 7 + t$

66. $7c - 2(3c + 1) = 5(4 - 2c)$

67. $-3(x - 4) + x = 5(3 - x)$

68. $-4(a + 1) - 3a = -7(2a - 3)$

69. Which solution strategies are incorrect? Why?

  a. Solve $(y - 2)(y + 2) = 4$ by setting each factor equal to 4.

  b. Solve $(x + 1)(x + 3) = 0$ by setting each factor equal to 0.

  c. Solve $z^2 + 5z + 6 = 0$ by factoring $z^2 + 5z + 6$ and setting each factor equal to 0.

  d. Solve $x^2 + 6x + 8 = 10$ by factoring $x^2 + 6x + 8$ and setting each factor equal to 0.

70. Describe two ways a linear equation differs from a quadratic equation.

Solve. See Examples 8 and 9.

71. One number exceeds another by five, and their product is 66. Find the numbers.

72. If the sum of two numbers is 4 and their product is $\dfrac{15}{4}$, find the numbers.

73. An electrician needs to run a cable from the top of a 60-foot tower to a transmitter box located 45 feet away from the base of the tower. Find how long he should make the cable.

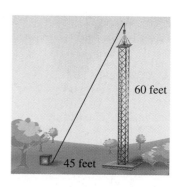

60 feet

45 feet

△ **74.** A stereo system installer needs to run speaker wire along the two diagonals of a rectangular room whose dimensions are 40 feet by 75 feet. Find how much speaker wire she needs.

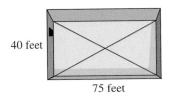

75. If the cost, $C(x)$, for manufacturing x units of a certain product is given by $C(x) = x^2 - 15x + 50$, find the number of units manufactured at a cost of $9500.

△ **76.** Determine whether any three consecutive integers represent the lengths of the sides of a right triangle.

△ **77.** The shorter leg of a right triangle is 3 centimeters less than the other leg. Find the length of the two legs if the hypotenuse is 15 centimeters.

△ **78.** The longer leg of a right triangle is 4 feet longer than the other leg. Find the length of the two legs if the hypotenuse is 20 feet.

△ **79.** Marie Mulroney has a rectangular board 12 inches by 16 inches around which she wants to put a uniform border of shells. If she has enough shells for a border whose area is 128 square inches, determine the width of the border.

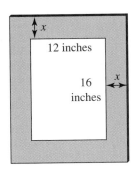

△ **80.** A gardener has a rose garden that measures 30 feet by 20 feet. He wants to put a uniform border of pine bark around the outside of the garden. Find how wide the border should be if he has enough pine bark to cover 336 square feet.

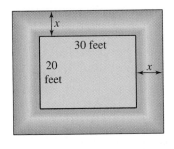

81. While hovering near the top of Ribbon Falls in Yosemite National Park at 1600 feet, a helicopter pilot accidentally drops his sunglasses. The height $h(t)$ of the sunglasses after t seconds is given by the polynomial function
$$h(t) = -16t^2 + 1600$$
When will the sunglasses hit the ground?

82. After t seconds, the height $h(t)$ of a model rocket launched from the ground into the air is given by the function
$$h(t) = -16t^2 + 80t$$
Find how long it takes the rocket to reach a height of 96 feet.

△ **83.** The floor of a shed has an area of 91 square feet. The floor is in the shape of a rectangle whose length is 6 feet more than the width. Find the length and the width of the floor of the shed.

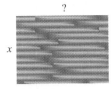

△ **84.** A vegetable garden with an area of 143 square feet is to be fertilized. If the width of the garden is 2 feet less than the length, find the dimensions of the garden.

85. The function $W(x) = 0.5x^2$ gives the number of servings of wedding cake that can be obtained from a two-layer x-inch square wedding cake tier. What size square wedding cake tier is needed to serve 50 people? (*Source:* Based on data from the *Wilton 2000 Yearbook of Cake Decorating*)

86. Use the function in Exercise 85 to determine what size wedding cake tier is needed to serve 200 people.

Match each polynomial function with its graph (A–F). See Example 10.

87. $f(x) = (x - 2)(x + 5)$

88. $g(x) = (x + 1)(x - 6)$

89. $h(x) = x(x + 3)(x - 3)$

90. $F(x) = (x + 1)(x - 2)(x + 5)$

91. $G(x) = 2x^2 + 9x + 4$

92. $H(x) = 2x^2 - 7x - 4$

A
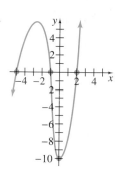

B
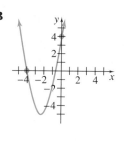

C
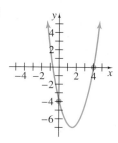

D
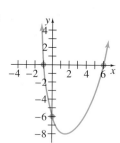

E
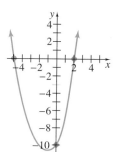

F
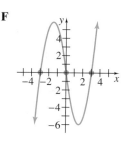

Write a quadratic equation that has the given numbers as solutions.

93. $5, 3$

94. $6, 7$

95. $-1, 2$

96. $4, -3$

REVIEW EXERCISES

Write the x- and y-intercepts for each graph and determine whether the graph is the graph of a function. See Sections 3.1 and 3.2.

97.
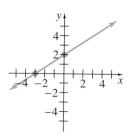

98.
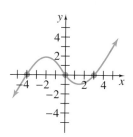

99.
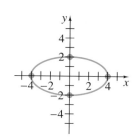

100.
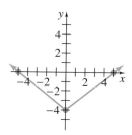

101. Draw a function with intercepts $(-3, 0)$, $(5, 0)$, and $(0, 4)$.

102. Draw a function with intercepts $(-7, 0)$, $\left(-\dfrac{1}{2}, 0\right)$, $(4, 0)$, and $(0, -1)$.

5.9   AN INTRODUCTION TO GRAPHING POLYNOMIAL FUNCTIONS

CD-ROM   SSM

SSG   Video

▶ **OBJECTIVES**

1. Analyze the graph of a polynomial function.
2. Graph quadratic functions.
3. Find the vertex of a parabola by using the vertex formula.
4. Graph cubic functions.

1

We discussed linear functions of the form $f(x) = mx + b$ in Chapter 3. In this chapter, we have thus far briefly discussed polynomial functions. In this section, we further discuss polynomial functions. As mentioned earlier, some polynomial functions are given special names according to their degree. For example,

$f(x) = 2x - 6$ is called a **linear function**; its **degree is one**.
$f(x) = 5x^2 - x + 3$ is called a **quadratic function; its degree is two**.
$f(x) = 7x^3 + 3x^2 - 1$ is called a **cubic function**; its **degree is three**.
$f(x) = -8x^4 - 3x^3 + 2x^2 + 20$ is called a **quartic function**; its **degree is four**.

All the above functions are also polynomial functions.

Before we practice graphing polynomial functions, let's analyze the graph of a polynomial function.

Example 1   Given the graph of the function $g(x)$

   a. Find the domain and the range of the function.
   b. List the x- and y-intercepts
   c. Find the coordinates of the point with the greatest y-value.
   d. Find the coordinates of the point with the least y-value.
   e. List the x-values whose y-values are equal to 0.
   f. List the x-values whose y-values are greater than 0.
   g. Find the solutions of $g(x) = 0$.

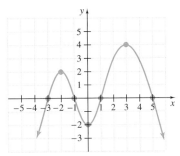

Solution   **a.** The domain is the set of all real numbers, or in interval notation, $(-\infty, \infty)$. The range is $(-\infty, 4]$.

   b. The x-intercepts are $(-3, 0)$, $(-1, 0)$, $(1, 0)$, and $(5, 0)$. The y-intercept is $(0, -2)$.

   c. The point with the greatest y-value corresponds to the "highest" point. This is the point with coordinates $(3, 4)$. (This means that for all real number values for x, the greatest y-value, or $f(x)$ value, is 4.)

d. The point with the least y-value corresponds to the "lowest" point. This graph contains no "lowest" point, so there is no point with the least y-value.

e. The y-values are equal to 0 when the graph lies on the x-axis. The x-values when this occurs are the x-intercepts $(-3, 0)$, $(-1, 0)$, $(1, 0)$, and $(5, 0)$. Notice that this tells us that $g(-3) = 0$, $g(-1) = 0$, $g(1) = 0$, and $g(5) = 0$.

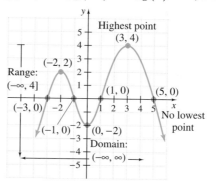

f. The y-values are greater than 0 when the graph lies above the x-axis. The x-values when this occurs are between $x = -3$ and $x = -1$ and between $x = 1$ and $x = 5$.

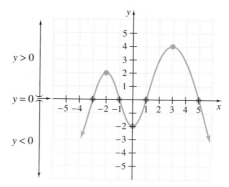

g. The solutions of $g(x) = 0$ are the x-intercepts of the graph. The x-intercepts are $(-3, 0)$, $(-1, 0)$, $(1, 0)$, and $(5, 0)$. This means that when $x = -3, -1, 1$, or 5, y or $g(x) = 0$. The solutions are $-3, -1, 1$, and 5.

The graph of any polynomial function (linear, quadratic, cubic, and so on) can be sketched by plotting a sufficient number of ordered pairs that satisfy the function and connecting them to form a smooth curve. The graph of all polynomial functions will pass the vertical line test since they are graphs of functions. To graph a linear function defined by $f(x) = mx + b$, recall that two ordered pair solutions will suffice since its graph is a line. To graph other polynomial functions, we need to find and plot more ordered pair solutions to ensure a reasonable picture of its graph.

2 Since we know how to graph linear functions (see Chapter 3), we will now graph quadratic functions and discuss special characteristics of their graphs.

QUADRATIC FUNCTION

A quadratic function is a function that can be written in the form

$$f(x) = ax^2 + bx + c$$

where a, b, and c are real numbers and $a \neq 0$.

We know that an equation of the form $f(x) = ax^2 + bx + c$ may be written as $y = ax^2 + bx + c$. Thus, both $f(x) = ax^2 + bx + c$ and $y = ax^2 + bx + c$ define quadratic functions as long as a is not 0.

Recall the graph of the quadratic function defined by $f(x) = x^2$ by plotting points. Choose $-3, -2, -1, 0, 1, 2$, and 3 as x-values, and find corresponding $f(x)$ or y-values.

x	$y = f(x)$
-3	9
-2	4
-1	1
0	0
1	1
2	4
3	9

Notice that the graph passes the vertical line test, as it should since it is a function. Recall that this curve is called a **parabola.** The highest point on a parabola that opens downward or the lowest point on a parabola that opens upward is called the **vertex** of the parabola. The vertex of this parabola is $(0, 0)$, the lowest point on the graph. If we fold the graph along the y-axis, we can see that the two sides of the graph coincide. This means that this curve is symmetric about the y-axis, and the y-axis, or the line $x = 0$, is called the **axis of symmetry.** The graph of every quadratic function is a parabola and has an axis of symmetry: the vertical line that passes through the vertex of the parabola.

Example 2   Graph the quadratic function $f(x) = -x^2 + 2x - 3$ by plotting points.

Solution   To graph, choose values for x and find corresponding $f(x)$ or y-values.

x	$y = f(x)$
-2	-11
-1	-6
0	-3
1	-2
2	-3
3	-6

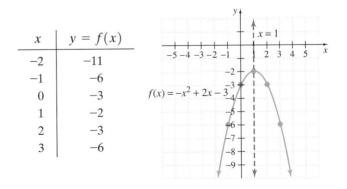

The vertex of this parabola is $(1, -2)$, the highest point on the graph. The vertical line $x = 1$ is the axis of symmetry. Recall that to find the x-intercepts of a graph, let $f(x)$ or $y = 0$. Since this graph has no x-intercepts, it means that $0 = -x^2 + 2x - 3$ has no real number solutions.

Notice that the parabola $f(x) = -x^2 + 2x - 3$ opens downward, whereas $f(x) = x^2$ opens upward. When the equation of a quadratic function is written in the form $f(x) = ax^2 + bx + c$, recall that the coefficient of the squared variable a determines whether the parabola opens downward or upward. If $a > 0$, the parabola opens upward, and if $a < 0$, the parabola opens downward.

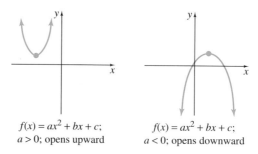

$f(x) = ax^2 + bx + c;$
$a > 0;$ opens upward

$f(x) = ax^2 + bx + c;$
$a < 0;$ opens downward

3 In both $f(x) = x^2$ and $f(x) = -x^2 + 2x - 3$, the vertex happens to be one of the points we chose to plot. Since this is not always the case, and since plotting the vertex allows us to draw the graph quickly, we need a consistent method for finding the vertex. One method is to use the following formula, which we shall derive in Chapter 8.

VERTEX FORMULA

The graph of $f(x) = ax^2 + bx + c, a \neq 0$, is a parabola with vertex

$$\left(\frac{-b}{2a}, f\left(\frac{-b}{2a} \right) \right)$$

We can also find the x- and y-intercepts of a parabola to aid in graphing. Recall that x-intercepts of the graph of any equation may be found by letting $y = 0$ in the equation and solving for x. Also, y-intercepts may be found by letting $x = 0$ in the equation and solving for y or $f(x)$.

Example 3 Graph $f(x) = x^2 + 2x - 3$. Find the vertex and any intercepts.

Solution To find the vertex, use the vertex formula. For the function $f(x) = x^2 + 2x - 3$, $a = 1$ and $b = 2$. Thus,

$$x = \frac{-b}{2a} = \frac{-2}{2(1)} = -1$$

Next find $f(-1)$.

$$f(-1) = (-1)^2 + 2(-1) - 3$$
$$= 1 - 2 - 3$$
$$= -4$$

The vertex is $(-1, -4)$, and since $a = 1$ is greater than 0, this parabola opens upward. This parabola will have two x-intercepts because its vertex lies below the x-axis and it opens upward. To find the x-intercepts, let y or $f(x) = 0$ and solve for x.

$$f(x) = x^2 + 2x - 3$$
$$0 = x^2 + 2x - 3 \qquad \text{Let } f(x) = 0.$$
$$0 = (x + 3)(x - 1) \qquad \text{Factor.}$$

$x + 3 = 0$	or	$x - 1 = 0$	Set each factor equal to 0.
$x = -3$	or	$x = 1$	Solve.

The x-intercepts are $(-3, 0)$ and $(1, 0)$.
To find the y-intercept, let $x = 0$.

$$f(x) = x^2 + 2x - 3$$
$$f(0) = 0^2 + 2(0) - 3$$
$$f(0) = -3$$

The y-intercept is $(0, -3)$
Now plot these points and connect them with a smooth curve.

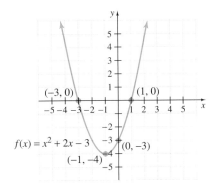

$f(x) = x^2 + 2x - 3$

HELPFUL HINT
Not all graphs of parabolas have x-intercepts. To see this, first plot the vertex of the parabola and decide whether the parabola opens upward or downward. Then use this information to decide whether the graph of the parabola has x-intercepts.

Example 4   Graph $f(x) = 3x^2 - 12x + 13$. Find the vertex and any intercepts.

Solution   To find the vertex, use the vertex formula. For the function $y = 3x^2 - 12x + 13$, $a = 3$ and $b = -12$. Thus,

$$x = \frac{-b}{2a} = \frac{-(-12)}{2(3)} = \frac{12}{6} = 2$$

Next find $f(2)$.

$$f(2) = 3(2)^2 - 12(2) + 13$$
$$= 3(4) - 24 + 13$$
$$= 1$$

The vertex is $(2, 1)$. Also, this parabola opens upward, since $a = 3$, which is greater than 0. Notice that this parabola has no x-intercepts: Its vertex lies above the x-axis, and it opens upward.

Exercise Set 5.9

For the graph of each function $f(x)$, answer the following. See Example 1.

a. *Find the domain and the range of the function.*

b. *List the x- and y-intercepts.*

c. *Find the coordinates of the point with the greatest y-value.*

d. *Find the coordinates of the point with the least y-value.*

e. *List the x-values whose y-values are equal to 0.*

f. *List the x-values whose y-values are greater than 0.*

g. *Find the solutions of $f(x) = 0$.*

1.

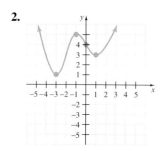

2.

3. The graph in Example 3 of this section.

4. The graph in Example 4 of this section.

5. The graph in Example 5 of this section.

6. The graph in Example 6 of this section.

Graph each quadratic function by plotting points. See Example 2.

7. $f(x) = 2x^2$

8. $f(x) = -3x^2$

9. $f(x) = x^2 + 1$

10. $f(x) = x^2 - 2$

11. $f(x) = -x^2$

12. $f(x) = \frac{1}{2}x^2$

Find the vertex of the graph of each function. See Examples 3 and 4.

13. $f(x) = x^2 + 8x + 7$

14. $f(x) = x^2 + 6x + 5$

15. $f(x) = 3x^2 + 6x + 4$

16. $f(x) = -2x^2 + 2x + 1$

17. $f(x) = -x^2 + 10x + 5$

18. $f(x) = -x^2 - 8x + 2$

19. If the vertex of a parabola lies below the x-axis and the parabola opens upward, how many x-intercepts will the graph have?

20. If the vertex of a parabola lies below the x-axis and the parabola opens downward, how many x-intercepts will the graph have?

21. If the vertex of a parabola lies above the x-axis and the parabola opens upward, how many x-intercepts will the graph have?

22. If the vertex of a parabola lies above the x-axis and the parabola opens downward, how many x-intercepts will the graph have?

23. If the vertex of a parabola is the origin, how many x-intercepts and how many y-intercepts will the graph have?

Graph each quadratic function. Find and label the vertex and intercepts. See Examples 3 and 4.

24. $f(x) = x^2 + 8x + 7$

25. $f(x) = x^2 + 6x + 5$

26. $f(x) = x^2 - 2x - 24$

27. $f(x) = x^2 - 12x + 35$

28. $f(x) = 2x^2 - 6x$

29. $f(x) = -3x^2 + 6x$

Graph each cubic function. Find any intercepts. See Examples 5 and 6.

30. $f(x) = 4x^3 - 9x$

31. $f(x) = 2x^3 - 5x^2 - 3x$

32. $f(x) = x^3 + 3x^2 - x - 3$

33. $f(x) = x^3 + x^2 - 4x - 4$

34. Can the graph of a function ever have more than one y-intercept point? Why?

35. In general, is there a limit to the number of x-intercepts for the graph of a function?

Graph each function. Find intercepts. If the function is a quadratic function, find the vertex.

36. $f(x) = x^2 + 4x - 5$

37. $f(x) = x^2 + 2x - 3$

38. $f(x) = (x - 2)(x + 2)(x + 1)$

39. $f(x) = x^3 - 4x^2 + 3x$

40. $f(x) = x^2 + 1$

41. $f(x) = x^2 + 4$

42. $f(x) = -5x^2 + 5x$

43. $f(x) = 3x^2 - 12x$

44. $f(x) = x^3 - 9x$

45. $f(x) = x^3 + x^2 - 12x$

46. $f(x) = -x^3 - x^2 + 2x$

47. $f(x) = x^3 + x^2 - 9x - 9$

48. $f(x) = x^2 - 4x + 4$

49. $f(x) = x^2 - 2x + 1$

50. $f(x) = -x^3 + x$ **51.** $f(x) = x^2 + 6x$

52. $f(x) = 2x^2 - x - 3$ **53.** $f(x) = (x + 2)(x - 2)$

54. $f(x) = -x^3 + 3x^2 + x - 3$

55. $f(x) = -x^3 + 25x$

56. $f(x) = x^2 - 10x + 26$ **57.** $f(x) = x^2 + 2x + 4$

58. $f(x) = x(x - 4)(x + 2)$

59. $f(x) = 3x(x - 3)(x + 5)$

60. $g(x) = x(x - 2)(x + 3)(x + 5)$

61. $h(x) = (x - 4)(x - 2)(2x + 1)(x + 3)$

 Use a graphing calculator to verify the graph in each exercise.

62. Exercise 36   **63.** Exercise 37

64. Exercise 54   **65.** Exercise 55

 Use a graphing calculator to approximate all x-intercepts to the nearest tenth.

66. $F(x) = -x^4 + 2.1x^2 + 5.6$

67. $G(x) = x^4 - 6.2x^2 - 6.2$

REVIEW EXERCISES

Simplify each fraction. See Sections 5.1 and 5.2.

68. $-\dfrac{8}{10}$ **69.** $-\dfrac{45}{100}$

70. $\dfrac{x^7 y^{10}}{x^3 y^{15}}$ **71.** $\dfrac{a^{14} b^2}{ab^4}$

72. $\dfrac{7n^{-9} m^{-2}}{14nm^{-5}}$ **73.** $\dfrac{20x^{-3} y^5}{25y^{-2}x}$

5

 For additional Chapter Projects, visit the Real World Activities Website by going to http://www.prenhall.com/martin-gay.

CHAPTER PROJECT

Investigating Earth's Water

Earth is covered by water. In fact, oceans cover nearly three-fourths of the surface of Earth. However, oceans aren't the only source of Earth's water. The melting of one of the other main sources of Earth's water, icecaps and glaciers, is expected to contribute to a global rise in ocean level due to global warming over the next 100 years. In this project, you will have the opportunity to investigate where Earth's water exists and how the ocean level will change. This project may be completed by working in groups or individually.

1. Refer to Table 1. Which accounts for more of Earth's water: groundwater or icecaps and glaciers?

2. Find the total volume of water that exists on planet Earth. Add this figure to the table.

3. Using the total you computed in Question 2, complete the percent column of the table. Discuss your findings.

Widespread industrialization during the nineteenth and twentieth centuries has led to an increase in the presence of carbon dioxide, methane, nitrous oxide, and chlorofluorocarbons in Earth's atmosphere. These so-called greenhouse gases are believed by some scientists to be responsible for an increase in the average global temperature of 0.2°C to 0.3°C in the last half of the twentieth century. If this global warming trend continues, one of its consequences may be a global increase in the level of the oceans. An overall increase in ocean level will be due to changes in icecaps and glaciers, as well as thermal expansion. Higher global temperatures lead to warming in the top layers of the ocean, causing the water to expand and elevate the sea level.

TABLE 1. WHERE EARTH'S WATER EXISTS

	Water Volume (cubic kilometers)	Percent
Atmosphere	1.3×10^4	
Average in stream channels	1.0×10^3	
Freshwater lakes	1.2×10^5	
Groundwater	8.3×10^6	
Icecaps and glaciers	2.9×10^7	
Oceans	1.32×10^9	
Saline lakes and inland seas	1.0×10^5	
Water in soil above groundwater	6.7×10^5	
Total		

(*Source:* Data from B.J. Skinner, *Earth Resources*, 2nd Ed., Prentice Hall, 1976)

Table 2 lists each contributor to overall changes in ocean level along with a polynomial model describing the projected rise y (in centimeters) each is expected to contribute x years after 2000.

4. By 2020, how much will the ocean level have risen due to thermal expansion?

5. Using the polynomial models given in Table 2, find a single polynomial model that gives the overall rise in ocean level from 1990 to 2100.

6. Using your model from Question 5, find the projected overall increase in ocean level for

    a. 2025   **b.** 2050

    c. 2075   **d.** 2100

7. Discuss the impact of your findings in Question 6.

TABLE 2. PROJECTIONS OF GLOBAL OCEAN LEVEL RISE BY CONTRIBUTOR, 1990–2100

Alpine glaciers:
$$y = 0.0006x^2 + 0.0936x + 0.8788$$
Greenland ice sheet:
$$y = 0.0004x^2 + 0.0164x + 0.1212$$
Antarctica ice sheet:
$$y = -0.0001x^2 - 0.0002x + 0.0076$$
Thermal expansion:
$$y = 0.0011x^2 + 0.1564x + 1.4545$$

(*Source:* Based on data from Frederick K. Lutgens, Edward J. Tarbuck, *The Atmosphere: An Introduction to Meteorology,* 7th Ed., Prentice Hall, 1998)

CHAPTER 5 VOCABULARY CHECK

Fill in each blank with one of the words or phrases listed below.

quadratic equation   scientific notation   polynomial   exponents   1   0   monomial

binomial   trinomial   degree of a polynomial   degree of a term   factoring

1. A _____ is a finite sum of terms in which all variables are raised to nonnegative integer powers and no variables appear in any denominator.

2. _____ is the process of writing a polynomial as a product.

3. _____ are used to write repeated factors in a more compact form.

4. The _____ is the sum of the exponents on the variables contained in the term.

5. A _____ is a polynomial with one term.

6. If a is not 0, $a^0 =$ ___ .

7. A _____ is a polynomial with three terms.

8. A polynomial equation of degree 2 is also called a _____ .

9. A positive number is written in _____ if it is written as the product of a number a, such that $1 \le a < 10$ and a power of 10.

10. The _____ is the largest degree of all of its terms.

11. A _____ is a polynomial with two terms.

12. If a and b are real numbers and $a \cdot b =$ ___ , then $a = 0$ or $b = 0$.

CHAPTER 5 HIGHLIGHTS

DEFINITIONS AND CONCEPTS	EXAMPLES

Section 5.1 Exponents and Scientific Notation

Product rule: $a^m \cdot a^n = a^{m+n}$
Zero exponent: $a^0 = 1, a \neq 0$

Quotient rule: $\dfrac{a^m}{a^n} = a^{m-n}$

Negative exponent: $a^{-n} = \dfrac{1}{a^n}$

A positive number is written in **scientific notation** if it is written as the product of a number a, where $1 \leq a < 10$, and an integer power of 10: $a \times 10^r$.

$x^2 \cdot x^3 = x^5$
$7^0 = 1, (-10)^0 = 1$

$\dfrac{y^{10}}{y^4} = y^{10-4} = y^6$

$3^{-2} = \dfrac{1}{3^2} = \dfrac{1}{9}, \dfrac{x^{-5}}{x^{-7}} = x^{-5-(-7)} = x^2$

Numbers written in scientific notation
$$568,000 = 5.68 \times 10^5$$
$$0.0002117 = 2.117 \times 10^{-4}$$

Section 5.2 More Work with Exponents and Scientific Notation

Power rules:

$$(a^m)^n = a^{m \cdot n}$$

$$(ab)^m = a^m b^m$$

$$\left(\dfrac{a}{b}\right)^n = \dfrac{a^n}{b^n}$$

$$(7^8)^2 = 7^{16}$$
$$(2y)^3 = 2^3 y^3 = 8y^3$$
$$\left(\dfrac{5x^{-3}}{x^2}\right)^{-2} = \dfrac{5^{-2} x^6}{x^{-4}}$$
$$= 5^{-2} \cdot x^{6-(-4)}$$
$$= \dfrac{x^{10}}{5^2}, \quad \text{or} \quad \dfrac{x^{10}}{25}$$

Section 5.3 Polynomials and Polynomial Functions

A **polynomial** is a finite sum of terms in which all variables have exponents raised to nonnegative integer powers and no variables appear in the denominator.

Polynomials

$1.3x^2$ (monomial)

$-\dfrac{1}{3}y + 5$ (binomial)

$6z^2 - 5z + 7$ (trinomial)

A function P is a **polynomial function** if $P(x)$ is a polynomial.

For the polynomial function
$$P(x) = -x^2 + 6x - 12, \text{find } P(-2)$$
$$P(-2) = -(-2)^2 + 6(-2) - 12 = -28.$$

To add polynomials, combine all like terms.

Add
$$(3y^2 x - 2yx + 11) + (-5y^2 x - 7)$$
$$= -2y^2 x - 2yx + 4$$

To subtract polynomials, change the signs of the terms of the polynomial being subtracted, then add.

Subtract
$$(-2z^3 - z + 1) - (3z^3 + z - 6)$$
$$= -2z^3 - z + 1 - 3z^3 - z + 6$$
$$= -5z^3 - 2z + 7$$

DEFINITIONS AND CONCEPTS	EXAMPLES

Section 5.4 Multiplying Polynomials

To multiply two polynomials, use the distributive property and multiply each term of one polynomial by each term of the other polynomial; then combine like terms.

Multiply

$$(x^2 - 2x)(3x^2 - 5x + 1)$$
$$= 3x^4 - 5x^3 + x^2 - 6x^3 + 10x^2 - 2x$$
$$= 3x^4 - 11x^3 + 11x^2 - 2x$$

Special products

$$(a + b)^2 = a^2 + 2ab + b^2$$
$$(a - b)^2 = a^2 - 2ab + b^2$$
$$(a + b)(a - b) = a^2 - b^2$$

$$(3m + 2n)^2 = 9m^2 + 12mn + 4n^2$$
$$(z^2 - 5)^2 = z^4 - 10z^2 + 25$$
$$(7y + 1)(7y - 1) = 49y^2 - 1$$

The FOIL method may be used when multiplying two binomials.

Multiply

$$(x^2 + 5)(2x^2 - 9)$$
$$\qquad \text{F} \qquad \text{O} \qquad \text{I} \qquad \text{L}$$
$$= x^2(2x^2) + x^2(-9) + 5(2x^2) + 5(-9)$$
$$= 2x^4 - 9x^2 + 10x^2 - 45$$
$$= 2x^4 + x^2 - 45$$

Section 5.5 The Greatest Common Factor and Factoring by Grouping

The greatest common factor (GCF) of the terms of a polynomial is the product of the GCF of the numerical coefficients and the GCF of the variable factors.

Factor: $14xy^3 - 2xy^2 = 2 \cdot 7 \cdot x \cdot y^3 - 2 \cdot x \cdot y^2$.

The GCF is $2 \cdot x \cdot y^2$, or $2xy^2$.

$$14xy^3 - 2xy^2 = 2xy^2(7y - 1)$$

To factor a polynomial by grouping, group the terms so that each group has a common factor. Factor out these common factors. Then see if the new groups have a common factor.

Factor $x^4y - 5x^3 + 2xy - 10$.

$$x^4y - 5x^3 + 2xy - 10 = x^3(xy - 5) + 2(xy - 5)$$
$$= (xy - 5)(x^3 + 2)$$

Section 5.6 Factoring Trinomials

To factor $ax^2 + bx + c$,

Step 1: Write all pairs of factors of ax^2.

Step 2: Write all pairs of factors of c.

Step 3: Try combinations of these factors until the middle term bx is found.

Factor $28x^2 - 27x - 10$.

Factors of $28x^2$: $28x$ and x, $2x$ and $14x$, $4x$ and $7x$.

Factors of -10: -2 and 5, 2 and -5, -10 and 1, 10 and -1.

$$28x^2 - 27x - 10 = (7x + 2)(4x - 5)$$

Section 5.7 Factoring by Special Products and Factoring Strategies

Perfect square trinomial

$$a^2 + 2ab + b^2 = (a + b)^2$$
$$a^2 - 2ab + b^2 = (a - b)^2$$

Factor

$$25x^2 + 30x + 9 = (5x + 3)^2$$
$$49z^2 - 28z + 4 = (7z - 2)^2$$

(continued)

DEFINITIONS AND CONCEPTS	EXAMPLES

Section 5.7 Factoring by Special Products and Factoring Strategies

Difference of two squares

$$a^2 - b^2 = (a + b)(a - b)$$

$$36x^2 - y^2 = (6x + y)(6x - y)$$

Sum and difference of two cubes

$$a^3 + b^3 = (a + b)(a^2 - ab + b^2)$$

$$a^3 - b^3 = (a - b)(a^2 + ab + b^2)$$

$$8y^3 + 1 = (2y + 1)(4y^2 - 2y + 1)$$

$$27p^3 - 64q^3 = (3p - 4q)(9p^2 + 12pq + 16q^2)$$

To factor a polynomial

Step 1: Factor out the GCF.

Step 2: If the polynomial is a binomial, see if it is a difference of two squares or a sum or difference of two cubes. If it is a trinomial, see if it is a perfect square trinomial. If not, try factoring by methods of Section 5.6. If it is a polynomial with 4 or more terms, try factoring by grouping.

Step 3: See if any factors can be factored further.

Factor $10x^4y + 5x^2y - 15y$.
$$10x^4y + 5x^2y - 15y = 5y(2x^4 + x^2 - 3)$$
$$= 5y(2x^2 + 3)(x^2 - 1)$$
$$= 5y(2x^2 + 3)(x + 1)(x - 1)$$

Section 5.8 Solving Equations by Factoring and Problem Solving

To solve polynomial equations by factoring:

Step 1: Write the equation so that one side is 0.

Step 2: Factor the polynomial completely.

Step 3: Set each factor equal to 0.

Step 4: Solve the resulting equations.

Step 5: Check each solution.

Solve

$$2x^3 - 5x^2 = 3x$$
$$2x^3 - 5x^2 - 3x = 0$$
$$x(2x + 1)(x - 3) = 0$$

$x = 0$ or $2x + 1 = 0$ or $x - 3 = 0$

$x = 0$ or $x = -\dfrac{1}{2}$ or $x = 3$

The solutions are $0, -\dfrac{1}{2}$, and 3.

Section 5.9 An Introduction to Graphing Polynomial Functions

To graph a polynomial function, find and plot x- and y-intercepts and a sufficient number of ordered pair solutions. Then connect the plotted points with a smooth curve.

Graph $f(x) = x^3 + 2x^2 - 3x$.
$$0 = x^3 + 2x^2 - 3x$$
$$0 = x(x - 1)(x + 3)$$
$$x = 0 \text{ or } x = 1 \text{ or } x = -3$$

The x-intercepts are $(0, 0)$, $(1, 0)$, and $(-3, 0)$.
$$f(0) = 0^3 + 2 \cdot 0^2 - 3 \cdot 0 = 0.$$

The y-intercept is $(0, 0)$

(continued)

DEFINITIONS AND CONCEPTS	EXAMPLES

Section 5.9 An Introduction to Graphing Polynomial Functions

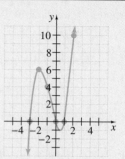

x	$f(x)$
-4	-20
-2	6
-1	4
$\frac{1}{2}$	$-\frac{7}{8}$
2	10

A quadratic function is a function that can be written in the form

$$f(x) = ax^2 + bx + c, a \neq 0$$

The graph of this quadratic function is a parabola with vertex $\left(\dfrac{-b}{2a}, f\left(\dfrac{-b}{2a}\right)\right)$.

Find the vertex of the graph of the quadratic function

$$f(x) = 2x^2 - 8x + 1$$

Here $a = 2$ and $b = -8$.

$$\frac{-b}{2a} = \frac{-(-8)}{2 \cdot 2} = 2$$

$$f(2) = 2 \cdot 2^2 - 8 \cdot (2) + 1 = -7$$

The vertex has coordinates $(2, -7)$.

CHAPTER 5 REVIEW

(5.1) *Evaluate.*

1. $(-2)^2$

2. $(-3)^4$

3. -2^2

4. -3^4

5. 8^0

6. -9^0

7. -4^{-2}

8. $(-4)^{-2}$

Simplify each expression. Use only positive exponents.

9. $-xy^2 \cdot y^3 \cdot xy^2z$

10. $(-4xy)(-3xy^2b)$

11. $a^{-14} \cdot a^5$

12. $\dfrac{a^{16}}{a^{17}}$

13. $\dfrac{x^{-7}}{x^4}$

14. $\dfrac{9a(a^{-3})}{18a^{15}}$

15. $\dfrac{y^{6p-3}}{y^{6p+2}}$

Write in scientific notation.

16. 36,890,000

17. -0.000362

Write each number without exponents.

18. 1.678×10^{-6}

19. 4.1×10^5

(5.2) *Simplify. Use only positive exponents.*

20. $(8^5)^3$

21. $\left(\dfrac{a}{4}\right)^2$

22. $(3x)^3$

23. $(-4x)^{-2}$

24. $\left(\dfrac{6x}{5}\right)^2$

25. $(8^6)^{-3}$

26. $\left(\dfrac{4}{3}\right)^{-2}$

27. $(-2x^3)^{-3}$

28. $\left(\dfrac{8p^6}{4p^4}\right)^{-2}$

29. $(-3x^{-2}y^2)^3$

30. $\left(\dfrac{x^{-5}y^{-3}}{z^3}\right)^{-5}$

31. $\dfrac{4^{-1}x^3yz}{x^{-2}yx^4}$

32. $(5xyz)^{-4}(x^{-2})^{-3}$

33. $\dfrac{2(3yz)^{-3}}{y^{-3}}$

Simplify each expression.

34. $x^{4a}(3x^{5a})^3$

35. $\dfrac{4y^{3x-3}}{2y^{2x+4}}$

Use scientific notation to find the quotient. Express each quotient in scientific notation.

36. $\dfrac{(0.00012)(144{,}000)}{0.0003}$

37. $\dfrac{(-0.00017)(0.00039)}{3000}$

Simplify. Use only positive exponents.

38. $\dfrac{27x^{-5}y^5}{18x^{-6}y^2}\cdot\dfrac{x^4y^{-2}}{x^{-2}y^3}$

39. $\dfrac{3x^5}{y^{-4}}\cdot\dfrac{(3xy^{-3})^{-2}}{(z^{-3})^{-4}}$

40. $\dfrac{(x^w)^2}{(x^{w-4})^{-2}}$

(5.3) *Find the degree of each polynomial.*

41. $x^2y - 3xy^3z + 5x + 7y$ **42.** $3x + 2$

Simplify by combining like terms.

43. $4x + 8x - 6x^2 - 6x^2y$

44. $-8xy^3 + 4xy^3 - 3x^3y$

Add or subtract as indicated.

45. $(3x + 7y) + (4x^2 - 3x + 7) + (y - 1)$

46. $(4x^2 - 6xy + 9y^2) - (8x^2 - 6xy - y^2)$

47. $(3x^2 - 4b + 28) + (9x^2 - 30) - (4x^2 - 6b + 20)$

48. Add $(9xy + 4x^2 + 18)$ and $(7xy - 4x^3 - 9x)$.

49. Subtract $(x - 7)$ from the sum of $(3x^2y - 7xy - 4)$ and $(9x^2y + x)$.

50. $x^2 - 5x + 7$
$\underline{\quad -\ (\ x + 4)\quad}$

51. $x^3 \quad\ + 2xy^2 - y$
$\underline{\quad +\ (x - 4xy^2 \qquad - 7)\quad}$

If $P(x) = 9x^2 - 7x + 8$, find the following.

52. $P(6)$ **53.** $P(-2)$

54. $P(-3)$

If $P(x) = 2x - 1$ and $Q(x) = x^2 + 2x - 5$, find the following.

55. $P(x) + Q(x)$ **56.** $2[P(x)] - Q(x)$

△ **57.** Find the perimeter of the rectangle.

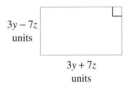

$x^2y + 5$ cm

$2x^2y - 6x + 1$ cm

(5.4) *Multiply.*

58. $-6x(4x^2 - 6x + 1)$

59. $-4ab^2(3ab^3 + 7ab + 1)$

60. $(x - 4)(2x + 9)$

61. $(-3xa + 4b)^2$

62. $(9x^2 + 4x + 1)(4x - 3)$

63. $(5x - 9y)(3x + 9y)$

64. $\left(x - \dfrac{1}{3}\right)\left(x + \dfrac{2}{3}\right)$

65. $(x^2 + 9x + 1)^2$

Multiply, using special products.

66. $(3x - y)^2$ **67.** $(4x + 9)^2$

68. $(x + 3y)(x - 3y)$

69. $[4 + (3a - b)][4 - (3a - b)]$

70. If $P(x) = 2x - 1$ and $Q(x) = x^2 + 2x - 5$, find $P(x)\cdot Q(x)$.

△ **71.** Find the area of the rectangle.

$3y - 7z$ units

$3y + 7z$ units

Multiply. Assume that all variable exponents represent integers.

72. $4a^b(3a^{b+2} - 7)$ **73.** $(4xy^z - b)^2$

74. $(3x^a - 4)(3x^a + 4)$

(5.5) *Factor out the greatest common factor.*

75. $16x^3 - 24x^2$ **76.** $36y - 24y^2$

77. $6ab^2 + 8ab - 4a^2b^2$ **78.** $14a^2b^2 - 21ab^2 + 7ab$

79. $6a(a + 3b) - 5(a + 3b)$

80. $4x(x - 2y) - 5(x - 2y)$

81. $xy - 6y + 3x - 18$ **82.** $ab - 8b + 4a - 32$

83. $pq - 3p - 5q + 15$ **84.** $x^3 - x^2 - 2x + 2$

△ **85.** A smaller square is cut from a larger rectangle. Write the area of the shaded region as a factored polynomial.

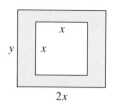

(5.6) *Completely factor each polynomial.*

86. $x^2 - 14x - 72$ **87.** $x^2 + 16x - 80$

88. $2x^2 - 18x + 28$ **89.** $3x^2 + 33x + 54$

90. $2x^3 - 7x^2 - 9x$ **91.** $3x^2 + 2x - 16$

92. $6x^2 + 17x + 10$ **93.** $15x^2 - 91x + 6$

94. $4x^2 + 2x - 12$ **95.** $9x^2 - 12x - 12$

96. $y^2(x + 6)^2 - 2y(x + 6)^2 - 3(x + 6)^2$

97. $(x + 5)^2 + 6(x + 5) + 8$

98. $x^4 - 6x^2 - 16$ **99.** $x^4 + 8x^2 - 20$

(5.7) *Factor each polynomial completely.*

100. $x^2 - 100$ **101.** $x^2 - 81$

102. $2x^2 - 32$ **103.** $6x^2 - 54$

104. $81 - x^4$ **105.** $16 - y^4$

106. $(y + 2)^2 - 25$ **107.** $(x - 3)^2 - 16$

108. $x^3 + 216$ **109.** $y^3 + 512$

110. $8 - 27y^3$ **111.** $1 - 64y^3$

112. $6x^4y + 48xy$ **113.** $2x^5 + 16x^2y^3$

114. $x^2 - 2x + 1 - y^2$ **115.** $x^2 - 6x + 9 - 4y^2$

116. $4x^2 + 12x + 9$ **117.** $16a^2 - 40ab + 25b^2$

△ **118.** The volume of the cylindrical shell is $\pi R^2 h - \pi r^2 h$ cubic units. Write this volume as a factored expression.

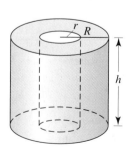

(5.8) *Solve each polynomial equation for the variable.*

119. $(3x - 1)(x + 7) = 0$

120. $3(x + 5)(8x - 3) = 0$

121. $5x(x - 4)(2x - 9) = 0$

122. $6(x + 3)(x - 4)(5x + 1) = 0$

123. $2x^2 = 12x$

124. $4x^3 - 36x = 0$

125. $(1 - x)(3x + 2) = -4x$

126. $2x(x - 12) = -40$

127. $3x^2 + 2x = 12 - 7x$

128. $2x^2 + 3x - 35$

129. $x^3 - 18x = 3x^2$

130. $19x^2 - 42x = -x^3$

131. $12x = 6x^3 + 6x^2$

132. $8x^3 + 10x^2 = 3x$

133. The sum of a number and twice its square is 105. Find the number.

△ **134.** The length of a rectangular piece of carpet is 2 meters less than 5 times its width. Find the dimensions of the carpet if its area is 16 square meters.

135. A scene from an adventure film calls for a stunt dummy to be dropped from above the second-story platform of the Eiffel Tower, a distance of 400 feet. Its height $h(t)$ at time t seconds is given by

$$h(t) = -16t^2 + 400$$

Determine when the stunt dummy will reach the ground.

400 feet

(5.9) *Exercises 136–139 refer to the following graph.*

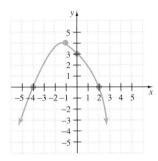

136. Find the domain and the range of the function.

137. List the *x*- and *y*-intercepts.

138. Find the coordinates of the point with the greatest *y*-value.

139. List the *x*-values for which the *y*-values are greater than 0.

Graph each polynomial function defined by the equation. Find all intercepts. If the function is a quadratic function, find the vertex.

140. $f(x) = x^2 + 6x + 9$

141. $f(x) = x^2 - 5x + 4$

142. $f(x) = (x - 1)(x^2 - 2x - 3)$

143. $f(x) = (x + 3)(x^2 - 4x + 3)$

144. $f(x) = 2x^2 - 4x + 5$

145. $f(x) = x^2 - 2x + 3$

146. $f(x) = x^3 - 16x$

147. $f(x) = x^3 + 5x^2 + 6x$

CHAPTER 5 TEST

Simplify. Use positive exponents to write the answers.

1. $(-9x)^{-2}$

2. $-3xy^{-2}(4xy^2)z$

3. $\dfrac{6^{-1}a^2b^{-3}}{3^{-2}a^{-5}b^2}$

4. $\left(\dfrac{-xy^{-5}z}{xy^3}\right)^{-5}$

Write in scientific notation.

5. 630,000,000

6. 0.01200

7. Write 5×10^{-6} without exponents.

8. Use scientific notation to find the quotient.

$$\frac{(0.0024)(0.00012)}{0.00032}$$

Perform the indicated operations.

9. $(4x^3 - 3x - 4) - (9x^3 + 8x + 5)$

10. $-3xy(4x + y)$

11. $(3x + 4)(4x - 7)$

12. $(5a - 2b)(5a + 2b)$

13. $(6m + n)^2$

14. $(2x - 1)(x^2 - 6x + 4)$

Factor each polynomial completely.

15. $16x^3y - 12x^2y^4$

16. $x^2 - 13x - 30$

17. $4y^2 + 20y + 25$

18. $6x^2 - 15x - 9$

19. $4x^2 - 25$

20. $x^3 + 64$

21. $3x^2y - 27y^3$

22. $6x^2 + 24$

23. $16y^3 - 2$

24. $x^2y - 9y - 3x^2 + 27$

Solve the equation for the variable.

25. $3(n - 4)(7n + 8) = 0$

26. $(x + 2)(x - 2) = 5(x + 4)$

Have you ever thought about how many feet, or even miles, of wiring are needed in your house, dormitory, or apartment building to make all of your lights and electrical appliances work? Without electricians to wire our homes and buildings, we all would probably be in the dark right now.

In addition to installing wiring and coaxial or fiber-optic cable, electricians also may repair or maintain electrical components. Most electricians learn their trade through a four-or five-year apprenticeship program that includes both on-the-job training and classes such as electrical theory and mathematics. Electricians use math and problem-solving skills in tasks such as estimating job costs, testing circuits, and reading blueprints.

 For more information about a career as an electrician, visit the National Electrical Contractors Association Website by first going to www.prenhall.com/martin-gay.

In the Spotlight on Decision Making feature on page 337, you will have the opportunity to make a decision as an electrician about which resistor to use to repair a power supply.

RATIONAL EXPRESSIONS

Polynomials are to algebra what integers are to arithmetic. We have added, subtracted, multiplied, and raised polynomials to powers, each operation yielding another polynomial, just as these operations on integers yield another integer. But when we divide one integer by another, the result may or may not be another integer. Likewise, when we divide one polynomial by another, we may or may not get a polynomial in return. The quotient $x \div (x + 1)$ is not a polynomial; it is a *rational expression* that can be written as $\dfrac{x}{x + 1}$.

In this chapter, we study these new algebraic forms known as rational expressions and the *rational functions* they generate.

6.1 RATIONAL FUNCTIONS AND MULTIPLYING AND DIVIDING RATIONAL EXPRESSIONS

CD-ROM   SSM

SSG   Video

▶ **O B J E C T I V E S**

1. Define a rational expression and a rational function.
2. Find values for which a rational expression is undefined.
3. Simplify rational expressions.
4. Multiply rational expressions.
5. Divide rational expressions.

---

1   Recall that a *rational number*, or *fraction*, is a number that can be written as the quotient $\frac{p}{q}$ of two integers p and q as long as q is not 0. A **rational expression** is an expression that can be written as the quotient $\frac{P}{Q}$ of two polynomials P and Q as long as Q is not 0.

Examples of Rational Expressions

$$\frac{3x + 7}{2} \qquad \frac{5x^2 - 3}{x - 1} \qquad \frac{7x - 2}{2x^2 + 7x + 6}$$

Rational expressions are sometimes used to describe functions. For example, we call the function $f(x) = \dfrac{x^2 + 2}{x - 3}$ a **rational function** since $\dfrac{x^2 + 2}{x - 3}$ is a rational expression.

Example 1   **COST FOR PRESSING COMPACT DISCS**

For the ICL Production Company, the rational function $C(x) = \dfrac{2.6x + 10,000}{x}$ describes the company's cost per disc of pressing x compact discs. Find the cost per disc for pressing

a. 100 compact discs
b. 1000 compact discs

Solution   **a.** $C(100) = \dfrac{2.6(100) + 10,000}{100} = \dfrac{10,260}{100} = 102.6$

The cost per disc for pressing 100 compact discs is $102.60.

b. $C(1000) = \dfrac{2.6(1000) + 10,000}{1000} = \dfrac{12,600}{1000} = 12.6$

The cost per disc for pressing 1000 compact discs is $12.60. Notice that as more compact discs are produced, the cost per disc decreases.

---

2   As with fractions, a rational expression is **undefined** if the denominator is 0. If a variable in a rational expression is replaced with a number that makes the denominator 0, we say that the rational expression is **undefined** for this value of the variable. For example, the rational expression $\dfrac{x^2 + 2}{x - 3}$ is undefined when x is 3, because replacing x with 3 results in a denominator of 0. For this reason, we must exclude 3 from the domain of the function defined by $f(x) = \dfrac{x^2 + 2}{x - 3}$.

The domain of f is then

$$\{x \mid x \text{ is a real number and } x \neq 3\}$$

"The set of all x such that x is a real number and x is not equal to 3."

Unless told otherwise, we assume that the domain of a function described by an equation is the set of all real numbers for which the equation is defined.

Example 2   Find the domain of each rational function.

a. $f(x) = \dfrac{8x^3 + 7x^2 + 20}{2}$ **b.** $g(x) = \dfrac{5x^2 - 3}{x - 1}$ **c.** $f(x) = \dfrac{7x - 2}{x^2 - 2x - 15}$

Solution   The domain of each function will contain all real numbers except those values that make the denominator 0.

a. No matter what the value of x, the denominator of $f(x) = \dfrac{8x^3 + 7x^2 + 20}{2}$ is never 0, so the domain of f is $\{x \mid x \text{ is a real number}\}$.

b. To find the values of x that make the denominator of $g(x)$ equal to 0, we solve the equation "denominator = 0":

$$x - 1 = 0, \quad \text{or} \quad x = 1$$

The domain of $g(x)$ must exclude 1 since the rational expression is undefined when x is 1. The domain of g is $\{x \mid x \text{ is a real number and } x \neq 1\}$.

c. We find the domain by setting the denominator equal to 0.

$$x^2 - 2x - 15 = 0 \qquad \text{\textit{Set the denominator equal to 0 and solve.}}$$
$$(x - 5)(x + 3) = 0$$
$$x - 5 = 0 \qquad \text{or} \qquad x + 3 = 0$$
$$x = 5 \qquad \text{or} \qquad x = -3$$

If x is replaced with 5 or with -3, the rational expression is undefined. The domain of f is $\{x \mid x \text{ is a real number and } x \neq 5 \text{ and } x \neq -3\}$.

3   Recall that a fraction is in lowest terms or simplest form if the numerator and denominator have no common factors other than 1 (or -1). For example, $\dfrac{3}{13}$ is in lowest terms since 3 and 13 have no common factors other than 1 (or -1).

To **simplify** a rational expression, or to write it in lowest terms, we use the fundamental principle of rational expressions.

FUNDAMENTAL PRINCIPLE OF RATIONAL EXPRESSIONS

For any rational expression $\dfrac{P}{Q}$ and any polynomial R, where $R \neq 0$,

$$\frac{PR}{QR} = \frac{P}{Q}$$

Thus, the fundamental principle says that multiplying or dividing the numerator and denominator of a rational expression by the same nonzero polynomial yields an equivalent rational expression.

To simplify a rational expression such as $\dfrac{(x + 2)^2}{x^2 - 4}$, factor the numerator and the denominator and then use the fundamental principle of rational expressions to divide out common factors.

$$\frac{(x + 2)^2}{x^2 - 4} = \frac{(x + 2)(x + 2)}{(x + 2)(x - 2)} = \frac{x + 2}{x - 2}$$

This means that the rational expression $\dfrac{(x + 2)^2}{x^2 - 4}$ has the same value as the rational expression $\dfrac{x + 2}{x - 2}$ for all values of x except 2 and −2. (Remember that when x is 2, the denominators of both rational expressions are 0 and that when x is −2, the original rational expression has a denominator of 0.)

As we simplify rational expressions, we will assume that the simplified rational expression is equivalent to the original rational expression for all real numbers except those for which either denominator is 0.

In general, the following steps may be used to simplify rational expressions or to write a rational expression in lowest terms.

SIMPLIFYING OR WRITING A RATIONAL EXPRESSION IN LOWEST TERMS

Step 1: Completely factor the numerator and denominator of the rational expression.

Step 2: Apply the fundamental principle of rational expressions to divide out factors common to both the numerator and denominator.

For now, we assume that variables in a rational expression do not represent values that make the denominator 0.

Example 3   Simplify $\dfrac{2x^2}{10x^3 - 2x^2}$.

Solution   Factor out $2x^2$ from the denominator. Then divide numerator and denominator by their GCF, $2x^2$.

$$\frac{2x^2}{10x^3 - 2x^2} = \frac{2x^2 \cdot 1}{2x^2 (5x - 1)} = \frac{1}{5x - 1}$$

When the terms in the numerator of a rational expression differ by sign from the terms of the denominator, the polynomials are opposites of each other and the expression simplifies to -1. To see this, factor out -1 from the numerator or the denominator. For example,

$$\frac{2-x}{x-2} = \frac{-1(-2+x)}{x-2} = \frac{-1(x-2)}{x-2} = -1$$

If -1 is factored from the denominator of the same rational expression, the result is the same.

$$\frac{2-x}{x-2} = \frac{2-x}{-1(-x+2)} = \frac{2-x}{-1(2-x)} = \frac{1}{-1} = -1$$

> **HELPFUL HINT**
> When the numerator and the denominator of a rational expression are opposites of each other, the expression simplifies to -1.

Example 4   Simplify $\dfrac{18 - 2x^2}{x^2 - 2x - 3}$.

Solution
$$\frac{18 - 2x^2}{x^2 - 2x - 3} = \frac{2(9 - x^2)}{(x+1)(x-3)} \qquad \text{Factor.}$$

$$= \frac{2(3+x)(3-x)}{(x+1)(x-3)} \qquad \text{Factor completely.}$$

$$= \frac{2(3+x) \cdot -1(x-3)}{(x+1)(x-3)} \qquad \begin{array}{l}\text{Notice the opposites } 3-x \\ \text{and } x-3. \text{ Write } 3-x \text{ as} \\ -1(x-3) \text{ and simplify.}\end{array}$$

$$= -\frac{2(3+x)}{x+1}$$

> **HELPFUL HINT**
> Recall that for a fraction $\dfrac{a}{b}$,
>
> $$\frac{a}{-b} = \frac{-a}{b} = -\frac{a}{b}$$
>
> For example
>
> $$\frac{-(x+1)}{(x+2)} = \frac{(x+1)}{-(x+2)} = -\frac{x+1}{x+2}$$

Example 5   Simplify each rational expression.

a. $\dfrac{x^3 + 8}{2 + x}$

b. $\dfrac{2y^2 + 2}{y^3 - 5y^2 + y - 5}$

Solution **a.** $\dfrac{x^3 + 8}{2 + x} = \dfrac{(x + 2)(x^2 - 2x + 4)}{x + 2}$ Factor the sum of the two cubes.

$\qquad\qquad\qquad = x^2 - 2x + 4$ Divide out common factors.

b. $\dfrac{2y^2 + 2}{y^3 - 5y^2 + y - 5} = \dfrac{2(y^2 + 1)}{(y^3 - 5y^2) + (y - 5)}$ Factor the numerator.

$\qquad\qquad\qquad\qquad = \dfrac{2(y^2 + 1)}{y^2(y - 5) + 1(y - 5)}$ Factor the denominator by grouping.

$\qquad\qquad\qquad\qquad = \dfrac{2(y^2 + 1)}{(y - 5)(y^2 + 1)}$

$\qquad\qquad\qquad\qquad = \dfrac{2}{y - 5}$ Divide out common factors.

---

4   Arithmetic operations on rational expressions are performed in the same way as they are on rational numbers.

MULTIPLYING RATIONAL EXPRESSIONS

The rule for multiplying rational expressions is

$$\frac{P}{Q} \cdot \frac{R}{S} = \frac{PR}{QS} \qquad \text{as long as } Q \neq 0 \text{ and } S \neq 0.$$

To multiply rational expressions, you may use these steps:

Step 1: Completely factor each numerator and denominator.
Step 2: Use the rule above and multiply the numerators and the denominators.
Step 3: Simplify the product by dividing the numerator and denominator by their common factors.

Example 6   Multiply.

a. $\dfrac{2x^3}{9y} \cdot \dfrac{y^2}{4x^3}$ **b.** $\dfrac{1 + 3n}{2n} \cdot \dfrac{2n - 4}{3n^2 - 2n - 1}$

Solution **a.** $\dfrac{2x^3}{9y} \cdot \dfrac{y^2}{4x^3} = \dfrac{2x^3 y^2}{36x^3 y}$

To simplify, divide the numerator and the denominator by the common factor, $2x^3 y$.

$$\frac{2x^3 y^2}{36x^3 y} = \frac{y(2x^3 y)}{18(2x^3 y)} = \frac{y}{18}$$

b. $\dfrac{1 + 3n}{2n} \cdot \dfrac{2n - 4}{3n^2 - 2n - 1} = \dfrac{1 + 3n}{2n} \cdot \dfrac{2(n - 2)}{(3n + 1)(n - 1)}$ Factor.

$$= \dfrac{(1 + 3n) \cdot 2(n - 2)}{2n(3n + 1)(n - 1)}$$ Multiply.

$$= \dfrac{n - 2}{n(n - 1)}$$ Divide out common factors.   ▬

When we multiply rational expressions, notice that we factor each numerator and denominator first. This helps when we apply the fundamental principle to write the product in lowest terms.

Example 7   Multiply.

a. $\dfrac{2x^2 + 3x - 2}{-4x - 8} \cdot \dfrac{16x^2}{4x^2 - 1}$ **b.** $\dfrac{x^3 - 1}{-3x + 3} \cdot \dfrac{15x^2}{x^2 + x + 1}$

Solution   **a.** $\dfrac{2x^2 + 3x - 2}{-4x - 8} \cdot \dfrac{16x^2}{4x^2 - 1} = \dfrac{(2x - 1)(x + 2)}{-4(x + 2)} \cdot \dfrac{16x^2}{(2x + 1)(2x - 1)}$ Factor.

$$= \dfrac{4 \cdot 4x^2(2x - 1)(x + 2)}{-1 \cdot 4(x + 2)(2x + 1)(2x - 1)}$$ Multiply.

$$= -\dfrac{4x^2}{2x + 1}$$ Divide out common factors.

b. $\dfrac{x^3 - 1}{-3x + 3} \cdot \dfrac{15x^2}{x^2 + x + 1} = \dfrac{(x - 1)(x^2 + x + 1)}{-3(x - 1)} \cdot \dfrac{15x^2}{x^2 + x + 1}$ Factor.

$$= \dfrac{(x - 1)(x^2 + x + 1) \cdot 3 \cdot 5x^2}{-1 \cdot 3(x - 1)(x^2 + x + 1)}$$ Factor.

$$= \dfrac{5x^2}{-1}$$ Divide out common factors.

$$= -5x^2$$ ▬

5   Recall that two numbers are reciprocals of each other if their product is 1. Similarly, if $\dfrac{P}{Q}$ is a rational expression, then $\dfrac{Q}{P}$ is its **reciprocal**, since

$$\dfrac{P}{Q} \cdot \dfrac{Q}{P} = \dfrac{P \cdot Q}{Q \cdot P} = 1$$

The following are examples of expressions and their reciprocals.

Expression	Reciprocal
$\dfrac{3}{x}$	$\dfrac{x}{3}$
$\dfrac{2 + x^2}{4x - 3}$	$\dfrac{4x - 3}{2 + x^2}$
x^3	$\dfrac{1}{x^3}$
0	no reciprocal

DIVIDING RATIONAL EXPRESSIONS

The rule for dividing rational expressions is

$$\frac{P}{Q} \div \frac{R}{S} = \frac{P}{Q} \cdot \frac{S}{R} = \frac{PS}{QR} \quad \text{as long as } Q \neq 0, S \neq 0, \text{ and } R \neq 0.$$

To divide by a rational expression, use the rule above and multiply by its reciprocal. Then simplify if possible.

Notice that division of rational expressions is the same as for rational numbers.

Example 8 Divide.

a. $\dfrac{3x}{5y} \div \dfrac{9y}{x^5}$

b. $\dfrac{8m^2}{3m^2 - 12} \div \dfrac{40}{2 - m}$

Solution **a.** $\dfrac{3x}{5y} \div \dfrac{9y}{x^5} = \dfrac{3x}{5y} \cdot \dfrac{x^5}{9y}$ Multiply by the reciprocal of the divisor.

$$= \frac{x^6}{15y^2} \quad \text{Simplify.}$$

b. $\dfrac{8m^2}{3m^2 - 12} \div \dfrac{40}{2 - m} = \dfrac{8m^2}{3m^2 - 12} \cdot \dfrac{2 - m}{40}$ Multiply by the reciprocal of the divisor.

$$= \frac{8m^2(2 - m)}{3(m + 2)(m - 2) \cdot 40} \quad \text{Factor and multiply.}$$

$$= \frac{8 \, m^2 \cdot -1(m - 2)}{3(m + 2)(m - 2) \cdot 8 \cdot 5} \quad \text{Write } (2 - m) \text{ as } -1(m - 2).$$

$$= -\frac{m^2}{15(m + 2)} \quad \text{Simplify.}$$

> ▼ **HELPFUL HINT**
> When dividing rational expressions, do not divide out common factors until the division problem is rewritten as a multiplication problem.

Example 9   Perform each indicated operation.

$$\frac{x^2 - 25}{(x + 5)^2} \cdot \frac{3x + 15}{4x} \div \frac{x^2 - 3x - 10}{x}$$

Solution $\dfrac{x^2 - 25}{(x + 5)^2} \cdot \dfrac{3x + 15}{4x} \div \dfrac{x^2 - 3x - 10}{x}$

$$= \frac{x^2 - 25}{(x + 5)^2} \cdot \frac{3x + 15}{4x} \cdot \frac{x}{x^2 - 3x - 10}$$ To divide, multiply by the reciprocal

$$= \frac{(x + 5)(x - 5)}{(x + 5)(x + 5)} \cdot \frac{3(x + 5)}{4x} \cdot \frac{x}{(x - 5)(x + 2)}$$

$$= \frac{3}{4(x + 2)}$$

SPOTLIGHT ON DECISION MAKING

Suppose you are an electrician at a small packaging plant. You are repairing machinery that heats the hot glue gun used for sealing boxes. You have determined that a resistor in the machinery's 50-volt direct current power supply must be replaced. To keep the glue warm, the power supply must dissipate about 2000 watts of power.

You know that the power P (in watts) dissipated by a resistor in a direct current circuit is given by the formula $P = \dfrac{V^2}{R}$, where V is the voltage (in volts) and R is the resistance (in ohms). Which of the three resistors shown in the parts list would you use to replace the faulty resistor? Why?

PARTS LIST RESISTORS		
Part Number	*Material*	*Resistance (in ohms)*
1298	Aluminum	0.95
3169	Nickel	1.81
4203	Tungsten	1.22

GRAPHING CALCULATOR EXPLORATIONS

Recall that since the rational expression $\dfrac{7x - 2}{(x - 2)(x + 5)}$ is not defined when $x = 2$ or when $x = -5$, we say that the domain of the rational function $f(x) = \dfrac{7x - 2}{(x - 2)(x + 5)}$ is all real numbers except 2 and -5. This domain can be written as $\{x \,|\, x$ is a real number and $x \neq 2$, $x \neq -5\}$. This means that the graph of $f(x)$ should not cross the vertical lines $x = 2$ and $x = -5$. The graph of $f(x)$ in *connected* mode follows. In connected mode the graphing calculator tries to connect all dots of the graph so that the result is a smooth curve. This is what has happened in the graph. Notice that the graph appears to contain vertical lines at $x = 2$ and at $x = -5$. We know that this cannot happen because the function is not defined at $x = 2$ and at $x = -5$. We also know that this cannot happen because the graph of this function would not pass the vertical line test.

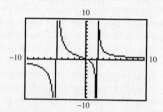

If we graph $f(x)$ in *dot* mode, the graph appears as follows. In dot mode the graphing calculator will not connect dots with a smooth curve. Notice that the vertical lines have disappeared, and we have a better picture of the graph. The graph, however, actually appears more like the hand-drawn graph to its right. By using a Table feature, a Calculate Value feature, or by tracing, we can see that the function is not defined at $x = 2$ and at $x = -5$.

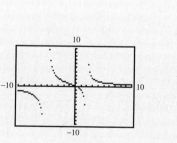

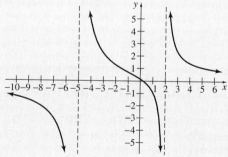

Find the domain of each rational function. Then graph each rational function and use the graph to confirm the domain.

1. $f(x) = \dfrac{x + 1}{x^2 - 4}$

2. $g(x) = \dfrac{5x}{x^2 - 9}$

3. $h(x) = \dfrac{x^2}{2x^2 + 7x - 4}$

4. $f(x) = \dfrac{3x + 2}{4x^2 - 19x - 5}$

Exercise Set 6.1

Find each function value. See Example 1.

1. $f(x) = \dfrac{x + 8}{2x - 1}; f(2), f(0), f(-1)$

2. $f(y) = \dfrac{y - 2}{-5 + y}; f(-5), f(0), f(10)$

3. $g(x) = \dfrac{x^2 + 8}{x^3 - 25x}; g(3), g(-2), g(1)$

4. $s(t) = \dfrac{t^3 + 1}{t^2 + 1}; s(-1), s(1), s(2)$

Find the domain of each rational function. See Example 2.

5. $f(x) = \dfrac{5x - 7}{4}$

6. $g(x) = \dfrac{4 - 3x}{2}$

7. $s(t) = \dfrac{t^2 + 1}{2t}$

8. $v(t) = -\dfrac{5t + t^2}{3t}$

9. $f(x) = \dfrac{3x}{7 - x}$

10. $f(x) = \dfrac{-4x}{-2 + x}$

11. $R(x) = \dfrac{3 + 2x}{x^3 + x^2 - 2x}$

12. $h(x) = \dfrac{5 - 3x}{2x^2 - 14x + 20}$

13. $C(x) = \dfrac{x + 3}{x^2 - 4}$

14. $R(x) = \dfrac{5}{x^2 - 7x}$

15. In your own words, explain how to find the domain of a rational function.

16. In your own words, explain how to simplify a rational expression or to write it in lowest terms.

Write each rational expression in lowest terms. See Examples 3 through 5.

17. $\dfrac{4x - 8}{3x - 6}$

18. $\dfrac{12 - 6x}{30 - 15x}$

19. $\dfrac{2x - 14}{7 - x}$

20. $\dfrac{9 - x}{5x - 45}$

21. $\dfrac{x^2 - 2x - 3}{x^2 - 6x + 9}$

22. $\dfrac{x^2 + 10x + 25}{x^2 + 8x + 15}$

23. $\dfrac{2x^2 + 12x + 18}{x^2 - 9}$

24. $\dfrac{x^2 - 4}{2x^2 + 8x + 8}$

25. $\dfrac{3x + 6}{x^2 + 2x}$

26. $\dfrac{3x + 4}{9x^2 + 4}$

27. $\dfrac{2x^2 - x - 3}{2x^3 - 3x^2 + 2x - 3}$

28. $\dfrac{3x^2 - 5x - 2}{6x^3 + 2x^2 + 3x + 1}$

29. $\dfrac{8q^2}{16q^3 - 16q^2}$

30. $\dfrac{3y}{6y^2 - 30y}$

31. $\dfrac{x^2 + 6x - 40}{10 + x}$

32. $\dfrac{x^2 - 8x + 16}{4 - x}$

33. $\dfrac{x^3 - 125}{5 - x}$

34. $\dfrac{4x + 4}{2x^3 + 2}$

35. $\dfrac{8x^3 - 27}{4x - 6}$

36. $\dfrac{9x^2 - 15x + 25}{27x^3 + 125}$

Multiply or divide as indicated. Simplify all answers. See Examples 6 through 9.

37. $\dfrac{3xy^3}{4x^3y^2} \cdot \dfrac{-8x^3y^4}{9x^4y^7}$

38. $-\dfrac{2xyz^3}{5x^2z^2} \cdot \dfrac{10xy}{x^3}$

39. $\dfrac{8a}{3a^4b^2} \div \dfrac{4b^5}{6a^2b}$

40. $\dfrac{3y^3}{14x^4} \div \dfrac{8y^3}{7x}$

41. $\dfrac{a^2b}{a^2 - b^2} \cdot \dfrac{a + b}{4a^3b}$

42. $\dfrac{3ab^2}{a^2 - 4} \cdot \dfrac{a - 2}{6a^2b^2}$

43. $\dfrac{x^2 - 9}{4} \div \dfrac{x^2 - 6x + 9}{x^2 - x - 6}$

44. $\dfrac{a - 5b}{a^2 + ab} \div \dfrac{15b - 3a}{b^2 - a^2}$

45. $\dfrac{9x + 9}{4x + 8} \cdot \dfrac{2x + 4}{3x^2 - 3}$

46. $\dfrac{x^2 - 1}{10x + 30} \cdot \dfrac{12x + 36}{3x - 3}$

47. $\dfrac{a + b}{ab} \div \dfrac{a^2 - b^2}{4a^3b}$

48. $\dfrac{6a^2b^2}{a^2 - 4} \div \dfrac{3ab^2}{a - 2}$

49. $\dfrac{2x^2 - 4x - 30}{5x^2 - 40x - 75} \div \dfrac{x^2 - 8x + 15}{x^2 - 6x + 9}$

50. $\dfrac{4a + 36}{a^2 - 7a - 18} \div \dfrac{a^2 - a - 6}{a^2 - 81}$

51. $\dfrac{2x^3 - 16}{6x^2 + 6x - 36} \cdot \dfrac{9x + 18}{3x^2 + 6x + 12}$

52. $\dfrac{x^2 - 3x + 9}{5x^2 - 20x - 105} \cdot \dfrac{x^2 - 49}{x^3 + 27}$

53. $\dfrac{15b - 3a}{b^2 - a^2} \div \dfrac{a - 5b}{ab + b^2}$

54. $\dfrac{4x + 4}{x - 1} \div \dfrac{x^2 - 4x - 5}{x^2 - 1}$

55. $\dfrac{a^3 + a^2b + a + b}{a^3 + a} \cdot \dfrac{6a^2}{2a^2 - 2b^2}$

56. $\dfrac{a^2 - 2a}{ab - 2b + 3a - 6} \cdot \dfrac{8b + 24}{3a + 6}$

57. $\dfrac{5a}{12} \cdot \dfrac{2}{25a^2} \cdot \dfrac{15a}{2}$

58. $\dfrac{4a}{7} \div \dfrac{a^2}{14} \cdot \dfrac{3}{a}$

59. $\dfrac{3x - x^2}{x^3 - 27} \div \dfrac{x}{x^2 + 3x + 9}$

60. $\dfrac{x^2 - 3x}{x^3 - 27} \div \dfrac{2x}{2x^2 + 6x + 18}$

61. $\dfrac{4a}{7} \div \left(\dfrac{a^2}{14} \cdot \dfrac{3}{a}\right)$

62. $\dfrac{a^2}{14} \cdot \dfrac{3}{a} \div \dfrac{4a}{7}$

63. $\dfrac{8b + 24}{3a + 6} \div \dfrac{ab - 2b + 3a - 6}{a^2 - 4a + 4}$

64. $\dfrac{2a^2 - 2b^2}{a^3 + a^2b + a + b} \div \dfrac{6a^2}{a^3 + a}$

65. $\dfrac{4}{x} \div \dfrac{3xy}{x^2} \cdot \dfrac{6x^2}{x^4}$

66. $\dfrac{4}{x} \cdot \dfrac{3xy}{x^2} \div \dfrac{6x^2}{x^4}$

67. $\dfrac{3x^2 - 5x - 2}{y^2 + y - 2} \cdot \dfrac{y^2 + 4y - 5}{12x^2 + 7x + 1} \div \dfrac{5x^2 - 9x - 2}{8x^2 - 2x - 1}$

68. $\dfrac{x^2 + x - 2}{3y^2 - 5y - 2} \cdot \dfrac{12y^2 + y - 1}{x^2 + 4x - 5} \div \dfrac{8y^2 - 6y + 1}{5y^2 - 9y - 2}$

69. $\dfrac{5a^2 - 20}{3a^2 - 12a} \div \dfrac{a^3 + 2a^2}{2a^2 - 8a} \cdot \dfrac{9a^3 + 6a^2}{2a^2 - 4a}$

70. $\dfrac{5a^2 - 20}{3a^2 - 12a} \div \left(\dfrac{a^3 + 2a^2}{2a^2 - 8a} \cdot \dfrac{9a^3 + 6a^2}{2a^2 - 4a}\right)$

71. $\dfrac{5x^4 + 3x^2 - 2}{x - 1} \cdot \dfrac{x + 1}{x^4 - 1}$

72. $\dfrac{3x^4 - 10x^2 - 8}{x - 2} \cdot \dfrac{3x + 6}{15x^2 + 10}$

△ **73.** Find the area of the rectangle.

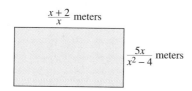

$\dfrac{x + 2}{x}$ meters

$\dfrac{5x}{x^2 - 4}$ meters

△ **74.** Find the area of the triangle.

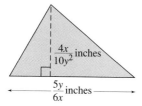

$\dfrac{4x}{10y^2}$ inches

$\dfrac{5y}{6x}$ inches

75. In our definition of division for
$$\dfrac{P}{Q} \div \dfrac{R}{S}$$
we stated that $Q \neq 0, S \neq 0,$ and $R \neq 0.$ Explain why R cannot equal 0.

76. Find the polynomial in the second numerator such that the following statement is true.
$$\dfrac{x^2 - 4}{x^2 - 7x + 10} \cdot \dfrac{?}{2x^2 + 11x + 14} = 1$$

△ **77.** A parallelogram has area $\dfrac{x^2 + x - 2}{x^3}$ square feet and height $\dfrac{x^2}{x - 1}$ feet. Express the length of its base as a rational expression in x. (*Hint:* Since $A = b \cdot h$, then $b = \dfrac{A}{h}$ or $b = A \div h$.)

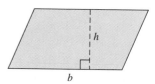

78. A lottery prize of $\dfrac{15x^3}{y^2}$ dollars is to be divided among $5x$ people. Express the amount of money each person is to receive as a rational expression in x and y.

79. Graph a portion of the function $f(x) = \dfrac{20x}{100 - x}$. To do so, complete the given table, plot the points, and then connect the plotted points with a smooth curve.

x	0	10	30	50	70	90	95	99
y or $f(x)$								

80. The domain of the function $f(x) = \dfrac{1}{x}$ is all real numbers except 0. This means that the graph of this function will be in two pieces: one piece corresponding to x values less than 0 and one piece corresponding to x values greater than 0. Graph the function by completing the following tables, separately plotting the points, and connecting each set of plotted points with a smooth curve.

x	$\frac{1}{4}$	$\frac{1}{2}$	1	2	4
y or $f(x)$					

x	-4	-2	-1	$-\frac{1}{2}$	$-\frac{1}{4}$
y or $f(x)$					

81. The function $f(x) = \dfrac{100,000x}{100 - x}$ models the cost in dollars for removing x percent of the pollutants from a bayou in which a nearby company dumped creosote.

   a. What is the domain of $f(x)$?

   b. Find the cost of removing 30% of the pollutants from the bayou. (*Hint:* Find $f(30).$)

   c. Find the cost of removing 60% of the pollutants and then 80% of the pollutants.

d. Find $f(90)$, then $f(95)$, and then $f(99)$. What happens to the cost as x approaches 100%?

82. The total revenue from the sale of a popular book is approximated by the rational function $R(x) = \dfrac{1000x^2}{x^2 + 4}$

where x is the number of years since publication and $R(x)$ is the total revenue in millions of dollars.

a. Find the total revenue at the end of the first year.
b. Find the total revenue at the end of the second year.
c. Find the revenue during the second year only.

REVIEW EXERCISES

Perform the indicated operations. See Section 1.3.

83. $\dfrac{4}{5} + \dfrac{3}{5}$

84. $\dfrac{4}{10} - \dfrac{7}{10}$

85. $\dfrac{5}{28} - \dfrac{2}{21}$

86. $\dfrac{5}{13} + \dfrac{2}{7}$

87. $\dfrac{3}{8} + \dfrac{1}{2} - \dfrac{3}{16}$

88. $\dfrac{2}{9} - \dfrac{1}{6} + \dfrac{2}{3}$

A Look Ahead

Example
Perform the following operation.

$$\frac{x^{2n} - 3x^n - 18}{x^{2n} - 9} \cdot \frac{3x^n + 9}{x^{2n}}$$

Solution $\dfrac{x^{2n} - 3x^n - 18}{x^{2n} - 9} \cdot \dfrac{3x^n + 9}{x^{2n}}$

$$= \frac{(x^n + 3)(x^n - 6) \cdot 3(x^n + 3)}{(x^n + 3)(x^n - 3) \cdot x^{2n}}$$

$$= \frac{3(x^n - 6)(x^n + 3)}{x^{2n}(x^n - 3)}$$

Perform the indicated operation. Write all answers in lowest terms. See the preceding example.

89. $\dfrac{x^{2n} - 4}{7x} \cdot \dfrac{14x^3}{x^n - 2}$

90. $\dfrac{x^{2n} + 4x^n + 4}{4x - 3} \cdot \dfrac{8x^2 - 6x}{x^n + 2}$

91. $\dfrac{y^{2n} + 9}{10y} \cdot \dfrac{y^n - 3}{y^{4n} - 81}$

92. $\dfrac{y^{4n} - 16}{y^{2n} + 4} \cdot \dfrac{6y}{y^n + 2}$

93. $\dfrac{y^{2n} - y^n - 2}{2y^n - 4} \div \dfrac{y^{2n} - 1}{1 + y^n}$

94. $\dfrac{y^{2n} + 7y^n + 10}{10} \div \dfrac{y^{2n} + 4y^n + 4}{5y^n + 25}$

6.2 ADDING AND SUBTRACTING RATIONAL EXPRESSIONS

CD-ROM   SSM

SSG   Video

▶ **OBJECTIVES**

1. Add or subtract rational expressions with common denominators.
2. Identify the least common denominator of two or more rational expressions.
3. Add or subtract rational expressions with unlike denominators.

1 Rational expressions, like rational numbers, can be added or subtracted. We define the sum or difference of rational expressions in the same way that we defined the sum or difference of rational numbers (fractions).

ADDING OR SUBTRACTING RATIONAL EXPRESSIONS WITH COMMON DENOMINATORS

If $\dfrac{P}{Q}$ and $\dfrac{R}{Q}$ are rational expressions, then

$$\frac{P}{Q} + \frac{R}{Q} = \frac{P + R}{Q} \quad \text{and} \quad \frac{P}{Q} - \frac{R}{Q} = \frac{P - R}{Q}$$

To add or subtract rational expressions with common denominators, add or subtract the numerators and write the sum or difference over the common denominator.

Example 1 Add or subtract.

a. $\dfrac{x}{4} + \dfrac{5x}{4}$

b. $\dfrac{x^2}{x + 7} - \dfrac{49}{x + 7}$

c. $\dfrac{x}{3y^2} - \dfrac{x + 1}{3y^2}$

Solution The rational expressions have common denominators, so add or subtract their numerators and place the sum or difference over their common denominator.

a. $\dfrac{x}{4} + \dfrac{5x}{4} = \dfrac{x + 5x}{4} = \dfrac{6x}{4} = \dfrac{3x}{2}$ Add the numerators and write the result over the common denominator.

b. $\dfrac{x^2}{x + 7} - \dfrac{49}{x + 7} = \dfrac{x^2 - 49}{x + 7}$ Subtract the numerators and write the result over the common denominator.

$\quad = \dfrac{(x + 7)(x - 7)}{x + 7}$ Factor the numerator.

$\quad = x - 7$ Simplify.

> **HELPFUL HINT**
> Be sure to insert parentheses here so that the entire numerator is subtracted.

c. $\dfrac{x}{3y^2} - \dfrac{x + 1}{3y^2} = \dfrac{x - (x + 1)}{3y^2}$ Subtract the numerators.

$\quad = \dfrac{x - x - 1}{3y^2}$ Use the distributive property.

$\quad = -\dfrac{1}{3y^2}$ Simplify.

2 To add or subtract rational expressions with unlike denominators, first write the rational expressions as equivalent rational expressions with common denominators.

The **least common denominator (LCD)** is usually the easiest common denominator to work with. The LCD of a list of rational expressions is a polynomial of least degree whose factors include the denominator factors in the list.

Use the following steps to find the LCD.

> **FINDING THE LEAST COMMON DENOMINATOR (LCD)**
>
> **Step 1:** Factor each denominator completely.
> **Step 2:** The LCD is the product of all unique factors each raised to the greatest power that appears in any factored denominator.

Example 2 Find the LCD of the rational expressions in each list.

a. $\dfrac{2}{3x^5y^2}, \dfrac{3z}{5xy^3}$

b. $\dfrac{7}{z + 1}, \dfrac{z}{z - 1}$

c. $\dfrac{m - 1}{m^2 - 25}, \dfrac{2m}{2m^2 - 9m - 5}, \dfrac{7}{m^2 - 10m + 25}$

d. $\dfrac{x}{x^2 - 4}, \dfrac{11}{6 - 3x}$

Solution   **a.** First we factor each denominator.

$$3x^5y^2 = 3 \cdot x^5 \cdot y^2$$
$$5xy^3 = 5 \cdot x \cdot y^3$$
$$\text{LCD} = 3 \cdot 5 \cdot x^5 \cdot y^3 = 15x^5y^3$$

> **▼ HELPFUL HINT**
> The greatest power of x is 5, so we have a factor of x^5. The greatest power of y is 3, so we have a factor of y^3.

b. The denominators $z + 1$ and $z - 1$ do not factor further. Thus,

$$\text{LCD} = (z + 1)(z - 1)$$

c. We first factor each denominator.

$$m^2 - 25 = (m + 5)(m - 5)$$
$$2m^2 - 9m - 5 = (2m + 1)(m - 5)$$
$$m^2 - 10m + 25 = (m - 5)(m - 5)$$
$$\text{LCD} = (m + 5)(2m + 1)(m - 5)^2$$

d. Factor each denominator.

$$x^2 - 4 = (x + 2)(x - 2)$$
$$6 - 3x = 3(2 - x) = 3(-1)(x - 2)$$
$$\text{LCD} = 3(-1)(x + 2)(x - 2)$$
$$= -3(x + 2)(x - 2)$$

> **▼ HELPFUL HINT**
> $(x - 2)$ and $(2 - x)$ are opposite factors. Notice that -1 was factored from $(2 - x)$ so that the factors are identical.

> **▼ HELPFUL HINT**
> If opposite factors occur, do not use both in the LCD. Instead, factor -1 from one of the opposite factors so that the factors are then identical.

3

To add or subtract rational expressions with unlike denominators, we write each rational expression as an equivalent rational expression so that their denominators are alike.

ADDING OR SUBTRACTING RATIONAL EXPRESSIONS WITH UNLIKE DENOMINATORS

Step 1: Find the LCD of the rational expressions.

Step 2: Write each rational expression as an equivalent rational expression whose denominator is the LCD found in Step 1.

Step 3: Add or subtract numerators, and write the result over the common denominator.

Step 4: Simplify the resulting rational expression.

Example 3   Perform the indicated operation.

a. $\dfrac{2}{x^2y} + \dfrac{5}{3x^3y}$ **b.** $\dfrac{3x}{x + 2} + \dfrac{2x}{x - 2}$ **c.** $\dfrac{x}{x - 1} - \dfrac{4}{1 - x}$

Solution   **a.** The LCD is $3x^3y$. Write each fraction as an equivalent fraction with denominator $3x^3y$. To do this, we multiply both the numerator and denominator of each fraction by the factors needed to obtain the LCD as denominator.

The first fraction is multiplied by $\dfrac{3x}{3x}$ so that the new denominator is the LCD.

$$\frac{2}{x^2y} + \frac{5}{3x^3y} = \frac{2 \cdot 3x}{x^2y \cdot 3x} + \frac{5}{3x^3y} \qquad \text{\small The second expression already has a denominator of } 3x^3y.$$

$$= \frac{6x}{3x^3y} + \frac{5}{3x^3y}$$

$$= \frac{6x + 5}{3x^3y} \qquad \text{\small Add the numerators.}$$

b. The LCD is the product of the two denominators: $(x + 2)(x - 2)$.

$$\frac{3x}{x + 2} + \frac{2x}{x - 2} = \frac{3x \cdot (x - 2)}{(x + 2) \cdot (x - 2)} + \frac{2x \cdot (x + 2)}{(x - 2) \cdot (x + 2)} \qquad \text{\small Write equivalent rational expressions.}$$

$$= \frac{3x(x - 2) + 2x(x + 2)}{(x + 2)(x - 2)} \qquad \text{\small Add the numerators.}$$

$$= \frac{3x^2 - 6x + 2x^2 + 4x}{(x + 2)(x - 2)} \qquad \text{\small Apply the distributive property.}$$

$$= \frac{5x^2 - 2x}{(x + 2)(x - 2)} \qquad \text{\small Simplify the numerator.}$$

c. The LCD is either $x - 1$ or $1 - x$. To get a common denominator of $x - 1$, we factor -1 from the denominator of the second rational expression.

$$\frac{x}{x - 1} - \frac{4}{1 - x} = \frac{x}{x - 1} - \frac{4}{-1(x - 1)} \qquad \text{\small Write } 1 - x \text{ as } -1(x - 1).$$

$$= \frac{x}{x - 1} - \frac{-1 \cdot 4}{x - 1} \qquad \text{\small Write } \frac{4}{-1(x - 1)} \text{ as } \frac{-1 \cdot 4}{x - 1}.$$

$$= \frac{x - (-4)}{x - 1}$$

$$= \frac{x + 4}{x - 1} \qquad \text{\small Simplify.} \qquad \blacksquare$$

Example 4   Subtract $\dfrac{5k}{k^2 - 4} - \dfrac{2}{k^2 + k - 2}$.

Solution $\dfrac{5k}{k^2 - 4} - \dfrac{2}{k^2 + k - 2} = \dfrac{5k}{(k + 2)(k - 2)} - \dfrac{2}{(k + 2)(k - 1)}$ $\text{\small Factor each denominator to find the LCD.}$

The LCD is $(k + 2)(k - 2)(k - 1)$. We write equivalent rational expressions with the LCD as denominators.

$$\frac{5k}{(k + 2)(k - 2)} - \frac{2}{(k + 2)(k - 1)} = \frac{5k \cdot (k - 1)}{(k + 2)(k - 2) \cdot (k - 1)} - \frac{2 \cdot (k - 2)}{(k + 2)(k - 1) \cdot (k - 2)}$$

$$= \frac{5k(k - 1) - 2(k - 2)}{(k + 2)(k - 2)(k - 1)} \qquad \text{\small Subtract the numerators.}$$

$$= \frac{5k^2 - 5k - 2k + 4}{(k + 2)(k - 2)(k - 1)} \qquad \text{Multiply in the numerator.}$$

$$= \frac{5k^2 - 7k + 4}{(k + 2)(k - 2)(k - 1)} \qquad \text{Simplify.}$$

■

Example 5   Add $\dfrac{2x - 1}{2x^2 - 9x - 5} + \dfrac{x + 3}{6x^2 - x - 2}$.

Solution $\dfrac{2x - 1}{2x^2 - 9x - 5} + \dfrac{x + 3}{6x^2 - x - 2} = \dfrac{2x - 1}{(2x + 1)(x - 5)} + \dfrac{x + 3}{(2x + 1)(3x - 2)} \quad \begin{array}{l}\text{Factor the}\\\text{denominators.}\end{array}$

The LCD is $(2x + 1)(x - 5)(3x - 2)$.

$$= \frac{(2x - 1) \cdot (3x - 2)}{(2x + 1)(x - 5) \cdot (3x - 2)} + \frac{(x + 3) \cdot (x - 5)}{(2x + 1)(3x - 2) \cdot (x - 5)}$$

$$= \frac{(2x - 1)(3x - 2) + (x + 3)(x - 5)}{(2x + 1)(x - 5)(3x - 2)} \qquad \text{Add the numerators.}$$

$$= \frac{6x^2 - 7x + 2 + x^2 - 2x - 15}{(2x + 1)(x - 5)(3x - 2)} \qquad \text{Multiply in the numerator.}$$

$$= \frac{7x^2 - 9x - 13}{(2x + 1)(x - 5)(3x - 2)} \qquad \text{Simplify.}$$

■

Example 6   Perform each indicated operation.

$$\frac{7}{x - 1} + \frac{10x}{x^2 - 1} - \frac{5}{x + 1}$$

Solution $\dfrac{7}{x - 1} + \dfrac{10x}{x^2 - 1} - \dfrac{5}{x + 1} = \dfrac{7}{x - 1} + \dfrac{10x}{(x - 1)(x + 1)} - \dfrac{5}{x + 1} \quad \begin{array}{l}\text{Factor the}\\\text{denominators.}\end{array}$

The LCD is $(x - 1)(x + 1)$.

$$= \frac{7 \cdot (x + 1)}{(x - 1) \cdot (x + 1)} + \frac{10x}{(x - 1)(x + 1)} - \frac{5 \cdot (x - 1)}{(x + 1) \cdot (x - 1)}$$

$$= \frac{7(x + 1) + 10x - 5(x - 1)}{(x - 1)(x + 1)} \qquad \text{Add and subtract the numerators.}$$

$$= \frac{7x + 7 + 10x - 5x + 5}{(x - 1)(x + 1)} \qquad \text{Multiply in the numerator.}$$

$$= \frac{12x + 12}{(x - 1)(x + 1)} \qquad \text{Simplify.}$$

$$= \frac{12(x + 1)}{(x - 1)(x + 1)} \qquad \text{Factor the numerator.}$$

$$= \frac{12}{x - 1} \qquad \text{Divide out common factors.}$$

■

GRAPHING CALCULATOR EXPLORATIONS

A graphing calculator can be used to support the results of operations on rational expressions. For example, to verify the result of Example 3b, graph

$$Y_1 = \frac{3x}{x+2} + \frac{2x}{x-2} \quad \text{and} \quad Y_2 = \frac{5x^2 - 2x}{(x+2)(x-2)}$$

on the same set of axes. The graphs should be the same. Use a Table feature or a Trace feature to see that this is true.

Exercise Set 6.2

Perform the indicated operation. If possible, simplify your answer. See Example 1.

1. $\dfrac{2}{x} - \dfrac{5}{x}$

2. $\dfrac{4}{x^2} + \dfrac{2}{x^2}$

3. $\dfrac{2}{x-2} + \dfrac{x}{x-2}$

4. $\dfrac{x}{5-x} + \dfrac{2}{5-x}$

5. $\dfrac{x^2}{x+2} - \dfrac{4}{x+2}$

6. $\dfrac{4}{x-2} - \dfrac{x^2}{x-2}$

7. $\dfrac{2x-6}{x^2+x-6} + \dfrac{3-3x}{x^2+x-6}$

8. $\dfrac{5x+2}{x^2+2x-8} + \dfrac{2-4x}{x^2+2x-8}$

△ **9.** Find the perimeter and the area of the square.

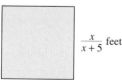

$\dfrac{x}{x+5}$ feet

△ **10.** Find the perimeter of the quadrilateral.

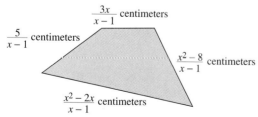

$\dfrac{3x}{x-1}$ centimeters

$\dfrac{5}{x-1}$ centimeters

$\dfrac{x^2-8}{x-1}$ centimeters

$\dfrac{x^2-2x}{x-1}$ centimeters

Find the LCD of the rational expressions in each list. See Example 2.

11. $\dfrac{2}{7}, \dfrac{3}{5x}$

12. $\dfrac{4}{5y}, \dfrac{3}{4y^2}$

13. $\dfrac{3}{x}, \dfrac{2}{x+1}$

14. $\dfrac{5}{2x}, \dfrac{7}{2+x}$

15. $\dfrac{12}{x+7}, \dfrac{8}{x-7}$

16. $\dfrac{1}{2x-1}, \dfrac{x}{2x+1}$

17. $\dfrac{5}{3x+6}, \dfrac{2x}{2x-4}$

18. $\dfrac{2}{3a+9}, \dfrac{5}{5a-15}$

19. $\dfrac{5+x}{(3x-1)(x+2)}, \dfrac{2}{3x-1}$

20. $\dfrac{6-x}{(x+3)(x-3)}, \dfrac{9}{x+3}$

21. $\dfrac{2a}{a^2-b^2}, \dfrac{1}{a^2-2ab+b^2}$

22. $\dfrac{2a}{a^2+8a+16}, \dfrac{7a}{a^2+a-12}$

23. $\dfrac{x}{x^2-9}, \dfrac{5x}{x}, \dfrac{7}{12-4x}$

24. $\dfrac{9}{x^2-25}, \dfrac{1}{50-10x}, \dfrac{6}{x}$

25. When is the LCD of two rational expressions equal to the product of their denominators? (*Hint:* What is the LCD of $\dfrac{1}{x}$ and $\dfrac{7}{x+5}$?)

26. When is the LCD of two rational expressions with different denominators equal to one of the denominators? (*Hint:* What is the LCD of $\dfrac{3x}{x+2}$ and $\dfrac{7x+1}{(x+2)^3}$?)

Perform the indicated operation. If possible, simplify your answer. Write each answer in lowest terms. See Example 3a and 3b.

27. $\dfrac{4}{3x} + \dfrac{3}{2x}$

28. $\dfrac{10}{7x} - \dfrac{5}{2x}$

29. $\dfrac{5}{2y^2} - \dfrac{2}{7y}$

30. $\dfrac{4}{11x^4y} - \dfrac{1}{4x^2y^3}$

31. $\dfrac{x-3}{x+4} - \dfrac{x+2}{x-4}$

32. $\dfrac{x-1}{x-5} - \dfrac{x+2}{x+5}$

33. $\dfrac{1}{x - 5} + \dfrac{x}{x^2 - x - 20}$

34. $\dfrac{x + 1}{x^2 - x - 20} - \dfrac{2}{x + 4}$

Perform the indicated operation. If possible, simplify your answer. See Example 3c.

35. $\dfrac{1}{a - b} + \dfrac{1}{b - a}$

36. $\dfrac{1}{a - 3} - \dfrac{1}{3 - a}$

37. $\dfrac{x + 1}{1 - x} + \dfrac{1}{x - 1}$

38. $\dfrac{5}{1 - x} - \dfrac{1}{x - 1}$

39. $\dfrac{5}{x - 2} + \dfrac{x + 4}{2 - x}$

40. $\dfrac{3}{5 - x} + \dfrac{x + 2}{x - 5}$

Perform each indicated operation. If possible, simplify your answer. Write each answer in lowest terms. See Examples 4 through 6.

41. $\dfrac{y + 1}{y^2 - 6y + 8} - \dfrac{3}{y^2 - 16}$

42. $\dfrac{x + 2}{x^2 - 36} - \dfrac{x}{x^2 + 9x + 18}$

43. $\dfrac{x + 4}{3x^2 + 11x + 6} + \dfrac{x}{2x^2 + x - 15}$

44. $\dfrac{x + 3}{5x^2 + 12x + 4} + \dfrac{6}{x^2 - x - 6}$

45. $\dfrac{7}{x^2 - x - 2} + \dfrac{x}{x^2 + 4x + 3}$

46. $\dfrac{a}{a^2 + 10a + 25} + \dfrac{4}{a^2 + 6a + 5}$

47. $\dfrac{2}{x + 1} - \dfrac{3x}{3x + 3} + \dfrac{1}{2x + 2}$

48. $\dfrac{5}{3x - 6} - \dfrac{x}{x - 2} + \dfrac{3 + 2x}{5x - 10}$

49. $\dfrac{3}{x + 3} + \dfrac{5}{x^2 + 6x + 9} - \dfrac{x}{x^2 - 9}$

50. $\dfrac{x + 2}{x^2 - 2x - 3} + \dfrac{x}{x - 3} - \dfrac{4}{x + 1}$

Add or subtract as indicated. If possible, simplify your answer.

51. $\dfrac{4}{3x^2y^3} + \dfrac{5}{3x^2y^3}$

52. $\dfrac{7}{2xy^4} + \dfrac{1}{2xy^4}$

53. $\dfrac{x - 5}{2x} - \dfrac{x + 5}{2x}$

54. $\dfrac{x + 4}{4x} - \dfrac{x - 4}{4x}$

55. $\dfrac{3}{2x + 10} + \dfrac{8}{3x + 15}$

56. $\dfrac{10}{3x - 3} + \dfrac{1}{7x - 7}$

57. $\dfrac{-2}{x^2 - 3x} - \dfrac{1}{x^3 - 3x^2}$

58. $\dfrac{-3}{2a + 8} - \dfrac{8}{a^2 + 4a}$

59. $\dfrac{ab}{a^2 - b^2} + \dfrac{b}{a + b}$

60. $\dfrac{x}{25 - x^2} + \dfrac{2}{3x - 15}$

61. $\dfrac{5}{x^2 - 4} - \dfrac{3}{x^2 + 4x + 4}$

62. $\dfrac{3z}{z^2 - 9} - \dfrac{2}{3 - z}$

63. $\dfrac{2}{a^2 + 2a + 1} + \dfrac{3}{a^2 - 1}$

64. $\dfrac{9x + 2}{3x^2 - 2x - 8} + \dfrac{7}{3x^2 + x - 4}$

65. In your own words, explain how to add rational expressions with different denominators.

66. In your own words, explain how to multiply rational expressions.

67. In your own words, explain how to divide rational expressions.

68. In your own words, explain how to subtract rational expressions with different denominators.

Perform the indicated operation. If possible, simplify your answer.

69. $\left(\dfrac{2}{3} - \dfrac{1}{x}\right) \cdot \left(\dfrac{3}{x} + \dfrac{1}{2}\right)$

70. $\left(\dfrac{2}{3} - \dfrac{1}{x}\right) \div \left(\dfrac{3}{x} + \dfrac{1}{2}\right)$

71. $\left(\dfrac{1}{x} + \dfrac{2}{3}\right) - \left(\dfrac{1}{x} - \dfrac{2}{3}\right)$

72. $\left(\dfrac{1}{2} + \dfrac{2}{x}\right) - \left(\dfrac{1}{2} - \dfrac{1}{x}\right)$

73. $\left(\dfrac{2a}{3}\right)^2 \div \left(\dfrac{a^2}{a + 1} - \dfrac{1}{a + 1}\right)$

74. $\left(\dfrac{x + 2}{2x} - \dfrac{x - 2}{2x}\right) \cdot \left(\dfrac{5x}{4}\right)^2$

75. $\left(\dfrac{2x}{3}\right)^2 \div \left(\dfrac{x}{3}\right)^2$

76. $\left(\dfrac{2x}{3}\right)^2 \cdot \left(\dfrac{3}{x}\right)^2$

77. $\dfrac{x}{x^2 - 9} + \dfrac{3}{x^2 - 6x + 9} - \dfrac{1}{x + 3}$

78. $\dfrac{3}{x^2 - 9} - \dfrac{x}{x^2 - 6x + 9} + \dfrac{1}{x + 3}$

79. $\left(\dfrac{x}{x + 1} - \dfrac{x}{x - 1}\right) \div \dfrac{x}{2x + 2}$

80. $\dfrac{x}{2x + 2} \div \left(\dfrac{x}{x + 1} + \dfrac{x}{x - 1}\right)$

81. $\dfrac{4}{x} \cdot \left(\dfrac{2}{x + 2} - \dfrac{2}{x - 2}\right)$

82. $\dfrac{1}{x + 1} \cdot \left(\dfrac{5}{x} + \dfrac{2}{x - 3}\right)$

Use a graphing calculator to support the results of each exercise.

83. Exercise 3

84. Exercise 4

85. Exercise 31

86. Exercise 32

REVIEW EXERCISES

Use the distributive property to multiply the following. See Section 1.4

87. $12\left(\dfrac{2}{3} + \dfrac{1}{6}\right)$

88. $14\left(\dfrac{1}{7} + \dfrac{3}{14}\right)$

89. $x^2\left(\dfrac{4}{x^2} + 1\right)$

90. $5y^2\left(\dfrac{1}{y^2} - \dfrac{1}{5}\right)$

Find each root. See Section 1.3.

91. $\sqrt{100}$

92. $\sqrt{25}$

93. $\sqrt[3]{8}$

94. $\sqrt[3]{27}$

95. $\sqrt[4]{81}$

96. $\sqrt[4]{16}$

Use the Pythagorean theorem to find each unknown length of a right triangle. See Section 5.8.

△ **97.**

3 meters

4 meters

△ **98.**

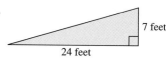

7 feet

24 feet

A Look Ahead

Example
Add $x^{-1} + 3x^{-2}$.

Solution

$$x^{-1} + 3x^{-2} = \frac{1}{x} + \frac{3}{x^2}$$

$$= \frac{1 \cdot x}{x \cdot x} + \frac{3}{x^2}$$

$$= \frac{x}{x^2} + \frac{3}{x^2}$$

$$= \frac{x + 3}{x^2}$$

Perform the indicated operation. See the preceding example.

99. $x^{-1} + (2x)^{-1}$

100. $3y^{-1} + (4y)^{-1}$

101. $4x^{-2} - 3x^{-1}$

102. $(4x)^{-2} - (3x)^{-1}$

103. $x^{-3}(2x + 1) - 5x^{-2}$

104. $4x^{-3} + x^{-4}(5x + 7)$

6.3 SIMPLIFYING COMPLEX FRACTIONS

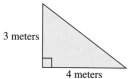

CD-ROM   SSM

SSG   Video

▶ **OBJECTIVES**

1. Simplify complex fractions by simplifying the numerator and denominator and then dividing.
2. Simplify complex fractions by multiplying by a common denominator.
3. Simplify expressions with negative exponents.

1 A rational expression whose numerator, denominator, or both contain one or more rational expressions is called a **complex rational expression** or a **complex fraction**.

Complex Fractions

$$\frac{\dfrac{1}{a}}{\dfrac{b}{2}} \qquad \frac{\dfrac{x}{2y^2}}{\dfrac{6x - 2}{9y}} \qquad \frac{x + \dfrac{1}{y}}{y + 1}$$

The parts of a complex fraction are

$$\dfrac{\dfrac{x}{y + 2}}{7 + \dfrac{1}{y}}$$

← Numerator of complex fraction.

← Main fraction bar.

← Denominator of complex fraction.

Our goal in this section is to simplify complex fractions. A complex fraction is simplified when it is in the form $\dfrac{P}{Q}$, where P and Q are polynomials that have no common factors. Two methods of simplifying complex fractions are introduced. The first method evolves from the definition of a fraction as a quotient.

SIMPLIFYING A COMPLEX FRACTION: METHOD I

Step 1: Simplify the numerator and the denominator of the complex fraction so that each is a single fraction.

Step 2: Perform the indicated division by multiplying the numerator of the complex fraction by the reciprocal of the denominator of the complex fraction.

Step 3: Simplify if possible.

Example 1   Simplify each complex fraction.

a. $\dfrac{\dfrac{2x}{27y^2}}{\dfrac{6x^2}{9}}$

b. $\dfrac{\dfrac{5x}{x+2}}{\dfrac{10}{x-2}}$

c. $\dfrac{\dfrac{x}{y^2}+\dfrac{1}{y}}{\dfrac{y}{x^2}+\dfrac{1}{x}}$

Solution   **a.** The numerator of the complex fraction is already a single fraction, and so is the denominator. Perform the indicated division by multiplying the numerator, $\dfrac{2x}{27y^2}$, by the reciprocal of the denominator, $\dfrac{6x^2}{9}$. Then simplify.

$$\dfrac{\dfrac{2x}{27y^2}}{\dfrac{6x^2}{9}} = \dfrac{2x}{27y^2} \div \dfrac{6x^2}{9}$$

$$= \dfrac{2x}{27y^2} \cdot \dfrac{9}{6x^2} \qquad \text{Multiply by the reciprocal of } \dfrac{6x^2}{9}.$$

$$= \dfrac{2x \cdot 9}{27y^2 \cdot 6x^2}$$

$$= \dfrac{1}{9xy^2}$$

The LCD of $\dfrac{1}{x}$, $\dfrac{2x}{y}$, $\dfrac{1}{x^2}$, and $\dfrac{1}{x^2 y}$ is $x^2 y$. Multiply both the numerator and denominator by $x^2 y$.

$$= \dfrac{\left(\dfrac{1}{x} + \dfrac{2x}{y}\right) \cdot x^2 y}{\left(\dfrac{1}{x^2} - \dfrac{1}{x^2 y}\right) \cdot x^2 y}$$

$$= \dfrac{\dfrac{1}{x} \cdot x^2 y + \dfrac{2x}{y} \cdot x^2 y}{\dfrac{1}{x^2} \cdot x^2 y - \dfrac{1}{x^2 y} \cdot x^2 y} \qquad \text{Apply the distributive property.}$$

$$= \dfrac{xy + 2x^3}{y - 1} \qquad \text{Simplify.}$$

Exercise Set 6.3

Simplify each complex fraction. See Examples 1 and 2.

1. $\dfrac{\dfrac{1}{3}}{\dfrac{2}{5}}$

2. $\dfrac{\dfrac{3}{5}}{\dfrac{4}{5}}$

3. $\dfrac{\dfrac{4}{x}}{\dfrac{5}{2x}}$

4. $\dfrac{\dfrac{5}{2x}}{\dfrac{4}{x}}$

5. $\dfrac{\dfrac{10}{3x}}{\dfrac{5}{6x}}$

6. $\dfrac{\dfrac{15}{2x}}{\dfrac{5}{6x}}$

7. $\dfrac{1 + \dfrac{2}{5}}{2 + \dfrac{3}{5}}$

8. $\dfrac{2 + \dfrac{1}{7}}{3 - \dfrac{4}{7}}$

9. $\dfrac{\dfrac{4}{x - 1}}{\dfrac{x}{x - 1}}$

10. $\dfrac{\dfrac{x}{x + 2}}{\dfrac{2}{x + 2}}$

11. $\dfrac{1 - \dfrac{2}{x}}{x - \dfrac{4}{9x}}$

12. $\dfrac{5 - \dfrac{3}{x}}{x + \dfrac{2}{3x}}$

13. $\dfrac{\dfrac{1}{x + 1} - 1}{\dfrac{1}{x - 1} + 1}$

14. $\dfrac{1 + \dfrac{1}{x - 1}}{1 - \dfrac{1}{x + 1}}$

Simplify. See Example 3.

15. $\dfrac{x^{-1}}{x^{-2} + y^{-2}}$

16. $\dfrac{a^{-3} + b^{-1}}{a^{-2}}$

17. $\dfrac{2a^{-1} + 3b^{-2}}{a^{-1} - b^{-1}}$

18. $\dfrac{x^{-1} + y^{-1}}{3x^{-2} + 5y^{-2}}$

19. $\dfrac{1}{x - x^{-1}}$

20. $\dfrac{x^{-2}}{x + 3x^{-1}}$

Simplify.

21. $\dfrac{\dfrac{x + 1}{7}}{\dfrac{x + 2}{7}}$

22. $\dfrac{\dfrac{y}{10}}{\dfrac{x + 1}{10}}$

23. $\dfrac{\dfrac{1}{2} - \dfrac{1}{3}}{\dfrac{3}{4} + \dfrac{2}{5}}$

24. $\dfrac{\dfrac{5}{6} - \dfrac{1}{2}}{\dfrac{1}{3} + \dfrac{1}{8}}$

25. $\dfrac{\dfrac{x + 1}{3}}{\dfrac{2x - 1}{6}}$

26. $\dfrac{\dfrac{x + 3}{12}}{\dfrac{4x - 5}{15}}$

27. $\dfrac{\dfrac{x}{3}}{\dfrac{2}{x + 1}}$

28. $\dfrac{\dfrac{x - 1}{5}}{\dfrac{3}{x}}$

29. $\dfrac{\dfrac{2}{x} + 3}{\dfrac{4}{x^2} - 9}$

30. $\dfrac{2 + \dfrac{1}{x}}{4x - \dfrac{1}{x}}$

31. $\dfrac{1 - \dfrac{x}{y}}{\dfrac{x^2}{y^2} - 1}$

32. $\dfrac{1 - \dfrac{2}{x}}{x - \dfrac{4}{x}}$

33. $\dfrac{\dfrac{-2x}{x - y}}{\dfrac{y}{x^2}}$

34. $\dfrac{\dfrac{7y}{x^2 + xy}}{\dfrac{y^2}{x^2}}$

35. $\dfrac{\dfrac{2}{x} + \dfrac{1}{x^2}}{\dfrac{y}{x^2}}$

36. $\dfrac{\dfrac{5}{x^2} - \dfrac{2}{x}}{\dfrac{1}{x} + 2}$

37. $\dfrac{\dfrac{x}{9} - \dfrac{1}{x}}{1 + \dfrac{3}{x}}$

38. $\dfrac{\dfrac{x}{4} - \dfrac{4}{x}}{1 - \dfrac{4}{x}}$

39. $\dfrac{\dfrac{x - 1}{x^2 - 4}}{1 + \dfrac{1}{x - 2}}$

40. $\dfrac{\dfrac{2}{x + 5} + \dfrac{4}{x + 3}}{\dfrac{3x + 13}{x^2 + 8x + 15}}$

41. $\dfrac{\dfrac{4}{5 - x} + \dfrac{5}{x - 5}}{\dfrac{2}{x} + \dfrac{3}{x - 5}}$

42. $\dfrac{\dfrac{3}{x - 4} - \dfrac{2}{4 - x}}{\dfrac{2}{x - 4} - \dfrac{2}{x}}$

43.  $\dfrac{\dfrac{x + 2}{x} - \dfrac{2}{x - 1}}{\dfrac{x + 1}{x} + \dfrac{x + 1}{x - 1}}$

44. $\dfrac{\dfrac{5}{a + 2} - \dfrac{1}{a - 2}}{\dfrac{3}{2 + a} + \dfrac{6}{2 - a}}$

45. $\dfrac{\dfrac{x - 2}{x + 2} + \dfrac{x + 2}{x - 2}}{\dfrac{x - 2}{x + 2} - \dfrac{x + 2}{x - 2}}$

46. $\dfrac{\dfrac{x - 1}{x + 1} - \dfrac{x + 1}{x - 1}}{\dfrac{x - 1}{x + 1} + \dfrac{x + 1}{x - 1}}$

47. $\dfrac{\dfrac{2}{y^2} - \dfrac{5}{xy} - \dfrac{3}{x^2}}{\dfrac{2}{y^2} + \dfrac{7}{xy} + \dfrac{3}{x^2}}$

48. $\dfrac{\dfrac{2}{x^2} - \dfrac{1}{xy} - \dfrac{1}{y^2}}{\dfrac{1}{x^2} - \dfrac{3}{xy} + \dfrac{2}{y^2}}$

49. $\dfrac{a^{-1} + 1}{a^{-1} - 1}$

50. $\dfrac{a^{-1} - 4}{4 + a^{-1}}$

51. $\dfrac{3x^{-1} + (2y)^{-1}}{x^{-2}}$

52. $\dfrac{5x^{-2} - 3y^{-1}}{x^{-1} + y^{-1}}$

53. $\dfrac{2a^{-1} + (2a)^{-1}}{a^{-1} + 2a^{-2}}$

54. $\dfrac{a^{-1} + 2a^{-2}}{2a^{-1} + (2a)^{-1}}$

55. $\dfrac{5x^{-1} + 2y^{-1}}{x^{-2}y^{-2}}$

56. $\dfrac{x^{-2}y^{-2}}{5x^{-1} + 2y^{-1}}$

57. $\dfrac{5x^{-1} - 2y^{-1}}{25x^{-2} - 4y^{-2}}$

58. $\dfrac{3x^{-1} + 3y^{-1}}{4x^{-2} - 9y^{-2}}$

59. $(x^{-1} + y^{-1})^{-1}$

60. $\dfrac{xy}{x^{-1} + y^{-1}}$

61. $\dfrac{x}{1 - \dfrac{1}{1 + \dfrac{1}{x}}}$

62. $\dfrac{1}{1 - \dfrac{1}{1 - \dfrac{1}{x}}}$

63. When the source of a sound is traveling toward a listener, the pitch that the listener hears due to the Doppler effect is given by the complex rational compression

$$\dfrac{a}{1 - \dfrac{s}{770}}, \text{ where } a \text{ is the actual pitch of the sound and } s$$

is the speed of the sound source. Simplify this expression.

64. Which of the following are equivalent to $\dfrac{\dfrac{1}{x}}{\dfrac{3}{y}}$?

a. $\dfrac{1}{x} \div \dfrac{3}{y}$

b. $\dfrac{1}{x} \cdot \dfrac{y}{3}$

c. $\dfrac{1}{x} \div \dfrac{y}{3}$

In the study of calculus, the difference quotient $\dfrac{f(a + h) - f(a)}{h}$ *is often found and simplified. Find and simplify this quotient for each function* $f(x)$ *by following steps* **a** *through* **d**.

a. *Find* $(a + h)$.

b. *Find* $f(a)$.

c. *Use steps* **a** *and* **b** *to find* $\dfrac{f(a + h) - f(a)}{h}$

d. *Simplify the result of step* **c**.

65. $f(x) = \dfrac{1}{x}$

66. $f(x) = \dfrac{5}{x}$

67. $\dfrac{3}{x+1}$

68. $\dfrac{2}{x^2}$

REVIEW EXERCISES

Simplify. See Sections 5.1 and 5.2.

69. $\dfrac{3x^3y^2}{12x}$

70. $\dfrac{-36xb^3}{9xb^2}$

71. $\dfrac{144x^5y^5}{-16x^2y}$

72. $\dfrac{48x^3y^2}{-4xy}$

Solve the following. See Sections 2.6 and 2.7

73. $|x-5|=9$

74. $|2y+1|=1$

75. $|x-5|<9$

76. $|2x+1|\geq 1$

A Look Ahead

Example

Simplify $\dfrac{2(a+b)^{-1}-5(a-b)^{-1}}{4(a^2-b^2)^{-1}}$

Solution

$$\dfrac{2(a+b)^{-1}-5(a-b)^{-1}}{4(a^2-b^2)^{-1}}=\dfrac{\dfrac{2}{a+b}-\dfrac{5}{a-b}}{\dfrac{4}{a^2-b^2}}$$

$$=\dfrac{\left(\dfrac{2}{a+b}-\dfrac{5}{a-b}\right)\cdot(a+b)(a-b)}{\left[\dfrac{4}{(a+b)(a-b)}\right]\cdot(a+b)(a-b)}$$

$$=\dfrac{\dfrac{2}{a+b}\cdot(a+b)(a-b)-\dfrac{5}{a-b}\cdot(a+b)(a-b)}{\dfrac{4(a+b)(a-b)}{(a+b)(a-b)}}$$

$$=\dfrac{2(a-b)-5(a+b)}{4}$$

$$=\dfrac{-3a-7b}{4}, \text{ or } -\dfrac{3a+7b}{4}$$

Simplify. See the preceding example.

77. $\dfrac{1}{1-(1-x)^{-1}}$

78. $\dfrac{1}{1+(1+x)^{-1}}$

79. $\dfrac{(x+2)^{-1}+(x-2)^{-1}}{(x^2-4)^{-1}}$

80. $\dfrac{(y-1)^{-1}-(y+4)^{-1}}{(y^2+3y-4)^{-1}}$

81. $\dfrac{3(a+1)^{-1}+4a^{-2}}{(a^3+a^2)^{-1}}$

82. $\dfrac{9x^{-1}-5(x-y)^{-1}}{4(x-y)^{-1}}$

6.4 DIVIDING POLYNOMIALS

CD-ROM   SSM

SSG   Video

▶ **OBJECTIVES**

1. Divide a polynomial by a monomial.
2. Divide by a polynomial.

1   Recall that a rational expression is a quotient of polynomials. An equivalent form of a rational expression can be obtained by performing the indicated division. For example, the rational expression $\dfrac{10x^3-5x^2+20x}{5x}$ can be thought of as the polynomial $10x^3-5x^2+20x$ divided by the monomial $5x$. To perform this division of a polynomial by a monomial (which we do below) recall the following addition fact for fractions with a common denominator.

$$\dfrac{a}{c}+\dfrac{b}{c}=\dfrac{a+b}{c}$$

If a, b, and c are monomials, we might read this equation from right to left and gain insight into dividing a polynomial by a monomial.

DIVIDING A POLYNOMIAL BY A MONOMIAL

Divide each term in the polynomial by the monomial.

$$\frac{a+b}{c} = \frac{a}{c} + \frac{b}{c}, \text{ where } c \neq 0$$

Example 1   Divide $10x^3 - 5x^2 + 20x$ by $5x$.

Solution   We divide each term of $10x^3 - 5x^2 + 20x$ by $5x$ and simplify.

$$\frac{10x^3 - 5x^2 + 20x}{5x} = \frac{10x^3}{5x} - \frac{5x^2}{5x} + \frac{20x}{5x} = 2x^2 - x + 4$$

Check: To check, see that (quotient) (divisor) = dividend, or

$$(2x^2 - x + 4)(5x) = 10x^3 - 5x^2 + 20x.$$

Example 2   Divide $\dfrac{3x^5y^2 - 15x^3y - x^2y - 6x}{x^2y}$

Solution   We divide each term in the numerator by x^2y.

$$\frac{3x^5y^2 - 15x^3y - x^2y - 6x}{x^2y} = \frac{3x^5y^2}{x^2y} - \frac{15x^3y}{x^2y} - \frac{x^2y}{x^2y} - \frac{6x}{x^2y}$$

$$= 3x^3y - 15x - 1 - \frac{6}{xy}$$

---

2   To divide a polynomial by a polynomial other than a monomial, we use **long division.** Polynomial long division is similar to long division of real numbers. We review long division of real numbers by dividing 7 into 296.

$$
\begin{array}{r}
42 \\
\text{Divisor: } 7\overline{)296} \\
-28 \\
\hline
16 \\
-14 \\
\hline
2 \\
\end{array}
$$

$4(7) = 28.$

Subtract and bring down the next digit in the dividend.

$2(7) = 14.$

Subtract. The remainder is 2.

The quotient is $42\dfrac{2}{7}\ \dfrac{\text{(remainder)}}{\text{(divisor)}}$.

Check: To check, notice that

$$42(7) + 2 = 296, \text{ the dividend.}$$

This same division process can be applied to polynomials, as shown next.

Example 3　Divide $2x^2 - x - 10$ by $x + 2$.

Solution　$2x^2 - x - 10$ is the dividend, and $x + 2$ is the divisor.

Step 1:　Divide $2x^2$ by x.

$$x + 2 \overline{)2x^2 - x - 10} \quad\quad \frac{2x}{}$$

$\dfrac{2x^2}{x} = 2x$, so $2x$ is the first term of the quotient.

Step 2:　Multiply $2x(x + 2)$.

$$\begin{array}{r} 2x \\ x + 2 \overline{)2x^2 - x - 10} \\ 2x^2 + 4x \end{array}$$

$2x(x + 2)$

Like terms are lined up vertically.

Step 3:　Subtract $(2x^2 + 4x)$ from $(2x^2 - x - 10)$ by changing the signs of $(2x^2 + 4x)$ and adding.

$$\begin{array}{r} 2x \\ x + 2 \overline{)2x^2 - x - 10} \\ -2x^2 - 4x \\ \hline -5x \end{array}$$

Step 4:　Bring down the next term, -10, and start the process over.

$$\begin{array}{r} 2x \\ x + 2 \overline{)2x^2 - x - 10} \\ -2x^2 - 4x \\ \hline -5x - 10 \end{array}$$

Step 5:　Divide $-5x$ by x.

$$\begin{array}{r} 2x - 5 \\ x + 2 \overline{)2x^2 - x - 10} \\ -2x^2 - 4x \\ \hline -5x - 10 \end{array}$$

$\dfrac{-5x}{x} = -5$, so -5 is the second term of the quotient.

Step 6:　Multiply $-5(x + 2)$.

$$\begin{array}{r} 2x - 5 \\ x + 2 \overline{)2x^2 - x - 10} \\ -2x^2 - 4x \\ \hline -5x - 10 \\ -5x - 10 \end{array}$$

$-5(x + 2)$

Like terms are lined up vertically.

Step 7:　Subtract $(-5x - 10)$ from $(-5x - 10)$.

$$\begin{array}{r} 2x - 5 \\ x + 2 \overline{)2x^2 - x - 10} \\ -2x^2 - 4x \\ \hline -5x - 10 \\ +5x + 10 \\ \hline 0 \end{array}$$

Then $\dfrac{2x^2 - x - 10}{x + 2} = 2x - 5$. There is no remainder.

Check:　Check this result by multiplying $2x - 5$ by $x + 2$. Their product is

$$(2x - 5)(x + 2) = 2x^2 - x - 10, \text{ the dividend.}$$

Example 4 Divide: $(6x^2 - 19x + 12) \div (3x - 5)$

Solution

$$
\begin{array}{r}
2x \\
3x - 5 \overline{)6x^2 - 19x + 12} \\
\underline{6x^2 \not\mp 10x} \\
-9x + 12
\end{array}
$$

Divide $\dfrac{6x^2}{3x} = 2x$.

Multiply $2x(3x - 5)$.

Subtract by adding the opposite.

Bring down the next term, $+ 12$.

$$
\begin{array}{r}
2x - 3 \\
3x - 5 \overline{)6x^2 - 19x + 12} \\
\underline{6x^2 \not\mp 10x} \\
-9x + 12 \\
\underline{\not\mp 9x \not\mp 15} \\
-3
\end{array}
$$

Divide $\dfrac{-9x}{3x} = -3$.

Multiply $-3(3x - 5)$.

Subtract by adding the opposite.

Check:

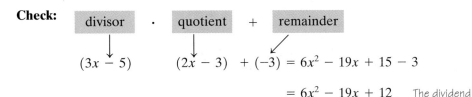

divisor $\cdot$ quotient $+$ remainder

$$(3x - 5) \qquad (2x - 3) + (-3) = 6x^2 - 19x + 15 - 3$$

$$= 6x^2 - 19x + 12 \qquad \text{The dividend}$$

The division checks, so

$$\frac{6x^2 - 19x + 12}{3x - 5} = 2x - 3 - \frac{3}{3x - 5}$$

> **HELPFUL HINT**
> This fraction is the remainder over the divisor.

Example 5 Divide $3x^4 + 2x^3 - 8x + 6$ by $x^2 - 1$.

Solution   Before dividing, we represent any "missing powers" by the product of 0 and the variable raised to the missing power. There is no x^2 term in the dividend, so we include $0x^2$ to represent the missing term. Also, there is no x term in the divisor, so we include $0x$ in the divisor.

$$
\begin{array}{r}
3x^2 + 2x + 3 \\
x^2 + 0x - 1 \overline{)3x^4 + 2x^3 + 0x^2 - 8x + 6} \\
\underline{3x^4 \not\mp 0x^3 \not\mp 3x^2} \\
2x^3 + 3x^2 - 8x \\
\underline{2x^3 \not\mp 0x^2 \not\mp 2x} \\
3x^2 - 6x + 6 \\
\underline{3x^2 \not\mp 0x \not\mp 3} \\
-6x + 9
\end{array}
$$

$\dfrac{3x^4}{x^2} = 3x^2$

$3x^2(x^2 + 0x - 1)$

Subtract. Bring down $-8x$.

$\dfrac{2x^3}{x^2} = 2x$, a term of the quotient.

$2x(x^2 + 0x - 1)$

Subtract. Bring down 6.

$\dfrac{3x^2}{x^2} = 3$, a term of the quotient.

$3(x^2 + 0x - 1)$

Subtract.

The division process is finished when the degree of the remainder polynomial is less than the degree of the divisor. Thus,

$$\frac{3x^4 + 2x^3 - 8x + 6}{x^2 - 1} = 3x^2 + 2x + 3 + \frac{-6x + 9}{x^2 - 1}$$

Example 6   Divide $27x^3 + 8$ by $3x + 2$.

Solution   We replace the missing terms in the dividend with $0x^2$ and $0x$.

$$
\begin{array}{r}
9x^2 - 6x + 4 \\
3x + 2 \overline{)27x^3 + 0x^2 + 0x + 8} \\
\underline{27x^3 + 18x^2} \qquad\quad \\
-18x^2 + 0x \\
\underline{+18x^2 + 12x} \\
12x + 8 \\
\underline{12x + 8}
\end{array}
$$

$9x^2(3x + 2)$

Subtract. Bring down $0x$.

$-6x(3x + 2)$

Subtract. Bring down 8.

$4(3x + 2)$

Thus, $\dfrac{27x^3 + 8}{3x + 2} = 9x^2 - 6x + 4$.

Exercise Set 6.4

Divide. See Examples 1 and 2

1. Divide $4a^2 + 8a$ by $2a$.

2. Divide $6x^4 - 3x^3$ by $3x^2$.

3. $\dfrac{12a^5b^2 + 16a^4b}{4a^4b}$

4. $\dfrac{4x^3y + 12x^2y^2 - 4xy^3}{4xy}$

5. $\dfrac{4x^2y^2 + 6xy^2 - 4y^2}{2x^2y}$

6. $\dfrac{6x^5 + 74x^4 + 24x^3}{2x^3}$

7. $\dfrac{4x^2 + 8x + 4}{4}$

8. $\dfrac{15x^3 - 5x^2 + 10x}{5x^2}$

9. A board of length $(3x^4 + 6x^2 - 18)$ meters is to be cut into three pieces of the same length. Find the length of each piece.

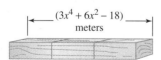

$(3x^4 + 6x^2 - 18)$ meters

△ **10.** The perimeter of a regular hexagon is given to be $12x^5 - 48x^3 + 3$ miles. Find the length of each side.

Divide. See Examples 3 through 6.

11. $(x^2 + 3x + 2) \div (x + 2)$

12. $(y^2 + 7y + 10) \div (y + 5)$

13. $(2x^2 - 6x - 8) \div (x + 1)$

14. $(3x^2 + 19x + 20) \div (x + 5)$

15. $2x^2 + 3x - 2$ by $2x + 4$

16. $6x^2 - 17x - 3$ by $3x - 9$

17. $(4x^3 + 7x^2 + 8x + 20) \div (2x + 4)$

18. $(18x^3 + x^2 - 90x - 5) \div (9x^2 - 45)$

△ **19.** If the area of the rectangle is $(15x^2 - 29x - 14)$ square inches and its length is $(5x + 2)$ inches, find its width.

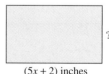

$(5x + 2)$ inches

△ **20.** If the area of a parallelogram is $(2x^2 - 17x + 35)$ square centimeters and its base is $(2x - 7)$ centimeters, find its height.

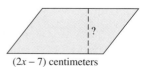

$(2x - 7)$ centimeters

Divide.

21. $25a^2b^{12}$ by $10a^5b^7$ **22.** $12a^2b^3$ by $8a^7b$

23. $(x^6y^6 - x^3y^3) \div x^3y^3$

24. $(25xy^2 + 75xyz + 125x^2yz) \div -5x^2y$

25. $(a^2 + 4a + 3) \div (a + 1)$

26. $(3x^2 - 14x + 16) \div (x - 2)$

27. $(2x^2 + x - 10) \div (x - 2)$

28. $(x^2 - 7x + 12) \div (x - 5)$

29. $-16y^3 + 24y^4$ by $-4y^2$

30. $-20a^2b + 12ab^2$ by $-4ab$

31. $(2x^2 + 13x + 15) \div (x - 5)$

32. $(2x^2 + 13x + 5) \div (2x + 3)$

33. $(20x^2y^3 + 6xy^4 - 12x^3y^5) \div 2xy^3$

34. $(3x^2y + 6x^2y^2 + 3xy) \div 3xy$

35. $(6x^2 + 16x + 8) \div (3x + 2)$

36. $(x^2 - 25) \div (x + 5)$

37. $(2y^2 + 7y - 15) \div (2y - 3)$

38. $(3x^2 - 4x + 6) \div (x - 2)$

39. $4x^2 - 9$ by $2x - 3$

40. $8x^2 + 6x - 27$ by $4x + 9$

41. $2x^3 + 6x - 4$ by $x + 4$

42. $4x^3 - 5x$ by $2x - 1$

43. $3x^2 - 4$ by $x - 1$

44. $x^2 - 9$ by $x + 4$

45. $(-13x^3 + 2x^4 + 16x^2 - 9x + 20) \div (5 - x)$

46. $(5x^2 - 5x + 2x^3 + 20) \div (4 + x)$

47. $3x^5 - x^3 + 4x^2 - 12x - 8$ by $x^2 - 2$

48. $-8x^3 + 2x^4 + 19x^2 - 33x + 15$ by $x^2 - x + 5$

49. $(3x^3 - 5) \div 3x^2$

50. $(14x^3 - 2) \div (7x - 1)$

51. Find $P(1)$ for the polynomial function
$P(x) = 3x^3 + 2x^2 - 4x + 3$. Next, divide
$3x^3 + 2x^2 - 4x + 3$ by $x - 1$. Compare the remainder
with $P(1)$.

52. Find $P(-2)$ for the polynomial function
$P(x) = x^3 - 4x^2 - 3x + 5$. Next, divide
$x^3 - 4x^2 - 3x + 5$ by $x + 2$. Compare the remainder
with $P(-2)$.

53. Find $P(-3)$ for the polynomial $P(x) = 5x^4 - 2x^2 + 3x - 6$.
Next, divide $5x^4 - 2x^2 + 3x - 6$ by $x + 3$. Compare
the remainder with $P(-3)$.

54. Find $P(2)$ for the polynomial function
$P(x) = -4x^4 + 2x^3 - 6x + 3$. Next, divide
$-4x^4 + 2x^3 - 6x + 3$ by $x - 2$. Compare the remainder with $P(2)$.

55. Write down any patterns you noticed from Exercises 51–54.

56. Explain how to check polynomial long division.

57. Try performing the following division without changing
the order of the terms. Describe why this makes the
process more complicated. Then perform the division
again after putting the terms in the dividend in descending order of exponents.
$$\frac{4x^2 - 12x - 12 + 3x^3}{x - 2}$$

58. Gateway is a leading direct marketer of personal computers. Gateway's annual net profit can be modeled by
the polynomial function
$$P(x) = -88.5x^3 + 454x^2 - 506.5x + 251,$$
where $P(x)$ is net profit in millions of dollars in the year x.
Gateway's annual revenue can be modeled by the function $R(x) = 1200.7x + 5059.7$, where $R(x)$ is revenue in
millions of dollars in the year x. In both models, $x = 0$ represents the year 1996. (*Source:* Gateway, Inc., 1996–1999)

  a. Suppose that a market analyst has found the model
  $P(x)$, and another analyst at the same firm has found
  the model $R(x)$. The analysts have been asked by
  their manager to work together to find a model for
  Gateway's net profit margin. The analysts know that
  a company's net profit margin is the ratio of its net
  profit to its revenue. Describe how these two analysts
  could collaborate to find a function $m(x)$ that models Gateway's net profit margin based on the work
  they have done independently.

  b. Without actually finding $m(x)$, give a general description of what you would expect the form of the
  result to be.

REVIEW EXERCISES

Insert $<$, $>$, or $=$ to make each statement true. See Section 1.3.

59. 3^2 _____ $(-3)^2$ **60.** $(-5)^2$ _____ 5^2

61. -2^3 _____ $(-2)^3$

62. 3^4 _____ $(-3)^4$

Solve each inequality. See Section 2.7.

63. $|x + 5| < 4$

64. $|x - 1| \le 8$

65. $|2x + 7| \ge 9$

66. $|4x + 2| > 10$

A Look Ahead

Example

$$\left(x^2 - \frac{7}{2}x + 4 \right) \div (x + 2)$$

Solution

$$
\begin{array}{r}
x - \dfrac{11}{2} \\
x + 2 \overline{) x^2 - \dfrac{7}{2}x + 4 } \\
\underline{x^2 + 2x } \\
-\dfrac{11}{2}x + 4 \\
\underline{-\dfrac{11}{2}x - 11} \\
15
\end{array}
$$

The quotient is $x - \dfrac{11}{2} + \dfrac{15}{x + 2}$.

Divide. See the preceding example.

67. $\left(x^4 + \dfrac{2}{2}x^3 + x \right) \div (x - 1)$

68. $\left(2x^3 + \dfrac{9}{2}x^2 - 4x - 10 \right) \div (x + 2)$

69. $\left(3x^4 - x - x^3 + \dfrac{1}{2} \right) \div (2x - 1)$

70. $\left(2x^4 + \dfrac{1}{2}x^3 + x^2 + x \right) \div (x - 2)$

71. $(5x^4 - 2x^2 + 10x^3 - 4x) \div (5x + 10)$

72. $(9x^5 + 6x^4 - 6x^2 - 4x) \div (3x + 2)$

6.5 SYNTHETIC DIVISION AND THE REMAINDER THEOREM

CD-ROM   SSM

SSG   Video

▶ **OBJECTIVES**

1. Use synthetic division to divide a polynomial by a binomial.
2. Use the remainder theorem to evaluate polynomials.

1   When a polynomial is to be divided by a binomial of the form $x - c$, a shortcut process called **synthetic division** may be used. On the left is an example of long division, and on the right, the same example showing the coefficients of the variables only.

$$
\begin{array}{r}
2x^2 + 5x + 2 \\
x - 3 \overline{) 2x^3 - x^2 - 13x + 1} \\
\underline{2x^3 - 6x^2 } \\
5x^2 - 13x \\
\underline{5x^2 - 15x } \\
2x + 1 \\
\underline{2x - 6} \\
7
\end{array}
\qquad
\begin{array}{r}
2 5 2 \\
1 - 3 \overline{) 2 - 1 - 13 + 1} \\
\underline{2 - 6 } \\
5 - 13 \\
\underline{5 - 15 } \\
2 + 1 \\
\underline{2 - 6} \\
7
\end{array}
$$

Notice that as long as we keep coefficients of powers of x in the same column, we can perform division of polynomials by performing algebraic operations on the coefficients only. This shortcut process of dividing with coefficients only in a special format is called synthetic division. To find $(2x^3 - x^2 - 13x + 1) \div (x - 3)$ by synthetic division, follow the next example.

Example 1   Use synthetic division to divide $2x^3 - x^2 - 13x + 1$ by $x - 3$.

Solution   To use synthetic division, the divisor must be in the form $x - c$. Since we are dividing by $x - 3$, c is 3. Write down 3 and the coefficients of the dividend.

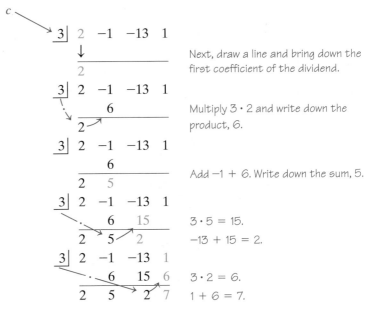

c

$$
\begin{array}{r|rrrr}
3 & 2 & -1 & -13 & 1 \\
  & \multicolumn{4}{c}{\downarrow} \\
\hline
  & 2 & & &
\end{array}
$$

Next, draw a line and bring down the first coefficient of the dividend.

$$
\begin{array}{r|rrrr}
3 & 2 & -1 & -13 & 1 \\
  &   & 6 &   &   \\
\hline
  & 2 &   &   &
\end{array}
$$

Multiply $3 \cdot 2$ and write down the product, 6.

$$
\begin{array}{r|rrrr}
3 & 2 & -1 & -13 & 1 \\
  &   & 6 &   &   \\
\hline
  & 2 & 5 &   &
\end{array}
$$

Add $-1 + 6$. Write down the sum, 5.

$$
\begin{array}{r|rrrr}
3 & 2 & -1 & -13 & 1 \\
  &   & 6 & 15 &   \\
\hline
  & 2 & 5 & 2   &
\end{array}
$$

$3 \cdot 5 = 15$.

$-13 + 15 = 2$.

$$
\begin{array}{r|rrrr}
3 & 2 & -1 & -13 & 1 \\
  &   & 6 & 15 & 6 \\
\hline
  & 2 & 5 & 2   & 7
\end{array}
$$

$3 \cdot 2 = 6$.

$1 + 6 = 7$.

The quotient is found in the bottom row. The numbers 2, 5, and 2 are the coefficients of the quotient polynomial, and the number 7 is the remainder. The degree of the quotient polynomial is one less than the degree of the dividend. In our example, the degree of the dividend is 3, so the degree of the quotient polynomial is 2. As we found when we performed the long division, the quotient is

$$2x^2 + 5x + 2, \qquad \text{remainder } 7$$

or

$$2x^2 + 5x + 2 + \frac{7}{x - 3}$$

Example 2   Use synthetic division to divide $x^4 - 2x^3 - 11x^2 + 5x + 34$ by $x + 2$.

Solution   The divisor is $x + 2$, which we write in the form $x - c$ as $x - (-2)$. Thus, c is -2. The dividend coefficients are $1, -2, -11, 5$, and 34.

c

$$
\begin{array}{r|rrrrr}
-2 & 1 & -2 & -11 & 5 & 34 \\
   &   & -2 & 8   & 6 & -22 \\
\hline
   & 1 & -4 & -3 & 11 & 12
\end{array}
$$

The dividend is a fourth-degree polynomial, so the quotient polynomial is a third-degree polynomial. The quotient is $x^3 - 4x^2 - 3x + 11$ with a remainder of 12. Thus,

$$\frac{x^4 - 2x^3 - 11x^2 + 5x + 34}{x + 2} = x^3 - 4x^2 - 3x + 11 + \frac{12}{x + 2}$$

> ▼ HELPFUL HINT
> Before dividing by synthetic division, write the dividend in descending order of variable exponents. Any "missing powers" of the variable should be represented by 0 times the variable raised to the missing power.

Example 3 If $P(x) = 2x^3 - 4x^2 + 5$

    a. Find $P(2)$ by substitution.
    b. Use synthetic division to find the remainder when $P(x)$ is divided by $x - 2$.

Solution   **a.** $P(x) = 2x^3 - 4x^2 + 5$
$$P(2) = 2(2)^3 - 4(2)^2 + 5$$
$$= 2(8) - 4(4) + 5 = 16 - 16 + 5 = 5$$

Thus, $P(2) = 5$.

    b. The coefficients of $P(x)$ are 2, -4, 0, and 5. The number 0 is a coefficient of the missing power of x^1. The divisor is $x - 2$, so c is 2.

$$
\begin{array}{c}
c \searrow \\
\underline{2|} \quad 2 \quad -4 \quad 0 \quad 5 \\
 \quad \quad \underline{4 \quad 0 \quad 0} \\
 \quad 2 \quad 0 \quad 0 \quad \underset{\uparrow\_\_\_\_\_}{5} \quad \text{remainder}
\end{array}
$$

The remainder when $P(x)$ is divided by $x - 2$ is 5. ◾

2

Notice in the preceding example that $P(2) = 5$ and that the remainder when $P(x)$ is divided by $x - 2$ is 5. This is no accident. This illustrates the **remainder theorem.**

REMAINDER THEOREM

If a polynomial $P(x)$ is divided by $x - c$, then the remainder is $P(c)$.

Example 4 Use the remainder theorem and synthetic division to find $P(4)$ if

$$P(x) = 4x^6 - 25x^5 + 35x^4 + 17x^2.$$

Solution To find $P(4)$ by the remainder theorem, we divide $P(x)$ by $x - 4$. The coefficients of $P(x)$ are 4, -25, 35, 0, 17, 0, and 0. Also, c is 4.

$$
\begin{array}{c}
c \searrow \\
\underline{4|} \quad 4 \quad -25 \quad 35 \quad 0 \quad 17 \quad 0 \quad 0 \\
 \quad \quad \underline{16 \quad -36 \quad -4 \quad -16 \quad 4 \quad 16} \\
 \quad 4 \cdot \quad -9 \quad -1 \quad -4 \quad 1 \quad 4 \quad \underset{\uparrow\_\_\_\_\_}{16} \quad \text{remainder}
\end{array}
$$

Thus, $P(4) = 16$, the remainder. ◾

Exercise Set 6.5

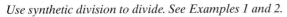

Use synthetic division to divide. See Examples 1 and 2.

1. $(x^2 + 3x - 40) \div (x - 5)$

2. $(x^2 - 14x + 24) \div (x - 2)$

3. $(x^2 + 5x - 6) \div (x + 6)$

4. $(x^2 + 12x + 32) \div (x + 4)$

5. $(x^3 - 7x^2 - 13x + 5) \div (x - 2)$

6. $(x^3 + 6x^2 + 4x - 7) \div (x + 5)$

7. $(4x^2 - 9) \div (x - 2)$

8. $(3x^2 - 4) \div (x - 1)$

For the given polynomial $P(x)$ and the given c, find $P(c)$ by (a) direct substitution and (b) the remainder theorem. See Examples 3 and 4.

9. $P(x) = 3x^2 - 4x - 1; P(2)$

10. $P(x) = x^2 - x + 3; P(5)$

11. $P(x) = 4x^4 + 7x^2 + 9x - 1; P(-2)$

12. $P(x) = 8x^5 + 7x + 4; P(-3)$

13. $P(x) = x^5 + 3x^4 + 3x - 7; P(-1)$

14. $P(x) = 5x^4 - 4x^3 + 2x - 1; P(-1)$

Use synthetic division to divide.

15. $(x^3 - 3x^2 + 2) \div (x - 3)$

16. $(x^2 + 12) \div (x + 2)$

17. $(6x^2 + 13x + 8) \div (x + 1)$

18. $(x^3 - 5x^2 + 7x - 4) \div (x - 3)$

19. $(2x^4 - 13x^3 + 16x^2 - 9x + 20) \div (x - 5)$

20. $(3x^4 + 5x^3 - x^2 + x - 2) \div (x + 2)$

21. $(3x^2 - 15) \div (x + 3)$

22. $(3x^2 + 7x - 6) \div (x + 4)$

23. $(3x^3 - 6x^2 + 4x + 5) \div \left(x - \dfrac{1}{2}\right)$

24. $(8x^3 - 6x^2 - 5x + 3) \div \left(x + \dfrac{3}{4}\right)$

25. $(3x^3 + 2x^2 - 4x + 1) \div \left(x - \dfrac{1}{3}\right)$

26. $(9y^3 + 9y^2 - y + 2) \div \left(y + \dfrac{2}{3}\right)$

27. $(7x^2 - 4x + 12 + 3x^3) \div (x + 1)$

28. $(x^4 + 4x^3 - x^2 - 16x - 4) \div (x - 2)$

29. $(x^3 - 1) \div (x - 1)$ **30.** $(y^3 - 8) \div (y - 2)$

31. $(x^2 - 36) \div (x + 6)$

32. $(4x^3 + 12x^2 + x - 12) \div (x + 3)$

For the given polynomial $P(x)$ and the given c, use the remainder theorem to find $P(c)$.

33. $P(x) = x^3 + 3x^2 - 7x + 4; 1$

34. $P(x) = x^3 + 5x^2 - 4x - 6; 2$

35. $P(x) = 3x^3 - 7x^2 - 2x + 5; -3$

36. $P(x) = 4x^3 + 5x^2 - 6x - 4; -2$

37. $P(x) = 4x^4 + x^2 - 2; -1$

38. $P(x) = x^4 - 3x^2 - 2x + 5; -2$

39. $P(x) = 2x^4 - 3x^2 - 2; \dfrac{1}{3}$

40. $P(x) = 4x^4 - 2x^3 + x^2 - x - 4; \dfrac{1}{2}$

41. $P(x) = x^5 + x^4 - x^3 + 3; \dfrac{1}{2}$

42. $P(x) = x^5 - 2x^3 + 4x^2 - 5x + 6; \dfrac{2}{3}$

43. Explain an advantage of using the remainder theorem instead of direct substitution.

44. Explain an advantage of using synthetic division instead of long division.

We say that 2 is a factor of 8 because 2 divides 8 evenly, or with a remainder of 0. In the same manner, the polynomial $x - 2$ is a factor of the polynomial $x^3 - 14x^2 + 24x$ because the remainder is 0 when $x^3 - 14x^2 + 24x$ is divided by $x - 2$. Use this information for Exercises 45 through 47.

45. Use synthetic division to show that $x + 3$ is a factor of $x^3 + 3x^2 + 4x + 12$.

46. Use synthetic division to show that $x - 2$ is a factor of $x^3 - 2x^2 - 3x + 6$.

47. From the remainder theorem, the polynomial $x - c$ is a factor of a polynomial function $P(x)$ if $P(c)$ is what value?

48. If a polynomial is divided by $x - 5$, the quotient is $2x^2 + 5x - 6$ and the remainder is 3. Find the original polynomial.

49. If a polynomial is divided by $x + 3$, the quotient is $x^2 - x + 10$ and the remainder is -2. Find the original polynomial.

△ **50.** If the area of a parallelogram is $\left(x^4 - 23x^2 + 9x - 5\right)$ square centimeters and its base is $(x + 5)$ centimeters, find its height.

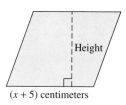

Height

$(x + 5)$ centimeters

△ **51.** If the volume of a box is $\left(x^4 + 6x^3 - 7x^2\right)$ cubic meters, its height is x^2 meters, and its length is $(x + 7)$ meters, find its width.

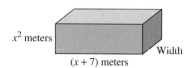

x^2 meters

Width

$(x + 7)$ meters

REVIEW EXERCISES

Solve each equation for x. See Sections 2.1 and 5.8.

52. $7x + 2 = x - 3$

53. $4 - 2x = 17 - 5x$

54. $x^2 = 4x - 4$

55. $5x^2 + 10x = 15$

56. $\dfrac{x}{3} - 5 = 13$

57. $\dfrac{2x}{9} + 1 = \dfrac{7}{9}$

Factor the following. See Sections 5.5 and 5.7.

58. $x^3 - 1$

59. $8y^3 + 1$

60. $125z^3 + 8$

61. $a^3 - 27$

62. $xy + 2x + 3y + 6$

63. $x^2 - x + xy - y$

64. $x^3 - 9x$

65. $2x^3 - 32x$

6.6 SOLVING EQUATIONS CONTAINING RATIONAL EXPRESSIONS

CD-ROM   SSM

SSG   Video

▶ **O B J E C T I V E**

1. Solve equations containing rational expressions.

1 In this section, we solve equations containing rational expressions. Before beginning this section, make sure that you understand the difference between an *equation* and an *expression*. An **equation** contains an equal sign and an **expression** does not.

Equation	*Expression*
$\dfrac{x}{2} + \dfrac{x}{6} = \dfrac{2}{3}$	$\dfrac{x}{2} + \dfrac{x}{6}$

SOLVING EQUATIONS CONTAINING RATIONAL EXPRESSIONS

To solve *equations* containing rational expressions, first clear the equation of fractions by multiplying both sides of the equation by the LCD of all rational expressions. Then solve as usual.

H E L P F U L   H I N T
The method described above is for equations only. It may *not* be used for performing operations on expressions.

Example 1   Solve: $\dfrac{4x}{5} + \dfrac{3}{2} = \dfrac{3x}{10}$

Solution   The LCD of $\dfrac{4x}{5}, \dfrac{3}{2}$, and $\dfrac{3x}{10}$ is 10. We multiply both sides of the equation by 10.

$$\frac{4x}{5} + \frac{3}{2} = \frac{3x}{10}$$

$$10\left(\frac{4x}{5} + \frac{3}{2}\right) = 10\left(\frac{3x}{10}\right) \qquad \text{Multiply both sides by the LCD.}$$

$$10 \cdot \frac{4x}{5} + 10 \cdot \frac{3}{2} = 10 \cdot \frac{3x}{10} \qquad \text{Use the distributive property.}$$

$$8x + 15 = 3x \qquad \text{Simplify.}$$

$$15 = -5x \qquad \text{Subtract } 8x \text{ from both sides.}$$

$$-3 = x \qquad \text{Solve.}$$

Verify this solution by replacing x with -3 in the original equation.

Check:
$$\frac{4x}{5} + \frac{3}{2} = \frac{3x}{10}$$

$$\frac{4(-3)}{5} + \frac{3}{2} \stackrel{?}{=} \frac{3(-3)}{10}$$

$$\frac{-12}{5} + \frac{3}{2} \stackrel{?}{=} \frac{-9}{10}$$

$$-\frac{24}{10} + \frac{15}{10} \stackrel{?}{=} -\frac{9}{10}$$

$$-\frac{9}{10} = -\frac{9}{10} \qquad \text{True.}$$

The solution is -3.

The important difference of the equations in this section is that the denominator of a rational expression may contain a variable. Recall that a rational expression is undefined for values of the variable that make the denominator 0. If a proposed solution makes the denominator 0, then it must be rejected as a solution of the original equation. Such proposed solutions are called **extraneous solutions**.

Example 2   Solve: $\dfrac{3}{x} - \dfrac{x + 21}{3x} = \dfrac{5}{3}$

Solution   The LCD of the denominators x, $3x$, and 3 is $3x$. We multiply both sides by $3x$.

$$\frac{3}{x} - \frac{x + 21}{3x} = \frac{5}{3}$$

$$3x\left(\frac{3}{x} - \frac{x + 21}{3x}\right) = 3x\left(\frac{5}{3}\right) \qquad \text{Multiply both sides by the LCD.}$$

$$3x \cdot \frac{3}{x} - 3x \cdot \frac{x + 21}{3x} = 3x \cdot \frac{5}{3} \qquad \text{Use the distributive property.}$$

$$9 - (x + 21) = 5x \qquad \text{Simplify.}$$

$$9 - x - 21 = 5x$$

$$-12 = 6x$$

$$-2 = x \qquad \text{Solve.}$$

The proposed solution is −2.

Check: Check the proposed solution in the original equation.

$$\frac{3}{x} - \frac{x + 21}{3x} = \frac{5}{3}$$

$$\frac{3}{-2} - \frac{-2 + 21}{3(-2)} \stackrel{?}{=} \frac{5}{3}$$

$$-\frac{9}{6} + \frac{19}{6} \stackrel{?}{=} \frac{5}{3}$$

$$\frac{10}{6} \stackrel{?}{=} \frac{5}{3} \qquad \textit{True.}$$

The solution is −2.

The following steps may be used to solve equations containing rational expressions.

SOLVING AN EQUATION CONTAINING RATIONAL EXPRESSIONS

Step 1: Multiply both sides of the equation by the LCD of all rational expressions in the equation.

Step 2: Simplify both sides.

Step 3: Determine whether the equation is linear, quadratic, or higher degree and solve accordingly.

Step 4: Check the solution in the original equation.

Example 3   Solve: $\dfrac{x + 6}{x - 2} = \dfrac{2(x + 2)}{x - 2}$

Solution   First we multiply both sides of the equation by the LCD, $x - 2$.

$$\frac{x + 6}{x - 2} = \frac{2(x + 2)}{x - 2}$$

$$(x - 2) \cdot \frac{x + 6}{x - 2} = (x - 2) \cdot \frac{2(x + 2)}{x - 2} \qquad \textit{Multiply both sides by } x - 2.$$

$$x + 6 = 2(x + 2) \qquad \textit{Simplify.}$$

$$x + 6 = 2x + 4 \qquad \textit{Use the distributive property.}$$

$$2 = x \qquad \textit{Solve.}$$

Check: The proposed solution is 2. Notice that 2 makes a denominator 0 in the original equation. This can also be seen in a check. Check the proposed solution 2 in the original equation.

$$\frac{x + 6}{x - 2} = \frac{2(x + 2)}{x - 2}$$

$$\frac{2 + 6}{2 - 2} = \frac{2(2 + 2)}{2 - 2}$$

$$\frac{8}{0} = \frac{2(4)}{0}$$

The denominators are 0, so 2 is not a solution of the original equation. The solution is $\{\quad\}$ or $\varnothing$.

Example 4   Solve: $\dfrac{2x}{2x - 1} + \dfrac{1}{x} = \dfrac{1}{2x - 1}$

Solution   The LCD is $x(2x - 1)$. Multiply both sides by $x(2x - 1)$. By the distributive property, this is the same as multiplying each term by $x(2x - 1)$.

$$x(2x - 1) \cdot \frac{2x}{2x - 1} + x(2x - 1) \cdot \frac{1}{x} = x(2x - 1) \cdot \frac{1}{2x - 1}$$

$$x(2x) + (2x - 1) = x \qquad \text{Simplify.}$$

$$2x^2 + 2x - 1 - x = 0$$

$$2x^2 + x - 1 = 0$$

$$(x + 1)(2x - 1) = 0$$

$$x + 1 = 0 \quad \text{or} \quad 2x - 1 = 0$$

$$x = -1 \qquad\qquad x = \frac{1}{2}$$

The number $\dfrac{1}{2}$ makes the denominator $2x - 1$ equal 0, so it is not a solution. The solution is -1.

Example 5   Solve: $\dfrac{2x}{x - 3} + \dfrac{6 - 2x}{x^2 - 9} = \dfrac{x}{x + 3}$

Solution   We factor the second denominator to find that the LCD is $(x + 3)(x - 3)$. We multiply both sides of the equation by $(x + 3)(x - 3)$. By the distributive property, this is the same as multiplying each term by $(x + 3)(x - 3)$.

$$\frac{2x}{x - 3} + \frac{6 - 2x}{x^2 - 9} = \frac{x}{x + 3}$$

$$(x + 3)(x - 3) \cdot \frac{2x}{x - 3} + (x + 3)(x - 3) \cdot \frac{6 - 2x}{(x + 3)(x - 3)}$$

$$= (x + 3)(x - 3)\left(\frac{x}{x + 3}\right)$$

$$2x(x + 3) + (6 - 2x) = x(x - 3) \qquad \text{Simplify.}$$

$$2x^2 + 6x + 6 - 2x = x^2 - 3x \qquad \text{Use the distributive property.}$$

Next we solve this quadratic equation by the factoring method. To do so, we first write the equation so that one side is 0.

$$x^2 + 7x + 6 = 0$$

$$(x + 6)(x + 1) = 0 \qquad \text{Factor.}$$

$$x = -6 \text{ or } x = -1 \qquad \text{Set each factor equal to 0.}$$

Neither -6 nor -1 makes any denominator 0 so they are both solutions. The solutions are -6 and -1.

Example 6 Solve: $\dfrac{z}{2z^2 + 3z - 2} - \dfrac{1}{2z} = \dfrac{3}{z^2 + 2z}$

Solution Factor the denominators to find that the LCD is $2z(z + 2)(2z - 1)$. Multiply both sides by the LCD. Remember, by using the distributive property, this is the same as multiplying each term by $2z(z + 2)(2z - 1)$.

$$\dfrac{z}{2z^2 + 3z - 2} - \dfrac{1}{2z} = \dfrac{3}{z^2 + 2z}$$

$$\dfrac{z}{(2z - 1)(z + 2)} - \dfrac{1}{2z} = \dfrac{3}{z(z + 2)}$$

$$2z(z + 2)(2z - 1) \cdot \dfrac{z}{(2z - 1)(z + 2)} - 2z(z + 2)(2z - 1) \cdot \dfrac{1}{2z}$$

$$= 2z(z + 2)(2z - 1) \cdot \dfrac{3}{z(z + 2)} \qquad \text{Apply the distributive property.}$$

$$2z(z) - (z + 2)(2z - 1) = 3 \cdot 2(2z - 1) \qquad \text{Simplify.}$$

$$2z^2 - (2z^2 + 3z - 2) = 12z - 6$$

$$2z^2 - 2z^2 - 3z + 2 = 12z - 6$$

$$-3z + 2 = 12z - 6$$

$$-15z = -8$$

$$z = \dfrac{8}{15} \qquad \text{Solve.}$$

The proposed solution $\dfrac{8}{15}$ does not make any denominator 0; the solution is $\dfrac{8}{15}$. ∎

A graph can be helpful in visualizing solutions of equations. For example, to visualize the solution of the equation $\dfrac{3}{x} - \dfrac{x + 21}{3x} = \dfrac{5}{3}$ in Example 2, the graph of the related rational function $f(x) = \dfrac{3}{x} - \dfrac{x + 21}{3x}$ is shown. A solution of the equation is an x-value that corresponds to a y-value of $\dfrac{5}{3}$.

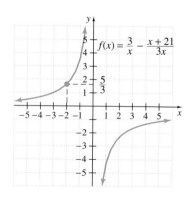

Notice that an x-value of -2 corresponds to a y-value of $\dfrac{5}{3}$. The solution of the equation is indeed -2 as shown in Example 2.

Exercise Set 6.6

Solve each equation. See Examples 1 and 2.

1. $\dfrac{x}{2} - \dfrac{x}{3} = 12$

2. $x = \dfrac{x}{2} - 4$

3. $\dfrac{x}{3} = \dfrac{1}{6} + \dfrac{x}{4}$

4. $\dfrac{x}{2} = \dfrac{21}{10} - \dfrac{x}{5}$

5. $\dfrac{2}{x} + \dfrac{1}{2} = \dfrac{5}{x}$

6. $\dfrac{5}{3x} + 1 = \dfrac{7}{6}$

7. $\dfrac{x + 3}{x} = \dfrac{5}{x}$

8. $\dfrac{4 - 3x}{2x} = -\dfrac{8}{2x}$

Solve each equation. See Examples 3 through 6.

9. $\dfrac{x + 5}{x + 3} = \dfrac{8}{x + 3}$

10. $\dfrac{5}{x - 2} - \dfrac{2}{x + 4} = -\dfrac{4}{x^2 + 2x - 8}$

11. $\dfrac{1}{x - 1} + \dfrac{1}{x + 1} = \dfrac{2}{x^2 - 1}$

12. $\dfrac{1}{x - 1} = \dfrac{2}{x + 1}$

13. $\dfrac{6}{x + 3} = \dfrac{4}{x - 3}$

14. $\dfrac{1}{x - 4} - \dfrac{3x}{x^2 - 16} = \dfrac{2}{x + 4}$

15. $\dfrac{3}{2x + 3} - \dfrac{1}{2x - 3} = \dfrac{4}{4x^2 - 9}$

16. $\dfrac{1}{x - 4} = \dfrac{8}{x^2 - 16}$

17. $\dfrac{2}{x^2 - 4} = \dfrac{1}{2x - 4}$

18. $\dfrac{1}{x - 2} - \dfrac{2}{x^2 - 2x} = 1$

19. $\dfrac{12}{3x^2 + 12x} = 1 - \dfrac{1}{x + 4}$

Solve each equation.

20. $\dfrac{5}{x} = \dfrac{20}{12}$

21. $\dfrac{2}{x} = \dfrac{10}{5}$

22. $1 - \dfrac{4}{a} = 5$

23. $7 + \dfrac{6}{a} = 5$

24. $\dfrac{1}{2x} - \dfrac{1}{x + 1} = \dfrac{1}{3x^2 + 3x}$

25. $\dfrac{2}{x - 5} + \dfrac{1}{2x} = \dfrac{5}{3x^2 - 15x}$

26. $\dfrac{1}{x} - \dfrac{x}{25} = 0$

27. $\dfrac{x}{4} + \dfrac{5}{x} = 3$

28. $5 - \dfrac{2}{2y - 5} = \dfrac{3}{2y - 5}$

29. $1 - \dfrac{5}{y + 7} = \dfrac{4}{y + 7}$

30. $\dfrac{x - 1}{x + 2} = \dfrac{2}{3}$

31. $\dfrac{6x + 7}{2x + 9} = \dfrac{5}{3}$

32. $\dfrac{x + 3}{x + 2} = \dfrac{1}{x + 2}$

33. $\dfrac{2x + 1}{4 - x} = \dfrac{9}{4 - x}$

34. $\dfrac{1}{a - 3} + \dfrac{2}{a + 3} = \dfrac{1}{a^2 - 9}$

35. $\dfrac{12}{9 - a^2} + \dfrac{3}{3 + a} = \dfrac{2}{3 - a}$

36. $\dfrac{64}{x^2 - 16} + 1 = \dfrac{2x}{x - 4}$

37. $2 + \dfrac{3}{x} = \dfrac{2x}{x + 3}$

38. $\dfrac{-15}{4y + 1} + 4 = y$

39. $\dfrac{36}{x^2 - 9} + 1 = \dfrac{2x}{x + 3}$

40. $\dfrac{28}{x^2 - 9} + \dfrac{2x}{x - 3} + \dfrac{6}{x + 3} = 0$

41. $\dfrac{x^2 - 20}{x^2 - 7x + 12} = \dfrac{3}{x - 3} + \dfrac{5}{x - 4}$

42. $\dfrac{x + 2}{x^2 + 7x + 10} = \dfrac{1}{3x + 6} - \dfrac{1}{x + 5}$

43. $\dfrac{3}{2x - 5} + \dfrac{2}{2x + 3} = 0$

44. The average cost of producing x game disks for a computer is given by the function $f(x) = 3.3 + \dfrac{5400}{x}$. Find the number of game disks that must be produced for the average cost to be \$5.10.

45. The average cost of producing x electric pencil sharpeners is given by the function $f(x) = 20 + \dfrac{4000}{x}$. Find the number of electric pencil sharpeners that must be produced for the average cost to be \$25.

Solve each equation. Begin by writing each equation with positive exponents only.

46. $x^{-2} - 19x^{-1} + 48 = 0$ **47.** $x^{-2} - 5x^{-1} - 36 = 0$

48. $p^{-2} + 4p^{-1} - 5 = 0$ **49.** $6p^{-2} - 5p^{-1} + 1 = 0$

Solve each equation. Round solutions to two decimal places.

50. $\dfrac{1.4}{x - 2.6} = \dfrac{-3.5}{x + 7.1}$ **51.** $\dfrac{-8.5}{x + 1.9} = \dfrac{5.7}{x - 3.6}$

52. $\dfrac{10.6}{y} - 14.7 = \dfrac{9.92}{3.2} + 7.6$

53. $\dfrac{12.2}{x} + 17.3 = \dfrac{9.6}{x} - 14.7$

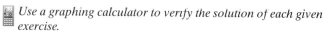 *Use a graphing calculator to verify the solution of each given exercise.*

54. Exercise 20   **55.** Exercise 21

56. Exercise 30   **57.** Exercise 31

REVIEW EXERCISES

Write each sentence as an equation and solve. See Section 2.2.

58. Four more than 3 times a number is 19.

59. The sum of two consecutive integers is 147.

60. The length of a rectangle is 5 inches more than the width. Its perimeter is 50 inches. Find the length and width.

61. The sum of a number and its reciprocal is $\dfrac{5}{2}$.

The following graph is from a survey of state and federal prisons. Use this histogram to answer Exercises 62–66.

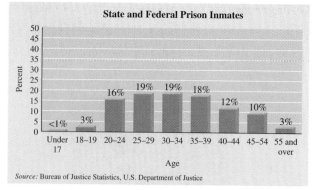

State and Federal Prison Inmates

Source: Bureau of Justice Statistics, U.S. Department of Justice

62. What percent of state and federal prison inmates are age 45 to 54?

63. What percent of state and federal prison inmates are 55 years old or older?

64. What age category shows the highest percent of prison inmates?

65. What percent of state and federal prison inmates are 20 to 34 years old?

66. At the end of 1998, there were 30,907 inmates under the jurisdiction of state and federal correctional authorities in the state of Louisiana. Approximately how many 25- to 29-year-old inmates would you expect to have been held in Louisiana at the end of 1998? Round to the nearest whole. (*Source:* Bureau of Justice Statistics)

A Look Ahead

Example

Solve $\left(\dfrac{x}{x + 1}\right)^2 - 7\left(\dfrac{x}{x + 1}\right) + 10 = 0.$

Solution

Let $u = \dfrac{x}{x + 1}$ and solve for u. Then substitute back and solve for x.

$$\left(\dfrac{x}{x + 1}\right)^2 - 7\left(\dfrac{x}{x + 1}\right) + 10 = 0$$

$$u^2 - 7u + 10 = 0 \qquad \text{Let } u = \dfrac{x}{x + 1}.$$

$$(u - 5)(u - 2) = 0 \qquad \text{Factor.}$$

$$u = 5 \quad \text{or} \quad u = 2 \qquad \text{Solve.}$$

Since $u = \dfrac{x}{x + 1}$, we have that $5 = \dfrac{x}{x + 1}$ or $2 = \dfrac{x}{x + 1}$.

Thus, there are two rational equations to solve.

1. $\qquad 5 = \dfrac{x}{x + 1}$ $\qquad$ **2.** $\qquad 2 = \dfrac{x}{x + 1}$

$\qquad 5 \cdot (x + 1) = x \qquad\qquad 2 \cdot (x + 1) = x$

$\qquad\qquad 5x + 5 = x \qquad\qquad\qquad 2x + 2 = x$

$\qquad\qquad\qquad 5 = -4x \qquad\qquad\qquad\quad 2 = -x$

$\qquad\qquad\qquad x = -\dfrac{5}{4} \qquad\qquad\qquad\quad x = -2$

Since neither $-\dfrac{5}{4}$ nor -2 makes the denominator 0, the solutions are $-\dfrac{5}{4}$ and -2.

Solve each equation by substitution. See the preceding example.

67. $(x - 1)^2 + 3(x - 1) + 2 = 0$

68. $(4 - x)^2 - 5(4 - x) + 6 = 0$

69. $\left(\dfrac{3}{x - 1}\right)^2 + 2\left(\dfrac{3}{x - 1}\right) + 1 = 0$

70. $\left(\dfrac{5}{2 + x}\right)^2 + \left(\dfrac{5}{2 + x}\right) - 20 = 0$

Supplementary Exercises on Expressions and Equations

It is very important that you understand the difference between an expression and an equation containing rational expressions. An equation contains an equal sign; an expression does not.

Expression to be Simplified

$$\frac{x}{2} + \frac{x}{6}$$

Write both rational expressions with the LCD, 6, as the denominator.

$$\frac{x}{2} + \frac{x}{6} = \frac{x \cdot 3}{2 \cdot 3} + \frac{x}{6}$$

$$= \frac{3x}{6} + \frac{x}{6}$$

$$= \frac{4x}{6} = \frac{2x}{3}$$

Equation to be Solved

$$\frac{x}{2} + \frac{x}{6} = \frac{2}{3}$$

Multiply both sides by the LCD, 6.

$$6\left(\frac{x}{2} + \frac{x}{6}\right) = 6\left(\frac{2}{3}\right)$$

$$3x + x = 4$$

$$4x = 4$$

$$x = 1$$

Check to see that the solution is 1.

HELPFUL HINT

Remember: Equations can be cleared of fractions; expressions cannot.

Perform each indicated operation and simplify, or solve the equation for the variable.

1. $\dfrac{x}{2} = \dfrac{1}{8} + \dfrac{x}{4}$

2. $\dfrac{x}{4} = \dfrac{3}{2} + \dfrac{x}{10}$

3. $\dfrac{1}{8} + \dfrac{x}{4}$

4. $\dfrac{3}{2} + \dfrac{x}{10}$

5. $\dfrac{4}{x + 2} - \dfrac{2}{x - 1}$

6. $\dfrac{5}{x - 2} - \dfrac{10}{x + 4}$

7. $\dfrac{4}{x + 2} = \dfrac{2}{x - 1}$

8. $\dfrac{5}{x - 2} = \dfrac{10}{x + 4}$

9. $\dfrac{2}{x^2 - 4} = \dfrac{1}{x + 2} - \dfrac{3}{x - 2}$

10. $\dfrac{3}{x^2 - 25} = \dfrac{1}{x + 5} + \dfrac{2}{x - 5}$

11. $\dfrac{5}{x^2 - 3x} + \dfrac{4}{2x - 6}$

12. $\dfrac{5}{x^2 - 3x} \div \dfrac{4}{2x - 6}$

13. $\dfrac{x - 1}{x + 1} + \dfrac{x + 7}{x - 1} = \dfrac{4}{x^2 - 1}$

14. $\left(1 - \dfrac{y}{x}\right) \div \left(1 - \dfrac{x}{y}\right)$

15. $\dfrac{a^2 - 9}{a - 6} \cdot \dfrac{a^2 - 5a - 6}{a^2 - a - 6}$

16. $\dfrac{2}{a - 6} + \dfrac{3a}{a^2 - 5a - 6} - \dfrac{a}{5a + 5}$

17. $\dfrac{2x + 3}{3x - 2} = \dfrac{4x + 1}{6x + 1}$

18. $\dfrac{5x - 3}{2x} = \dfrac{10x + 3}{4x + 1}$

19. $\dfrac{a}{9a^2 - 1} + \dfrac{2}{6a - 2}$

20. $\dfrac{3}{4a - 8} - \dfrac{a + 2}{a^2 - 2a}$

21. $-\dfrac{3}{x^2} - \dfrac{1}{x} + 2 = 0$

22. $\dfrac{x}{2x + 6} + \dfrac{5}{x^2 - 9}$

23. $\dfrac{x - 8}{x^2 - x - 2} + \dfrac{2}{x - 2}$

24. $\dfrac{x - 8}{x^2 - x - 2} + \dfrac{2}{x - 2} = \dfrac{3}{x + 1}$

25. $\dfrac{3}{a} - 5 = \dfrac{7}{a} - 1$

26. $\dfrac{7}{3z - 9} + \dfrac{5}{z}$

6.7 RATIONAL EQUATIONS AND PROBLEM SOLVING

CD-ROM

SSM

SSG

Video

▶ **OBJECTIVES**

1. Solve an equation containing rational expressions for a specified variable.
2. Solve problems by writing equations containing rational expressions.

1 In Section 2.3 we solved equations for a specified variable. In this section, we continue practicing this skill by solving equations containing rational expressions for a specified variable. The steps given in Section 2.3 for solving equations for a specified variable are repeated here.

SOLVING EQUATIONS FOR A SPECIFIED VARIABLE

Step 1: Clear the equation of fractions or rational expressions by multiplying each side of the equation by the least common denominator (LCD) of all denominators in the equation.

Step 2: Use the distributive property to remove grouping symbols such as parentheses.

Step 3: Combine like terms on each side of the equation.

Step 4: Use the addition property of equality to rewrite the equation as an equivalent equation with terms containing the specified variable on one side and all other terms on the other side.

Step 5: Use the distributive property and the multiplication property of equality to get the specified variable alone.

Example 1 Solve $\dfrac{1}{x} + \dfrac{1}{y} = \dfrac{1}{z}$ for x.

Solution To clear this equation of fractions, we multiply both sides of the equation by xyz, the LCD of $\dfrac{1}{x}, \dfrac{1}{y},$ and $\dfrac{1}{z}$.

$$\frac{1}{x} + \frac{1}{y} = \frac{1}{z}$$

$$xyz\left(\frac{1}{x} + \frac{1}{y}\right) = xyz\left(\frac{1}{z}\right) \qquad \text{Multiply both sides by } xyz.$$

$$xyz\left(\frac{1}{x}\right) + xyz\left(\frac{1}{y}\right) = xyz\left(\frac{1}{z}\right) \qquad \text{Use the distributive property.}$$

$$yz + xz = xy \qquad \text{Simplify.}$$

Notice the two terms that contain the specified variable x.

Next, we subtract xz from both sides so that all terms containing the specified variable x are on one side of the equation and all other terms are on the other side.

$$yz = xy - xz$$

Now we use the distributive property to factor x from $xy - xz$ and then the multiplication property of equality to solve for x.

$$yz = x(y - z)$$

$$\frac{yz}{y - z} = x \quad \text{or} \quad x = \frac{yz}{y - z} \qquad \text{Divide both sides by } y - z.$$

---

2 Problem solving sometimes involves modeling a described situation with an equation containing rational expressions. In Examples 2 through 5, we practice solving such problems and use the problem-solving steps first introduced in Section 2.2.

Example 2 FINDING AN UNKNOWN NUMBER

If a certain number is subtracted from the numerator and added to the denominator of $\dfrac{9}{19}$, the new fraction is equivalent to $\dfrac{1}{3}$. Find the number.

Solution 1. **UNDERSTAND** the problem. Read and reread the problem and try guessing the solution. For example, if the unknown number is 3, we have

$$\frac{9 - 3}{19 + 3} = \frac{1}{3}$$

To see if this is a true statement, we simplify the fraction on the left side.

$$\frac{6}{22} = \frac{1}{3} \quad \text{or} \quad \frac{3}{11} = \frac{1}{3} \qquad \text{False.}$$

Since this is not a true statement, 3 is not the correct number. Remember that the purpose of this step is not to guess the correct solution but to gain an understanding of the problem posed.

We will let n = the number to be subtracted from the numerator and added to the denominator.

2. TRANSLATE the problem.

In words:

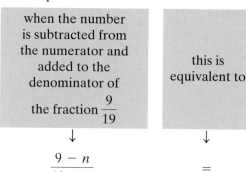

| when the number is subtracted from the numerator and added to the denominator of the fraction $\frac{9}{19}$ | this is equivalent to | $\frac{1}{3}$ |

$\downarrow$ $\downarrow$ $\downarrow$

Translate: $\qquad \dfrac{9-n}{19+n} \qquad\qquad = \qquad \dfrac{1}{3}$

3. SOLVE the equation for n.

$$\frac{9-n}{19+n} = \frac{1}{3}$$

To solve for n, we begin by multiplying both sides by the LCD $3(19+n)$.

$$3(19+n) \cdot \frac{9-n}{19+n} = 3(19+n) \cdot \frac{1}{3} \qquad \text{Multiply both sides by the LCD.}$$

$$3(9-n) = 19+n \qquad \text{Simplify.}$$

$$27-3n = 19+n$$

$$8 = 4n$$

$$2 = n \qquad \text{Solve.}$$

4. INTERPRET the results.

Check: If we subtract 2 from the numerator and add 2 to the denominator of $\frac{9}{19}$, we have $\dfrac{9-2}{19+2} = \dfrac{7}{21} = \dfrac{1}{3}$, and the problem checks.

State: The unknown number is 2.

Example 3 FINDING THE DISTANCE OF A LIGHT SOURCE

The intensity I of light, as measured in foot-candles, x feet from its source is given by the rational equation

$$I = \frac{320}{x^2}$$

How far away is the source if the intensity of light is 5 foot-candles?

Solution   1. **UNDERSTAND.** Read and reread the problem, and guess a solution. Since an equation has been given that describes the relationship between I and x, we replace x with a few values to help us become familiar with the equation.

To find the intensity I of light 1 foot from the source, we let $x = 1$.

$$I = \frac{320}{1^2} = \frac{320}{1} = 320 \text{ foot-candles}$$

To find the intensity I of light 3 feet from the source, we let $x = 3$.

$$I = \frac{320}{3^2} = \frac{320}{9} = 35\frac{5}{9} \text{ foot-candles}$$

Notice that as x increases, I decreases. That is, as the number of feet from the light source increases, the intensity decreases, as expected.

2. **TRANSLATE.** We are given that the intensity I is 5 foot-candles, and we are asked to find how far away the light source, x is. To do so, we let $I = 5$.

$$I = \frac{320}{x^2}$$

$$5 = \frac{320}{x^2} \qquad \text{Let } I = 5.$$

3. **SOLVE** the equation for x.

$$5 = \frac{320}{x^2}$$

$$x^2 \cdot 5 = x^2 \cdot \frac{320}{x^2} \qquad \text{Multiply both sides by } x^2.$$

$$5x^2 = 320 \qquad \text{Simplify.}$$

$$5x^2 - 320 = 0 \qquad \text{Subtract 320.}$$

$$5(x^2 - 64) = 0 \qquad \text{Factor.}$$

$$5(x + 8)(x - 8) = 0 \qquad \text{Factor.}$$

$$x = -8 \quad \text{or} \quad x = 8$$

4. **INTERPRET.** Since x represents distance and distance cannot be negative, the proposed solution -8 must be rejected. *Check* the solution 8 feet in the given formula. Then *state* the conclusion: The source of light is 8 feet away when the intensity is 5 foot-candles.   ▬

The following work example leads to an equation containing rational expressions.

Example 4   **CALCULATING WORK HOURS**

Melissa Scarlatti can clean the house in 4 hours, whereas her husband, Zack, can do the same job in 5 hours. They have agreed to clean together so that they can finish in time to watch a movie on TV that starts in 2 hours. How long will it take them to clean the house together? Can they finish before the movie starts?

Solution   1. **UNDERSTAND.** Read and reread the problem. The key idea here is the relationship between the *time* (in hours) it takes to complete the job and the *part of the job* completed in 1 unit of time (1 hour). For example, if the *time* it takes Melissa to complete the job is 4 hours, the *part of the job* she can complete in 1 hour is $\frac{1}{4}$. Similarly, Zack can complete $\frac{1}{5}$ of the job in 1 hour.

We will let t = *the time* in hours it takes Melissa and Zack to clean the house together. Then $\frac{1}{t}$ represents the *part of the job* they complete in 1 hour. We summarize the given information in a chart.

	Hours to Complete the Job	Part of Job Completed in 1 Hour
MELISSA ALONE	4	$\frac{1}{4}$
ZACK ALONE	5	$\frac{1}{5}$
TOGETHER	t	$\frac{1}{t}$

2. TRANSLATE.

In words:

part of job Melissa can complete in 1 hour	added to	part of job Zack can complete in 1 hour	is equal to	part of job they can complete together in 1 hour
↓	↓	↓	↓	↓
$\frac{1}{4}$	$+$	$\frac{1}{5}$	$=$	$\frac{1}{t}$

Translate:

3. SOLVE.

$$\frac{1}{4} + \frac{1}{5} = \frac{1}{t}$$

$$20t\left(\frac{1}{4} + \frac{1}{5}\right) = 20t\left(\frac{1}{t}\right) \qquad \text{Multiply both sides by the LCD, } 20t.$$

$$5t + 4t = 20$$

$$9t = 20$$

$$t = \frac{20}{9} \quad \text{or} \quad 2\frac{2}{9} \qquad \text{Solve.}$$

4. INTERPRET.

Check: The proposed solution is $2\frac{2}{9}$. That is, Melissa and Zack would take $2\frac{2}{9}$ hours to clean the house together. This proposed solution is reasonable since $2\frac{2}{9}$ hours is more than half of Melissa's time and less than half of Zack's time. Check this solution in the originally stated problem.

State: Melissa and Zack can clean the house together in $2\frac{2}{9}$ hours. They cannot complete the job before the movie starts.

Example 5   **FINDING THE SPEED OF A CURRENT**

Steve Deitmer takes $1\frac{1}{2}$ times as long to go 72 miles upstream in his boat as he does to return. If the boat cruises at 30 mph in still water, what is the speed of the current?

Solution   1. **UNDERSTAND.** Read and reread the problem. Guess a solution. Suppose that the current is 4 mph. The speed of the boat upstream is slowed down by the current: $30 - 4$, or 26 mph, and the speed of the boat downstream is speeded up by the current: $30 + 4$, or 34 mph. Next let's find out how long it takes to travel 72 miles upstream and 72 miles downstream. To do so, we use the formula $d = rt$, or $\dfrac{d}{r} = t$.

Upstream	**Downstream**
$\dfrac{d}{r} = t$	$\dfrac{d}{r} = t$
$\dfrac{72}{26} = t$	$\dfrac{72}{34} = t$
$2\dfrac{10}{13} = t$	$2\dfrac{2}{17} = t$

Since the time upstream $\left(2\dfrac{10}{13} \text{ hours} \right)$ is not $1\dfrac{1}{2}$ times the time downstream $\left(2\dfrac{2}{17} \text{ hours} \right)$, our guess is not correct. We do, however, have a better understanding of the problem.

We will let
$$x = \text{the speed of the current}$$
$$30 + x = \text{the speed of the boat downstream}$$
$$30 - x = \text{the speed of the boat upstream}$$

This information is summarized in the following chart, where we use the formula $\dfrac{d}{r} = t$.

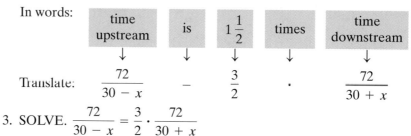

	Distance	Rate	Time $\left(\dfrac{d}{r}\right)$
UPSTREAM	72	$30 - x$	$\dfrac{72}{30 - x}$
DOWNSTREAM	72	$30 + x$	$\dfrac{72}{30 + x}$

2. TRANSLATE. Since the time spent traveling upstream is $1\frac{1}{2}$ times the time spent traveling downstream, we have

In words:

time upstream	is	$1\frac{1}{2}$	times	time downstream
↓	↓	↓	↓	↓

Translate: $\dfrac{72}{30 - x}$ $=$ $\dfrac{3}{2}$ $\cdot$ $\dfrac{72}{30 + x}$

3. SOLVE. $\dfrac{72}{30 - x} = \dfrac{3}{2} \cdot \dfrac{72}{30 + x}$

First we multiply both sides by the LCD, $2(30 + x)(30 - x)$.

$$2(30 + x)(30 - x) \cdot \frac{72}{30 - x} = 2(30 + x)(30 - x)\left(\frac{3}{2} \cdot \frac{72}{30 + x}\right)$$

$72 \cdot 2(30 + x) = 3 \cdot 72 \cdot (30 - x)$ Simplify.

$2(30 + x) = 3(30 - x)$ Divide both sides by 72.

$60 + 2x = 90 - 3x$ Use the distributive property.

$5x = 30$

$x = 6$ Solve.

4. INTERPRET.

Check: Check the proposed solution of 6 mph in the originally stated problem.

State: The current's speed is 6 mph.

SPOTLIGHT ON DECISION MAKING

Suppose you are an aviation safety inspector. You are testing the accuracy of the radioaltimeter on an airplane. To be acceptable, the altitude reading given by the altimeter must be within 3% of the actual altitude. You know that you can check the altimeter's altitude reading with the equation $t = \dfrac{2a}{c}$, where t is the time it takes a radar pulse aimed downward from the airplane to bounce off Earth's surface and return to the radioaltimeter, a is the altitude, and c is the speed of light, 3×10^8 meters per second.

During your test, you find that it takes 5×10^{-5} second for the radar pulse emitted by the altimeter to be returned. The altimeter reads an altitude of 7420 meters. Is the altimeter reading acceptable? Explain.

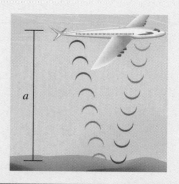

Exercise Set 6.7

Solve each equation for the specified variable. See Example 1.

1. $F = \dfrac{9}{5}C + 32$ for C (Meteorology)

△ **2.** $V = \dfrac{1}{3}\pi r^2 h$ for h (Volume)

3. $Q = \dfrac{A - I}{L}$ for I (Finance)

4. $P = 1 - \dfrac{C}{S}$ for S (Finance)

5. $\dfrac{1}{R} = \dfrac{1}{R_1} + \dfrac{1}{R_2}$ for R (Electronics)

6. $\dfrac{1}{R} = \dfrac{1}{R_1} + \dfrac{1}{R_2}$ for R_1 (Electronics)

7. $S = \dfrac{n(a + L)}{2}$ for n (Sequences)

8. $S = \dfrac{n(a + L)}{2}$ for a (Sequences)

△ **9.** $A = \dfrac{h(a + b)}{2}$ for b (Geometry)

△ **10.** $A = \dfrac{h(a + b)}{2}$ for h (Geometry)

11. $\dfrac{P_1 V_1}{T_1} = \dfrac{P_2 V_2}{T_2}$ for T_2 (Chemistry)

12. $H = \dfrac{kA(T_1 - T_2)}{L}$ for T_2 (Physics)

13. $f = \dfrac{f_1 f_2}{f_1 + f_2}$ for f_2 (Optics)

14. $I = \dfrac{E}{R + r}$ for r (Electronics)

15. $\lambda = \dfrac{2L}{n}$ for L (Physics)

16. $S = \dfrac{a_1 - a_n r}{1 - r}$ for a_1 (Sequences)

17. $\dfrac{\theta}{\omega} = \dfrac{2L}{c}$ for c

18. $F = \dfrac{-GMm}{r^2}$ for M (Physics)

Solve. See Example 2.

19. The sum of a number and 5 times its reciprocal is 6. Find the number(s).

20. The quotient of a number and 9 times its reciprocal is 1. Find the number(s).

21. If a number is added to the numerator of $\dfrac{12}{41}$ and twice the number is added to the denominator of $\dfrac{12}{41}$, the resulting fraction is equivalent to $\dfrac{1}{3}$. Find the number.

22. If a number is subtracted from the numerator of $\dfrac{13}{8}$ and added to the denominator of $\dfrac{13}{8}$, the resulting fraction is equivalent to $\dfrac{2}{5}$. Find the number.

In electronics, the relationship among the resistances R_1 and R_2 of two resistors wired in a parallel circuit and their combined resistance R is described by the formula $\dfrac{1}{R} = \dfrac{1}{R_1} + \dfrac{1}{R_2}$. Use this formula to solve Exercises 23 through 26. See Example 3.

23. If the combined resistance is 2 ohms and one of the two resistances is 3 ohms, find the other resistance.

24. Find the combined resistance of two resistors of 12 ohms each when they are wired in a parallel circuit.

25. The relationship among resistance of two resistors wired in a parallel circuit and their combined resistance may be extended to three resistors of resistances R_1, R_2, and R_3. Write an equation you believe may describe the relationship, and use it to find the combined resistance if R_1, is 5 R_2 is 6, and R_3 is 2.

26. Use your formula from Exercise 25 to find the combined resistance if R_1 is 3, R_2 is 5, and R_3 is 15.

Solve. See Example 4.

27. Alan Cantrell can word process a research paper in 6 hours. With Steve Isaac's help, the paper can be processed in 4 hours. Find how long it takes Steve to word process the paper alone.

28. An experienced roofer can roof a house in 26 hours. A beginning roofer needs 39 hours to complete the same job. Find how long it takes for the two to do the job together.

29. A new printing press can print newspapers twice as fast as the old one can. The old one can print the afternoon edition in 4 hours. Find how long it takes to print the afternoon edition if both printers are operating.

30. Three postal workers can sort a stack of mail in 20 minutes, 30 minutes, and 60 minutes, respectively. Find how long it takes to sort the mail if all three work together.

Solve. See Example 5

31. An F-100 plane and a Toyota truck leave the same town at sunrise and head for a town 450 miles away. The speed of the plane is three times the speed of the truck, and the plane arrives 6 hours ahead of the truck. Find the speed of the truck.

32. Mattie Evans drove 150 miles in the same amount of time that it took a turbo propeller plane to travel 600 miles. The speed of the plane was 150 mph faster than the speed of the car. Find the speed of the plane.

33. The speed of a boat in still water is 24 mph. If the boat travels 54 miles upstream in the same time that it takes to travel 90 miles downstream, find the speed of the current.

34. The speed of Lazy River's current is 5 mph. If a boat travels 20 miles downstream in the same time that it takes to travel 10 miles upstream, find the speed of the boat in still water.

Solve.

35. The sum of the reciprocals of two consecutive odd integers is $\frac{20}{99}$. Find the two integers.

36. The sum of the reciprocals of two consecutive integers is $-\frac{15}{56}$. Find the two integers.

37. If Sarah Clark can do a job in 5 hours and Dick Belli and Sarah working together can do the same job in 2 hours, find how long it takes Dick to do the job alone.

38. One hose can fill a goldfish pond in 45 minutes, and two hoses can fill the same pond in 20 minutes. Find how long it takes the second hose alone to fill the pond.

39. The speed of a bicyclist is 10 mph faster than the speed of a walker. If the bicyclist travels 26 miles in the same amount of time that the walker travels 6 miles, find the speed of the bicyclist.

40. Two trains going in opposite directions leave at the same time. One train travels 15 mph faster than the other. In 6 hours the trains are 630 miles apart. Find the speed of each.

41. The numerator of a fraction is 4 less than the denominator. If both the numerator and the denominator are increased by 2, the resulting fraction is equivalent to $\frac{2}{3}$. Find the fraction.

42. The denominator of a fraction is 1 more than the numerator. If both the numerator and the denominator are decreased by 3, the resulting fraction is equivalent to $\frac{4}{5}$. Find the fraction.

43. Cyclist Lance Armstrong of the United States won the 1999 Tour de France. An amateur cyclist training for a road race rode the first 20-mile portion of his workout at a constant rate. For the 16-mile cool-down portion of his workout, he reduced his speed by 2 miles per hour. Each portion of the workout took equal time. Find the cyclist's rate during the first portion and his rate during the cool-down portion.

44. Moo Dairy has three machines to fill gallon milk cartons. The machines can fill the daily quota in 5 hours, 6 hours, and 7.5 hours, respectively. Find how long it takes to fill the daily quota if all three machines are running.

45. The inlet pipe of an oil tank can fill the tank in 1 hour 30 minutes. The outlet pipe can empty the tank in 1 hour. Find how long it takes to empty a full tank if both pipes are open.

46. A plane flies 465 miles with the wind and 345 miles against the wind in the same length of time. If the speed of the wind is 20 mph, find the speed of the plane in still air.

47. Two rockets are launched. The first travels at 9000 mph. Fifteen minutes later the second is launched at 10,000 mph. Find the distance at which both rockets are an equal distance from Earth.

48. Two joggers, one averaging 8 mph and one averaging 6 mph, start from a designated initial point. The slower jogger arrives at the end of the run a half hour after the other jogger. Find the distance of the run.

49. Smith Engineering is in the process of reviewing the salaries of their surveyors. During this review, the company has found that an experienced surveyor surveys a roadbed in 4 hours. An apprentice surveyor needs 5 hours to survey the same stretch of road. If the two work together, find how long it takes them to complete the job.

50. A semi truck travels 300 miles through the flatland in the same amount of time that it travels 180 miles through the Great Smoky mountains. The rate of the truck is 20 miles per hour slower in the mountains than in the flatland. Find both the flatland rate and mountain rate.

51. An experienced bricklayer constructs a small wall in 3 hours. An apprentice completes the job in 6 hours. Find how long it takes if they work together.

52. A marketing manager travels 1080 miles in a corporate jet and then an additional 240 miles by car. If the car ride takes 1 hour longer, and if the rate of the jet is 6 times the rate of the car, find the time the manager travels by jet and find the time she travels by car.

53. Gary Marcus and Tony Alva work at Lombardo's Pipe and Concrete. Mr. Lombardo is preparing an estimate for a customer. He knows that Gary lays a slab of concrete in 6 hours. Tony lays the same size slab in 4 hours. If both work on the job and the cost of labor is $45 per hour, determine what the labor estimate should be.

54. In 2 minutes, a conveyor belt moves 300 pounds of recyclable aluminum from the delivery truck to a storage area. A smaller belt moves the same quantity of cans the same distance in 6 minutes. If both belts are used, find how long it takes to move the cans to the storage area.

55. Mr. Dodson can paint his house by himself in four days. His son needs an additional day to complete the job if he works by himself. If they work together, find how long it takes to paint the house.

56. While road testing a new make of car, the editor of a consumer magazine finds that she can go 10 miles into a 3-mile-per-hour wind in the same amount of time that she can go 11 miles with a 3-mile-per-hour wind behind her. Find the speed of the car in still air.

57. The world record for the largest white bass caught is held by Ronald Sprouse of Virginia. The bass weighed 6 pounds 13 ounces. If Ronald rows to his favorite fishing spot 9 miles downstream in the same amount of time that he rows 3 miles upstream, and if the current is 6 miles per hour, find how long it takes him to cover the 12 miles.

Calculating body-mass index is a way to gauge whether a person should lose weight. Doctors recommend that body-mass index values fall between 19 and 25. The formula for body-mass index B is $B = \dfrac{705w}{h^2}$, where w is weight in pounds and h is height in inches. Use this formula to answer Exercises 58 and 59.

 58. A patient is 5 ft 8 in. tall. What should his or her weight be to have a bodymass index of 25? Round to the nearest whole pound.

 59. A doctor recorded a body-mass index of 47 on a patient's chart. Later, a nurse notices that the doctor recorded the patient's weight as 240 pounds but neglected to record the patient's height. Explain how the nurse can use the information from the chart to find the patient's height. Then find the height.

In physics, when the source of a sound is traveling toward an observer, the relationship between the actual pitch a of the sound and the pitch h that the observer hears due to the Doppler effect is described by the formula $h = \dfrac{a}{1 - \dfrac{s}{770}}$, where s is the speed of the sound source in miles per hour. Use this formula to answer Exercise 60.

 60. An emergency vehicle has a single-tone siren with the pitch of the musical note E. As it approaches an observer standing by the road, the vehicle is traveling 50 miles per hour. Is the pitch that the observer hears due to the Doppler effect lower or higher than the actual pitch? To which musical note is the pitch that the observer hears closest?

Pitch of an Octave of Musical Notes in Hertz (Hz)	
Note	Pitch
Middle C	261.63
D	293.66
E	329.63
F	349.23
G	392.00
A	440.00
B	493.88

Note: Greater numbers indicate higher pitches (acoustically).
(*Source:* American Standards Association)

REVIEW EXERCISES

Solve each equation for x. See Section 2.1.

61. $\dfrac{x}{5} = \dfrac{x+2}{3}$

62. $\dfrac{x}{4} = \dfrac{x+3}{6}$

63. $\dfrac{x-3}{2} = \dfrac{x-5}{6}$

64. $\dfrac{x-6}{4} = \dfrac{x-2}{5}$

6.8 VARIATION AND PROBLEM SOLVING

CD-ROM   SSM

SSG   Video

▶ **O B J E C T I V E S**

1. Solve problems involving direct variation.
2. Solve problems involving inverse variation.
3. Solve problems involving joint variation.
4. Solve problems involving combined variation.

---

1 A very familiar example of direct variation is the relationship of the circumference C of a circle to its radius r. The formula $C = 2\pi r$ expresses that the circumference is always 2π times the radius. In other words, C is always a constant multiple (2π) of r. Because it is, we say that **C varies directly as r**, that **C varies directly with r**, or that **C is directly proportional to r.**

> **DIRECT VARIATION**
>
> **y varies directly as x, or y is directly proportional to x,** if there is a nonzero constant k such that
>
> $$y = kx$$
>
> The number k is called the **constant of variation** or the **constant of proportionality.**

In the above definition, the relationship described between x and y is a linear one. In other words, the graph of $y = kx$ is a line. The slope of the line is k, and the line passes through the origin.

For example, the graph of the direct variation equation $C = 2\pi r$ is shown. The horizontal axis represents the radius r, and the vertical axis is the circumference C. From the graph we can read that when the radius is 6 units, the circumference is approximately 38 units. Also, when the circumference is 45 units, the radius is between 7 and 8 units. Notice that as the radius increases, the circumference increases.

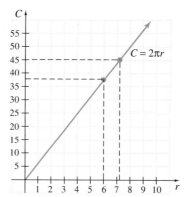

Example 1 Suppose that y varies directly as x. If y is 5 when x is 30, find the constant of variation and the direct variation equation.

Solution   Since y varies directly as x, we write $y = kx$. If $y = 5$ when $x = 30$, we have that

$$y = kx$$
$$5 = k(30) \quad \text{Replace } y \text{ with 5 and } x \text{ with 30.}$$
$$\frac{1}{6} = k \quad \text{Solve for } k.$$

The constant of variation is $\frac{1}{6}$.

After finding the constant of variation k, the direct variation equation can be written as $y = \frac{1}{6}x$.

Example 2   USING DIRECT VARIATION AND HOOKE'S LAW

Hooke's law states that the distance a spring stretches is directly proportional to the weight attached to the spring. If a 40-pound weight attached to the spring stretches the spring 5 inches, find the distance that a 65-pound weight attached to the spring stretches the spring.

Solution   1. UNDERSTAND. Read and reread the problem. Notice that we are given that the distance a spring stretches is **directly proportional** to the weight attached. We let

$$d = \text{the distance stretched}$$
$$w = \text{the weight attached}$$

The constant of variation is represented by k.

2. TRANSLATE. Because d is directly proportional to w, we write

$$d = kw$$

3. SOLVE. When a weight of 40 pounds is attached, the spring stretches 5 inches. That is, when $w = 40, d = 50$.

$$d = kw$$
$$5 = k(40) \quad \text{Replace } d \text{ with 5 and } w \text{ with 40.}$$
$$\frac{1}{8} = k \quad \text{Solve for } k.$$

Now when we replace k with $\frac{1}{8}$ in the equation

$$d = kw, \text{ we have}$$
$$d = \frac{1}{8}w$$

To find the stretch when a weight of 65 pounds is attached, we replace w with 65 to find d.

$$d = \frac{1}{8}(65)$$

$$= \frac{65}{8} = 8\frac{1}{8} \quad \text{or} \quad 8.125$$

4. INTERPRET.

   Check: Check the proposed solution of 8.125 inches in the original problem.

   State: The spring stetches 8.125 inches when a 65-pound weight is attached.   ▬

2

When y is proportional to the **reciprocal** of another variable x, we say that **y varies inversely as x**, or that **y is inversely proportional to x**. An example of the inverse variation relationship is the relationship between the pressure that a gas exerts and the volume of its container. As the volume of a container decreases, the pressure of the gas it contains increases.

INVERSE VARIATION

y varies inversely as x, or **y is inversely proportional to x**, if there is a nonzero constant k such that

$$y = \frac{k}{x}$$

The number k is called the **constant of variation** or the **constant of proportionality**.

Notice that $y = \frac{k}{x}$ is a rational equation. Its graph for $k > 0$ and $x > 0$ is shown.

From the graph, we can see that as x increases, y decreases.

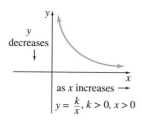

y decreases

as x increases →

$y = \frac{k}{x}, k > 0, x > 0$

Example 3   Suppose that u varies inversely as w. If u is 3 when w is 5, find the constant of variation and the inverse variation equation.

Solution   Since u varies inversely as w, we have $u = \frac{k}{w}$. We let $u = 3$ and $w = 5$, and we solve for k.

$$u = \frac{k}{w}$$

$$3 = \frac{k}{5} \qquad \text{Let } u = 3 \text{ and } w = 5.$$

$$15 = k \qquad \text{Multiply both sides by 5.}$$

The constant of variation k is 15. This gives the inverse variation equation

$$u = \frac{15}{w}$$

Example 4 **USING INVERSE VARIATION AND BOYLE'S LAW**

Boyle's law says that if the temperature stays the same, the pressure P of a gas is inversely proportional to the volume V. If a cylinder in a steam engine has a pressure of 960 kilopascals when the volume is 1.4 cubic meters, find the pressure when the volume increases to 2.5 cubic meters.

Solution
1. UNDERSTAND. Read and reread the problem. Notice that we are given that the pressure of a gas is *inversely proportional* to the volume. We will let P = the pressure and V = the volume. The constant of variation is represented by k.

2. TRANSLATE. Because P is inversely proportional to V, we write

$$P = \frac{k}{V}$$

When P = 960 kilopascals, the volume V = 1.4 cubic meters. We use this information to find k.

$$960 = \frac{k}{1.4} \qquad \text{Let } P = 960 \text{ and } V = 1.4.$$

$$1344 = k \qquad \text{Multiply both sides by 1.4.}$$

Thus, the value of k is 1344. Replacing k with 1344 in the variation equation, we have

$$P = \frac{1344}{V}$$

Next we find P when V is 2.5 cubic meters.

3. SOLVE.

$$P = \frac{1344}{2.5} \qquad \text{Let } V = 2.5.$$

$$= 537.6$$

4. INTERPRET. *Check* the proposed solution in the original problem.

   State: When the volume is 2.5 cubic meters, the pressure is 537.6 kilopascals.

3 Sometimes the ratio of a variable to the product of many other variables is constant. For example, the ratio of distance traveled to the product of speed and time traveled is always 1.

$$\frac{d}{rt} = 1 \qquad \text{or} \qquad d = rt$$

Such a relationship is called **joint variation.**

JOINT VARIATION

If the ratio of a variable y to the product of two or more variables is constant, then y **varies jointly as,** or **is jointly proportional to,** the other variables. If

$$y = kxz$$

then the number k is the **constant of variation** or the **constant of proportionality.**

△ **Example 5**   **EXPRESSING SURFACE AREA**

The surface area of a cylinder varies jointly as its radius and height. Express surface area S in terms of radius r and height h.

Solution   Because the surface area varies jointly as the radius r and the height h, we equate S to a constant multiple of r and h.

$$S = krh$$

In the equation, $S = krh$, it can be determined that the constant k is 2π, and we then have the formula $S = 2\pi rh$. (This formula does not include the areas of the two circular bases.)

4 Some examples of variation involve combinations of direct, inverse, and joint variation. We will call these variations **combined variation.**

△ **Example 6**   **FINDING COLUMN WEIGHT**

The maximum weight that a circular column can support is directly proportional to the fourth power of its diameter and is inversely proportional to the square of its height. A 2-meter-diameter column that is 8 meters in height can support 1 ton. Find the weight that a 1-meter-diameter column that is 4 meters in height can support.

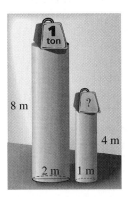

Solution   1. **UNDERSTAND.** Read and reread the problem. Let w = weight, d = diameter, h = height, and k = the constant of variation.

2. **TRANSLATE.** Since w is directly proportional to d^4 and inversely proportional to h^2, we have

$$w = \frac{kd^4}{h^2}$$

3. **SOLVE.** To find k, we are given that a 2-meter-diameter column that is 8 meters in height can support 1 ton. That is, $w = 1$ when $d = 2$ and $h = 8$, or

$$1 = \frac{k \cdot 2^4}{8^2} \qquad \text{Let } w = 1, d = 2, \text{ and } h = 8.$$

$$1 = \frac{k \cdot 16}{64}$$

$$4 = k \qquad \text{Solve for } k.$$

Now replace k with 4 in the equation $w = \dfrac{kd^4}{h^2}$ and we have

$$w = \frac{4d^4}{h^2}$$

To find weight w for a 1-meter-diameter column that is 4 meters in height, let $d = 1$ and $h = 4$.

$$w = \frac{4 \cdot 1^4}{4^2}$$

$$w = \frac{4}{16} = \frac{1}{4}$$

4. **INTERPRET.** *Check* the proposed solution in the original problem. *State:* The 1-meter-diameter column that is 4 meters in height can hold $\dfrac{1}{4}$ ton of weight. ▬

SPOTLIGHT ON DECISION MAKING

Suppose you are painting the ceilings of your one-story home, whose layout is shown in the figure. The amount of paint you need is directly proportional to the area of what is to be painted. A clerk at the paint store says that 450 square feet can be painted with 4 quarts of paint. Quarts of paint cost $5.95 each and gallons of paint cost $21.50 each. You have brought only $50 with you to the store.

Can you get all the paint you need for the project with the money you have brought? If so, explain how. If not, how much more money will you need?

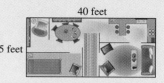

40 feet

25 feet

Exercise Set 6.8

If y varies directly as x, find the constant of variation k and the direct variation equation for each situation. See Example 1.

1. $y = 4$ when $x = 20$

2. $y = 5$ when $x = 30$

3. $y = 6$ when $x = 4$

4. $y = 12$ when $x = 8$

5. $y = 7$ when $x = \frac{1}{2}$

6. $y = 11$ when $x = \frac{1}{3}$

7. $y = 0.2$ when $x = 0.8$

8. $y = 0.4$ when $x = 2.5$

Solve. See Example 2.

9. The weight of a synthetic ball varies directly with the cube of its radius. A ball with a radius of 2 inches weighs 1.20 pounds. Find the weight of a ball of the same material with a 3-inch radius.

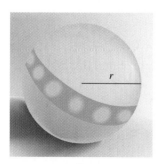

r

10. At sea, the distance to the horizon is directly proportional to the square root of the elevation of the observer. If a person who is 36 feet above the water can see 7.4 miles, find how far a person 64 feet above the water can see. Round answer to one decimal place.

11. The amount P of pollution varies directly with the population N of people. Kansas City has a population of 450,000 and produces 260,000 tons of pollutants. Find how many tons of pollution we should expect St. Louis to produce, if we know that its population is 980,000. Round answer to the nearest whole ton.

12. Charles' law states that if the pressure P stays the same, the volume V of a gas is directly proportional to its temperature T. If a balloon is filled with 20 cubic meters of a gas at a temperature of 300 K, find the new volume if the temperature rises to 360 K while the pressure stays the same.

If y varies inversely as x, find the constant of variation k and the inverse variation equation for each situation. See Example 3.

13. $y = 6$ when $x = 5$

14. $y = 20$ when $x = 9$

15. $y = 100$ when $x = 7$

16. $y = 63$ when $x = 3$

17. $y = \frac{1}{8}$ when $x = 16$

18. $y = \frac{1}{10}$ when $x = 40$

19. $y = 0.2$ when $x = 0.7$

20. $y = 0.6$ when $x = 0.3$

Solve. See Example 4.

21. Pairs of markings a set distance apart are made on highways so that police can detect drivers exceeding the speed limit. Over a fixed distance, the speed R varies inversely with the time T. In one particular pair of markings, R is 45 mph when T is 6 seconds. Find the speed of a car that travels the given distance in 5 seconds.

22. The weight of an object on or above the surface of Earth varies inversely as the square of the distance between the object and Earth's center. If a person weighs 160 pounds on Earth's surface, find the individual's weight if he moves 200 miles above Earth. Round answer to the nearest pound. (Assume that Earth's radius is 4000 miles.)

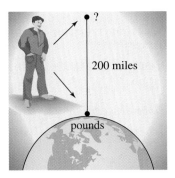

23. If the voltage V in an electric circuit is held constant, the current I is inversely proportional to the resistance R. If the current is 40 amperes when the resistance is 270 ohms, find the current when the resistance is 150 ohms.

24. Because it is more efficient to produce larger numbers of items, the cost of producing Dysan computer disks is inversely proportional to the number produced. If 4000 can be produced at a cost of $1.20 each, find the cost per disk when 6000 are produced.

25. The intensity I of light varies inversely as the square of the distance d from the light source. If the distance from the light source is doubled (see the figure at the bottom of this column and the figure at the top of the next column), determine what happens to the intensity of light at the new location.

△ **26.** The maximum weight that a circular column can hold is inversely proportional to the square of its height. If an 8-foot column can hold 2 tons, find how much weight a 10-foot column can hold.

Write each statement as an equation. See Example 5.

27. x varies jointly as y and z.

28. P varies jointly as R and the square of S.

29. r varies jointly as s and the cube of t.

30. a varies jointly as b and c.

Solve. See Examples 5 and 6.

31. The maximum weight that a rectangular beam can support varies jointly as its width and the square of its height and inversely as its length. If a beam $\frac{1}{2}$ foot wide, $\frac{1}{3}$ foot high, and 10 feet long can support 12 tons, find how much a similar beam can support if the beam is $\frac{2}{3}$ foot wide, $\frac{1}{2}$ foot high, and 16 feet long.

32. The number of cars manufactured on an assembly line at a General Motors plant varies jointly as the number of workers and the time they work. If 200 workers can produce 60 cars in 2 hours, find how many cars 240 workers should be able to make in 3 hours.

△ **33.** The volume of a cone varies jointly as the square of its radius and its height. If the volume of a cone is 32π cubic inches when the radius is 4 inches and the height is 6 inches, find the volume of a cone when the radius is 3 inches and the height is 5 inches.

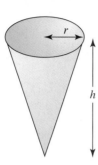

34. When a wind blows perpendicularly against a flat surface, its force is jointly proportional to the surface area and the speed of the wind. A sail whose surface area is 12 square feet experiences a 20-pound force when the wind speed is 10 miles per hour. Find the force on an 8-square-foot sail if the wind speed is 12 miles per hour.

35. The horsepower that can be safely transmitted to a shaft varies jointly as the shaft's angular speed of rotation (in revolutions per minute) and the cube of its diameter. A 2-inch shaft making 120 revolutions per minute safely transmits 40 horsepower. Find how much horsepower can be safely transmitted by a 3-inch shaft making 80 revolutions per minute.

△ **36.** The maximum weight that a rectangular beam can support varies jointly as its width and the square of its height and inversely as its length. If a beam $\frac{1}{3}$ foot wide, 1 foot high, and 10 feet long can support 3 tons, find how much weight a similar beam can support if it is 1 foot wide, $\frac{1}{3}$ foot high, and 9 feet long.

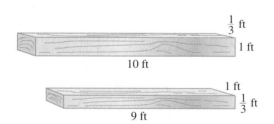

37. The atmospheric pressure y (in millibars) is inversely proportional to the altitude x (in kilometers). If the atmospheric pressure is 400 millibars at an altitude of 8 kilometers, find the atmospheric pressure at an altitude of 4 kilometers.

38. The horsepower to drive a boat varies directly as the cube of the speed of the boat. If the speed of the boat is to double, determine the corresponding increase in horsepower required.

△ **39.** The volume of a cylinder varies jointly as the height and the square of the radius. If the height is halved and the radius is doubled, determine what happens to the volume.

40. Suppose that y varies directly as x. If x is doubled, what is the effect on y?

41. Suppose that y varies directly as x^2. If x is doubled, what is the effect on y?

Complete the following table for the inverse variation $y = \dfrac{k}{x}$ over each given value of k. Plot the points on a rectangular coordinate system.

x	$\frac{1}{4}$	$\frac{1}{2}$	1	2	4
$y = \dfrac{k}{x}$					

42. $k = 1$

43. $k = 3$

44. $k = 5$

45. $k = \frac{1}{2}$

REVIEW EXERCISES

Find the exact circumference and area of each circle. See the inside cover for a list of geometric formulas.

△ **46.**

4 in.

△ **47.**

6 cm

△ **48.**

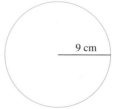

9 cm

△ **49.**

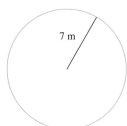

7 m

Find each square root. See Section 1.3

50. $\sqrt{81}$ **51.** $\sqrt{36}$

52. $\sqrt{1}$ **53.** $\sqrt{4}$

54. $\sqrt{\dfrac{1}{4}}$ **55.** $\sqrt{\dfrac{1}{25}}$

56. $\sqrt{\dfrac{4}{9}}$ **57.** $\sqrt{\dfrac{25}{121}}$

 For additional Chapter Projects, visit the Real World Activities
Website by going to http://www.prenhall.com/martin-gay.

CHAPTER PROJECT

Modeling Electricity Production

According to the U.S. Department of Energy, energy produced by renewable sources (including hydro-electric, geothermal, wind, and solar powers) accounted for nearly 7% of the United States' total production of energy in 1997. Wind energy can be harnessed by windmills to produce electricity, but it is the least utilized of these renewable energy sources. However, progressive communities are experimenting with fields of windmills for communal electricity needs, examining exactly how wind speed affects the amount of electricity produced.

A community in California is experimenting with electricity generated by windmills. City engineers are analyzing data they have gathered about their field of windmills. The engineers are familiar with other research demonstrating that the amount of electricity that a windmill generates hourly (in watt-hours) is directly proportional to the cube of the wind speed (in miles per hour). In this project, you will use this fact to help the engineers analyze the amount of electricity generated by the windmill field. This project may be completed by working in groups or individually.

1. The city engineers have documented that when the wind speed is exactly 10 miles per hour, a windmill generates electricity at a rate of 15

watt-hours. Find a formula that models the relationship between the wind speed and the amount of electricity generated hourly by a windmill.

2. Complete the following table for the given wind speeds. Then use the table to estimate the wind speed required to obtain: **a.** 100 watt-hours, and **b.** 400 watt-hours.

Wind Speed (miles per hour)	Electricity Generated (watt-hours)
15	
17	
19	
21	
23	
25	
27	
29	
31	
33	
35	

3. Plot the ordered pairs from the table. Describe the trend shown by the graph.

4. The engineers' data show that for several days the wind speed was more or less steady at 20 miles per hour, and the windmills generated the expected 120 watt-hours. According to the weather forecast for the coming few days, wind speed will fluctuate wildly, but will still average 20 miles per hour. Should the engineers still expect the windmills to generate 120 watt-hours? Demonstrate your reasoning with a numerical example.

5. During one three-day period, each windmill generated 150 watt-hours. The forecast predicts that the wind speed for the coming few days will drop by half. How many watt-hours should the engineers now expect each windmill to generate? In general, if the wind speed yields c watt-hours, how many watt-hours does half the wind speed yield?

CHAPTER 6 VOCABULARY CHECK

Fill in each blank with one of the words or phrases listed below.

rational expression   equation   complex fraction   opposites   synthetic division
least common denominator   expression   long division   jointly   directly   inversely

1. A rational expression whose numerator, denominator, or both contain one or more rational expressions is called a _____.

2. To divide a polynomial by a polynomial other than a monomial, we use _____.

3. In the equation $y = kx$, y varies _____ as x.

4. In the equation $y = \dfrac{k}{x}$, y varies _____ as x.

5. The _____ of a list of rational expressions is a polynomial of least degree whose factors include the denominator factors in the list.

6. When a polynomial is to be divided by a binomial of the form $x - c$, a shortcut process called _____ may be used.

7. In the equation $y = kxz$, y varies _____ as x and z.

8. The expressions $(x - 5)$ and $(5 - x)$ are called _____.

9. A _____ is an expression that can be written as the quotient $\dfrac{P}{Q}$ of two polynomials P and Q as long as Q is not 0.

10. Which is an expression and which is an equation? An example of an _____ is $\dfrac{2}{x} + \dfrac{2}{x^2} = 7$ and an example of an _____ is $\dfrac{2}{x} + \dfrac{5}{x^2}$.

CHAPTER 6 HIGHLIGHTS

DEFINITIONS AND CONCEPTS	EXAMPLES

Section 6.1 Rational Functions and Multiplying and Dividing Rational Expressions

A **rational expression** is the quotient $\dfrac{P}{Q}$ of two polynomials P and Q, as long as Q is not 0.

$$\frac{2x - 6}{7}, \qquad \frac{t^2 - 3t + 5}{t - 1}$$

To Simplify a Rational Expression

Step 1: Completely factor the numerator and the denominator.

Step 2: Apply the fundamental principle of rational expressions.

Simplify.

$$\frac{2x^2 + 9x - 5}{x^2 - 25} = \frac{(2x - 1)(x + 5)}{(x - 5)(x + 5)}$$

$$= \frac{2x - 1}{x - 5}$$

To Multiply Rational Expressions

Step 1: Completely factor numerators and denominators.

Step 2: Multiply the numerators and multiply the denominators.

Step 3: Apply the fundamental principle of rational expressions.

Multiply $\dfrac{x^3 + 8}{12x - 18} \cdot \dfrac{14x^2 - 21x}{x^2 + 2x}$.

$$= \frac{(x + 2)(x^2 - 2x + 4)}{6(2x - 3)} \cdot \frac{7x(2x - 3)}{x(x + 2)}$$

$$= \frac{7(x^2 - 2x + 4)}{6}$$

To Divide Rational Expressions

Multiply the first rational expression by the reciprocal of the second rational expression.

Divide $\dfrac{x^2 + 6x + 9}{5xy - 5y} \div \dfrac{x + 3}{10y}$.

$$= \frac{(x + 3)(x + 3)}{5y(x - 1)} \cdot \frac{2 \cdot 5y}{x + 3}$$

$$= \frac{2(x + 3)}{x - 1}$$

A **rational function** is a function described by a rational expression.

$$f(x) = \frac{2x - 6}{7}, \qquad h(t) = \frac{t^2 - 3t + 5}{t - 1}$$

Section 6.2 Adding and Subtracting Rational Expressions

To Add or Subtract Rational Expressions

Step 1: Find the LCD.

Step 2: Write each rational expression as an equivalent rational expression whose denominator is the LCD.

Step 3: Add or subtract numerators and write the result over the common denominator.

Step 4: Simplify the resulting rational expression.

Subtract $\dfrac{3}{x + 2} - \dfrac{x + 1}{x - 3}$.

$$= \frac{3 \cdot (x - 3)}{(x + 2) \cdot (x - 3)} - \frac{(x + 1) \cdot (x + 2)}{(x - 3) \cdot (x + 2)}$$

$$= \frac{3(x - 3) - (x + 1)(x + 2)}{(x + 2)(x - 3)}$$

$$= \frac{3x - 9 - (x^2 + 3x + 2)}{(x + 2)(x - 3)}$$

$$= \frac{3x - 9 - x^2 - 3x - 2}{(x + 2)(x - 3)}$$

$$= \frac{-x^2 - 11}{(x + 2)(x - 3)}$$

DEFINITIONS AND CONCEPTS	EXAMPLES

Section 6.3 Simplifying Complex Fractions

Method 1: Simplify the numerator and the denominator so that each is a single fraction. Then perform the indicated division and simplify if possible.

Simplify $\dfrac{\dfrac{x+2}{x}}{x-\dfrac{4}{x}}$.

Method 1: $\dfrac{\dfrac{x+2}{x}}{\dfrac{x \cdot x}{1 \cdot x}-\dfrac{4}{x}} = \dfrac{\dfrac{x+2}{x}}{\dfrac{x^2-4}{x}}$

$= \dfrac{x+2}{x} \cdot \dfrac{x}{(x+2)(x-2)} = \dfrac{1}{x-2}$

Method 2: Multiply the numerator and the denominator of the complex fraction by the LCD of the fractions in both the numerator and the denominator. Then simplify if possible.

Method 2: $\dfrac{\left(\dfrac{x+2}{x}\right) \cdot x}{\left(x-\dfrac{4}{x}\right) \cdot x} = \dfrac{x+2}{x \cdot x - \dfrac{4}{x} \cdot x}$

$= \dfrac{x+2}{x^2-4} = \dfrac{x+2}{(x+2)(x-2)} = \dfrac{1}{x-2}$

Section 6.4 Dividing Polynomials

To divide a polynomial by a monomial:
Divide each term in the polynomial by the monomial.

Divide $\dfrac{12a^5b^3 - 6a^2b^2 + ab}{6a^2b^2}$.

$= \dfrac{12a^5b^3}{6a^2b^2} - \dfrac{6a^2b^2}{6a^2b^2} + \dfrac{ab}{6a^2b^2}$

$= 2a^3b - 1 + \dfrac{1}{6ab}$

To divide a polynomial by a polynomial, other than a monomial:
Use **long division.**

Divide $2x^3 - x^2 - 8x - 1$ by $x - 2$.

$$
\begin{array}{r}
2x^2 + 3x - 2 \\
x-2\overline{)2x^3 - x^2 - 8x - 1} \\
\underline{2x^3 - 4x^2} \\
3x^2 - 8x \\
\underline{3x^2 - 6x} \\
-2x - 1 \\
\underline{-2x + 4} \\
-5
\end{array}
$$

The quotient is $2x^2 + 3x - 2 - \dfrac{5}{x-2}$.

Section 6.5 Synthetic Division and the Remainder Theorem

A shortcut method called **synthetic division** may be used to divide a polynomial by a binomial of the form $x - c$.

Use synthetic division to divide $2x^3 - x^2 - 8x - 1$ by $x - 2$.

$$
\begin{array}{r|rrrr}
2 & 2 & -1 & -8 & -1 \\
  &   & 4 & 6 & -4 \\
\hline
  & 2 & 3 & -2 & -5
\end{array}
$$

The quotient is $2x^2 + 3x - 2 - \dfrac{5}{x-2}$.

DEFINITIONS AND CONCEPTS	EXAMPLES

Section 6.6 Solving Equations Containing Rational Expressions

To solve an equation containing rational expressions: Multiply both sides of the equation by the LCD of all rational expressions. Then apply the distributive property and simplify. Solve the resulting equation and then check each proposed solution to see whether it makes the denominator 0. If so, it is an **extraneous solution.**

Solve $x - \dfrac{3}{x} = \dfrac{1}{2}$.

$$2x\left(x - \frac{3}{x}\right) = 2x\left(\frac{1}{2}\right) \qquad \text{The LCD is } 2x.$$

$$2x \cdot x - 2x\left(\frac{3}{x}\right) = 2x\left(\frac{1}{2}\right) \qquad \text{Distribute.}$$

$$2x^2 - 6 = x$$

$$2x^2 - x - 6 = 0 \qquad \text{Subtract } x.$$

$$(2x + 3)(x - 2) = 0 \qquad \text{Factor.}$$

$$x = -\frac{3}{2} \quad \text{or} \quad x = 2 \qquad \text{Solve.}$$

Both $-\dfrac{3}{2}$ and 2 check. The solutions are 2 and $-\dfrac{3}{2}$.

Section 6.7 Rational Equations and Problem Solving

Solving an Equation for a Specified Variable

Treat the specified variable as the only variable of the equation and solve as usual.

Solve for x.

$$A = \frac{2x + 3y}{5}$$

$$5A = 2x + 3y \qquad \text{Multiply both sides by 5.}$$

$$5A - 3y = 2x \qquad \text{Subtract } 3y \text{ from both sides.}$$

$$\frac{5A - 3y}{2} = x \qquad \text{Divide both sides by 2.}$$

Problem-Solving Steps to Follow

Jeanee and David Dillon volunteer every year to clean a strip of Lake Ponchartrain beach. Jeanee can clean all the trash in this area of beach in 6 hours; David takes 5 hours. Find how long it will take them to clean the area of beach together.

1. UNDERSTAND.

1. Read and reread the problem.
   Let x = time in hours that it takes Jeanee and David to clean the beach together.

	Hours to Complete	Part Completed in 1 Hour
JEANEE ALONE	6	$\dfrac{1}{6}$
DAVID ALONE	5	$\dfrac{1}{5}$
TOGETHER	x	$\dfrac{1}{x}$

(continued)

DEFINITIONS AND CONCEPTS	EXAMPLES

Section 6.7 Rational Equations and Problem Solving

2. TRANSLATE.

2. In words:

part Jeanee can complete in 1 hour		part David can complete in 1 hour		part they can complete together in 1 hour
↓	+	↓	=	↓

Translate:

$$\frac{1}{6} \quad + \quad \frac{1}{5} \quad = \quad \frac{1}{x}$$

3. SOLVE.

3. $\dfrac{1}{6} + \dfrac{1}{5} = \dfrac{1}{x}$ *Multiply both sides by 30x.*

$$5x + 6x = 30$$

$$11x = 30$$

$$x = \frac{30}{11} \quad \text{or} \quad 2\frac{8}{11}$$

4. INTERPRET.

4. *Check* and then *state.* Together, they can clean the beach in $2\dfrac{8}{11}$ hours.

Section 6.8 Variation and Problem Solving

y **varies directly as** *x*, or *y* is **directly proportional to** *x*, if there is a nonzero constant *k* such that

$$y = kx$$

The circumference of a circle *C* varies directly as its radius *r*.

$$C = \underbrace{2\pi}_{k} r$$

y **varies inversely as** *x*, or *y* is **inversely proportional to** x, if there is a nonzero constant *k* such that

$$y = \frac{k}{x}$$

Pressure *P* varies inversely with volume *V*.

$$P = \frac{k}{V}$$

y **varies jointly as** *x* and *z* or *y* is **jointly proportional to** *x* and *z* if there is a nonzero constant *k* such that

$$y = kxz$$

The lateral surface area *S* of a cylinder varies jointly as its radius *r* and height *h*.

$$S = \underbrace{2\pi}_{k} rh$$

CHAPTER 6 REVIEW

Find the domain for each rational function.

1. $f(x) = \dfrac{3 - 5x}{7}$

2. $g(x) = \dfrac{2x + 4}{11}$

3. $F(x) = \dfrac{-3x^2}{x - 5}$

4. $h(x) = \dfrac{4x}{3x - 12}$

5. $f(x) = \dfrac{x^3 + 2}{x^2 + 8x}$

6. $G(x) = \dfrac{20}{3x^2 - 48}$

Write each rational expression in lowest terms.

7. $\dfrac{15x^4}{45x^2}$

8. $\dfrac{x + 2}{2 + x}$

9. $\dfrac{18m^6 p^2}{10m^4 p}$

10. $\dfrac{x - 12}{12 - x}$

11. $\dfrac{5x - 15}{25x - 75}$

12. $\dfrac{22x + 8}{11x + 4}$

13. $\dfrac{2x}{2x^2 - 2x}$

14. $\dfrac{x + 7}{x^2 - 49}$

15. $\dfrac{2x^2 + 4x - 30}{x^2 + x - 20}$

16. $\dfrac{xy - 3x + 2y - 6}{x^2 + 4x + 4}$

17. The average cost of manufacturing x bookcases is given by the rational function

$$C(x) = \frac{35x + 4200}{x}$$

   a. Find the average cost per bookcase of manufacturing 50 bookcases.

   b. Find the average cost per bookcase of manufacturing 100 bookcases.

   c. As the number of bookcases increases, does the average cost per bookcase increase or decrease? (See parts **a** and **b**.)

Perform the indicated operation. If possible, simplify your answer.

18. $\dfrac{5}{x^3} \cdot \dfrac{x^2}{15}$

19. $\dfrac{3x^4 y z^3}{15x^2 y^2} \cdot \dfrac{10xy}{z^6}$

20. $\dfrac{4 - x}{5} \cdot \dfrac{15}{2x - 8}$

21. $\dfrac{x^2 - 6x + 9}{2x^2 - 18} \cdot \dfrac{4x + 12}{5x - 15}$

22. $\dfrac{a - 4b}{a^2 + ab} \cdot \dfrac{b^2 - a^2}{8b - 2a}$

23. $\dfrac{x^2 - x - 12}{2x^2 - 32} \cdot \dfrac{x^2 + 8x + 16}{3x^2 + 21x + 36}$

24. $\dfrac{2x^3 + 54}{5x^2 + 5x - 30} \cdot \dfrac{6x + 12}{3x^2 - 9x + 27}$

25. $\dfrac{3}{4x} \div \dfrac{8}{2x^2}$

26. $\dfrac{4x + 8y}{3} \div \dfrac{5x + 10y}{9}$

27. $\dfrac{5ab}{14c^3} \div \dfrac{10a^4 b^2}{6ac^5}$

28. $\dfrac{2}{5x} \div \dfrac{4 - 18x}{6 - 27x}$

29. $\dfrac{x^2 - 25}{3} \div \dfrac{x^2 - 10x + 25}{x^2 - x - 20}$

30. $\dfrac{a - 4b}{a^2 + ab} \div \dfrac{20b - 5a}{b^2 - a^2}$

31. $\dfrac{7x + 28}{2x + 4} \div \dfrac{x^2 + 2x - 8}{x^2 - 2x - 8}$

32. $\dfrac{3x + 3}{x - 1} \div \dfrac{x^2 - 6x - 7}{x^2 - 1}$

33. $\dfrac{2x - x^2}{x^3 - 8} \div \dfrac{x^2}{x^2 + 2x + 4}$

34. $\dfrac{5a^2 - 20}{a^3 + 2a^2 + a + 2} \div \dfrac{7a}{a^3 + a}$

35. $\dfrac{2a}{21} \div \dfrac{3a^2}{7} \cdot \dfrac{4}{a}$

36. $\dfrac{5x - 15}{3 - x} \cdot \dfrac{x + 2}{10x + 20} \cdot \dfrac{x^2 - 9}{x^2 - x - 6}$

37. $\dfrac{4a + 8}{5a^2 - 20} \cdot \dfrac{3a^2 - 6a}{a + 3} \div \dfrac{2a^2}{5a + 15}$

(6.2) *Find the LCD of the rational expressions in the list.*

38. $\dfrac{4}{9}, \dfrac{5}{2}$

39. $\dfrac{5}{4x^2 y^5}, \dfrac{3}{10x^2 y^4}, \dfrac{x}{6y^4}$

40. $\dfrac{5}{2x}, \dfrac{7}{x - 2}$

41. $\dfrac{3}{5x}, \dfrac{2}{x - 5}$

42. $\dfrac{1}{5x^3}, \dfrac{4}{x^2 + 3x - 28}, \dfrac{11}{10x^2 - 30x}$

Perform the indicated operation. If possible, simplify your answer.

43. $\dfrac{2}{15} + \dfrac{4}{15}$

44. $\dfrac{4}{x - 4} + \dfrac{x}{x - 4}$

45. $\dfrac{4}{3x^2} + \dfrac{2}{3x^2}$

46. $\dfrac{1}{x - 2} - \dfrac{1}{4 - 2x}$

47. $\dfrac{2x + 1}{x^2 + x - 6} + \dfrac{2 - x}{x^2 + x - 6}$

48. $\dfrac{7}{2x} + \dfrac{5}{6x}$

49. $\dfrac{1}{3x^2y^3} - \dfrac{1}{5x^4y}$

50. $\dfrac{1}{10 - x} + \dfrac{x - 1}{x - 10}$

51. $\dfrac{x}{x + 1} \cdot \dfrac{2}{} - \dfrac{x - 3}{x - 1}$

52. $\dfrac{x}{9 - x^2} - \dfrac{2}{5x - 15}$

53. $2x + 1 - \dfrac{1}{x - 3}$

54. $\dfrac{2}{a^2 - 2a + 1} + \dfrac{3}{a^2 - 1}$

55. $\dfrac{x}{9x^2 + 12x + 16} - \dfrac{3x + 4}{27x^3 - 64}$

Perform the indicated operation. If possible, simplify your answer.

56. $\dfrac{2}{x - 1} - \dfrac{3x}{3x - 3} + \dfrac{1}{2x - 2}$

57. $\dfrac{3}{2x} \cdot \left(\dfrac{2}{x + 1} - \dfrac{2}{x - 3} \right)$

58. $\left(\dfrac{2}{x} - \dfrac{1}{5} \right) \cdot \left(\dfrac{2}{x} + \dfrac{1}{3} \right)$

59. $\dfrac{2}{x^2 - 16} - \dfrac{3x}{x^2 + 8x + 16} + \dfrac{3}{x + 4}$

△ **60.** Find the perimeter of the heptagon (polygon with 7 sides).

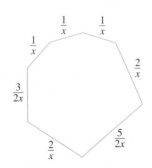

(6.3) *Simplify each complex fraction.*

61. $\dfrac{\dfrac{2}{5}}{\dfrac{3}{5}}$

62. $\dfrac{1 - \dfrac{3}{4}}{2 + \dfrac{1}{4}}$

63. $\dfrac{\dfrac{1}{x} - \dfrac{2}{3x}}{\dfrac{5}{2x} - \dfrac{1}{3}}$

64. $\dfrac{\dfrac{x^2}{15}}{\dfrac{x + 1}{5x}}$

65. $\dfrac{\dfrac{3}{y^2}}{\dfrac{6}{y^3}}$

66. $\dfrac{\dfrac{x + 2}{3}}{\dfrac{5}{x - 2}}$

67. $\dfrac{2 - \dfrac{3}{2x}}{x - \dfrac{2}{5x}}$

68. $\dfrac{1 + \dfrac{x}{y}}{\dfrac{x^2}{y^2} - 1}$

69. $\dfrac{\dfrac{5}{x} + \dfrac{1}{xy}}{\dfrac{3}{x^2}}$

70. $\dfrac{\dfrac{x}{3} - \dfrac{3}{x}}{1 + \dfrac{3}{x}}$

71. $\dfrac{\dfrac{1}{x - 1} + 1}{\dfrac{1}{x + 1} - 1}$

72. $\dfrac{2}{1 - \dfrac{2}{x}}$

73. $\dfrac{1}{1 + \dfrac{2}{1 - \dfrac{1}{x}}}$

74. $\dfrac{\dfrac{x^2 + 5x - 6}{4x + 3}}{\dfrac{(x + 6)^2}{8x + 6}}$

75. $\dfrac{\dfrac{x - 3}{x + 3} + \dfrac{x + 3}{x - 3}}{\dfrac{x - 3}{x + 3} - \dfrac{x + 3}{x - 3}}$

76. $\dfrac{\dfrac{3}{x - 1} - \dfrac{2}{1 - x}}{\dfrac{2}{x - 1} - \dfrac{2}{x}}$

77. If $f(x) = \dfrac{3}{x}$, find each of the following:

    a. $f(a + h)$ **b.** $f(a)$

    c. Use parts **a** and **b** to find $\dfrac{f(a + h) - f(a)}{h}$.

    d. Simplify the results of part **c**.

(6.4) *Divide.*

78. Divide $3x^5yb^9$ by $9xy^7$.

79. Divide $-9xb^4z^3$ by $-4axb^2$.

80. $(4xy + 2x^2 - 9) \div 4xy$

81. Divide $12xb^2 + 16xb^4$ by $4xb^3$.

82. $(3x^4 - 25x^2 - 20) \div (x - 3)$

83. $(-x^2 + 2x^4 + 5x - 12) \div (x + 2)$

84. $(2x^4 - x^3 + 2x^2 - 3x + 1) \div \left(x - \dfrac{1}{2} \right)$

85. $(2x^3 + 3x^2 - 2x + 2) \div \left(x + \dfrac{3}{2} \right)$

86. $(3x^4 + 5x^3 + 7x^2 + 3x - 2) \div (x^2 + x + 2)$

87. $(9x^4 - 6x^3 + 3x^2 - 12x - 30) \div (3x^2 - 2x - 5)$

(6.5) *Use synthetic division to find each quotient.*

88. $(3x^3 + 12x - 4) \div (x - 2)$

89. $(3x^3 + 2x^2 - 4x - 1) \div \left(x + \dfrac{3}{2} \right)$

90. $(x^5 - 1) \div (x + 1)$

91. $(x^3 - 81) \div (x - 3)$

92. $(x^3 - x^2 + 3x^4 - 2) \div (x - 4)$

93. $(3x^4 - 2x^2 + 10) \div (x + 2)$

If $P(x) = 3x^5 - 9x + 7$, use the remainder theorem to find the following.

94. $P(4)$ **95.** $P(-5)$

96. $P\left(\dfrac{2}{3}\right)$ **97.** $P\left(-\dfrac{1}{2}\right)$

△ **98.** If the area of the rectangle is $(x^4 - x^3 - 6x^2 - 6x + 18)$ square miles and its width is $(x - 3)$ miles, find the length.

$$\boxed{\begin{array}{c} x^4 - x^3 - 6x^2 - 6x + 18 \\ \text{square miles} \end{array}} \quad \begin{array}{c} \uparrow \\ x - 3 \\ \text{miles} \\ \downarrow \end{array}$$

(6.6) *Solve each equation for x.*

99. $\dfrac{2}{5} = \dfrac{x}{15}$

100. $\dfrac{3}{x} + \dfrac{1}{3} = \dfrac{5}{x}$

101. $4 + \dfrac{8}{x} = 8$

102. $\dfrac{2x + 3}{5x - 9} = \dfrac{3}{2}$

103. $\dfrac{1}{x - 2} - \dfrac{3x}{x^2 - 4} = \dfrac{2}{x + 2}$

104. $\dfrac{7}{x} - \dfrac{x}{7} = 0$

105. $\dfrac{x - 2}{x^2 - 7x + 10} = \dfrac{1}{5x - 10} - \dfrac{1}{x - 5}$

Solve the equations for x or perform the indicated operation. Simplify.

106. $\dfrac{5}{x^2 - 7x} + \dfrac{4}{2x - 14}$

107. $3 - \dfrac{5}{x} - \dfrac{2}{x^2} = 0$

108. $\dfrac{4}{3 - x} - \dfrac{7}{2x - 6} + \dfrac{5}{x}$

(6.7) *Solve the equation for the specified variable.*

△ **109.** $A = \dfrac{h(a + b)}{2}$, a

110. $\dfrac{1}{R} = \dfrac{1}{R_1} + \dfrac{1}{R_2}$, R_2

111. $I = \dfrac{E}{R + r}$, R

112. $A = P + Prt$, r

113. $H = \dfrac{kA(T_1 - T_2)}{L}$, A

Solve.

114. The sum of a number and twice its reciprocal is 3. Find the number(s).

115. If a number is added to the numerator of $\dfrac{3}{7}$, and twice that number is added to the denominator of $\dfrac{3}{7}$, the result is equivalent to $\dfrac{10}{21}$. Find the number.

116. The denominator of a fraction is 2 more than the numerator. If the numerator is decreased by 3 and the denominator is increased by 5, the resulting fraction is equivalent to $\frac{2}{3}$. Find the fraction.

117. The sum of the reciprocals of two consecutive even integers is $-\frac{9}{40}$. Find the two integers.

118. Three boys can paint a fence in 4 hours, 5 hours, and 6 hours, respectively. Find how long it will take all three boys to paint the fence.

119. If Sue Katz can type a certain number of mailing labels in 6 hours and Tom Neilson and Sue working together can type the same number of mailing labels in 4 hours, find how long it takes Tom alone to type the mailing labels.

120. The inlet pipe of a water tank can fill the tank in 2 hours and 30 minutes. The outlet pipe can empty the tank in 2 hours. Find how long it takes to empty a full tank if both pipes are open.

121. Timmy Garnica drove 210 miles in the same amount of time that it took a DC-10 jet to travel 1715 miles. The speed of the jet was 430 mph faster than the speed of the car. Find the speed of the jet.

122. The combined resistance R of two resistors in parallel with resistances R_1 and R_2 is given by the formula $\frac{1}{R} = \frac{1}{R_1} + \frac{1}{R_2}$. If the combined resistance is $\frac{30}{11}$ ohms and the resistance of one of the two resistors is 5 ohms, find the resistance of the other resistor.

123. The speed of a Ranger boat in still water is 32 mph. If the boat travels 72 miles upstream in the same time that

it takes to travel 120 miles downstream, find the speed of the current.

124. A B737 jet flies 445 miles with the wind and 355 miles against the wind in the same length of time. If the speed of the jet in still air is 400 mph, find the speed of the wind.

125. The speed of a jogger is 3 mph faster than the speed of a walker. If the jogger travels 14 miles in the same amount of time that the walker travels 8 miles, find the speed of the walker.

126. Two Amtrak trains traveling on parallel tracks leave Tucson at the same time. The speed of one train is 18 mph faster than the other. If the faster train travels 378 miles in the same time that the other train travels 270 miles, find the speed of each train.

(6.8) *Solve each variation problem.*

127. A is directly proportional to B. If $A = 6$ when $B = 14$, find A when $B = 21$.

128. C is inversely proportional to D. If $C = 12$ when $D = 8$, find C when $D = 24$.

129. According to Boyle's law, the pressure exerted by a gas is inversely proportional to the volume, as long as the temperature stays the same. If a gas exerts a pressure of 1250 pounds per square inch when the volume is 2 cubic feet, find the volume when the pressure is 800 pounds per square inch.

△ **130.** The surface area of a sphere varies directly as the square of its radius. If the surface area is 36π square inches when the radius is 3 inches, find the surface area when the radius is 4 inches.

CHAPTER 6 TEST

Find the domain of each rational function.

1. $f(x) = \dfrac{5x^2}{1 - x}$

2. $g(x) = \dfrac{9x^2 - 9}{x^2 + 4x + 3}$

5. $\dfrac{x^2 - 4x}{x^2 + 5x - 36}$

Write each rational expression in lowest terms.

3. $\dfrac{5x^7}{3x^4}$

4. $\dfrac{7x - 21}{24 - 8x}$

Perform the indicated operation. If possible, simplify your answer.

6. $\dfrac{x}{x - 2} \cdot \dfrac{x^2 - 4}{5x}$

7. $\dfrac{2x^3 + 16}{6x^2 + 12x} \cdot \dfrac{5}{x^2 - 2x + 4}$

8. $\dfrac{26ab}{7c} \div \dfrac{13a^2c^5}{14a^4b^3}$

9. $\dfrac{3x^2 - 12}{x^2 + 2x - 8} \div \dfrac{6x + 18}{x + 4}$

10. $\dfrac{4x - 12}{2x - 9} \div \dfrac{3 - x}{4x^2 - 81} \cdot \dfrac{x + 3}{5x + 15}$

11. $\dfrac{5}{4x^3} + \dfrac{7}{4x^3}$

12. $\dfrac{3 + 2x}{10 - x} + \dfrac{13 + x}{x - 10}$

13. $\dfrac{3}{x^2 - x - 6} + \dfrac{2}{x^2 - 5x + 6}$

14. $\dfrac{5}{x - 7} - \dfrac{2x}{3x - 21} + \dfrac{x}{2x - 14}$

15. $\dfrac{3x}{5} \cdot \left(\dfrac{5}{x} - \dfrac{5}{2x} \right)$

Simplify each complex fraction.

16. $\dfrac{\dfrac{4x}{13}}{\dfrac{20x}{13}}$

17. $\dfrac{\dfrac{5}{x} - \dfrac{7}{3x}}{\dfrac{9}{8x} - \dfrac{1}{x}}$

18. $\dfrac{\dfrac{x^2 - 5x + 6}{x + 3}}{\dfrac{x^2 - 4x + 4}{x^2 - 9}}$

Divide.

19. $\left(4x^2y + 9x + z \right) \div 3xz$

20. $\left(x^6 + 3x^5 - 2x^4 + x^2 - 3x + 2 \right) \div (x - 2)$

21. Use synthetic division to divide $(4x^4 - 3x^3 + 2x^2 - x - 1)$ by $(x + 3)$.

22. If $P(x) = 4x^4 + 7x^2 - 2x - 5$, use the remainder theorem to find $P(-2)$.

Solve each equation for x.

23. $\dfrac{5x + 3}{3x - 7} = \dfrac{19}{7}$

24. $\dfrac{5}{x - 5} + \dfrac{x}{x + 5} = -\dfrac{29}{21}$

25. $\dfrac{x}{x - 4} = 3 - \dfrac{4}{x - 4}$

26. Solve for x: $\dfrac{x + b}{a} = \dfrac{4x - 7a}{b}$

27. The product of one more than a number and twice the reciprocal of the number is $\dfrac{12}{5}$. Find the number.

28. If Jan can weed the garden in 2 hours and her husband can weed it in 1 hour and 30 minutes, find how long, it takes them to weed the garden together.

29. Suppose that W is inversely proportional to V. If $W = 20$ when $V = 12$, find W when $V = 15$.

30. Suppose that Q is jointly proportional to R and the square of S. If $Q = 24$ when $R = 3$ and $S = 4$, find Q when $R = 2$ and $S = 3$.

31. When an anvil is dropped into a gorge, the speed with which it strikes the ground is directly proportional to the square root of the distance it falls. An anvil that falls 400 feet hits the ground at a speed of 160 feet per second. Find the height of a cliff over the gorge if a dropped anvil hits the ground at a speed of 128 feet per second.

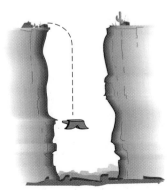

CHAPTER 6 CUMULATIVE REVIEW

1. Translate each phrase to an algebraic expression. Use the variable x to represent each unknown number.

    a. Eight times a number

    b. Three more than eight times a number

    c. The quotient of a number and -7

    d. One and six-tenths subtracted from twice a number

2. Solve for y: $\dfrac{y}{3} - \dfrac{y}{4} = \dfrac{1}{6}$

3. In the United States, the annual consumption of cigarettes is declining. The consumption c in billions of cigarettes per year since the year 1985 can be approximated by the formula

$$c = -14.25t + 598.69$$

where t is the number of years after 1985. Use this formula to predict the years that the consumption of cigarettes will be less than 200 billion per year.

4. Solve: $\left| \dfrac{3x + 1}{2} \right| = -2$

5. Solve for x: $\left| \dfrac{2(x + 1)}{3} \right| \leq 0$

6. Graph the equation $y = -2x + 3$.

7. Which of the following relations are also functions?

    a. $\{(-2, 5), (2, 7), (-3, 5), (9, 9)\}$

    b.

    c.

Input	Correspondence	Output
People in a certain city	Each person's age	The set of nonnegative integers

8. Graph $x - 3y = 6$ by plotting intercept points.

9. Find an equation of the line with slope -3 containing the point $(1, -5)$. Write the equation in slope–intercept form $y = mx + b$.

10. Graph the intersection of $x \geq 1$ and $y \geq 2x - 1$.

11. Use the elimination method to solve the system.

$$\begin{cases} 3x - 2y = 10 \\ 4x - 3y = 15 \end{cases}$$

12. Solve the system.

$$\begin{cases} 2x - 4y + 8z = 2 \\ -x - 3y + z = 11 \\ x - 2y + 4z = 0 \end{cases}$$

13. The measure of the largest angle of a triangle is $80°$ more than the measure of the smallest angle, and the measure of the remaining angle is $10°$ more than the measure of the smallest angle. Find the measure of each angle.

14. Use matrices to solve the system.

$$\begin{cases} x + 2y + z = 2 \\ -2x - y + 2z = 5 \\ x + 3y - 2z = -8 \end{cases}$$

15. Evaluate the following.

    a. 7^0

    b. -7^0

    c. $(2x + 5)^0$

    d. $2x^0$

16. Simplify each. Assume that a and b are integers and that x and y are not 0.

    a. $x^{-b}(2x^b)^2$

    b. $\dfrac{(y^{3a})^2}{y^{a-6}}$

17. Find the degree of each term.

    a. $3x^2$

    b. -2^3x^5

    c. y

    d. $12x^2yz^3$

    e. 5

18. Multiply $\left[3 + (2a + b)\right]^2$.

19. Factor $ab - 6a + 2b - 12$

20. $2n^2 - 38n + 80$

21. Factor $x^2 + 4x + 4 - y^2$

22. Solve $(x + 2)(x - 6) = 0$

23. Graph $f(x) = -x^3$. Find any intercepts.

24. Subtract $\dfrac{5k}{k^2 - 4} - \dfrac{2}{k^2 + k - 2}$.

25. Solve: $\dfrac{3}{x} - \dfrac{x + 21}{3x} = \dfrac{5}{3}$

Studying Human Behavior

Psychology is the scientific study of the human mind and behavior. Over 150,000 psychologists practice in the United States in such diverse areas as experimental psychology, clinical psychology, industrial psychology, educational psychology, counseling psychology, psychotherapy, military psychology, consumer psychology, family psychology, and sports psychology.

Although psychology careers in teaching, research, and counseling frequently require advanced degrees, there are many career paths in which a two- or four-year degree is useful. Employment counselors, child protection workers, corrections officers, social service directors, day-care-center supervisors, and hospital patient service representatives are all examples of positions for which advanced psychology degrees are not necessarily required. No matter which educational path is chosen, psychologists must have good communication, interpersonal, research, and analytical skills, including the ability to reason numerically, interpret statistics, read tables and graphs, and solve problems.

 For more information about psychology careers, visit the American Psychological Association Website by first going to www.prenhall.com/martin-gay.

In the Spotlight on Decision Making feature on page 441, you will have the opportunity to make a decision about assigning subjects to the appropriate test groups for a psychology experiment.

RATIONAL EXPONENTS, RADICALS, AND COMPLEX NUMBERS

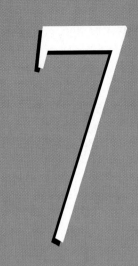

In this chapter, radical notation is reviewed, and then rational exponents are introduced. As the name implies, rational exponents are exponents that are rational numbers. We present an interpretation of rational exponents that is consistent with the meaning and rules already established for integer exponents, and we present two forms of notation for roots: radical and exponent. We conclude this chapter with complex numbers, a natural extension of the real number system.

7.1 RADICALS AND RADICAL FUNCTIONS

CD-ROM   SSM

SSG   Video

▶ **OBJECTIVES**

1. Find square roots.
2. Approximate roots using a calculator.
3. Find cube roots.
4. Find nth roots.
5. Find $\sqrt[n]{a^n}$ where a is a real number.
6. Graph square and cube root functions.

1

Recall from Section 1.3 that to find a **square root** of a number a, we find a number that was squared to get a.

Thus, because

$$5^2 = 25 \quad \text{and} \quad (-5)^2 = 25, \text{then}$$

both 5 and -5 are square roots of 25.

Recall that we denote the **nonnegative**, or **principal**, **square root** with the **radical sign**.

$$\sqrt{25} = 5$$

We denote the **negative square root** with the **negative radical sign**.

$$-\sqrt{25} = -5$$

An expression containing a radical sign is called a **radical expression**. An expression within, or "under," a radical sign is called a **radicand**.

radical expression: $\sqrt{a}$

PRINCIPAL AND NEGATIVE SQUARE ROOTS

The **principal square root** of a nonnegative number a is its nonnegative square root. The principal square root is written as $\sqrt{a}$. The **negative square root** of a is written as $-\sqrt{a}$.

◆ **Example 1** Simplify. Assume that all variables represent positive numbers.

    a. $\sqrt{36}$ **b.** $\sqrt{0}$ **c.** $\sqrt{\dfrac{4}{49}}$ **d.** $\sqrt{0.25}$ **e.** $\sqrt{x^6}$ **f.** $\sqrt{9x^{10}}$ **g.** $-\sqrt{81}$

Solution   **a.** $\sqrt{36} = 6$ because $6^2 = 36$ and 6 is not negative.
    b. $\sqrt{0} = 0$ because $0^2 = 0$ and 0 is not negative.
    c. $\sqrt{\dfrac{4}{49}} = \dfrac{2}{7}$ because $\left(\dfrac{2}{7}\right)^2 = \dfrac{4}{49}$ and $\dfrac{2}{7}$ is not negative.
    d. $\sqrt{0.25} = 0.5$ because $(0.5)^2 = 0.25$.
    e. $\sqrt{x^6} = x^3$ because $\left(x^3\right)^2 = x^6$.

f. $\sqrt{9x^{10}} = 3x^5$ because $\left(3x^5\right)^2 = 9x^{10}$.

g. $-\sqrt{81} = -9$. The negative in front of the radical indicates the negative square root of 81.

Can we find the square root of a negative number, say $\sqrt{-4}$? That is, can we find a real number whose square is -4? No, there is no real number whose square is -4, and we say that $\sqrt{-4}$ is not a real number. In general:

The square root of a negative number is not a real number.

> ▼
> **HELPFUL HINT**
> Don't forget, the square root of a negative number, such as $\sqrt{-9}$, is not a real number. In Section 7.7, we will see what kind of a number $\sqrt{-9}$ is.

2

Recall that numbers such as 1, 4, 9, and 25 are called **perfect squares**, since $1 = 1^2$, $4 = 2^2$, $9 = 3^2$, and $25 = 5^2$. Square roots of perfect square radicands simplify to rational numbers. What happens when we try to simplify a root such as $\sqrt{3}$? Since 3 is not a perfect square, $\sqrt{3}$ is not a rational number. It is called an **irrational number**, and we can find a decimal **approximation** of it. To find decimal approximations, use a calculator. For example, an approximation for $\sqrt{3}$ is

$$\sqrt{3} \approx 1.732$$
$$\uparrow$$

approximation symbol

To see if the approximation is reasonable, notice that since

$$1 < 3 < 4, \text{ then}$$
$$\sqrt{1} < \sqrt{3} < \sqrt{4}, \text{ or}$$
$$1 < \sqrt{3} < 2.$$

We found $\sqrt{3} \approx 1.732$, a number between 1 and 2, so our result is reasonable.

Example 2   Use a calculator to approximate $\sqrt{20}$. Round the approximation to 3 decimal places and check to see that your approximation is reasonable.

Solution
$$\sqrt{20} \approx 4.472$$

Is this reasonable? Since $16 < 20 < 25$, then $\sqrt{16} < \sqrt{20} < \sqrt{25}$, or $4 < \sqrt{20} < 5$. The approximation is between 4 and 5 and thus is reasonable.

3

Finding roots can be extended to other roots such as cube roots. For example, since $2^3 = 8$, we call 2 the **cube root** of 8. In symbols, we write

$$\sqrt[3]{8} = 2$$

CUBE ROOT

The **cube root** of a real number a is written as $\sqrt[3]{a}$, and

$$\sqrt[3]{a} = b \text{ only if } b^3 = a$$

From this definition, we have

$$\sqrt[3]{64} = 4 \text{ since } 4^3 = 64$$
$$\sqrt[3]{-27} = -3 \text{ since } (-3)^3 = -27$$
$$\sqrt[3]{x^3} = x \text{ since } x^3 = x^3$$

Notice that, unlike with square roots, *it is possible to have a negative radicand when finding a cube root.* This is so because the *cube* of a negative number is a negative number. Therefore, the *cube root* of a negative number is a negative number.

Example 3 Find the cube roots.

 a. $\sqrt[3]{1}$ **b.** $\sqrt[3]{-64}$ **c.** $\sqrt[3]{\dfrac{8}{125}}$ **d.** $\sqrt[3]{x^6}$ **e.** $\sqrt[3]{-8x^9}$

Solution **a.** $\sqrt[3]{1} = 1$ because $1^3 = 1$.

  b. $\sqrt[3]{-64} = -4$ because $(-4)^3 = -64$.

  c. $\sqrt[3]{\dfrac{8}{125}} = \dfrac{2}{5}$ because $\left(\dfrac{2}{5}\right)^3 = \dfrac{8}{125}$.

  d. $\sqrt[3]{x^6} = x^2$ because $(x^2)^3 = x^6$.

  e. $\sqrt[3]{-8x^9} = -2x^3$ because $(-2x^3)^3 = -8x^9$.

---

4 Just as we can raise a real number to powers other than 2 or 3, we can find roots other than square roots and cube roots. In fact, we can find the **nth root** of a number, where n is any natural number. In symbols, the nth root of a is written as $\sqrt[n]{a}$, where n is called the **index**. The index 2 is usually omitted for square roots.

> ▼**HELPFUL HINT**
>
> If the index is even, such as $\sqrt{}$, $\sqrt[4]{}$, $\sqrt[6]{}$, and so on, the radicand must be non-negative for the root to be a real number. For example,
>
> $$\sqrt[4]{16} = 2, \text{ but } \sqrt[4]{-16} \text{ is not a real number.}$$
>
> $$\sqrt[6]{64} = 2, \text{ but } \sqrt[6]{-64} \text{ is not a real number.}$$
>
> If the index is odd, such as $\sqrt[3]{}$, $\sqrt[5]{}$, and so on, the radicand may be any real number. For example,
>
> $$\sqrt[3]{64} = 4 \text{ and } \sqrt[3]{-64} = -4$$
>
> $$\sqrt[5]{32} = 2 \text{ and } \sqrt[5]{-32} = -2$$

Example 4 Simplify the following expressions.

 a. $\sqrt[4]{81}$ **b.** $\sqrt[5]{-243}$ **c.** $-\sqrt{25}$ **d.** $\sqrt[4]{-81}$ **e.** $\sqrt[3]{64x^3}$

Solution **a.** $\sqrt[4]{81} = 3$ because $3^4 = 81$ and 3 is positive.

  b. $\sqrt[5]{-243} = -3$ because $(-3)^5 = -243$.

c. $-\sqrt{25} = -5$ because -5 is the opposite of $\sqrt{25}$.

d. $\sqrt[4]{-81}$ is not a real number. There is no real number that, when raised to the fourth power, is -81.

e. $\sqrt[3]{64x^3} = 4x$ because $(4x)^3 = 64x^3$.

5

Recall that the notation $\sqrt{a^2}$ indicates the positive square root of a^2 only. For example,

$$\sqrt{(-5)^2} = \sqrt{25} = 5$$

When variables are present in the radicand and it is unclear whether the variable represents a positive number or a negative number, absolute value bars are sometimes needed to ensure that the result is a positive number. For example,

$$\sqrt{x^2} = |x|$$

This ensures that the result is positive. This same situation may occur when the index is any *even* positive integer. When the index is any *odd* positive integer, absolute value bars are not necessary.

FINDING $\sqrt[n]{a^n}$

If n is an *even* positive integer, then $\sqrt[n]{a^n} = |a|$.

If n is an *odd* positive integer, then $\sqrt[n]{a^n} = a$.

Example 5 Simplify.

a. $\sqrt{(-3)^2}$ **b.** $\sqrt{x^2}$ **c.** $\sqrt[4]{(x-2)^4}$ **d.** $\sqrt[3]{(-5)^3}$ **e.** $\sqrt[5]{(2x-7)^5}$

Solution **a.** $\sqrt{(-3)^2} = |-3| = 3$ When the index is even, the absolute value bars ensure us that our result is not negative.

b. $\sqrt{x^2} = |x|$

c. $\sqrt[4]{(x-2)^4} = |x-2|$

d. $\sqrt[3]{(-5)^3} = -5$

e. $\sqrt[5]{(2x-7)^5} = 2x - 7$ Absolute value bars are not needed when the index is odd.

6

Recall that an equation in x and y describes a function if each x-value is paired with exactly one y-value. With this in mind, does the equation

$$y = \sqrt{x}$$

describe a function? First, notice that replacement values for x must be nonnegative real numbers, since $\sqrt{x}$ is not a real number if $x < 0$. The notation $\sqrt{x}$ denotes the principal square root of x, so for every nonnegative number x, there is exactly one number, $\sqrt{x}$. Therefore, $y = \sqrt{x}$ describes a function, and we may write it as

$$f(x) = \sqrt{x}$$

Recall that the domain of a function in x is the set of all possible replacement values for x. This means that the domain of this function is the set of all nonnegative numbers, or $\{x \mid x \geq 0\}$.

We find function values for $f(x)$ as usual. For example,

$$f(0) = \sqrt{0} = 0$$
$$f(1) = \sqrt{1} = 1$$
$$f(4) = \sqrt{4} = 2$$
$$f(9) = \sqrt{9} = 3$$

Choosing perfect squares for x ensures us that $f(x)$ is a rational number, but it is important to stress that $f(x) = \sqrt{x}$ is defined for all nonnegative real numbers. For example,

$$f(3) = \sqrt{3} \approx 1.732$$

Example 6   Graph the square root function $f(x) = \sqrt{x}$.

Solution   To graph, we identify the domain, evaluate the function for several values of x, plot the resulting points, and connect the points with a smooth curve. The domain of this function is the set of all nonnegative numbers or $\{x \mid x \geq 0\}$. The table comes from the function values obtained earlier.

x	$f(x) = \sqrt{x}$
0	0
1	1
3	$\sqrt{3} \approx 1.7$
4	2
9	3

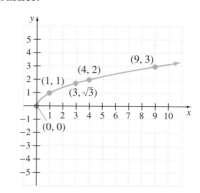

Notice that the graph of this function passes the vertical line test, as expected.

The equation $f(x) = \sqrt[3]{x}$ also describes a function. Here x may be any real number, so the domain of this function is the set of all real numbers. A few function values are given next.

$$f(0) = \sqrt[3]{0} = 0$$
$$f(1) = \sqrt[3]{1} = 1$$
$$f(-1) = \sqrt[3]{-1} = -1$$
$$f(6) = \sqrt[3]{6}$$
$$f(-6) = \sqrt[3]{-6}$$
$$f(8) = \sqrt[3]{8} = 2$$
$$f(-8) = \sqrt[3]{-8} = -2$$

Here, the radicands are not perfect cubes. The radicals do not simplify to rational numbers.

Example 7 Graph the function $f(x) = \sqrt[3]{x}$.

Solution To graph, we identify the domain, plot points, and connect the points with a smooth curve. The domain of this function is the set of all real numbers. The table comes from the function values obtained earlier. We have approximated $\sqrt[3]{6}$ and $\sqrt[3]{-6}$ for graphing purposes.

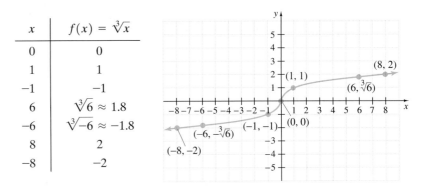

x	$f(x) = \sqrt[3]{x}$
0	0
1	1
−1	−1
6	$\sqrt[3]{6} \approx 1.8$
−6	$\sqrt[3]{-6} \approx -1.8$
8	2
−8	−2

The graph of this function passes the vertical line test, as expected.

SPOTLIGHT ON DECISION MAKING

Suppose you are a scientist working for NASA. A new moon, S/2001U1, has been discovered orbiting the planet Uranus in our outer solar system. You have been asked to check whether it is possible for this moon to have an oxygen atmosphere. You can do so by comparing the average speed of an oxygen molecule (480 meters per second) to the moon's **escape velocity**, the speed an object must travel to permanently leave the moon's gravitational pull. If the moon's escape velocity is greater than the average speed of oxygen molecules, then it is possible for the moon to retain oxygen in its atmosphere—that is, if oxygen exists on the moon at all.

Data about the new moon are listed in the table. Use that along with the escape velocity formula given below to decide whether it is possible for S/2001U1 to have an oxygen atmosphere.

$$v = \sqrt{\frac{2GM}{r}}, \text{ where}$$

v is the escape velocity (in meters per second, m/s),

M is the mass of the moon (in kilograms, kg),

r is the radius of the moon (in meters, m), and

G is the universal constant of gravitation where

$$\left(G = 6.67 \times 10^{-11} \frac{m^3}{kg \cdot s^2}\right).$$

S/2001U1 Parameters	
Mass	9.07×10^{20} kg
Radius	620,000 m
Visual geometric albedo	0.07
Orbital period	7.2 days

Exercise Set 7.1

Simplify. Assume that variables represent positive real numbers. See Example 1.

1. $\sqrt{100}$

2. $\sqrt{400}$

3. $\sqrt{\dfrac{1}{4}}$

4. $\sqrt{\dfrac{9}{25}}$

5. $\sqrt{0.0001}$

6. $\sqrt{0.04}$

7. $-\sqrt{36}$

8. $-\sqrt{9}$

9. $\sqrt{x^{10}}$

10. $\sqrt{x^{16}}$

11. $\sqrt{16y^6}$

12. $\sqrt{64y^{20}}$

Use a calculator to approximate each square root to 3 decimal places. Check to see that each approximation is reasonable. See Example 2.

13. $\sqrt{7}$

14. $\sqrt{11}$

15. $\sqrt{38}$

16. $\sqrt{56}$

17. $\sqrt{200}$

18. $\sqrt{300}$

Find each cube root. See Example 3.

19. $\sqrt[3]{64}$

20. $\sqrt[3]{27}$

21. $\sqrt[3]{\dfrac{1}{8}}$

22. $\sqrt[3]{\dfrac{27}{64}}$

23. $\sqrt[3]{-1}$

24. $\sqrt[3]{-125}$

25. $\sqrt[3]{x^{12}}$

26. $\sqrt[3]{x^{15}}$

27. $\sqrt[3]{-27x^9}$

28. $\sqrt[3]{-64x^6}$

Find each root. Assume that all variables represent nonnegative real numbers. See Example 4.

29. $-\sqrt[4]{16}$

30. $\sqrt[5]{-243}$

31. $\sqrt[4]{-16}$

32. $\sqrt[5]{-16}$

33. $\sqrt[5]{-32}$

34. $\sqrt[5]{-1}$

35. $\sqrt[5]{x^{20}}$

36. $\sqrt[4]{x^{20}}$

37. $\sqrt[6]{64x^{12}}$

38. $\sqrt[5]{-32x^{15}}$

39. $\sqrt{81x^4}$

40. $\sqrt[4]{81x^4}$

41. $\sqrt[4]{256x^8}$

42. $\sqrt{256x^8}$

Simplify. Assume that the variables represent any real number. See Example 5.

43. $\sqrt{(-8)^2}$

44. $\sqrt{(-7)^2}$

45. $\sqrt[3]{(-8)^3}$

46. $\sqrt[5]{(-7)^5}$

47. $\sqrt{4x^2}$

48. $\sqrt[4]{16x^4}$

49. $\sqrt[3]{x^3}$

50. $\sqrt[5]{x^5}$

51. $\sqrt{(x-5)^2}$

52. $\sqrt{(y-6)^2}$

53. $\sqrt{x^2+4x+4}$
(*Hint:* Factor the polynomial first.)

54. $\sqrt{x^2-8x+16}$
(*Hint:* Factor the polynomial first.)

Simplify each radical. Assume that all variables represent positive real numbers.

55. $-\sqrt{121}$

56. $-\sqrt[3]{125}$

57. $\sqrt[3]{8x^3}$

58. $\sqrt{16x^8}$

59. $\sqrt{y^{12}}$

60. $\sqrt[3]{y^{12}}$

61. $\sqrt{25a^2b^{20}}$

62. $\sqrt{9x^4y^6}$

63. $\sqrt[3]{-27x^{12}y^9}$

64. $\sqrt[3]{-8a^{21}b^6}$

65. $\sqrt[4]{a^{16}b^4}$

66. $\sqrt[4]{x^8y^{12}}$

67. $\sqrt[5]{-32x^{10}y^5}$

68. $\sqrt[5]{-243z^{15}}$

69. $\sqrt{\dfrac{25}{49}}$

70. $\sqrt{\dfrac{4}{81}}$

71. $\sqrt{\dfrac{x^2}{4y^2}}$

72. $\sqrt{\dfrac{y^{10}}{9x^6}}$

73. $-\sqrt[3]{\dfrac{z^{21}}{27x^3}}$

74. $-\sqrt[3]{\dfrac{64a^3}{b^9}}$

75. $\sqrt[4]{\dfrac{x^4}{16}}$

76. $\sqrt[4]{\dfrac{y^4}{81x^4}}$

If $f(x) = \sqrt{2x+3}$ and $g(x) = \sqrt[3]{x-8}$, find the following function values. See Examples 6 and 7.

77. $f(0)$

78. $g(0)$

79. $g(7)$

80. $f(-1)$

81. $g(-19)$

82. $f(3)$

83. $f(2)$

84. $g(1)$

Identify the domain and then graph each function. See Example 6.

85. $f(x) = \sqrt{x} + 2$

86. $f(x) = \sqrt{x} - 2$

87. $f(x) = \sqrt{x-3}$; use the following table.

x	$f(x)$
3	
4	
7	
12	

88. $f(x) = \sqrt{x+1}$; use the following table.

x	$f(x)$
-1	
0	
3	
8	

Identify the domain and then graph each function. See Example 7.

89. $f(x) = \sqrt[3]{x} + 1$

90. $f(x) = \sqrt[3]{x} - 2$

91. $g(x) = \sqrt[3]{x - 1}$; use the following table.

x	$g(x)$
1	0
2	1
0	−1
9	2
−7	−2

92. $g(x) = \sqrt[3]{x + 1}$; use the following table.

x	$g(x)$
−1	0
0	1
−2	−1
7	2
−9	−2

93. Suppose that a friend tells you that $\sqrt{13} \approx 5.7$. Without a calculator, how can you convince your friend that he must have made an error?

 94. Escape velocity is the minimum speed that an object must reach to escape a planet's pull of gravity. Escape velocity v is given by the equation $v = \sqrt{\dfrac{2GM}{r}}$, where M is the mass of the planet, r is its radius, and G is the universal gravitational constant, which has a value of $G = 6.67 \times 10^{-11}$ m³/kg·s². The mass of Earth is 5.97×10^{24} kg and its radius is 6.37×10^6 m. Use this information to find the escape velocity for Earth. Round to the nearest whole number. (*Source:* National Space Science Data Center)

Use a graphing calculator to verify the domain of each function and its graph.

95. Exercise 85   **96.** Exercise 86

97. Exercise 89   **98.** Exercise 90

REVIEW EXERCISES

Simplify each exponential expression. See Sections 5.1 and 5.2.

99. $\left(-2x^3y^2\right)^5$ **100.** $\left(4y^6z^7\right)^3$

101. $\left(-3x^2y^3z^5\right)\left(20x^5y^7\right)$ **102.** $\left(-14a^5bc^2\right)\left(2abc^4\right)$

103. $\dfrac{7x^{-1}y}{14\left(x^5y^2\right)^{-2}}$ **104.** $\dfrac{\left(2a^{-1}b^2\right)^3}{\left(8a^2b\right)^{-2}}$

7.2 RATIONAL EXPONENTS

CD-ROM   SSM

SSG   Video

▶ **OBJECTIVES**

1. Understand the meaning of $a^{1/n}$.
2. Understand the meaning of $a^{m/n}$.
3. Understand the meaning of $a^{-m/n}$.
4. Use rules for exponents to simplify expressions that contain rational exponents.
5. Use rational exponents to simplify radical expressions.

1 So far in this text, we have not defined expressions with rational exponents such as $3^{1/2}$, $x^{2/3}$, and $-9^{-1/4}$. We will define these expressions so that the rules for exponents will apply to these rational exponents as well.

Suppose that $x = 5^{1/3}$. Then

$$x^3 = \left(5^{1/3}\right)^3 = 5^{1/3 \cdot 3} = 5^1 \text{ or } 5$$

└ using rules ↑
for exponents

Since $x^3 = 5$, then x is the number whose cube is 5, or $x = \sqrt[3]{5}$. Notice that we also know that $x = 5^{1/3}$. This means

$$5^{1/3} = \sqrt[3]{5}$$

DEFINITION OF $a^{1/n}$

If n is a positive integer greater than 1 and $\sqrt[n]{a}$ is a real number, then

$$a^{1/n} = \sqrt[n]{a}$$

Notice that the denominator of the rational exponent corresponds to the index of the radical.

Example 1 Use radical notation to write the following. Simplify if possible.

    a. $4^{1/2}$ **b.** $64^{1/3}$ **c.** $x^{1/4}$ **d.** $0^{1/6}$ **e.** $-9^{1/2}$ **f.** $\left(81x^8\right)^{1/4}$ **g.** $(5y)^{1/3}$

Solution **a.** $4^{1/2} = \sqrt{4} = 2$ **b.** $64^{1/3} = \sqrt[3]{64} = 4$

        c. $x^{1/4} = \sqrt[4]{x}$ **d.** $0^{1/6} = \sqrt[6]{0} = 0$

        e. $-9^{1/2} = -\sqrt{9} = -3$ **f.** $\left(81x^8\right)^{1/4} = \sqrt[4]{81x^8} = 3x^2$

        g. $(5y)^{1/3} = \sqrt[3]{5y}$

2 As we expand our use of exponents to include $\dfrac{m}{n}$, we define their meaning so that rules for exponents still hold true. For example, by properties of exponents,

$$8^{2/3} = \left(8^{1/3}\right)^2 = \left(\sqrt[3]{8}\right)^2 \qquad \text{or}$$

$$8^{2/3} = \left(8^2\right)^{1/3} = \sqrt[3]{8^2}$$

DEFINITION OF $a^{m/n}$

If m and n are positive integers greater than 1 with $\dfrac{m}{n}$ in lowest terms, then

$$a^{m/n} = \sqrt[n]{a^m} = \left(\sqrt[n]{a}\right)^m$$

as long as $\sqrt[n]{a}$ is a real number.

Notice that the denominator n of the rational exponent corresponds to the index of the radical. The numerator m of the rational exponent indicates that the base is to be raised to the mth power. This means

$$8^{2/3} = \sqrt[3]{8^2} = \sqrt[3]{64} = 4 \qquad \text{or}$$

$$8^{2/3} = \left(\sqrt[3]{8}\right)^2 = 2^2 = 4$$

> **HELPFUL HINT**
> Most of the time, $\left(\sqrt[n]{a}\right)^m$ will be easier to calculate than $\sqrt[n]{a^m}$.

Example 2 Use radical notation to write the following. Then simplify if possible.

a. $4^{3/2}$ **b.** $-16^{3/4}$ **c.** $(-27)^{2/3}$ **d.** $\left(\dfrac{1}{9}\right)^{3/2}$ **e.** $(4x - 1)^{3/5}$

Solution

a. $4^{3/2} = \left(\sqrt{4}\right)^3 = 2^3 = 8$

b. $-16^{3/4} = -\left(\sqrt[4]{16}\right)^3 = -(2)^3 = -8$

c. $(-27)^{2/3} = \left(\sqrt[3]{-27}\right)^2 = (-3)^2 = 9$

d. $\left(\dfrac{1}{9}\right)^{3/2} = \left(\sqrt{\dfrac{1}{9}}\right)^3 = \left(\dfrac{1}{3}\right)^3 = \dfrac{1}{27}$

e. $(4x - 1)^{3/5} = \sqrt[5]{(4x - 1)^3}$

> **HELPFUL HINT**
> The *denominator* of a rational exponent is the index of the corresponding radical.
> For example, $x^{1/5} = \sqrt[5]{x}$ and $z^{2/3} = \sqrt[3]{z^2}$, or $z^{2/3} = \left(\sqrt[3]{z}\right)^2$.

3 The rational exponents we have given meaning to exclude negative rational numbers. To complete the set of definitions, we define $a^{-m/n}$.

> **DEFINITION OF $a^{-m/n}$**
>
> $$a^{-m/n} = \dfrac{1}{a^{m/n}}$$
>
> as long as $a^{m/n}$ is a nonzero real number.

Example 3 Write each expression with a positive exponent, and then simplify.

a. $16^{-3/4}$ **b.** $(-27)^{-2/3}$

Solution

a. $16^{-3/4} = \dfrac{1}{16^{3/4}} = \dfrac{1}{\left(\sqrt[4]{16}\right)^3} = \dfrac{1}{2^3} = \dfrac{1}{8}$

b. $(-27)^{-2/3} = \dfrac{1}{(-27)^{2/3}} = \dfrac{1}{\left(\sqrt[3]{-27}\right)^2} = \dfrac{1}{(-3)^2} = \dfrac{1}{9}$

▼
HELPFUL HINT

If an expression contains a negative rational exponent, such as $9^{-3/2}$, you may want to first write the expression with a positive exponent and then interpret the rational exponent. Notice that the sign of the base is not affected by the sign of its exponent. For example,

$$9^{-3/2} = \frac{1}{9^{3/2}} = \frac{1}{(\sqrt{9})^3} = \frac{1}{27}$$

Also,

$$(-27)^{-1/3} = \frac{1}{(-27)^{1/3}} = -\frac{1}{3}$$

---

4   It can be shown that the properties of integer exponents hold for rational exponents. By using these properties and definitions, we can now simplify expressions that contain rational exponents.

These rules are repeated here for review.

SUMMARY OF EXPONENT RULES

If m and n are rational numbers, and a, b, and c are numbers for which the expressions below exist, then

Product rule for exponents:	$a^m \cdot a^n = a^{m+n}$
Power rule for exponents:	$(a^m)^n = a^{m \cdot n}$
Power rules for products and quotients:	$(ab)^n = a^n b^n$ and
	$\left(\dfrac{a}{c}\right)^n = \dfrac{a^n}{c^n}, c \neq 0$
Quotient rule for exponents:	$\dfrac{a^m}{a^n} = a^{m-n}, a \neq 0$
Zero exponent:	$a^0 = 1, a \neq 0$
Negative exponent:	$a^{-n} = \dfrac{1}{a^n}, a \neq 0$

Example 4   Use properties of exponents to simplify. Write results with only positive exponents.

a. $x^{1/2} x^{1/3}$ **b.** $\dfrac{7^{1/3}}{7^{4/3}}$ **c.** $\dfrac{(2x^{2/5} y^{-1/3})^5}{x^2 y}$

Solution   **a.** $x^{1/2} x^{1/3} = x^{(1/2 + 1/3)} = x^{3/6 + 2/6} = x^{5/6}$

b. $\dfrac{7^{1/3}}{7^{4/3}} = 7^{1/3 - 4/3} = 7^{-3/3} = 7^{-1} = \dfrac{1}{7}$

c. We begin by using the power rule $(ab)^m = a^m b^m$ to simplify the numerator.

$$\frac{(2x^{2/5}y^{-1/3})^5}{x^2 y} = \frac{2^5(x^{2/5})^5(y^{-1/3})^5}{x^2 y} = \frac{32x^2 y^{-5/3}}{x^2 y}$$

$$= 32x^{2-2}y^{-5/3-3/3} \quad \text{Apply the quotient rule.}$$

$$= 32x^0 y^{-8/3}$$

$$= \frac{32}{y^{8/3}}$$

Example 5   Multiply.

a. $z^{2/3}(z^{1/3} - z^5)$

b. $(x^{1/3} - 5)(x^{1/3} + 2)$

Solution   **a.** $z^{2/3}(z^{1/3} - z^5) = z^{2/3}z^{1/3} - z^{2/3}z^5$ Apply the distributive property.

$$= z^{(2/3+1/3)} - z^{(2/3+5)} \quad \text{Use the product rule.}$$

$$= z^{3/3} - z^{(2/3+15/3)}$$

$$= z - z^{17/3}$$

b. $(x^{1/3} - 5)(x^{1/3} + 2) = x^{2/3} + 2x^{1/3} - 5x^{1/3} - 10$ Think of $(x^{1/3} - 5)$ and $(x^{1/3} + 2)$ as 2 binomials, and FOIL.

$$= x^{2/3} - 3x^{1/3} - 10$$

Example 6   Factor $x^{-1/2}$ from the expression $3x^{-1/2} - 7x^{5/2}$. Assume that all variables represent positive numbers.

Solution $3x^{-1/2} - 7x^{5/2} = (x^{-1/2})(3) - (x^{-1/2})(7x^{6/2})$

$$= x^{-1/2}(3 - 7x^3)$$

To check, multiply $x^{-1/2}(3 - 7x^3)$ to see that the product is $3x^{-1/2} - 7x^{5/2}$.

5   Some radical expressions are easier to simplify when we first write them with rational exponents. We can simplify some radical expressions by first writing the expression with rational exponents. Use properties of exponents to simplify, and then convert back to radical notation.

Example 7   Use rational exponents to simplify. Assume that variables represent positive numbers.

a. $\sqrt[6]{25}$

b. $\sqrt[8]{x^4}$

c. $\sqrt[4]{r^2 s^6}$

Solution   **a.** $\sqrt[6]{25} = 25^{1/6} = (5^2)^{1/6} = 5^{2/6} = 5^{1/3} = \sqrt[3]{5}$

b. $\sqrt[8]{x^4} = x^{4/8} = x^{1/2} = \sqrt{x}$

c. $\sqrt[4]{r^2 s^6} = (r^2 s^6)^{1/4} = r^{2/4}s^{6/4} = r^{1/2}s^{3/2} = (rs^3)^{1/2} = \sqrt{rs^3}$

Example 8   Use rational exponents to write as a single radical.

a. $\sqrt{x} \cdot \sqrt[4]{x}$ **b.** $\dfrac{\sqrt{x}}{\sqrt[3]{x}}$ **c.** $\sqrt[3]{3} \cdot \sqrt{2}$

Solution   **a.** $\sqrt{x} \cdot \sqrt[4]{x} = x^{1/2} \cdot x^{1/4} = x^{1/2+1/4}$

$= x^{3/4} = \sqrt[4]{x^3}$

b. $\dfrac{\sqrt{x}}{\sqrt[3]{x}} = \dfrac{x^{1/2}}{x^{1/3}} = x^{1/2-1/3} = x^{3/6-2/6}$

$= x^{1/6} = \sqrt[6]{x}$

c. $\sqrt[3]{3} \cdot \sqrt{2} = 3^{1/3} \cdot 2^{1/2}$ Write with rational exponents.

$= 3^{2/6} \cdot 2^{3/6}$ Write the exponents so that they have the same denominator.

$= \left(3^2 \cdot 2^3\right)^{1/6}$ Use $a^n b^n = (ab)^n$.

$= \sqrt[6]{3^2 \cdot 2^3}$ Write with radical notation.

$= \sqrt[6]{72}$ Multiply $3^2 \cdot 2^3$.

SPOTLIGHT ON DECISION MAKING

Suppose you are a telecommunications industry analyst. A colleague has just formulated a mathematical model for the number of cellular telephone subscriptions in the United States from 1985 to 1998. The model is $y = 341.8x^{21/5}$, where y is the number of cellular telephone subscriptions x years after 1980. The actual data from 1985 to 1998 are listed in the table.

Your colleague has asked your help in evaluating whether this model represents the actual data well. By comparing the numbers of subscriptions given by the model to the actual data given in the table, decide whether this mathematical model is acceptable. Explain your reasoning.

U.S. CELLULAR TELEPHONE SUBSCRIPTIONS, 1985–1998

Year	Subscriptions
1985	340,213
1986	681,825
1987	1,230,855
1988	2,069,441
1989	3,508,944
1990	5,283,055
1991	7,557,148
1992	11,032,753
1993	16,009,461
1994	24,134,421
1995	33,785,661
1996	44,042,992
1997	55,312,293
1998	69,209,321

(*Source:* The CTIA Semi-Annual Wireless Survey)

Exercise Set 7.2

Use radical notation to write each expression. Simplify if possible. See Example 1.

1. $49^{1/2}$ **2.** $64^{1/3}$

3. $27^{1/3}$ **4.** $8^{1/3}$

5. $\left(\dfrac{1}{16}\right)^{1/4}$ **6.** $\left(\dfrac{1}{64}\right)^{1/2}$

7. $169^{1/2}$ **8.** $81^{1/4}$

9. $2m^{1/3}$ **10.** $(2m)^{1/3}$

11. $(9x^4)^{1/2}$ **12.** $(16x^8)^{1/2}$

13. $(-27)^{1/3}$ **14.** $-64^{1/2}$

15. $-16^{1/4}$ **16.** $(-32)^{1/5}$

Use radical notation to write each expression. Simplify if possible. See Example 2.

17. $16^{3/4}$ **18.** $4^{5/2}$

19. $(-64)^{2/3}$ **20.** $(-8)^{4/3}$

21. $(-16)^{3/4}$ **22.** $(-9)^{3/2}$

23. $(2x)^{3/5}$ **24.** $2x^{3/5}$

25. $(7x + 2)^{2/3}$ **26.** $(x - 4)^{3/4}$

27. $\left(\dfrac{16}{9}\right)^{3/2}$ **28.** $\left(\dfrac{49}{25}\right)^{3/2}$

Write with positive exponents. Simplify if possible. See Example 3.

29. $8^{-4/3}$ **30.** $64^{-2/3}$

31. $(-64)^{-2/3}$ **32.** $(-8)^{-4/3}$

33. $(-4)^{-3/2}$ **34.** $(-16)^{-5/4}$

35. $x^{-1/4}$ **36.** $y^{-1/6}$

37. $\dfrac{1}{a^{-2/3}}$ **38.** $\dfrac{1}{n^{-8/9}}$

39. $\dfrac{5}{7x^{-3/4}}$ **40.** $\dfrac{2}{3y^{-5/7}}$

41. Explain how writing x^{-7} with positive exponents is similar to writing $x^{-1/4}$ with positive exponents.

42. Explain how writing $2x^{-5}$ with positive exponents is similar to writing $2x^{-3/4}$ with positive exponents.

Use the properties of exponents to simplify each expression. Write with positive exponents. See Example 4.

43. $a^{2/3}a^{5/3}$ **44.** $b^{9/5}b^{8/5}$

45. $x^{-2/5} \cdot x^{7/5}$ **46.** $y^{4/3} \cdot y^{-1/3}$

47. $3^{1/4} \cdot 3^{3/8}$ **48.** $5^{1/2} \cdot 5^{1/6}$

49. $\dfrac{y^{1/3}}{y^{1/6}}$ **50.** $\dfrac{x^{3/4}}{x^{1/8}}$

51. $(4u^2)^{3/2}$ **52.** $(32^{1/5}x^{2/3})^3$

53. $\dfrac{b^{1/2}b^{3/4}}{-b^{1/4}}$ **54.** $\dfrac{a^{1/4}a^{-1/2}}{a^{2/3}}$

55. $\dfrac{(3x^{1/4})^3}{x^{1/12}}$ **56.** $\dfrac{(2x^{1/5})^4}{x^{3/10}}$

Multiply. See Example 5.

57. $y^{1/2}(y^{1/2} - y^{2/3})$ **58.** $x^{1/2}(x^{1/2} + x^{3/2})$

59. $x^{2/3}(2x - 2)$ **60.** $3x^{1/2}(x + y)$

61. $(2x^{1/3} + 3)(2x^{1/3} - 3)$ **62.** $(y^{1/2} + 5)(y^{1/2} + 5)$

Factor the common factor from the given expression. See Example 6.

63. $x^{8/3}$; $x^{8/3} + x^{10/3}$ **64.** $x^{3/2}$; $x^{5/2} - x^{3/2}$

65. $x^{1/5}$; $x^{2/5} - 3x^{1/5}$ **66.** $x^{2/7}$; $x^{3/7} - 2x^{2/7}$

67. $x^{-1/3}$; $5x^{-1/3} + x^{2/3}$ **68.** $x^{-3/4}$; $x^{-3/4} + 3x^{1/4}$

Use rational exponents to simplify each radical. Assume that all variables represent positive numbers. See Example 7.

69. $\sqrt[6]{x^3}$ **70.** $\sqrt[9]{a^3}$

71. $\sqrt[4]{4}$ **72.** $\sqrt[4]{36}$

73. $\sqrt[4]{16x^2}$ **74.** $\sqrt[8]{4y^2}$

75. $\sqrt[8]{x^4y^4}$ **76.** $\sqrt[9]{y^6z^3}$

Use rational expressions to write as a single radical expression. See Example 8.

77. $\sqrt[3]{y} \cdot \sqrt[5]{y^2}$ **78.** $\sqrt[3]{y^2} \cdot \sqrt[6]{y}$

79. $\dfrac{\sqrt[3]{b^2}}{\sqrt[4]{b}}$ **80.** $\dfrac{\sqrt[4]{a}}{\sqrt[5]{a}}$

81. $\dfrac{\sqrt[3]{a^2}}{\sqrt[6]{a}}$ **82.** $\dfrac{\sqrt[5]{b^2}}{\sqrt[10]{b^3}}$

83. $\sqrt{3} \cdot \sqrt[3]{4}$ **84.** $\sqrt[3]{5} \cdot \sqrt{2}$

85. $\sqrt[5]{7} \cdot \sqrt[3]{y}$ **86.** $\sqrt[4]{5} \cdot \sqrt[3]{x}$

87. In physics, the speed of a wave traveling over a stretched string with tension t and density u is given by the expression $\dfrac{\sqrt{t}}{\sqrt{u}}$. Write this expression with rational exponents.

88. In electronics, the angular frequency of oscillations in a certain type of circuit is given by the expression $(LC)^{-1/2}$. Use radical notation to write this expression.

Basal metabolic rate (BMR) is the number of calories per day a person needs to maintain life. A person's basal metabolic rate $B(w)$ in calories per day can be estimated with the function $B(w) = 70w^{3/4}$, where w is the person's weight in kilograms.

89. Estimate the BMR for a person who weighs 50 kilograms. Round to the nearest calorie. (Note: 50 kilograms is approximately 110 pounds.)

90. Estimate the BMR for a person who weighs 85 kilograms. Round to the nearest calorie. (Note: 85 kilograms is approximately 187 pounds.)

91. Hewlett-Packard (HP) is a global leader in computing and imaging products. HP's annual net revenue can be modeled by the function $f(x) = 6550x^{43/50}$, where $f(x)$ is net revenue in millions of dollars in the year x, and $x = 0$ represents the year 1990. (*Source:* Hewlett-Packard Company, 1995–1999)

    a. Use this model to find HP's net revenue in 1999.
    b. Predict HP's net revenue in 2004.

Fill in the box with the correct expression.

92. $\boxed{} \cdot a^{2/3} = a^{3/3}$, or a **93.** $\boxed{} \cdot x^{1/8} = x^{4/8}$, or $x^{1/2}$

94. $\dfrac{\boxed{}}{x^{-2/5}} = x^{3/5}$ **95.** $\dfrac{\boxed{}}{y^{-3/4}} = y^{4/4}$, or y

Use a calculator to write a four-decimal-place approximation of each.

96. $8^{1/4}$ **97.** $20^{1/5}$

98. $18^{3/5}$ **99.** $76^{5/7}$

REVIEW EXERCISES

Write each integer as a product of two integers such that one of the factors is a perfect square. For example, write 18 as $9 \cdot 2$, because 9 is a perfect square.

100. 75   **101.** 20

102. 48   **103.** 45

Write each integer as a product of two integers such that one of the factors is a perfect cube. For example, write 24 as $8 \cdot 3$, because 8 is a perfect cube.

104. 16   **105.** 56

106. 54   **107.** 80

7.3 SIMPLIFYING RADICAL EXPRESSIONS

CD-ROM   SSM

SSG   Video

▶ **OBJECTIVES**

1. Use the product rule for radicals.
2. Use the quotient rule for radicals.
3. Simplify radicals.

1   It is possible to simplify some radicals that do not evaluate to rational numbers. To do so, we use a product rule and a quotient rule for radicals. To discover the product rule, notice the following pattern.

$$\sqrt{9} \cdot \sqrt{4} = 3 \cdot 2 = 6$$
$$\sqrt{9 \cdot 4} = \sqrt{36} = 6$$

Since both expressions simplify to 6, it is true that

$$\sqrt{9} \cdot \sqrt{4} = \sqrt{9 \cdot 4}$$

This pattern suggests the following product rule for radicals.

PRODUCT RULE FOR RADICALS

If $\sqrt[n]{a}$ and $\sqrt[n]{b}$ are real numbers, then

$$\sqrt[n]{a} \cdot \sqrt[n]{b} = \sqrt[n]{ab}$$

Notice that the product rule is the relationship $a^{1/n} \cdot b^{1/n} = (ab)^{1/n}$ stated in radical notation.

Example 1   Multiply.

a. $\sqrt{3} \cdot \sqrt{5}$ **b.** $\sqrt{21} \cdot \sqrt{x}$ **c.** $\sqrt[3]{4} \cdot \sqrt[3]{2}$ **d.** $\sqrt[4]{5y^2} \cdot \sqrt[4]{2x^3}$ **e.** $\sqrt{\dfrac{2}{a}} \cdot \sqrt{\dfrac{b}{3}}$

Solution   **a.** $\sqrt{3} \cdot \sqrt{5} = \sqrt{3 \cdot 5} = \sqrt{15}$

b. $\sqrt{21} \cdot \sqrt{x} = \sqrt{21x}$

c. $\sqrt[3]{4} \cdot \sqrt[3]{2} = \sqrt[3]{4 \cdot 2} = \sqrt[3]{8} = 2$

d. $\sqrt[4]{5y^2} \cdot \sqrt[4]{2x^3} = \sqrt[4]{5y^2 \cdot 2x^3} = \sqrt[4]{10y^2x^3}$

e. $\sqrt{\dfrac{2}{a}} \cdot \sqrt{\dfrac{b}{3}} = \sqrt{\dfrac{2}{a} \cdot \dfrac{b}{3}} = \sqrt{\dfrac{2b}{3a}}$

2   To discover a quotient rule for radicals, notice the following pattern.

$$\sqrt{\dfrac{4}{9}} = \dfrac{2}{3}$$

$$\dfrac{\sqrt{4}}{\sqrt{9}} = \dfrac{2}{3}$$

Since both expressions simplify to $\dfrac{2}{3}$, it is true that

$$\sqrt{\dfrac{4}{9}} = \dfrac{\sqrt{4}}{\sqrt{9}}$$

This pattern suggests the following quotient rule for radicals.

QUOTIENT RULE FOR RADICALS

If $\sqrt[n]{a}$ and $\sqrt[n]{b}$ are real numbers and $\sqrt[n]{b}$ is not zero, then

$$\sqrt[n]{\dfrac{a}{b}} = \dfrac{\sqrt[n]{a}}{\sqrt[n]{b}}$$

Notice that the quotient rule is the relationship $\left(\dfrac{a}{b}\right)^{1/n} = \dfrac{a^{1/n}}{b^{1/n}}$ stated in radical notation. We can use the quotient rule to simplify radical expressions by reading the rule from left to right, or to divide radicals by reading the rule from right to left. For example,

$$\sqrt{\dfrac{x}{16}} = \dfrac{\sqrt{x}}{\sqrt{16}} = \dfrac{\sqrt{x}}{4} \qquad \text{Using } \sqrt[n]{\dfrac{a}{b}} = \dfrac{\sqrt[n]{a}}{\sqrt[n]{b}}$$

$$\dfrac{\sqrt{75}}{\sqrt{3}} = \sqrt{\dfrac{75}{3}} = \sqrt{25} = 5 \qquad \text{Using } \dfrac{\sqrt[n]{a}}{\sqrt[n]{b}} = \sqrt[n]{\dfrac{a}{b}}$$

Note: *For the remainder of this chapter, we will assume that variables represent positive real numbers. Since this is so, we need not insert absolute value bars when we simplify even roots.*

Example 2   Use the quotient rule to simplify.

a. $\sqrt{\dfrac{25}{49}}$ b. $\sqrt{\dfrac{x}{9}}$ c. $\sqrt[3]{\dfrac{8}{27}}$ d. $\sqrt[4]{\dfrac{3}{16y^4}}$

Solution   a. $\sqrt{\dfrac{25}{49}} = \dfrac{\sqrt{25}}{\sqrt{49}} = \dfrac{5}{7}$

b. $\sqrt{\dfrac{x}{9}} = \dfrac{\sqrt{x}}{\sqrt{9}} = \dfrac{\sqrt{x}}{3}$

c. $\sqrt[3]{\dfrac{8}{27}} = \dfrac{\sqrt[3]{8}}{\sqrt[3]{27}} = \dfrac{2}{3}$

d. $\sqrt[4]{\dfrac{3}{16y^4}} = \dfrac{\sqrt[4]{3}}{\sqrt[4]{16y^4}} = \dfrac{\sqrt[4]{3}}{2y}$

---

3   Both the product and quotient rules can be used to simplify a radical. If the product rule is read from right to left, we have that $\sqrt[n]{ab} = \sqrt[n]{a} \cdot \sqrt[n]{b}$. This is used to simplify the following radicals.

Example 3   Simplify the following.

a. $\sqrt{50}$ b. $\sqrt[3]{24}$ c. $\sqrt{26}$ d. $\sqrt[4]{32}$

Solution   a. Factor 50 such that one factor is the largest perfect square that divides 50. The largest perfect square factor of 50 is 25, so we write 50 as $25 \cdot 2$ and use the product rule for radicals to simplify.

$$\sqrt{50} = \sqrt{25 \cdot 2} = \sqrt{25} \cdot \sqrt{2} = 5\sqrt{2}$$

> **HELPFUL HINT**
> Don't forget that, for example, $5\sqrt{2}$ means $5 \cdot \sqrt{2}$.

⤷ The largest perfect square factor of 50.

b. $\sqrt[3]{24} = \sqrt[3]{8 \cdot 3} = \sqrt[3]{8} \cdot \sqrt[3]{3} = 2\sqrt[3]{3}$

⤷ The largest perfect cube factor of 24.

c. $\sqrt{26}$ The largest perfect square factor of 26 is 1, so $\sqrt{26}$ cannot be simplified further.

d. $\sqrt[4]{32} = \sqrt[4]{16 \cdot 2} = \sqrt[4]{16} \cdot \sqrt[4]{2} = 2\sqrt[4]{2}$

⤷ The largest fourth power factor of 32.

After simplifying a radical such as a square root, always check the radicand to see that it contains no other perfect square factors. It may, if the largest perfect square factor of the radicand was not originally recognized. For example,

$$\sqrt{200} = \sqrt{4 \cdot 50} = \sqrt{4} \cdot \sqrt{50} = 2\sqrt{50}$$

Notice that the radicand 50 still contains the perfect square factor 25. This is because 4 is not the largest perfect square factor of 200. We continue as follows.

$$2\sqrt{50} = 2\sqrt{25 \cdot 2} = 2 \cdot \sqrt{25} \cdot \sqrt{2} = 2 \cdot 5 \cdot \sqrt{2} = 10\sqrt{2}$$

The radical is now simplified since 2 contains no perfect square factors (other than 1).

HELPFUL HINT
To help you recognize largest perfect power factors of a radicand, it will help if you are familiar with some perfect powers. A few are listed below.

Perfect Squares $\underset{1^2}{1},\ \ \underset{2^2}{4},\ \ \underset{3^2}{9},\ \ \underset{4^2}{16},\ \ \underset{5^2}{25},\ \ \underset{6^2}{36},\ \ \underset{7^2}{49},\ \ \underset{8^2}{64},\ \ \underset{9^2}{81},\ \ \underset{10^2}{100},\ \ \underset{11^2}{121},\ \ \underset{12^2}{144}$

Perfect Cubes $\underset{1^3}{1},\ \ \underset{2^3}{8},\ \ \underset{3^3}{27},\ \ \underset{4^3}{64},\ \ \underset{5^3}{125}$

Perfect Fourth
Powers $\underset{1^4}{1},\ \ \underset{2^4}{16},\ \ \underset{3^4}{81},\ \ \underset{4^4}{256}$

In general, we say that a radicand of the form $\sqrt[n]{a}$ is simplified when a contains no factors that are perfect nth powers (other than 1 or -1).

Example 4   Use the product rule to simplify.

   a. $\sqrt{25x^3}$ **b.** $\sqrt[3]{54x^6y^8}$ **c.** $\sqrt[4]{81z^{11}}$

Solution   **a.** $\sqrt{25x^3} = \sqrt{25x^2 \cdot x}$ Find the largest perfect square factor.

                $= \sqrt{25x^2} \cdot \sqrt{x}$ Apply the product rule.

                $= 5x\sqrt{x}$ Simplify.

   b. $\sqrt[3]{54x^6y^8} = \sqrt[3]{27 \cdot 2 \cdot x^6 \cdot y^6 \cdot y^2}$ Factor the radicand and identify perfect cube factors.

                $= \sqrt[3]{27x^6y^6 \cdot 2y^2}$

                $= \sqrt[3]{27x^6y^6} \cdot \sqrt[3]{2y^2}$ Apply the product rule.

                $= 3x^2y^2\sqrt[3]{2y^2}$ Simplify.

   c. $\sqrt[4]{81z^{11}} = \sqrt[4]{81 \cdot z^8 \cdot z^3}$ Factor the radicand and identify perfect fourth power factors.

                $= \sqrt[4]{81z^8} \cdot \sqrt[4]{z^3}$ Apply the product rule.

                $= 3z^2\sqrt[4]{z^3}$ Simplify.

Example 5   Use the quotient rule to divide, and simplify if possible.

a. $\dfrac{\sqrt{20}}{\sqrt{5}}$

b. $\dfrac{\sqrt{50x}}{2\sqrt{2}}$

c. $\dfrac{7\sqrt[3]{48x^4y^8}}{\sqrt[3]{6y^2}}$

Solution   **a.** $\dfrac{\sqrt{20}}{\sqrt{5}} = \sqrt{\dfrac{20}{5}}$ Apply the quotient rule.

$= \sqrt{4}$ Simplify.

$= 2$ Simplify.

b. $\dfrac{\sqrt{50x}}{2\sqrt{2}} = \dfrac{1}{2} \cdot \sqrt{\dfrac{50x}{2}}$ Apply the quotient rule.

$= \dfrac{1}{2} \cdot \sqrt{25x}$ Simplify.

$= \dfrac{1}{2} \cdot \sqrt{25} \cdot \sqrt{x}$ Factor 25x.

$= \dfrac{1}{2} \cdot 5 \cdot \sqrt{x}$ Simplify.

$= \dfrac{5}{2} \sqrt{x}$

c. $\dfrac{7\sqrt[3]{48x^4y^8}}{\sqrt[3]{6y^2}} = 7 \cdot \sqrt[3]{\dfrac{48x^4y^8}{6y^2}}$ Apply the quotient rule.

$= 7 \cdot \sqrt[3]{8x^4y^6}$ Simplify.

$= 7\sqrt[3]{8x^3y^6 \cdot x}$ Factor.

$= 7 \cdot \sqrt[3]{8x^3y^6} \cdot \sqrt[3]{x}$ Apply the product rule.

$= 7 \cdot 2xy^2 \cdot \sqrt[3]{x}$ Simplify.

$= 14xy^2\sqrt[3]{x}$

Exercise Set 7.3

Use the product rule to multiply. See Example 1.

1. $\sqrt{7} \cdot \sqrt{2}$

2. $\sqrt{11} \cdot \sqrt{10}$

3. $\sqrt[4]{8} \cdot \sqrt[4]{2}$

4. $\sqrt[4]{27} \cdot \sqrt[4]{3}$

5. $\sqrt[3]{4} \cdot \sqrt[3]{9}$

6. $\sqrt[3]{10} \cdot \sqrt[3]{5}$

7. $\sqrt{2} \cdot \sqrt{3x}$

8. $\sqrt{3y} \cdot \sqrt{5x}$

9. $\sqrt{\dfrac{7}{x}} \cdot \sqrt{\dfrac{2}{y}}$

10. $\sqrt{\dfrac{6}{m}} \cdot \sqrt{\dfrac{n}{5}}$

11. $\sqrt[4]{4x^3} \cdot \sqrt[4]{5}$

12. $\sqrt[4]{ab^2} \cdot \sqrt[4]{27ab}$

Use the quotient rule to simplify. See Examples 2 and 3.

13. $\sqrt{\dfrac{6}{49}}$

14. $\sqrt{\dfrac{8}{81}}$

15. $\sqrt{\dfrac{2}{49}}$

16. $\sqrt{\dfrac{5}{121}}$

17. $\sqrt[4]{\dfrac{x^3}{16}}$

18. $\sqrt[4]{\dfrac{y}{81x^4}}$

19. $\sqrt[3]{\dfrac{4}{27}}$

20. $\sqrt[3]{\dfrac{3}{64}}$

21. $\sqrt[4]{\dfrac{8}{x^8}}$

22. $\sqrt[4]{\dfrac{a^3}{81}}$

23. $\sqrt[3]{\dfrac{2x}{81y^{12}}}$

24. $\sqrt[3]{\dfrac{3}{8x^6}}$

25. $\sqrt{\dfrac{x^2y}{100}}$

26. $\sqrt{\dfrac{y^2z}{36}}$

27. $\sqrt{\dfrac{5x^2}{4y^2}}$

28. $\sqrt{\dfrac{y^{10}}{9x^6}}$

29. $-\sqrt[3]{\dfrac{z^7}{27x^3}}$

30. $-\sqrt[3]{\dfrac{64a}{b^9}}$

Simplify. See Examples 3 and 4.

31. $\sqrt{32}$

32. $\sqrt{27}$

33. $\sqrt[3]{192}$

34. $\sqrt[3]{108}$

35. $5\sqrt{75}$

36. $3\sqrt{8}$

37. $\sqrt{24}$

38. $\sqrt{20}$

39. $\sqrt{100x^5}$

40. $\sqrt{64y^9}$

41. $\sqrt[3]{16y^7}$

42. $\sqrt[3]{64y^9}$

43. $\sqrt[4]{a^8b^7}$

44. $\sqrt[5]{32z^{12}}$

45. $\sqrt{y^5}$

46. $\sqrt[3]{y^5}$

47. $\sqrt{25a^2b^3}$

48. $\sqrt{9x^5y^7}$

49. $\sqrt[5]{-32x^{10}y}$

50. $\sqrt[5]{-243z^9}$

51. $\sqrt[3]{50x^{14}}$

52. $\sqrt[3]{40y^{10}}$

53. $-\sqrt{32a^8b^7}$

54. $-\sqrt{20ab^6}$

55. $\sqrt{9x^7y^9}$

56. $\sqrt{12r^9s^{12}}$

57. $\sqrt[3]{125r^9s^{12}}$

58. $\sqrt[3]{8a^6b^9}$

Use the quotient rule to divide. Then simplify if possible. See Example 5.

59. $\dfrac{\sqrt{14}}{\sqrt{7}}$

60. $\dfrac{\sqrt{45}}{\sqrt{9}}$

61. $\dfrac{\sqrt[3]{24}}{\sqrt[3]{3}}$

62. $\dfrac{\sqrt[3]{10}}{\sqrt[3]{2}}$

63. $\dfrac{5\sqrt[4]{48}}{\sqrt[4]{3}}$

64. $\dfrac{7\sqrt[4]{162}}{\sqrt[4]{2}}$

65. $\dfrac{\sqrt{x^5y^3}}{\sqrt{xy}}$

66. $\dfrac{\sqrt{a^7b^6}}{\sqrt{a^3b^2}}$

67. $\dfrac{8\sqrt[3]{54m^7}}{\sqrt[3]{2m}}$

68. $\dfrac{\sqrt[3]{128x^3}}{-3\sqrt[3]{2x}}$

69. $\dfrac{3\sqrt{100x^2}}{2\sqrt{2x^{-1}}}$

70. $\dfrac{\sqrt{270y^2}}{5\sqrt{3y^{-4}}}$

71. $\dfrac{\sqrt[4]{96a^{10}b^3}}{\sqrt[4]{3a^2b^3}}$

72. $\dfrac{\sqrt[5]{64x^{10}y^3}}{\sqrt[5]{2x^3y^{-7}}}$

73. The formula for the surface area A of a cone with height h and radius r is given by
$$A = \pi r\sqrt{r^2 + h^2}$$

 a. Find the surface area of a cone whose height is 3 centimeters and whose radius is 4 centimeters.

 b. Approximate to two decimal places the surface area of a cone whose height is 7.2 feet and whose radius is 6.8 feet.

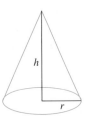

74. Before Mount Vesuvius, a volcano in Italy, erupted violently in 79 A.D., its height was 4190 feet. Vesuvius was roughly cone-shaped, and its base had a radius of approximately 25,200 feet. Use the formula for the surface area of a cone, given in Exercise 73, to approximate the surface area this volcano had before it erupted. (*Source: Global Volcanism Network*)

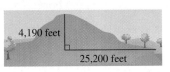

4,190 feet
25,200 feet

75. The owner of Knightime Video has determined that the demand equation for renting older releases is given by the equation $F(x) = 0.6\sqrt{49 - x^2}$, where x is the price in dollars per two-day rental and $F(x)$ is the number of times the video is demanded per week.

 a. Approximate to one decimal place the demand per week of an older release if the rental price is $3 per two-day rental.

 b. Approximate to one decimal place the demand per week of an older release if the rental price is $5 per two-day rental.

 c. Explain how the owner of the video store can use this equation to predict the number of copies of each tape that should be in stock.

REVIEW EXERCISES

Perform each indicated operation. See Sections 1.4 and 5.4.

76. $6x + 8x$

77. $(6x)(8x)$

78. $(2x + 3)(x - 5)$

79. $(2x + 3) + (x - 5)$

80. $9y^2 - 8y^2$

81. $(9y^2)(-8y^2)$

82. $-3(x + 5)$

83. $-3 + x + 5$

84. $(x - 4)^2$

85. $(2x + 1)^2$

7.4 ADDING, SUBTRACTING, AND MULTIPLYING RADICAL EXPRESSIONS

CD-ROM SSM

SSG Video

▶ **OBJECTIVES**

1. Add or subtract radical expressions.
2. Multiply radical expressions.

---

1 We have learned that sums or differences of like terms can be simplified. To simplify these sums or differences, we use the distributive property. For example,

$$2x + 3x = (2 + 3)x = 5x \quad \text{and} \quad 7x^2y - 4x^2y = (7 - 4)x^2y = 3x^2y$$

The distributive property can also be used to add **like radicals.**

LIKE RADICALS

Radicals with the same index and the same radicand are like radicals.

For example, $2\sqrt{7} + 3\sqrt{7} = (2 + 3)\sqrt{7} = 5\sqrt{7}$. Also,

$$5\sqrt{3x} - 7\sqrt{3x} = (5 - 7)\sqrt{3x} = -2\sqrt{3x}$$

The expression $2\sqrt{7} + 2\sqrt[3]{7}$ cannot be simplified further since $2\sqrt{7}$ and $2\sqrt[3]{7}$ are not like radicals.

Example 1 Add or subtract. Assume that variables represent positive real numbers.

    a. $\sqrt{20} + 2\sqrt{45}$ **b.** $\sqrt[3]{54} - 5\sqrt[3]{16} + \sqrt[3]{2}$ **c.** $\sqrt{27x} - 2\sqrt{9x} + \sqrt{72x}$

    d. $\sqrt[3]{98} + \sqrt{98}$ **e.** $\sqrt[3]{48y^4} + \sqrt[3]{6y^4}$

Solution   First, simplify each radical. Then add or subtract any like radicals.

    a. $\sqrt{20} + 2\sqrt{45} = \sqrt{4 \cdot 5} + 2\sqrt{9 \cdot 5}$ Factor 20 and 45.

                     $= \sqrt{4} \cdot \sqrt{5} + 2 \cdot \sqrt{9} \cdot \sqrt{5}$ Use the product rule.

                     $= 2 \cdot \sqrt{5} + 2 \cdot 3 \cdot \sqrt{5}$ Simplify $\sqrt{4}$ and $\sqrt{9}$.

                     $= 2\sqrt{5} + 6\sqrt{5}$

                     $= 8\sqrt{5}$ Add like radicals.

    b. $\sqrt[3]{54} - 5\sqrt[3]{16} + \sqrt[3]{2}$

           $= \sqrt[3]{27} \cdot \sqrt[3]{2} - 5 \cdot \sqrt[3]{8} \cdot \sqrt[3]{2} + \sqrt[3]{2}$ Factor and use the product rule.

           $= 3 \cdot \sqrt[3]{2} - 5 \cdot 2 \cdot \sqrt[3]{2} + \sqrt[3]{2}$ Simplify $\sqrt[3]{27}$ and $\sqrt[3]{8}$.

           $= 3\sqrt[3]{2} - 10\sqrt[3]{2} + \sqrt[3]{2}$ Write $5 \cdot 2$ as 10.

           $= -6\sqrt[3]{2}$ Combine like radicals.

c. $\sqrt{27x} - 2\sqrt{9x} + \sqrt{72x}$

$\quad = \sqrt{9} \cdot \sqrt{3x} - 2 \cdot \sqrt{9} \cdot \sqrt{x} + \sqrt{36} \cdot \sqrt{2x}$ Factor and use the product rule.

$\quad = 3 \cdot \sqrt{3x} - 2 \cdot 3 \cdot \sqrt{x} + 6 \cdot \sqrt{2x}$ Simplify $\sqrt{9}$ and $\sqrt{36}$.

$\quad = 3\sqrt{3x} - 6\sqrt{x} + 6\sqrt{2x}$ Write $2 \cdot 3$ as 6.

> **HELPFUL HINT**
> None of these terms contain like radicals. We can simplify no further.

d. $\sqrt[3]{98} + \sqrt{98} = \sqrt[3]{98} + \sqrt{49} \cdot \sqrt{2}$ Factor and use the product rule.

$\quad\quad\quad\quad\quad = \sqrt[3]{98} + 7\sqrt{2}$ No further simplification is possible.

e. $\sqrt[3]{48y^4} + \sqrt[3]{6y^4} = \sqrt[3]{8y^3} \cdot \sqrt[3]{6y} + \sqrt[3]{y^3} \cdot \sqrt[3]{6y}$ Factor and use the product rule.

$\quad\quad\quad\quad\quad\quad = 2y\sqrt[3]{6y} + y\sqrt[3]{6y}$ Simplify $\sqrt[3]{8y^3}$ and $\sqrt[3]{y^3}$.

$\quad\quad\quad\quad\quad\quad = 3y\sqrt[3]{6y}$ Combine like radicals. ∎

Example 2   Add or subtract as indicated.

a. $\dfrac{\sqrt{45}}{4} - \dfrac{\sqrt{5}}{3}$ **b.** $\sqrt[3]{\dfrac{7x}{8}} + 2\sqrt[3]{7x}$

Solution   **a.** $\dfrac{\sqrt{45}}{4} - \dfrac{\sqrt{5}}{3} = \dfrac{3\sqrt{5}}{4} - \dfrac{\sqrt{5}}{3}$ To subtract, notice that the LCD is 12.

$\quad\quad\quad\quad\quad = \dfrac{3\sqrt{5} \cdot 3}{4 \cdot 3} - \dfrac{\sqrt{5} \cdot 4}{3 \cdot 4}$ Write each expression as an equivalent expression with a denominator of 12.

$\quad\quad\quad\quad\quad = \dfrac{9\sqrt{5}}{12} - \dfrac{4\sqrt{5}}{12}$ Multiply factors in the numerator and the denominator.

$\quad\quad\quad\quad\quad = \dfrac{5\sqrt{5}}{12}$ Subtract.

b. $\sqrt[3]{\dfrac{7x}{8}} + 2\sqrt[3]{7x} = \dfrac{\sqrt[3]{7x}}{\sqrt[3]{8}} + 2\sqrt[3]{7x}$ Apply the quotient rule for radicals.

$\quad\quad\quad\quad\quad\quad = \dfrac{\sqrt[3]{7x}}{2} + 2\sqrt[3]{7x}$ Simplify.

$\quad\quad\quad\quad\quad\quad = \dfrac{\sqrt[3]{7x}}{2} + \dfrac{2\sqrt[3]{7x} \cdot 2}{2}$ Write each expression as an equivalent expression with a denominator of 2.

$\quad\quad\quad\quad\quad\quad = \dfrac{\sqrt[3]{7x}}{2} + \dfrac{4\sqrt[3]{7x}}{2}$

$\quad\quad\quad\quad\quad\quad = \dfrac{5\sqrt[3]{7x}}{2}$ Add. ∎

2   We can multiply radical expressions by using many of the same properties used to multiply polynomial expressions. For instance, to multiply $\sqrt{2}(\sqrt{6} - 3\sqrt{2})$, we use the distributive property and multiply $\sqrt{2}$ by each term inside the parentheses.

$$\sqrt{2}(\sqrt{6} - 3\sqrt{2}) = \sqrt{2}(\sqrt{6}) - \sqrt{2}(3\sqrt{2}) \qquad \text{Use the distributive property.}$$

$$= \sqrt{2 \cdot 6} - 3\sqrt{2 \cdot 2}$$

$$= \sqrt{2 \cdot 2 \cdot 3} - 3 \cdot 2 \qquad \text{Use the product rule for radicals.}$$

$$= 2\sqrt{3} - 6$$

Example 3   Multiply.

a. $\sqrt{3}(5 + \sqrt{30})$ **b.** $(\sqrt{5} - \sqrt{6})(\sqrt{7} + 1)$ **c.** $(7\sqrt{x} + 5)(3\sqrt{x} - \sqrt{5})$

d. $(4\sqrt{3} \quad 1)^2$ **e.** $(\sqrt{2x} - 5)(\sqrt{2x} + 5)$

Solution   **a.** $\sqrt{3}(5 + \sqrt{30}) = \sqrt{3}(5) + \sqrt{3}(\sqrt{30})$

$$= 5\sqrt{3} + \sqrt{3 \cdot 30}$$

$$= 5\sqrt{3} + \sqrt{3 \cdot 3 \cdot 10}$$

$$= 5\sqrt{3} + 3\sqrt{10}$$

b.   To multiply, we can use the FOIL method.

$$\overset{\text{First}}{} \qquad \overset{\text{Outer}}{} \qquad \overset{\text{Inner}}{} \qquad \overset{\text{Last}}{}$$

$$(\sqrt{5} - \sqrt{6})(\sqrt{7} + 1) = \sqrt{5} \cdot \sqrt{7} + \sqrt{5} \cdot 1 - \sqrt{6} \cdot \sqrt{7} - \sqrt{6} \cdot 1$$

$$= \sqrt{35} + \sqrt{5} - \sqrt{42} - \sqrt{6}$$

c. $(7\sqrt{x} + 5)(3\sqrt{x} - \sqrt{5}) = 7\sqrt{x}(3\sqrt{x}) - 7\sqrt{x}(\sqrt{5}) + 5(3\sqrt{x}) - 5(\sqrt{5})$

$$= 21x - 7\sqrt{5x} + 15\sqrt{x} - 5\sqrt{5}$$

d. $(4\sqrt{3} - 1)^2 = (4\sqrt{3} - 1)(4\sqrt{3} - 1)$

$$= 4\sqrt{3}(4\sqrt{3}) - 4\sqrt{3}(1) - 1(4\sqrt{3}) - 1(-1)$$

$$= 16 \cdot 3 - 4\sqrt{3} - 4\sqrt{3} + 1$$

$$= 48 - 8\sqrt{3} + 1$$

$$= 49 - 8\sqrt{3}$$

e. $(\sqrt{2x} - 5)(\sqrt{2x} + 5) = \sqrt{2x} \cdot \sqrt{2x} + 5\sqrt{2x} - 5\sqrt{2x} - 5 \cdot 5$

$$= 2x - 25$$

MENTAL MATH

Simplify. Assume that all variables represent positive real numbers.

1. $2\sqrt{3} + 4\sqrt{3}$ **2.** $5\sqrt{7} + 3\sqrt{7}$ **3.** $8\sqrt{x} - 5\sqrt{x}$

4. $3\sqrt{y} + 10\sqrt{y}$ **5.** $7\sqrt[3]{x} + 5\sqrt[3]{x}$ **6.** $8\sqrt[3]{z} - 2\sqrt[3]{z}$

Exercise Set 7.4

Add or subtract. See Examples 1 and 2.

1. $\sqrt{8} - \sqrt{32}$

2. $\sqrt{27} - \sqrt{75}$

3. $2\sqrt{2x^3} + 4x\sqrt{8x}$

4. $3\sqrt{45x^3} + x\sqrt{5x}$

5. $2\sqrt{50} - 3\sqrt{125} + \sqrt{98}$

6. $4\sqrt{32} - \sqrt{18} + 2\sqrt{128}$

7. $\sqrt[3]{16x} - \sqrt[3]{54x}$

8. $2\sqrt[3]{3a^4} - 3a\sqrt[3]{81a}$

9. $\sqrt{9b^3} - \sqrt{25b^3} + \sqrt{49b^3}$

10. $\sqrt{4x^7} + 9x^2\sqrt{x^3} - 5x\sqrt{x^5}$

11. $\dfrac{5\sqrt{2}}{3} + \dfrac{2\sqrt{2}}{5}$

12. $\dfrac{\sqrt{3}}{2} + \dfrac{4\sqrt{3}}{3}$

13. $\sqrt[3]{\dfrac{11}{8}} - \dfrac{\sqrt[3]{11}}{6}$

14. $\dfrac{2\sqrt[3]{4}}{7} - \dfrac{\sqrt[3]{4}}{14}$

15. $\dfrac{\sqrt{20x}}{9} + \sqrt{\dfrac{5x}{9}}$

16. $\dfrac{3x\sqrt{7}}{5} + \sqrt{\dfrac{7x^2}{100}}$

17. $7\sqrt{9} - 7 + \sqrt{3}$

18. $\sqrt{16} - 5\sqrt{10} + 7$

19. $2 + 3\sqrt{y^2} - 6\sqrt{y^2} + 5$

20. $3\sqrt{7} - \sqrt[3]{x} + 4\sqrt{7} - 3\sqrt[3]{x}$

21. $3\sqrt{108} - 2\sqrt{18} - 3\sqrt{48}$

22. $-\sqrt{75} + \sqrt{12} - 3\sqrt{3}$

23. $-5\sqrt[3]{625} + \sqrt[3]{40}$

24. $-2\sqrt[3]{108} - \sqrt[3]{32}$

25. $\sqrt{9b^3} - \sqrt{25b^3} + \sqrt{16b^3}$

26. $\sqrt{4x^7y^5} + 9x^2\sqrt{x^3y^5} - 5xy\sqrt{x^5y^3}$

27. $5y\sqrt{8y} + 2\sqrt{50y^3}$

28. $3\sqrt{8x^2y^3} - 2x\sqrt{32y^3}$

29. $\sqrt[3]{54xy^3} - 5\sqrt[3]{2xy^3} + y\sqrt[3]{128x}$

30. $2\sqrt[3]{24x^3y^4} + 4x\sqrt[3]{81y^4}$

31. $6\sqrt[3]{11} + 8\sqrt{11} - 12\sqrt{11}$

32. $3\sqrt[3]{5} + 4\sqrt{5}$

33. $-2\sqrt[4]{x^7} + 3\sqrt[4]{16x^7}$

34. $6\sqrt[3]{24x^3} - 2\sqrt[3]{81x^3} - x\sqrt[3]{3}$

35. $\dfrac{4\sqrt{3}}{3} - \dfrac{\sqrt{12}}{3}$

36. $\dfrac{\sqrt{45}}{10} + \dfrac{7\sqrt{5}}{10}$

37. $\dfrac{\sqrt[3]{8x^4}}{7} + \dfrac{3x\sqrt[3]{x}}{7}$

38. $\dfrac{\sqrt[4]{48}}{5x} - \dfrac{2\sqrt[4]{3}}{10x}$

39. $\sqrt{\dfrac{28}{x^2}} + \sqrt{\dfrac{7}{4x^2}}$

40. $\dfrac{\sqrt{99}}{5x} - \sqrt{\dfrac{44}{x^2}}$

41. $\sqrt[3]{\dfrac{16}{27}} - \dfrac{\sqrt[3]{54}}{6}$

42. $\dfrac{\sqrt[3]{3}}{10} + \sqrt[3]{\dfrac{24}{125}}$

43. $-\dfrac{\sqrt[3]{2x^4}}{9} + \sqrt[3]{\dfrac{250x^4}{27}}$

44. $\dfrac{\sqrt[3]{y^5}}{8} + \dfrac{5y\sqrt[3]{y^2}}{4}$

△ **45.** Find the perimeter of the trapezoid.

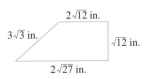

2√12 in.

3√3 in.   √12 in.

2√27 in.

△ **46.** Find the perimeter of the triangle.

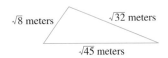

√8 meters   √32 meters

√45 meters

Multiply, and then simplify if possible. See Example 3.

47. $\sqrt{7}(\sqrt{5} + \sqrt{3})$

48. $\sqrt{5}(\sqrt{15} - \sqrt{35})$

49. $(\sqrt{5} - \sqrt{2})^2$

50. $(3x - \sqrt{2})(3x - \sqrt{2})$

51. $\sqrt{3x}(\sqrt{3} - \sqrt{x})$

52. $\sqrt{5y}(\sqrt{y} + \sqrt{5})$

53. $(2\sqrt{x} - 5)(3\sqrt{x} + 1)$

54. $(8\sqrt{y} + z)(4\sqrt{y} - 1)$

55. $(\sqrt[3]{a} - 4)(\sqrt[3]{a} + 5)$

56. $(\sqrt[3]{a} + 2)(\sqrt[3]{a} + 7)$

57. $6(\sqrt{2} - 2)$

58. $\sqrt{5}(6 - \sqrt{5})$

59. $\sqrt{2}(\sqrt{2} + x\sqrt{6})$

60. $\sqrt{3}(\sqrt{3} - 2\sqrt{5x})$

61. $(2\sqrt{7} + 3\sqrt{5})(\sqrt{7} - 2\sqrt{5})$

62. $(\sqrt{6} - 4\sqrt{2})(3\sqrt{6} + 1)$

63. $(\sqrt{x} - y)(\sqrt{x} + y)$

64. $(3\sqrt{x} + 2)(\sqrt{3x} - 2)$

65. $(\sqrt{3} + x)^2$

66. $(\sqrt{y} - 3x)^2$

67. $(\sqrt{5x} - 3\sqrt{2})(\sqrt{5x} - 3\sqrt{3})$

68. $(5\sqrt{3x} - \sqrt{y})(4\sqrt{x} + 1)$

69. $(\sqrt[3]{4} + 2)(\sqrt[3]{2} - 1)$

70. $(\sqrt[3]{3} + \sqrt[3]{2})(\sqrt[3]{9} - \sqrt[3]{4})$

71. $(\sqrt[3]{x} + 1)(\sqrt[3]{x} - 4\sqrt{x} + 7)$

72. $(\sqrt[3]{3x} + 3)(\sqrt[3]{2x} - 3x - 1)$

△ **73.** Baseboard needs to be installed around the perimeter of a rectangular room.

a. Find how much baseboard should be ordered by finding the perimeter of the room.

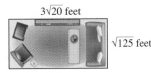

3√20 feet

√125 feet

b. Find the area of the room.

△ **74.** A border of wallpaper is to be used around the perimeter of the odd-shaped room shown.

   a. Find how much wallpaper border is needed by finding the perimeter of the room.

2√63 meters

2√27 meters

6√3 meters

7√7 meters

   b. Find the area of the room. (*Hint:* The area of a trapezoid is the product of half the height $6\sqrt{3}$ meters and the sum of the bases $2\sqrt{63}$ and $7\sqrt{7}$ meters.)

75. Explain how simplifying $2x + 3x$ is similar to simplifying $2\sqrt{x} + 3\sqrt{x}$.

76. Explain how multiplying $(x - 2)(x + 3)$ is similar to multiplying $(\sqrt{x} - \sqrt{2})(\sqrt{x} + 3)$.

REVIEW EXERCISES

Factor each numerator and denominator. Then simplify if possible. See Section 6.1.

77. $\dfrac{2x - 14}{2}$

78. $\dfrac{8x - 24y}{4}$

79. $\dfrac{7x - 7y}{x^2 - y^2}$

80. $\dfrac{x^3 - 8}{4x - 8}$

81. $\dfrac{6a^2b - 9ab}{3ab}$

82. $\dfrac{14r - 28r^2s^2}{7rs}$

83. $\dfrac{-4 + 2\sqrt{3}}{6}$

84. $\dfrac{-5 + 10\sqrt{7}}{5}$

7.5   RATIONALIZING DENOMINATORS AND NUMERATORS OF RADICAL EXPRESSIONS

CD-ROM   SSM

SSG   Video

▶ **OBJECTIVES**

1. Rationalize denominators.
2. Rationalize numerators.
3. Rationalize denominators or numerators having two terms.

1   Often in mathematics, it is helpful to write a radical expression such as $\dfrac{\sqrt{3}}{\sqrt{2}}$ either without a radical in the denominator or without a radical in the numerator. The process of writing this expression as an equivalent expression but without a radical in the denominator is called **rationalizing the denominator**. To rationalize the denominator of $\dfrac{\sqrt{3}}{\sqrt{2}}$, we use the fundamental principle of fractions and multiply the numerator and the denominator by $\sqrt{2}$. Recall that this is the same as multiplying by $\dfrac{\sqrt{2}}{\sqrt{2}}$, which simplifies to 1.

$$\frac{\sqrt{3}}{\sqrt{2}} = \frac{\sqrt{3} \cdot \sqrt{2}}{\sqrt{2} \cdot \sqrt{2}} = \frac{\sqrt{6}}{\sqrt{4}} = \frac{\sqrt{6}}{2}$$

Example 1   Rationalize the denominator of each expression.

   a. $\dfrac{2}{\sqrt{5}}$ **b.** $\dfrac{2\sqrt{16}}{\sqrt{9x}}$ **c.** $\sqrt[3]{\dfrac{1}{2}}$

Solution   **a.** To rationalize the denominator, we multiply the numerator and denominator by a factor that makes the radicand in the denominator a perfect square.

$$\frac{2}{\sqrt{5}} = \frac{2 \cdot \sqrt{5}}{\sqrt{5} \cdot \sqrt{5}} = \frac{2\sqrt{5}}{5}$$ The denominator is now rationalized.

b. First, we simplify the radicals and then rationalize the denominator.

$$\frac{2\sqrt{16}}{\sqrt{9x}} = \frac{2(4)}{3\sqrt{x}} = \frac{8}{3\sqrt{x}}$$

To rationalize the denominator, multiply the numerator and denominator by $\sqrt{x}$. Then

$$\frac{8}{3\sqrt{x}} = \frac{8 \cdot \sqrt{x}}{3\sqrt{x} \cdot \sqrt{x}} = \frac{8\sqrt{x}}{3x}$$

c. $\sqrt[3]{\frac{1}{2}} = \frac{\sqrt[3]{1}}{\sqrt[3]{2}} = \frac{1}{\sqrt[3]{2}}$. Now we rationalize the denominator. Since $\sqrt[3]{2}$ is a cube root, we want to multiply by a value that will make the radicand 2 a perfect cube. If we multiply by $\sqrt[3]{2^2}$, we get $\sqrt[3]{2^3} = \sqrt[3]{8} = 2$.

$$\frac{1 \cdot \sqrt[3]{2^2}}{\sqrt[3]{2} \cdot \sqrt[3]{2^2}} = \frac{\sqrt[3]{4}}{\sqrt[3]{2^3}} = \frac{\sqrt[3]{4}}{2} \quad \text{Multiply numerator and denominator by } \sqrt[3]{2^2} \text{ and then simplify.}$$

Example 2   Rationalize the denominator of $\sqrt{\dfrac{7x}{3y}}$.

Solution $\sqrt{\dfrac{7x}{3y}} = \dfrac{\sqrt{7x}}{\sqrt{3y}}$ Use the quotient rule. No radical may be simplified further.

$$= \frac{\sqrt{7x} \cdot \sqrt{3y}}{\sqrt{3y} \cdot \sqrt{3y}}$$ Multiply numerator and denominator by $\sqrt{3y}$ so that the radicand in the denominator is a perfect square.

$$= \frac{\sqrt{21xy}}{3y}$$ Use the product rule in the numerator and denominator. Remember that $\sqrt{3y} \cdot \sqrt{3y} = 3y$.

Example 3   Rationalize the denominator of $\dfrac{\sqrt[4]{x}}{\sqrt[4]{81y^5}}$.

Solution   First, simplify each radical if possible.

$$\frac{\sqrt[4]{x}}{\sqrt[4]{81y^5}} = \frac{\sqrt[4]{x}}{\sqrt[4]{81y^4} \cdot \sqrt[4]{y}}$$ Use the product rule in the denominator.

$$= \frac{\sqrt[4]{x}}{3y\sqrt[4]{y}}$$ Write $\sqrt[4]{81y^4}$ as $3y$.

$$= \frac{\sqrt[4]{x} \cdot \sqrt[4]{y^3}}{3y\sqrt[4]{y} \cdot \sqrt[4]{y^3}}$$ Multiply numerator and denominator by $\sqrt[4]{y^3}$ so that the radicand in the denominator is a perfect fourth power.

$$= \frac{\sqrt[4]{xy^3}}{3y\sqrt[4]{y^4}}$$ Use the product rule in the numerator and denominator.

$$= \frac{\sqrt[4]{xy^3}}{3y^2}$$ In the denominator, $\sqrt[4]{y^4} = y$ and $3y \cdot y = 3y^2$.

2

As mentioned earlier, it is also often helpful to write an expression such as $\dfrac{\sqrt{3}}{\sqrt{2}}$ as an equivalent expression without a radical in the numerator. This process is called **rationalizing the numerator**. To rationalize the numerator of $\dfrac{\sqrt{3}}{\sqrt{2}}$, we multiply the numerator and the denominator by $\sqrt{3}$.

$$\frac{\sqrt{3}}{\sqrt{2}} = \frac{\sqrt{3} \cdot \sqrt{3}}{\sqrt{2} \cdot \sqrt{3}} = \frac{\sqrt{9}}{\sqrt{6}} = \frac{3}{\sqrt{6}}$$

Example 4   Rationalize the numerator of $\dfrac{\sqrt{7}}{\sqrt{45}}$.

Solution   First we simplify $\sqrt{45}$.

$$\frac{\sqrt{7}}{\sqrt{45}} = \frac{\sqrt{7}}{\sqrt{9 \cdot 5}} = \frac{\sqrt{7}}{3\sqrt{5}}$$

Next we rationalize the numerator by multiplying the numerator and the denominator by $\sqrt{7}$.

$$\frac{\sqrt{7}}{3\sqrt{5}} = \frac{\sqrt{7} \cdot \sqrt{7}}{3\sqrt{5} \cdot \sqrt{7}} = \frac{7}{3\sqrt{5} \cdot 7} = \frac{7}{3\sqrt{35}}$$

Example 5   Rationalize the numerator of $\dfrac{\sqrt[3]{2x^2}}{\sqrt[3]{5y}}$.

Solution   The numerator and the denominator of this expression are already simplified. To rationalize the numerator, $\sqrt[3]{2x^2}$, we multiply the numerator and denominator by a factor that will make the radicand a perfect cube. If we multiply $\sqrt[3]{2x^2}$ by $\sqrt[3]{4x}$, we get $\sqrt[3]{8x^3} = 2x$.

$$\frac{\sqrt[3]{2x^2}}{\sqrt[3]{5y}} = \frac{\sqrt[3]{2x^2} \cdot \sqrt[3]{4x}}{\sqrt[3]{5y} \cdot \sqrt[3]{4x}} = \frac{\sqrt[3]{8x^3}}{\sqrt[3]{20xy}} - \frac{2x}{\sqrt[3]{20xy}}$$

3

Remember the product of the sum and difference of two terms?

$$(a + b)(a - b) = a^2 - b^2$$

These two expressions are called conjugates of each other.

To rationalize a numerator or denominator that is a sum or difference of two terms, we use conjugates. To see how and why this works, let's rationalize the denominator of the expression $\dfrac{5}{\sqrt{3} - 2}$. To do so, we multiply both the numerator and the denominator by $\sqrt{3} + 2$, the **conjugate** of the denominator $\sqrt{3} - 2$, and see what happens.

$$\frac{5}{\sqrt{3} - 2} = \frac{5(\sqrt{3} + 2)}{(\sqrt{3} - 2)(\sqrt{3} + 2)}$$

$$= \frac{5(\sqrt{3} + 2)}{(\sqrt{3})^2 - 2^2} \qquad \text{Multiply the sum and difference of two terms: } (a + b)(a - b) = a^2 - b^2.$$

$$= \frac{5(\sqrt{3} + 2)}{3 - 4}$$

$$= \frac{5(\sqrt{3} + 2)}{-1}$$

$$= -5(\sqrt{3} + 2) \quad \text{or} \quad -5\sqrt{3} - 10$$

Notice in the denominator that the product of $(\sqrt{3} - 2)$ and its conjugate, $(\sqrt{3} + 2)$, is -1. In general, the product of an expression and its conjugate will contain no radical terms. This is why, when rationalizing a denominator or a numerator containing two terms, we multiply by its conjugate. Examples of conjugates are

$$\sqrt{a} - \sqrt{b} \qquad \text{and} \qquad \sqrt{a} + \sqrt{b}$$

$$x + \sqrt{y} \qquad \text{and} \qquad x - \sqrt{y}$$

Example 6   Rationalize each denominator.

a. $\dfrac{2}{3\sqrt{2} + 4}$ **b.** $\dfrac{\sqrt{6} + 2}{\sqrt{5} - \sqrt{3}}$ **c.** $\dfrac{2\sqrt{m}}{3\sqrt{x} + \sqrt{m}}$

Solution   **a.** Multiply the numerator and denominator by the conjugate of the denominator, $3\sqrt{2} + 4$.

$$\frac{2}{3\sqrt{2} + 4} = \frac{2(3\sqrt{2} - 4)}{(3\sqrt{2} + 4)(3\sqrt{2} - 4)}$$

$$= \frac{2(3\sqrt{2} - 4)}{(3\sqrt{2})^2 - 4^2}$$

$$= \frac{2(3\sqrt{2} - 4)}{18 - 16}$$

$$= \frac{2(3\sqrt{2} - 4)}{2}, \quad \text{or} \quad 3\sqrt{2} - 4$$

It is often helpful to leave a numerator in factored form to help determine whether the expression can be simplified.

b. Multiply the numerator and denominator by the conjugate of $\sqrt{5} - \sqrt{3}$.

$$\frac{\sqrt{6} + 2}{\sqrt{5} - \sqrt{3}} = \frac{(\sqrt{6} + 2)(\sqrt{5} + \sqrt{3})}{(\sqrt{5} - \sqrt{3})(\sqrt{5} + \sqrt{3})}$$

$$= \frac{\sqrt{6}\sqrt{5} + \sqrt{6}\sqrt{3} + 2\sqrt{5} + 2\sqrt{3}}{(\sqrt{5})^2 - (\sqrt{3})^2}$$

$$= \frac{\sqrt{30} + \sqrt{18} + 2\sqrt{5} + 2\sqrt{3}}{5 - 3}$$

$$= \frac{\sqrt{30} + 3\sqrt{2} + 2\sqrt{5} + 2\sqrt{3}}{2}$$

c. Multiply by the conjugate of $3\sqrt{x} + \sqrt{m}$ to eliminate the radicals from the denominator.

$$\frac{2\sqrt{m}}{3\sqrt{x} + \sqrt{m}} = \frac{2\sqrt{m}(3\sqrt{x} - \sqrt{m})}{(3\sqrt{x} + \sqrt{m})(3\sqrt{x} - \sqrt{m})} = \frac{6\sqrt{mx} - 2m}{(3\sqrt{x})^2 - (\sqrt{m})^2}$$

$$= \frac{6\sqrt{mx} - 2m}{9x - m}$$

Example 7 Rationalize the numerator of $\dfrac{\sqrt{x} + 2}{5}$.

Solution We multiply the numerator and the denominator by the conjugate of the numerator, $\sqrt{x} + 2$.

$$\frac{\sqrt{x} + 2}{5} = \frac{(\sqrt{x} + 2)(\sqrt{x} - 2)}{5(\sqrt{x} - 2)} \qquad \text{Multiply by } \sqrt{x} - 2 \text{, the conjugate of } \sqrt{x} + 2.$$

$$= \frac{(\sqrt{x})^2 - 2^2}{5(\sqrt{x} - 2)} \qquad (a + b)(a - b) = a^2 - b^2.$$

$$= \frac{x - 4}{5(\sqrt{x} - 2)}$$

MENTAL MATH

Find the conjugate of each expression.

1. $\sqrt{2} + x$ **2.** $\sqrt{3} + y$ **3.** $5 - \sqrt{a}$

4. $6 - \sqrt{b}$ **5.** $7\sqrt{5} + 8\sqrt{x}$ **6.** $9\sqrt{2} - 6\sqrt{y}$

Exercise Set 7.5

Rationalize each denominator. See Examples 1 through 3.

1. $\dfrac{\sqrt{2}}{\sqrt{7}}$ **2.** $\dfrac{\sqrt{3}}{\sqrt{2}}$ **3.** $\sqrt{\dfrac{1}{5}}$ **4.** $\sqrt{\dfrac{1}{2}}$

5. $\sqrt[3]{\dfrac{3}{4}}$

6. $\sqrt[3]{\dfrac{2}{9}}$

7. $\dfrac{4}{\sqrt[3]{3}}$

8. $\dfrac{6}{\sqrt[3]{9}}$

9. $\dfrac{3}{\sqrt{8x}}$

10. $\dfrac{5}{\sqrt{27a}}$

11. $\dfrac{3}{\sqrt[3]{4x^2}}$

12. $\dfrac{5}{\sqrt[3]{3y}}$

13. $\sqrt{\dfrac{4}{x}}$

14. $\sqrt{\dfrac{25}{y}}$

15. $\dfrac{9}{\sqrt{3a}}$

16. $\dfrac{x}{\sqrt{5}}$

17. $\dfrac{3}{\sqrt[3]{2}}$

18. $\dfrac{5}{\sqrt[3]{9}}$

19. $\dfrac{2\sqrt{3}}{\sqrt{7}}$

20. $\dfrac{-5\sqrt{2}}{\sqrt{11}}$

21. $\sqrt{\dfrac{2x}{5y}}$

22. $\sqrt{\dfrac{13a}{2b}}$

23. $\sqrt[4]{\dfrac{81}{8}}$

24. $\sqrt[4]{\dfrac{1}{9}}$

25. $\sqrt[4]{\dfrac{16}{9x^7}}$

26. $\sqrt[5]{\dfrac{32}{m^6 n^{13}}}$

27. $\dfrac{5a}{\sqrt[5]{8a^9 b^{11}}}$

28. $\dfrac{9y}{\sqrt[4]{4y^9}}$

Rationalize each numerator. See Examples 4 and 5.

29. $\sqrt{\dfrac{5}{3}}$

30. $\sqrt{\dfrac{3}{2}}$

31. $\sqrt{\dfrac{18}{5}}$

32. $\sqrt{\dfrac{12}{7}}$

33. $\dfrac{\sqrt{4x}}{7}$ $\quad \sqrt{x}$

34. $\dfrac{\sqrt{3x^5}}{6}$

35. $\dfrac{\sqrt[3]{5y^2}}{\sqrt[3]{4x}}$

36. $\dfrac{\sqrt[3]{4x}}{\sqrt[3]{z^4}}$

37. $\sqrt{\dfrac{2}{5}}$

38. $\sqrt{\dfrac{3}{7}}$

39. $\dfrac{\sqrt{2x}}{11}$

40. $\dfrac{\sqrt{y}}{7}$

41. $\sqrt[3]{\dfrac{7}{8}}$

42. $\sqrt[3]{\dfrac{25}{2}}$

43. $\dfrac{\sqrt[3]{3x^5}}{10}$

44. $\sqrt[3]{\dfrac{9y}{7}}$

45. $\sqrt{\dfrac{18x^4 y^6}{3z}}$

46. $\sqrt{\dfrac{8x^5 y}{2z}}$

47. When rationalizing the denominator of $\dfrac{\sqrt{5}}{\sqrt{7}}$, explain why both the numerator and the denominator must be multiplied by $\sqrt{7}$.

48. When rationalizing the numerator of $\dfrac{\sqrt{5}}{\sqrt{7}}$, explain why both the numerator and the denominator must be multiplied by $\sqrt{5}$.

Rationalize each denominator. See Example 6.

49. $\dfrac{6}{2 - \sqrt{7}}$

50. $\dfrac{3}{\sqrt{7} - 4}$

51. $\dfrac{-7}{\sqrt{x} - 3}$

52. $\dfrac{-8}{\sqrt{y} + 4}$

53. $\dfrac{\sqrt{2} - \sqrt{3}}{\sqrt{2} + \sqrt{3}}$

54. $\dfrac{\sqrt{3} + \sqrt{4}}{\sqrt{2} + \sqrt{3}}$

55. $\dfrac{\sqrt{a} + 1}{2\sqrt{a} - \sqrt{b}}$

56. $\dfrac{2\sqrt{a} - 3}{2\sqrt{a} - \sqrt{b}}$

57. $\dfrac{8}{1 + \sqrt{10}}$

58. $\dfrac{-3}{\sqrt{6} - 2}$

59. $\dfrac{\sqrt{x}}{\sqrt{x} + \sqrt{y}}$

60. $\dfrac{2\sqrt{a}}{2\sqrt{x} - \sqrt{y}}$

61. $\dfrac{2\sqrt{3} + \sqrt{6}}{4\sqrt{3} - \sqrt{6}}$

62. $\dfrac{4\sqrt{5} + \sqrt{2}}{2\sqrt{5} - \sqrt{2}}$

Rationalize each numerator. See Example 7.

63. $\dfrac{2 - \sqrt{11}}{6}$

64. $\dfrac{\sqrt{15} + 1}{2}$

65. $\dfrac{2 - \sqrt{7}}{-5}$

66. $\dfrac{\sqrt{5} + 2}{\sqrt{2}}$

67. $\dfrac{\sqrt{x} + 3}{\sqrt{x}}$

68. $\dfrac{5 + \sqrt{2}}{\sqrt{2x}}$

69. $\dfrac{\sqrt{2} - 1}{\sqrt{2} + 1}$

70. $\dfrac{\sqrt{8} - \sqrt{3}}{\sqrt{2} + \sqrt{3}}$

71. $\dfrac{\sqrt{x} + 1}{\sqrt{x} - 1}$

72. $\dfrac{\sqrt{x} + \sqrt{y}}{\sqrt{x} - \sqrt{y}}$

△ **73.** The formula of the radius of a sphere r with surface area A is given by the formula

$$r = \sqrt{\dfrac{A}{4\pi}}$$

Rationalize the denominator of the radical expression in this formula.

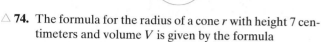

△ **74.** The formula for the radius of a cone r with height 7 centimeters and volume V is given by the formula

$$r = \sqrt{\frac{3V}{7\pi}}$$

Rationalize the numerator of the radical expression in this formula.

75. Explain why rationalizing the denominator does not change the value of the original expression.

76. Explain why rationalizing the numerator does not change the value of the original expression.

REVIEW EXERCISES

Solve each equation. See Sections 2.1 and 5.8.

77. $2x - 7 = 3(x - 4)$ **78.** $9x - 4 = 7(x - 2)$

79. $(x - 6)(2x + 1) = 0$ **80.** $(y + 2)(5y + 4) = 0$

81. $x^2 - 8x = -12$ **82.** $x^3 = x$

7.6 RADICAL EQUATIONS AND PROBLEM SOLVING

CD-ROM   SSM

SSG   Video

▶ **OBJECTIVES**

1. Solve equations that contain radical expressions.
2. Use the Pythagorean theorem to model problems.

1 In this section, we present techniques to solve equations containing radical expressions such as

$$\sqrt{2x - 3} = 9$$

We use the power rule to help us solve these radical equations.

POWER RULE

If both sides of an equation are raised to the same power, **all** solutions of the original equation are **among** the solutions of the new equation.

This property *does not* say that raising both sides of an equation to a power yields an equivalent equation. A solution of the new equation *may or may not* be a solution of the original equation. Thus, *each solution of the new equation must be checked* to make sure it is a solution of the original equation. Recall that a proposed solution that is not a solution of the original equation is called an **extraneous solution**.

Example 1   Solve $\sqrt{2x - 3} = 9$.

Solution   We use the power rule to square both sides of the equation to eliminate the radical.

$$\sqrt{2x - 3} = 9$$
$$(\sqrt{2x - 3})^2 = 9^2$$
$$2x - 3 = 81$$
$$2x = 84$$
$$x = 42$$

Now we, check the solution in the original equation.

Check:
$$\sqrt{2x - 3} = 9$$
$$\sqrt{2(42) - 3} \stackrel{?}{=} 9 \qquad \text{Let } x = 42.$$
$$\sqrt{84 - 3} \stackrel{?}{=} 9$$
$$\sqrt{81} \stackrel{?}{=} 9$$
$$9 = 9 \qquad \text{True.}$$

The solution checks, so we conclude that the solution is 42.

To solve a radical equation, first isolate a radical on one side of the equation.

Example 2   Solve $\sqrt{-10x - 1} + 3x = 0$.

Solution   First, isolate the radical on one side of the equation. To do this, we subtract $3x$ from both sides.

$$\sqrt{-10x - 1} + 3x = 0$$
$$\sqrt{-10x - 1} + 3x - 3x = 0 - 3x$$
$$\sqrt{-10x - 1} = -3x$$

Next we use the power rule to eliminate the radical.

$$\left(\sqrt{-10x - 1}\right)^2 = (-3x)^2$$
$$-10x - 1 = 9x^2$$

Since this is a quadratic equation, we can set the equation equal to 0 and try to solve by factoring.

$$9x^2 + 10x + 1 = 0$$
$$(9x + 1)(x + 1) = 0 \qquad \text{Factor.}$$
$$9x + 1 = 0 \quad \text{or} \quad x + 1 = 0 \qquad \text{Set each factor equal to 0.}$$
$$x = -\frac{1}{9} \qquad\qquad x = -1$$

Check: Let $x = -\frac{1}{9}$.

$$\sqrt{-10x - 1} + 3x = 0$$
$$\sqrt{-10\left(-\frac{1}{9}\right) - 1} + 3\left(-\frac{1}{9}\right) \stackrel{?}{=} 0$$
$$\sqrt{\frac{10}{9} - \frac{9}{9}} - \frac{3}{9} \stackrel{?}{=} 0$$
$$\sqrt{\frac{1}{9}} - \frac{1}{3} \stackrel{?}{=} 0$$
$$\frac{1}{3} - \frac{1}{3} = 0 \qquad \text{True.}$$

Let $x = -1$.

$$\sqrt{-10x - 1} + 3x = 0$$
$$\sqrt{-10(-1) - 1} + 3(-1) \stackrel{?}{=} 0$$
$$\sqrt{10 - 1} - 3 \stackrel{?}{=} 0$$
$$\sqrt{9} - 3 \stackrel{?}{=} 0$$
$$3 - 3 = 0 \qquad \text{True.}$$

Both solutions check. The solutions are $-\frac{1}{9}$ and -1.

The following steps may be used to solve a radical equation.

SOLVING A RADICAL EQUATION

Step 1: Isolate one radical on one side of the equation.
Step 2: Raise each side of the equation to a power equal to the index of the radical and simplify.
Step 3: If the equation still contains a radical term, repeat Steps 1 and 2. If not, solve the equation.
Step 4: Check all proposed solutions in the original equation.

Example 3 Solve $\sqrt[3]{x + 1} + 5 = 3$.

Solution First we isolate the radical by subtracting 5 from both sides of the equation.

$$\sqrt[3]{x + 1} + 5 = 3$$
$$\sqrt[3]{x + 1} = -2$$

Next we raise both sides of the equation to the third power to eliminate the radical.

$$\left(\sqrt[3]{x + 1}\right)^3 = (-2)^3$$
$$x + 1 = -8$$
$$x = -9$$

The solution checks in the original equation, so the solution is -9. ▄

Example 4 Solve $\sqrt{4 - x} = x - 2$.

Solution

$$\sqrt{4 - x} = x - 2$$
$$\left(\sqrt{4 - x}\right)^2 = (x - 2)^2$$
$$4 - x = x^2 - 4x + 4$$
$$x^2 - 3x = 0 \qquad \text{Write the quadratic equation in standard form.}$$
$$x(x - 3) = 0 \qquad \text{Factor.}$$
$$x = 0 \quad \text{or} \quad x - 3 = 0 \qquad \text{Set each factor equal to 0.}$$
$$x = 3$$

Check:

$$\sqrt{4 - x} = x - 2 \qquad\qquad \sqrt{4 - x} = x - 2$$
$$\sqrt{4 - 0} \stackrel{?}{=} 0 - 2 \quad \text{Let } x = 0. \qquad \sqrt{4 - 3} \stackrel{?}{=} 3 - 2 \quad \text{Let } x = 3.$$
$$2 = -2 \quad \text{False.} \qquad\qquad 1 = 1 \quad \text{True.}$$

The proposed solution 3 checks, but 0 does not. Since 0 is an extraneous solution, the only solution is 3. ▄

> **HELPFUL HINT**
> In Example 4, notice that $(x - 2)^2 = x^2 - 4x + 4$. Make sure binomials are squared correctly.

Example 5   Solve $\sqrt{2x + 5} + \sqrt{2x} = 3$.

Solution   We get one radical alone by subtracting $\sqrt{2x}$ from both sides.

$$\sqrt{2x + 5} + \sqrt{2x} = 3$$
$$\sqrt{2x + 5} = 3 - \sqrt{2x}$$

Now we use the power rule to begin eliminating the radicals. First we square both sides.

$$\left(\sqrt{2x + 5}\right)^2 = \left(3 - \sqrt{2x}\right)^2$$

$$2x + 5 = 9 - 6\sqrt{2x} + 2x \qquad \text{Multiply}$$
$$\left(3 - \sqrt{2x}\right)\left(3 - \sqrt{2x}\right).$$

There is still a radical in the equation, so we get the radical alone again. Then we square both sides.

$$2x + 5 = 9 - 6\sqrt{2x} + 2x \qquad \textit{Get the radical alone.}$$

$$6\sqrt{2x} = 4$$

$$36(2x) = 16 \qquad \textit{Square both sides of the equation to eliminate the radical.}$$

$$72x = 16 \qquad \textit{Multiply.}$$

$$x = \frac{16}{72} \qquad \textit{Solve.}$$

$$x = \frac{2}{9} \qquad \textit{Simplify.}$$

The proposed solution, $\frac{2}{9}$, checks in the original equation. The solution is $\frac{2}{9}$.

HELPFUL HINT
Make sure expressions are squared correctly. In Example 5, we squared $\left(3 - \sqrt{2x}\right)$ as

$$\left(3 - \sqrt{2x}\right)^2 = \left(3 - \sqrt{2x}\right)\left(3 - \sqrt{2x}\right)$$
$$= 3 \cdot 3 - 3\sqrt{2x} - 3\sqrt{2x} + \sqrt{2x} \cdot \sqrt{2x}$$
$$= 9 - 6\sqrt{2x} + 2x$$

---

2   Recall that the Pythagorean theorem states that in a right triangle, the length of the hypotenuse squared equals the sum of the lengths of each of the legs squared.

PYTHAGOREAN THEOREM

If a and b are the lengths of the legs of a right triangle and c is the length of the hypotenuse, then $a^2 + b^2 = c^2$.

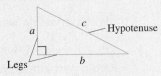

△ **Example 6**   Find the length of the unknown leg of the right triangle.

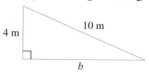

Solution   In the formula $a^2 + b^2 = c^2$, c is the hypotenuse. Here, $c = 10$, the length of the hypotenuse, and $a = 4$. We solve for b. Then $a^2 + b^2 = c^2$ becomes

$$4^2 + b^2 = 10^2$$
$$16 + b^2 = 100$$
$$b^2 = 84 \qquad \text{Subtract 16 from both sides.}$$

Since b is a length and thus is positive, we have that

$$b = \sqrt{84} = \sqrt{4 \cdot 21} = 2\sqrt{21}$$

The unknown leg of the triangle is $2\sqrt{21}$ meters long.

△ **Example 7**   **CALCULATING PLACEMENT OF A WIRE**

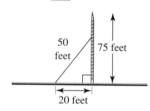

A 50-foot supporting wire is to be attached to a 75-foot antenna. Because of surrounding buildings, sidewalks, and roadways, the wire must be anchored exactly 20 feet from the base of the antenna.

a. How high from the base of the antenna is the wire attached?

b. Local regulations require that a supporting wire be attached at a height no less than $\dfrac{3}{5}$ of the total height of the antenna. From part **a**, have local regulations been met?

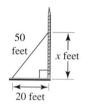

Solution   1. UNDERSTAND. Read and reread the problem. From the diagram we notice that a right triangle is formed with hypotenuse 50 feet and one leg 20 feet. Let x be the height from the base of the antenna to the attached wire.

2. TRANSLATE. Use the Pythagorean theorem.

$$a^2 + b^2 = c^2$$
$$20^2 + x^2 = 50^2 \qquad a = 20, c = 50$$

3. SOLVE. $20^2 + x^2 = 50^2$

$$400 + x^2 = 2500$$
$$x^2 = 2100 \qquad \text{Subtract 400 from both sides.}$$
$$x = \sqrt{2100}$$
$$= 10\sqrt{21}$$

4. INTERPRET. *Check* the work and *state* the solution.

   a. The wire is attached exactly $10\sqrt{21}$ feet from the base of the pole, or approximately 45.8 feet.

   b. The supporting wire must be attached at a height no less than $\dfrac{3}{5}$ of the total height of the antenna. This height is $\dfrac{3}{5}$ (75 feet), or 45 feet. Since we know from part **a** that the wire is to be attached at a height of approximately 45.8 feet, local regulations have been met.

GRAPHING CALCULATOR EXPLORATIONS

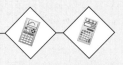

We can use a graphing calculator to solve radical equations. For example, to use a graphing calculator to approximate the solutions of the equation solved in Example 4, we graph the following.

$$Y_1 = \sqrt{4 - x} \quad \text{and} \quad Y_2 = x - 2$$

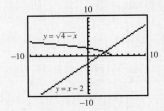

The x-value of the point of intersection is the solution. Use the Intersect feature or the Zoom and Trace features of your graphing calculator to see that the solution is 3.

Use a graphing calculator to solve each radical equation. Round all solutions to the nearest hundredth.

1. $\sqrt{x + 7} = x$
2. $\sqrt{3x + 5} = 2x$
3. $\sqrt{2x + 1} = \sqrt{2x} + 2$
4. $\sqrt{10x - 1} = \sqrt{-10x + 10} - 1$
5. $1.2x = \sqrt{3.1x + 5}$
6. $\sqrt{1.9x^2 - 2.2} = -0.8x + 3$

SPOTLIGHT ON DECISION MAKING

Suppose you are a psychologist studying a person's ability to recognize patterns. You theorize that IQ is linked to pattern-recognition ability and design a research study using human subjects to test your theory. As part of your study, you have decided to form three groups of test subjects based roughly on IQ. Group A will consist of subjects having IQ's under 90, Group B will consist of subjects having IQ's from 90 to 105, and Group C will consist of subjects having IQ's over 105.

While preparing for your research study, you came across the findings of another psychologist suggesting that the number S of nonsense syllables that a person can repeat consecutively depends on his or her IQ score I according to the equation $S = 2\sqrt{I} - 9$. Because administering IQ tests can be time-consuming and because your groupings by IQ need only be approximate, you decide to use this equation as a quick way to assign test subjects to Groups A, B, and C. Each subject is individually screened by listening to a string of 20 random nonsense syllables and then repeating as many as possible. The results for the first 5 test subjects are listed in the table. For each subject, decide to which group—A, B, or C—the subject should be assigned.

TEST SUBJECT SCREENING

Subject	S—the number of Nonsense Syllables Successfully Repeated
1	11
2	13
3	9
4	12
5	10

Exercise Set 7.6

Solve. See Examples 1 and 2.

1. $\sqrt{2x} = 4$

2. $\sqrt{3x} = 3$

3. $\sqrt{x - 3} = 2$

4. $\sqrt{x + 1} = 5$

5. $\sqrt{2x} = -4$

6. $\sqrt{5x} = -5$

7. $\sqrt{4x - 3} - 5 = 0$

8. $\sqrt{x - 3} - 1 = 0$

9. $\sqrt{2x - 3} - 2 = 1$

10. $\sqrt{3x + 3} - 4 = 8$

Solve. See Example 3.

11. $\sqrt[3]{6x} = -3$

12. $\sqrt[3]{4x} = -2$

13. $\sqrt[3]{x - 2} - 3 = 0$

14. $\sqrt[3]{2x - 6} - 4 = 0$

Solve. See Examples 4 and 5.

15. $\sqrt{13 - x} = x - 1$

16. $\sqrt{2x - 3} = 3 - x$

17. $x - \sqrt{4 - 3x} = -8$

18. $2x + \sqrt{x + 1} = 8$

19. $\sqrt{y + 5} = 2 - \sqrt{y - 4}$

20. $\sqrt{x + 3} + \sqrt{x - 5} = 3$

21. $\sqrt{x - 3} + \sqrt{x + 2} = 5$

22. $\sqrt{2x - 4} - \sqrt{3x + 4} = -2$

Solve. See Examples 1 through 5.

23. $\sqrt{3x - 2} = 5$

24. $\sqrt{5x - 4} = 9$

25. $-\sqrt{2x} + 4 = -6$

26. $-\sqrt{3x + 9} = -12$

27. $\sqrt{3x + 1} + 2 = 0$

28. $\sqrt{3x + 1} - 2 = 0$

29. $\sqrt[4]{4x + 1} - 2 = 0$

30. $\sqrt[4]{2x - 9} - 3 = 0$

31. $\sqrt{4x - 3} = 7$

32. $\sqrt{3x + 9} = 6$

33. $\sqrt[3]{6x - 3} - 3 = 0$

34. $\sqrt[3]{3x} + 4 = 7$

35. $\sqrt[3]{2x - 3} - 2 = -5$

36. $\sqrt[3]{x - 4} - 5 = -7$

37. $\sqrt{x + 4} = \sqrt{2x - 5}$

38. $\sqrt{3y + 6} = \sqrt{7y - 6}$

39. $x - \sqrt{1 - x} = -5$

40. $x - \sqrt{x - 2} = 4$

41. $\sqrt[3]{-6x - 1} = \sqrt[3]{-2x - 5}$

42. $x + \sqrt{x + 5} = 7$

43. $\sqrt{5x - 1} - \sqrt{x + 2} = 3$

44. $\sqrt{2x - 1} - 4 = -\sqrt{x - 4}$

45. $\sqrt{2x - 1} = \sqrt{1 - 2x}$

46. $\sqrt{7x - 4} = \sqrt{4 - 7x}$

47. $\sqrt{3x + 4} - 1 = \sqrt{2x + 1}$

48. $\sqrt{x - 2} + 3 = \sqrt{4x + 1}$

49. $\sqrt{y + 3} - \sqrt{y - 3} = 1$

50. $\sqrt{x + 1} - \sqrt{x - 1} = 2$

51. What is wrong with the following steps?

$$\sqrt{2x + 5} + \sqrt{4 - x} = 8$$
$$\left(\sqrt{2x + 5} + \sqrt{4 - x}\right)^2 = 8^2$$
$$(2x + 5) + (4 - x) = 64$$
$$x + 9 = 64$$
$$x = 55$$

52. How can you immediately tell that the equation $\sqrt{2y + 3} = -4$ has no real solution?

Find the length of the unknown side of each triangle. See Example 6.

△ **53.**

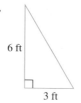

6 ft

3 ft

△ **54.**   7 in.

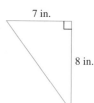

8 in.

△ **55.**

3 m

7 m

△ **56.**   4 cm

7 cm

Find the length of each unknown side of each triangle. Give the exact length and a one-decimal-place approximation. See Example 6.

△ **57.**

9 m

$11\sqrt{5}$ m

△ **58.**

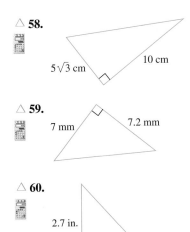

5√3 cm   10 cm

△ **59.**

7 mm   7.2 mm

△ **60.**

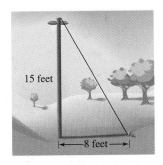

2.7 in.

2.3 in.

Solve. See Example 7. Give exact answers and two-decimal-place approximations where appropriate.

△ **61.** A wire is needed to support a vertical pole 15 feet high. The cable will be anchored to a stake 8 feet from the base of the pole. How much cable is needed?

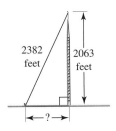

15 feet

8 feet

△ **62.** The tallest structure in the United States is a TV tower in Blanchard, North Dakota. Its height is 2063 feet. A 2382-foot length of wire is to be used as a guy wire attached to the top of the tower. Approximate to the nearest foot how far from the base of the tower the guy wire must be anchored. (*Source:* U.S. Geological Survey)

2382 feet   2063 feet

?

△ **63.** A spotlight is mounted on the eaves of a house 12 feet above the ground. A flower bed runs between the house and the sidewalk, so the closest the ladder can be placed to the house is 5 feet. How long a ladder is needed so

that an electrician can reach the place where the light is mounted?

12 feet

5 feet

△ **64.** A wire is to be attached to support a telephone pole. Because of surrounding buildings, sidewalks, and roadways, the wire must be anchored exactly 15 feet from the base of the pole. Telephone company workers have only 30 feet of cable, and 2 feet of that must be used to attach the cable to the pole and to the stake on the ground. How high from the base of the pole can the wire be attached?

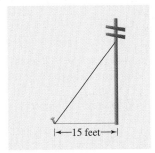

15 feet

△ **65.** The radius of the Moon is 1080 miles. Use the formula for the radius r of a sphere given its surface area A,

$$r = \sqrt{\frac{A}{4\pi}}$$

to find the surface area of the Moon. Round to the nearest square mile. (*Source:* National Space Science Data Center)

66. Police departments find it very useful to be able to approximate the speed of a car when they are given the distance that the car skidded before it came to a stop. If the road surface is wet concrete, the function $S(x) = \sqrt{10.5x}$ is used, where $S(x)$ is the speed of the car in miles per hour and x is the distance skidded in feet. Find how fast a car was moving if it skidded 280 feet on wet concrete.

67. The formula $v = \sqrt{2gh}$ gives the velocity v, in feet per second, of an object when it falls h feet accelerated by gravity g, in feet per second squared. If g is approximately 32 feet per second squared, find how far an object has fallen if its velocity is 80 feet per second.

68. Two tractors are pulling a tree stump from a field. If two forces A and B pull at right angles (90°) to each other, the size of the resulting force R is given by the formula $R = \sqrt{A^2 + B^2}$. If tractor A is exerting 600 pounds of force and the resulting force is 850 pounds, find how much force tractor B is exerting.

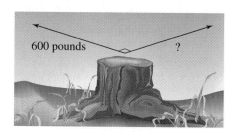

600 pounds   ?

69. Solve: $\sqrt{\sqrt{x + 3} + \sqrt{x}} = \sqrt{3}$

70. The maximum distance $D(h)$ that a person can see from a height h kilometers above the ground is given by the function $D(h) = 111.7\sqrt{h}$. Find the height that would allow a person to see 80 kilometers.

71. The cost $C(x)$ in dollars per day to operate a small delivery service is given by $C(x) = 80\sqrt[3]{x} + 500$, where x is the number of deliveries per day. In July, the manager decides that it is necessary to keep delivery costs below $1620. Find the greatest number of deliveries this company can make per day and still keep overhead below $1620.

72. Explain why proposed solutions of radical equations must be checked.

73. Consider the equations $\sqrt{2x} = 4$ and $\sqrt[3]{2x} = 4$.
   a. Explain the difference in solving these equations.
   b. Explain the similarity in solving these equations.

REVIEW EXERCISES

Use the vertical line test to determine whether each graph represents the graph of a function. See Section 3.2.

74.

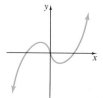

75.

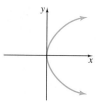

76.

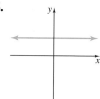

77.

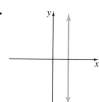

78.

79.

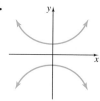

Simplify. See Section 6.4.

80. $\dfrac{\dfrac{x}{6}}{\dfrac{2x}{3} + \dfrac{1}{2}}$

81. $\dfrac{\dfrac{1}{y} + \dfrac{4}{5}}{\dfrac{-3}{20}}$

82. $\dfrac{\dfrac{z}{5} + \dfrac{1}{10}}{\dfrac{z}{20} - \dfrac{z}{5}}$

83. $\dfrac{\dfrac{1}{y} + \dfrac{1}{x}}{\dfrac{1}{y} - \dfrac{1}{x}}$

A Look Ahead

Example
Solve $(t^2 - 3t) - 2\sqrt{t^2 - 3t} = 0$.

Solution
Substitution can be used to make this problem somewhat simpler. Since $t^2 - 3t$ occurs more than once, let $x = t^2 - 3t$.

$$(t^2 - 3t) - 2\sqrt{t^2 - 3t} = 0$$
$$x - 2\sqrt{x} = 0 \qquad \text{Let } x = t^2 - 3t.$$
$$x = 2\sqrt{x}$$
$$x^2 = (2\sqrt{x})^2$$
$$x^2 = 4x$$
$$x^2 - 4x = 0$$
$$x(x - 4) = 0$$
$$x = 0 \quad \text{or} \quad x - 4 = 0$$
$$x = 4$$

Now we "undo" the substitution.

$x = 0$ Replace x with $t^2 - 3t$.
$$t^2 - 3t = 0$$
$$t(t - 3) = 0$$
$$t = 0 \quad \text{or} \quad t - 3 = 0$$
$$t = 3$$

$x = 4$ Replace x with $t^2 - 3t$.
$$t^2 - 3t = 4$$
$$t^2 - 3t - 4 = 0$$
$$(t - 4)(t + 1) = 0$$
$$t - 4 = 0 \quad \text{or} \quad t + 1 = 0$$
$$t = 4 \qquad\qquad t = -1$$

In this problem, we have four possible solutions: 0, 3, 4, and −1. All four solutions check in the original equation, so the solutions are −1, 0, 3, 4.

Solve. See the preceding example.

84. $3\sqrt{x^2 - 8x} = x^2 - 8x$

85. $\sqrt{(x^2 - x) + 7} = 2(x^2 - x) - 1$

86. $7 - (x^2 - 3x) = \sqrt{(x^2 - 3x) + 5}$

87. $x^2 + 6x = 4\sqrt{x^2 + 6x}$

7.7 COMPLEX NUMBERS

CD-ROM

SSM

SSG

Video

▶ **OBJECTIVES**

1. Define imaginary and complex numbers.
2. Add or subtract complex numbers.
3. Multiply complex numbers.
4. Divide complex numbers.
5. Raise i to powers.

1

Our work with radical expressions has excluded expressions such as $\sqrt{-16}$ because $\sqrt{-16}$ is not a real number; there is no real number whose square is −16. In this section, we discuss a number system that includes roots of negative numbers. This number system is the **complex number system**, and it includes the set of real numbers as a subset. The complex number system allows us to solve equations such as $x^2 + 1 = 0$ that have no real number solutions. The set of complex numbers includes the **imaginary unit**.

IMAGINARY UNIT

The imaginary unit, written i, is the number whose square is −1. That is,
$$i^2 = -1 \quad \text{and} \quad i = \sqrt{-1}$$

To write the square root of a negative number in terms of i, use the property that if a is a positive number, then
$$\sqrt{-a} = \sqrt{-1} \cdot \sqrt{a}$$
$$= i \cdot \sqrt{a}$$

Using i, we can write $\sqrt{-16}$ as
$$\sqrt{-16} = \sqrt{-1 \cdot 16} = \sqrt{-1} \cdot \sqrt{16} = i \cdot 4, \text{ or } 4i$$

Example 1   Write with i notation.

a. $\sqrt{-36}$

b. $\sqrt{-5}$

c. $-\sqrt{-20}$

Solution   a. $\sqrt{-36} = \sqrt{-1 \cdot 36} = \sqrt{-1} \cdot \sqrt{36} = i \cdot 6, \text{ or } 6i$

b. $\sqrt{-5} = \sqrt{-1(5)} = \sqrt{-1} \cdot \sqrt{5} = i\sqrt{5}$. Since $\sqrt{5}i$ can easily be confused with $\sqrt{5i}$, we write $\sqrt{5}i$ as $i\sqrt{5}$.

c. $-\sqrt{-20} = -\sqrt{-1 \cdot 20} = -\sqrt{-1} \cdot \sqrt{4 \cdot 5} = -i \cdot 2\sqrt{5} = -2i\sqrt{5}$

The product rule for radicals does not necessarily hold true for imaginary numbers. *To multiply square roots of negative numbers, first we write each number in terms of the imaginary unit i.* For example, to multiply $\sqrt{-4}$ and $\sqrt{-9}$, we first write each number in the form bi.

$$\sqrt{-4}\,\sqrt{-9} = 2i(3i) = 6i^2 = 6(-1) = -6$$

We will also use this method to simplify quotients of square roots of negative numbers.

Example 2 Multiply or divide as indicated.

a. $\sqrt{-3} \cdot \sqrt{-5}$ **b.** $\sqrt{-36} \cdot \sqrt{-1}$ **c.** $\sqrt{8} \cdot \sqrt{-2}$ **d.** $\dfrac{\sqrt{-125}}{\sqrt{5}}$

Solution   **a.** $\sqrt{-3} \cdot \sqrt{-5} = i\sqrt{3}\,(i\sqrt{5}) = i^2\sqrt{15} = -1\sqrt{15} = -\sqrt{15}$

b. $\sqrt{-36} \cdot \sqrt{-1} = 6i(i) = 6i^2 = 6(-1) = -6$

c. $\sqrt{8} \cdot \sqrt{-2} = 2\sqrt{2}\,(i\sqrt{2}) = 2i(\sqrt{2}\,\sqrt{2}) = 2i(2) = 4i$

d. $\dfrac{\sqrt{-125}}{\sqrt{5}} = \dfrac{i\sqrt{125}}{\sqrt{5}} = i\sqrt{25} = 5i$

Now that we have practiced working with the imaginary unit, we define complex numbers.

COMPLEX NUMBERS

A **complex number** is a number that can be written in the form $a + bi$, where a and b are real numbers.

Notice that the set of real numbers is a subset of the complex numbers since any real number can be written in the form of a complex number. For example,

$$16 = 16 + 0i$$

In general, a complex number $a + bi$ is a real number if $b = 0$. Also, a complex number is called an **imaginary number** if $a = 0$. For example,

$$3i = 0 + 3i \qquad \text{and} \qquad i\sqrt{7} = 0 + i\sqrt{7}$$

are imaginary numbers.

The following diagram shows the relationship between complex numbers and their subsets.

Complex numbers
$a + bi$:
$6, 1 - 2i, \frac{3}{5}i, \sqrt[3]{7}$

Real numbers
$a + bi, b = 0$:
$4, -7, 1.8, \sqrt{5}, -\frac{9}{11}, 0$

Rational numbers:
$6, -\frac{8}{3}, \frac{4}{5}, 0, -1.2$

Irrational numbers:
$\sqrt[3]{2}, \pi, -\sqrt{11}$

Complex numbers that are not real numbers
$a + bi, b \neq 0$:
$6 - 2i, 3i, \frac{1}{2} + \frac{3}{4}i, -7.2i$

Imaginary numbers
$a + bi, a = 0, b \neq 0$:
$4i, -2.6i, \frac{7}{8}i$

Other complex numbers
$a + bi, a \neq 0, b \neq 0$:
$3 + 5i, 6 - 0.2i, \frac{2}{3} + \frac{7}{3}i$

2

Two complex numbers $a + bi$ and $c + di$ are equal if and only if $a = c$ and $b = d$. Complex numbers can be added or subtracted by adding or subtracting their real parts and then adding or subtracting their imaginary parts.

SUM OR DIFFERENCE OF COMPLEX NUMBERS

If $a + bi$ and $c + di$ are complex numbers, then their sum is

$$(a + bi) + (c + di) = (a + c) + (b + d)i$$

Their difference is

$$(a + bi) - (c + di) = a + bi - c - di = (a - c) + (b - d)i$$

Example 3 Add or subtract the complex numbers. Write the sum or difference in the form $a + bi$.

a. $(2 + 3i) + (-3 + 2i)$ **b.** $(5i) - (1 - i)$ **c.** $(-3 - 7i) - (-6)$

Solution **a.** $(2 + 3i) + (-3 + 2i) = (2 - 3) + (3 + 2)i = -1 + 5i$

b. $5i - (1 - i) = 5i - 1 + i$

$$= -1 + (5 + 1)i$$

$$= -1 + 6i$$

c. $(-3 - 7i) - (-6) = -3 - 7i + 6$

$$= (-3 + 6) - 7i$$

$$= 3 - 7i$$

3 To multiply two complex numbers of the form $a + bi$, we multiply as though they are binomials. Then we use the relationship $i^2 = -1$ to simplify.

Example 4 Multiply the complex numbers. Write the product in the form $a + bi$.

a. $-7i \cdot 3i$ **b.** $3i(2 - i)$ **c.** $(2 - 5i)(4 + i)$

d. $(2 - i)^2$ **e.** $(7 + 3i)(7 - 3i)$

Solution   **a.** $-7i \cdot 3i = -21i^2$

$$= -21(-1) \quad \text{Replace } i^2 \text{ with } -1.$$

$$= 21$$

b. $3i(2 - i) = 3i \cdot 2 - 3i \cdot i \quad \text{Use the distributive property.}$

$$= 6i - 3i^2 \quad \text{Multiply}$$

$$= 6i - 3(-1) \quad \text{Replace } i^2 \text{ with } -1.$$

$$= 6i + 3$$

$$= 3 + 6i$$

Use the FOIL method. (First, Outer, Inner, Last)

c. $(2 - 5i)(4 + i) = 2(4) + 2(i) - 5i(4) - 5i(i)$

$$\qquad\qquad\qquad\quad \text{F} \qquad \text{O} \qquad \text{I} \qquad \text{L}$$

$$= 8 + 2i - 20i - 5i^2$$

$$= 8 - 18i - 5(-1) \quad i^2 = -1.$$

$$= 8 - 18i + 5$$

$$= 13 - 18i$$

d. $(2 - i)^2 = (2 - i)(2 - i)$

$$= 2(2) - 2(i) - 2(i) + i^2$$

$$= 4 - 4i + (-1) \quad i^2 = -1.$$

$$= 3 - 4i$$

e. $(7 + 3i)(7 - 3i) = 7(7) - 7(3i) + 3i(7) - 3i(3i)$

$$= 49 - 21i + 21i - 9i^2$$

$$= 49 - 9(-1) \quad i^2 = -1.$$

$$= 49 + 9$$

$$= 58$$

Notice that if you add, subtract, or multiply two complex numbers, just like real numbers, the result is a complex number.

4 From Example 4e, notice that the product of $7 + 3i$ and $7 - 3i$ is a real number. These two complex numbers are called **complex conjugates** of one another. In general, we have the following definition.

COMPLEX CONJUGATES

The complex numbers $(a + bi)$ and $(a - bi)$ are called **complex conjugates** of each other, and $(a + bi)(a - bi) = a^2 + b^2$.

To see that the product of a complex number $a + bi$ and its conjugate $a - bi$ is the real number $a^2 + b^2$ we multiply.

$$(a + bi)(a - bi) = a^2 - abi + abi - b^2i^2$$
$$= a^2 - b^2(-1)$$
$$= a^2 + b^2$$

We use complex conjugates to divide by a complex number.

Example 5   Find each quotient. Write in the form $a + bi$.

  a. $\dfrac{2 + i}{1 - i}$

  b. $\dfrac{7}{3i}$

Solution   **a.** Multiply the numerator and denominator by the complex conjugate of $1 - i$ to eliminate the imaginary number in the denominator.

$$\frac{2 + i}{1 - i} = \frac{(2 + i)(1 + i)}{(1 - i)(1 + i)}$$

$$= \frac{2(1) + 2(i) + 1(i) + i^2}{1^2 - i^2}$$

$$= \frac{2 + 3i - 1}{1 + 1}$$

$$= \frac{1 + 3i}{2} \quad \text{or} \quad \frac{1}{2} + \frac{3}{2}i$$

> **HELPFUL HINT**
> Recall that division can be checked by multiplication.
> To check that $\dfrac{2 + i}{1 - i} = \dfrac{1}{2} + \dfrac{3}{2}i$, in Example 5a, multiply $\left(\dfrac{1}{2} + \dfrac{3}{2}i\right)(1 - i)$ to verify that the product is $2 + i$.

b. Multiply the numerator and denominator by the conjugate of $3i$. Note that $3i = 0 + 3i$, so its conjugate is $0 - 3i$ or $-3i$.

$$\frac{7}{3i} = \frac{7(-3i)}{(3i)(-3i)} = \frac{-21i}{-9i^2} = \frac{-21i}{-9(-1)} = \frac{-21i}{9} = \frac{-7i}{3} \quad \text{or} \quad 0 - \frac{7}{3}i$$

5

We can use the fact that $i^2 = -1$ to find higher powers of i. To find i^3, we rewrite it as the product of i^2 and i.

$$i^3 = i^2 \cdot i = (-1)i = -i$$
$$i^4 = i^2 \cdot i^2 = (-1) \cdot (-1) = 1$$

We continue this process and use the fact that $i^4 = 1$ and $i^2 = -1$ to simplify i^5 and i^6.

$$i^5 = i^4 \cdot i = 1 \cdot i = i$$
$$i^6 = i^4 \cdot i^2 = 1 \cdot (-1) = -1$$

If we continue finding powers of i, we generate the following pattern. Notice that the values $i, -1, -i$, and 1 repeat as i is raised to higher and higher powers.

$i^1 = i$	$i^5 = i$	$i^9 = i$
$i^2 = -1$	$i^6 = -1$	$i^{10} = -1$
$i^3 = -i$	$i^7 = -i$	$i^{11} = -i$
$i^4 = 1$	$i^8 = 1$	$i^{12} = 1$

This pattern allows us to find other powers of i. To do so, we will use the fact that $i^4 = 1$ and rewrite a power of i in terms of i^4.
For example, $i^{22} = i^{20} \cdot i^2 = (i^4)^5 \cdot i^2 = 1^5 \cdot (-1) = 1 \cdot (-1) = -1$.

Example 6   Find the following powers of i.

a. i^7 **b.** i^{20} **c.** i^{46} **d.** i^{-12}

Solution   **a.** $i^7 = i^4 \cdot i^3 = 1(-i) = -i$

b. $i^{20} = (i^4)^5 = 1^5 = 1$

c. $i^{46} = i^{44} \cdot i^2 = (i^4)^{11} \cdot i^2 = 1^{11}(-1) = -1$

d. $i^{-12} = \dfrac{1}{i^{12}} = \dfrac{1}{(i^4)^3} = \dfrac{1}{(1)^3} = \dfrac{1}{1} = 1$

MENTAL MATH

Simplify. See Example 1.

1. $\sqrt{-81}$ **2.** $\sqrt{-49}$ **3.** $\sqrt{-7}$ **4.** $\sqrt{-3}$
5. $-\sqrt{16}$ **6.** $-\sqrt{4}$ **7.** $\sqrt{-64}$ **8.** $\sqrt{-100}$

Exercise Set 7.7

Write in terms of i. See Example 1.

1. $\sqrt{-24}$ **2.** $\sqrt{-32}$

3. $-\sqrt{-36}$ **4.** $-\sqrt{-121}$

5. $8\sqrt{-63}$ **6.** $4\sqrt{-20}$

7. $-\sqrt{54}$ **8.** $\sqrt{-63}$

Multiply or divide. See Example 2.

9. $\sqrt{-2} \cdot \sqrt{-7}$ **10.** $\sqrt{-11} \cdot \sqrt{-3}$

11. $\sqrt{-5} \cdot \sqrt{-10}$ **12.** $\sqrt{-2} \cdot \sqrt{-6}$

13. $\sqrt{16} \cdot \sqrt{-1}$ **14.** $\sqrt{3} \cdot \sqrt{-27}$

15. $\dfrac{\sqrt{-9}}{\sqrt{3}}$ **16.** $\dfrac{\sqrt{49}}{\sqrt{-10}}$

17. $\dfrac{\sqrt{-80}}{\sqrt{-10}}$

18. $\dfrac{\sqrt{-40}}{\sqrt{-8}}$

Add or subtract. Write the sum or difference in the form a + bi. See Example 3.

19. $(4 - 7i) + (2 + 3i)$

20. $(2 - 4i) - (2 - i)$

21. $(6 + 5i) - (8 - i)$

22. $(8 - 3i) + (-8 + 3i)$

23. $6 - (8 + 4i)$

24. $(9 - 4i) - 9$

Multiply. Write the product in the form a + bi. See Example 4.

25. $6i(2 - 3i)$

26. $5i(4 - 7i)$

27. $(\sqrt{3} + 2i)(\sqrt{3} - 2i)$

28. $(\sqrt{5} - 5i)(\sqrt{5} + 5i)$

29. $(4 - 2i)^2$

30. $(6 - 3i)^2$

Write each quotient in the form a + bi. See Example 5.

31. $\dfrac{4}{i}$

32. $\dfrac{5}{6i}$

33. $\dfrac{7}{4 + 3i}$

34. $\dfrac{9}{1 - 2i}$

35. $\dfrac{3 + 5i}{1 + i}$

36. $\dfrac{6 + 2i}{4 - 3i}$

37. $\dfrac{5 - i}{3 - 2i}$

38. $\dfrac{6 - i}{2 + i}$

Perform the indicated operation. Write the result in the form a + bi.

39. $(7i)(-9i)$

40. $(-6i)(-4i)$

41. $(6 - 3i) - (4 - 2i)$

42. $(-2 - 4i) - (6 - 8i)$

43. $(6 - 2i)(3 + i)$

44. $(2 - 4i)(2 - i)$

45. $(8 - 3i) + (2 + 3i)$

46. $(7 + 4i) + (4 - 4i)$

47. $(1 - i)(1 + i)$

48. $(6 + 2i)(6 - 2i)$

49. $\dfrac{16 + 15i}{-3i}$

50. $\dfrac{2 - 3i}{-7i}$

51. $(9 + 8i)^2$

52. $(4 - 7i)^2$

53. $\dfrac{2}{3 + i}$

54. $\dfrac{5}{3 - 2i}$

55. $(5 - 6i) - 4i$

56. $(6 - 2i) + 7i$

57. $\dfrac{2 - 3i}{2 + i}$

58. $\dfrac{6 + 5i}{6 - 5i}$

59. $(2 + 4i) + (6 - 5i)$

60. $(5 - 3i) + (7 - 8i)$

Find each power of i. See Example 6.

61. i^8

62. i^{10}

63. i^{21}

64. i^{15}

65. i^{11}

66. i^{40}

67. i^{-6}

68. i^{-9}

Write in the form a + bi.

69. $i^3 + i^4$

70. $i^8 - i^7$

71. $i^6 + i^8$

72. $i^4 + i^{12}$

73. $2 + \sqrt{-9}$

74. $5 - \sqrt{-16}$

75. $\dfrac{6 + \sqrt{-18}}{3}$

76. $\dfrac{4 - \sqrt{-8}}{2}$

77. $\dfrac{5 - \sqrt{-75}}{10}$

78. Describe how to find the conjugate of a complex number.

79. Explain why the product of a complex number and its complex conjugate is a real number.

Simplify.

80. $(8 - \sqrt{-3}) - (2 + \sqrt{-12})$

81. $(8 - \sqrt{-4}) - (2 + \sqrt{-16})$

82. Determine whether $2i$ is a solution of $x^2 + 4 = 0$.

83. Determine whether $-1 + i$ is a solution of $x^2 + 2x = -2$.

REVIEW EXERCISES

Recall that the sum of the measures of the angles of a triangle is 180°. Find the unknown angle in each triangle. See Section 4.3.

△ **84.**

△ **85.**

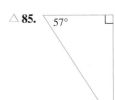

Use synthetic division to divide the following. See Section 6.5.

86. $(x^3 - 6x^2 + 3x - 4) \div (x - 1)$

87. $(5x^4 - 3x^2 + 2) \div (x + 2)$

Thirty people were recently polled about their average monthly balance in their checking accounts. The results of this poll are shown in the following histogram. Use this graph to answer Exercises 88 through 93. See Section 1.2.

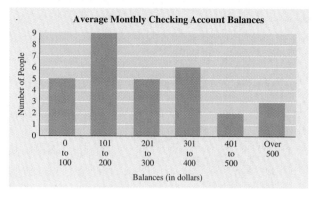

Average Monthly Checking Account Balances

88. How many people polled reported an average checking balance of $201 to $300?

89. How many people polled reported an average checking balance of $0 to $100?

90. How many people polled reported an average checking balance of $200 or less?

91. How many people polled reported an average checking balance of $301 or more?

92. What percent of people polled reported an average checking balance of $201 to $300?

93. What percent of people polled reported an average checking balance of $0 to $100?

For additional Chapter Projects, visit the Real World Activities Website by going to http://www.prenhall.com/martin-gay.

CHAPTER PROJECT

Calculating the Length and Period of a Pendulum

A simple pendulum of a given length, like the kind found in a clock, has a unique property. The time required to complete one full back-and-forth swing (called the **period**) is the same regardless of the mass of the pendulum or the distance it travels. The time to complete one full swing *does*, however, depend on the pendulum's length. In this project, you will have the opportunity to investigate the relationship between the length of a pendulum and its period. You will need at least 1 meter of string, a weight of some sort, a meter stick, a stopwatch, and a calculator. This project may be completed by working in groups or individually.

Make a simple pendulum by securely tying the string to the weight.

The formula relating a pendulum's period T (in seconds) to its length l (in centimeters) is

$$T = 2\pi\sqrt{\frac{l}{980}}$$

The period of a pendulum is defined as the time it takes the pendulum to complete one full back-and-forth swing. In this project, you will be measuring your simple pendulum's period with a stopwatch. Because the periods will be only a few seconds long, it will be more accurate for you to time a total of 5 complete swings and then find the average time of one complete swing.

1. For each of the pendulum (string) lengths l given in Table 1, measure the time required for 5 complete swings and record it in the appropriate column. Next, divide this value by 5 to find the measured period of the pendulum for the given length and record it in the Measured Period T_m column in the table. Use the given formula to calculate the theoretical period T for the same pendulum length and record it in the appropriate column. (Round to two decimal places.) Find and record in the last column the difference between the measured period and the theoretical period.

2. For each of the periods T given in Table 2, use the given formula to calculate the theoretical pendulum length l required to yield the given period. Record l in the appropriate column; round to one decimal place. Next, using this length l, measure and record the time for 5 complete swings. Divide this time by 5 to find the measured period T_m, and record it. Then find and record in the last column the difference between the theoretical period and the measured period.

3. Use the general trends you find in the tables to describe the relationship between a pendulum's period and its length.

4. Discuss the differences you found between the values of the theoretical period and the measured period. What factors contributed to these differences?

TABLE 1

Length l (in centimeters)	Time for 5 Swings (in seconds)	Measured Period T_m (in seconds)	Theoretical Period T (in seconds)	Difference $|T - T_m|$
30				
55				
70				

TABLE 2

Period l (in seconds)	Theoretical Length l (in centimeters)	Time for 5 swings (in seconds)	Measured Periods T_m	Difference $|T - T_m|$
1				
1.25				
2				

CHAPTER 7 VOCABULARY CHECK

Fill in each blank with one of the words or phrases listed below.

index   rationalizing   conjugate   principal square root   cube root
complex number   like radicals   radicand   imaginary unit

1. The _____ of $\sqrt{3} + 2$ is $\sqrt{3} - 2$.

2. The _____ of a nonnegative number a is written as $\sqrt{a}$.

3. The process of writing a radical expression as an equivalent expression but without a radical in the denominator is called _____ the denominator.

4. The _____, written i, is the number whose square is -1.

5. The _____ of a number is written as $\sqrt[3]{a}$.

6. In the notation $\sqrt[n]{a}$, n is called the _____ and a is called the _____.

7. Radicals with the same index and the same radicand are called _____.

8. A _____ is a number that can be written in the form $a + bi$ where a and b are real numbers.

CHAPTER 7 HIGHLIGHTS

DEFINITIONS AND CONCEPTS	EXAMPLES

Section 7.1 Radicals and Radical Functions

The **positive**, or **principal**, **square root** of a nonnegative number a is written as $\sqrt{a}$.

$$\sqrt{a} = b \text{ only if } b^2 = a \text{ and } b \geq 0$$

The **negative square root** of a is written as $-\sqrt{a}$.

The **cube root** of a real number a is written as $\sqrt[3]{a}$.

$$\sqrt[3]{a} = b \text{ only if } b^3 = a$$

If n is an even positive integer, then $\sqrt[n]{a^n} = |a|$.

If n is an odd positive integer, then $\sqrt[n]{a^n} = a$.

A **radical function** in x is a function defined by an expression containing a root of x.

$$\sqrt{36} = 6 \qquad \sqrt{\frac{9}{100}} = \frac{3}{10}$$
$$-\sqrt{36} = -6 \qquad \sqrt{0.04} = 0.2$$
$$\sqrt[3]{27} = 3 \qquad \sqrt[3]{-\frac{1}{8}} = -\frac{1}{2}$$
$$\sqrt[3]{y^6} = y^2 \qquad \sqrt[3]{64x^9} = 4x^3$$
$$\sqrt{(-3)^2} = |-3| = 3$$
$$\sqrt[3]{(-7)^3} = -7$$

If $f(x) = \sqrt{x} + 2$,
$$f(1) = \sqrt{1} + 2 = 1 + 2 = 3$$
$$f(3) = \sqrt{3} + 2 \approx 3.73$$

Section 7.2 Rational Exponents

$a^{1/n} = \sqrt[n]{a}$ if $\sqrt[n]{a}$ is a real number.

If m and n are positive integers greater than 1 with $\frac{m}{n}$ in lowest terms and $\sqrt[n]{a}$ is a real number, then

$$a^{m/n} = \left(a^{1/n}\right)^m = \left(\sqrt[n]{a}\right)^m$$

$a^{-m/n} = \dfrac{1}{a^{m/n}}$ as long as $a^{m/n}$ is a nonzero number.

Exponent rules are true for rational exponents.

$$81^{1/2} = \sqrt{81} = 9$$
$$(-8x^3)^{1/3} = \sqrt[3]{-8x^3} = -2x$$
$$4^{5/2} = \left(\sqrt{4}\right)^5 = 2^5 = 32$$
$$27^{2/3} = \left(\sqrt[3]{27}\right)^2 = 3^2 = 9$$
$$16^{-3/4} = \frac{1}{16^{3/4}} = \frac{1}{\left(\sqrt[4]{16}\right)^3} = \frac{1}{2^3} = \frac{1}{8}$$
$$x^{2/3} \cdot x^{-5/6} = x^{2/3-5/6} = x^{-1/6} = \frac{1}{x^{1/6}}$$
$$\left(8^{14}\right)^{1/7} = 8^2 = 64$$
$$\frac{a^{4/5}}{a^{-2/5}} = a^{4/5-(-2/5)} = a^{6/5}$$

Section 7.3 Simplifying Radical Expressions

Product and Quotient Rules

If $\sqrt[n]{a}$ and $\sqrt[n]{b}$ are real numbers,

$$\sqrt[n]{a} \cdot \sqrt[n]{b} = \sqrt[n]{a \cdot b}$$
$$\frac{\sqrt[n]{a}}{\sqrt[n]{b}} = \sqrt[n]{\frac{a}{b}}, \text{ provided } \sqrt[n]{b} \neq 0$$

A radical of the form $\sqrt[n]{a}$ is **simplified** when a contains no factors that are perfect nth powers.

Multiply or divide as indicated:
$$\sqrt{11} \cdot \sqrt{3} = \sqrt{33}$$
$$\frac{\sqrt[3]{40x}}{\sqrt[3]{5x}} = \sqrt[3]{8} = 2$$

$$\sqrt{40} = \sqrt{4 \cdot 10} = 2\sqrt{10}$$
$$\sqrt{36x^5} = \sqrt{36x^4 \cdot x} = 6x^2\sqrt{x}$$
$$\sqrt[3]{24x^7y^3} = \sqrt[3]{8x^6y^3 \cdot 3x} = 2x^2y\sqrt[3]{3x}$$
$$\sqrt{36x^4 \cdot x} = 6x^2\sqrt{x}$$

DEFINITIONS AND CONCEPTS	EXAMPLES

Section 7.4 Adding, Subtracting, and Multiplying Radical Expressions

Radicals with the same index and the same radicand are **like radicals**.

The distributive property can be used to add like radicals.

$$5\sqrt{6} + 2\sqrt{6} = (5 + 2)\sqrt{6} = 7\sqrt{6}$$
$$-\sqrt[3]{3x} - 10\sqrt[3]{3x} + 3\sqrt[3]{10x}$$
$$= (-1 - 10)\sqrt[3]{3x} + 3\sqrt[3]{10x}$$
$$= -11\sqrt[3]{3x} + 3\sqrt[3]{10x}$$

Radical expressions are multiplied by using many of the same properties used to multiply polynomials.

Multiply.
$$(\sqrt{5} - \sqrt{2x})(\sqrt{2} + \sqrt{2x})$$
$$= \sqrt{10} + \sqrt{10x} - \sqrt{4x} - 2x$$
$$= \sqrt{10} + \sqrt{10x} - 2\sqrt{x} - 2x$$
$$(2\sqrt{3} - \sqrt{8x})(2\sqrt{3} + \sqrt{8x})$$
$$= 4(3) - 8x = 12 - 8x$$

Section 7.5 Rationalizing Denominators and Numerators of Radical Expressions

The **conjugate** of $a + b$ is $a - b$.

The process of writing the denominator of a radical expression without a radical is called **rationalizing the denominator**.

The conjugate of $\sqrt{7} + \sqrt{3}$ is $\sqrt{7} - \sqrt{3}$

Rationalize each denominator.
$$\frac{\sqrt{5}}{\sqrt{3}} = \frac{\sqrt{5} \cdot \sqrt{3}}{\sqrt{3} \cdot \sqrt{3}} = \frac{\sqrt{15}}{3}$$

$$\frac{6}{\sqrt{7} + \sqrt{3}} = \frac{6(\sqrt{7} - \sqrt{3})}{(\sqrt{7} + \sqrt{3})(\sqrt{7} - \sqrt{3})}$$
$$= \frac{6(\sqrt{7} - \sqrt{3})}{7 - 3}$$
$$= \frac{6(\sqrt{7} - \sqrt{3})}{4} = \frac{3(\sqrt{7} - \sqrt{3})}{2}$$

The process of writing the numerator of a radical expression without a radical is called **rationalizing the numerator**.

Rationalize each numerator.
$$\frac{\sqrt[3]{9}}{\sqrt[3]{5}} = \frac{\sqrt[3]{9} \cdot \sqrt[3]{3}}{\sqrt[3]{5} \cdot \sqrt[3]{3}} = \frac{\sqrt[3]{27}}{\sqrt[3]{15}} = \frac{3}{\sqrt[3]{15}}$$
$$\frac{\sqrt{9} + \sqrt{3x}}{12} = \frac{(\sqrt{9} + \sqrt{3x})(\sqrt{9} - \sqrt{3x})}{12(\sqrt{9} - \sqrt{3x})}$$
$$= \frac{9 - 3x}{12(\sqrt{9} - \sqrt{3x})}$$
$$= \frac{3(3 - x)}{3 \cdot 4(3 - \sqrt{3x})} = \frac{3 - x}{4(3 - \sqrt{3x})}$$

Section 7.6 Radical Equations and Problem Solving

To Solve a Radical Equation

Step 1: Write the equation so that one radical is by itself on one side of the equation.

Step 2: Raise each side of the equation to a power equal to the index of the radical and simplify.

Step 3: If the equation still contains a radical, repeat Steps 1 and 2. If not, solve the equation.

Step 4: Check all proposed solutions in the original equation.

Solve $x = \sqrt{4x + 9} + 3$.

1. $x - 3 = \sqrt{4x + 9}$

2. $(x - 3)^2 = (\sqrt{4x + 9})^2$
$x^2 - 6x + 9 = 4x + 9$

3. $x^2 - 10x = 0$
$x(x - 10) = 0$
$x = 0$ or $x = 10$

4. The proposed solution 10 checks, but 0 does not. The solution is 10.

DEFINITIONS AND CONCEPTS	EXAMPLES

Section 7.7 Complex Numbers

$i^2 = -1$ and $i = \sqrt{-1}$

Simplify $\sqrt{-9}$.

$$\sqrt{-9} = \sqrt{-1 \cdot 9} = \sqrt{-1} \cdot \sqrt{9} = i \cdot 3 \text{ or } 3i$$

A **complex number** is a number that can be written in the form $a + bi$, where a and b are real numbers.

Complex Numbers	*Written in form $a + bi$*
12	$12 + 0i$
$-5i$	$0 + (-5)i$
$-2 - 3i$	$-2 + (-3)i$

Multiply.

$$\sqrt{-3} \cdot \sqrt{-7} = i\sqrt{3} \cdot i\sqrt{7}$$
$$= i^2\sqrt{21}$$
$$= -\sqrt{21}$$

To add or subtract complex numbers, add or subtract their real parts and then add or subtract their imaginary parts.

Perform each indicated operation.

$$(-3 + 2i) - (7 - 4i) = -3 + 2i - 7 + 4i$$
$$= -10 + 6i$$

To multiply complex numbers, multiply as though they are binomials.

$$(-7 - 2i)(6 + i) = -42 - 7i - 12i - 2i^2$$
$$= -42 - 19i - 2(-1)$$
$$= -42 - 19i + 2$$
$$= -40 - 19i$$

The complex numbers $(a + bi)$ and $(a - bi)$ are called **complex conjugates.**

The complex conjugate of

$$(3 + 6i) \text{ is } (3 - 6i).$$

Their product is a real number.

$$(3 - 6i)(3 + 6i) = 9 - 36i^2$$
$$= 9 - 36(-1) = 9 + 36 = 45$$

To divide complex numbers, multiply the numerator and the denominator by the conjugate of the denominator.

Divide.

$$\frac{4}{2 - i} = \frac{4(2 + i)}{(2 - i)(2 + i)}$$
$$= \frac{4(2 + i)}{4 - i^2}$$
$$= \frac{4(2 + i)}{5}$$
$$= \frac{8 + 4i}{5} = \frac{8}{5} + \frac{4}{5}i$$

CHAPTER 7 REVIEW

(7.1) *Find the root. Assume that all variables represent positive numbers.*

1. $\sqrt{81}$
2. $\sqrt[4]{81}$
3. $\sqrt[3]{-8}$
4. $\sqrt[4]{-16}$
5. $-\sqrt{\dfrac{1}{49}}$
6. $\sqrt{x^{64}}$
7. $-\sqrt{36}$
8. $\sqrt[3]{64}$
9. $\sqrt[3]{-a^6 b^9}$
10. $\sqrt{16a^4 b^{12}}$
11. $\sqrt[5]{32a^5 b^{10}}$
12. $\sqrt[5]{-32x^{15} y^{20}}$
13. $\sqrt{\dfrac{x^{12}}{36y^2}}$
14. $\sqrt[3]{\dfrac{27y^3}{z^{12}}}$

Simplify. Use absolute value bars when necessary.

15. $\sqrt{(-x)^2}$
16. $\sqrt[4]{(x^2 - 4)^4}$
17. $\sqrt[3]{(-27)^3}$
18. $\sqrt[5]{(-5)^5}$
19. $-\sqrt[5]{x^5}$
20. $\sqrt[4]{16(2y + z)^{12}}$
21. $\sqrt{25(x - y)^{10}}$
22. $\sqrt[5]{-y^5}$
23. $\sqrt[9]{-x^9}$

Identify the domain and then graph each function.

24. $f(x) = \sqrt{x} + 3$
25. $g(x) = \sqrt[3]{x} - 3$; use the accompanying table.

x	-5	2	3	4	11
$g(x)$					

(7.2) *Evaluate the following.*

26. $\left(\dfrac{1}{81}\right)^{1/4}$
27. $\left(-\dfrac{1}{27}\right)^{1/3}$
28. $(-27)^{-1/3}$
29. $(-64)^{-1/3}$
30. $-9^{3/2}$
31. $64^{-1/3}$
32. $(-25)^{5/2}$
33. $\left(\dfrac{25}{49}\right)^{-3/2}$
34. $\left(\dfrac{8}{27}\right)^{-2/3}$
35. $\left(-\dfrac{1}{36}\right)^{-1/4}$

Write with rational exponents.

36. $\sqrt[3]{x^2}$
37. $\sqrt[5]{5x^2 y^3}$

Write with radical notation.

38. $y^{4/5}$
39. $5(xy^2 z^5)^{1/3}$
40. $(x + 2y)^{-1/2}$

Simplify each expression. Assume that all variables represent positive numbers. Write with only positive exponents.

41. $a^{1/3} a^{4/3} a^{1/2}$
42. $\dfrac{b^{1/3}}{b^{4/3}}$
43. $(a^{1/2} a^{-2})^3$
44. $(x^{-3} y^6)^{1/3}$
45. $\left(\dfrac{b^{3/4}}{a^{-1/2}}\right)^8$
46. $\dfrac{x^{1/4} x^{-1/2}}{x^{2/3}}$
47. $\left(\dfrac{49 c^{5/3}}{a^{-1/4} b^{5/6}}\right)^{-1}$
48. $a^{-1/4}(a^{5/4} - a^{9/4})$

Use a calculator and write a three-decimal-place approximation.

49. $\sqrt{20}$
50. $\sqrt[3]{-39}$
51. $\sqrt[4]{726}$
52. $56^{1/3}$
53. $-78^{3/4}$
54. $105^{-2/3}$

Use rational exponents to write each radical with the same index. Then multiply.

55. $\sqrt[3]{2} \cdot \sqrt{7}$
56. $\sqrt[3]{3} \cdot \sqrt[4]{x}$

(7.3) *Perform the indicated operations and then simplify if possible. For the remainder of this review, assume that variables represent positive numbers only.*

57. $\sqrt{3} \cdot \sqrt{8}$
58. $\sqrt[3]{7y} \cdot \sqrt[3]{x^2 z}$
59. $\dfrac{\sqrt{44x^3}}{\sqrt{11x}}$
60. $\dfrac{\sqrt[4]{a^6 b^{13}}}{\sqrt[4]{a^2 b}}$

Simplify.

61. $\sqrt{60}$
62. $-\sqrt{75}$
63. $\sqrt[3]{162}$
64. $\sqrt[3]{-32}$
65. $\sqrt{36x^7}$
66. $\sqrt[3]{24a^5 b^7}$
67. $\sqrt{\dfrac{p^{17}}{121}}$
68. $\sqrt[3]{\dfrac{y^5}{27x^6}}$
69. $\sqrt[4]{\dfrac{xy^6}{81}}$
70. $\sqrt{\dfrac{2x^3}{49y^4}}$

△ 71. The formula for the radius r of a circle of area A is

$$r = \sqrt{\dfrac{A}{\pi}}$$

a. Find the exact radius of a circle whose area is 25 square meters.

b. Approximate to two decimal places the radius of a circle whose area is 104 square inches.

(7.4) *Perform the indicated operation.*

72. $x\sqrt{75xy} - \sqrt{27x^3 y}$
73. $2\sqrt{32x^2 y^3} - xy\sqrt{98y}$

74. $\sqrt[3]{128} + \sqrt[3]{250}$

75. $3\sqrt[4]{32a^5} - a\sqrt[4]{162a}$

76. $\dfrac{5}{\sqrt{4}} + \dfrac{\sqrt{3}}{3}$

77. $\sqrt{\dfrac{8}{x^2}} - \sqrt{\dfrac{50}{16x^2}}$

78. $2\sqrt{50} - 3\sqrt{125} + \sqrt{98}$

79. $2a\sqrt[4]{32b^5} - 3b\sqrt[4]{162a^4b} + \sqrt[4]{2a^4b^5}$

Multiply and then simplify if possible.

80. $\sqrt{3}(\sqrt{27} - \sqrt{3})$

81. $(\sqrt{x} - 3)^2$

82. $(\sqrt{5} - 5)(2\sqrt{5} + 2)$

83. $(2\sqrt{x} - 3\sqrt{y})(2\sqrt{x} + 3\sqrt{y})$

84. $(\sqrt{a} + 3)(\sqrt{a} - 3)$

85. $(\sqrt[3]{a} + 2)^2$

86. $(\sqrt[3]{5x} + 9)(\sqrt[3]{5x} - 9)$

87. $(\sqrt[3]{a} + 4)(\sqrt[3]{a^2} - 4\sqrt[3]{a} + 16)$

(7.5) *Rationalize each denominator.*

88. $\dfrac{3}{\sqrt{7}}$

89. $\sqrt{\dfrac{x}{12}}$

90. $\dfrac{5}{\sqrt[3]{4}}$

91. $\sqrt{\dfrac{24x^5}{3y^2}}$

92. $\sqrt[3]{\dfrac{15x^6y^7}{z^2}}$

93. $\dfrac{5}{2 - \sqrt{7}}$

94. $\dfrac{3}{\sqrt{y} - 2}$

95. $\dfrac{\sqrt{2} - \sqrt{3}}{\sqrt{2} + \sqrt{3}}$

Rationalize each numerator.

96. $\dfrac{\sqrt{11}}{3}$

97. $\sqrt{\dfrac{18}{y}}$

98. $\dfrac{\sqrt[3]{9}}{7}$

99. $\sqrt{\dfrac{24x^5}{3y^2}}$

100. $\sqrt[3]{\dfrac{xy^2}{10z}}$

101. $\dfrac{\sqrt{x} + 5}{-3}$

(7.6) *Solve each equation for the variable.*

102. $\sqrt{y - 7} = 5$

103. $\sqrt{2x + 10} = 4$

104. $\sqrt[3]{2x - 6} = 4$

105. $\sqrt{x + 6} = \sqrt{x + 2}$

106. $2x - 5\sqrt{x} = 3$

107. $\sqrt{x + 9} = 2 + \sqrt{x - 7}$

Find each unknown length.

△ **108.**

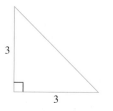

△ **109.**

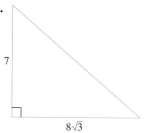

△ **110.** Beverly Hillis wants to determine the distance x across a pond on her property. She is able to measure the distances shown on the following diagram. Find how wide the lake is at the crossing point, indicated by the triangle, to the nearest tenth of a foot.

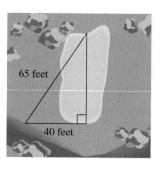

△ **111.** A pipe fitter needs to connect two underground pipelines that are offset by 3 feet, as pictured in the diagram. Neglecting the joints needed to join the pipes, find the length of the shortest possible connecting pipe rounded to the nearest hundredth of a foot.

(7.7) *Perform the indicated operation and simplify. Write the result in the form $a + bi$.*

112. $\sqrt{-8}$

113. $-\sqrt{-6}$

114. $\sqrt{-4} + \sqrt{-16}$

115. $\sqrt{-2} \cdot \sqrt{-5}$

116. $(12 - 6i) + (3 + 2i)$

117. $(-8 - 7i) - (5 - 4i)$

118. $(\sqrt{3} + \sqrt{2}) + (3\sqrt{2} - \sqrt{-8})$

119. $2i(2 - 5i)$

120. $-3i(6 - 4i)$

121. $(3 + 2i)(1 + i)$

122. $(2 - 3i)^2$

123. $(\sqrt{6} - 9i)(\sqrt{6} + 9i)$

124. $\dfrac{2 + 3i}{2i}$

125. $\dfrac{1 + i}{-3i}$

CHAPTER 7 TEST

Raise to the power or find the root. Assume that all variables represent positive numbers. Write with only positive exponents.

1. $\sqrt{216}$

2. $-\sqrt[4]{x^{64}}$

3. $\left(\dfrac{1}{125}\right)^{1/3}$

4. $\left(\dfrac{1}{125}\right)^{-1/3}$

5. $\left(\dfrac{8x^3}{27}\right)^{2/3}$

6. $\sqrt[3]{-a^{18}b^9}$

7. $\left(\dfrac{64c^{4/3}}{a^{-2/3}b^{5/6}}\right)^{1/2}$

8. $a^{-2/3}\left(a^{5/4} - a^3\right)$

Find the root. Use absolute value bars when necessary.

9. $\sqrt[4]{(4xy)^4}$

10. $\sqrt[3]{(-27)^3}$

Rationalize the denominator. Assume that all variables represent positive numbers.

11. $\sqrt{\dfrac{9}{y}}$

12. $\dfrac{4 - \sqrt{x}}{4 + 2\sqrt{x}}$

13. $\dfrac{\sqrt[3]{ab}}{\sqrt[3]{ab^2}}$

14. Rationalize the numerator of $\dfrac{\sqrt{6} + x}{8}$ and simplify.

Perform the indicated operations. Assume that all variables represent positive numbers.

15. $\sqrt{125x^3} - 3\sqrt{20x^3}$

16. $\sqrt{3}(\sqrt{16} - \sqrt{2})$

17. $(\sqrt{x} + 1)^2$

18. $(\sqrt{2} - 4)(\sqrt{3} + 1)$

19. $(\sqrt{5} + 5)(\sqrt{5} - 5)$

 Use a calculator to approximate each to three decimal places.

20. $\sqrt{561}$

21. $386^{-2/3}$

Solve.

22. $x = \sqrt{x - 2} + 2$

23. $\sqrt{x^2 - 7} + 3 = 0$

24. $\sqrt{x + 5} = \sqrt{2x - 1}$

Perform the indicated operation and simplify. Write the result in the form $a + bi$.

25. $\sqrt{-2}$

26. $-\sqrt{-8}$

27. $(12 - 6i) - (12 - 3i)$

28. $(6 - 2i)(6 + 2i)$

29. $(4 + 3i)^2$

30. $\dfrac{1 + 4i}{1 - i}$

△ **31.** Find x.

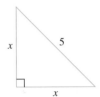

32. Identify the domain of $g(x)$. Then complete the accompanying table and graph $g(x)$.

$$g(x) = \sqrt{x + 2}$$

x	-2	-1	2	7
$g(x)$				

 Solve.

33. The function $V(r) = \sqrt{2.5r}$ can be used to estimate the maximum safe velocity V in miles per hour at which a car can travel if it is driven along a curved road with a *radius of curvature r* in feet. To the nearest whole number, find the maximum safe speed if a cloverleaf exit on an expressway has a radius of curvature of 300 feet.

34. Use the formula from Exercise 33 to find the radius of curvature if the safe velocity is 30 mph.

CHAPTER 7 CUMULATIVE REVIEW

1. Simplify each expression.

   a. $3xy - 2xy + 5 - 7 + xy$

   b. $7x^2 + 3 - 5(x^2 - 4)$

   c. $(2.1x - 5.6) - (-x - 5.3)$

2. Solve for x: $\dfrac{x + 5}{2} + \dfrac{1}{2} = 2x - \dfrac{x - 3}{8}$

3. A salesperson earns \$600 per month plus a commission of 20% of sales. Find the minimum amount of sales needed to receive a total income of at least \$1500 per month.

4. Solve: $2|x| + 25 = 23$

5. Solve: $\left|\dfrac{x}{3} - 1\right| - 7 \geq -5$

6. Graph the equation $y = |x|$.

7. Determine the domain and range of each relation.

   a. $\{(2, 3), (2, 4), (0, -1), (3, -1)\}$

   b.

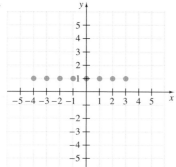

   c.   Input: Output:

        Cities   Population
                       (in thousands)

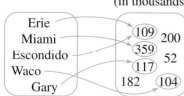

8. Graph $y = -3$.

9. Find the slope of the line $x = -5$.

10. Use the substitution method to solve the system.

$$\begin{cases} -\dfrac{x}{6} + \dfrac{y}{2} = \dfrac{1}{2} \\[2mm] \dfrac{x}{3} - \dfrac{y}{6} = -\dfrac{3}{4} \end{cases}$$

11. Use the product rule to simplify.

   a. $2^2 \cdot 2^5$

   b. $x^7 x^3$

   c. $y \cdot y^2 \cdot y^4$

12. Use scientific notation to simplify $\dfrac{2000 \times 0.000021}{700}$.

13. If $P(x) = 3x^2 - 2x - 5$, find the following.

   a. $P(1)$

   b. $P(-2)$

14. Multiply and simplify the product if possible.

   a. $(x + 3)(2x + 5)$

   b. $(2x - 3)(5x^2 - 6x + 7)$

15. Find the GCF of $20x^3y$, $10x^2y^2$, and $35x^3$.

16. Simplify each rational expression.

   a. $\dfrac{x^3 + 8}{2 + x}$

   b. $\dfrac{2y^2 + 2}{y^3 - 5y^2 + y - 5}$

17. Perform the indicated operation.

   a. $\dfrac{2}{x^2y} + \dfrac{5}{3x^3y}$

   b. $\dfrac{3x}{x + 2} + \dfrac{2x}{x - 2}$

   c. $\dfrac{x}{x - 1} - \dfrac{4}{1 - x}$

18. Simplify each complex fraction.

   a. $\dfrac{\dfrac{5x}{x + 2}}{\dfrac{10}{x - 2}}$

   b. $\dfrac{\dfrac{x}{y^2} + \dfrac{1}{y}}{\dfrac{y}{x^2} + \dfrac{1}{x}}$

19. Divide $10x^3 - 5x^2 + 20x$ by $5x$.

20. Use synthetic division to divide $2x^3 - x^2 - 13x + 1$ by $x - 3$.

21. Solve: $\dfrac{x + 6}{x - 2} = \dfrac{2(x + 2)}{x - 2}$

22. Solve $\dfrac{1}{x} + \dfrac{1}{y} = \dfrac{1}{z}$ for x.

23. Suppose that u varies inversely as w. If u is 3 when w is 5, find the constant of variation and the inverse variation equation.

24. Write each expression with a positive exponent, and then simplify.

   a. $16^{-3/4}$ **b.** $(-27)^{-2/3}$

25. Rationalize the numerator of $\dfrac{\sqrt{x} + 2}{5}$.

Allies of Good Nutrition

Diet and nutrition play a major role in good health. Diets low in saturated fats and dietary cholesterol tend to lower the risk of cardiovascular disease. High sodium intakes have been associated with high blood pressure and stroke. Antioxidants, such as beta carotene and vitamin C, can help protect against heart disease and some cancers. It is no wonder, then, that public interest in healthy eating habits is soaring.

Registered dieticians, food and nutrition experts, are valuable allies in an effort to eat right. They plan nutrition programs, supervise food preparation, and educate about the health benefits of good nutrition. Registered dieticians work in diverse environments: hospitals, schools, day-care centers, nursing homes, government or university laboratories, private practice, corporate wellness programs, food producing companies, pharmaceutical companies, restaurant management, and community health settings. Dieticians use math and problem-solving skills in tasks such as analyzing the nutritional content of a recipe or food product, assessing a client's diet, and determining an individual's nutritional requirements.

For more information about careers in dietetics, visit the American Dietetic Association Web site by first going to www.prenhall.com/martin-gay.

In the Spotlight on Decision Making feature on page 480, you will have the opportunity to make a decision about the adequacy of vitamin A intake as a registered dietician.

QUADRATIC EQUATIONS AND FUNCTIONS

An important part of the study of algebra is learning to model and solve problems. Often, the model of a problem is a quadratic equation or a function containing a second-degree polynomial. In this chapter, we continue the work begun in Chapter 5, when we solved polynomial equations in one variable by factoring. Two additional methods of solving quadratic equations are analyzed, as well as methods of solving nonlinear inequalities in one variable.

8.1 SOLVING QUADRATIC EQUATIONS BY COMPLETING THE SQUARE

▶ **OBJECTIVES**

CD-ROM   SSM

SSG   Video

1. Use the square root property to solve quadratic equations.
2. Solve quadratic equations by completing the square.
3. Use quadratic equations to solve problems.

1

In Chapter 5, we solved quadratic equations by factoring. Recall that a **quadratic, or second-degree, equation** is an equation that can be written in the form $ax^2 + bx + c = 0$, where a, b, and c are real numbers and a is not 0. To solve a quadratic equation such as $x^2 = 9$ by factoring, we use the zero-factor theorem. To use the zero-factor theorem, the equation must first be written in standard form, $ax^2 + bx + c = 0$.

$$x^2 = 9$$

$$x^2 - 9 = 0 \qquad \text{Subtract 9 from both sides.}$$

$$(x + 3)(x - 3) = 0 \qquad \text{Factor.}$$

$$x + 3 = 0 \quad \text{or} \quad x - 3 = 0 \qquad \text{Set each factor equal to 0.}$$

$$x = -3 \qquad\qquad x = 3 \qquad \text{Solve.}$$

The solution set is $\{-3, 3\}$, the positive and negative square roots of 9. Not all quadratic equations can be solved by factoring, so we need to explore other methods. Notice that the solutions of the equation $x^2 = 9$ are two numbers whose square is 9.

$$3^2 = 9 \qquad \text{and} \qquad (-3)^2 = 9$$

Thus, we can solve the equation $x^2 = 9$ by taking the square root of both sides. Be sure to include both $\sqrt{9}$ and $-\sqrt{9}$ as solutions since both $\sqrt{9}$ and $-\sqrt{9}$ are numbers whose square is 9.

$$x^2 = 9$$

The notation $\pm\sqrt{9}$ (read as "plus or minus $\sqrt{9}$") indicates the pair of numbers $+\sqrt{9}$ and $-\sqrt{9}$.

$$\sqrt{x^2} = \pm\sqrt{9}$$

$$x = \pm 3$$

This illustrates the square root property.

▼
HELPFUL HINT
The notation ± 3, for example, is read as "plus or minus 3." It is a shorthand notation for the pair of numbers $+3$ and -3.

SQUARE ROOT PROPERTY

If b is a real number and if $a^2 = b$, then $a = \pm\sqrt{b}$.

Example 1   Use the square root property to solve $x^2 = 50$.

Solution $x^2 = 50$

$x = \pm\sqrt{50}$ Use the square root property.

$x = \pm 5\sqrt{2}$ Simplify the radical.

Check   Let $x = 5\sqrt{2}$.   Let $x = -5\sqrt{2}$.

$x^2 = 50$ $x^2 = 50$

$(5\sqrt{2})^2 \stackrel{?}{=} 50$ $(-5\sqrt{2})^2 \stackrel{?}{=} 50$

$25 \cdot 2 \stackrel{?}{=} 50$ $25 \cdot 2 \stackrel{?}{=} 50$

$50 = 50$ True. $50 = 50$ True.

The solutions are $5\sqrt{2}$ and $-5\sqrt{2}$.

Example 2   Use the square root property to solve $2x^2 = 14$.

Solution   First we get the squared variable alone on one side of the equation.

$$2x^2 = 14$$

$$x^2 = 7 \qquad \text{Divide both sides by 2.}$$

$$x = \pm\sqrt{7} \qquad \text{Use the square root property.}$$

Check to see that the solutions are $\sqrt{7}$ and $-\sqrt{7}$.

Example 3   Use the square root property to solve $(x + 1)^2 = 12$.

Solution $(x + 1)^2 = 12$

$x + 1 = \pm\sqrt{12}$ Use the square root property.

$x + 1 = \pm 2\sqrt{3}$ Simplify the radical.

$x = -1 \pm 2\sqrt{3}$ Subtract 1 from both sides.

Check   Below is a check for $-1 + 2\sqrt{3}$. The check for $-1 - 2\sqrt{3}$ is almost the same and is left for you to do on your own.

$$(x + 1)^2 = 12$$

$$(-1 + 2\sqrt{3} + 1)^2 \stackrel{?}{=} 12$$

$$(2\sqrt{3})^2 \stackrel{?}{=} 12$$

$$4 \cdot 3 \stackrel{?}{=} 12$$

$$12 = 12 \qquad \text{True.}$$

The solutions are $-1 + 2\sqrt{3}$, $-1 - 2\sqrt{3}$.

Example 4 Use the square root property to solve $(2x - 5)^2 = -16$.

Solution $(2x - 5)^2 = -16$

$2x - 5 = \pm\sqrt{-16}$ Use the square root property.

$2x - 5 = \pm 4i$ Simplify the radical.

$2x = 5 \pm 4i$ Add 5 to both sides.

$x = \dfrac{5 \pm 4i}{2}$ Divide both sides by 2.

The solutions are $\dfrac{5 + 4i}{2}$ and $\dfrac{5 - 4i}{2}$.

Notice from Examples 3 and 4 that, if we write a quadratic equation so that one side is the square of a binomial, we can solve by using the square root property. To write the square of a binomial, we write perfect square trinomials. Recall that a perfect square trinomial is a trinomial that can be factored into two identical binomial factors.

Perfect Square Trinomials	*Factored Form*
$x^2 + 8x + 16$	$(x + 4)^2$
$x^2 - 6x + 9$	$(x - 3)^2$
$x^2 + 3x + \dfrac{9}{4}$	$\left(x + \dfrac{3}{2}\right)^2$

Notice that for each perfect square trinomial, **the constant term of the trinomial is the square of half the coefficient of the x-term.** For example,

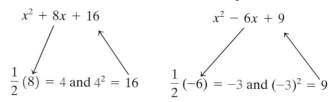

$x^2 + 8x + 16$

$\dfrac{1}{2}(8) = 4$ and $4^2 = 16$

$x^2 - 6x + 9$

$\dfrac{1}{2}(-6) = -3$ and $(-3)^2 = 9$

2 The process of writing a quadratic equation so that one side is a perfect square trinomial is called **completing the square.**

Example 5 Solve $p^2 + 2p = 4$ by completing the square.

Solution First, add the square of half the coefficient of p to both sides so that the resulting trinomial will be a perfect square trinomial. The coefficient of p is 2.

$$\frac{1}{2}(2) = 1 \quad \text{and} \quad 1^2 = 1$$

Add 1 to both sides of the original equation.

$$p^2 + 2p = 4$$

$$p^2 + 2p + 1 = 4 + 1 \qquad \text{Add 1 to both sides.}$$

$$(p + 1)^2 = 5 \qquad \text{Factor the trinomial; simplify the right side.}$$

We may now use the square root property and solve for p.

$$p + 1 = \pm\sqrt{5} \qquad \text{Use the square root property.}$$

$$p = -1 \pm \sqrt{5} \qquad \text{Subtract 1 from both sides.}$$

Notice that there are two solutions: $-1 + \sqrt{5}$ and $-1 - \sqrt{5}$.

Example 6   Solve $m^2 - 7m - 1 = 0$ for m by completing the square.

Solution   First, add 1 to both sides of the equation so that the left side has no constant term.

$$m^2 - 7m - 1 = 0$$

$$m^2 - 7m = 1$$

Now find the constant term that makes the left side a perfect square trinomial by squaring half the coefficient of m. Add this constant to both sides of the equation.

$$\frac{1}{2}(-7) = -\frac{7}{2} \quad \text{and} \quad \left(-\frac{7}{2}\right)^2 = \frac{49}{4}$$

$$m^2 - 7m + \frac{49}{4} = 1 + \frac{49}{4} \qquad \text{Add } \frac{49}{4} \text{ to both sides of the equation.}$$

$$\left(m - \frac{7}{2}\right)^2 = \frac{53}{4} \qquad \text{Factor the perfect square trinomial and simplify the right side.}$$

$$m - \frac{7}{2} = \pm\sqrt{\frac{53}{4}} \qquad \text{Apply the square root property.}$$

$$m = \frac{7}{2} \pm \frac{\sqrt{53}}{2} \qquad \text{Add } \frac{7}{2} \text{ to both sides and simplify } \sqrt{\frac{53}{4}}.$$

$$m = \frac{7 \pm \sqrt{53}}{2} \qquad \text{Simplify.}$$

The solutions are $\dfrac{7 + \sqrt{53}}{2}$ and $\dfrac{7 - \sqrt{53}}{2}$.

Example 7   Solve $2x^2 - 8x + 3 = 0$.

Solution   Our procedure for finding the constant term to complete the square works only if the coefficient of the squared variable term is 1. Therefore, to solve this equation, the first step is to divide both sides by 2, the coefficient of x^2.

$$2x^2 - 8x + 3 = 0$$

$$x^2 - 4x + \frac{3}{2} = 0 \qquad \text{Divide both sides by 2.}$$

$$x^2 - 4x = -\frac{3}{2} \qquad \text{Subtract } \frac{3}{2} \text{ from both sides.}$$

Next find the square of half of -4.

$$\frac{1}{2}(-4) = -2 \quad \text{and} \quad (-2)^2 = 4$$

Add 4 to both sides of the equation to complete the square.

$$x^2 - 4x + 4 = -\frac{3}{2} + 4$$

$$(x - 2)^2 = \frac{5}{2} \qquad \text{Factor the perfect square and simplify the right side.}$$

$$x - 2 = \pm\sqrt{\frac{5}{2}} \qquad \text{Apply the square root property.}$$

$$x - 2 = \pm\frac{\sqrt{10}}{2} \qquad \text{Rationalize the denominator.}$$

$$x = 2 \pm \frac{\sqrt{10}}{2} \qquad \text{Add 2 to both sides.}$$

$$= \frac{4}{2} \pm \frac{\sqrt{10}}{2} \qquad \text{Find the common denominator.}$$

$$= \frac{4 \pm \sqrt{10}}{2} \qquad \text{Simplify.}$$

The solutions are $\dfrac{4 + \sqrt{10}}{2}$ and $\dfrac{4 - \sqrt{10}}{2}$.

The following steps may be used to solve a quadratic equation such as $ax^2 + bx + c = 0$ by completing the square. This method may be used whether or not the polynomial $ax^2 + bx + c$ is factorable.

SOLVING A QUADRATIC EQUATION IN x BY COMPLETING THE SQUARE

Step 1: If the coefficient of x^2 is 1, go to Step 2. Otherwise, divide both sides of the equation by the coefficient of x^2.

Step 2: Isolate all variable terms on one side of the equation.

Step 3: Complete the square for the resulting binomial by adding the square of half of the coefficient of x to both sides of the equation.

Step 4: Factor the resulting perfect square trinomial and write it as the square of a binomial.

Step 5: Use the square root property to solve for x.

Example 8   Solve $3x^2 - 9x + 8 = 0$ by completing the square.

Solution $3x^2 - 9x + 8 = 0$

Step 1: $\quad x^2 - 3x + \dfrac{8}{3} = 0$ _____ Divide both sides of the equation by 3.

Step 2: $\qquad x^2 - 3x = -\dfrac{8}{3}$ _____ Subtract $\dfrac{8}{3}$ from both sides.

Since $\dfrac{1}{2}(-3) = -\dfrac{3}{2}$ and $\left(-\dfrac{3}{2}\right)^2 = \dfrac{9}{4}$, we add $\dfrac{9}{4}$ to both sides of the equation.

Step 3: $\quad x^2 - 3x + \dfrac{9}{4} = -\dfrac{8}{3} + \dfrac{9}{4}$

Step 4: $\qquad \left(x - \dfrac{3}{2}\right)^2 = -\dfrac{5}{12}$ _____ Factor the perfect square trinomial.

Step 5: $\quad x - \dfrac{3}{2} = \pm\sqrt{-\dfrac{5}{12}}$ _____ Apply the square root property.

$$x - \dfrac{3}{2} = \pm\dfrac{i\sqrt{5}}{2\sqrt{3}}$$ _____ Simplify the radical.

$$x - \dfrac{3}{2} = \pm\dfrac{i\sqrt{15}}{6}$$ _____ Rationalize the denominator.

$$x = \dfrac{3}{2} \pm \dfrac{i\sqrt{15}}{6}$$ _____ Add $\dfrac{3}{2}$ to both sides.

$$= \dfrac{9}{6} \pm \dfrac{i\sqrt{15}}{6}$$ _____ Find a common denominator.

$$= \dfrac{9 \pm i\sqrt{15}}{6}$$ _____ Simplify.

The solutions are $\dfrac{9 + i\sqrt{15}}{6}$ and $\dfrac{9 - i\sqrt{15}}{6}$.

3 Recall the **simple interest** formula $I = Prt$, where I is the interest earned, P is the principal, r is the rate of interest, and t is time. If \$100 is invested at a simple interest rate of 5% annually, at the end of 3 years the total interest I earned is

$$I = P \cdot r \cdot t$$

or

$$I = 100 \cdot 0.05 \cdot 3 = \$15$$

and the new principal is

$$\$100 + \$15 = \$115$$

Most of the time, the interest computed on money borrowed or money deposited is **compound interest.** Compound interest, unlike simple interest, is computed on original principal *and* on interest already earned. To see the difference between simple interest and compound interest, suppose that \$100 is invested at a rate of 5% compounded annually. To find the total amount of money at the end of 3 years, we calculate as follows.

$$I = P \cdot r \cdot t$$

First year: Interest = $\$100 \cdot 0.05 \cdot 1 = \$5.00$
New principal = $\$100.00 + \$5.00 = \$105.00$

Second year: Interest = $\$105.00 \cdot 0.05 \cdot 1 = \$5.25$
New principal = $\$105.00 + \$5.25 = \$110.25$

Third year: Interest = $\$110.25 \cdot 0.05 \cdot 1 \approx \$5.51$
New principal = $\$110.25 + \$5.51 = \$115.76$

At the end of the third year, the total compound interest earned is \$15.76, whereas the total simple interest earned is \$15.

It is tedious to calculate compound interest as we did above, so we use a compound interest formula. The formula for calculating the total amount of money when interest is compounded annually is

$$A = P(1 + r)^t$$

where P is the original investment, r is the interest rate per compounding period, and t is the number of periods. For example, the amount of money A at the end of 3 years if \$100 is invested at 5% compounded annually is

$$A = \$100(1 + 0.05)^3 \approx \$100(1.1576) = \$115.76$$

as we previously calculated.

Example 9   **FINDING INTEREST RATES**

Find the interest rate r if \$2000 compounded annually grows to \$2420 in 2 years.

Solution   1. UNDERSTAND the problem. Since the \$2000 is compounded annually, we use the compound interest formula. For this example, make sure that you understand the formula for compounding interest annually.

2. TRANSLATE. We substitute the given values into the formula.

$$A = P(1 + r)^t$$

$$2420 = 2000(1 + r)^2 \qquad \text{Let } A = 2420, P = 2000, \text{ and } t = 2.$$

3. SOLVE. Solve the equation for r.

$$2420 = 2000(1 + r)^2$$

$$\frac{2420}{2000} = (1 + r)^2 \qquad \text{Divide both sides by 2000.}$$

$$\frac{121}{100} = (1 + r)^2 \qquad \text{Simplify the fraction.}$$

$$\pm\sqrt{\frac{121}{100}} = 1 + r \qquad \text{Use the square root property.}$$

$$\pm\frac{11}{10} = 1 + r \qquad \text{Simplify.}$$

$$-1 \pm \frac{11}{10} = r$$

$$-\frac{10}{10} \pm \frac{11}{10} = r$$

$$\frac{1}{10} = r \quad \text{or} \quad -\frac{21}{10} = r$$

4. INTERPRET. The rate cannot be negative, so we reject $-\dfrac{21}{10}$.

Check: $\dfrac{1}{10} = 0.10 = 10\%$ per year. If we invest \$2000 at 10% compounded annually, in 2 years the amount in the account would be $2000(1 + 0.10)^2 = 2420$ dollars, the desired amount.

State: The interest rate is 10% compounded annually.

GRAPHING CALCULATOR EXPLORATIONS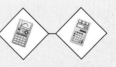

In Section 5.8, we showed how we can use a grapher to approximate real number solutions of a quadratic equation written in standard form. We can also use a grapher to solve a quadratic equation when it is not written in standard form. For example, to solve $(x + 1)^2 = 12$, the quadratic equation in Example 3, we graph the following on the same set of axes. Use Xmin $= -10$, Xmax $= 10$, Ymin $= -13$, and Ymax $= 13$.

$$Y_1 = (x + 1)^2 \quad \text{and} \quad Y_2 = 12$$

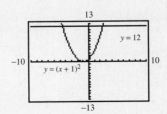

Use the Intersect feature or the Zoom and Trace features to locate the points of intersection of the graphs. The x-values of these points are the solutions of $(x + 1)^2 = 12$. The solutions, rounded to two decimal places, are 2.46 and −4.46.

Check to see that these numbers are approximations of the exact solutions $-1 \pm 2\sqrt{3}$.

Use a graphing calculator to solve each quadratic equation. Round all solutions to the nearest hundredth.

1. $x(x - 5) = 8$

2. $x(x + 2) = 5$

3. $x^2 + 0.5x = 0.3x + 1$

4. $x^2 - 2.6x = -2.2x + 3$

5. Use a grapher and solve $(2x - 5)^2 = -16$, Example 4 in this section, using the window

$$\text{Xmin} = -20$$

$$\text{Xmax} = 20$$

$$\text{Xscl} = 1$$

$$\text{Ymin} = -20$$

$$\text{Ymax} = 20$$

$$\text{Yscl} = 1$$

Explain the results. Compare your results with the solution found in Example 4.

6. What are the advantages and disadvantages of using a grapher to solve quadratic equations?

Exercise Set 8.1

Use the square root property to solve each equation. These equations have real-number solutions. See Examples 1 through 3.

1. $x^2 = 16$

2. $x^2 = 49$

3. $x^2 - 7 = 0$

4. $x^2 - 11 = 0$

5. $x^2 = 18$

6. $y^2 = 20$

7. $3z^2 - 30 = 0$

8. $2x^2 = 4$

9. $(x + 5)^2 = 9$

10. $(y - 3)^2 = 4$

11. $(z - 6)^2 = 18$

12. $(y + 4)^2 = 27$

13. $(2x - 3)^2 = 8$

14. $(4x + 9)^2 = 6$

Use the square root property to solve each equation. See Examples 1 through 4.

15. $x^2 + 9 = 0$

16. $x^2 + 4 = 0$

17. $x^2 - 6 = 0$

18. $y^2 - 10 = 0$

19. $2z^2 + 16 = 0$

20. $3p^2 + 36 = 0$

21. $(x - 1)^2 = -16$

22. $(y + 2)^2 = -25$

23. $(z + 7)^2 = 5$

24. $(x + 10)^2 = 11$

25. $(x + 3)^2 = -8$

26. $(y - 4)^2 = -18$

Add the proper constant to each binomial so that the resulting trinomial is a perfect square trinomial. Then factor the trinomial.

27. $x^2 + 16x$

28. $y^2 + 2y$

29. $z^2 - 12z$

30. $x^2 - 8x$

31. $p^2 + 9p$

32. $n^2 + 5n$

33. $x^2 + x$

34. $y^2 - y$

Find two possible missing terms so that each is a perfect square trinomial.

35. $x^2 + \quad + 16$

36. $y^2 + \quad + 9$

37. $z^2 + \quad + \dfrac{25}{4}$

38. $x^2 + \quad + \dfrac{1}{4}$

Solve each equation by completing the square. These equations have real number solutions. See Examples 5 through 7.

39. $x^2 + 8x = -15$

40. $y^2 + 6y = -8$

41. $x^2 + 6x + 2 = 0$

42. $x^2 - 2x - 2 = 0$

43. $x^2 + x - 1 = 0$

44. $x^2 + 3x - 2 = 0$

45. $x^2 + 2x - 5 = 0$

46. $y^2 + y - 7 = 0$

47. $3p^2 - 12p + 2 = 0$

48. $2x^2 + 14x - 1 = 0$

49. $4y^2 - 12y - 2 = 0$

50. $6x^2 - 3 = 6x$

51. $2x^2 + 7x = 4$

52. $3x^2 - 4x = 4$

53. $x^2 - 4x - 5 = 0$

54. $y^2 + 6y - 8 = 0$

55. $x^2 + 8x + 1 = 0$

56. $x^2 - 10x + 2 = 0$

57. $3y^2 + 6y - 4 = 0$

58. $2y^2 + 12y + 3 = 0$

59. $2x^2 - 3x - 5 = 0$

60. $5x^2 + 3x - 2 = 0$

Solve each equation by completing the square. See Examples 5 through 8.

61. $y^2 + 2y + 2 = 0$

62. $x^2 + 4x + 6 = 0$

63. $x^2 - 6x + 3 = 0$

64. $x^2 - 7x - 1 = 0$

65. $2a^2 + 8a = -12$

66. $3x^2 + 12x = -14$

67. $5x^2 + 15x - 1 = 0$

68. $16y^2 + 16y - 1 = 0$

69. $2x^2 - x + 6 = 0$

70. $4x^2 - 2x + 5 = 0$

71. $x^2 + 10x + 28 = 0$

72. $y^2 + 8y + 18 = 0$

73. $z^2 + 3z - 4 = 0$

74. $y^2 + y - 2 = 0$

75. $2x^2 - 4x + 3 = 0$

76. $9x^2 - 36x = -40$

77. $3x^2 + 3x = 5$

78. $5y^2 - 15y = 1$

Use the formula $A = P(1 + r)^t$ to solve Exercises 79–82. See Example 9.

79. Find the rate r at which $3000 grows to $4320 in 2 years.

80. Find the rate r at which $800 grows to $882 in 2 years.

81. Find the rate at which $810 grows to $1000 in 2 years.

82. Find the rate at which $2000 grows to $2880 in 2 years.

83. In your own words, what is the difference between simple interest and compound interest?

84. If you are depositing money in an account that pays 4%, would you prefer the interest to be simple or compound? Explain why.

85. If you are borrowing money at a rate of 10%, would you prefer the interest to be simple or compound? Explain why.

Neglecting air resistance, the distance $s(t)$ in feet traveled by a freely falling object is given by the function $s(t) = 16t^2$, where t is time in seconds. Use this formula to solve Exercises 86 through 89. Round answers to two decimal places.

86. The Petronas Towers in Kuala Lumpur, built in 1997, are the tallest buildings in Malaysia. Each tower is 1483 feet tall. How long would it take an object to fall to the ground from the top of one of the towers? (*Source:* Council on Tall Buildings and Urban Habitat, Lehigh University)

87. The height of the Chicago Beach Tower Hotel, built in 1998 in Dubai, United Arab Emirates, is 1053 feet. How long would it take an object to fall to the ground from the top of the building? (*Source:* Council on Tall Buildings and Urban Habitat, Lehigh University)

88. The height of the Nurek Dam in Tajikistan (part of the former USSR that borders Afghanistan) is 984 feet. How long would it take an object to fall from the top to the base of the dam? (*Source:* U.S. Committee on Large Dams of the International Commission on Large Dams)

89. The Hoover Dam, located on the Colorado River on the border of Nevada and Arizona near Las Vegas, is 725 feet tall. How long would it take an object to fall from the top to the base of the dam? (*Source:* U.S. Committee on Large Dams of the International Commission on Large Dams)

Solve.

△ **90.** The area of a square room is 225 square feet. Find the dimensions of the room.

△ **91.** The area of a circle is 36π square inches. Find the radius of the circle.

△ **92.** An isosceles right triangle has legs of equal length. If the hypotenuse is 20 centimeters long, find the length of each leg.

△ **93.** A 27-inch TV is advertised in the *Daily Sentry* newspaper. If 27 inches is the measure of the diagonal of the picture tube, find the measure of the side of the picture tube.

 A common equation used in business is a demand equation. It expresses the relationship between the unit price of some commodity and the quantity demanded. For Exercises 94 and 95, p represents the unit price and x represents the quantity demanded in thousands.

94. A manufacturing company has found that the demand equation for a certain type of scissors is given by the equation $p = -x^2 + 47$. Find the demand for the scissors if the price is $11 per pair.

95. Acme, Inc., sells desk lamps and has found that the demand equation for a certain style of desk lamp is given by the equation $p = -x^2 + 15$. Find the demand for the desk lamp if the price is $7 per lamp.

REVIEW EXERCISES

Simplify each expression. See Section 7.1.

96. $\dfrac{3}{4} - \sqrt{\dfrac{25}{16}}$

97. $\dfrac{3}{5} + \sqrt{\dfrac{16}{25}}$

98. $\dfrac{1}{2} - \sqrt{\dfrac{9}{4}}$

99. $\dfrac{9}{10} - \sqrt{\dfrac{49}{100}}$

Simplify each expression. See Section 7.5.

100. $\dfrac{6 + 4\sqrt{5}}{2}$

101. $\dfrac{10 - 20\sqrt{3}}{2}$

102. $\dfrac{3 - 9\sqrt{5}}{6}$

103. $\dfrac{12 - 8\sqrt{7}}{16}$

Evaluate $\sqrt{b^2 - 4ac}$ for each set of values. See Section 7.3.

104. $a = 2, b = 4, c = -1$ **105.** $a = 1, b = 6, c = 2$

106. $a = 3, b = -1, c = -2$ **107.** $a = 1, b = -3, c = -1$

8.2 SOLVING QUADRATIC EQUATIONS BY THE QUADRATIC FORMULA

▶ **OBJECTIVES**

CD-ROM   SSM

SSG   Video

1. Solve quadratic equations by using the quadratic formula.
2. Determine the number and type of solutions of a quadratic equation by using the discriminant.
3. Solve geometric pr\oblems modeled by quadratic equations.

1   Any quadratic equation can be solved by completing the square. Since the same sequence of steps is repeated each time we complete the square, let's complete the square for a general quadratic equation, $ax^2 + bx + c = 0$. By doing so, we find a pattern for the solutions of a quadratic equation known as the **quadratic formula.**

Recall that to complete the square for an equation such as $ax^2 + bx + c = 0$, we first divide both sides by the coefficient of x^2.

$$ax^2 + bx + c = 0$$

$$x^2 + \frac{b}{a}x + \frac{c}{a} = 0 \qquad \text{Divide both sides by } a, \text{ the coefficient of } x^2.$$

$$x^2 + \frac{b}{a}x = -\frac{c}{a} \qquad \text{Subtract the constant } \frac{c}{a} \text{ from both sides.}$$

Next, find the square of half $\frac{b}{a}$, the coefficient of x.

$$\frac{1}{2}\left(\frac{b}{a}\right) = \frac{b}{2a} \quad \text{and} \quad \left(\frac{b}{2a}\right)^2 = \frac{b^2}{4a^2}$$

Add this result to both sides of the equation.

$$x^2 + \frac{b}{a}x + \frac{b^2}{4a^2} = -\frac{c}{a} + \frac{b^2}{4a^2} \qquad \text{Add } \frac{b^2}{4a^2} \text{ to both sides.}$$

$$x^2 + \frac{b}{a}x + \frac{b^2}{4a^2} = \frac{-c \cdot 4a}{a \cdot 4a} + \frac{b^2}{4a^2} \qquad \text{Find a common denominator on the right side.}$$

$$x^2 + \frac{b}{a}x + \frac{b^2}{4a^2} = \frac{b^2 - 4ac}{4a^2} \qquad \text{Simplify the right side.}$$

$$\left(x + \frac{b}{2a}\right)^2 = \frac{b^2 - 4ac}{4a^2} \qquad \text{Factor the perfect square trinomial on the left side.}$$

$$x + \frac{b}{2a} = \pm\sqrt{\frac{b^2 - 4ac}{4a^2}} \qquad \text{Apply the square root property.}$$

$$x + \frac{b}{2a} = \pm\frac{\sqrt{b^2 - 4ac}}{2a} \qquad \text{Simplify the radical.}$$

$$x = -\frac{b}{2a} \pm \frac{\sqrt{b^2 - 4ac}}{2a} \qquad \text{Subtract } \frac{b}{2a} \text{ from both sides.}$$

$$x = \frac{-b \pm \sqrt{b^2 - 4ac}}{2a} \qquad \text{Simplify.}$$

This equation identifies the solutions of the general quadratic equation in standard form and is called the quadratic formula. It can be used to solve any equation written in standard form $ax^2 + bx + c = 0$ as long as a is not 0.

QUADRATIC FORMULA

A quadratic equation written in the form $ax^2 + bx + c = 0$ has the solutions

$$x = \frac{-b \pm \sqrt{b^2 - 4ac}}{2a}$$

Example 1 Solve $3x^2 + 16x + 5 = 0$ for x.

Solution This equation is in standard form, so $a = 3, b = 16$, and $c = 5$. Substitute these values into the quadratic formula.

$$x = \frac{-b \pm \sqrt{b^2 - 4ac}}{2a} \qquad \text{Quadratic formula.}$$

$$= \frac{-16 \pm \sqrt{16^2 - 4(3)(5)}}{2 \cdot 3} \qquad \text{Use } a = 3, b = 16, \text{ and } c = 5.$$

$$= \frac{-16 \pm \sqrt{256 - 60}}{6}$$

$$= \frac{-16 \pm \sqrt{196}}{6} = \frac{-16 \pm 14}{6}$$

$$x = \frac{-16 + 14}{6} = -\frac{1}{3} \quad \text{or} \quad x = \frac{-16 - 14}{6} = -\frac{30}{6} = -5$$

The solutions are $-\dfrac{1}{3}$ and -5.

Example 2 Solve $2x^2 - 4x = 3$.

Solution First write the equation in standard form by subtracting 3 from both sides.

$$2x^2 - 4x - 3 = 0$$

Now $a = 2, b = -4$, and $c = -3$. Substitute these values into the quadratic formula.

> **HELPFUL HINT**
> To replace a, b, and c correctly in the quadratic formula, write the quadratic equation in standard form $ax^2 + bx + c = 0$.

$$x = \frac{-b \pm \sqrt{b^2 - 4ac}}{2a}$$

$$= \frac{-(-4) \pm \sqrt{(-4)^2 - 4(2)(-3)}}{2 \cdot 2}$$

$$= \frac{4 \pm \sqrt{16 + 24}}{4}$$

$$= \frac{4 \pm \sqrt{40}}{4} = \frac{4 \pm 2\sqrt{10}}{4}$$

$$= \frac{2(2 \pm \sqrt{10})}{2 \cdot 2} = \frac{2 \pm \sqrt{10}}{2}$$

The solutions are $\dfrac{2 + \sqrt{10}}{2}$ and $\dfrac{2 - \sqrt{10}}{2}$.

> **HELPFUL HINT**
> To simplify the expression $\dfrac{4 \pm 2\sqrt{10}}{4}$ in the preceding example, note that 2 is factored out of both terms of the numerator *before* simplifying.
>
> $$\frac{4 \pm 2\sqrt{10}}{4} = \frac{2(2 \pm \sqrt{10})}{2 \cdot 2} = \frac{2 \pm \sqrt{10}}{2}$$

Example 3 Solve $\frac{1}{4}m^2 - m + \frac{1}{2} = 0$.

Solution We could use the quadratic formula with $a = \frac{1}{4}$, $b = -1$, and $c = \frac{1}{2}$. Instead, we find a simpler, equivalent standard form equation whose coefficients are not fractions. Multiply both sides of the equation by 4 to clear fractions.

$$4\left(\frac{1}{4}m^2 - m + \frac{1}{2}\right) = 4 \cdot 0$$

$$m^2 - 4m + 2 = 0 \qquad \text{Simplify.}$$

Substitute $a = 1$, $b = -4$, and $c = 2$ into the quadratic formula and simplify.

$$m = \frac{-(-4) \pm \sqrt{(-4)^2 - 4(1)(2)}}{2 \cdot 1} = \frac{4 \pm \sqrt{16 - 8}}{2}$$

$$= \frac{4 \pm \sqrt{8}}{2} = \frac{4 \pm 2\sqrt{2}}{2} = \frac{2(2 \pm \sqrt{2})}{2}$$

$$= 2 \pm \sqrt{2}$$

The solutions are $2 + \sqrt{2}$ and $2 - \sqrt{2}$. ▪

Example 4 Solve $x = -3x^2 - 3$.

Solution The equation in standard form is $3x^2 + x + 3 = 0$. Thus, let $a = 3$, $b = 1$, and $c = 3$ in the quadratic formula.

$$x = \frac{-1 \pm \sqrt{1^2 - 4(3)(3)}}{2 \cdot 3} = \frac{-1 \pm \sqrt{1 - 36}}{6} = \frac{-1 \pm \sqrt{-35}}{6} = \frac{-1 \pm i\sqrt{35}}{6}$$

The solutions are $\dfrac{-1 + i\sqrt{35}}{6}$ and $\dfrac{-1 - i\sqrt{35}}{6}$. ▪

In Example 1, the equation $3x^2 + 16x + 5 = 0$ had 2 real roots, $-\frac{1}{3}$ and -5. In Example 4, the equation $3x^2 + x + 3 = 0$ (written in standard form) had no real roots. How do their related graphs compare? Recall that the x-intercepts of $f(x) = 3x^2 + 16x + 5$ occur where $f(x) = 0$ or where $3x^2 + 16x + 5 = 0$. Since this equation has 2 real roots, the graph has 2 x-intercepts. Similarly, since the equation $3x^2 + x + 3 = 0$ has no real roots, the graph of $f(x) = 3x^2 + x + 3$ has no x-intercepts.

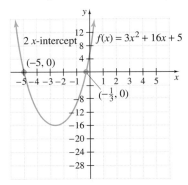

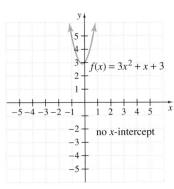

2 In the quadratic formula, $x = \dfrac{-b \pm \sqrt{b^2 - 4ac}}{2a}$, the radicand $b^2 - 4ac$ is called the **discriminant** because, by knowing its value, we can **discriminate** among the possible number and type of solutions of a quadratic equation. Possible values of the discriminant and their meanings are summarized next.

DISCRIMINANT

The following table corresponds the discriminant $b^2 - 4ac$ of a quadratic equation of the form $ax^2 + bx + c = 0$ with the number and type of solutions of the equation.

$b^2 - 4ac$	Number and Type of Solutions
Positive	Two real solutions
Zero	One real solution
Negative	Two complex but not real solutions

Example 5 Use the discriminant to determine the number and type of solutions of each quadratic equation.

a. $x^2 + 2x + 1 = 0$ **b.** $3x^2 + 2 = 0$ **c.** $2x^2 - 7x - 4 = 0$

Solution **a.** In $x^2 + 2x + 1 = 0$, $a = 1$, $b = 2$, and $c = 1$. Thus,

$$b^2 - 4ac = 2^2 - 4(1)(1) = 0$$

Since $b^2 - 4ac = 0$, this quadratic equation has one real solution.

b. In this equation, $a = 3$, $b = 0$, $c = 2$. Then $b^2 - 4ac = 0 - 4(3)(2) = -24$. Since $b^2 - 4ac$ is negative, the quadratic equation has two complex but not real solutions.

c. In this equation, $a = 2$, $b = -7$, and $c = -4$. Then

$$b^2 - 4ac = (-7)^2 - 4(2)(-4) = 81$$

Since $b^2 - 4ac$ is positive, the quadratic equation has two real solutions.

The discriminant helps us determine the number and type of solutions of a quadratic equation, $ax^2 + bx + c = 0$. Recall that the solutions of this equation are the same as the x-intercepts of its related graph $f(x) = ax^2 + bx + c$. This means that the discriminant of $ax^2 + bx + c = 0$ also tells us the number of x-intercepts for the graph of $f(x) = ax^2 + bx + c$.

GRAPH OF $f(x) = ax^2 + bx + c$

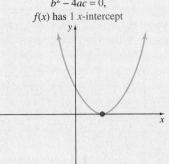

$b^2 - 4ac > 0$,
$f(x)$ has 2 x-intercepts

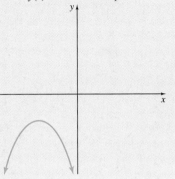

$b^2 - 4ac = 0$,
$f(x)$ has 1 x-intercept

$b^2 - 4ac < 0$,
$f(x)$ has no x-intercepts

3 The quadratic formula is useful in solving problems that are modeled by quadratic equations.

△ **Example 6** **CALCULATING DISTANCE SAVED**

At a local university, students often leave the sidewalk and cut across the lawn to save walking distance. Given the diagram below of a favorite place to cut across the lawn, approximate how many feet of walking distance a student saves by cutting across the lawn instead of walking on the sidewalk.

Solution 1. UNDERSTAND. Read and reread the problem. In the diagram, notice that a triangle is formed. Since the corner of the block forms a right angle, we use the Pythagorean theorem for right triangles. You may want to review this theorem.

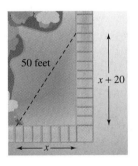

50 feet

$x + 20$

x

2. TRANSLATE. By the Pythagorean theorem, we have

In words: $(\text{leg})^2 + (\text{leg})^2 = (\text{hypotenuse})^2$

Translate: $x^2 + (x + 20)^2 = 50^2$

3. SOLVE. Use the quadratic formula to solve.

$$x^2 + x^2 + 40x + 400 = 2500 \qquad \text{Square } (x + 20) \text{ and } 50.$$

$$2x^2 + 40x - 2100 = 0 \qquad \text{Set the equation equal to 0.}$$

$$x^2 + 20x - 1050 = 0 \qquad \text{Divide by 2.}$$

Here, $a = 1, b = 20, c = -1050$. By the quadratic formula,

$$x = \frac{-20 \pm \sqrt{20^2 - 4(1)(-1050)}}{2 \cdot 1}$$

$$= \frac{-20 \pm \sqrt{400 + 4200}}{2} = \frac{-20 \pm \sqrt{4600}}{2}$$

$$= \frac{-20 \pm \sqrt{100 \cdot 46}}{2} = \frac{-20 \pm 10\sqrt{46}}{2}$$

$$= -10 \pm 5\sqrt{46} \qquad \text{Simplify.}$$

4. **INTERPRET.**

   Check: Your calculations in the quadratic formula. The length of a side of a triangle can't be negative, so we reject $-10 - 5\sqrt{46}$. Since $-10 + 5\sqrt{46} \approx 24$ feet, the walking distance along the sidewalk is

   $$x + (x + 20) \approx 24 + (24 + 20) = 68 \text{ feet.}$$

   State: A student saves $68 - 50$ or 18 feet of walking distance by cutting across the lawn.

SPOTLIGHT ON DECISION MAKING

Suppose you are a registered dietician. Recently, you read an article in a nutrition journal that described a relationship between weight and the Recommended Dietary Allowance (RDA) for vitamin A in children up to age 10. The relationship is $y = 0.149x^2 - 4.475x + 406.478$, where y is the RDA for vitamin A in micrograms for a child whose weight is x pounds. (*Source:* Food and Nutrition Board, National Academy of Sciences—Institute of Medicine, 1989)

   You are working with a 4-year-old patient who weighs 40 pounds. After analyzing her diet, you are able to determine that she is currently getting an average of 400 micrograms of vitamin A daily. Decide whether her current vitamin A intake is adequate. If not, how much more is needed each day? In either case, determine how much weight she will need to gain before a daily intake of 500 micrograms of vitamin A is appropriate.

Exercise Set 8.2

Use the quadratic formula to solve each equation. These equations have real number solutions. See Examples 1 through 3.

1. $m^2 + 5m - 6 = 0$

2. $p^2 + 11p - 12 = 0$

3. $2y = 5y^2 - 3$

4. $5x^2 - 3 = 14x$

5. $x^2 - 6x + 9 = 0$

6. $y^2 + 10y + 25 = 0$

7. $x^2 + 7x + 4 = 0$

8. $y^2 + 5y + 3 = 0$

9. $8m^2 - 2m = 7$

10. $11n^2 - 9n = 1$

11. $3m^2 - 7m = 3$

12. $x^2 - 13 = 5x$

13. $\frac{1}{2}x^2 - x - 1 = 0$

14. $\frac{1}{6}x^2 + x + \frac{1}{3} = 0$

15. $\frac{2}{5}y^2 + \frac{1}{5}y = \frac{3}{5}$

16. $\frac{1}{8}x^2 + x = \frac{5}{2}$

17. $\frac{1}{3}y^2 - y - \frac{1}{6} = 0$

18. $\frac{1}{2}y^2 = y + \frac{1}{2}$

19. Solve Exercise 1 by factoring. Explain the result.

20. Solve Exercise 2 by factoring. Explain the result.

Use the quadratic formula to solve each equation. See Example 4.

21. $6 = -4x^2 + 3x$

22. $9x^2 + x + 2 = 0$

23. $(x + 5)(x - 1) = 2$

24. $x(x + 6) = 2$

25. $10y^2 + 10y + 3 = 0$

26. $3y^2 + 6y + 5 = 0$

The solutions of the quadratic equation $ax^2 + bx + c = 0$ are

$$\frac{-b + \sqrt{b^2 - 4ac}}{2a} \quad and \quad \frac{-b - \sqrt{b^2 - 4ac}}{2a}$$

27. Show that the sum of these solutions is $\dfrac{-b}{a}$.

28. Show that the product of these solutions is $\dfrac{c}{a}$.

Use the discriminant to determine the number and type of solutions of each equation. See Example 5.

29. $9x - 2x^2 + 5 = 0$

30. $5 - 4x + 12x^2 = 0$

31. $4x^2 + 12x = -9$

32. $9x^2 + 1 = 6x$

33. $3x = -2x^2 + 7$

34. $3x^2 = 5 - 7x$

35. $6 = 4x - 5x^2$

36. $8x = 3 - 9x^2$

Use the quadratic formula to solve each equation. These equations have real number solutions.

37. $x^2 + 5x = -2$

38. $y^2 - 8 = 4y$

39. $(m + 2)(2m - 6) = 5(m - 1) - 12$

40. $7p(p - 2) + 2(p + 4) = 3$

41. $\dfrac{x^2}{3} - x = \dfrac{5}{3}$

42. $\dfrac{x^2}{2} - 3 = -\dfrac{9}{2}x$

43. $x(6x + 2) - 3 = 0$

44. $x(7x + 1) = 2$

Use the quadratic formula to solve each equation.

45. $x^2 + 6x + 13 = 0$

46. $x^2 + 2x + 2 = 0$

47. $\dfrac{2}{5}y^2 + \dfrac{1}{5}y + \dfrac{3}{5} = 0$

48. $\dfrac{1}{8}x^2 + x + \dfrac{5}{2} = 0$

49. $\dfrac{1}{2}y^2 = y - \dfrac{1}{2}$

50. $\dfrac{2}{3}x^2 - \dfrac{20}{3}x = -\dfrac{100}{6}$

51. $(n - 2)^2 = 15n$

52. $\left(p - \dfrac{1}{2}\right)^2 = \dfrac{p}{2}$

Solve. See Example 6.

△ **53.** Nancy, Thelma, and John Varner live on a corner lot. Often, neighborhood children cut across their lot to save walking distance. Given the diagram below, approximate to the nearest foot how many feet of walking distance is saved by cutting across their property instead of walking around the lot.

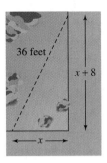

△ **54.** Given the diagram below, approximate to the nearest foot how many feet of walking distance a person saves by cutting across the lawn instead of walking on the sidewalk.

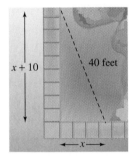

△ **55.** The hypotenuse of an isosceles right triangle is 2 centimeters longer than either of its legs. Find the exact length of each side. (*Hint:* An isosceles right triangle is a right triangle whose legs are the same length.)

△ **56.** The hypotenuse of an isosceles right triangle is one meter longer than either of its legs. Find the length of each side.

△ **57.** Uri Chechov's rectangular dog pen for his Irish setter must have an area of 400 square feet. Also, the length must be 10 feet longer than the width. Find the dimensions of the pen.

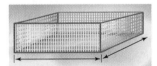

△ **58.** An entry in the Peach Festival Poster Contest must be rectangular and have an area of 1200 square inches. Furthermore, its length must be 20 inches longer than its width. Find the dimensions each entry must have.

△ **59.** A holding pen for cattle must be square and have a diagonal length of 100 meters.

   a. Find the length of a side of the pen.

   b. Find the area of the pen.

△ **60.** A rectangle is three times longer than it is wide. It has a diagonal of length 50 centimeters.

a. Find the dimensions of the rectangle.

b. Find the perimeter of the rectangle.

61. If a point *B* divides a line segment such that the smaller portion is to the larger portion as the larger is to the whole, the whole is the length of the *golden ratio.*

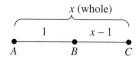

The golden ratio was thought by the Greeks to be the most pleasing to the eye, and many of their buildings contained numerous examples of the golden ratio. The value of the golden ratio is the positive solution of

$$\underset{\text{(larger)}}{\overset{\text{(smaller)}}{\frac{x-1}{1}}} = \underset{\text{(whole)}}{\overset{\text{(larger)}}{\frac{1}{x}}}$$

Find this value.

△ **62.** The base of a triangle is four more than twice its height. If the area of the triangle is 42 square centimeters, find its base and height.

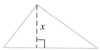

The Wollomombi Falls in Australia have a height of 1100 feet. A pebble is thrown upward from the top of the falls with an initial velocity of 20 feet per second. The height of the pebble h after t seconds is given by the equation $h = -16t^2 + 20t + 1100$. Use this equation for Exercises 63 and 64.

63. How long after the pebble is thrown will it hit the ground? Round to the nearest tenth of a second.

64. How long after the pebble is thrown will it be 550 feet from the ground? Round to the nearest tenth of a second.

A ball is thrown downward from the top of a 180-foot building with an initial velocity of 20 feet per second. The height of the ball h after t seconds is given by the equation $h = -16t^2 - 20t + 180$. Use this equation to answer Exercises 65 and 66.

65. How long after the ball is thrown will it strike the ground? Round the result to the nearest tenth of a second.

66. How long after the ball is thrown will it be 50 feet from the ground? Round the result to the nearest tenth of a second.

The accompanying graph shows the daily low temperatures for one week in New Orleans, Louisiana.

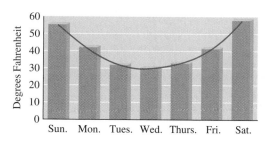

67. Which day of the week shows the greatest decrease in low temperature?

68. Which day of the week shows the greatest increase in low temperature?

69. Which day of the week had the lowest low temperature?

70. Use the graph to estimate the low temperature on Thursday.

Notice that the shape of the temperature graph is similar to a parabola (see Section 5.9). In fact, this graph can be modeled by the quadratic function $f(x) = 3x^2 - 18x + 56$, where $f(x)$ is the temperature in degrees Fahrenheit and x is the number of days from Sunday. (This graph is shown in red above.) Use this function to answer Exercises 71 and 72.

71. Use the quadratic function given to approximate the temperature on Thursday. Does your answer agree with the graph above?

72. Use the function given and the quadratic formula to find when the temperature was 35°F. [*Hint:* Let $f(x) = 35$ and solve for *x*.] Round your answer to one decimal place and interpret your result. Does your answer agree with the graph above?

73. Wal-Mart Stores' net income can be modeled by the quadratic function $f(x) = 128.5x^2 - 69.5x + 2681$, where $f(x)$ is net income in millions of dollars and *x* is the number of years after 1995. (*Source:* Based on data from Wal-Mart Stores, Inc.)

a. Find Wal-Mart's net income in 1997.

b. If the trend described by the model continues, predict the year after 1995 in which Wal-Mart's net income will be $15,000 million. Round to the nearest whole year.

74. The number of inmates in custody in U.S. prisons and jails can be modeled by the quadratic function

$p(x) = -716.2x^2 + 87,453.7x + 1,148,702$ where $p(x)$ is the number of inmates and x is the number of years after 1990. (*Source:* Based on data from the Bureau of Justice Statistics, U.S. Department of Justice, 1990–1998) Round **a** and **b** to the nearest ten thousand.

  a. Find the number of prison inmates in the United States in 1992.

  b. Find the number of prison inmates in the United States in 1998.

 75. Use a graphing calculator to solve Exercises 63 and 65.

 76. Use a graphing calculator to solve Exercises 64 and 66.

Recall that the discriminant also tells us the number of x-intercepts of the related function.

 77. Check the results of Exercise 29 by graphing $y = 9x - 2x^2 + 5$.

 78. Check the results of Exercise 30 by graphing $y = 5 - 4x + 12x^2$.

REVIEW EXERCISES

Solve each equation. See Sections 6.6 and 7.6.

79. $\sqrt{5x - 2} = 3$

80. $\sqrt{y + 2} + 7 = 12$

81. $\dfrac{1}{x} + \dfrac{2}{5} = \dfrac{7}{x}$

82. $\dfrac{10}{z} = \dfrac{5}{z} - \dfrac{1}{3}$

Factor. See Section 5.7.

83. $x^4 + x^2 - 20$

84. $2y^4 + 11y^2 - 6$

85. $z^4 - 13z^2 + 36$

86. $x^4 - 1$

A Look Ahead

Example

Solve $x^2 - 3\sqrt{2}x + 2 = 0$.

Solution

In this equation, $a = 1$, $b = -3\sqrt{2}$, and $c = 2$. By the quadratic formula, we have

$$x = \frac{-b \pm \sqrt{b^2 - 4ac}}{2a}$$

$$= \frac{3\sqrt{2} \pm \sqrt{(-3\sqrt{2})^2 - 4(1)(2)}}{2(1)}$$

$$= \frac{3\sqrt{2} \pm \sqrt{18 - 8}}{2} = \frac{3\sqrt{2} \pm \sqrt{10}}{2}$$

The solution set is $\left\{ \dfrac{3\sqrt{2} + \sqrt{10}}{2}, \dfrac{3\sqrt{2} - \sqrt{10}}{2} \right\}$.

Use the quadratic formula to solve each quadratic equation. See the preceding example.

87. $3x^2 - \sqrt{12}x + 1 = 0$

88. $5x^2 + \sqrt{20}x + 1 = 0$

89. $x^2 + \sqrt{2}x + 1 = 0$

90. $x^2 - \sqrt{2}x + 1 = 0$

91. $2x^2 - \sqrt{3}x - 1 = 0$

92. $7x^2 + \sqrt{7}x - 2 = 0$

8.3 SOLVING EQUATIONS BY USING QUADRATIC METHODS

▶ **OBJECTIVES**

  1. Solve various equations that are quadratic in form.
  2. Solve problems that lead to quadratic equations.

1 In this section, we discuss various types of equations that can be solved in part by using the methods for solving quadratic equations.

  Once each equation is simplified, you may want to use these steps when deciding what method to use to solve the quadratic equation.

SOLVING A QUADRATIC EQUATION

Step 1: If the equation is in the form $(ax + b)^2 = c$, use the square root property and solve. If not, go to Step 2.

Step 2: Write the equation in standard form: $ax^2 + bx + c = 0$.

Step 3: Try to solve the equation by the factoring method. If not possible, go to Step 4.

Step 4: Solve the equation by the quadratic formula.

The first example is a radical equation that becomes a quadratic equation once we square both sides.

Example 1   Solve $x - \sqrt{x} - 6 = 0$.

Solution   Recall that to solve a radical equation, first get the radical alone on one side of the equation. Then square both sides.

$$x - 6 = \sqrt{x} \qquad \text{Add } \sqrt{x} \text{ to both sides.}$$

$$(x - 6)^2 = (\sqrt{x})^2 \qquad \text{Square both sides.}$$

$$x^2 - 12x + 36 = x$$

$$x^2 - 13x + 36 = 0 \qquad \text{Set the equation equal to 0.}$$

$$(x - 9)(x - 4) = 0$$

$$x - 9 = 0 \quad \text{or} \quad x - 4 = 0$$

$$x = 9 \qquad\qquad x = 4$$

Check

$$\text{Let } x = 9 \qquad\qquad\qquad \text{Let } x = 4$$

$$x - \sqrt{x} - 6 = 0 \qquad\qquad x - \sqrt{x} - 6 = 0$$

$$9 - \sqrt{9} - 6 \stackrel{?}{=} 0 \qquad\qquad 4 - \sqrt{4} - 6 \stackrel{?}{=} 0$$

$$9 - 3 - 6 \stackrel{?}{=} 0 \qquad\qquad 4 - 2 - 6 \stackrel{?}{=} 0$$

$$0 = 0 \quad \text{True.} \qquad\qquad -4 = 0 \quad \text{False.}$$

The solution is 9.

Example 2   Solve $\dfrac{3x}{x - 2} - \dfrac{x + 1}{x} = \dfrac{6}{x(x - 2)}$.

Solution   In this equation, x cannot be either 2 or 0, because these values cause denominators to equal zero. To solve for x, we first multiply both sides of the equation by $x(x - 2)$ to clear the fractions. By the distributive property, this means that we multiply each term by $x(x - 2)$.

$$x(x - 2)\left(\frac{3x}{x - 2}\right) - x(x - 2)\left(\frac{x + 1}{x}\right) = x(x - 2)\left[\frac{6}{x(x - 2)}\right]$$

$$3x^2 - (x - 2)(x + 1) = 6 \qquad \text{Simplify.}$$

$$3x^2 - (x^2 - x - 2) = 6 \qquad \text{Multiply.}$$

$$3x^2 - x^2 + x + 2 = 6$$

$$2x^2 + x - 4 = 0 \qquad \text{Simplify.}$$

This equation cannot be factored using integers, so we solve by the quadratic formula.

$$x = \frac{-1 \pm \sqrt{1^2 - 4(2)(-4)}}{2 \cdot 2} \qquad \begin{array}{l}\text{Use } a = 2, b = 1, \text{ and } c = -4 \text{ in} \\ \text{the quadratic formula.}\end{array}$$

$$= \frac{-1 \pm \sqrt{1 + 32}}{4} \qquad \text{Simplify.}$$

$$= \frac{-1 \pm \sqrt{33}}{4}$$

Neither proposed solution will make the denominators 0.

The solutions are $\dfrac{-1 + \sqrt{33}}{4}$ and $\dfrac{-1 - \sqrt{33}}{4}$.   ▪

Example 3   Solve $p^4 - 3p^2 - 4 = 0$.

Solution   First we factor the trinomial.

$$p^4 - 3p^2 - 4 = 0$$

$$(p^2 - 4)(p^2 + 1) = 0 \qquad \text{Factor.}$$

$$(p - 2)(p + 2)(p^2 + 1) = 0 \qquad \begin{array}{l}\text{Factor further.} \\ \text{Set each factor}\end{array}$$

$$p - 2 = 0 \quad \text{or} \quad p + 2 = 0 \quad \text{or} \quad p^2 + 1 = 0 \qquad \begin{array}{l}\text{equal to 0 and solve.}\end{array}$$

$$p = 2 \qquad\qquad p = -2 \qquad\qquad p^2 = -1$$

$$p = \pm\sqrt{-1} = \pm i$$

The solutions are $2, -2, i$ and $-i$.   ▪

> **HELPFUL HINT**
> Example 3 can be solved using substitution also. Think of
> $p^4 - 3p^2 - 4 = 0$ as
> $(p^2)^2 - 3p^2 - 4 = 0$ Then let $x = p^2$, and solve and substitute back. The
>   solutions will be the same.
> $x^2 - 3x - 4 = 0$

Example 4   Solve $(x - 3)^2 - 3(x - 3) - 4 = 0$.

Solution   Notice that the quantity $(x - 3)$ is repeated in this equation. Sometimes it is help-ful to substitute a variable (in this case other than x) for the repeated quantity. We will let $y = x - 3$. Then

$$(x - 3)^2 - 3(x - 3) - 4 = 0$$

becomes

$$y^2 - 3y - 4 = 0 \qquad \text{Let } x - 3 = y.$$

$$(y - 4)(y + 1) = 0 \qquad \text{Factor.}$$

To solve, we use the zero factor property.

$$y - 4 = 0 \quad \text{or} \quad y + 1 = 0 \qquad \text{Set each factor equal to 0.}$$

$$y = 4 \qquad\qquad y = -1 \qquad \text{Solve.}$$

To find values of x, we substitute back. That is, we substitute $x - 3$ for y.

$$x - 3 = 4 \quad \text{or} \quad x - 3 = -1$$

$$x = 7 \qquad\qquad x = 2$$

> **HELPFUL HINT**
> When using substitution, don't forget to substitute back to the original variable.

Both 2 and 7 check. The solutions are 2 and 7.

Example 5   Solve $x^{2/3} - 5x^{1/3} + 6 = 0$.

Solution   The key to solving this equation is recognizing that $x^{2/3} = (x^{1/3})^2$. We replace $x^{1/3}$ with m so that

$$(x^{1/3})^2 - 5x^{1/3} + 6 = 0$$

becomes

$$m^2 - 5m + 6 = 0$$

Now we solve by factoring.

$$m^2 - 5m + 6 = 0$$

$$(m - 3)(m - 2) = 0 \qquad\qquad \text{Factor.}$$

$$m - 3 = 0 \quad \text{or} \quad m - 2 = 0 \qquad \text{Set each factor equal to 0.}$$

$$m = 3 \qquad\qquad m = 2$$

Since $m = x^{1/3}$, we have

$$x^{1/3} = 3 \qquad\qquad \text{or} \quad x^{1/3} = 2$$

$$x = 3^3 = 27 \quad \text{or} \qquad x = 2^3 = 8$$

Both 8 and 27 check. The solutions are 8 and 27.

2

The next example is a work problem. This problem is modeled by a rational equation that simplifies to a quadratic equation.

Example 6 FINDING WORK TIME

Together, an experienced typist and an apprentice typist can process a document in 6 hours. Alone, the experienced typist can process the document 2 hours faster than the apprentice typist can. Find the time in which each person can process the document alone.

Solution
1. UNDERSTAND. Read and reread the problem. The key idea here is the relationship between the *time* (hours) it takes to complete the job and the *part of the job* completed in one unit of time (hour). For example, because they can complete the job together in 6 hours, the *part of the job* they can complete in 1 hour is $\frac{1}{6}$. Let

x = the *time* in hours it takes the apprentice typist to complete the job alone

$x - 2$ = the *time* in hours it takes the experienced typist to complete the job alone

We can summarize in a chart the information discussed

	Total Hours to Complete Job	*Part of Job Completed in 1 Hour*
APPRENTICE TYPIST	x	$\dfrac{1}{x}$
EXPERIENCED TYPIST	$x - 2$	$\dfrac{1}{x - 2}$
TOGETHER	6	$\dfrac{1}{6}$

2. TRANSLATE.

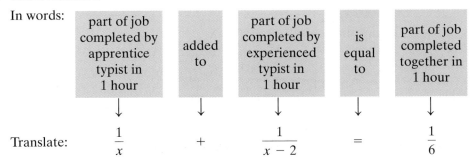

In words:

part of job completed by apprentice typist in 1 hour	added to	part of job completed by experienced typist in 1 hour	is equal to	part of job completed together in 1 hour
↓	↓	↓	↓	↓

Translate: $\dfrac{1}{x}$ $+$ $\dfrac{1}{x - 2}$ $=$ $\dfrac{1}{6}$

3. SOLVE.

$$\frac{1}{x} + \frac{1}{x - 2} = \frac{1}{6}$$

$$6x(x - 2)\left(\frac{1}{x} + \frac{1}{x - 2}\right) = 6x(x - 2) \cdot \frac{1}{6}$$

Multiply both sides by the LCD, $6x(x - 2)$.

$$6x(x - 2) \cdot \frac{1}{x} + 6x(x - 2) \cdot \frac{1}{x - 2} = 6x(x - 2) \cdot \frac{1}{6}$$

Use the distributive property.

$$6(x - 2) + 6x = x(x - 2)$$

$$6x - 12 + 6x = x^2 - 2x$$

$$0 = x^2 - 14x + 12$$

Now we can substitute $a = 1$, $b = -14$, and $c = 12$ into the quadratic formula and simplify.

$$x = \frac{-(-14) \pm \sqrt{(-14)^2 - 4(1)(12)}}{2 \cdot 1} = \frac{14 \pm \sqrt{148}}{2}$$

Using a calculator or a square root table, we see that $\sqrt{148} \approx 12.2$ rounded to one decimal place. Thus,

$$x \approx \frac{14 \pm 12.2}{2}$$

$$x \approx \frac{14 + 12.2}{2} = 13.1 \quad \text{or} \quad x \approx \frac{14 - 12.2}{2} = 0.9$$

4. INTERPRET.

Check: If the apprentice typist completes the job alone in 0.9 hours, the experienced typist completes the job alone in $x - 2 = 0.9 - 2 = -1.1$ hours. Since this is not possible, we reject the solution of 0.9. The approximate solution thus is 13.1 hours.

State: The apprentice typist can complete the job alone in approximately 13.1 hours, and the experienced typist can complete the job alone in approximately

$$x - 2 = 13.1 - 2 = 11.1 \text{ hours.}$$

Example 7   FINDING SPEED

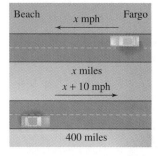

Beach and Fargo are about 400 miles apart. A salesperson travels from Fargo to Beach one day at a certain speed. She returns to Fargo the next day and drives 10 mph faster. Her total travel time was $14\frac{2}{3}$ hours. Find her speed to Beach and the return speed to Fargo.

Solution 1. UNDERSTAND. Read and reread the problem. Let

$$x = \text{the speed to Beach, so}$$

$$x + 10 = \text{the return speed to Fargo.}$$

Then organize the given information in a table.

HELPFUL HINT
Since $d = rt$, then
$t = \dfrac{d}{r}$. The time
column was
completed using $\dfrac{d}{r}$.

	distance	=	rate	·	time
TO BEACH	400		x		$\dfrac{400}{x}$ ←distance ←rate
RETURN TO FARGO	400		$x + 10$		$\dfrac{400}{x + 10}$ ←distance ←rate

2. TRANSLATE.

In words:

time to Beach	+	return time to Fargo	=	$14\dfrac{2}{3}$ hours

Translate: $\dfrac{400}{x} + \dfrac{400}{x + 10} = \dfrac{44}{3}$

3. SOLVE.

$$\frac{400}{x} + \frac{400}{x + 10} = \frac{44}{3}$$

$$\frac{100}{x} + \frac{100}{x + 10} = \frac{11}{3} \qquad \text{Divide both sides by 4.}$$

$$3x(x + 10)\left(\frac{100}{x} + \frac{100}{x + 10}\right) = 3x(x + 10) \cdot \frac{11}{3} \qquad \text{Multiply both sides by the LCD } 3x(x + 10).$$

$$3x(x + 10) \cdot \frac{100}{x} + 3x(x + 10) \cdot \frac{100}{x + 10} = 3x(x + 10) \cdot \frac{11}{3} \qquad \text{Use the distributive property.}$$

$$3(x + 10) \cdot 100 + 3x \cdot 100 = x(x + 10) \cdot 11$$

$$300x + 3000 + 300x = 11x^2 + 110x$$

$$0 = 11x^2 - 490x - 3000 \qquad \text{Set equation equal to 0.}$$

$$0 = (11x + 60)(x - 50) \qquad \text{Factor.}$$

$$11x + 60 = 0 \quad \text{or} \quad x - 50 = 0 \qquad \text{Set each factor equal to 0.}$$

$$x = -\frac{60}{11} \quad \text{or} \quad -5\frac{5}{11} \qquad x = 50$$

4. INTERPRET.

Check The speed is not negative, so it's not $-5\dfrac{5}{11}$. The number 50 does check.

State The speed to Beach was 50 mph and her return speed to Fargo was 60 mph.

Exercise Set 8.3

Solve. See Example 1.

1. $2x = \sqrt{10 + 3x}$

2. $3x = \sqrt{8x + 1}$

3. $x - 2\sqrt{x} = 8$

4. $x - \sqrt{2x} = 4$

5. $\sqrt{9x} = x + 2$

6. $\sqrt{16x} = x + 3$

Solve. See Example 2.

7. $\dfrac{2}{x} + \dfrac{3}{x - 1} = 1$

8. $\dfrac{6}{x^2} = \dfrac{3}{x + 1}$

9. $\dfrac{3}{x} + \dfrac{4}{x + 2} = 2$

10. $\dfrac{5}{x - 2} + \dfrac{4}{x + 2} = 1$

11. $\dfrac{7}{x^2 - 5x + 6} = \dfrac{2x}{x - 3} - \dfrac{x}{x - 2}$

12. $\dfrac{11}{2x^2 + x - 15} = \dfrac{5}{2x - 5} - \dfrac{x}{x + 3}$

Solve. See Example 3.

13. $p^4 - 16 = 0$

14. $x^4 + 2x^2 - 3 = 0$

15. $4x^4 + 11x^2 = 3$

16. $z^4 = 81$

17. $z^4 - 13z^2 + 36 = 0$

18. $9x^4 + 5x^2 - 4 = 0$

Solve. See Examples 4 and 5.

19. $x^{2/3} - 3x^{1/3} - 10 = 0$

20. $x^{2/3} + 2x^{1/3} + 1 = 0$

21. $(5n + 1)^2 + 2(5n + 1) - 3 = 0$

22. $(m - 6)^2 + 5(m - 6) + 4 = 0$

23. $2x^{2/3} - 5x^{1/3} = 3$

24. $3x^{2/3} + 11x^{1/3} = 4$

25. $1 + \dfrac{2}{3t - 2} = \dfrac{8}{(3t - 2)^2}$

26. $2 - \dfrac{7}{x + 6} = \dfrac{15}{(x + 6)^2}$

27. $20x^{2/3} - 6x^{1/3} - 2 = 0$

28. $4x^{2/3} + 16x^{1/3} = -15$

Solve. See Examples 1 through 5.

29. $a^4 - 5a^2 + 6 = 0$

30. $x^4 - 12x^2 + 11 = 0$

31. $\dfrac{2x}{x - 2} + \dfrac{x}{x + 3} = -\dfrac{5}{x + 3}$

32. $\dfrac{5}{x - 3} + \dfrac{x}{x + 3} = \dfrac{19}{x^2 - 9}$

33. $(p + 2)^2 = 9(p + 2) - 20$

34. $2(4m - 3)^2 - 9(4m - 3) = 5$

35. $2x = \sqrt{11x + 3}$

36. $4x = \sqrt{2x + 3}$

37. $x^{2/3} - 8x^{1/3} + 15 = 0$

38. $x^{2/3} - 2x^{1/3} - 8 = 0$

39. $y^3 + 9y - y^2 - 9 = 0$

40. $x^3 + x - 3x^2 - 3 = 0$

41. $2x^{2/3} + 3x^{1/3} - 2 = 0$

42. $6x^{2/3} - 25x^{1/3} - 25 = 0$

43. $x^{-2} - x^{-1} - 6 = 0$

44. $y^{-2} - 8y^{-1} + 7 = 0$

45. $x - \sqrt{x} = 2$

46. $x - \sqrt{3x} = 6$

47. $\dfrac{x}{x - 1} + \dfrac{1}{x + 1} = \dfrac{2}{x^2 - 1}$

48. $\dfrac{x}{x - 5} + \dfrac{5}{x + 5} = -\dfrac{1}{x^2 - 25}$

49. $p^4 - p^2 - 20 = 0$

50. $x^4 - 10x^2 + 9 = 0$

51. $2x^3 = -54$

52. $y^3 - 216 = 0$

53. $1 = \dfrac{4}{x - 7} + \dfrac{5}{(x - 7)^2}$

54. $3 + \dfrac{1}{2p + 4} = \dfrac{10}{(2p + 4)^2}$

55. $27y^4 + 15y^2 = 2$

56. $8z^4 + 14z^2 = -5$

Solve. See Examples 6 and 7.

57. A jogger ran 3 miles, decreased her speed by 1 mile per hour, and then ran another 4 miles. If her total time jogging was $1\dfrac{3}{5}$ hours, find her speed for each part of her run.

58. Mark Keaton's workout consists of jogging for 3 miles, and then riding his bike for 5 miles at a speed 4 miles per hour faster than he jogs. If his total workout time is 1 hour, find his jogging speed and his biking speed.

59. A Chinese restaurant in Mandeville, Louisiana, has a large goldfish pond around the restaurant. Suppose that an inlet pipe and a hose together can fill the pond in 8 hours. The inlet pipe alone can complete the job in one hour less time than the hose alone. Find the time that the hose can complete the job alone and the time that the inlet pipe can complete the job alone. Round each to the nearest tenth of an hour.

60. A water tank on a farm in Flatonia, Texas, can be filled with a large inlet pipe and a small inlet pipe in 3 hours. The large inlet pipe alone can fill the tank in 2 hours less time than the small inlet pipe alone. Find the time to the nearest tenth of an hour each pipe can fill the tank alone.

61. Roma Sherry drove 330 miles from her hometown to Tucson. During her return trip, she was able to increase her speed by 11 mph. If her return trip took 1 hour less time, find her original speed and her speed returning home.

62. A salesperson drove to Portland, a distance of 300 miles. During the last 80 miles of his trip, heavy rainfall forced him to decrease his speed by 15 mph. If his total driving time was 6 hours, find his original speed and his speed during the rainfall.

63. Bill Shaughnessy and his son Billy can clean the house together in 4 hours. When the son works alone, it takes him an hour longer to clean than it takes his dad alone. Find how long to the nearest tenth of an hour it takes the son to clean alone.

64. Together, Noodles and Freckles eat a 50-pound bag of dog food in 30 days. Noodles by himself eats a 50-pound bag in 2 weeks less time than Freckles does by himself. How many days to the nearest whole day would a 50-pound bag of dog food last Freckles?

65. The product of a number and 4 less than the number is 96. Find the number.

66. A whole number increased by its square is two more than twice itself. Find the number.

△ **67.** Suppose that an open box is to be made from a square sheet of cardboard by cutting out squares from each corner as shown and then folding along the dotted lines. If the box is to have a volume of 300 cubic centimeters, find the original dimensions of the sheet of cardboard.

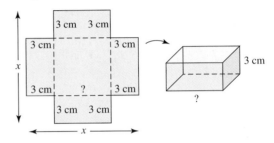

   a. The ? in the drawing to the left will be the length (and also the width) of the box as shown in the drawing above. Represent this length in terms of x.

   b. Use the formula for volume of a box, $V = l \cdot w \cdot h$, to write an equation in x.

   c. Solve the equation for x and give the dimensions of the sheet of cardboard. Check your solution.

△ **68.** Suppose that an open box is to be made from a square sheet of cardboard by cutting out squares from each corner as shown and then folding along the dotted lines. If the box is to have a volume of 128 cubic inches, find the original dimensions of the sheet of cardboard. (*Hint:* Use Exercise 67 Parts **a**, **b**, and **c** to help you.)

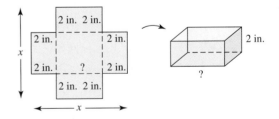

69. During the 2000 Grand Prix of Miami auto race, Juan Montoya posted the fastest lap speed but Max Papis won the race. The track is 7920 feet (1.5 miles) long. Montoya's fastest lap speed was 3.8 feet per second faster than Papis' fastest lap speed. Traveling at these fastest speeds, Papis would have taken 0.376 seconds longer than Montoya to complete a lap. (*Source:* Championship Auto Racing Teams, Inc.)

   a. Find Max Papis' fastest lap speed during the race. Round to one decimal place.

b. Find Juan Montoya's fastest lap speed during the race. Round to one decimal place.

c. Convert each speed to miles per hour. Round to one decimal place.

70. Use a graphing calculator to solve Exercise 29. Compare the solution with the solution from Exercise 29. Explain any differences.

71. Write a polynomial equation that has three solutions: 2, 5, and −7.

72. Write a polynomial equation that has three solutions: 0, 2i, and −2i.

REVIEW EXERCISES

Solve each inequality. See Section 2.4.

73. $\dfrac{5x}{3} + 2 \le 7$

74. $\dfrac{2x}{3} + \dfrac{1}{6} \ge 2$

75. $\dfrac{y-1}{15} > -\dfrac{2}{5}$

76. $\dfrac{z-2}{12} < \dfrac{1}{4}$

Find the domain and range of each graphed relation. Decide which relations are also functions. See Section 3.2.

77.

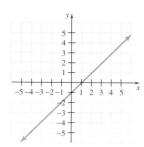

78.

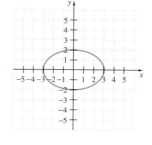

79.

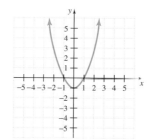

80.

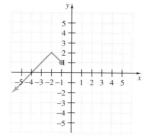

8.4 NONLINEAR INEQUALITIES IN ONE VARIABLE

▶ **OBJECTIVES**

1. Solve polynomial inequalities of degree 2 or greater.
2. Solve inequalities that contain rational expressions with variables in the denominator.

1   Just as we can solve linear inequalities in one variable, so can we also solve quadratic inequalities in one variable. A **quadratic inequality** is an inequality that can be written so that one side is a quadratic expression and the other side is 0. Here are examples of quadratic inequalities in one variable. Each is written in **standard form.**

$$x^2 - 10x + 7 \le 0 \qquad 3x^2 + 2x - 6 > 0$$

$$2x^2 + 9x - 2 < 0 \qquad x^2 - 3x + 11 \ge 0$$

A solution of a quadratic inequality in one variable is a value of the variable that makes the inequality a true statement.

The value of an expression such as $x^2 - 3x - 10$ will sometimes be positive, sometimes negative, and sometimes 0, depending on the value substituted for x. To solve the inequality $x^2 - 3x - 10 < 0$, we are looking for all values of x that make the expression $x^2 - 3x - 10$ **less than 0,** or **negative.** To understand how we find these values, we'll study the graph of the quadratic function $y = x^2 - 3x - 10$.

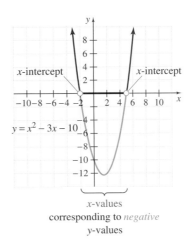

x-values
corresponding to *negative*
y-values

Notice that the x-values for which y is positive are separated from the x values for which y is negative by the x-intercepts. (Recall that the x-intercepts correspond to values of x for which $y = 0$.) Thus, the solution set of $x^2 - 3x - 10 < 0$ consists of all real numbers from -2 to 5, or in interval notation, $(-2, 5)$.

It is not necessary to graph $y = x^2 - 3x - 10$ to solve the related inequality $x^2 - 3x - 10 < 0$. Instead, we can draw a number line representing the x-axis and keep the following in mind: *A region on the number line for which the value of $x^2 - 3x - 10$ is positive is separated from a region on the number line for which the value of $x^2 - 3x - 10$ is negative by a value for which the expression is 0.*

Let's find these values for which the expression is 0 by solving the related equation:

$$x^2 - 3x - 10 = 0$$

$$(x - 5)(x + 2) = 0 \qquad \text{Factor.}$$

$$x - 5 = 0 \quad \text{or} \quad x + 2 = 0 \qquad \text{Set each factor equal to 0.}$$

$$x = 5 \qquad\qquad x = -2 \qquad \text{Solve.}$$

These two numbers -2 and 5, divide the number line into three regions. We will call the regions A, B, and C. These regions are important because, if the value of $x^2 - 3x - 10$ is negative when a number from a region is substituted for x, then $x^2 - 3x - 10$ is negative when any number in that region is substituted for x. The same is true if the value of $x^2 - 3x - 10$ is positive for a particular value of x in a region.

To see whether the inequality $x^2 - 3x - 10 < 0$ is true or false in each region, we choose a test point from each region and substitute its value for x in the inequality

$x^2 - 3x - 10 < 0$. If the resulting inequality is true, the region containing the test point is a solution region.

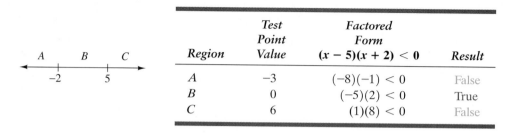

Region	Test Point Value	Factored Form $(x - 5)(x + 2) < 0$	Result
A	-3	$(-8)(-1) < 0$	False
B	0	$(-5)(2) < 0$	True
C	6	$(1)(8) < 0$	False

The values in region B satisfy the inequality. The numbers -2 and 5 are not included in the solution set since the inequality symbol is $<$. The solution set is $(-2, 5)$, and its graph is shown.

$$A \qquad B \qquad C$$
$$\text{F } -2 \quad \text{T} \quad 5 \text{ F}$$

Example 1   Solve $(x + 3)(x - 3) > 0$.

Solution   First we solve the related equation $(x + 3)(x - 3) = 0$.

$$(x + 3)(x - 3) = 0$$
$$x + 3 = 0 \quad \text{or} \quad x - 3 = 0$$
$$x = -3 \qquad\qquad x = 3$$

The two numbers -3 and 3 separate the number line into three regions, A, B, and C.

Now we substitute the value of a test point from each region. If the test value satisfies the inequality, every value in the region containing the test value is a solution.

Region	Test Point Value	$(x + 3)(x - 3) > 0$	Result
A	-4	$(-1)(-7) > 0$	True
B	0	$(3)(-3) > 0$	False
C	4	$(7)(1) > 0$	True

The points in regions A and C satisfy the inequality. The numbers -3 and 3 are not included in the solution since the inequality symbol is $>$. The solution set is $(-\infty, -3) \cup (3, \infty)$, and its graph is shown.

$$A \qquad B \qquad C$$
$$\text{T } -3 \quad \text{F} \quad 3 \text{ T}$$

The following steps may be used to solve a polynomial inequality.

SOLVING A POLYNOMIAL INEQUALITY

Step 1: Write the inequality in standard form and then solve the related equation.

Step 2: Separate the number line into regions with the solutions from Step 1.

Step 3: For each region, choose a test point and determine whether its value satisfies the *original inequality*.

Step 4: The solution set includes the regions whose test point value is a solution. If the inequality symbol is $\leq$ or $\geq$, the values from Step 1 are solutions; if $<$ or $>$, they are not.

Example 2 Solve $x^2 - 4x \leq 0$.

Solution First we solve the related equation $x^2 - 4x = 0$.

$$x^2 - 4x = 0$$
$$x(x - 4) = 0$$
$$x = 0 \quad \text{or} \quad x = 4$$

The numbers 0 and 4 separate the number line into three regions, A, B, and C.

Check a test value in each region in the original inequality. Values in region B satisfy the inequality. The numbers 0 and 4 are included in the solution since the inequality symbol is $\leq$. The solution set is $[0, 4]$, and its graph is shown.

Example 3 Solve $(x + 2)(x - 1)(x - 5) \leq 0$.

Solution First we solve $(x + 2)(x - 1)(x - 5) = 0$. By inspection, we see that the solutions are $-2, 1$, and 5. They separate the number line into four regions, A, B, C, and D. Next we check test points from each region.

Region	Test Point Value	$(x + 2)(x - 1)$ $(x - 5) \leq 0$	Result
A	-3	$(-1)(-4)(-8) \leq 0$	True
B	0	$(2)(-1)(-5) \leq 0$	False
C	2	$(4)(1)(-3) \leq 0$	True
D	6	$(8)(5)(1) \leq 0$	False

The solution set is $(-\infty, -2] \cup [1, 5]$, and its graph is shown. We include the numbers $-2, 1$, and 5 because the inequality symbol is $\leq$.

$$A \quad B \quad C \quad D$$
$$T\,{-}2\ F\ 1\ T\ 5\ F$$

2 Inequalities containing rational expressions with variables in the denominator are solved by using a similar procedure.

Example 4 Solve $\dfrac{x + 2}{x - 3} \leq 0$.

Solution First we find all values that make the denominator equal to 0. To do this, we solve $x - 3 = 0$ and find that $x = 3$.

Next, we solve the related equation $\dfrac{x + 2}{x - 3} = 0$.

$$\frac{x + 2}{x - 3} = 0$$

$$x + 2 = 0 \qquad \text{Multiply both sides by the LCD, } x - 3.$$

$$x = -2$$

Now we place these numbers on a number line and proceed as before, checking test point values in the original inequality.

$$A \quad B \quad C$$
$$-2 \qquad 3$$

Choose -3 from region A.

$$\frac{x + 2}{x - 3} \leq 0$$

$$\frac{-3 + 2}{-3 - 3} \leq 0$$

$$\frac{-1}{-6} \leq 0$$

$$\frac{1}{6} \leq 0 \qquad \text{False.}$$

Choose 0 from region B.

$$\frac{x + 2}{x - 3} \leq 0$$

$$\frac{0 + 2}{0 - 3} \leq 0$$

$$-\frac{2}{3} \leq 0 \qquad \text{True.}$$

Choose 4 from region C.

$$\frac{x + 2}{x - 3} \leq 0$$

$$\frac{4 + 2}{4 - 3} \leq 0$$

$$6 \leq 0 \qquad \text{False.}$$

The solution set is $[-2, 3)$. This interval includes -2 because -2 satisfies the original inequality. This interval does not include 3, because 3 would make the denominator 0.

$$A \quad B \quad C$$
$$F\,{-}2 \quad T \quad 3\ F$$

The following steps may be used to solve a rational inequality with variables in the denominator.

SOLVING A RATIONAL INEQUALITY

Step 1: Solve for values that make all denominators 0.
Step 2: Solve the related equation.
Step 3: Separate the number line into regions with the solutions from Steps 1 and 2.
Step 4: For each region, choose a test point and determine whether its value satisfies the *original inequality.*
Step 5: The solution set includes the regions whose test point value is a solution. Check whether to include values from Step 2. Be sure *not* to include values that make any denominator 0.

Example 5   Solve $\dfrac{5}{x + 1} < -2$.

Solution   First we find values for x that make the denominator equal to 0.

$$x + 1 = 0$$
$$x = -1$$

Next we solve $\dfrac{5}{x + 1} = -2$.

$$(x + 1) \cdot \frac{5}{x + 1} = (x + 1) \cdot -2 \qquad \text{Multiply both sides by the LCD, } x + 1.$$
$$5 = -2x - 2 \qquad \text{Simplify.}$$
$$7 = -2x$$
$$-\frac{7}{2} = x$$

We use these two solutions to divide a number line into three regions and choose test points. Only a test point value from region B satisfies the *original inequality.* The solution set is $\left(-\dfrac{7}{2}, -1\right)$, and its graph is shown.

Exercise Set 8.4

Solve each quadratic inequality. Graph the solution set and write the solution set in interval notation. See Examples 1 through 3.

1. $(x + 1)(x + 5) > 0$

2. $(x + 1)(x + 5) \leq 0$

3. $(x - 3)(x + 4) \leq 0$

4. $(x + 4)(x - 1) > 0$

5. $x^2 - 7x + 10 \leq 0$

6. $x^2 + 8x + 15 \geq 0$

7. $3x^2 + 16x < -5$

8. $2x^2 - 5x < 7$

9. $(x - 6)(x - 4)(x - 2) > 0$

10. $(x - 6)(x - 4)(x - 2) \leq 0$

11. $x(x - 1)(x + 4) \leq 0$

12. $x(x - 6)(x + 2) > 0$

13. $(x^2 - 9)(x^2 - 4) > 0$

14. $(x^2 - 16)(x^2 - 1) \leq 0$

Solve each inequality. Graph the solution set and write the solution set in interval notation. See Example 4.

15. $\dfrac{x+7}{x-2} < 0$ **16.** $\dfrac{x-5}{x-6} > 0$ **17.** $\dfrac{5}{x+1} > 0$

18. $\dfrac{3}{y-5} < 0$ **19.** $\dfrac{x+1}{x-4} \geq 0$ **20.** $\dfrac{x+1}{x-4} \leq 0$

21. Explain why $\dfrac{x+2}{x-3} > 0$ and $(x+2)(x-3) > 0$ have the same solutions.

22. Explain why $\dfrac{x+2}{x-3} \geq 0$ and $(x+2)(x-3) \geq 0$ do not have the same solutions.

Solve each inequality. Graph the solution set and write the solution set in interval notation. See Example 5.

23. $\dfrac{3}{x-2} < 4$ **24.** $\dfrac{-2}{y+3} > 2$ **25.** $\dfrac{x^2+6}{5x} \geq 1$

26. $\dfrac{y^2+15}{8y} \leq 1$

Solve each inequality. Graph the solution set and write the solution set in interval notation.

27. $(x-8)(x+7) > 0$ **28.** $(x-5)(x+1) < 0$

29. $(2x-3)(4x+5) \leq 0$ **30.** $(6x+7)(7x-12) > 0$

31. $x^2 > x$

32. $x^2 < 25$

33. $(2x-8)(x+4)(x-6) \leq 0$

34. $(3x-12)(x+5)(2x-3) \geq 0$

35. $6x^2 - 5x \geq 6$

36. $12x^2 + 11x \leq 15$

37. $4x^3 + 16x^2 - 9x - 36 > 0$

38. $x^3 + 2x^2 - 4x - 8 < 0$

39. $x^4 - 26x^2 + 25 \geq 0$

40. $16x^4 - 40x^2 + 9 \leq 0$

41. $(2x-7)(3x+5) > 0$

42. $(4x-9)(2x+5) < 0$

43. $\dfrac{x}{x-10} < 0$ **44.** $\dfrac{x+10}{x-10} > 0$

45. $\dfrac{x-5}{x+4} \geq 0$ **46.** $\dfrac{x-3}{x+2} \leq 0$

47. $\dfrac{x(x+6)}{(x-7)(x+1)} \geq 0$

48. $\dfrac{(x-2)(x+2)}{(x+1)(x-4)} \leq 0$

49. $\dfrac{-1}{x-1} > -1$ **50.** $\dfrac{4}{y+2} < -2$

51. $\dfrac{x}{x+4} \leq 2$ **52.** $\dfrac{4x}{x-3} \geq 5$

53. $\dfrac{z}{z-5} \geq 2z$ **54.** $\dfrac{p}{p+4} \leq 3p$

55. $\dfrac{(x+1)^2}{5x} > 0$ **56.** $\dfrac{(2x-3)^2}{x} < 0$

Find all numbers that satisfy each of the following.

57. A number minus its reciprocal is less than zero. Find the numbers.

58. Twice a number added to its reciprocal is nonnegative. Find the numbers.

59. The total profit function $P(x)$ for a company producing x thousand units is given by
$$P(x) = -2x^2 + 26x - 44$$
Find the values of x for which the company makes a profit. [*Hint:* The company makes a profit when $P(x) > 0$.]

60. A projectile is fired straight up from the ground with an initial velocity of 80 feet per second. Its height $s(t)$ in feet at any time t is given by the function
$$s(t) = -16t^2 + 80t$$
Find the interval of time for which the height of the projectile is greater than 96 feet.

Use a graphing calculator to check each exercise.

61. Exercise 27.   **62.** Exercise 28.

63. Exercise 39.   **64.** Exercise 40.

REVIEW EXERCISES

Recall that the graph of $f(x) + K$ is the same as the graph of $f(x)$ shifted K units upward if $K > 0$ and $|K|$ units downward if $K < 0$. Use the graph of $f(x) = |x|$ below to sketch the graph of each function. (See Sections 3.1 and 3.3.)

65. $g(x) = |x| + 2$ **66.** $H(x) = |x| - 2$

67. $F(x) = |x| - 1$ **68.** $h(x) = |x| + 5$

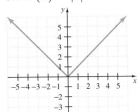

Use the graph of $f(x) = x^2$ below to sketch the graph of each function.

69. $F(x) = x^2 - 3$ **70.** $h(x) = x^2 - 4$

71. $H(x) = x^2 + 1$ **72.** $g(x) = x^2 + 3$

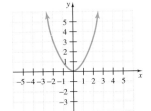

8.5 QUADRATIC FUNCTIONS AND THEIR GRAPHS

▶ **OBJECTIVES**

CD-ROM

SSM

SSG

Video

1. Graph quadratic functions of the form $f(x) = x^2 + k$.
2. Graph quadratic functions of the form $f(x) = (x - h)^2$.
3. Graph quadratic functions of the form $f(x) = (x - h)^2 + k$.
4. Graph quadratic functions of the form $f(x) = ax^2$.
5. Graph quadratic functions of the form $f(x) = a(x - h)^2 + k$.

1

We first graphed the quadratic equation $y = x^2$ in Section 3.1. In Section 3.2, we learned that this graph defines a function, and we wrote $y = x^2$ as $f(x) = x^2$. Quadratic functions and their graphs were studied further in Section 5.9. In these sections, we discovered that the graph of a quadratic function is a parabola opening upward or downward. In this section, we continue our study of quadratic functions and their graphs.

First, let's recall the definition of a quadratic function.

QUADRATIC FUNCTION

A quadratic function is a function that can be written in the form $f(x) = ax^2 + bx + c$, where a, b, and c are real numbers and $a \neq 0$.

Notice that equations of the form $y = ax^2 + bx + c$, where $a \neq 0$, define quadratic functions, since y is a function of x or $y = f(x)$.

Recall that if $a > 0$, the parabola opens upward and if $a < 0$, the parabola opens downward. Also, the vertex of a parabola is the lowest point if the parabola opens upward and the highest point if the parabola opens downward. The axis of symmetry is the vertical line that passes through the vertex.

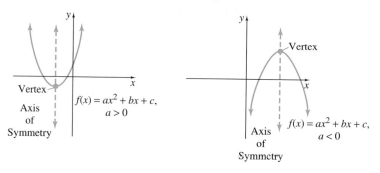

Example 1 Graph $f(x) = x^2$ and $g(x) = x^2 + 3$ on the same set of axes.

Solution First we construct a table of values for $f(x)$ and plot the points. Notice that for each x-value, the corresponding value of $g(x)$ must be 3 more than the corresponding value of $f(x)$ since $f(x) = x^2$ and $g(x) = x^2 + 3$. In other words, the graph of $g(x) = x^2 + 3$ is the same as the graph of $f(x) = x^2$ shifted upward 3 units. The axis of symmetry for both graphs is the y-axis.

x	$f(x) = x^2$	$g(x) = x^2 + 3$
-2	4	7
-1	1	4
0	0	3
1	1	4
2	4	7

Each y-value is increased by 3.

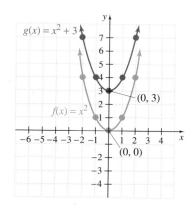

In general, we have the following properties.

GRAPHING THE PARABOLA DEFINED BY $f(x) = x^2 + k$

If k is positive, the graph of $f(x) = x^2 + k$ is the graph of $y = x^2$ shifted upward k units.

If k is negative, the graph of $f(x) = x^2 + k$ is the graph of $y = x^2$ shifted downward $|k|$ units.

The vertex is $(0, k)$, and the axis of symmetry is the y-axis.

Example 2   Graph each function.

  a. $F(x) = x^2 + 2$ **b.** $g(x) = x^2 - 3$

Solution   **a.** $F(x) = x^2 + 2$

The graph of $F(x) = x^2 + 2$ is obtained by shifting the graph of $y = x^2$ upward 2 units.

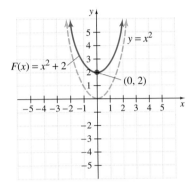

b. $g(x) = x^2 - 3$

The graph of $g(x) = x^2 - 3$ is obtained by shifting the graph of $y = x^2$ downward 3 units.

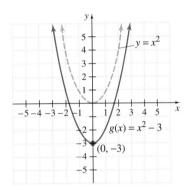

2   Now we will graph functions of the form $f(x) = (x - h)^2$.

Example 3   Graph $f(x) = x^2$ and $g(x) = (x - 2)^2$ on the same set of axes.

Solution   By plotting points, we see that for each x-value, the corresponding value of $g(x)$ is the same as the value of $f(x)$ when the x-value is increased by 2. Thus, the graph of $g(x) = (x - 2)^2$ is the graph of $f(x) = x^2$ shifted to the right 2 units. The axis of symmetry for the graph of $g(x) = (x - 2)^2$ is also shifted 2 units to the right and is the line $x = 2$.

x	$f(x) = x^2$	x	$g(x) = (x-2)^2$
-2	4	0	4
-1	1	1	1
0	0	2	0
1	1	3	1
2	4	4	4

Each x-value increased by 2 corresponds to same y-value.

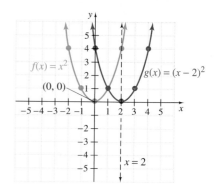

In general, we have the following properties.

GRAPHING THE PARABOLA DEFINED BY $f(x) = (x - h)^2$

If h is positive, the graph of $f(x) = (x - h)^2$ is the graph of $y = x^2$ shifted to the right h units.

If h is negative, the graph of $f(x) = (x - h)^2$ is the graph of $y = x^2$ shifted to the left $|h|$ units.

The vertex is $(h, 0)$, and the axis of symmetry is the vertical line $x = h$.

Example 4   Graph each function.

a. $G(x) = (x - 3)^2$

b. $F(x) = (x + 1)^2$

Solution   **a.** The graph of $G(x) = (x - 3)^2$ is obtained by shifting the graph of $y = x^2$ to the right 3 units. The graph of $G(x)$ is below on the left.

b. The equation $F(x) = (x + 1)^2$ can be written as $F(x) = [x - (-1)]^2$. The graph of $F(x) = [x - (-1)]^2$ is obtained by shifting the graph of $y = x^2$ to the left 1 unit. The graph of $F(x)$ is below on the right.

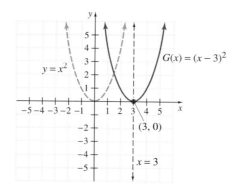

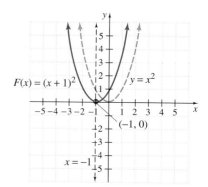

3   As we will see in graphing functions of the form $f(x) = (x - h)^2 + k$, it is possible to combine vertical and horizontal shifts.

GRAPHING THE PARABOLA DEFINED BY $f(x) = (x - h)^2 + k$

The parabola has the same shape as $y = x^2$.
The vertex is (h, k), and the axis of symmetry is the vertical line $x = h$.

Example 5   Graph $F(x) = (x - 3)^2 + 1$.

Solution   The graph of $F(x) = (x - 3)^2 + 1$ is the graph of $y = x^2$ shifted 3 units to the right and 1 unit up. The vertex is then $(3, 1)$, and the axis of symmetry is $x = 3$. A few ordered pair solutions are plotted to aid in graphing.

x	$F(x) = (x - 3)^2 + 1$
1	5
2	2
4	2
5	5

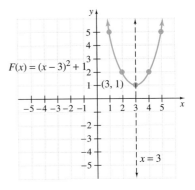

4   Next, we discover the change in the shape of the graph when the coefficient of x^2 is not 1.

Example 6   Graph $f(x) = x^2$, $g(x) = 3x^2$, and $h(x) = \dfrac{1}{2}x^2$ on the same set of axes.

Solution   Comparing the tables of values, we see that for each x-value, the corresponding value of $g(x)$ is triple the corresponding value of $f(x)$. Similarly, the value of $h(x)$ is half the value of $f(x)$.

x	$f(x) = x^2$
-2	4
-1	1
0	0
1	1
2	4

x	$g(x) = 3x^2$
-2	12
-1	3
0	0
1	3
2	12

x	$h(x) = \dfrac{1}{2}x^2$
-2	2
-1	$\dfrac{1}{2}$
0	0
1	$\dfrac{1}{2}$
2	2

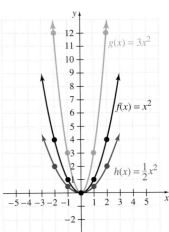

The result is that the graph of $g(x) = 3x^2$ is narrower than the graph of $f(x) = x^2$ and the graph of $h(x) = \frac{1}{2}x^2$ is wider. The vertex for each graph is $(0, 0)$, and the axis of symmetry is the y-axis.

GRAPHING THE PARABOLA DEFINED BY $f(x) = ax^2$

If a is positive, the parabola opens upward, and if a is negative, the parabola opens downward.
If $|a| > 1$, the graph of the parabola is narrower than the graph of $y = x^2$.
If $|a| < 1$, the graph of the parabola is wider than the graph of $y = x^2$.

Example 7   Graph $f(x) = -2x^2$.

Solution   Because $a = -2$, a negative value, this parabola opens downward. Since $|-2| = 2$ and $2 > 1$, the parabola is narrower than the graph of $y = x^2$. The vertex is $(0, 0)$, and the axis of symmetry is the y-axis. We verify this by plotting a few points.

x	$f(x) = -2x^2$
-2	-8
-1	-2
0	0
1	-2
2	-8

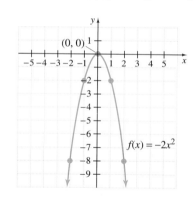

5   Now we will see the shape of the graph of a quadratic function of the form $f(x) = a(x - h)^2 + k$.

Example 8   Graph $g(x) = \frac{1}{2}(x + 2)^2 + 5$. Find the vertex and the axis of symmetry.

Solution   The function $g(x) = \frac{1}{2}(x + 2)^2 + 5$ may be written as $g(x) = \frac{1}{2}[x - (-2)]^2 + 5$. Thus, this graph is the same as the graph of $y = x^2$ shifted 2 units to the left and 5 units up, and it is wider because a is $\frac{1}{2}$. The vertex is $(-2, 5)$, and the axis of symmetry is $x = -2$. We plot a few points to verify.

x	$g(x) = \dfrac{1}{2}(x+2)^2 + 5$
-4	7
-3	$5\dfrac{1}{2}$
-2	5
-1	$5\dfrac{1}{2}$
0	7

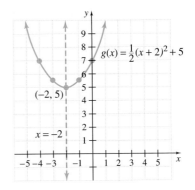

In general, the following holds.

GRAPH OF A QUADRATIC FUNCTION

The graph of a quadratic function written in the form $f(x) = a(x-h)^2 + k$ is a parabola with vertex (h, k). If $a > 0$, the parabola opens upward, and if $a < 0$, the parabola opens downward. The axis of symmetry is the line whose equation is $x = h$.

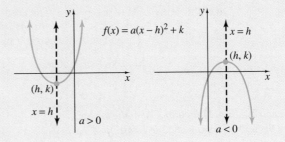

GRAPHING CALCULATOR EXPLORATIONS

Use a graphing calculator to graph the first function of each pair that follows. Then use its graph to predict the graph of the second function. Check your prediction by graphing both on the same set of axes.

1. $F(x) = \sqrt{x}$; $G(x) = \sqrt{x} + 1$
3. $H(x) = |x|$; $f(x) = |x - 5|$
5. $f(x) = |x + 4|$; $F(x) = |x + 4| + 3$

2. $g(x) = x^3$; $H(x) = x^3 - 2$
4. $h(x) = x^3 + 2$; $g(x) = (x - 3)^3 + 2$
6. $G(x) = \sqrt{x} - 2$; $g(x) = \sqrt{x - 4} - 2$

MENTAL MATH

State the vertex of the graph of each quadratic function.

1. $f(x) = x^2$
2. $f(x) = -5x^2$
3. $g(x) = (x - 2)^2$
4. $g(x) = (x + 5)^2$
5. $f(x) = 2x^2 + 3$
6. $h(x) = x^2 - 1$
7. $g(x) = (x + 1)^2 + 5$
8. $h(x) = (x - 10)^2 - 7$

Exercise Set 8.5

Sketch the graph of each quadratic function. Label the vertex, and sketch and label the axis of symmetry. See Examples 1 through 5.

1. $f(x) = x^2 - 1$ **2.** $g(x) = x^2 + 3$

3. $h(x) = x^2 + 5$ **4.** $h(x) = x^2 - 4$

5. $g(x) = x^2 + 7$ **6.** $f(x) = x^2 - 2$

7. $f(x) = (x - 5)^2$ **8.** $g(x) = (x + 5)^2$

9. $h(x) = (x + 2)^2$ **10.** $H(x) = (x - 1)^2$

11. $G(x) = (x + 3)^2$ **12.** $f(x) = (x - 6)^2$

13. $f(x) = (x - 2)^2 + 5$ **14.** $g(x) = (x - 6)^2 + 1$

15. $h(x) = (x + 1)^2 + 4$ **16.** $G(x) = (x + 3)^2 + 3$

17. $g(x) = (x + 2)^2 - 5$ **18.** $h(x) = (x + 4)^2 - 6$

Sketch the graph of each quadratic function. Label the vertex, and sketch and label the axis of symmetry. See Examples 6 and 7.

19. $g(x) = -x^2$ **20.** $f(x) = 5x^2$

21. $h(x) = \dfrac{1}{3}x^2$ **22.** $g(x) = -3x^2$

23. $H(x) = 2x^2$ **24.** $f(x) = -\dfrac{1}{4}x^2$

Sketch the graph of each quadratic function. Label the vertex, and sketch and label the axis of symmetry. See Example 8.

25. $f(x) = 2(x - 1)^2 + 3$ **26.** $g(x) = 4(x - 4)^2 + 2$

27. $h(x) = -3(x + 3)^2 + 1$ **28.** $f(x) = -(x - 2)^2 - 6$

29. $H(x) = \dfrac{1}{2}(x - 6)^2 - 3$ **30.** $G(x) = \dfrac{1}{5}(x + 4)^2 + 3$

Sketch the graph of each quadratic function. Label the vertex, and sketch and label the axis of symmetry.

31. $f(x) = -(x - 2)^2$ **32.** $g(x) = -(x + 6)^2$

33. $F(x) = -x^2 + 4$ **34.** $H(x) = -x^2 + 10$

35. $F(x) = 2x^2 - 5$ **36.** $g(x) = \dfrac{1}{2}x^2 - 2$

37. $h(x) = (x - 6)^2 + 4$ **38.** $f(x) = (x - 5)^2 + 2$

39. $F(x) = \left(x + \dfrac{1}{2}\right)^2 - 2$ **40.** $H(x) = \left(x + \dfrac{1}{2}\right)^2 - 3$

41. $F(x) = \dfrac{3}{2}(x + 7)^2 + 1$ **42.** $g(x) = -\dfrac{3}{2}(x - 1)^2 - 5$

43. $f(x) = \dfrac{1}{4}x^2 - 9$ **44.** $H(x) = \dfrac{3}{4}x^2 - 2$

45. $G(x) = 5\left(x + \dfrac{1}{2}\right)^2$ **46.** $F(x) = 3\left(x - \dfrac{3}{2}\right)^2$

47. $h(x) = -(x - 1)^2 - 1$

48. $f(x) = -3(x + 2)^2 + 2$

49. $g(x) = \sqrt{3}(x + 5)^2 + \dfrac{3}{4}$

50. $G(x) = \sqrt{5}(x - 7)^2 - \dfrac{1}{2}$

51. $h(x) = 10(x + 4)^2 - 6$

52. $h(x) = 8(x + 1)^2 + 9$

53. $f(x) = -2(x - 4)^2 + 5$

54. $G(x) = -4(x + 9)^2 - 1$

Write the equation of the parabola that has the same shape as $f(x) = 5x^2$ but with the following vertex.

55. $(2, 3)$ **56.** $(1, 6)$

57. $(-3, 6)$ **58.** $(4, -1)$

The shifting properties covered in this section apply to the graphs of all functions. Given the accompanying graph of $y = f(x)$, sketch the graph of each of the following.

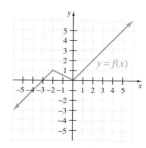

59. $y = f(x) + 1$ **60.** $y = f(x) - 2$

61. $y = f(x - 3)$ **62.** $y = f(x + 3)$

63. $y = f(x + 2) + 2$ **64.** $y = f(x - 1) + 1$

REVIEW EXERCISES

Add the proper constant to each binomial so that the resulting trinomial is a perfect square trinomial. See Section 8.1.

65. $x^2 + 8x$ **66.** $y^2 + 4y$

67. $z^2 - 16z$ **68.** $x^2 - 10x$

69. $y^2 + y$ **70.** $z^2 - 3z$

Solve by completing the square. See Section 8.1.

71. $x^2 + 4x = 12$ **72.** $y^2 + 6y = -5$

73. $z^2 + 10z - 1 = 0$ **74.** $x^2 + 14x + 20 = 0$

75. $z^2 - 8z = 2$ **76.** $y^2 - 10y = 3$

8.6 FURTHER GRAPHING OF QUADRATIC FUNCTIONS

▶ **OBJECTIVES**

1. Write quadratic functions in the form $y = a(x - h)^2 + k$.
2. Derive a formula for finding the vertex of a parabola.
3. Find the minimum or maximum value of a quadratic function.

1

We know that the graph of a quadratic function is a parabola. If a quadratic function is written in the form

$$f(x) = a(x - h)^2 + k$$

we can easily find the vertex (h, k) and graph the parabola. To write a quadratic function in this form, complete the square. (See Section 8.1 for a review of completing the square.)

Example 1   Graph $f(x) = x^2 - 4x - 12$. Find the vertex and any intercepts.

Solution   The graph of this quadratic function is a parabola. To find the vertex of the parabola, we will write the function in the form $y = (x - h)^2 + k$. To do this, we complete the square on the binomial $x^2 - 4x$. To simplify our work, we let $f(x) = y$.

$$y = x^2 - 4x - 12 \qquad \text{Let } f(x) = y.$$
$$y + 12 = x^2 - 4x \qquad \begin{array}{l}\text{Add 12 to both sides to get the}\\ \text{x-variable terms alone.}\end{array}$$

Now we add the square of half of -4 to both sides.

$$\frac{1}{2}(-4) = -2 \quad \text{and} \quad (-2)^2 = 4$$

$$y + 12 + 4 = x^2 - 4x + 4 \qquad \text{Add 4 to both sides.}$$
$$y + 16 = (x - 2)^2 \qquad \text{Factor the trinomial.}$$
$$y = (x - 2)^2 - 16 \qquad \text{Subtract 16 from both sides.}$$
$$f(x) = (x - 2)^2 - 16 \qquad \text{Replace } y \text{ with } f(x).$$

From this equation, we can see that the vertex of the parabola is $(2, -16)$, a point in quadrant IV, and the axis of symmetry is the line $x = 2$.

Notice that $a = 1$. Since $a > 0$, the parabola opens upward. This parabola opening upward with vertex $(2, -16)$ will have two x-intercepts and one y-intercept. (See the Helpful Hint after this example.)

x-intercepts: let y or $f(x) = 0$ $\qquad$ y-intercept: let $x = 0$

$$f(x) = x^2 - 4x - 12 \qquad\qquad f(x) = x^2 - 4x - 12$$
$$0 = x^2 - 4x - 12 \qquad\qquad f(0) = 0^2 - 4 \cdot 0 - 12$$
$$0 = (x - 6)(x + 2) \qquad\qquad = -12$$
$$0 = x - 6 \quad \text{or} \quad 0 = x + 2$$
$$6 = x \qquad\qquad -2 = x$$

The two x-intercepts are $(6, 0)$ and $(-2, 0)$. The y-intercept is $(0, -12)$. The sketch of $f(x) = x^2 - 4x - 12$ is shown.

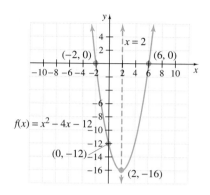

HELPFUL HINT

Parabola Opens Upward
Vertex in I or II: no x-intercept
Vertex in III or IV: 2 x-intercepts

Parabola Opens Downward
Vertex in I or II: 2 x-intercept
Vertex in III or IV: no x-intercepts.

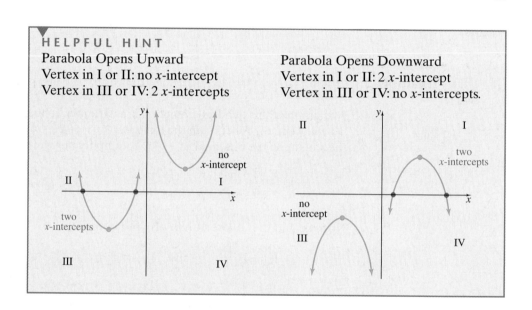

Example 2   Graph $f(x) = 3x^2 + 3x + 1$. Find the vertex and any intercepts.

Solution   Replace $f(x)$ with y and complete the square on x to write the equation in the form $y = a(x - h)^2 + k$.

$$y = 3x^2 + 3x + 1 \qquad \text{Replace } f(x) \text{ with } y.$$

$$y - 1 = 3x^2 + 3x \qquad \text{Isolate } x\text{-variable terms.}$$

Factor 3 from the terms $3x^2 + 3x$ so that the coefficient of x^2 is 1.

$$y - 1 = 3(x^2 + x) \qquad \text{Factor out 3.}$$

The coefficient of x in the parentheses above is 1. Then $\dfrac{1}{2}(1) = \dfrac{1}{2}$ and $\left(\dfrac{1}{2}\right)^2 = \dfrac{1}{4}$.

Since we are adding $\dfrac{1}{4}$ inside the parentheses, we are really adding $3\left(\dfrac{1}{4}\right)$, so we *must* add $3\left(\dfrac{1}{4}\right)$ to the left side.

$$y - 1 + 3\left(\frac{1}{4}\right) = 3\left(x^2 + x + \frac{1}{4}\right)$$

$$y - \frac{1}{4} = 3\left(x + \frac{1}{2}\right)^2 \qquad \text{Simplify the left side and factor the right side.}$$

$$y = 3\left(x + \frac{1}{2}\right)^2 + \frac{1}{4} \qquad \text{Add } \frac{1}{4} \text{ to both sides.}$$

$$f(x) = 3\left(x + \frac{1}{2}\right)^2 + \frac{1}{4} \qquad \text{Replace } y \text{ with } f(x).$$

Then $a = 3$, $h = -\dfrac{1}{2}$, and $k = \dfrac{1}{4}$. This means that the parabola opens upward with vertex $\left(-\dfrac{1}{2}, \dfrac{1}{4}\right)$ and that the axis of symmetry is the line $x = -\dfrac{1}{2}$.

To find the y-intercept, let $x = 0$. Then

$$f(0) = 3(0)^2 + 3(0) + 1 = 1$$

Thus the y-intercept is $(0, 1)$.

This parabola has no x-intercepts since the vertex is in the second quadrant and opens upward. Use the vertex, axis of symmetry, and y-intercept to sketch the parabola.

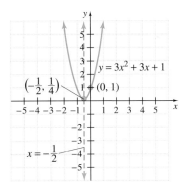

Example 3

Graph $f(x) = -x^2 - 2x + 3$. Find the vertex and any intercepts.

Solution We write $f(x)$ in the form $a(x - h)^2 + k$ by completing the square. First we replace $f(x)$ with y.

$$f(x) = -x^2 - 2x + 3$$

$$y = -x^2 - 2x + 3$$

$$y - 3 = -x^2 - 2x \qquad \text{Subtract 3 from both sides to get the } x\text{-variable terms alone.}$$

$$y - 3 = -1(x^2 + 2x) \qquad \text{Factor } -1 \text{ from the terms } -x^2 - 2x.$$

The coefficient of x is 2. Then $\dfrac{1}{2}(2) = 1$ and $1^2 = 1$. We add 1 to the right side inside the parentheses and add $-1(1)$ to the left side.

$$y - 3 - 1(1) = -1(x^2 + 2x + 1)$$

$$y - 4 = -1(x + 1)^2 \qquad \text{Simplify the left side and factor the right side.}$$

$$y = -1(x + 1)^2 + 4 \qquad \text{Add 4 to both sides.}$$

$$\underline{f(x) = -1(x + 1)^2 + 4} \qquad \text{Replace } y \text{ with } f(x).$$

> **HELPFUL HINT**
> This can be written as
> $f(x) =$
> $-1[x - (-1)]^2 + 4$.
> Notice that the vertex
> is $(-1, 4)$.

Since $a = -1$, the parabola opens downward with vertex $(-1, 4)$ and axis of symmetry $x = -1$.

To find the y-intercept, we let $x = 0$ and solve for y. Then

$$f(0) = -0^2 - 2(0) + 3 = 3$$

Thus, $(0, 3)$ is the y-intercept.

To find the x-intercepts, we let y or $f(x) = 0$ and solve for x.

$$f(x) = -x^2 - 2x + 3$$

$$0 = -x^2 - 2x + 3 \qquad \text{Let } f(x) = 0.$$

Now we divide both sides by -1 so that the coefficient of x^2 is 1.

$$\frac{0}{-1} = \frac{-x^2}{-1} - \frac{2x}{-1} + \frac{3}{-1} \qquad \text{Divide both sides by } -1.$$

$$0 = x^2 + 2x - 3 \qquad \text{Simplify.}$$

$$0 = (x + 3)(x - 1) \qquad \text{Factor.}$$

$$x + 3 = 0 \quad \text{or} \quad x - 1 = 0 \qquad \text{Set each factor equal to 0.}$$

$$x = -3 \qquad\qquad x = 1 \qquad \text{Solve.}$$

The x-intercepts are $(-3, 0)$ and $(1, 0)$. Use these points to sketch the parabola.

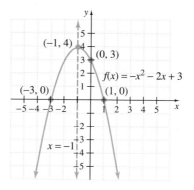

Recall from Section 5.9 that we introduced a formula for finding the vertex of a parabola. Now that we have practiced completing the square, we will show that the x-coordinate of the vertex of the graph of $f(x)$ or $y = ax^2 + bx + c$ can be found by the formula $x = \dfrac{-b}{2a}$. To do so, we complete the square on x and write the equation in the form $y = a(x - h)^2 + k$.

First, isolate the x-variable terms by subtracting c from both sides.

$$y = ax^2 + bx + c$$

$$y - c = ax^2 + bx$$

Next, factor a from the terms $ax^2 + bx$.

$$y - c = a\left(x^2 + \frac{b}{a}x\right)$$

Next, add the square of half of $\frac{b}{a}$, or $\left(\frac{b}{2a}\right)^2 = \frac{b^2}{4a^2}$, to the right side inside the paren-

theses. Because of the factor a, what we really added was $a\left(\frac{b^2}{4a^2}\right)$ and this must be

added to the left side.

$$y - c + a\left(\frac{b^2}{4a^2}\right) = a\left(x^2 + \frac{b}{a}x + \frac{b^2}{4a^2}\right)$$

$$y - c + \frac{b^2}{4a} = a\left(x + \frac{b}{2a}\right)^2 \qquad \text{Simplify the left side and factor the right side.}$$

$$y = a\left(x + \frac{b}{2a}\right)^2 + c - \frac{b^2}{4a} \qquad \begin{array}{l}\text{Add } c \text{ to both sides and subtract} \\ \dfrac{b^2}{4a} \text{ from both sides.}\end{array}$$

Compare this form with $f(x)$ or $y = a(x - h)^2 + k$ and see that h is $\frac{-b}{2a}$, which means

that the x-coordinate of the vertex of the graph of $f(x) = ax^2 + bx + c$ is $\frac{-b}{2a}$.

VERTEX FORMULA

The graph of $f(x) = ax^2 + bx + c$, when $a \neq 0$, is a parabola with vertex

$$\left(\frac{-b}{2a}, f\left(\frac{-b}{2a}\right)\right)$$

Let's use this formula to find the vertex of the parabola we graphed in Example 1.

Example 4   Find the vertex of the graph of $f(x) = x^2 - 4x - 12$.

Solution   In the quadratic function $f(x) = x^2 - 4x - 12$, notice that $a = 1$, $b = -4$, and $c = -12$. Then

$$\frac{-b}{2a} = \frac{-(-4)}{2(1)} = 2$$

The x-value of the vertex is 2. To find the corresponding $f(x)$ or y-value, find $f(2)$. Then

$$f(2) = 2^2 - 4(2) - 12 = 4 - 8 - 12 = -16$$

The vertex is $(2, -16)$. These results agree with our findings in Example 1.

3

The vertex of a parabola gives us some important information about its corresponding quadratic function. The quadratic function whose graph is a parabola that opens upward has a minimum value, and the quadratic function whose graph is a parabola that opens downward has a maximum value. The $f(x)$ or y-value of the vertex is the minimum or maximum value of the function.

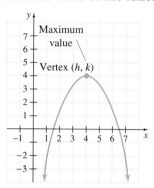

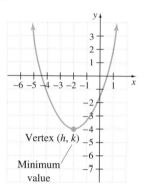

Example 5   FINDING MAXIMUM HEIGHT

A rock is thrown upward from the ground. Its height in feet above ground after t seconds is given by the function $f(t) = -16t^2 + 20t$. Find the maximum height of the rock and the number of seconds it took for the rock to reach its maximum height.

Solution   1. **UNDERSTAND.** The maximum height of the rock is the largest value of $f(t)$. Since the function $f(t) = -16t^2 + 20t$ is a quadratic function, its graph is a parabola. It opens downward since $-16 < 0$. Thus, the maximum value of $f(t)$ is the $f(t)$ or y-value of the vertex of its graph.

2. **TRANSLATE.** To find the vertex (h, k), notice that for $f(t) = -16t^2 + 20t$, $a = -16$, $b = 20$, and $c = 0$. We will use these values and the vertex formula

$$\left(\frac{-b}{2a},\ f\left(\frac{-b}{2a} \right) \right)$$

3. **SOLVE.**

$$h = \frac{-b}{2a} = \frac{-20}{-32} = \frac{5}{8}$$

$$f\left(\frac{5}{8} \right) = -16\left(\frac{5}{8} \right)^2 + 20\left(\frac{5}{8} \right)$$

$$= -16\left(\frac{25}{64} \right) + \frac{25}{2}$$

$$= -\frac{25}{4} + \frac{50}{4} = \frac{25}{4}$$

4. **INTERPRET.** The graph of $f(t)$ is a parabola opening downward with vertex $\left(\frac{5}{8}, \frac{25}{4} \right)$. This means that the rock's maximum height is $\frac{25}{4}$ feet, or $6\frac{1}{4}$ feet, which was reached in $\frac{5}{8}$ second.

SPOTLIGHT ON DECISION MAKING

Suppose you are a member of a community theater group, the Slidell Players. For an upcoming performance of *Grease,* your group must decide on a ticket price. The graph shows the relationship between ticket price and box office receipts for past Slidell Players performances.

What ticket price would you suggest that the Slidell Players charge for its performance of *Grease?* Explain your reasoning.

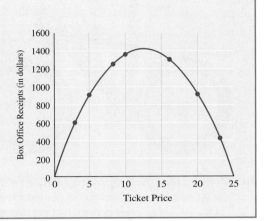

Exercise Set 8.6

Find the vertex of the graph of each quadratic function. See Examples 1 through 4.

1. $f(x) = x^2 + 8x + 7$ **2.** $f(x) = x^2 + 6x + 5$

3. $f(x) = -x^2 + 10x + 5$ **4.** $f(x) = -x^2 - 8x + 2$

5. $f(x) = 5x^2 - 10x + 3$ **6.** $f(x) = -3x^2 + 6x + 4$

7. $f(x) = -x^2 + x + 1$ **8.** $f(x) = x^2 - 9x + 8$

Match each function with its graph. See Examples 1 through 4.

A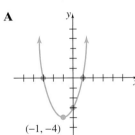

$(-1, -4)$

B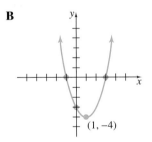

$(1, -4)$

C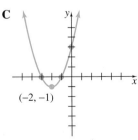

$(-2, -1)$

D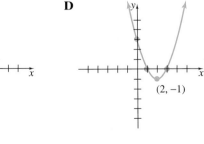

$(2, -1)$

9. $f(x) = x^2 - 4x + 3$ **10.** $f(x) = x^2 + 2x - 3$

11. $f(x) = x^2 - 2x - 3$ **12.** $f(x) = x^2 + 4x + 3$

Find the vertex of the graph of each quadratic function. Determine whether the graph opens upward or downward, find any intercepts, and sketch the graph. See Examples 1 through 3.

13. $f(x) = x^2 + 4x - 5$ **14.** $f(x) = x^2 + 2x - 3$

15. $f(x) = -x^2 + 2x - 1$ **16.** $f(x) = -x^2 + 4x - 4$

17. $f(x) = x^2 - 4$ **18.** $f(x) = x^2 - 1$

19. $f(x) = 4x^2 + 4x - 3$ **20.** $f(x) = 2x^2 - x - 3$

21. $f(x) = x^2 + 8x + 15$ **22.** $f(x) = x^2 + 10x + 9$

23. $f(x) = x^2 - 6x + 5$ **24.** $f(x) = x^2 - 4x + 3$

25. $f(x) = x^2 - 4x + 5$ **26.** $f(x) = x^2 - 6x + 11$

27. $f(x) = 2x^2 + 4x + 5$ **28.** $f(x) = 3x^2 + 12x + 16$

29. $f(x) = -2x^2 + 12x$ **30.** $f(x) = -4x^2 + 8x$

31. $f(x) = x^2 + 1$ **32.** $f(x) = x^2 + 4$

33. $f(x) = x^2 - 2x - 15$ **34.** $f(x) = x^2 - 4x + 3$

35. $f(x) = -5x^2 + 5x$ **36.** $f(x) = 3x^2 - 12x$

37. $f(x) = -x^2 + 2x - 12$ **38.** $f(x) = -x^2 + 8x - 17$

39. $f(x) = 3x^2 - 12x + 15$ **40.** $f(x) = 2x^2 - 8x + 11$

41. $f(x) = x^2 + x - 6$ **42.** $f(x) = x^2 + 3x - 18$

43. $f(x) = -2x^2 - 3x + 35$ **44.** $f(x) = 3x^2 - 13x - 10$

Solve. See Example 5.

45. The cost C in dollars of manufacturing x bicycles at Holladay's Production Plant is given by the function $C(x) = 2x^2 - 800x + 92,000$.

     a. Find the number of bicycles that must be manufactured to minimize the cost.

b. Find the minimum cost.

46. If a projectile is fired straight upward from the ground with an initial speed of 96 feet per second, then its height h in feet after t seconds is given by the equation

$$h(t) = -16t^2 + 96t$$

Find the maximum height of the projectile.

47. If Rheam Gaspar throws a ball upward with an initial speed of 32 feet per second, then its height h in feet after t seconds is given by the equation

$$h(t) = -16t^2 + 32t$$

Find the maximum height of the ball.

48. The Utah Ski Club sells calendars to raise money. The profit P, in cents, from selling x calendars is given by the equation $P(x) = 360x - x^2$.

   a. Find how many calendars must be sold to maximize profit.

   b. Find the maximum profit.

49. Find two numbers whose sum is 60 and whose product is as large as possible. [*Hint:* Let x and $60 - x$ be the two positive numbers. Their product can be described by the function $f(x) = x(60 - x)$.]

50. Find two numbers whose sum is 11 and whose product is as large as possible. (Use the hint for Exercise 49.)

51. Find two numbers whose difference is 10 and whose product is as small as possible. (Use the hint for Exercise 49.)

52. Find two numbers whose difference is 8 and whose product is as small as possible.

△ **53.** The length and width of a rectangle must have a sum of 40. Find the dimensions of the rectangle that will have the maximum area. (Use the hint for Exercise 49.)

△ **54.** The length and width of a rectangle must have a sum of 50. Find the dimensions of the rectangle that will have maximum area.

55. Methane is a gas produced by landfills, natural gas systems, and coal mining that contributes to the greenhouse effect and global warming. Methane emissions in the United States can be modeled by the quadratic function

$f(x) = -0.74x^2 + 8.66x + 159.07$, where $f(x)$ is the amount of methane produced in million metric tons and x is the number of years after 1990. (*Source:* based on data from the U.S. Environmental Protection Agency, 1993–1998)

   a. If this trend continues, what will U.S. emissions of methane be in 2004?

   b. In what year were methane emissions in the United States at their maximum? Round to the nearest whole year.

   c. Use the result of part b. to determine the maximum methane emissions level.

56. The number of inmates in custody in U.S. prisons and jails can be modeled by the quadratic function $p(x) = -716.2x^2 + 87,453.7x + 1,148,702$, where $p(x)$ is the number of inmates and x is the number of years after 1990. (*Source:* based on data from the Bureau of Justice Statistics, U.S. Department of Justice, 1990–1998)

   a. Will this function have a maximum or a minimum? How can you tell?

   b. According to this model, when will the number of prison inmates in custody in the United States be at its maximum/minimum?

   c. What is the number of inmates predicted for that year? Round answer to the nearest hundred inmates.

Find the vertex of the graph of each quadratic function. Determine whether the graph opens upward or downward, find the y-intercept, approximate the x-intercepts to one decimal place, and sketch the graph.

57. $f(x) = x^2 + 10x + 15$ **58.** $f(x) = x^2 - 6x + 4$

59. $f(x) = 3x^2 - 6x + 7$ **60.** $f(x) = 2x^2 + 4x - 1$

Use a graphing calculator to check each exercise.

61. Exercise 27   **62.** Exercise 28

63. Exercise 37   **64.** Exercise 38

Find the maximum or minimum value of each function. Approximate to two decimal places.

65. $f(x) = 2.3x^2 - 6.1x + 3.2$

66. $f(x) = 7.6x^2 + 9.8x - 2.1$

67. $f(x) = -1.9x^2 + 5.6x - 2.7$

68. $f(x) = -5.2x^2 - 3.8x + 5.1$

73. $f(x) = (x + 5)^2 + 2$ **74.** $f(x) = 2(x - 3)^2 + 2$

75. $f(x) = 3(x - 4)^2 + 1$ **76.** $f(x) = (x + 1)^2 + 4$

77. $f(x) = -(x - 4)^2 + \dfrac{3}{2}$

78. $f(x) = -2(x + 7)^2 + \dfrac{1}{2}$

REVIEW EXERCISES

Sketch the graph of each function. See Section 8.5.

69. $f(x) = x^2 + 2$ **70.** $f(x) = (x - 3)^2$

71. $g(x) = x + 2$ **72.** $h(x) = x - 3$

For additional Chapter Projects, visit the Real World Activities Website by going to http://www.prenhall.com/martin-gay.

CHAPTER PROJECT

Fitting a Quadratic Model to Data

Throughout the twentieth century, the eating habits of Americans changed noticeably. Americans started consuming less whole milk and butter, and started consuming more skim and low-fat milk and margarine. We also started eating more poultry and fish. In this project, you will have the opportunity to investigate trends in per capita consumption of poultry during the twentieth century. This project may be completed by working in groups or individually.

We will start by finding a quadratic model, $y = ax^2 + bx + c$, that has ordered pair solutions that correspond to the data for U.S. per capita consumption of poultry given in the table. To do so, substitute each data pair into the equation. Each time, the result is an equation in three unknowns: $a, b,$ and c. Because there are three pairs of data, we can form a system of three linear equations in three unknowns. Solving for the values of $a, b,$ and c gives a quadratic model that represents the given data.

1. Write the system of equations that must be solved to find the values of $a, b,$ and c needed for a quadratic model of the given data.
2. Solve the system of equations for $a, b,$ and c. Recall the various methods of solving linear systems used in Chapter 4. You might consider using matrices, Cramer's rule, or a graphing calculator to do so. Round to the nearest thousandth.
3. Write the quadratic model for the data. Note that the variable x represents the number of years after 1900.
4. In 1939, the actual U.S. per capita consumption of poultry was 12 pounds per person. Based on this information, how accurate do you think this model is for years other than those given in the table?
5. Use your model to estimate the per capita consumption of poultry in 1950.
6. According to the model, in what year was per capita consumption of poultry 50 pounds per person?
7. In what year was the per capita consumption of poultry at its lowest level? What was that level?
8. Who might be interested in a model like this and how would it be helpful?

U.S. PER CAPITA CONSUMPTION OF POULTRY (IN POUNDS)

Year	x	Poultry Consumption, y (in pounds)
1909	9	11
1969	69	33
1998	98	68

(*Source:* Economic research service, U.S. Department of Agriculture)

CHAPTER 8 VOCABULARY CHECK

Fill in each blank with one of the words or phrases listed below.

quadratic formula	quadratic	discriminant	$\pm\sqrt{b}$
completing the square	quadratic inequality		

(h, k) $\quad$ $(0, k)$ $\quad$ $(h, 0)$ $\quad$ $\dfrac{-b}{2a}$

1. The _____ helps us know find the number and type of solutions of a quadratic equation.

2. If $a^2 = b$, then $a =$ _____.

3. The graph of $f(x) = ax^2 + bx + c$ where a is not 0 is a parabola whose vertex has x-value of ____.

4. A(n) _____ is an inequality that can be written so that one side is a quadratic expression and the other side is 0.

5. The process of writing a quadratic equation so that one side is a perfect square trinomial is called _____.

6. The graph of $f(x) = x^2 + k$ has vertex _____.

7. The graph of $f(x) = (x - h)^2$ has vertex _____.

8. The graph of $f(x) = (x - h)^2 + k$ has vertex _____.

9. The formula $x = \dfrac{-b \pm \sqrt{b^2 - 4ac}}{2a}$ is called the _____.

10. A _____ equation is one that can be written in the form $ax^2 + bx + c = 0$ where $a, b,$ and c are real numbers and a is not 0.

CHAPTER 8 HIGHLIGHTS

DEFINITIONS AND CONCEPTS	EXAMPLES

Section 8.1 Solving Quadratic Equations by Completing the Square

Square root property If b is a real number and if $a^2 = b$, then $a = \pm\sqrt{b}$.	Solve $(x + 3)^2 = 14$. $x + 3 = \pm\sqrt{14}$ $x = -3 \pm \sqrt{14}$

To solve a quadratic equation in x by completing the square **Step 1:** If the coefficient of x^2 is not 1, divide both sides of the equation by the coefficient of x^2. **Step 2:** Isolate the variable terms. **Step 3:** Complete the square by adding the square of half of the coefficient of x to both sides. **Step 4:** Write the resulting trinomial as the square of a binomial. **Step 5:** Apply the square root property and solve for x.	Solve $3x^2 - 12x - 18 = 0$. 1. $x^2 - 4x - 6 = 0$ 2. $\quad\quad x^2 - 4x = 6$ 3. $\dfrac{1}{2}(-4) = -2$ and $(-2)^2 = 4$ $\quad\quad x^2 - 4x + 4 = 6 + 4$ 4. $\quad\quad (x - 2)^2 = 10$ 5. $\quad\quad x - 2 = \pm\sqrt{10}$ $\quad\quad x = 2 \pm \sqrt{10}$

DEFINITIONS AND CONCEPTS	EXAMPLES

Section 8.2 Solving Quadratic Equations by the Quadratic Formula

A quadratic equation written in the form $ax^2 + bx + c = 0$ has solutions

$$x = \frac{-b \pm \sqrt{b^2 - 4ac}}{2a}$$

Solve $x^2 - x - 3 = 0$.

$a = 1, b = -1, c = -3$

$$x = \frac{-(-1) \pm \sqrt{(-1)^2 - 4(1)(-3)}}{2 \cdot 1}$$

$$x = \frac{1 \pm \sqrt{13}}{2}$$

Section 8.3 Solving Equations by Using Quadratic Methods

Substitution is often helpful in solving an equation that contains a repeated variable expression.

Solve $(2x + 1)^2 - 5(2x + 1) + 6 = 0$.
Let $m = 2x + 1$. Then

$$m^2 - 5m + 6 = 0 \quad \text{Let } m = 2x + 1.$$
$$(m - 3)(m - 2) = 0$$
$$m = 3 \quad \text{or} \quad m = 2$$
$$2x + 1 = 3 \quad \text{or} \quad 2x + 1 = 2 \quad \text{Substitute}$$
$$x = 1 \quad \text{or} \quad x = \frac{1}{2} \quad \text{back.}$$

Section 8.4 Nonlinear Inequalities in One Variable

To solve a polynomial inequality

Step 1: Write the inequality in standard form.

Step 2: Solve the related equation.

Step 3: Use solutions from Step 2 to separate the number line into regions.

Step 4: Use test points to determine whether values in each region satisfy the original inequality.

Step 5: Write the solution set as the union of regions whose test point value is a solution.

Solve $x^2 \geq 6x$.

1. $x^2 - 6x \geq 0$

2. $x^2 - 6x = 0$

   $x(x - 6) = 0$

   $x = 0 \quad \text{or} \quad x = 6$

3.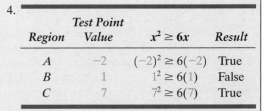

4.

Region	Test Point Value	$x^2 \geq 6x$	Result
A	-2	$(-2)^2 \geq 6(-2)$	True
B	1	$1^2 \geq 6(1)$	False
C	7	$7^2 \geq 6(7)$	True

5.

The solution set is $(-\infty, 0] \cup [6, \infty)$.

(continued)

DEFINITIONS AND CONCEPTS	EXAMPLES

Section 8.4 Nonlinear Inequalities in One Variable

To solve a rational inequality

Step 1: Solve for values that make all denominators 0.
Step 2: Solve the related equation.
Step 3: Use solutions from Steps 1 and 2 to separate the number line into regions.
Step 4: Use test points to determine whether values in each region satisfy the original inequality.
Step 5: Write the solution set as the union of regions whose test point value is a solution.

Solve $\dfrac{6}{x-1} < -2$.

1. $x - 1 = 0$ *Set denominator equal to 0.*
   $x = 1$

2. $\dfrac{6}{x-1} = -2$

   $6 = -2(x-1)$ *Multiply by $(x-1)$.*
   $6 = -2x + 2$
   $4 = -2x$
   $-2 = x$

3.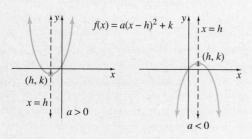

4. Only a test value from region B satisfies the original inequality.

5.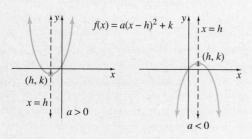

The solution set is $(-2, 1)$.

Section 8.5 Quadratic Functions and Their Graphs

Graph of a quadratic function

The graph of a quadratic function written in the form $f(x) = a(x-h)^2 + k$ is a parabola with vertex (h, k). If $a > 0$, the parabola opens upward; if $a < 0$, the parabola opens downward. The axis of symmetry is the line whose equation is $x = h$.

Graph $g(x) = 3(x-1)^2 + 4$.

The graph is a parabola with vertex $(1, 4)$ and axis of symmetry $x = 1$. Since $a = 3$ is positive, the graph opens upward.

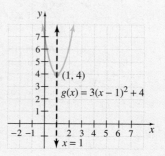

Section 8.6 Further Graphing of Quadratic Functions

The graph of $f(x) = ax^2 + bx + c$, where $a \neq 0$, is a parabola with vertex

$$\left(\dfrac{-b}{2a}, f\left(\dfrac{-b}{2a}\right)\right)$$

Graph $f(x) = x^2 - 2x - 8$. Find the vertex and x- and y-intercepts.

$$\dfrac{-b}{2a} = \dfrac{-(-2)}{2 \cdot 1} = 1$$

(continued)

DEFINITIONS AND CONCEPTS	EXAMPLES

Section 8.6 Further Graphing of Quadratic Functions

$$f(1) = 1^2 - 2(1) - 8 = -9$$

The vertex is $(1, -9)$.

$$0 = x^2 - 2x - 8$$
$$0 = (x - 4)(x + 2)$$
$$x = 4 \quad \text{or} \quad x = -2$$

The x-intercepts are $(4, 0)$ and $(-2, 0)$.

$$f(0) = 0^2 - 2 \cdot 0 - 8 = -8$$

The y-intercept is $(0, -8)$.

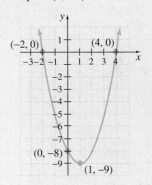

CHAPTER 8 REVIEW

(8.1) *Solve by factoring.*

1. $x^2 - 15x + 14 = 0$

2. $x^2 - x - 30 = 0$

3. $10x^2 = 3x + 4$ **4.** $7a^2 = 29a + 30$

Solve by using the square root property.

5. $4m^2 = 196$ **6.** $9y^2 = 36$

7. $(9n + 1)^2 = 9$ **8.** $(5x - 2)^2 = 2$

Solve by completing the square.

9. $z^2 + 3z + 1 = 0$ **10.** $x^2 + x + 7 = 0$

11. $(2x + 1)^2 = x$ **12.** $(3x - 4)^2 = 10x$

13. If P dollars are originally invested, the formula $A = P(1 + r)^2$ gives the amount A in an account paying interest rate r compounded annually after 2 years. Find the interest rate r such that $2500 increases to $2717 in 2 years. Round the result to the nearest hundredth of a percent.

14. Two ships leave a port at the same time and travel at the same speed. One ship is traveling due north and the other due east. In a few hours, the ships are 150 miles apart. How many miles has each ship traveled? Give an exact answer and a one-decimal-place approximation.

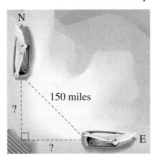

(8.2) *If the discriminant of a quadratic equation has the given value, determine the number and type of solutions of the equation.*

15. -8

16. 48

17. 100

18. 0

Solve by using the quadratic formula.

19. $x^2 - 16x + 64 = 0$

20. $x^2 + 5x = 0$

21. $x^2 + 11 = 0$

22. $2x^2 + 3x = 5$

23. $6x^2 + 7 = 5x$

24. $9a^2 + 4 = 2a$

25. $(5a - 2)^2 - a = 0$

26. $(2x - 3)^2 = x$

27. Cadets graduating from military school usually toss their hats high into the air at the end of the ceremony. One cadet threw his hat so that its distance $d(t)$ in feet above the ground t seconds after it was thrown was $d(t) = -16t^2 + 30t + 6$

a. Find the distance above the ground of the hat 1 second after it was thrown.

b. Find the time it takes the hat to hit the ground. Give an exact time and a one-decimal-place approximation.

28. The hypotenuse of an isosceles right triangle is 6 centimeters longer than either of the legs. Find the length of the legs.

(8.3) *Solve each equation for the variable.*

29. $x^3 = 27$

30. $y^3 = -64$

31. $\dfrac{5}{x} + \dfrac{6}{x - 2} = 3$

32. $\dfrac{7}{8} = \dfrac{8}{x^2}$

33. $x^4 - 21x^2 - 100 = 0$

34. $5(x + 3)^2 - 19(x + 3) = 4$ $\quad -\frac{16}{5}, 1$

35. $x^{2/3} - 6x^{1/3} + 5 = 0$

36. $x^{2/3} - 6x^{1/3} = -8$

37. $a^6 - a^2 = a^4 - 1$

38. $y^{-2} + y^{-1} = 20$ $\quad -\frac{1}{5}, \frac{1}{4}$

39. Two postal workers, Jerome Grant and Tim Bozik, can sort a stack of mail in 5 hours. Working alone, Tim can sort the mail in 1 hour less time than Jerome can. Find the time that each postal worker can sort the mail alone. Round the result to one decimal place.

40. A negative number decreased by its reciprocal is $-\dfrac{24}{5}$. Find the number.

(8.4) *Solve each inequality for x. Graph the solution set and write each solution set in interval notation.*

41. $2x^2 - 50 \le 0$

42. $\dfrac{1}{4}x^2 < \dfrac{1}{16}$

43. $(2x - 3)(4x + 5) \ge 0$

44. $(x^2 - 16)(x^2 - 1) > 0$

45. $\dfrac{x - 5}{x - 6} < 0$

46. $\dfrac{x(x + 5)}{4x - 3} \ge 0$

47. $\dfrac{(4x + 3)(x - 5)}{x(x + 6)} > 0$

48. $(x + 5)(x - 6)(x + 2) \le 0$

49. $x^3 + 3x^2 - 25x - 75 > 0$

50. $\dfrac{x^2 + 4}{3x} \le 1$

51. $\dfrac{(5x + 6)(x - 3)}{x(6x - 5)} < 0$

52. $\dfrac{3}{x - 2} > 2$

(8.5) Sketch the graph of each function. Label the vertex and the axis of symmetry.

53. $f(x) = x^2 - 4$

54. $g(x) = x^2 + 7$

55. $H(x) = 2x^2$

56. $h(x) = -\dfrac{1}{3}x^2$

57. $F(x) = (x - 1)^2$

58. $G(x) = (x + 5)^2$

59. $f(x) = (x - 4)^2 - 2$

60. $f(x) = -3(x - 1)^2 + 1$

(8.6) Sketch the graph of each function. Find the vertex and the intercepts.

61. $f(x) = x^2 + 10x + 25$

62. $f(x) = -x^2 + 6x - 9$

63. $f(x) = 4x^2 - 1$

64. $f(x) = -5x^2 + 5$

65. Find the vertex of the graph of $f(x) = -3x^2 - 5x + 4$. Determine whether the graph opens upward or down-ward, find the y-intercept, approximate the x-intercepts to one decimal place, and sketch the graph.

66. The function $h(t) = -16t^2 + 120t + 300$ gives the height in feet of a projectile fired from the top of a building in t seconds.

    a. When will the object reach a height of 350 feet? Round your answer to one decimal place.

    b. Explain why Part **a** has two answers.

67. Find two numbers whose product is as large as possible, given that their sum is 420.

68. Write an equation of a quadratic function whose graph is a parabola that has vertex $(-3, 7)$ and that passes through the origin.

CHAPTER 8 TEST

Solve each equation for the variable.

1. $5x^2 - 2x = 7$

2. $(x + 1)^2 = 10$

3. $m^2 - m + 8 = 0$

4. $u^2 - 6u + 2 = 0$

5. $7x^2 + 8x + 1 = 0$

6. $a^2 - 3a = 5$

7. $\dfrac{4}{x + 2} + \dfrac{2x}{x - 2} = \dfrac{6}{x^2 - 4}$

8. $x^4 - 8x^2 - 9 = 0$

9. $x^6 + 1 = x^4 + x^2$

10. $(x + 1)^2 - 15(x + 1) + 56 = 0$

Solve the equation for the variable by completing the square.

11. $x^2 - 6x = -2$

12. $2a^2 + 5 = 4a$

Solve each inequality for x. Graph the solution set and then write the solution set in interval notation.

13. $2x^2 - 7x > 15$

14. $(x^2 - 16)(x^2 - 25) > 0$

15. $\dfrac{5}{x + 3} < 1$

16. $\dfrac{7x - 14}{x^2 - 9} \le 0$

Graph each function. Label the vertex.

17. $f(x) = 3x^2$

18. $G(x) = -2(x - 1)^2 + 5$

Graph each function. Find and label the vertex, y-intercept, and x-intercepts (if any).

19. $h(x) = x^2 - 4x + 4$

20. $F(x) = 2x^2 - 8x + 9$

21. A 10-foot ladder is leaning against a house. The distance from the bottom of the ladder to the house is 4 feet less than the distance from the top of the ladder to the ground. Find how far the top of the ladder is from the ground. Give an exact answer and a one-decimal-place approximation.

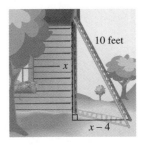

22. Dave and Sandy Hartranft can paint a room together in 4 hours. Working alone, Dave can paint the room in 2 hours less time than Sandy can. Find how long it takes Sandy to paint the room alone.

23. A stone is thrown upward from a bridge. The stone's height in feet, $s(t)$, above the water t seconds after the stone is thrown is a function given by the equation $s(t) = -16t^2 + 32t + 256$.

    a. Find the maximum height of the stone.

b. Find the time it takes the stone to hit the water. Round the answer to two decimal places.

256 feet

by cutting across the lawn instead of walking on the sidewalk.

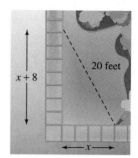

$x + 8$

20 feet

x

△ **24.** Given the diagram shown, approximate to the nearest foot how many feet of walking distance a person saves

CHAPTER 8 CUMULATIVE REVIEW

1. Write each sentence using mathematical symbols.
  a. The sum of 5 and y is greater than or equal to 7.
  b. 11 is not equal to z.
  c. 20 is less than the difference of 5 and twice x.

2. Find the slope of the line containing the points $(0, 3)$ and $(2, 5)$. Graph the line.

3. Use the elimination method to solve the system:
$$\begin{cases} x - 5y = -12 \\ -x + y = 4 \end{cases}$$

4. Multiply.
  a. $(2x - 7)(3x - 4)$
  b. $(3x + y)(5x - 2y)$

5. Factor.
  a. $8x^2 + 4$
  b. $5x - 2z^4$
  c. $6x^2 - 3x^3$

Factor.

6. $x^2 - 12x + 35$

7. $3a^2x - 12abx + 12b^2x$

8. Solve $3(x^2 + 4) + 5 = -6(x^2 + 2x) + 13$.

9. Graph the quadratic function $f(x) = -x^2 + 2x - 3$ by plotting points.

10. Simplify.
$$\frac{2x^2}{10x^3 - 2x^2}$$

11. Add $\dfrac{2x - 1}{2x^2 - 9x - 5} + \dfrac{x + 3}{6x^2 - x - 2}$.

12. Simplify.
$$\frac{x^{-1} + 2xy^{-1}}{x^{-2} - x^{-2}y^{-1}}$$

13. Divide: $\dfrac{3x^5y^2 - 15x^3y - x^2y - 6x}{x^2y}$

14. If $P(x) = 2x^3 - 4x^2 + 5$
  a. Find $P(2)$ by substitution.
  b. Use synthetic division to find the remainder when $P(x)$ is divided by $x - 2$.

15. Solve: $\dfrac{4x}{5} + \dfrac{3}{2} = \dfrac{3x}{10}$

16. If a certain number is subtracted from the numerator and added to the denominator of $\dfrac{9}{19}$, the new fraction is equivalent to $\dfrac{1}{3}$. Find the number.

17. Suppose that y varies directly as x. If y is 5 when x is 30, find the constant of variation and the direct variation equation.

18. Simplify.
  a. $\sqrt{(-3)^2}$
  b. $\sqrt{x^2}$
  c. $\sqrt[4]{(x - 2)^4}$
  d. $\sqrt[3]{(-5)^3}$
  e. $\sqrt[5]{(2x - 7)^5}$

19. Use rational exponents to simplify. Assume that variables represent positive numbers.

  a. $\sqrt[6]{25}$ **b.** $\sqrt[8]{x^4}$

  c. $\sqrt[4]{r^2 s^6}$

20. Use the product rule to simplify.

  a. $\sqrt{25x^3}$ **b.** $\sqrt[3]{54x^6 y^8}$

  c. $\sqrt[4]{81z^{11}}$

21. Rationalize the denominator of each expression.

  a. $\dfrac{2}{\sqrt{5}}$ **b.** $\dfrac{2\sqrt{16}}{\sqrt{9x}}$

  c. $\sqrt[3]{\dfrac{1}{2}}$

22. Solve $\sqrt{2x + 5} + \sqrt{2x} = 3$.

23. Find each quotient. Write in the form $a + bi$.

  a. $\dfrac{2 + i}{1 - i}$

  b. $\dfrac{7}{3i}$

24. Use the square root property to solve $(x + 1)^2 = 12$.

25. Solve $x - \sqrt{x} - 6 = 0$.

Designing Your World

Schools, homes, hospitals, airports, auditoriums, community centers, jails, theaters, day-care centers, and office buildings are just some of the types of structures designed by architects to be safe, economical, and functional.

To become a licensed architect, a person must have a professional degree in architecture, complete a three-year internship, and pass the Architect Registration Examination. An architecture degree typically includes courses in building design, computer-aided design and drafting (CADD), physics and other physical sciences, architectural history, and mathematics. Architects need solid computer and communication skills. They also need a good understanding of geometry and spatial relationships to visualize a building during the design process.

For more information about a career in architecture, visit The American Institute of Architects Web site by first going to **www.prenhall.com/martin-gay.**

In the Spotlight on Decision Making feature on page 553, you will have the opportunity to make a decision as an architect about redesigning a bridge arch in the shape of a half-ellipse.

CONIC SECTIONS

In Chapter 8, we analyzed some of the important connections between a parabola and its equation. Parabolas are interesting in their own right but are more interesting still because they are part of a collection of curves known as conic sections. This chapter is devoted to quadratic equations in two variables and their conic section graphs: the parabola, circle, ellipse, and hyperbola.

9.1 THE PARABOLA AND THE CIRCLE

▶ **OBJECTIVES**

CD-ROM   SSM

SSG   Video

1. Graph parabolas of the form $x = a(y - k)^2 + h$ and $y = a(x - h)^2 + k$.
2. Use the distance formula and the midpoint formula.
3. Graph circles of the form $(x - h)^2 + (y - k)^2 = r^2$.
4. Write the equation of a circle, given its center and radius.
5. Find the center and the radius of a circle, given its equation.

Conic sections derive their name because each conic section is the intersection of a right circular cone and a plane. The circle, parabola, ellipse, and hyperbola are the conic sections.

Circle

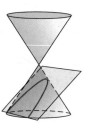

Parabola

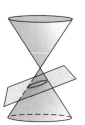

Ellipse

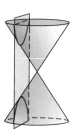

Hyperbola

1

Thus far, we have seen that $f(x)$ or $y = a(x - h)^2 + k$ is the equation of a parabola that opens upward if $a > 0$ or downward if $a < 0$. Parabolas can also open left or right, or even on a slant. Equations of these parabolas are not functions of x, of course, since a parabola opening any way other than upward or downward fails the vertical line test. In this section, we introduce parabolas that open to the left and to the right. Parabolas opening on a slant will not be developed in this book.

Just as $y = a(x - h)^2 + k$ is the equation of a parabola that opens upward or downward, $x = a(y - k)^2 + h$ is the equation of a parabola that opens to the right or to the left. The parabola opens to the right if $a > 0$ and to the left if $a < 0$. The parabola has vertex (h, k), and its axis of symmetry is the line $y = k$.

PARABOLAS

$$y = a(x - h)^2 + k$$

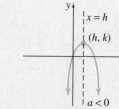

$$x = a(y - k)^2 + h$$

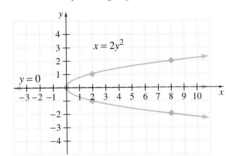

| $a > 0$ | $a < 0$ |

The equations $y = a(x - h)^2 + k$ and $x = a(y - k)^2 + h$ are called **standard forms.**

Example 1   Graph the parabola $x = 2y^2$.

Solution   Written in standard form, the equation $x = 2y^2$ is $x = 2(y - 0)^2 + 0$ with $a = 2$, $h = 0$, and $k = 0$. Its graph is a parabola with vertex $(0, 0)$, and its axis of symmetry is the line $y = 0$. Since $a > 0$, this parabola opens to the right. The table shows a few more ordered pair solutions of $x = 2y^2$. Its graph is also shown.

x	y
8	−2
2	−1
0	0
2	1
8	2

Example 2   Graph the parabola $x = -3(y - 1)^2 + 2$.

Solution   The equation $x = -3(y - 1)^2 + 2$ is in the form $x = a(y - k)^2 + h$ with $a = -3$, $k = 1$, and $h = 2$. Since $a < 0$, the parabola opens to the left. The vertex (h, k) is $(2, 1)$, and the axis of symmetry is the line $y = 1$. When $y = 0$, $x = -1$, so the x-intercept is $(-1, 0)$. Again, we obtain a few ordered pair solutions and then graph the parabola.

x	y
2	1
−1	0
−1	2
−10	3
−10	−1

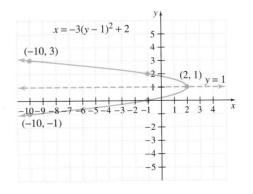

Example 3 Graph $y = -x^2 - 2x + 15$.

Solution Complete the square on x to write the equation in standard form.

$$y - 15 = -x^2 - 2x \qquad \text{Subtract 15 from both sides.}$$

$$y - 15 = -1(x^2 + 2x) \qquad \text{Factor} -1 \text{ from the terms } -x^2 - 2x.$$

The coefficient of x is 2. Find the square of half of 2.

$$\frac{1}{2}(2) = 1 \quad \text{and} \quad 1^2 = 1$$

$$y - 15 - 1(1) = -1(x^2 + 2x + 1) \qquad \text{Add} -1(1) \text{ to both sides.}$$

$$y - 16 = -1(x + 1)^2 \qquad \begin{array}{l}\text{Simplify the left side and}\\ \text{factor the right side.}\end{array}$$

$$y = -(x + 1)^2 + 16 \qquad \text{Add 16 to both sides.}$$

The equation is now in standard form $y = a(x - h)^2 + k$ with $a = -1, h = -1$, and $k = 16$.

The vertex is then (h, k), or $(-1, 16)$.

A second method for finding the vertex is by using the formula $\dfrac{-b}{2a}$.

$$x = \frac{-(-2)}{2(-1)} = \frac{2}{-2} = -1$$

$$y = -(-1)^2 - 2(-1) + 15 = -1 + 2 + 15 = 16$$

Again, we see that the vertex is $(-1, 16)$, and the axis of symmetry is the vertical line $x = -1$. The y-intercept is $(0, 15)$. Now we can use a few more ordered pair solutions to graph the parabola.

x	y
-1	16
0	15
-2	15
1	12
-3	12
3	0
-5	0

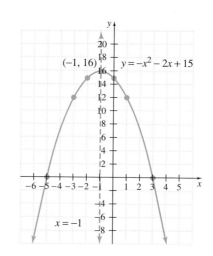

Example 4   Graph $x = 2y^2 + 4y + 5$.

Solution   Notice that this equation is quadratic in y, so its graph is a parabola that opens to the left or the right. We can complete the square on y or we can use the formula $\dfrac{-b}{2a}$ to find the vertex.

Since the equation is quadratic in y, the formula gives us the y-value of the vertex.

$$y = \frac{-4}{2 \cdot 2} = \frac{-4}{4} = -1$$

$$x = 2(-1)^2 + 4(-1) + 5 = 2 \cdot 1 - 4 + 5 = 3$$

The vertex is $(3, -1)$, and the axis of symmetry is the line $y = -1$. The parabola opens to the right since $a > 0$. The x-intercept is $(5, 0)$.

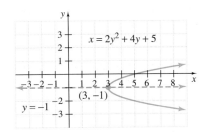

2   Another conic section is the circle. Before we review the circle, we need a formula to calculate the distance between points of the Cartesian coordinate system. To find the distance between two points, we use the distance formula, which is derived from the Pythagorean theorem.

To find the distance d between two points (x_1, y_1) and (x_2, y_2) as shown to the left, notice that the length of leg a is $x_2 - x_1$ and that the length of leg b is $y_2 - y_1$.

Thus, the Pythagorean theorem tells us that

$$d^2 = a^2 + b^2$$

or

$$d^2 = (x_2 - x_1)^2 + (y_2 - y_1)^2$$

or

$$d = \sqrt{(x_2 - x_1)^2 + (y_2 - y_1)^2}$$

This formula gives us the distance between any two points on the real plane.

DISTANCE FORMULA

The distance d between two points (x_1, y_1) and (x_2, y_2) is given by

$$d = \sqrt{(x_2 - x_1)^2 + (y_2 - y_1)^2}$$

Example 5 Find the distance between $(2, -5)$ and $(1, -4)$. Give an exact distance and a three-decimal-place approximation.

Solution To use the distance formula, it makes no difference which point we call (x_1, y_1) and which point we call (x_2, y_2). We will let $(x_1, y_1) = (2, -5)$ and $(x_2, y_2) = (1, -4)$.

$$d = \sqrt{(x_2 - x_1)^2 + (y_2 - y_1)^2}$$
$$= \sqrt{(1 - 2)^2 + [-4 - (-5)]^2}$$
$$= \sqrt{(-1)^2 + (1)^2}$$
$$= \sqrt{1 + 1}$$
$$= \sqrt{2} \approx 1.414$$

The distance between the two points is exactly $\sqrt{2}$ units, or approximately 1.414 uniits.

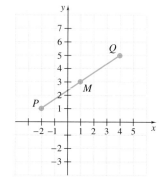

The **midpoint** of a line segment is the **point** located exactly halfway between the two endpoints of the line segment. On the graph to the left, the point M is the midpoint of line segment PQ. Thus, the distance between M and P equals the distance between M and Q.

The x-coordinate of M is at half the distance between the x-coordinates of P and Q, and the y-coordinate of M is at half the distance between the y-coordinates of P and Q. That is, the x-coordinate of M is the average of the x-coordinates of P and Q; the y-coordinate of M is the average of the y-coordinates of P and Q.

MIDPOINT FORMULA

The midpoint of the line segment whose endpoints are (x_1, y_1) and (x_2, y_2) is the point with coordinates

$$\left(\frac{x_1 + x_2}{2}, \frac{y_1 + y_2}{2} \right)$$

Example 6 Find the midpoint of the line segment that joins points $P(-3, 3)$ and $Q(1, 0)$.

Solution Use the midpoint formula. It makes no difference which point we call (x_1, y_1) or which point we call (x_2, y_2). Let $(x_1, y_1) = (-3, 3)$ and $(x_2, y_2) = (1, 0)$.

$$\text{midpoint} = \left(\frac{x_1 + x_2}{2}, \frac{y_1 + y_2}{2} \right)$$
$$= \left(\frac{-3 + 1}{2}, \frac{3 + 0}{2} \right)$$
$$= \left(\frac{-2}{2}, \frac{3}{2} \right)$$
$$= \left(-1, \frac{3}{2} \right)$$

The midpoint of the segment is $\left(-1, \frac{3}{2} \right)$.

3

Another conic section is the **circle.** A circle is the set of all points in a plane that are the same distance from a fixed point called the **center.** The distance is called the **radius** of the circle. To find a standard equation for a circle, let (h, k) represent the center of the circle, and let (x, y) represent any point on the circle. The distance between (h, k) and (x, y) is defined to be the circle's radius, r units. We can find this distance r by using the distance formula.

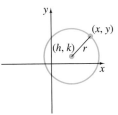

$$r = \sqrt{(x - h)^2 + (y - k)^2}$$

$$r^2 = (x - h)^2 + (y - k)^2 \qquad \text{Square both sides.}$$

CIRCLE

The graph of $(x - h)^2 + (y - k)^2 = r^2$ is a circle with center (h, k) and radius r.

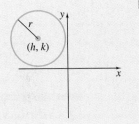

The equation $(x - h)^2 + (y - k)^2 = r^2$ is called **standard form.**

If an equation can be written in the standard form

$$(x - h)^2 + (y - k)^2 = r^2$$

then its graph is a circle, which we can draw by graphing the center (h, k) and using the radius r.

Example 7   Graph $x^2 + y^2 = 4$.

Solution   The equation can be written in standard form as

$$(x - 0)^2 + (y - 0)^2 = 2^2$$

The center of the circle is $(0, 0)$, and the radius is 2. Its graph is shown.

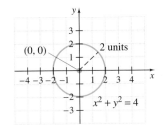

HELPFUL HINT

Notice the difference between the equation of a circle and the equation of a parabola. The equation of a circle contains both x^2 and y^2 terms on the same side of the equation with equal coefficients. The equation of a parabola has either an x^2 term or a y^2 term but not both.

Example 8   Graph $(x + 1)^2 + y^2 = 8$.

Solution   The equation can be written as $(x + 1)^2 + (y - 0)^2 = 8$ with $h = -1$, $k = 0$, and $r = \sqrt{8}$. The center is $(-1, 0)$, and the radius is $\sqrt{8} = 2\sqrt{2} \approx 2.8$.

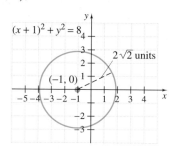

4   Since a circle is determined entirely by its center and radius, this information is all we need to write the equation of a circle.

Example 9   Find an equation of the circle with center $(-7, 3)$ and radius 10.

Solution   Using the given values $h = -7$, $k = 3$, and $r = 10$, we write the equation

$$(x - h)^2 + (y - k)^2 = r^2$$

or

$$[x - (-7)]^2 + (y - 3)^2 = 10^2 \qquad \text{Substitute the given values.}$$

or

$$(x + 7)^2 + (y - 3)^2 = 100$$

5   To find the center and the radius of a circle from its equation, write the equation in standard form. To write the equation of a circle in standard form, we complete the square on both x and y.

Example 10   Graph $x^2 + y^2 + 4x - 8y = 16$.

Solution   Since this equation contains x^2 and y^2 terms on the same side of the equation with equal coefficients, its graph is a circle. To write the equation in standard form, group the terms involving x and the terms involving y, and then complete the square on each variable.

$$(x^2 + 4x) + (y^2 - 8y) = 16$$

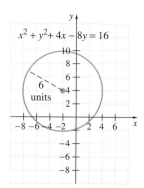

Thus, $\frac{1}{2}(4) = 2$ and $2^2 = 4$. Also, $\frac{1}{2}(-8) = -4$ and $(-4)^2 = 16$. Add 4 and then 16 to both sides.

$$(x^2 + 4x + 4) + (y^2 - 8y + 16) = 16 + 4 + 16$$
$$(x + 2)^2 + (y - 4)^2 = 36 \qquad \text{Factor.}$$

This circle has the center $(-2, 4)$ and radius 6, as shown.

GRAPHING CALCULATOR EXPLORATIONS

To graph an equation such as $x^2 + y^2 = 25$ with a graphing calculator, we first solve the equation for y.

$$x^2 + y^2 = 25$$
$$y^2 = 25 - x^2$$
$$y = \pm\sqrt{25 - x^2}$$

The graph of $y = \sqrt{25 - x^2}$ will be the top half of the circle, and the graph of $y = -\sqrt{25 - x^2}$ will be the bottom half of the circle.

To graph, press $\boxed{Y =}$ and enter $Y_1 = \sqrt{25 - x^2}$ and $Y_2 = -\sqrt{25 - x^2}$. Insert parentheses around $25 - x^2$ so that $\sqrt{25 - x^2}$ and not $\sqrt{25} - x^2$ is graphed.

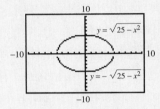

The graph does not appear to be a circle because we are currently using a standard window and the screen is rectangular. This causes the tick marks on the x-axis to be farther apart than the tick marks on the y-axis and, thus, creates the distorted circle. If we want the graph to appear circular, we must define a square window by using a feature of the graphing calculator or by redefining the window to show the x-axis from -15 to 15 and the y-axis from -10 to 10. Using a square window, the graph appears as follows.

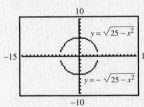

Use a graphing calculator to graph each circle.

1. $x^2 + y^2 = 55$
2. $x^2 + y^2 = 20$
3. $5x^2 + 5y^2 = 50$
4. $6x^2 + 6y^2 = 105$
5. $2x^2 + 2y^2 - 34 = 0$
6. $4x^2 + 4y^2 - 48 = 0$
7. $7x^2 + 7y^2 - 89 = 0$
8. $3x^2 + 3y^2 - 35 = 0$

MENTAL MATH

The graph of each equation is a parabola. Determine whether the parabola opens upward, downward, to the left, or to the right.

1. $y = x^2 - 7x + 5$
2. $y = -x^2 + 16$
3. $x = -y^2 - y + 2$
4. $x = 3y^2 + 2y - 5$
5. $y = -x^2 + 2x + 1$
6. $x = -y^2 + 2y - 6$

Exercise Set 9.1

The graph of each equation is a parabola. Find the vertex of the parabola and sketch its graph. See Examples 1 through 4.

1. $x = 3y^2$

2. $x = -2y^2$

3. $x = (y - 2)^2 + 3$

4. $x = (y - 4)^2 - 1$

5. $y = 3(x - 1)^2 + 5$

6. $x = -4(y - 2)^2 + 2$

7. $x = y^2 + 6y + 8$

8. $x = y^2 - 6y + 6$

9. $y = x^2 + 10x + 20$

10. $y = x^2 + 4x - 5$

11. $x = -2y^2 + 4y + 6$

12. $x = 3y^2 + 6y + 7$

Find the distance between each pair of points. Approximate the distance in Exercises 21 and 22 to two decimal places. See Example 5.

13. $(5, 1)$ and $(8, 5)$

14. $(2, 3)$ and $(14, 8)$

15. $(-3, 2)$ and $(1, -3)$

16. $(3, -2)$ and $(-4, 1)$

17. $(-9, 4)$ and $(-8, 1)$

18. $(-5, -2)$ and $(-6, -6)$

19. $(0, -\sqrt{2})$ and $(\sqrt{3}, 0)$

20. $(-\sqrt{5}, 0)$ and $(0, \sqrt{7})$

21. $(1.7, -3.6)$ and $(-8.6, 5.7)$

22. $(9.6, 2.5)$ and $(-1.9, -3.7)$

23. $(2\sqrt{3}, \sqrt{6})$ and $(-\sqrt{3}, 4\sqrt{6})$

24. $(5\sqrt{2}, -4)$ and $(-3\sqrt{2}, -8)$

Find the midpoint of the line segment whose endpoints are given. See Example 6.

25. $(6, -8), (2, 4)$

26. $(3, 9), (7, 11)$

27. $(-2, -1), (-8, 6)$

28. $(-3, -4), (6, -8)$

29. $(7, 3), (-1, -3)$

30. $(-2, 5), (-1, 6)$

31. $\left(\frac{1}{2}, \frac{3}{8}\right), \left(-\frac{3}{2}, \frac{5}{8}\right)$

32. $\left(-\frac{2}{5}, \frac{7}{15}\right), \left(-\frac{2}{5}, -\frac{4}{15}\right)$

33. $(\sqrt{2}, 3\sqrt{5}), (\sqrt{2}, -2\sqrt{5})$

34. $(\sqrt{8}, -\sqrt{12}), (3\sqrt{2}, 7\sqrt{3})$

35. $(4.6, -3.5), (7.8, -9.8)$

36. $(-4.6, 2.1), (-6.7, 1.9)$

The graph of each equation is a circle. Find the center and the radius, and then sketch. See Examples 7, 8, and 10.

37. $x^2 + y^2 = 9$

38. $x^2 + y^2 = 25$

39. $x^2 + (y - 2)^2 = 1$

40. $(x - 3)^2 + y^2 = 9$

41. $(x - 5)^2 + (y + 2)^2 = 1$

42. $(x + 3)^2 + (y + 3)^2 = 4$

43. $x^2 + y^2 + 6y = 0$

44. $x^2 + 10x + y^2 = 0$

45. $x^2 + y^2 + 2x - 4y = 4$

46. $x^2 + 6x - 4y + y^2 = 3$

47. $x^2 + y^2 - 4x - 8y - 2 = 0$

48. $x^2 + y^2 - 2x - 6y - 5 = 0$

Write an equation of the circle with the given center and radius. See Example 9.

49. $(2, 3); 6$

50. $(-7, 6); 2$

51. $(0, 0); \sqrt{3}$

52. $(0, -6); \sqrt{2}$

53. $(-5, 4); 3\sqrt{5}$

54. the origin; $4\sqrt{7}$

55. If you are given a list of equations of circles and parabolas and none are in standard form, explain how you would determine which is an equation of a circle and which is an equation of a parabola. Explain also how you would distinguish the upward or downward parabolas from the left-opening or right-opening parabolas.

Sketch the graph of each equation. If the graph is a parabola, find its vertex. If the graph is a circle, find its center and radius.

56. $x = y^2 + 2$

57. $x = y^2 - 3$

58. $y = (x + 3)^2 + 3$

59. $y = (x - 2)^2 - 2$

60. $x^2 + y^2 = 49$

61. $x^2 + y^2 = 1$

62. $x = (y - 1)^2 + 4$

63. $x = (y + 3)^2 - 1$

64. $(x + 3)^2 + (y - 1)^2 = 9$

65. $(x - 2)^2 + (y - 2)^2 = 16$

66. $x = -2(y + 5)^2$

67. $x = -(y - 1)^2$

68. $x^2 + (y + 5)^2 = 5$

69. $(x - 4)^2 + y^2 = 7$

70. $y = 3(x - 4)^2 + 2$

71. $y = 5(x + 5)^2 + 3$

72. $2x^2 + 2y^2 = \frac{1}{2}$

73. $\frac{x^2}{8} + \frac{y^2}{8} = 2$

74. $y = x^2 - 2x - 15$

75. $y = x^2 + 7x + 6$

76. $x^2 + y^2 + 6x + 10y - 2 = 0$

77. $x^2 + y^2 + 2x + 12y - 12 = 0$

78. $x = y^2 + 6y + 2$

79. $x = y^2 + 8y - 4$

80. $x^2 + y^2 - 8y + 5 = 0$

81. $x^2 - 10y + y^2 + 4 = 0$

82. $x = -2y^2 - 4y$

83. $x = -3y^2 + 30y$

84. $\frac{x^2}{3} + \frac{y^2}{3} = 2$

85. $5x^2 + 5y^2 = 25$

86. $y = 4x^2 - 40x + 105$

87. $y = 5x^2 - 20x + 16$

Solve.

88. Two surveyors need to find the distance across a lake. They place a reference pole at point *A* in the diagram. Point *B* is 3 meters east and 1 meter north of the reference point A. Point C is 19 meters east and 13 meters north of point A. Find the distance across the lake, from B to C.

100 meters and the maximum height of the arch is 40 meters.

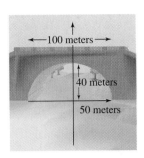

△ **89.** Determine whether the triangle with vertices $(2, 6)$, $(0, -2)$, and $(5, 1)$ is an isosceles triangle.

△ **90.** Cindy Brown, an architect, is drawing plans on grid paper for a circular pool with a fountain in the middle. The paper is marked off in centimeters, and each centimeter represents 1 foot. On the paper, the diameter of the "pool" is 20 centimeters, and "fountain" is the point $(0, 0)$.

   a. Sketch the architect's drawing. Be sure to label the axes.

   b. Write an equation that describes the circular pool.

   c. Cindy plans to place a circle of lights around the fountain such that each light is 5 feet from the fountain. Write an equation for the circle of lights and sketch the circle on your drawing.

91. A bridge constructed over a bayou has a supporting arch in the shape of a parabola. Find an equation of the parabolic arch if the length of the road over the arch is

Use a graphing calculator to verify each exercise. Use a square viewing window.

92. Exercise 84.   **93.** Exercise 85.

94. Exercise 86.   **95.** Exercise 87.

REVIEW EXERCISES

Graph each equation. See Section 3.3.

96. $y = 2x + 5$ **97.** $y = -3x + 3$

98. $y = 3$ **99.** $x = -2$

Rationalize each denominator and simplify if possible. See Section 7.5.

100. $\dfrac{1}{\sqrt{3}}$ **101.** $\dfrac{\sqrt{5}}{\sqrt{8}}$

102. $\dfrac{4\sqrt{7}}{\sqrt{6}}$ **103.** $\dfrac{10}{\sqrt{5}}$

9.2 THE ELLIPSE AND THE HYPERBOLA

CD-ROM   SSM

SSG   Video

▶ **OBJECTIVES**

1. Define and graph an ellipse.
2. Define and graph a hyperbola.

1   An **ellipse** can be thought of as the set of points in a plane such that the sum of the distances of those points from two fixed points is constant. Each of the two fixed points is called a **focus**. (The plural of focus is **foci**.) The point midway between the foci is called the **center.**

    An ellipse may be drawn by hand by using two thumbtacks, a piece of string, and a pencil. Secure the two thumbtacks in a piece of cardboard, for example, and tie each end of the string to a tack. Use your pencil to pull the string tight and draw the ellipse. The two thumbtacks are the foci of the drawn ellipse.

 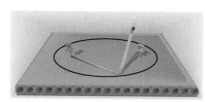 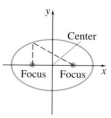

ELLIPSE WITH CENTER $(0, 0)$

The graph of an equation of the form $\dfrac{x^2}{a^2} + \dfrac{y^2}{b^2} = 1$ is an ellipse with center $(0, 0)$. The x-intercepts are $(a, 0)$ and $(-a, 0)$, and the y-intercepts are $(0, b)$, and $(0, -b)$.

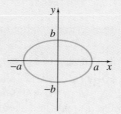

The **standard form** of an ellipse with center $(0, 0)$ is $\dfrac{x^2}{a^2} + \dfrac{y^2}{b^2} = 1$.

Example 1   Graph $\dfrac{x^2}{9} + \dfrac{y^2}{16} = 1$.

Solution   The equation is of the form $\dfrac{x^2}{a^2} + \dfrac{y^2}{b^2} = 1$, with $a = 3$ and $b = 4$, so its graph is an ellipse with center $(0, 0)$, x-intercepts $(3, 0)$ and $(-3, 0)$, and y-intercepts $(0, 4)$ and $(0, -4)$.

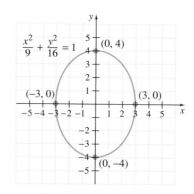

EXPONENTIAL AND LOGARITHMIC FUNCTIONS

10

In this chapter, we discuss two closely related functions: exponential and logarithmic functions. These functions are vital to applications in economics, finance, engineering, the sciences, education, and other fields. Models of tumor growth and learning curves are two examples of the uses of exponential and logarithmic functions.

10.1 THE ALGEBRA OF FUNCTIONS; COMPOSITE FUNCTIONS

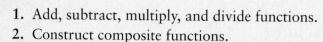

▶ **OBJECTIVES**

1. Add, subtract, multiply, and divide functions.
2. Construct composite functions.

 CD-ROM   SSM

SSG   Video

1

As we have seen in earlier chapters, it is possible to add, subtract, multiply, and divide functions. Although we have not stated it as such, the sums, differences, products, and quotients of functions are themselves functions. For example, if $f(x) = 3x$ and $g(x) = x + 1$, their product, $f(x) \cdot g(x) = 3x(x + 1) = 3x^2 + 3x$, is a new function. We can use the notation $(f \cdot g)(x)$ to denote this new function. Finding the sum, difference, product, and quotient of functions to generate new functions is called the **algebra of functions.**

ALGEBRA OF FUNCTIONS

Let f and g be functions. New functions from f and g are defined as follows.

Sum	$(f + g)(x) = f(x) + g(x)$
Difference	$(f - g)(x) = f(x) - g(x)$
Product	$(f \cdot g)(x) = f(x) \cdot g(x)$
Quotient	$\left(\dfrac{f}{g}\right)(x) = \dfrac{f(x)}{g(x)}, g(x) \neq 0$

Example 1   If $f(x) = x - 1$ and $g(x) = 2x - 3$, find

a. $(f + g)(x)$

b. $(f - g)(x)$

c. $(f \cdot g)(x)$

d. $\left(\dfrac{f}{g}\right)(x)$

Solution   Use the algebra of functions and replace $f(x)$ by $x - 1$ and $g(x)$ by $2x - 3$. Then we simplify.

a. $(f + g)(x) = f(x) + g(x)$

$$= (x - 1) + (2x - 3)$$

$$= 3x - 4$$

b. $(f - g)(x) = f(x) - g(x)$

$$= (x - 1) - (2x - 3)$$

$$= x - 1 - 2x + 3$$

$$= -x + 2$$

c. $(f \cdot g)(x) = f(x) \cdot g(x)$

$$= (x - 1)(2x - 3)$$

$$= 2x^2 - 5x + 3$$

d. $\left(\dfrac{f}{g}\right)(x) = \dfrac{f(x)}{g(x)} = \dfrac{x - 1}{2x - 3}$, where $x \neq \dfrac{3}{2}$

There is an interesting but not surprising relationship between the graphs of functions and the graphs of their sum, difference, product, and quotient. For example, the graph of $(f + g)(x)$ can be found by adding the graph of $f(x)$ to the graph of $g(x)$. We add two graphs by adding corresponding y-values.

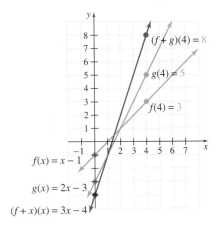

2 Another way to combine functions is called **function composition.** To understand this new way of combining functions, study the tables below. The first table shows degrees Celsius $C(x)$ as a function of degrees Fahrenheit x. The second table shows Kelvins $K(C)$ as a function of degrees Celsius C. (The Kelvin scale is a temperature scale devised by Lord Kelvin in 1848.) The function represented by the first table we will call C, and the second function we will call K.

x = Degrees Fahrenheit (Input)	-31	-13	32	68	149	212
$C(x)$ = Degrees Celsius (Output)	-35	-25	0	20	65	100

C = Degrees Celsius (Input)	-35	-25	0	20	65	100
$K(C)$ = Kelvins (Output)	238.15	248.15	273.15	293.15	338.15	373.15

Suppose that we want a table that shows a direct conversion from degrees Fahrenheit to kelvins. In other words, suppose that a table is needed that shows kelvins as a function of degrees Fahrenheit. This can easily be done because in the tables, the output of the first table $C(x)$ is the same as the input of the second table. If we use $C(x)$ to represent this, then we get the following table.

$x =$ Degrees Fahrenheit (Input)	-31	-13	32	68	149	212
$K(C(x)) =$ Kelvins (Output)	238.15	248.15	273.15	293.15	338.15	373.15

Since the output of the first table is used as the input of the second table, we write the new function as $K(C(x))$. The new function is formed from the composition of the other two functions. The mathematical symbol for this composition is $(K \circ C)(x)$. Thus, $(K \circ C)(x) = K(C(x))$.

It is possible to find an equation for the composition of the two functions C and K. In other words, we can find a function that converts degrees Fahrenheit directly to kelvins. The function $C(x) = \dfrac{5}{9}(x - 32)$ converts degrees Fahrenheit to degrees Celsius, and the function $K(C) = C + 273.15$ converts degrees Celsius to kelvins. Thus,

$$(K \circ C)(x) = K(C(x)) = K\left(\frac{5}{9}(x - 32)\right) = \frac{5}{9}(x - 32) + 273.15$$

In general, the notation $f(g(x))$ means "f composed with g" and can be written as $(f \circ g)(x)$. Also $g(f(x))$, or $(g \circ f)(x)$, means "g composed with f."

COMPOSITION OF FUNCTIONS

The composition of functions f and g is

$$(f \circ g)(x) = f(g(x))$$

HELPFUL HINT
$(f \circ g)(x)$ does not mean the same as $(f \cdot g)(x)$.
$$(f \circ g)(x) = f(g(x)) \text{ while } (f \cdot g)(x) = f(x) \cdot g(x)$$

Example 2 If $f(x) = x^2$ and $g(x) = x + 3$, find each composition.

a. $(f \circ g)(2)$ and $(g \circ f)(2)$

b. $(f \circ g)(x)$ and $(g \circ f)(x)$

Solution **a.** $(f \circ g)(2) = f(g(2))$

$\qquad\qquad = f(5)$ Replace $g(2)$ with 5. [Since $g(x) = x + 3$, then

$\qquad\qquad = 5^2 = 25$ $g(2) = 2 + 3 = 5$.]

$\qquad (g \circ f)(2) = g(f(2))$

$\qquad\qquad = g(4)$ Since $f(x) = x^2$, then $f(2) = 2^2 = 4$.

$\qquad\qquad = 4 + 3 = 7$

b. $(f \circ g)(x) = f(g(x))$

$\qquad\qquad = f(x + 3)$ Replace $g(x)$ with $x + 3$.

$\qquad\qquad = (x + 3)^2$ $f(x + 3) = (x + 3)^2$

$\qquad\qquad = x^2 + 6x + 9$ Square $(x + 3)$.

$(g \circ f)(x) = g(f(x))$

$\qquad\qquad = g(x^2)$ Replace $f(x)$ with x^2.

$\qquad\qquad = x^2 + 3$ $g(x^2) = x^2 + 3$

Example 3   If $f(x) = |x|$ and $g(x) = x - 2$, find each composition.

a. $(f \circ g)(x)$

b. $(g \circ f)(x)$

Solution   **a.** $(f \circ g)(x) = f(g(x)) = f(x - 2) = |x - 2|$

b. $(g \circ f)(x) = g(f(x)) = g(|x|) = |x| - 2$

> **HELPFUL HINT**
> In Examples 2 and 3, notice that $(g \circ f)(x) \neq (f \circ g)(x)$. In general, $(g \circ f)(x)$ *may* or *may not* equal $(f \circ g)(x)$.

Example 4   If $f(x) = 5x$, $g(x) = x - 2$, and $h(x) = \sqrt{x}$, write each function as a composition using two of the given functions.

a. $F(x) = \sqrt{x - 2}$

b. $G(x) = 5x - 2$

Solution   **a.** Notice the order in which the function F operates on an input value x. First, 2 is subtracted from x. This is the function $g(x) = x - 2$. Then the square root *of that result* is taken. The square root function is $h(x) = \sqrt{x}$. This means that $F = h \circ g$. To check, we find $h \circ g$.

$$(h \circ g)(x) = h(g(x)) = h(x - 2) = \sqrt{x - 2}$$

b. Notice the order in which the function G operates on an input value x. First, x is multiplied by 5, and then 2 is subtracted from the result. This means that $G = g \circ f$. To check, we find $g \circ f$.

$$(g \circ f)(x) = g(f(x)) = g(5x) = 5x - 2$$

GRAPHING CALCULATOR EXPLORATIONS

If $f(x) = \dfrac{1}{2}x + 2$ and $g(x) = \dfrac{1}{3}x^2 + 4$, then

$$(f + g)(x) = f(x) + g(x)$$

$$= \left(\frac{1}{2}x + 2\right) + \left(\frac{1}{3}x^2 + 4\right)$$

$$= \frac{1}{3}x^2 + \frac{1}{2}x + 6.$$

To visualize this addition of functions with a graphing calculator, graph

$$Y_1 = \frac{1}{2}x + 2, \qquad Y_2 = \frac{1}{3}x^2 + 4, \qquad Y_3 = \frac{1}{3}x^2 + \frac{1}{2}x + 6$$

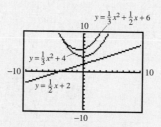

Use a TABLE feature to verify that for a given x value, $Y_1 + Y_2 = Y_3$. For example, verify that when $x = 0$, $Y_1 = 2$, $Y_2 = 4$, and $Y_3 = 2 + 4 = 6$.

Exercise Set 10.1

*For the functions f and g, find **a.** $(f + g)(x)$, **b.** $(f - g)(x)$,
c. $(f \cdot g)(x)$, and **d.** $\left(\dfrac{f}{g}\right)(x)$. See Example 1.*

1. $f(x) = x - 7, g(x) = 2x + 1$

2. $f(x) = x + 4, g(x) = 5x - 2$

3. $f(x) = x^2 + 1, g(x) = 5x$

4. $f(x) = x^2 - 2, g(x) = 3x$

5. $f(x) = \sqrt{x}, g(x) = x + 5$

6. $f(x) = \sqrt[3]{x}, g(x) = x - 3$

7. $f(x) = -3x, g(x) = 5x^2$

8. $f(x) = 4x^3, g(x) = -6x$

If $f(x) = x^2 - 6x + 2$, $g(x) = -2x$, and $h(x) = \sqrt{x}$, find each composition. See Example 2.

9. $(f \circ g)(2)$

10. $(h \circ f)(-2)$

11. $(g \circ f)(-1)$

12. $(f \circ h)(1)$

13. $(g \circ h)(0)$

14. $(h \circ g)(0)$

Find $(f \circ g)(x)$ and $(g \circ f)(x)$. See Examples 2 and 3.

15. $f(x) = x^2 + 1, g(x) = 5x$

16. $f(x) = x - 3, g(x) = x^2$

17. $f(x) = 2x - 3, g(x) = x + 7$

18. $f(x) = x + 10, g(x) = 3x + 1$

19. $f(x) = x^3 + x - 2, g(x) = -2x$

20. $f(x) = -4x, g(x) = x^3 + x^2 - 6$

21. $f(x) = \sqrt{x}, g(x) = -5x + 2$

22. $f(x) = 7x - 1, g(x) = \sqrt[3]{x}$

If $f(x) = 3x$, $g(x) = \sqrt{x}$, and $h(x) = x^2 + 2$, write each function as a composition using two of the given functions. See Example 4.

23. $H(x) = \sqrt{x^2 + 2}$

24. $G(x) = \sqrt{3x}$

25. $F(x) = 9x^2 + 2$

26. $H(x) = 3x^2 + 6$

27. $G(x) = 3\sqrt{x}$

28. $F(x) = x + 2$

Find $f(x)$ and $g(x)$ so that the given function $h(x) = (f \circ g)(x)$.

29. $h(x) = (x + 2)^2$

30. $h(x) = |x - 1|$

31. $h(x) = \sqrt{x + 5} + 2$

32. $h(x) = (3x + 4)^2 + 3$

33. $h(x) = \dfrac{1}{2x - 3}$

34. $h(x) = \dfrac{1}{x + 10}$

Given that $f(-1) = 4 \quad g(-1) = -4$
$f(0) = 5 \quad g(0) = -3$
$f(2) = 7 \quad g(2) = -1$
$f(7) = 1 \quad g(7) = 4$

Find each function value.

35. $(f + g)(2)$

36. $(f - g)(7)$

37. $(f \circ g)(2)$

38. $(g \circ f)(2)$

39. $(f \cdot g)(7)$

40. $(f \cdot g)(0)$

41. $\left(\dfrac{f}{g}\right)(-1)$

42. $\left(\dfrac{g}{f}\right)(-1)$

Solve.

43. Business people are concerned with cost functions, revenue functions, and profit functions. Recall that the profit $P(x)$ obtained from x units of a product is equal to the revenue $R(x)$ from selling the x units minus the cost $C(x)$ of manufacturing the x units. Write an equation expressing this relationship among $C(x)$, $R(x)$, and $P(x)$.

44. Suppose the revenue $R(x)$ for x units of a product can be described by $R(x) = 25x$, and the cost $C(x)$ can be described by $C(x) = 50 + x^2 + 4x$. Find the profit $P(x)$ for x units.

REVIEW EXERCISES

Solve each equation for y. See Section 2.3.

45. $x = y + 2$

46. $x = y - 5$

47. $x = 3y$

48. $x = -6y$

49. $x = -2y - 7$

50. $x = 4y + 7$

10.2 INVERSE FUNCTIONS

CD-ROM SSM SSG Video

▶ **OBJECTIVES**

1. Determine whether a function is a one-to-one function.
2. Use the horizontal line test to decide whether a function is a one-to-one function.
3. Find the inverse of a function.
4. Find the equation of the inverse of a function.
5. Graph functions and their inverses.
6. Determine whether two functions are inverses of each other.

1

In the next section, we begin a study of two new functions: exponential and logarithmic functions. As we learn more about these functions, we will discover that they share a special relation to each other: They are inverses of each other.

Before we study these functions, we need to learn about inverses. We begin by defining one-to-one functions.

Study the following table.

Degrees Fahrenheit (Input)	-31	-13	32	68	149	212
Degrees Celsius (Output)	-35	-25	0	20	65	100

Recall that since each degrees Fahrenheit (input) corresponds to exactly one degrees Celsius (output), this table of inputs and outputs does describe a function. Also notice that each output corresponds to a different input. This type of function is given a special name—a one-to-one function.

Does the set $f = \{(0, 1), (2, 2), (-3, 5), (7, 6)\}$ describe a one-to-one function? It is a function since each x-value corresponds to a unique y-value. For this particular function f, each y-value corresponds to a unique x-value. Thus, this function is also a **one-to-one function.**

ONE-TO-ONE FUNCTION

For a **one-to-one function,** each x-value (input) corresponds to only one y-value (output), and each y-value (output) corresponds to only one x-value (input).

Example 1 Determine whether each function described is one-to-one.

a. $f = \{(6, 2), (5, 4), (-1, 0), (7, 3)\}$

b. $g = \{(3, 9), (-4, 2), (-3, 9), (0, 0)\}$

c. $h = \{(1, 1), (2, 2), (10, 10), (-5, -5)\}$

d.

MINERAL (INPUT)	Talc	Gypsum	Diamond	Topaz	Stibnite
HARDNESS ON THE MOHS SCALE (OUTPUT)	1	2	10	8	2

e.

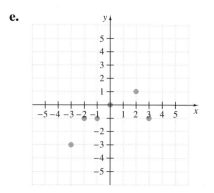

Solution   **a.** f is one-to-one since each y-value corresponds to only one x-value.

b. g is not one-to-one because the y-value 9 in $(3, 9)$ and $(-3, 9)$ corresponds to two different x-values.

c. h is a one-to-one function since each y-value corresponds to only one x-value.

d. This table does not describe a one-to-one function since the output 2 corresponds to two different inputs, gypsum and stibnite.

e. This graph does not describe a one-to-one function since the y-value -1 corresponds to three different x-values, $-2, -1,$ and 3.

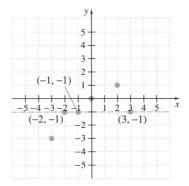

2   Recall that we recognize the graph of a function when it passes the vertical line test. Since every x-value of the function corresponds to exactly one y-value, each vertical line intersects the function's graph at most once. The graph shown next, for instance, is the graph of a function.

   Is this function a *one-to-one* function? The answer is no. To see why not, notice that the y-value of the ordered pair $(-3, 3)$, for example, is the same as the y-value of the ordered pair $(3, 3)$. This function is therefore not one-to-one.

   To test whether a graph is the graph of a one-to-one function, apply the vertical line test to see if it is a function, and then apply a similar **horizontal line test** to see if it is a one-to-one function.

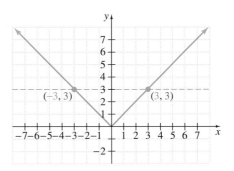

HORIZONTAL LINE TEST

If every horizontal line intersects the graph of a function at most once, then the function is a one-to-one function.

Example 2   Determine whether each graph is the graph of a one-to-one function.

a.

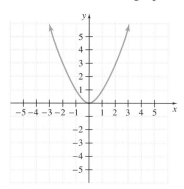

b.

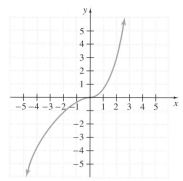

c.

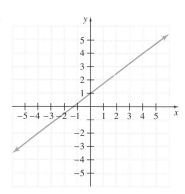

d.

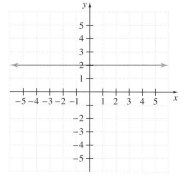

e.

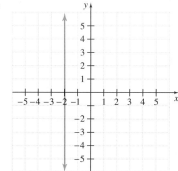

Solution   Graphs **a**, **b**, **c**, and **d** all pass the vertical line test, so only these graphs are graphs of functions. But, of these, only **b** and **c** pass the horizontal line test, so only **b** and **c** are graphs of one-to-one functions.

> ▼
> **HELPFUL HINT**
> All linear equations are one-to-one functions except those whose graphs are horizontal or vertical lines. A vertical line does not pass the vertical line test and hence is not the graph of a function. A horizontal line is the graph of a function but does not pass the horizontal line test and hence is not the graph of a one-to-one function.

3 One-to-one functions are special in that their graphs pass both the vertical and horizontal line tests. They are special, too, in another sense: For each one-to-one function, we can find its **inverse function** by switching the coordinates of the ordered pairs of the function, or the inputs and the outputs. For example, the inverse of the one-to-one function

Degrees Fahrenheit (Input)	−31	−13	32	68	149	212
Degrees Celsius (Output)	−35	−25	0	20	65	100

is the function

Degrees Celsius (Input)	−35	−25	0	20	65	100
Degrees Fahrenheit (Output)	−31	−13	32	68	149	212

Notice that the ordered pair $(-31, -35)$ of the function, for example, becomes the ordered pair $(-35, -31)$ of its inverse.

Also, the inverse of the one-to-one function $f = \{(2, -3), (5, 10), (9, 1)\}$ is $\{(-3, 2), (10, 5), (1, 9)\}$. For a function f, we use the notation f^{-1}, read "f inverse," to denote its inverse function. Notice that since the coordinates of each ordered pair have been switched, the domain (set of inputs) of f is the range (set of outputs) of f^{-1}, and the range of f is the domain of f^{-1}. See the definition of inverse function.

INVERSE FUNCTION

The inverse of a one-to-one function f is the one-to-one function f^{-1} that consists of the set of all ordered pairs (y, x) where (x, y) belongs to f.

Example 3 Find the inverse of the one-to-one function.

$$f = \{(0, 1), (-2, 7), (3, -6), (4, 4)\}$$

Solution $f^{-1} = \{(1, 0), (7, -2), (-6, 3), (4, 4)\}$

Switch coordinates of each ordered pair.

HELPFUL HINT
The symbol f^{-1} is the single symbol used to denote the inverse of the function f.
It is read as "f inverse." This symbol *does not mean* $\dfrac{1}{f}$.

---

4 If a one-to-one function f is defined as a set of ordered pairs, we can find f^{-1} by interchanging the x- and y-coordinates of the ordered pairs. If a one-to-one function f is given in the form of an equation, we can find f^{-1} by using a similar procedure.

FINDING THE INVERSE OF A ONE-TO-ONE FUNCTION $f(x)$

Step 1: Replace $f(x)$ with y.
Step 2: Interchange x and y.
Step 3: Solve the equation for y.
Step 4: Replace y with the notation $f^{-1}(x)$.

Example 4   Find an equation of the inverse of $f(x) = x + 3$.

Solution $f(x) = x + 3$

Step 1: $y = x + 3$ Replace $f(x)$ with y.
Step 2: $x = y + 3$ Interchange x and y.
Step 3: $x - 3 = y$ Solve for y.
Step 4: $f^{-1}(x) = x - 3$ Replace y with $f^{-1}(x)$.

The inverse of $f(x) = x + 3$ is $f^{-1}(x) = x - 3$. Notice that, for example,

$$f(1) = 1 + 3 = 4 \quad \text{and} \quad f^{-1}(4) = 4 - 3 = 1$$

Ordered pair: $(1, 4)$ Ordered pair: $(4, 1)$

The coordinates are
switched, as expected.

Example 5   Find the equation of the inverse of $f(x) = 3x - 5$. Graph f and f^{-1} on the same set of axes.

Solution $f(x) = 3x - 5$

Step 1: $y = 3x - 5$ Replace $f(x)$ with y.
Step 2: $x = 3y - 5$ Interchange x and y.
Step 3: $3y = x + 5$ Solve for y.

$$y = \frac{x + 5}{3}$$

Step 4: $f^{-1}(x) = \dfrac{x + 5}{3}$ Replace y with $f^{-1}(x)$.

Now we graph $f(x)$ and $f^{-1}(x)$ on the same set of axes. Both $f(x) = 3x - 5$ and

$f^{-1}(x) = \dfrac{x + 5}{3}$ are linear functions, so each graph is a line.

	$f(x) = 3x - 5$			$f^{-1}(x) = \dfrac{x + 5}{3}$

x	$y = f(x)$		x	$y = f^{-1}(x)$
1	-2		-2	1
0	-5		-5	0
$\dfrac{5}{3}$	0		0	$\dfrac{5}{3}$

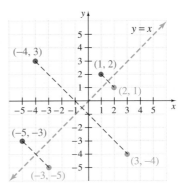

5 Notice that the graphs of f and f^{-1} in Example 5 are mirror images of each other, and the "mirror" is the dashed line $y = x$. This is true for every function and its inverse. For this reason, we say that *the graphs of f and f^{-1} are symmetric about the line $y = x$*.

To see why this happens, study the graph of a few ordered pairs and their switched coordinates.

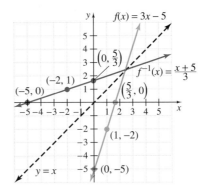

6 Notice also in the table of values in Example 5 that $f(0) = -5$ and $f^{-1}(-5) = 0$, as expected. Also, for example, $f(1) = -2$ and $f^{-1}(-2) = 1$. In words, we say that for some input x, the function f^{-1} takes the output of x, called $f(x)$, back to x.

$$x \rightarrow f(x) \quad \text{and} \quad f^{-1}(f(x)) \rightarrow x$$
$$\downarrow \qquad \downarrow \qquad\qquad \downarrow \qquad \downarrow$$
$$f(0) = -5 \quad \text{and} \quad f^{-1}(-5) = \quad 0$$
$$f(1) = -2 \quad \text{and} \quad f^{-1}(-2) = \quad 1$$

In general,

> If f is a one-to-one function, then the inverse of f is the function f^{-1} such that
>
> $$(f^{-1} \circ f)(x) = x \quad \text{and} \quad (f \circ f^{-1})(x) = x$$

Example 6   Graph the inverse of each function.

Solution   The function is graphed in blue and the inverse is graphed in red.

a.

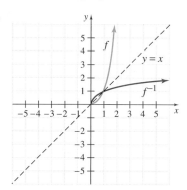

b.

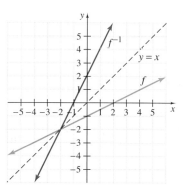

Example 7   Show that if $f(x) = 3x + 2$, then $f^{-1}(x) = \dfrac{x - 2}{3}$.

Solution   See that $f^{-1}(f(x)) = x$ and $f(f^{-1}(x)) = x$.

$$(f^{-1} \circ f)(x) = f^{-1}(f(x))$$

$$= f^{-1}(3x + 2) \qquad \text{Replace } f(x) \text{ with } 3x + 2.$$

$$= \frac{3x + 2 - 2}{3}$$

$$= \frac{3x}{3}$$

$$= x$$

$$(f \circ f^{-1})(x) = f(f^{-1}(x))$$

$$= f\left(\frac{x - 2}{3}\right) \qquad \text{Replace } f^{-1}(x) \text{ with } \frac{x - 2}{3}.$$

$$= 3\left(\frac{x - 2}{3}\right) + 2$$

$$= x - 2 + 2$$

$$= x$$

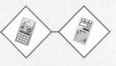

GRAPHING CALCULATOR EXPLORATIONS

A graphing calculator can be used to visualize the results of Example 7. Recall that the graph of a function f and its inverse f^{-1} are mirror images of each other across the line $y = x$. To see this for the function from Example 7, use a square window and graph

the given function: $Y_1 = 3x + 2$

its inverse: $Y_2 = \dfrac{x - 2}{3}$

and the line: $Y_3 = x$

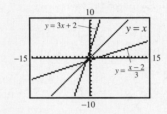

Exercises will follow in Exercise Set 10.2.

Exercise Set 10.2

Determine whether each function is a one-to-one function. If it is one-to-one, list the inverse function by switching coordinates, or inputs and outputs. See Examples 1 and 3.

1. $f = \{(-1, -1), (1, 1), (0, 2), (2, 0)\}$

2. $g = \{(8, 6), (9, 6), (3, 4), (-4, 4)\}$

3. $h = \{(10, 10)\}$

4. $r = \{(1, 2), (3, 4), (5, 6), (6, 7)\}$

5. $f = \{(11, 12), (4, 3), (3, 4), (6, 6)\}$

6. $g = \{(0, 3), (3, 7), (6, 7), (-2, -2)\}$

7.

Month of 1998 (Input)	January	February	March	April	May	June
Thousands of Houses on Sale at Month's End (Output)	282	277	281	285	282	287

(*Source:* U.S. Department of Housing and Urban Development)

8.

State (Input)	Washington	Ohio	Georgia	Colorado	California	Arizona
Electoral Votes (Output)	11	21	13	8	54	8

(*Source:* U.S. Bureau of the Census)

9.

State (Input)	California	Vermont	Virginia	Texas	South Dakota
Rank in Population (Output)	1	49	12	2	45

(*Source:* U.S. Bureau of the Census)

10.

Shape (Input)	Triangle	Pentagon	Quadrilateral	Hexagon	Decagon
Number of Sides (Output)	3	5	4	6	10

Given the one-to-one function $f(x) = x^3 + 2$, *find the following. [Hint: You do not need to find the equation for* $f^{-1}(x)$.]

11. a. $f(1)$
   b. $f^{-1}(3)$

12. a. $f(0)$
   b. $f^{-1}(2)$

13. a. $f(-1)$
   b. $f^{-1}(1)$

14. a. $f(-2)$
   b. $f^{-1}(-6)$

Determine whether the graph of each function is the graph of a one-to-one function. See Example 2.

15.

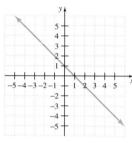

16.

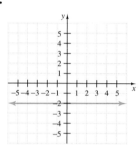

17.

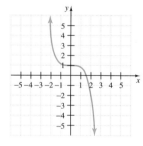

18.

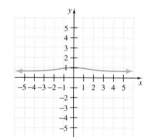

19.

20.

21.

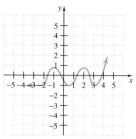

22.

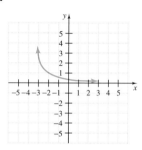

Each of the following functions is one-to-one. Find the inverse of each function and graph the function and its inverse on the same set of axes. See Examples 4 and 5.

23. $f(x) = x + 4$

24. $f(x) = x - 5$

25. $f(x) = 2x - 3$

26. $f(x) = 4x + 9$

27. $f(x) = \dfrac{1}{2}x - 1$

28. $f(x) = -\dfrac{1}{2}x + 2$

29. $f(x) = x^3$

30. $f(x) = x^3 - 1$

Find the inverse of each one-to-one function. See Examples 4 and 5.

31. $f(x) = 5x + 2$

32. $f(x) = 6x - 1$

33. $f(x) = \dfrac{x - 2}{5}$

34. $f(x) = \dfrac{4x - 3}{2}$

35. $f(x) = \sqrt[3]{x}$

36. $f(x) = \sqrt[3]{x + 1}$

37. $f(x) = \dfrac{5}{3x + 1}$

38. $f(x) = \dfrac{7}{2x + 4}$

39. $f(x) = (x + 2)^3$

40. $f(x) = (x - 5)^3$

Graph the inverse of each function on the same set of axes. See Example 6.

41.

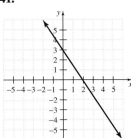

42.

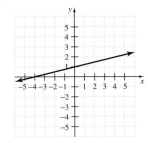

43.

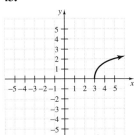

44.

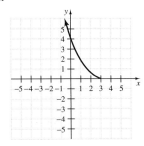

45.

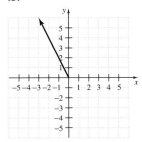

46.

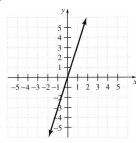

Solve. See Example 7.

47. If $f(x) = 2x + 1$, show that $f^{-1}(x) = \dfrac{x - 1}{2}$.

48. If $f(x) = 3x - 10$, show that $f^{-1}(x) = \dfrac{x + 10}{3}$.

49. If $f(x) = x^3 + 6$, show that $f^{-1}(x) = \sqrt[3]{x - 6}$.

50. If $f(x) = x^3 - 5$, show that $f^{-1}(x) = \sqrt[3]{x + 5}$.

For Exercises 51 and 52,

    a. Write the ordered pairs for $f(x)$ whose points are highlighted. (Include the points whose coordinates are given.)

b. Write the corresponding ordered pairs for the inverse of f, f^{-1}.

c. Graph the ordered pairs for f^{-1} found in Part **b.**

d. Graph $f^{-1}(x)$ by drawing a smooth curve through the plotted points.

51.

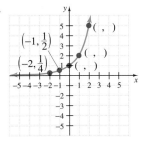

52.

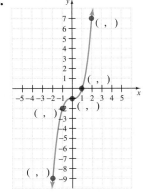

Find the inverse of each given one-to-one function. Then graph the function and its inverse on a square window.

53. $f(x) = 3x + 1$ **54.** $f(x) = -2x - 6$

55. $f(x) = \sqrt[3]{x + 1}$ **56.** $f(x) = x^3 - 3$

REVIEW EXERCISES

Evaluate each of the following. See Section 7.2.

57. $25^{1/2}$ **58.** $49^{1/2}$

59. $16^{3/4}$ **60.** $27^{2/3}$

61. $9^{-3/2}$ **62.** $81^{-3/4}$

If $f(x) = 3^x$, find the following. In Exercises 65 and 66, give an exact answer and a two-decimal-place approximation. See Sections 3.2 and 5.1.

63. $f(2)$ **64.** $f(0)$

65. $f\left(\tfrac{1}{2}\right)$ **66.** $f\left(\tfrac{2}{3}\right)$

10.3 EXPONENTIAL FUNCTIONS

▶ **OBJECTIVES**

CD-ROM   SSM

SSG   Video

1. Graph exponential functions.
2. Solve equations of the form $b^x = b^y$.
3. Solve problems modeled by exponential equations.

1

In earlier chapters, we gave meaning to exponential expressions such as 2^x, where x is a rational number. For example,

$$2^3 = 2 \cdot 2 \cdot 2 \qquad \text{Three factors, each factor is 2}$$

$$2^{3/2} = (2^{1/2})^3 = \sqrt{2} \cdot \sqrt{2} \cdot \sqrt{2} \qquad \text{Three factors, each factor is } \sqrt{2}$$

When x is an irrational number (for example, $\sqrt{3}$), what meaning can we give to $2^{\sqrt{3}}$?

It is beyond the scope of this book to give precise meaning to 2^x if x is irrational. We can confirm your intuition and say that $2^{\sqrt{3}}$ is a real number, and since $1 < \sqrt{3} < 2$, then $2^1 < 2^{\sqrt{3}} < 2^2$. We can also use a calculator and approximate $2^{\sqrt{3}}$: $2^{\sqrt{3}} \approx 3.321997$. In fact, as long as the base b is positive, b^x is a real number for all real numbers x. Finally, the rules of exponents apply whether x is rational or irrational, as long as b is positive. In this section, we are interested in functions of the form $f(x) = b^x$, where $b > 0$. A function of this form is called an **exponential function.**

EXPONENTIAL FUNCTION

A function of the form

$$f(x) = b^x$$

is called an **exponential function** if $b > 0$, b is not 1, and x is a real number.

Next, we practice graphing exponential functions.

◆ **Example 1**   Graph the exponential functions defined by $f(x) = 2^x$ and $g(x) = 3^x$ on the same set of axes.

Solution   Graph each function by plotting points. Set up a table of values for each of the two functions.

$f(x) = 2^x$

x	0	1	2	3	−1	−2
$f(x)$	1	2	4	8	$\dfrac{1}{2}$	$\dfrac{1}{4}$

$g(x) = 3^x$

x	0	1	2	3	-1	-2
$g(x)$	1	3	9	27	$\dfrac{1}{3}$	$\dfrac{1}{9}$

If each set of points is plotted and connected with a smooth curve, the following graphs result.

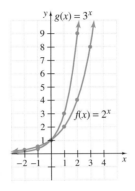

A number of things should be noted about the two graphs of exponential functions in Example 1. First, the graphs show that $f(x) = 2^x$ and $g(x) = 3^x$ are one-to-one functions since each graph passes the vertical and horizontal line tests. The y-intercept of each graph is $(0, 1)$, but neither graph has an x-intercept. From the graph, we can also see that the domain of each function is all real numbers and that the range is $(0, \infty)$. We can also see that as x-values are increasing, y-values are increasing also.

Example 2   Graph the exponential functions $y = \left(\dfrac{1}{2}\right)^x$ and $y = \left(\dfrac{1}{3}\right)^x$ on the same set of axes.

Solution   As before, plot points and connect them with a smooth curve.

$y = \left(\dfrac{1}{2}\right)^x$

x	0	1	2	3	-1	-2
y	1	$\dfrac{1}{2}$	$\dfrac{1}{4}$	$\dfrac{1}{8}$	2	4

$y = \left(\dfrac{1}{3}\right)^x$

x	0	1	2	3	-1	-2
y	1	$\dfrac{1}{3}$	$\dfrac{1}{9}$	$\dfrac{1}{27}$	3	9

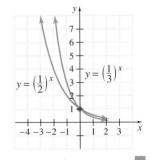

Each function in Example 2 again is a one-to-one function. The y-intercept of both is $(0, 1)$. The domain is the set of all real numbers, and the range is $(0, \infty)$.

Notice the difference between the graphs of Example 1 and the graphs of Example 2. An exponential function is always increasing if the base is greater than 1.

When the base is between 0 and 1, the graph is always decreasing. The following figures summarize these characteristics of exponential functions.

$$f(x) = b^x, \quad b > 0, \quad b \neq 1$$

- one-to-one function
- y-intercept $(0, 1)$
- no x-intercept

- domain: $(-\infty, \infty)$
- range: $(0, \infty)$

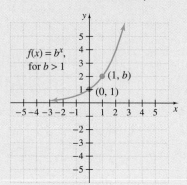

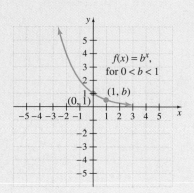

Example 3

Graph the exponential function $f(x) = 3^{x+2}$.

Solution   As before, we find and plot a few ordered pair solutions. Then we connect the points with a smooth curve.

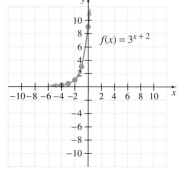

$y = 3^{x+2}$

x	0	-1	-2	-3	-4
y	9	3	1	$\dfrac{1}{3}$	$\dfrac{1}{9}$

2   We have seen that an exponential function $y = b^x$ is a one-to-one function. Another way of stating this fact is a property that we can use to solve exponential equations.

UNIQUENESS OF b^x

Let $b > 0$ and $b \neq 1$. Then $b^x = b^y$ is equivalent to $x = y$.

Example 4

Solve each equation for x.

a. $2^x = 16$ **b.** $9^x = 27$ **c.** $4^{x+3} = 8^x$

Solution   **a.** We write 16 as a power of 2 and then use the uniqueness of b^x to solve.

$$2^x = 16$$
$$2^x = 2^4$$

Since the bases are the same and are nonnegative, by the uniqueness of b^x, we then have that the exponents are equal. Thus,

$$x = 4$$

The solution is 4.

b. Notice that both 9 and 27 are powers of 3.

$$9^x = 27$$
$$(3^2)^x = 3^3 \qquad \text{Write 9 and 27 as powers of 3.}$$
$$3^{2x} = 3^3$$
$$2x = 3 \qquad \text{Apply the uniqueness of } b^x.$$
$$x = \frac{3}{2} \qquad \text{Divide by 2.}$$

To check, replace x with $\frac{3}{2}$ in the original expression, $9^x = 27$. The solution is $\frac{3}{2}$.

c. Write both 4 and 8 as powers of 2.

$$4^{x+3} = 8^x$$
$$(2^2)^{x+3} = (2^3)^x$$
$$2^{2x+6} = 2^{3x}$$
$$2x + 6 = 3x \qquad \text{Apply the uniqueness of } b^x.$$
$$6 = x \qquad \text{Subtract } 2x \text{ from both sides.}$$

The solution is 6.

There is one major problem with the preceding technique. Often the two sides of an equation cannot easily be written as powers of a common base. We explore how to solve an equation such as $4 = 3^x$ with the help of **logarithms** later.

3 The bar graph here shows the increase in the number of cellular phone users. Notice that the graph of the exponential function $y = 6.052(1.378)^x$ approximates the heights of the bars.

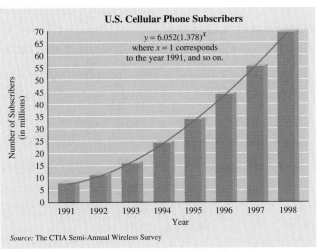

U.S. Cellular Phone Subscribers

$y = 6.052(1.378)^x$
where $x = 1$ corresponds
to the year 1991, and so on.

Number of Subscribers (in millions)

Year

Source: The CTIA Semi-Annual Wireless Survey

The graph above shows just one example of how the world abounds with patterns that can be modeled by exponential functions. To make these applications realistic, we use numbers that warrant a calculator. Another application of an exponential function has to do with interest rates on loans.

The exponential function defined by $A = P\left(1 + \dfrac{r}{n}\right)^{nt}$ models the dollars A accrued (or owed) after P dollars are invested (or loaned) at an annual rate of interest r compounded n times each year for t years. This function is known as the compound interest formula.

Example 5   **USING THE COMPOUND INTEREST FORMULA**

Find the amount owed at the end of 5 years if $1600 is loaned at a rate of 9% compounded monthly.

Solution   We use the formula $A = P\left(1 + \dfrac{r}{n}\right)^{nt}$, with the following values.

$$P = \$1600 \text{ (the amount of the loan)}$$

$$r = 9\% = 0.09 \text{ (the annual rate of interest)}$$

$$n = 12 \text{ (the number of times interest is compounded each year)}$$

$$t = 5 \text{ (the duration of the loan, in years)}$$

$$A = P\left(1 + \dfrac{r}{n}\right)^{nt} \qquad \text{Compound interest formula}$$

$$= 1600\left(1 + \dfrac{0.09}{12}\right)^{12(5)} \qquad \text{Substitute known values.}$$

$$= 1600(1.0075)^{60}$$

To approximate A, use the $\boxed{y^x}$ or $\boxed{\wedge}$ key on your calculator.

$$\boxed{2505.0896}$$

Thus, the amount A owed is approximately $2505.09.   ▬

Example 6   **ESTIMATING PERCENT OF RADIOACTIVE MATERIAL**

As a result of the Chernobyl nuclear accident, radioactive debris was carried through the atmosphere. One immediate concern was the impact that the debris had on the milk supply. The percent y of radioactive material in raw milk after t days is estimated by $y = 100\,(2.7)^{-0.1t}$. Estimate the expected percent of radioactive material in the milk after 30 days.

Solution   Replace t with 30 in the given equation.

$$y = 100(2.7)^{-0.1t}$$

$$= 100(2.7)^{-0.1(30)} \qquad \text{Let } t = 30.$$

$$= 100(2.7)^{-3}$$

To approximate the percent y, the following keystrokes may be used on a scientific calculator.

$$\boxed{2.7}\ \boxed{y^x}\ \boxed{3}\ \boxed{+/-}\ \boxed{=}\ \boxed{\times}\ \boxed{100}\ \boxed{=}$$

The display should read

$$5.0805263$$

Thus, approximately 5% of the radioactive material still remained in the milk supply after 30 days.

GRAPHING CALCULATOR EXPLORATIONS

We can use a graphing calculator and its TRACE feature to solve Example 6 graphically.

To estimate the expected percent of radioactive material in the milk after 30 days, enter $Y_1 = 100(2.7)^{-0.1x}$. (The variable t in Example 6 is changed to x here to better accommodate our work on the graphing calculator.) The graph does not appear on a standard viewing window, so we need to determine an appropriate viewing window. Because it doesn't make sense to look at radioactivity *before* the Chernobyl nuclear accident, we use Xmin = 0. We are interested in finding the percent of radioactive material in the milk when $x = 30$, so we choose Xmax = 35 to leave enough space to see the graph at $x = 30$. Because the values of y are percents, it seems appropriate that $0 \le y \le 100$. (We also use Xscl = 1 and Yscl = 10.) Now we graph the function.

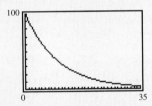

We can use the TRACE feature to obtain an approximation of the expected percent of radioactive material in the milk when $x = 30$. (A TABLE feature may also be used to approximate the percent.) To obtain a better approximation, let's use the ZOOM feature several times to zoom in near $x = 30$.

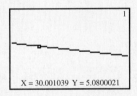

The percent of radioactive material in the milk 30 days after the Chernobyl accident was 5.08%, accurate to two decimal places.

Use a graphing calculator to find each percent. Approximate your solutions so that they are accurate to two decimal places.

1. Estimate the expected percent of radioactive material in the milk 2 days after the Chernobyl nuclear accident.

2. Estimate the expected percent of radioactive material in the milk 10 days after the Chernobyl nuclear accident.

3. Estimate the expected percent of radioactive material in the milk 15 days after the Chernobyl nuclear accident.

4. Estimate the expected percent of radioactive material in the milk 25 days after the Chernobyl nuclear accident.

Exercise Set 10.3

Graph each exponential function. See Examples 1 through 3.

1. $y = 4^x$

2. $y = 5^x$

3. $y = 2^x + 1$

4. $y = 3^x - 1$

5. $y = \left(\dfrac{1}{4}\right)^x$

6. $y = \left(\dfrac{1}{5}\right)^x$

7. $y = \left(\dfrac{1}{2}\right)^x - 2$

8. $y = \left(\dfrac{1}{3}\right)^x + 2$

9. $y = -2^x$

10. $y = -3^x$

11. $y = -\left(\dfrac{1}{4}\right)^x$

12. $y = -\left(\dfrac{1}{5}\right)^x$

13. $f(x) = 2^{x+1}$

14. $f(x) = 3^{x-1}$

15. $f(x) = 4^{x-2}$

16. $f(x) = 2^{x+3}$

17. Explain why the graph of an exponential function $y = b^x$ contains the point $(1, b)$.

18. Explain why an exponential function $y = b^x$ has a y-intercept of $(0, 1)$.

Solve each equation for x. See Example 4.

19. $3^x = 27$

20. $6^x = 36$

21. $16^x = 8$

22. $64^x = 16$

23. $32^{2x-3} = 2$

24. $9^{2x+1} = 81$

25. $\dfrac{1}{4} = 2^{3x}$

26. $\dfrac{1}{27} = 3^{2x}$

27. $5^x = 625$

28. $2^x = 64$

29. $4^x = 8$

30. $32^x = 4$

31. $27^{x+1} = 9$

32. $125^{x-2} = 25$

33. $81^{x-1} = 27^{2x}$

34. $4^{3x-7} = 32^{2x}$

Match each exponential equation with its graph.

35. $f(x) = \left(\dfrac{1}{2}\right)^x$

36. $f(x) = 2^x$

37. $f(x) = \left(\dfrac{1}{4}\right)^x$

38. $f(x) = 3^x$

A

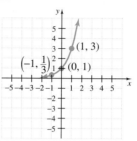

B

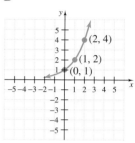

C

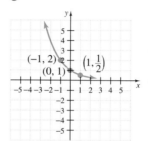

D

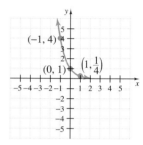

Solve. Unless otherwise indicated, round results to one decimal place. See Example 6.

39. One type of uranium has a daily radioactive decay rate of 0.4%. If 30 pounds of this uranium is available today, find how much will still remain after 50 days. Use $y = 30(2.7)^{-0.004t}$, and let t be 50.

40. The nuclear waste from an atomic energy plant decays at a rate of 3% each century. If 150 pounds of nuclear waste is disposed of, find how much of it will still remain after 10 centuries. Use $y = 150(2.7)^{-0.03t}$, and let t be 10.

41. The size of the rat population of a wharf area grows at a rate of 8% monthly. If there are 200 rats in January, find how many rats (rounded to the nearest whole) should be expected by next January. Use $y = 200(2.7)^{0.08t}$.

42. National Park Service personnel are trying to increase the size of the bison population of Theodore Roosevelt National Park. If 260 bison currently live in the park, and if the population's rate of growth is 2.5% annually, find how many bison (rounded to the nearest whole) there should be in 10 years. Use $y = 260(2.7)^{0.025t}$.

43. A rare isotope of a nuclear material is very unstable, decaying at a rate of 15% each second. Find how much isotope remains 10 seconds after 5 grams of the isotope is created. Use $y = 5(2.7)^{-0.15t}$.

44. An accidental spill of 75 grams of radioactive material in a local stream has led to the presence of radioactive debris decaying at a rate of 4% each day. Find how much debris still remains after 14 days. Use $y = 75(2.7)^{-0.04t}$.

45. Mexico City is growing at a rate of 0.7% annually. If there were 15,525,000 residents of Mexico City in 1994, find how many (to the nearest ten-thousand) are living in the city in 2000. Use $y = 15,525,000(2.7)^{0.007t}$.

46. An unusually wet spring has caused the size of the Cape Cod mosquito population to increase by 8% each day. If an estimated 200,000 mosquitoes are on Cape Cod on May 12, find how many thousands of mosquitoes will inhabit the Cape on May 25. Use $y = 200,000(2.7)^{0.08t}$.

Solve. Use $A = P\left(1 + \dfrac{r}{n}\right)^{nt}$. Round answers to two decimal places. See Example 5.

47. Find the amount Erica owes at the end of 3 years if $6000 is loaned to her at a rate of 8% compounded monthly.

48. Find the amount owed at the end of 5 years if $3000 is loaned at a rate of 10% compounded quarterly.

49. Find the total amount Janina has in a college savings account if $2000 was invested and earned 6% compounded semiannually for 12 years.

50. Find the amount accrued if $500 is invested and earns 7% compounded monthly for 4 years.

Use a graphing calculator to solve. Estimate each result to two decimal places.

51. Verify the results of Exercise 39.

52. From Exercise 39, estimate the number of pounds of uranium that will be available after 100 days.

53. From Exercise 39, estimate the number of pounds of uranium that will be available after 120 days.

54. Verify the results of Exercise 44.

55. From Exercise 44, estimate the amount of debris that remains after 10 days.

56. From Exercise 44, estimate the amount of debris that remains after 20 days.

Solve.

57. The world population is currently growing at a rate of 1.32% annually. In 1998, the midyear population of the world was 5,926,466,814 people. Predict the midyear world population (to the nearest million) in 2005. Use $y = 5,926,466,814(2.7)^{0.0132t}$, where t is the number of years after 1998. (*Source:* Based on data from the U.S. Bureau of the Census, International Data Base)

58. Retail revenue from shopping on the Internet is expected to grow at a rate of 64% per year. In 1997, a total of $2.4 billion in revenue was collected through Internet retail sales. To make the following predictions, use $y = 2.4(1.64)^t$, where t is the number of years after 1997.

(*Source:* Based on data from Forrester Research Inc.)

a. What level of retail revenues from Internet shopping is expected in 2001?

b. Predict the level of Internet shopping revenues in 2010.

59. Carbon dioxide (CO_2) is a greenhouse gas that contributes to global warming. Due to the combustion of fossil fuels, the amount of CO_2 in Earth's atmosphere has been increasing by 0.4% annually over the past century. In 1994, the concentration of CO_2 in the atmosphere was 358 parts per million by volume. To make the following predictions, use $y = 358(1.004)^t$, where t is the number of years after 1994. (*Source:* Based on data from the United Nations Environment Programme's Information Unit for Conventions)

a. Predict the concentration of CO_2 in the atmosphere in the year 2004.

b. Predict the concentration of CO_2 in the atmosphere in the year 2025.

The formula $y = 6.052(1.378)^x$ gives the number of cellular phone users y (in millions) in the United States for the years 1991 through 1998. In this formula, $x = 0$ corresponds to 1991, $x = 1$ corresponds to 1992, and so on. Use this formula to solve exercises 60 and 61.

60. Use this model to predict the number of cellular phone users in the year 2005.

61. Use this model to predict the number of cellular phone users in the year 2008.

REVIEW EXERCISES

Solve each equation. See Sections 2.1 and 5.8.

62. $5x - 2 = 18$

63. $3x - 7 = 11$

64. $3x - 4 = 3(x + 1)$

65. $2 - 6x = 6(1 - x)$

66. $x^2 + 6 = 5x$

67. $18 = 11x - x^2$

By inspection, find the value for x that makes each statement true.

68. $2^x = 8$

69. $3^x = 9$

70. $5^x = \dfrac{1}{5}$

71. $4^x = 1$

10.4 LOGARITHMIC FUNCTIONS

▶ **O B J E C T I V E S**

CD-ROM   SSM

SSG   Video

1. Write exponential equations with logarithmic notation and write logarithmic equations with exponential notation.
2. Solve logarithmic equations by using exponential notation.
3. Identify and graph logarithmic functions.

1

Since the exponential function $f(x) = 2^x$ is a one-to-one function, it has an inverse. We can create a table of values for f^{-1} by switching the coordinates in the accompanying table of values for $f(x) = 2^x$.

x	$y = f(x)$
-3	$\dfrac{1}{8}$
-2	$\dfrac{1}{4}$
-1	$\dfrac{1}{2}$
0	1
1	2
2	4
3	8

x	$y = f^{-1}(x)$
$\dfrac{1}{8}$	-3
$\dfrac{1}{4}$	-2
$\dfrac{1}{2}$	-1
1	0
2	1
4	2
8	3

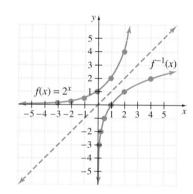

The graphs of $f(x)$ and its inverse are shown above. Notice that the graphs of f and f^{-1} are symmetric about the line $y = x$, as expected.

Now we would like to be able to write an equation for f^{-1}. To do so, we follow the steps for finding an inverse.

$$f(x) = 2^x$$

Step 1: Replace $f(x)$ by y. $y = 2^x$

Step 2: Interchange x and y. $x = 2^y$

Step 3: Solve for y.

At this point, we are stuck. To solve this equation for y, a new notation, the **logarithmic notation,** is needed. The symbol $\log_b x$ means "the power to which b is raised in order to produce a result of x."

$$\log_b x = y \quad \text{means} \quad b^y = x$$

We say that $\log_b x$ is "the logarithm of x to the base b" or "the log of x to the base b."

LOGARITHMIC DEFINITION

If $b > 0$ and $b \neq 1$, then

$$y = \log_b x \text{ means } x = b^y$$

for every $x > 0$ and every real number y.

Before returning to the function $x = 2^y$ and solving it for y in terms of x, let's practice using the new notation $\log_b x$.

It is important to be able to write exponential equations with logarithmic notation, and vice versa. The following table shows examples of both forms.

Logarithmic Equation	Corresponding Exponential Equation
$\log_3 9 = 2$	$3^2 = 9$
$\log_6 1 = 0$	$6^0 = 1$
$\log_2 8 = 3$	$2^3 = 8$
$\log_4 \dfrac{1}{16} = -2$	$4^{-2} = \dfrac{1}{16}$
$\log_8 2 = \dfrac{1}{3}$	$8^{1/3} = 2$

Example 1   Write as an exponential equation.

a. $\log_5 25 = 2$ **b.** $\log_6 \dfrac{1}{6} = -1$ **c.** $\log_2 \sqrt{2} = \dfrac{1}{2}$

Solution   **a.** $\log_5 25 = 2$ means $5^2 = 25$

b. $\log_6 \dfrac{1}{6} = -1$ means $6^{-1} = \dfrac{1}{6}$

c. $\log_2 \sqrt{2} = \dfrac{1}{2}$ means $2^{1/2} = \sqrt{2}$

Example 2   Write as a logarithmic equation.

a. $9^3 = 729$ **b.** $6^{-2} = \dfrac{1}{36}$ **c.** $5^{1/3} = \sqrt[3]{5}$

Solution   **a.** $9^3 = 729$ means $\log_9 729 = 3$

b. $6^{-2} = \dfrac{1}{36}$ means $\log_6 \dfrac{1}{36} = -2$

c. $5^{1/3} = \sqrt[3]{5}$ means $\log_5 \sqrt[3]{5} = \dfrac{1}{3}$

Example 3   Find the value of each logarithmic expression.

a. $\log_4 16$ **b.** $\log_{10} \dfrac{1}{10}$ **c.** $\log_9 3$

Solution   **a.** $\log_4 16 = 2$ because $4^2 = 16$ **b.** $\log_{10} \dfrac{1}{10} = -1$ because $10^{-1} = \dfrac{1}{10}$

c. $\log_9 3 = \dfrac{1}{2}$ because $9^{1/2} = \sqrt{9} = 3$

▼
HELPFUL HINT
Another method for evaluating logarithms such as those in Example 3 is to set the expression equal to x and then write them in exponential form to find x. For example:

a. $\log_4 16 = x$ means $4^x = 16$. Since $4^2 = 16$, $x = 2$ or $\log_4 16 = 2$.

b. $\log_{10} \dfrac{1}{10} = x$ means $10^x = \dfrac{1}{10}$. Since $10^{-1} = \dfrac{1}{10}$, $x = -1$ or $\log_{10} \dfrac{1}{10} = -1$.

c. $\log_9 3 = x$ means $9^x = 3$. Since $9^{1/2} = 3$, $x = \dfrac{1}{2}$ or $\log_9 3 = \dfrac{1}{2}$.

---

2   The ability to interchange the logarithmic and exponential forms of a statement is often the key to solving logarithmic equations.

Example 4   Solve each equation for x.

a. $\log_4 \dfrac{1}{4} = x$ **b.** $\log_5 x = 3$ **c.** $\log_x 25 = 2$

d. $\log_3 1 = x$ **e.** $\log_b 1 = x$

Solution   **a.** $\log_4 \dfrac{1}{4} = x$ means $4^x = \dfrac{1}{4}$. Solve $4^x = \dfrac{1}{4}$ for x.

$$4^x = \frac{1}{4}$$

$$4^x = 4^{-1}$$

Since the bases are the same, by the uniqueness of b^x, we have that

$$x = -1$$

The solution is -1. To check, see that $\log_4 \dfrac{1}{4} = -1$, since $4^{-1} = \dfrac{1}{4}$.

b. $\log_5 x = 3$ means $5^3 = x$ or

$$x = 125$$

The solution is 125.

c. $\log_x 25 = 2$ means $x^2 = 25$ and $x > 0$ and $x \neq 1$.

$$x = 5$$

Even though $(-5)^2 = 25$, the base b of a logarithm must be positive. The solution is 5.

d. $\log_3 1 = x$ means $3^x = 1$. Either solve this equation by inspection or solve by writing 1 as 3^0 as shown.

$$3^x = 3^0 \qquad \text{Write 1 as } 3^0.$$

$$x = 0 \qquad \text{Apply the uniqueness of } b^x.$$

The solution is 0.

e. $\log_b 1 = x$ means $b^x = 1$ and $b > 0$ and $b \neq 1$.

$$b^x = b^0 \qquad \text{Write 1 as } b^0.$$

$$x = 0 \qquad \text{Apply the uniqueness of } b^x.$$

The solution is 0. ▬

In Example **4e** we proved an important property of logarithms. That is, $\log_b 1$ is always 0. This property as well as two important others are given next.

PROPERTIES OF LOGARITHMS

If b is a real number, $b > 0$, and $b \neq 1$, then

1. $\log_b 1 = 0$ 2. $\log_b b^x = x$ 3. $b^{\log_b x} = x$

To see that $\log_b b^x = x$, change the logarithmic form to exponential form. Then, $\log_b b^x = x$ means $b^x = b^x$. In exponential form, the statement is true, so in logarithmic form, the statement is also true.

Example 5   Simplify.

a. $\log_3 3^2$ **b.** $\log_7 7^{-1}$ **c.** $5^{\log_5 3}$ **d.** $2^{\log_2 6}$

Solution   **a.** From Property 2, $\log_3 3^2 = 2$.

b. From Property 2, $\log_7 7^{-1} = -1$.

c. From Property 3, $5^{\log_5 3} = 3$.

d. From Property 3, $2^{\log_2 6} = 6$. ▬

3

Let us now return to the function $f(x) = 2^x$ and write an equation for its inverse, $f^{-1}(x)$. Recall our earlier work.

$$f(x) = 2^x$$

Step 1:   Replace $f(x)$ by y. $y = 2^x$

Step 2:   Interchange x and y. $x = 2^y$

Having gained proficiency with the notation $\log_b x$, we can now complete the steps for writing the inverse equation.

Step 3:   Solve for y. $y = \log_2 x$

Step 4:   Replace y with $f^{-1}(x)$. $f^{-1}(x) = \log_2 x$

Thus, $f^{-1}(x) = \log_2 x$ defines a function that is the inverse function of the function $f(x) = 2^x$. The function $f^{-1}(x)$ or $y = \log_2 x$ is called a **logarithmic function.**

LOGARITHMIC FUNCTION

If x is a positive real number, b is a constant positive real number, and b is not 1, then a **logarithmic function** is a function that can be defined by

$$f(x) = \log_b x$$

The domain of f is the set of positive real numbers, and the range of f is the set of real numbers.

We can explore logarithmic functions by graphing them.

Example 6   Graph the logarithmic function $y = \log_2 x$.

Solution   First we write the equation with exponential notation as $2^y = x$. Then we find some ordered pair solutions that satisfy this equation. Finally, we plot the points and connect them with a smooth curve. The domain of this function is $(0, \infty)$, and the range is all real numbers.

Since $x = 2^y$ is solved for x, we choose y-values and compute corresponding x-values.

If $y = 0, x = 2^0 = 1$

If $y = 1, x - 2^1 = 2$

If $y = 2, x = 2^2 = 4$

If $y = -1, x = 2^{-1} = \dfrac{1}{2}$

$x = 2^y$	y
1	0
2	1
4	2
$\dfrac{1}{2}$	-1

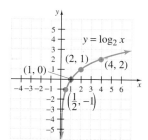

Example 7   Graph the logarithmic function $f(x) = \log_{1/3} x$.

Solution   Replace $f(x)$ with y, and write the result with exponential notation.

$$f(x) = \log_{1/3} x$$

$$y = \log_{1/3} x \qquad \text{Replace } f(x) \text{ with } y.$$

$$\left(\frac{1}{3}\right)^y = x \qquad \text{Write in exponential form.}$$

Now we can find ordered pair solutions that satisfy $\left(\dfrac{1}{3}\right)^y = x$, plot these points, and connect them with a smooth curve.

If $y = 0, x = \left(\dfrac{1}{3}\right)^0 = 1$

If $y = 1, x = \left(\dfrac{1}{3}\right)^1 = \dfrac{1}{3}$

If $y = -1, x = \left(\dfrac{1}{3}\right)^{-1} = 3$

If $y = -2, x = \left(\dfrac{1}{3}\right)^{-2} = 9$

$x = \left(\dfrac{1}{3}\right)^y$	y
1	0
$\dfrac{1}{3}$	1
3	-1
9	-2

The domain of this function is $(0, \infty)$, and the range is the set of all real numbers.

The following figures summarize characteristics of logarithmic functions.

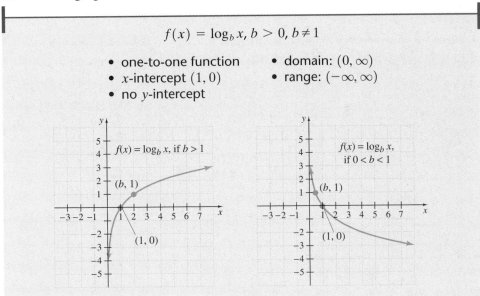

$$f(x) = \log_b x, b > 0, b \neq 1$$

- one-to-one function
- x-intercept $(1, 0)$
- no y-intercept

- domain: $(0, \infty)$
- range: $(-\infty, \infty)$

SPOTLIGHT ON DECISION MAKING

Suppose you are the Webmaster for a small but growing company. One of your duties is to ensure that your company's newly established Web site can adequately handle the number of visitors to it. You decide to find a mathematical model for recent Web site usage statistics to help predict future numbers of visitors. Ultimately, you would like to use this model to predict when your Web site's server capacity must be expanded.

The first step in finding a model for the usage statistics is to decide what type of mathematical model to use: linear, quadratic, exponential, or logarithmic. The graph shows the number of visitors to your company's Web site in each of the first five months since it was established. Use the graph to decide which type of mathematical model to use. Explain your reasoning.

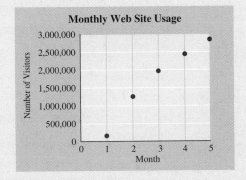

Month	1	2	3	4	5
Visitors	166,511	1,320,978	1,996,298	2,475,445	2,847,100

Exercise Set 10.4

Write each as an exponential equation. See Example 1.

1. $\log_6 36 = 2$

2. $\log_2 32 = 5$

3. $\log_3 \dfrac{1}{27} = -3$

4. $\log_5 \dfrac{1}{25} = -2$

5. $\log_{10} 1000 = 3$

6. $\log_{10} 10 = 1$

7. $\log_e x = 4$

8. $\log_e \dfrac{1}{e} = -1$

9. $\log_e \dfrac{1}{e^2} = -2$

10. $\log_e y = 7$

11. $\log_7 \sqrt{7} = \dfrac{1}{2}$

12. $\log_{11} \sqrt[4]{11} = \dfrac{1}{4}$

Write each as a logarithmic equation. See Example 2.

13. $2^4 = 16$

14. $5^3 = 125$

15. $10^2 = 100$

16. $10^4 = 10,000$

17. $e^3 = x$

18. $e^5 = y$

19. $10^{-1} = \dfrac{1}{10}$

20. $10^{-2} = \dfrac{1}{100}$

21. $4^{-2} = \dfrac{1}{16}$

22. $3^{-4} = \dfrac{1}{81}$

23. $5^{1/2} = \sqrt{5}$

24. $4^{1/3} = \sqrt[3]{4}$

Find the value of each logarithmic expression. See Example 3.

25. $\log_2 8$

26. $\log_3 9$

27. $\log_3 \dfrac{1}{9}$

28. $\log_2 \dfrac{1}{32}$

29. $\log_{25} 5$

30. $\log_8 \dfrac{1}{2}$

31. $\log_{1/2} 2$

32. $\log_{2/3} \dfrac{4}{9}$

33. $\log_7 1$

34. $\log_9 9$

35. $\log_2 2^4$

36. $\log_6 6^{-2}$

37. $\log_{10} 100$

38. $\log_{10} \dfrac{1}{10}$

39. $3^{\log_3 5}$

40. $5^{\log_5 7}$

41. $\log_3 81$

42. $\log_2 16$

43. $\log_4 \dfrac{1}{64}$

44. $\log_3 \dfrac{1}{9}$

45. Explain why negative numbers are not included as logarithmic bases.

46. Explain why 1 is not included as a logarithmic base.

Solve each equation for x. See Example 4.

47. $\log_3 9 = x$

48. $\log_2 8 = x$

49. $\log_3 x = 4$

50. $\log_2 x = 3$

51. $\log_x 49 = 2$

52. $\log_x 8 = 3$

53. $\log_2 \dfrac{1}{8} = x$

54. $\log_3 \dfrac{1}{81} = x$

55. $\log_3 \dfrac{1}{27} = x$

56. $\log_5 \dfrac{1}{125} = x$

57. $\log_8 x = \dfrac{1}{3}$

58. $\log_9 x = \dfrac{1}{2}$

59. $\log_4 16 = x$

60. $\log_2 16 - x$

61. $\log_{3/4} x = 3$

62. $\log_{2/3} x = 2$

63. $\log_x 100 = 2$

64. $\log_x 27 = 3$

Simplify. See Example 5.

65. $\log_5 5^3$

66. $\log_6 6^2$

67. $2^{\log_2 3}$

68. $7^{\log_7 4}$

69. $\log_9 9$

70. $\log_8 (8)^{-1}$

Graph each logarithmic function. Label any intercepts. See Examples 6 and 7.

71. $y = \log_3 x$

72. $y = \log_2 x$

73. $f(x) = \log_{1/4} x$

74. $f(x) = \log_{1/2} x$

75. $f(x) = \log_5 x$

76. $f(x) = \log_6 x$

77. $f(x) = \log_{1/6} x$

78. $f(x) = \log_{1/5} x$

Graph each function and its inverse function on the same set of axes. Label any intercepts.

79. $y = 4^x;\ y = \log_4 x$

80. $y = 3^x;\ y = \log_3 x$

81. $y = \left(\dfrac{1}{3}\right)^x;\ y = \log_{1/3} x$

82. $y = \left(\dfrac{1}{2}\right)^x;\ y = \log_{1/2} x$

83. The formula $\log_{10}(1 - k) = \dfrac{-0.3}{H}$ models the relationship between the half-life H of a radioactive material and its rate of decay k. Find the rate of decay of the iodine isotope I-131 if its half-life is 8 days. Round to 4 decimal places.

84. Explain why the graph of the function $y = \log_b x$ contains the point $(1, 0)$ no matter what b is.

85. $\text{Log}_3 10$ is between which two integers? Explain your answer.

REVIEW EXERCISES

Simplify each rational expression. See Section 6.1.

86. $\dfrac{x + 3}{3 + x}$

87. $\dfrac{x - 5}{5 - x}$

88. $\dfrac{x^2 - 8x + 16}{2x - 8}$

89. $\dfrac{x^2 - 3x - 10}{2 + x}$

Add or subtract as indicated. See Section 6.2.

90. $\dfrac{2}{x} + \dfrac{3}{x^2}$

91. $\dfrac{3x}{x + 3} + \dfrac{9}{x + 3}$

92. $\dfrac{m^2}{m + 1} - \dfrac{1}{m + 1}$

93. $\dfrac{5}{y + 1} - \dfrac{4}{y - 1}$

10.5 PROPERTIES OF LOGARITHMS

▶ **OBJECTIVES**

CD-ROM   SSM

SSG   Video

1. Use the product property of logarithms.
2. Use the quotient property of logarithms.
3. Use the power property of logarithms.
4. Use the properties of logarithms together.

In the previous section we explored some basic properties of logarithms. We now introduce and explore additional properties. Because a logarithm is an exponent, logarithmic properties are just restatements of exponential properties.

1 The first of these properties is called the **product property of logarithms,** because it deals with the logarithm of a product.

PRODUCT PROPERTY OF LOGARITHMS

If x, y, and b are positive real numbers and $b \neq 1$, then

$$\log_b xy = \log_b x + \log_b y$$

To prove this, let $\log_b x = M$ and $\log_b y = N$. Now write each logarithm with exponential notation.

$$\log_b x = M \quad \text{is equivalent to} \quad b^M = x$$
$$\log_b y = N \quad \text{is equivalent to} \quad b^N = y$$

Multiply the left sides and the right sides of the exponential equations, and we have that

$$xy = (b^M)(b^N) = b^{M+N}$$

If we write the equation $xy = b^{M+N}$ in equivalent logarithmic form, we have

$$\log_b xy = M + N$$

But since $M = \log_b x$ and $N = \log_b y$, we can write

$$\log_b xy = \log_b x + \log_b y \qquad \text{Let } M = \log_b x \text{ and } N = \log_b y.$$

In other words, the logarithm of a product is the sum of the logarithms of the factors. This property is sometimes used to simplify logarithmic expressions.

In the examples that follow, assume that variables represent positive numbers.

Example 1 Write each sum as a single logarithm.

a. $\log_{11} 10 + \log_{11} 3$ **b.** $\log_3 \dfrac{1}{2} + \log_3 12$ **c.** $\log_2 (x + 2) + \log_2 x$

Solution In each case, both terms have a common logarithmic base.

a. $\log_{11} 10 + \log_{11} 3 = \log_{11} (10 \cdot 3)$ *Apply the product property.*

$= \log_{11} 30$

> **HELPFUL HINT**
> Check your logarithm properties. Make sure you understand that $\log_2 (x + 2)$ *is not* $\log_2 x + \log_2 2$.

b. $\log_3 \dfrac{1}{2} + \log_3 12 = \log_3 \left(\dfrac{1}{2} \cdot 12 \right) = \log_3 6$

c. $\log_2 (x + 2) + \log_2 x = \log_2 [(x + 2) \cdot x] = \log_2 (x^2 + 2x)$

2 The second property is the **quotient property of logarithms.**

QUOTIENT PROPERTY OF LOGARITHMS

If x, y, and b are positive real numbers and $b \neq 1$, then

$$\log_b \frac{x}{y} = \log_b x - \log_b y$$

The proof of the quotient property of logarithms is similar to the proof of the product property. Notice that the quotient property says that the logarithm of a quotient is the difference of the logarithms of the dividend and divisor.

Example 2 Write each difference as a single logarithm.

a. $\log_{10} 27 - \log_{10} 3$ **b.** $\log_5 8 - \log_5 x$ **c.** $\log_3 (x^2 + 5) - \log_3 (x^2 + 1)$

Solution All terms have a common logarithmic base.

a. $\log_{10} 27 - \log_{10} 3 = \log_{10} \dfrac{27}{3} = \log_{10} 9$

b. $\log_5 8 - \log_5 x = \log_5 \dfrac{8}{x}$

c. $\log_3 (x^2 + 5) - \log_3 (x^2 + 1) = \log_3 \dfrac{x^2 + 5}{x^2 + 1}$ *Apply the quotient property.*

3 The third and final property we introduce is the **power property of logarithms.**

POWER PROPERTY OF LOGARITHMS

If x and b are positive real numbers, $b \neq 1$, and r is a real number, then

$$\log_b x^r = r \log_b x$$

Example 3 Use the power property to rewrite each expression.

a. $\log_5 x^3$ **b.** $\log_4 \sqrt{2}$

Solution **a.** $\log_5 x^3 = 3 \log_5 x$

b. $\log_4 \sqrt{2} = \log_4 2^{1/2} = \dfrac{1}{2} \log_4 2$

4 Many times we must use more than one property of logarithms to simplify a logarithmic expression.

Example 4 Write as a single logarithm.

a. $2 \log_5 3 + 3 \log_5 2$ **b.** $3 \log_9 x - \log_9 (x + 1)$ **c.** $\log_4 25 + \log_4 3 - \log_4 5$

Solution In each case, both terms have a common logarithmic base.

a. $2 \log_5 3 + 3 \log_5 2 = \log_5 3^2 + \log_5 2^3$ Apply the power property.

$$= \log_5 9 + \log_5 8$$

$$= \log_5 (9 \cdot 8)$$ Apply the product property.

$$= \log_5 72$$

b. $3 \log_9 x - \log_9 (x + 1) = \log_9 x^3 - \log_9 (x + 1)$ Apply the power property.

$$= \log_9 \frac{x^3}{x + 1}$$ Apply the quotient property.

c. Use both the product and quotient properties.

$$\log_4 25 + \log_4 3 - \log_4 5 = \log_4 (25 \cdot 3) - \log_4 5$$ Apply the product property.

$$= \log_4 75 - \log_4 5$$ Simplify.

$$= \log_4 \frac{75}{5}$$ Apply the quotient property.

$$= \log_4 15$$ Simplify.

Example 5 Write each expression as sums or differences of multiples of logarithms.

a. $\log_3 \dfrac{5 \cdot 7}{4}$

b. $\log_2 \dfrac{x^5}{y^2}$

Solution a. $\log_3 \dfrac{5 \cdot 7}{4} = \log_3 (5 \cdot 7) - \log_3 4$ Apply the quotient property.

$\qquad\qquad = \log_3 5 + \log_3 7 - \log_3 4$ Apply the product property.

b. $\log_2 \dfrac{x^5}{y^2} = \log_2 (x^5) - \log_2 (y^2)$ Apply the quotient property.

$\qquad\qquad = 5 \log_2 x - 2 \log_2 y$ Apply the power property.

> **HELPFUL HINT**
> Notice that we are not able to simplify further a logarithmic expression such as $\log_5 (2x - 1)$. None of the basic properties gives a way to write the logarithm of a difference in some equivalent form.

Example 6 If $\log_b 2 = 0.43$ and $\log_b 3 = 0.68$, use the properties of logarithms to evaluate.

a. $\log_b 6$ b. $\log_b 9$ c. $\log_b \sqrt{2}$

Solution a. $\log_b 6 = \log_b (2 \cdot 3)$ Write 6 as $2 \cdot 3$.

$\qquad\qquad = \log_b 2 + \log_b 3$ Apply the product property.

$\qquad\qquad = 0.43 + 0.68$ Substitute given values.

$\qquad\qquad = 1.11$ Simplify.

b. $\log_b 9 = \log_b 3^2$ Write 9 as 3^2.

$\qquad\qquad = 2 \log_b 3$

$\qquad\qquad = 2(0.68)$ Substitute 0.68 for $\log_b 3$.

$\qquad\qquad = 1.36$ Simplify.

c. First, recall that $\sqrt{2} = 2^{1/2}$. Then

$\log_b \sqrt{2} = \log_b 2^{1/2}$ Write $\sqrt{2}$ as $2^{1/2}$.

$\qquad\qquad = \dfrac{1}{2} \log_b 2$ Apply the power property.

$\qquad\qquad = \dfrac{1}{2} (0.43)$ Substitute the given value.

$\qquad\qquad = 0.215$ Simplify.

A summary of the basic properties of logarithms that we have developed so far is given next.

PROPERTIES OF LOGARITHMS

If x, y, and b are positive real numbers, $b \neq 1$, and r is a real number, then

1. $\log_b 1 = 0$	4. $\log_b xy = \log_b x + \log_b y$	*Product property.*
2. $\log_b b^x = x$	5. $\log_b \dfrac{x}{y} = \log_b x - \log_b y$	*Quotient property.*
3. $b^{\log_b x} = x$	6. $\log_b x^r = r \log_b x$	*Power property.*

SPOTLIGHT ON DECISION MAKING

Suppose you are a quality assurance inspector for an electronics manufacturer. Your department has conducted reliability studies of a new model of CD player. Your studies show that the CD player's reliability can be described by the exponential function $R(t) = 2.7^{-(1/3)t}$, where the reliability R is the probability that the CD player is still working t years after it is manufactured.

The marketing department asks for your input in choosing a warranty period for the CD player. Popular warranty periods for similar competing CD players are 1 year, 2 years, and 3 years. Using the graph of the reliability for this CD player, which warranty period would you recommend? Explain your reasoning. What other factors would you want to consider?

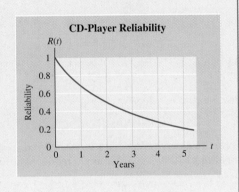

CD-Player Reliability

Exercise Set 10.5

Write each sum as the logarithm of a single expression. Assume that variables represent positive numbers. See Example 1.

1. $\log_5 2 + \log_5 7$
2. $\log_3 8 + \log_3 4$
3. $\log_4 9 + \log_4 x$
4. $\log_2 x + \log_2 y$
5. $\log_{10} 5 + \log_{10} 2 + \log_{10} (x^2 + 2)$
6. $\log_6 3 + \log_6 (x + 4) + \log_6 5$

Write each as the logarithm of a single expression. Assume that variables represent positive numbers. See Examples 2 and 4.

7. $\log_5 12 - \log_5 4$
8. $\log_7 20 - \log_7 4$
9. $\log_2 x - \log_2 y$
10. $\log_3 12 - \log_3 z$

11. $\log_4 2 + \log_4 10 - \log_4 5$
12. $\log_6 18 + \log_6 2 - \log_6 9$

Use the power property to rewrite each expression. See Example 3.

13. $\log_3 x^2$
14. $\log_2 x^5$
15. $\log_4 5^{-1}$
16. $\log_6 7^{-2}$
17. $\log_5 \sqrt{y}$
18. $\log_5 \sqrt[3]{x}$

Write each as a single logarithm. Assume that variables represent positive numbers. See Example 4.

19. $2 \log_2 5$
20. $3 \log_5 2$
21. $3 \log_5 x + 6 \log_5 z$

22. $2 \log_7 y + 6 \log_7 z$

23. $\log_{10} x - \log_{10} (x + 1) + \log_{10} (x^2 - 2)$

24. $\log_9 (4x) - \log_9 (x - 3) + \log_9 (x^3 + 1)$

25. $\log_4 5 + \log_4 7$

26. $\log_3 2 + \log_3 5$

27. $\log_3 8 - \log_3 2$

28. $\log_5 12 - \log_5 3$

29. $\log_7 6 + \log_7 3 - \log_7 4$

30. $\log_8 5 + \log_8 15 - \log_8 20$

31. $3 \log_4 2 + \log_4 6$

32. $2 \log_3 5 + \log_3 2$

33. $3 \log_2 x + \dfrac{1}{2} \log_2 x - 2 \log_2 (x + 1)$

34. $2 \log_5 x + \dfrac{1}{3} \log_5 x - 3 \log_5 (x + 5)$

35. $2 \log_8 x - \dfrac{2}{3} \log_8 x + 4 \log_8 x$

36. $5 \log_6 x - \dfrac{3}{4} \log_6 x + 3 \log_6 x$

Write each expression as a sum or difference of multiples of logarithms. Assume that variables represent positive numbers. See Example 5.

37. $\log_2 \dfrac{7 \cdot 11}{3}$

38. $\log_5 \dfrac{2 \cdot 9}{13}$

39. $\log_3 \dfrac{4y}{5}$

40. $\log_4 \dfrac{2}{9z}$

41. $\log_2 \dfrac{x^3}{y}$

42. $\log_5 \dfrac{x}{y^4}$

43. $\log_b \sqrt{7x}$

44. $\log_b \sqrt{\dfrac{3}{y}}$

45. $\log_7 \dfrac{5x}{4}$

46. $\log_9 \dfrac{7}{y}$

47. $\log_5 x^3 (x + 1)$

48. $\log_2 y^3 z$

49. $\log_6 \dfrac{x^2}{x + 3}$

50. $\log_3 \dfrac{(x + 5)^2}{x}$

If $\log_b 3 = 0.5$ and $\log_b 5 = 0.7$, evaluate the following. See Example 6. If necessary, round to three decimal places.

51. $\log_b \dfrac{5}{3}$

52. $\log_b 25$

53. $\log_b 15$

54. $\log_b \dfrac{3}{5}$

55. $\log_b \sqrt[3]{5}$

56. $\log_b \sqrt[4]{3}$

Answer the following true or false.

57. $\log_2 x^3 = 3 \log_2 x$

58. $\log_3 (x + y) = \log_3 x + \log_3 y$

59. $\dfrac{\log_7 10}{\log_7 5} = \log_7 2$

60. $\log_7 \dfrac{14}{8} = \log_7 14 - \log_7 8$

61. $\dfrac{\log_7 x}{\log_7 y} = (\log_7 x) - (\log_7 y)$

62. $(\log_3 6) \cdot (\log_3 4) = \log_3 24$

If $\log_b 2 = 0.43$ and $\log_b 3 = 0.68$, evaluate the following.

63. $\log_b 8$

64. $\log_b 81$

65. $\log_b \dfrac{3}{9}$

66. $\log_b \dfrac{4}{32}$

67. $\log_b \sqrt{\dfrac{2}{3}}$

68. $\log_b \sqrt{\dfrac{3}{2}}$

REVIEW EXERCISES

69. Graph the functions $y = 10^x$ and $y = \log_{10} x$ on the same set of axes. See Section 10.4.

Evaluate each expression. See Section 10.4.

70. $\log_{10} 100$

71. $\log_{10} \dfrac{1}{10}$

72. $\log_7 7^2$

73. $\log_7 \sqrt{7}$

10.6 COMMON LOGARITHMS, NATURAL LOGARITHMS, AND CHANGE OF BASE

▶ **OBJECTIVES**

CD-ROM   SSM

SSG   Video

1. Identify common logarithms and approximate them by calculator.
2. Evaluate common logarithms of powers of 10.
3. Identify natural logarithms and approximate them by calculator.
4. Evaluate natural logarithms of powers of e.
5. Use the change of base formula.

In this section we look closely at two particular logarithmic bases. These two logarithmic bases are used so frequently that logarithms to their bases are given special names. **Common logarithms** are logarithms to base 10. **Natural logarithms** are logarithms to base e, which we introduce in this section. The work in this section is based on the use of the calculator, which has both the common "log" ⟨LOG⟩ and the natural "log" ⟨LN⟩ keys.

1   Logarithms to base 10, common logarithms, are used frequently because our number system is a base 10 decimal system. The notation $\log x$ means the same as $\log_{10} x$.

COMMON LOGARITHMS

$$\log x \text{ means } \log_{10} x$$

Example 1   Use a calculator to approximate log 7 to four decimal places.

Solution   Press the following sequence of keys.

⟨7⟩ ⟨LOG⟩   or   ⟨LOG⟩ ⟨7⟩ ⟨ENTER⟩

To four decimal places,

$$\log 7 \approx 0.8451$$

2   To evaluate the common log of a power of 10, a calculator is not needed. According to the property of logarithms,

$$\log_b b^x = x$$

It follows that if b is replaced with 10, we have

$$\log 10^x = x$$

> **HELPFUL HINT**
> Remember that $\log 10^x$ means $\log_{10} 10^x = x$.

Example 2 Find the exact value of each logarithm.

a. $\log 10$ **b.** $\log 1000$ **c.** $\log \dfrac{1}{10}$ **d.** $\log \sqrt{10}$

Solution **a.** $\log 10 = \log 10^1 = 1$ **b.** $\log 1000 = \log 10^3 = 3$

c. $\log \dfrac{1}{10} = \log 10^{-1} = -1$ **d.** $\log \sqrt{10} = \log 10^{1/2} = \dfrac{1}{2}$ ∎

As we will soon see, equations containing common logs are useful models of many natural phenomena.

Example 3 Solve $\log x = 1.2$ for x. Give an exact solution, and then approximate the solution to four decimal places.

Solution Remember that the base of a common log is understood to be 10.

> **HELPFUL HINT**
> The understood base is 10.

$$\log x = 1.2$$

$$10^{1.2} = x \qquad \textit{Write with exponential notation.}$$

The exact solution is $10^{1.2}$. To four decimal places, $x \approx 15.8489$.   ∎

The Richter scale measures the intensity, or magnitude, of an earthquake. The formula for the magnitude R of an earthquake is $R - \log\left(\dfrac{a}{T}\right) + B$, where a is the amplitude in micrometers of the vertical motion of the ground at the recording station, T is the number of seconds between successive seismic waves, and B is an adjustment factor that takes into account the weakening of the seismic wave as the distance increases from the epicenter of the earthquake.

Example 4 **FINDING THE MAGNITUDE OF AN EARTHQUAKE**

Find an earthquake's magnitude on the Richter scale if a recording station measures an amplitude of 300 micrometers and 2.5 seconds between waves. Assume that B is 4.2. Approximate the solution to the nearest tenth.

Solution   Substitute the known values into the formula for earthquake intensity.

$$R = \log\left(\frac{a}{T}\right) + B \qquad \text{Richter scale formula}$$

$$= \log\left(\frac{300}{2.5}\right) + 4.2 \qquad \text{Let } a = 300, T = 2.5, \text{ and } B = 4.2.$$

$$= \log(120) + 4.2$$

$$\approx 2.1 + 4.2 \qquad \text{Approximate } \log 120 \text{ by } 2.1.$$

$$= 6.3$$

This earthquake had a magnitude of 6.3 on the Richter scale.

3   **Natural logarithms** are also frequently used, especially to describe natural events; hence the label "natural logarithm." Natural logarithms are logarithms to the base e, which is a constant approximately equal to 2.7183. The number e is an irrational number, as is π. The notation $\log_e x$ is usually abbreviated to $\ln x$. (The abbreviation ln is read "el en.")

NATURAL LOGARITHMS

$$\ln x \text{ means } \log_e x$$

The graph of $y = \ln x$ is shown to the right.

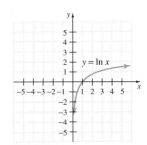

Example 5   Use a calculator to approximate $\ln 8$ to four decimal places.

Solution   Press the following sequence of keys.

$$\boxed{8}\ \boxed{\text{LN}} \qquad \text{or} \qquad \boxed{\text{LN}}\ \boxed{8}\ \boxed{\text{ENTER}}$$

To four decimal places,

$$\ln 8 \approx 2.0794$$

4   As a result of the property $\log_b b^x = x$, we know that $\log_e e^x = x$, or $\ln e^x = x$.

Example 6 Find the exact value of each natural logarithm.

a. $\ln e^3$ **b.** $\ln \sqrt[5]{e}$

Solution   **a.** $\ln e^3 = 3$ **b.** $\ln \sqrt[5]{e} = \ln e^{1/5} = \dfrac{1}{5}$

Example 7 Solve $\ln 3x = 5$. Give an exact solution, and then approximate the solution to four decimal places.

Solution   Remember that the base of a natural logarithm is understood to be e.

> **HELPFUL HINT**
> The understood base is e.

$$\ln 3x = 5$$

$$e^5 = 3x \qquad \text{Write with exponential notation.}$$

$$\frac{e^5}{3} = x \qquad \text{Solve for } x.$$

The exact solution is $\dfrac{e^5}{3}$. To four decimal places,

$$x \approx 49.4711.$$

Recall from Section 10.3 the formula $A = P\left(1 + \dfrac{r}{n}\right)^{nt}$ for compound interest, where n represents the number of compoundings per year. When interest is compounded continuously, the formula $A = Pe^{rt}$ is used, where r is the annual interest rate and interest is compounded continuously for t years.

Example 8 **FINDING FINAL LOAN PAYMENT**

Find the amount owed at the end of 5 years if $1600 is loaned at a rate of 9% compounded continuously.

Solution   Use the formula $A = Pe^{rt}$, where

$$P = \$1600 \text{ (the size of the loan)}$$
$$r = 9\% = 0.09 \text{ (the rate of interest)}$$
$$t = 5 \text{ (the 5-year duration of the loan)}$$
$$A = Pe^{rt}$$
$$= 1600e^{0.09(5)} \qquad \text{Substitute in known values.}$$
$$= 1600e^{0.45}$$

Now we can use a calculator to approximate the solution.

$$A \approx 2509.30$$

The total amount of money owed is $2509.30.

5   Calculators are handy tools for approximating natural and common logarithms. Unfortunately, some calculators cannot be used to approximate logarithms to bases other than e or 10—at least not directly. In such cases, we use the change of base formula.

CHANGE OF BASE

If a, b, and c are positive real numbers and neither b nor c is 1, then

$$\log_b a = \frac{\log_c a}{\log_c b}$$

Example 9   Approximate $\log_5 3$ to four decimal places.

Solution   Use the change of base property to write $\log_5 3$ as a quotient of logarithms to base 10.

$$\log_5 3 = \frac{\log 3}{\log 5} \qquad \text{Use the change of base property. In the change of base property, we let } a = 3, b = 5, \text{ and } c = 10.$$

$$\approx \frac{0.4771213}{0.69897} \qquad \text{Approximate logarithms by calculator.}$$

$$\approx 0.6826062 \qquad \text{Simplify by calculator.}$$

To four decimal places, $\log_5 3 \approx 0.6826$.

Exercise Set 10.6

Use a calculator to approximate each logarithm to four decimal places. See Examples 1 and 5.

1. $\log 8$ **2.** $\log 6$ **3.** $\log 2.31$

4. $\log 4.86$ **5.** $\ln 2$ **6.** $\ln 3$

7. $\ln 0.0716$ **8.** $\ln 0.0032$ **9.** $\log 12.6$

10. $\log 25.9$ **11.** $\ln 5$ **12.** $\ln 7$

13. $\log 41.5$ **14.** $\ln 41.5$

15. Use a calculator and try to approximate $\log 0$. Describe what happens and explain why.

16. Use a calculator and try to approximate $\ln 0$. Describe what happens and explain why.

Find the exact value. See Examples 2 and 6.

17. $\log 100$ **18.** $\log 10{,}000$

19. $\log\left(\dfrac{1}{1000}\right)$ **20.** $\log\left(\dfrac{1}{100}\right)$

21. $\ln e^2$ **22.** $\ln e^4$

23. $\ln \sqrt[4]{e}$ **24.** $\ln \sqrt[5]{e}$

25. $\log 10^3$ **26.** $\ln e^5$

27. $\ln e^2$ **28.** $\log 10^7$

29. $\log 0.0001$ **30.** $\log 0.001$

31. $\ln \sqrt{e}$ **32.** $\log \sqrt{10}$

33. Without using a calculator, explain which of $\log 50$ or $\ln 50$ must be larger.

34. Without using a calculator, explain which of $\log 50^{-1}$ or $\ln 50^{-1}$ must be larger.

Solve each equation for x. Give an exact solution and a four-decimal-place approximation. See Examples 3 and 7.

35. $\log x = 1.3$ **36.** $\log x = 2.1$

37. $\log 2x = 1.1$ **38.** $\log 3x = 1.3$

39. $\ln x = 1.4$ **40.** $\ln x = 2.1$

41. $\ln (3x - 4) = 2.3$ **42.** $\ln (2x + 5) = 3.4$

43. $\log x = 2.3$ **44.** $\log x = 3.1$

45. $\ln x = -2.3$ **46.** $\ln x = -3.7$

47. $\log (2x + 1) = -0.5$ **48.** $\log (3x - 2) = -0.8$

49. $\ln 4x = 0.18$ **50.** $\ln 3x = 0.76$

Approximate each logarithm to four decimal places. See Example 9.

51. $\log_2 3$ **52.** $\log_3 2$

53. $\log_{1/2} 5$ **54.** $\log_{1/3} 2$

55. $\log_4 9$ **56.** $\log_9 4$

57. $\log_3 \dfrac{1}{6}$

58. $\log_6 \dfrac{2}{3}$

59. $\log_8 6$

60. $\log_6 8$

Use the formula $R = \log\left(\dfrac{a}{T}\right) + B$ to find the intensity R on the Richter scale of the earthquakes that fit the descriptions given. Round answers to one decimal place. See Example 4.

61. Amplitude a is 200 micrometers, time T between waves is 1.6 seconds, and B is 2.1.

62. Amplitude a is 150 micrometers, time T between waves is 3.6 seconds, and B is 1.9.

63. Amplitude a is 400 micrometers, time T between waves is 2.6 seconds, and B is 3.1.

64. Amplitude a is 150 micrometers, time T between waves is 4.2 seconds, and B is 2.7.

Use the formula $A = Pe^{rt}$ to solve. See Example 8.

65. Find how much money Dana Jones has after 12 years if $1400 is invested at 8% interest compounded continuously.

66. Determine the size of an account in which $3500 earns 6% interest compounded continuously for 1 year.

67. Find the amount of money Barbara Mack owes at the end of 4 years if 6% interest is compounded continuously on her $2000 debt.

68. Find the amount of money for which a $2500 certificate of deposit is redeemable if it has been paying 10% interest compounded continuously for 3 years.

Graph each function by finding ordered pair solutions, plotting the solutions, and then drawing a smooth curve through the plotted points.

69. $f(x) = e^x$

70. $f(x) = e^{2x}$

71. $f(x) = e^{-3x}$

72. $f(x) = e^{-x}$

73. $f(x) = e^x + 2$

74. $f(x) = e^x - 3$

75. $f(x) = e^{x-1}$

76. $f(x) = e^{x+4}$

77. $f(x) = 3e^x$

78. $f(x) = -2e^x$

79. $f(x) = \ln x$

80. $f(x) = \log x$

81. $f(x) = -2 \log x$

82. $f(x) = 3 \ln x$

83. $f(x) = \log(x + 2)$

84. $f(x) = \log(x - 2)$

85. $f(x) = \ln x - 3$

86. $f(x) = \ln x + 3$

87. Graph $f(x) = e^x$ (Exercise 69), $f(x) = e^x + 2$ (Exercise 73), and $f(x) = e^x - 3$ (Exercise 74) on the same screen. Discuss any trends shown on the graphs.

88. Graph $f(x) = \ln x$ (Exercise 79), $f(x) = \ln x - 3$ (Exercise 85), and $f(x) = \ln x + 3$ (Exercise 86). Discuss any trends shown on the graphs.

REVIEW EXERCISES

Solve each equation for x. See Sections 2.1 and 5.8.

89. $6x - 3(2 - 5x) = 6$

90. $2x + 3 = 5 - 2(3x - 1)$

91. $2x + 3y = 6x$

92. $4x - 8y = 10x$

93. $x^2 + 7x = -6$

94. $x^2 + 4x = 12$

Solve each system of equations. See Section 4.1.

95. $\begin{cases} x + 2y = -4 \\ 3x - y = 9 \end{cases}$

96. $\begin{cases} 5x + y = 5 \\ -3x - 2y = -10 \end{cases}$

10.7 EXPONENTIAL AND LOGARITHMIC EQUATIONS AND APPLICATIONS

▶ **OBJECTIVES**

CD-ROM   SSM

SSG   Video

1. Solve exponential equations.
2. Solve logarithmic equations.
3. Solve problems that can be modeled by exponential and logarithmic equations.

1

In Section 10.3 we solved exponential equations such as $2^x = 16$ by writing 16 as a power of 2 and applying the uniqueness of b^x.

$$2^x = 16$$

$$2^x = 2^4 \qquad \text{Write 16 as } 2^4.$$

$$x = 4 \qquad \text{Use the uniqueness of } b^x.$$

Solving the equation in this manner is possible since 16 is a power of 2. If solving an equation such as $2^x = a$ *number,* where the number is not a power of 2, we use logarithms. For example, to solve an equation such as $3^x = 7$, we use the fact that $f(x) = \log_b x$ is a one-to-one function. Another way of stating this fact is as a property of equality.

LOGARITHM PROPERTY OF EQUALITY

Let a, b, and c be real numbers such that $\log_b a$ and $\log_b c$ are real numbers and b is not 1. Then

$$\log_b a = \log_b c \text{ is equivalent to } a = c$$

Example 1 Solve $3^x = 7$.

Solution To solve, we use the logarithm property of equality and take the logarithm of both sides. For this example, we use the common logarithm.

$$3^x = 7$$

$$\log 3^x = \log 7 \qquad \text{Take the common log of both sides.}$$

$$x \log 3 = \log 7 \qquad \text{Apply the power property of logarithms.}$$

$$x = \frac{\log 7}{\log 3} \qquad \text{Divide both sides by log 3.}$$

The exact solution is $\dfrac{\log 7}{\log 3}$. If a decimal approximation is preferred,

$$\frac{\log 7}{\log 3} \approx \frac{0.845098}{0.4771213} \approx 1.7712 \text{ to four decimal places.}$$

The solution is $\dfrac{\log 7}{\log 3}$, or *approximately* 1.7712.

2

By applying the appropriate properties of logarithms, we can solve a broad variety of logarithmic equations.

Solution   We are given that $P = \$2000$ and $r = 5\% = 0.05$. Compounding quarterly means 4 times a year, so $n = 4$. The investment is to double, so A must be $\$4000$. Substitute these values and solve for t.

$$A = P\left(1 + \frac{r}{n}\right)^{nt}$$

$$4000 = 2000\left(1 + \frac{0.05}{4}\right)^{4t} \qquad \text{Substitute in known values.}$$

$$4000 = 2000(1.0125)^{4t} \qquad \text{Simplify } 1 + \frac{0.05}{4}.$$

$$2 = (1.0125)^{4t} \qquad \text{Divide both sides by 2000.}$$

$$\log 2 = \log 1.0125^{4t} \qquad \text{Take the logarithm of both sides.}$$

$$\log 2 = 4t(\log 1.0125) \qquad \text{Apply the power property.}$$

$$\frac{\log 2}{4 \log 1.0125} = t \qquad \text{Divide both sides by 4 log 1.0125.}$$

$$13.949408 \approx t \qquad \text{Approximate by calculator.}$$

Thus, it takes nearly 14 years for the money to double in value.

GRAPHING CALCULATOR EXPLORATIONS

Use a graphing calculator to find how long it takes an investment of $\$1500$ to triple if it is invested at 8% interest compounded monthly.

First, let $P = \$1500$, $r = 0.08$, and $n = 12$ (for 12 months) in the formula

$$A = P\left(1 + \frac{r}{n}\right)^{nt}$$

Notice that when the investment has tripled, the accrued amount A is $\$4500$. Thus,

$$4500 = 1500\left(1 + \frac{0.08}{12}\right)^{12t}$$

Determine an appropriate viewing window and enter and graph the equations

$$Y_1 = 1500\left(1 + \frac{0.08}{12}\right)^{12x}$$

and

$$Y_2 = 4500$$

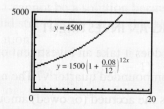

The point of intersection of the two curves is the solution. The *x*-coordinate tells how long it takes for the investment to triple.

Use a TRACE feature or an INTERSECT feature to approximate the coordinates of the point of intersection of the two curves. It takes approximately 13.78 years, or 13 years and 9 months, for the investment to triple in value to $4500.

Use this graphical solution method to solve each problem. Round each answer to the nearest hundredth.

1. Find how long it takes an investment of $5000 to grow to $6000 if it is invested at 5% interest compounded quarterly.

2. Find how long it takes an investment of $1000 to double if it is invested at 4.5% interest compounded daily. (Use 365 days in a year.)

3. Find how long it takes an investment of $10,000 to quadruple if it is invested at 6% interest compounded monthly.

4. Find how long it takes $500 to grow to $800 if it is invested at 4% interest compounded semiannually.

Exercise Set 10.7

Solve each equation. Give an exact solution, and also approximate the solution to four decimal places. See Example 1.

1. $3^x = 6$

2. $4^x = 7$

3. $3^{2x} = 3.8$

4. $5^{3x} = 5.6$

5. $2^{x-3} = 5$

6. $8^{x-2} = 12$

7. $9^x = 5$

8. $3^x = 11$

9. $4^{x+7} = 3$

10. $6^{x+3} = 2$

11. $7^{3x-4} = 11$

12. $5^{2x-6} = 12$

13. $e^{6x} = 5$

14. $e^{2x} = 8$

Solve each equation. See Examples 2 through 4.

15. $\log_2 (x + 5) = 4$

16. $\log_6 (x^2 - x) = 1$

17. $\log_3 x^2 = 4$

18. $\log_2 x^2 = 6$

19. $\log_4 2 + \log_4 x = 0$

20. $\log_3 5 + \log_3 x = 1$

21. $\log_2 6 - \log_2 x = 3$

22. $\log_4 10 - \log_4 x = 2$

23. $\log_4 x + \log_4 (x + 6) = 2$

24. $\log_3 x + \log_3 (x + 6) = 3$

25. $\log_5 (x + 3) - \log_5 x = 2$

26. $\log_6 (x + 2) - \log_6 x = 2$

27. $\log_3 (x - 2) = 2$

28. $\log_2 (x - 5) = 3$

29. $\log_4 (x^2 - 3x) = 1$

30. $\log_8 (x^2 - 2x) = 1$

31. $\ln 5 + \ln x = 0$

32. $\ln 3 + \ln (x - 1) = 0$

33. $3 \log x - \log x^2 = 2$

34. $2 \log x - \log x = 3$

35. $\log_2 x + \log_2 (x + 5) = 1$

36. $\log_4 x + \log_4 (x + 7) = 1$

37. $\log_4 x - \log_4 (2x - 3) = 3$

38. $\log_2 x - \log_2 (3x + 5) = 4$

39. $\log_2 x + \log_2 (3x + 1) = 1$

40. $\log_3 x + \log_3 (x - 8) = 2$

Solve. See Example 5.

41. The size of the wolf population at Isle Royale National Park increases at a rate of 4.3% per year. If the size of the current population is 83 wolves, find how many there should be in 5 years. Use $y = y_0 e^{0.043t}$ and round to the nearest whole.

42. The number of victims of a flu epidemic is increasing at a rate of 7.5% per week. If 20,000 persons are currently infected, find in how many days we can expect 45,000 to have the flu. Use $y = y_0 e^{0.075t}$ and round to the nearest whole. (Hint: Don't forget to convert your answer to days.)

43. The size of the population of Senegal is increasing at a rate of 2.6% per year. If 10,052,000 people lived in Senegal in 1999, find how many inhabitants there will be by 2005. Round to the nearest ten-thousand. Use $y = y_0 e^{0.026t}$.

44. In 1999, 1001 million people were citizens of India. Find how long it will take India's population to reach a size of 1500 million (that is, 1.5 billion) if the population size is growing at a rate of 1.7% per year. Use $y = y_0 e^{0.017t}$ and round to the nearest tenth. (*Source:* U.S. Bureau of the Census, International Data Base)

45. In 1999, Russia had a population of 146,394 thousand. At that time, Russia's population was declining at a rate of 0.5% per year. How long will it take for Russia's population to reach 120,000 thousand? Use $y = y_0 e^{-0.005t}$ and round to the nearest tenth. (*Source:* U.S. Bureau of the Census, International Data Base)

46. The population of Italy has been decreasing at a rate of 0.1% per year. If there were 56,735,000 people living in Italy in 1999, how many inhabitants will there be by 2020? Use $y = y_0 e^{-0.001t}$ and round to the nearest whole number. (*Source:* U.S. Bureau of the Census, International Data Base)

Use the formula $A = P\left(1 + \dfrac{r}{n}\right)^{nt}$ to solve these compound interest problems. Round to the nearest tenth. See Example 6.

47. Find how long it takes $600 to double if it is invested at 7% interest compounded monthly.

48. Find how long it takes $600 to double if it is invested at 12% interest compounded monthly.

49. Find how long it takes a $1200 investment to earn $200 interest if it is invested at 9% interest compounded quarterly.

50. Find how long it takes a $1500 investment to earn $200 interest if it is invested at 10% compounded semiannually.

51. Find how long it takes $1000 to double if it is invested at 8% interest compounded semiannually.

52. Find how long it takes $1000 to double if it is invested at 8% interest compounded monthly.

The formula $w = 0.00185h^{2.67}$ is used to estimate the normal weight w of a boy h inches tall. Use this formula to solve the height–weight problems. Round to the nearest tenth.

53. Find the expected weight of a boy who is 35 inches tall.

54. Find the expected weight of a boy who is 43 inches tall.

55. Find the expected height of a boy who weighs 85 pounds.

56. Find the expected height of a boy who weighs 140 pounds.

The formula $P = 14.7e^{-0.21x}$ gives the average atmospheric pressure P, in pounds per square inch, at an altitude x, in miles above sea level. Use this formula to solve these pressure problems. Round answers to the nearest tenth.

57. Find the average atmospheric pressure of Denver, which is 1 mile above sea level.

58. Find the average atmospheric pressure of Pikes Peak, which is 2.7 miles above sea level.

59. Find the elevation of a Delta jet if the atmospheric pressure outside the jet is 7.5 lb/in.^{2}.

60. Find the elevation of a remote Himalayan peak if the atmospheric pressure atop the peak is 6.5 lb/in.^{2}.

Psychologists call the graph of the formula $t = \dfrac{1}{c}\ln\left(\dfrac{A}{A - N}\right)$ the learning curve, since the formula relates time t passed, in

weeks, to a measure N of learning achieved, to a measure A of maximum learning possible, and to a measure c of an individual's learning style. Round to the nearest week.

61. Norman is learning to type. If he wants to type at a rate of 50 words per minute (N is 50) and his expected maximum rate is 75 words per minute (A is 75), find how many weeks it should take him to achieve his goal. Assume that c is 0.09.

62. An experiment with teaching chimpanzees sign language shows that a typical chimp can master a maximum of 65 signs. Find how many weeks it should take a chimpanzee to master 30 signs if c is 0.03.

63. Janine is working on her dictation skills. She wants to take dictation at a rate of 150 words per minute and believes that the maximum rate she can hope for is 210 words per minute. Find how many weeks it should take her to achieve the 150 words per minute level if c is 0.07.

64. A psychologist is measuring human capability to memorize nonsense syllables. Find how many weeks it should take a subject to learn 15 nonsense syllables if the maximum possible to learn is 24 syllables and c is 0.17.

Use a graphing calculator to solve each equation. For example, to solve Exercise 65, let $Y_1 = e^{0.3x}$ and $Y_2 = 8$, and graph the equations. The x-value of the point of intersection is the solution. Round all solutions to two decimal places.

65. $e^{0.3x} = 8$

66. $10^{0.5x} = 7$

67. $2\log(-5.6x + 1.3) = -x - 1$

68. $\ln(1.3x - 2.1) = -3.5x + 5$

69. Check Exercise 11.

70. Check Exercise 12.

71. Check Exercise 31.

72. Check Exercise 32.

REVIEW EXERCISES

If $x = -2$, $y = 0$, and $z = 3$, find the value of each expression. See Section 1.4.

73. $\dfrac{x^2 - y + 2z}{3x}$

74. $\dfrac{x^3 - 2y + z}{2z}$

75. $\dfrac{3z - 4x + y}{x + 2z}$

76. $\dfrac{4y - 3x + z}{2x + y}$

Find the inverse function of each one-to-one function. See Section 10.2.

77. $f(x) = 5x + 2$

78. $f(x) = \dfrac{x - 3}{4}$

10

For additional Chapter Projects, visit the Real World Activities Website by going to http://www.prenhall.com/martin-gay.

CHAPTER PROJECT

Modeling Temperature

When a cold object is placed in a warm room, the object's temperature gradually rises until it becomes, or nearly becomes, room temperature. Similarly, if a hot object is placed in a cooler room, the object's temperature gradually falls to room temperature. The way in which a cold or hot object warms up or cools off is modeled by an exact mathematical relationship, known as Newton's law of cooling. This law relates the temperature of an object to the time elapsed since its warming or cooling began. In this project, you will have the opportunity to investigate this model of cooling and warming. This project may be completed by working in groups or individually.

To investigate Newton's law of cooling in this project, you will collect experimental data in one of two methods: Method 1, using a stopwatch and thermometer, or Method 2, using Texas Instruments' Calculator-Based Laboratory (CBL™) or Second Generation Calculator-Based Laboratory (CBL 2™).

Method 1 Materials

- Container of either cold or hot liquid
- Thermometer
- Stopwatch
- Graphing calculator with regression capabilities

Method 2 Materials

- Container of either cold or hot liquid
- A TI-82, TI-83, or TI-85 graphing calculator with unit-to-unit link cable
- CBL™ or CBL 2™ unit with temperature probe

DATA TABLE

Time, t	Temperature, T
0	

Steps for Collecting Data with Method 1:

a. Insert the thermometer into the liquid and allow a thermometer reading to register. Take a temperature reading T as you start the stopwatch (at $t = 0$) and record it in the accompanying data table.

b. Continue taking temperature readings at uniform intervals anywhere between 5 and 10 minutes long. At each reading use the stopwatch to measure the length of time that has elapsed since the temperature readings started with your first reading at $t = 0$. Record your time t and liquid temperature T in the data table. Gather data for six to twelve readings.

c. Plot the data from the data table. Plot t on the horizontal axis and T on the vertical axis.

Steps for Collecting Data with Method 2:

a. Enter the HEAT program appropriate for your calculator.

b. Prepare the CBL or CBL 2 and the graphing calculator. Insert the temperature probe into the liquid.

c. Start the HEAT program on the graphing calculator and follow its instructions to begin collecting data. The program will collect 36 temperature readings in degrees Celsius and plot them in real time with t on the horizontal axis and T on the vertical axis.

1. Which of the following mathematical models best fits the data you collected? Explain your reasoning. (Assume $a > 0$.)

   a. $T = ab^t + c$
   b. $T = ab^{-t} + c$
   c. $T = -ab^{-t} + c$
   d. $T = \ln(-ax + b) + c$
   e. $T = -\ln(-ax + b) + c$

2. What does the constant c represent in the model you chose? What is the value of c in this activity?

3. (Optional) Subtract the value of c from each of your observations of T. Enter the new

ordered pairs $(t, T - c)$ into a graphing calculator. Use the exponential or logarithmic regression feature to find a model for your experimental data. Graph the ordered pairs $(t, T - c)$ with the model you found. How well does the model fit the data? How does the model compare with your selection from Question 1?

Graphing Calculator Programs
TI-82 or TI-83 Program

```
PROGRAM:HEAT82
:PlotsOff
:Func
:FnOff
:AxesOn
:ClrDraw
:ClrList L3, L4
:-10→Ymin
:90→Ymax
:10→Yscl
:ClrHome
:{1, 0}→L1
:Send (L1)
:{1, 1, 1}→L1
:Send (L1)
:36→dim L3
:36→dim L4
:Disp "HOW MUCH TIME"
:Disp "BETWEEN POINTS"
:Disp "IN SECONDS?"
:Input T
:-2*T→Xmin
:36*T→Xmax
:T→Xscl
:seq(K, K, T, 36*T, T)→L3
:ClrHome
:Disp "PRESS ENTER"
:Disp "TO START"
:Pause
:ClrHome
:{3, T, -1, 0}→L1
:Send(L1)
:For (K, 1, 36, 1)
:Get (L4 (K))
:Pt-On(L3 (K), L4 (K))
:End
:ClrHome
:Plotl(Scatter, L3, L4,·)
:DispGraph
:Stop
```

TI-85 Program

```
PROGRAM:HEAT85
:Func
:FnOff
:AxesOn
:ClDrw
:1→dimL L3:1→dimL L4
:-10→yMin
:90→yMax
:10→yScl
:Cl LCD
:{1, 0}→L1
:Outpt("CBLSEND", L1)
:{1, 1, 1}→L1
:Outpt ("CBLSEND", L1)
:36→dimL L3
:36→dimL L4
:Disp "HOW MUCH TIME"
:Disp "BETWEEN POINTS"
:Disp "IN SECONDS"
:Input T
:-2*T→xMin
:36*T→xMax
:T→xScl
:seq(K, K, T, 36*T, T)→L3
:ClLCD
:Disp "PRESS ENTER"
:Disp "TO START"
:Pause
:ClLCD
:{3, T, -1, 0}→L1
:Outpt ("CBLSEND", L1)
:For (K, 1, 36, 1)
:Input "CBLGET", L4(K)
:PtOn (L3(K), L4(K))
:End
:ClLCD
:Scatter L3, L4
:DispG
:Stop
```

CHAPTER 10 VOCABULARY CHECK

Fill in each blank with one of the words or phrases listed below.

inverse	common	composition	symmetric	exponential
vertical	logarithmic	natural	horizontal	

1. For each one-to-one function, we can find its _____ function by switching the coordinates of the ordered pairs of the function.

2. The _____ of functions f and g is $(f \circ g)(x) = f(g(x))$.

3. A function of the form $f(x) = b^x$ is called an _____ function if $b > 0, b$ is not 1, and x is a real number.

4. The graphs of f and f^{-1} are _____ about the line $y = x$.

5. _____ logarithms are logarithms to base e.

6. _____ logarithms are logarithms to base 10.

7. To see whether a graph is the graph of a one-to-one function, apply the _____ line test to see if it is a function, and then apply the _____ line test to see if it is a one-to-one function.

8. A _____ function is a function that can be defined by $f(x) = \log_b x$ where x is a positive real number, b is a constant positive real number, and b is not 1.

CHAPTER 10 HIGHLIGHTS

DEFINITIONS AND CONCEPTS	EXAMPLES

Section 10.1 The Algebra of Functions; Composite Functions

Algebra of Functions

Sum $(f + g)(x) = f(x) + g(x)$

Difference $(f - g)(x) = f(x) - g(x)$

Product $(f \cdot g)(x) = f(x) \cdot g(x)$

Quotient $\left(\dfrac{f}{g}\right)(x) = \dfrac{f(x)}{g(x)}, g(x) \neq 0$

If $f(x) = 7x$ and $g(x) = x^2 + 1$,

$(f + g)(x) = f(x) + g(x) = 7x + x^2 + 1$

$(f - g)(x) = f(x) - g(x) = 7x - (x^2 + 1)$
$= 7x - x^2 - 1$

$(f \cdot g)(x) = f(x) \cdot g(x) = 7x(x^2 + 1)$
$= 7x^3 + 7x$

$\left(\dfrac{f}{g}\right)(x) = \dfrac{f(x)}{g(x)} = \dfrac{7x}{x^2 + 1}$

Composite Functions

The notation $(f \circ g)(x)$ means "f composed with g."

$(f \circ g)(x) = f(g(x))$

$(g \circ f)(x) = g(f(x))$

If $f(x) = x^2 + 1$ and $g(x) = x - 5$, find $(f \circ g)(x)$.

$(f \circ g)(x) = f(g(x))$
$= f(x - 5)$
$= (x - 5)^2 + 1$
$= x^2 - 10x + 26$

DEFINITIONS AND CONCEPTS	EXAMPLES

Section 10.2 Inverse Functions

If f is a function, then f is a **one-to-one function** only if each y-value (output) corresponds to only one x-value (input).

Horizontal Line Test

If every horizontal line intersects the graph of a function at most once, then the function is a one-to-one function.

Determine whether each graph is a one-to-one function.

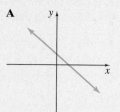

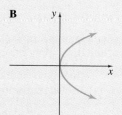

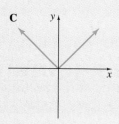

Graphs A and C pass the vertical line test, so only these are graphs of functions. Of graphs A and C, only graph A passes the horizontal line test, so only graph A is the graph of a one-to-one function.

The **inverse** of a one-to-one function f is the one-to-one function f^{-1} that is the set of all ordered pairs (b, a) such that (a, b) belongs to f.

To Find the Inverse of a One-to-One Function f(x)

Step 1: Replace $f(x)$ with y.
Step 2: Interchange x and y.
Step 3: Solve for y.
Step 4: Replace y with $f^{-1}(x)$.

Find the inverse of $f(x) = 2x + 7$.

$$y = 2x + 7 \qquad \text{Replace } f(x) \text{ with } y.$$

$$x = 2y + 7 \qquad \text{Interchange } x \text{ and } y.$$

$$2y = x - 7 \qquad \text{Solve for } y.$$

$$y = \frac{x - 7}{2}$$

$$f^{-1}(x) = \frac{x - 7}{2} \qquad \text{Replace } y \text{ with } f^{-1}(x).$$

The inverse of $f(x) = 2x + 7$ is $f^{-1}(x) = \dfrac{x - 7}{2}$.

DEFINITIONS AND CONCEPTS	EXAMPLES

Section 10.3 Exponential Functions

A function of the form $f(x) = b^x$ is an **exponential function**, where $b > 0, b \neq 1$, and x is a real number.

Graph the exponential function $y = 4^x$.

x	y
-2	$\dfrac{1}{16}$
-1	$\dfrac{1}{4}$
0	1
1	4
2	16

Uniqueness of b^x

If $b > 0$ and $b \neq 1$, then $b^x = b^y$ is equivalent to $x = y$.

Solve $2^{x+5} = 8$.

$$2^{x+5} = 2^3 \qquad \text{Write 8 as } 2^3.$$

$$x + 5 = 3 \qquad \text{Use the uniqueness of } b^x.$$

$$x = -2 \qquad \text{Subtract 5 from both sides.}$$

Section 10.4 Logarithmic Functions

Logarithmic Definition

If $b > 0$ and $b \neq 1$, then

$$y = \log_b x \quad \text{means} \quad x = b^y$$

for any positive number x and real number y.

Logarithmic Form	Corresponding Exponential Statement
$\log_5 25 = 2$	$5^2 = 25$
$\log_9 3 = \dfrac{1}{2}$	$9^{1/2} = 3$

Properties of Logarithms

If b is a real number, $b > 0$ and $b \neq 1$, then

$$\log_b 1 = 0, \quad \log_b b^x = x, \quad b^{\log_b x} = x$$

$$\log_5 1 = 0, \quad \log_7 7^2 = 2, \quad 3^{\log_3 6} = 6$$

Logarithmic Function

If $b > 0$ and $b \neq 1$, then a **logarithmic function** is a function that can be defined as

$$f(x) = \log_b x$$

The domain of f is the set of positive real numbers, and the range of f is the set of real numbers.

Graph $y = \log_3 x$.
Write $y = \log_3 x$ as $3^y = x$. Plot the ordered pair solutions listed in the table, and connect them with a smooth curve.

x	y
3	1
1	0
$\dfrac{1}{3}$	-1
$\dfrac{1}{9}$	-2

DEFINITIONS AND CONCEPTS	EXAMPLES

Section 10.5 Properties of Logarithms

Let x, y, and b be positive numbers and $b \neq 1$.

Product Property

$$\log_b xy = \log_b x + \log_b y$$

Quotient Property

$$\log_b \frac{x}{y} = \log_b x - \log_b y$$

Power Property

$$\log_b x^r = r \log_b x$$

Write as a single logarithm.

$2 \log_5 6 + \log_5 x - \log_5 (y + 2)$

$= \log_5 6^2 + \log_5 x - \log_5 (y + 2)$ Power property

$= \log_5 36 \cdot x - \log_5 (y + 2)$ Product property

$= \log_5 \dfrac{36x}{y + 2}$ Quotient property

Section 10.6 Common Logarithms, Natural Logarithms, and Change of Base

Common Logarithms

$$\log x \quad \text{means} \quad \log_{10} x$$

Natural Logarithms

$$\ln x \quad \text{means} \quad \log_e x$$

Continuously Compounded Interest Formula

$$A = Pe^{rt}$$

where r is the annual interest rate for P dollars invested for t years.

$\log 5 = \log_{10} 5 \approx 0.69897$

$\ln 7 = \log_e 7 \approx 1.94591$

Find the amount in an account at the end of 3 years if $1000 is invested at an interest rate of 4% compounded continuously.

Here, $t = 3$ years, $P = \$1000$, and $r = 0.04$.

$A = Pe^{rt}$

$= 1000e^{0.04(3)}$

$\approx \$1127.50$

Section 10.7 Exponential and Logarithmic Equations and Applications

Logarithm Property of Equality

Let $\log_b a$ and $\log_b c$ be real numbers and $b \neq 1$. Then

$\log_b a = \log_b c$ is equivalent to $a = c$

Solve $2^x = 5$.

$\log 2^x = \log 5$ Log property of equality

$x \log 2 = \log 5$ Power property

$x = \dfrac{\log 5}{\log 2}$ Divide both sides by log 2.

$x \approx 2.3219$ Use a calculator.

CHAPTER 10 REVIEW

(10.1) *If* $f(x) = x - 5$ *and* $g(x) = 2x + 1$, *find*

1. $(f + g)(x)$

2. $(f - g)(x)$

3. $(f \cdot g)(x)$

4. $\left(\dfrac{g}{f}\right)(x)$

If $f(x) = x^2 - 2$, $g(x) = x + 1$, and $h(x) = x^3 - x^2$, find each composition.

5. $(f \circ g)(x)$

6. $(g \circ f)(x)$

7. $(h \circ g)(2)$

8. $(f \circ f)(x)$

9. $(f \circ g)(-1)$

10. $(h \circ h)(2)$

(10.2) *Determine whether each function is a one-to-one function. If it is one-to-one, list the elements of its inverse.*

11. $h = \{(-9, 14), (6, 8), (-11, 12), (15, 15)\}$

12. $f = \{(-5, 5), (0, 4), (13, 5), (11, -6)\}$

13.

U.S. Region (Input)	West	Midwest	South	Northeast
Rank in Automobile Thefts (Output)	2	4	1	3

△ **14.**

Shape (Input)	Square	Triangle	Parallelogram	Rectangle
Number of Sides (Output)	4	3	4	4

Given that $f(x) = \sqrt{x + 2}$ is a one-to-one function, find the following.

15. a. $f(7)$

  b. $f^{-1}(3)$

16. a. $f(-1)$

  b. $f^{-1}(1)$

Determine whether each function is a one-to-one function.

17.

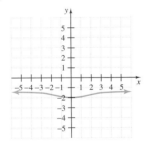

18.

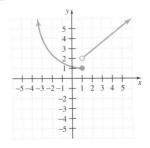

19.

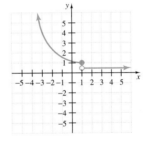

20.

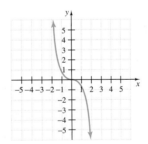

Find an equation defining the inverse function of the given one-to-one function.

21. $f(x) = x - 9$

22. $f(x) = x + 8$

23. $f(x) = 6x + 11$

24. $f(x) = 12x$

25. $f(x) = x^3 - 5$

26. $f(x) = \sqrt[3]{x + 2}$

27. $g(x) = \dfrac{12x - 7}{6}$

28. $r(x) = \dfrac{13}{2}x - 4$

On the same set of axes, graph the given one-to-one function and its inverse.

29. $g(x) = \sqrt{x}$

30. $h(x) = 5x - 5$

31. Find the inverse of the one-to-one function $f(x) = 2x - 3$. Then graph both $f(x)$ and $f^{-1}(x)$ with a square window.

(10.3) Solve each equation for x.

32. $4^x = 64$

33. $3^x = \dfrac{1}{9}$

34. $2^{3x} = \dfrac{1}{16}$

35. $5^{2x} = 125$

36. $9^{x+1} = 243$

37. $8^{3x-2} = 4$

Graph each exponential function.

38. $y = 3^x$

39. $y = \left(\dfrac{1}{3}\right)^x$

40. $y = 4 \cdot 2^x$

41. $y = 2^x + 4$

Use the formula $A = P\left(1 + \dfrac{r}{n}\right)^{nt}$ to solve the interest problems. In this formula,

A = amount accrued (or owed)
P = principal invested (or loaned)
r = rate of interest
n = number of compounding periods per year
t = time in years

42. Find the amount accrued if $1600 is invested at 9% interest compounded semiannually for 7 years.

43. A total of $800 is invested in a 7% certificate of deposit for which interest is compounded quarterly. Find the value that this certificate will have at the end of 5 years.

44. Use a graphing calculator to verify the results of Exercise 40.

(10.4) Write each equation with logarithmic notation.

45. $49 = 7^2$

46. $2^{-4} = \dfrac{1}{16}$

Write each logarithmic equation with exponential notation.

47. $\log_{1/2} 16 = -4$

48. $\log_{0.4} 0.064 = 3$

Solve for x.

49. $\log_4 x = -3$

50. $\log_3 x = 2$

51. $\log_3 1 = x$

52. $\log_4 64 = x$

53. $\log_x 64 = 2$

54. $\log_x 81 = 4$

55. $\log_4 4^5 = x$

56. $\log_7 7^{-2} = x$

57. $5^{\log_5 4} = x$

58. $2^{\log_2 9} = x$

59. $\log_2 (3x - 1) = 4$

60. $\log_3 (2x + 5) = 2$

61. $\log_4 (x^2 - 3x) = 1$

62. $\log_8 (x^2 + 7x) = 1$

Graph each pair of equations on the same coordinate system.

63. $y = 2^x$ and $y = \log_2 x$

64. $y = \left(\dfrac{1}{2}\right)^x$ and $y = \log_{1/2} x$

(10.5) Write each of the following as single logarithms.

65. $\log_3 8 + \log_3 4$

66. $\log_2 6 + \log_2 3$

67. $\log_7 15 - \log_7 20$

68. $\log 18 - \log 12$

69. $\log_{11} 8 + \log_{11} 3 - \log_{11} 6$

70. $\log_5 14 + \log_5 3 - \log_5 21$

71. $2 \log_5 x - 2 \log_5 (x + 1) + \log_5 x$

72. $4 \log_3 x - \log_3 x + \log_3 (x + 2)$

Use properties of logarithms to write each expression as a sum or difference of multiples of logarithms.

73. $\log_3 \dfrac{x^3}{x + 2}$

74. $\log_4 \dfrac{x + 5}{x^2}$

75. $\log_2 \dfrac{3x^2 y}{z}$

76. $\log_7 \dfrac{yz^3}{x}$

If $\log_b 2 = 0.36$ and $\log_b 5 = 0.83$, find the following.

77. $\log_b 50$

78. $\log_b \dfrac{4}{5}$

(10.6) *Use a calculator to approximate the logarithm to four decimal places.*

79. $\log 3.6$

80. $\log 0.15$

81. $\ln 1.25$

82. $\ln 4.63$

Find the exact value.

83. $\log 1000$

84. $\log \dfrac{1}{10}$

85. $\ln \dfrac{1}{e}$

86. $\ln e^4$

Solve each equation for x.

87. $\ln (2x) = 2$

88. $\ln (3x) = 1.6$

89. $\ln (2x - 3) = -1$

90. $\ln (3x + 1) = 2$

Use the formula $\ln \dfrac{I}{I_0} = -kx$ to solve radiation problems. In this formula,

$$x = \text{depth in millimeters}$$
$$I = \text{intensity of radiation}$$
$$I_0 = \text{initial intensity}$$
$$k = \text{a constant measure dependent on the material}$$

Round answers to two decimal places.

91. Find the depth at which the intensity of the radiation passing through a lead shield is reduced to 3% of the original intensity if the value of k is 2.1.

92. If k is 3.2, find the depth at which 2% of the original radiation will penetrate.

Approximate the logarithm to four decimal places.

93. $\log_5 1.6$

94. $\log_3 4$

Use the formula $A = Pe^{rt}$ to solve the interest problems in which interest is compounded continuously. In this formula,

$$A = \text{amount accrued (or owed)}$$
$$P = \text{principal invested (or loaned)}$$
$$r = \text{rate of interest}$$
$$t = \text{time in years}$$

95. Bank of New York offers a 5-year, 6% continuously compounded investment option. Find the amount accrued if \$1450 is invested.

96. Find the amount to which a \$940 investment grows if it is invested at 11% compounded continuously for 3 years.

(10.7) *Solve each exponential equation for x. Give an exact solution and also approximate the solution to four decimal places.*

97. $3^{2x} = 7$

98. $6^{3x} = 5$

99. $3^{2x+1} = 6$

100. $4^{3x+2} = 9$

101. $5^{3x-5} = 4$

102. $8^{4x-2} = 3$

103. $2 \cdot 5^{x-1} = 1$

104. $3 \cdot 4^{x+5} = 2$

Solve the equation for x.

105. $\log_5 2 + \log_5 x = 2$

106. $\log_3 x + \log_3 10 = 2$

107. $\log(5x) - \log(x + 1) = 4$

108. $\ln(3x) - \ln(x - 3) = 2$

109. $\log_2 x + \log_2 2x - 3 = 1$

110. $-\log_6(4x + 7) + \log_6 x = 1$

Use the formula $y = y_0 e^{kt}$ to solve the population growth problems. In this formula,

$$y = \text{size of population}$$
$$y_0 = \text{initial count of population}$$
$$k = \text{rate of growth}$$
$$t = \text{time}$$

Round each answer to the nearest whole.

111. The population of mallard ducks in Nova Scotia is expected to grow at a rate of 6% per week during the spring migration. If 155,000 ducks are already in Nova Scotia, find how many are expected by the end of 4 weeks.

112. The population of Indonesia is growing at a rate of 1.5% per year. If the population in 1998 was 212,942,000, find the expected population by the year 2006. (*Source:* U.S. Bureau of the Census, International Data Base)

113. Japan is experiencing an annual growth rate of 0.2%. In 1998, the population of Japan was 125,932,000. How long will it take for the population to be 140,000,000? (*Source:* U.S. Bureau of the Census, International Data Base)

114. In 1998, Canada had a population of 30,675,000. How long will it take Canada to double in population if its growth rate is 1.1% annually? (*Source:* U.S. Bureau of the Census, International Data Base)

115. Egypt's population is increasing at a rate of 1.9% per year. How long will it take for its 1998 population of 66,050,000 to double in size? (*Source:* U.S. Bureau of the Census, International Data Base)

Use the compound interest equation $A = P\left(1 + \dfrac{r}{n}\right)^{nt}$ to solve the following. (See the directions for Exercises 42 and 43 for an explanation of this formula. Round answers to the nearest tenth.)

116. Find how long it will take a $5000 investment to grow to $10,000 if it is invested at 8% interest compounded quarterly.

117. An investment of $6000 has grown to $10,000 while the money was invested at 6% interest compounded monthly. Find how long it was invested.

Use a graphing calculator to solve each equation. Round all solutions to two decimal places.

118. $e^x = 2$ **119.** $10^{0.3x} = 7$

CHAPTER 10 TEST

If $f(x) = x$, $g(x) = x - 7$, and $h(x) = x^2 - 6x + 5$, find the following.

1. $(f \circ h)(0)$

2. $(g \circ f)(x)$

3. $(g \circ h)(x)$

On the same set of axes, graph the given one-to-one function and its inverse.

4. $f(x) = 7x - 14$

Determine whether the given graph is the graph of a one-to-one function.

5.

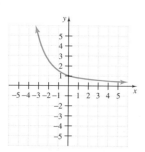

6.

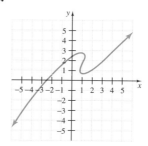

Determine whether each function is one-to-one. If it is one-to-one, find an equation or a set of ordered pairs that defines the inverse function of the given function.

7. $y = 6 - 2x$

8. $f = \{(0, 0), (2, 3), (-1, 5)\}$

9.

Word (Input)	Dog	Cat	House	Desk	Circle
First Letter of Word (Output)	d	c	h	d	c

Use the properties of logarithms to write each expression as a single logarithm.

10. $\log_3 6 + \log_3 4$

11. $\log_5 x + 3 \log_5 x - \log_5 (x + 1)$

12. Write the expression $\log_6 \dfrac{2x}{y^3}$ as the sum or difference of multiples of logarithms.

13. If $\log_b 3 = 0.79$ and $\log_b 5 = 1.16$, find the value of $\log_b \dfrac{3}{25}$.

14. Approximate $\log_7 8$ to four decimal places.

15. Solve $8^{x-1} = \dfrac{1}{64}$ for x. Give an exact solution.

16. Solve $3^{2x+5} = 4$ for x. Give an exact solution, and also approximate the solution to four decimal places.

Solve each logarithmic equation for x. Give an exact solution.

17. $\log_3 x = -2$

18. $\ln \sqrt{e} = x$

19. $\log_8 (3x - 2) = 2$

20. $\log_5 x + \log_5 3 = 2$

21. $\log_4 (x + 1) - \log_4 (x - 2) = 3$

22. Solve $\ln (3x + 7) = 1.31$ accurate to four decimal places.

23. Graph $y = \left(\dfrac{1}{2}\right)^x + 1$.

24. Graph the functions $y = 3^x$ and $y = \log_3 x$ on the same coordinate system.

Use the formula $A = P\left(1 + \dfrac{r}{n}\right)^{nt}$ to solve Exercises 25 and 26.

25. Find the amount in the account if $4000 is invested for 3 years at 9% interest compounded monthly.

26. Find how long it will take $2000 to grow to $3000 if the money is invested at 7% interest compounded semiannually. Round to the nearest whole.

Use the population growth formula $y = y_0 e^{kt}$ to solve Exercises 27 and 28.

27. The prairie dog population of the Grand Rapids area now stands at 57,000 animals. If the population is growing at a rate of 2.6% annually, find how many prairie dogs there will be in that area 5 years from now.

28. In an attempt to save an endangered species of wood duck, naturalists would like to increase the wood duck population from 400 to 1000 ducks. If the annual population growth rate is 6.2%, find how long it will take the naturalists to reach their goal. Round to the nearest whole year.

29. The formula $\log (1 + k) = \dfrac{0.3}{D}$ relates the doubling time D, in days, and the growth rate k for a population of mice. Find the rate at which the population is increasing if the doubling time is 56 days. Round to the nearest tenth of a percent.

30. Use a graphing calculator to approximate the solution of
$$e^{0.2x} = e^{-0.4x} + 2$$
to two decimal places.

CHAPTER 10 CUMULATIVE REVIEW

1. Multiply.

   a. $(-8)(-1)$

   b. $(-2)\dfrac{1}{6}$

   c. $3(-3)$

   d. $0(11)$

   e. $\left(\dfrac{1}{5}\right)\left(-\dfrac{10}{11}\right)$

   f. $(7)(1)(-2)(-3)$

   g. $8(-2)(0)$

2. Graph $y = x^2$.

3. Solve the system.
$$\begin{cases} x - 5y - 2z = 6 \\ -2x + 10y + 4z = -12 \\ \dfrac{1}{2}x - \dfrac{5}{2}y - z = 3 \end{cases}$$

4. Use the quotient rule to simplify.

a. $\dfrac{x^7}{x^4}$

b. $\dfrac{5^8}{5^2}$

c. $\dfrac{20x^6}{4x^5}$

d. $\dfrac{12y^{10}z^7}{14y^8z^7}$

5. For the ICL Production Company, the rational function
$C(x) = \dfrac{2.6x + 10,000}{x}$ describes the company's cost per disc of pressing x compact discs. Find the cost per disc for pressing:

a. 100 compact discs

b. 1000 compact discs

6. Add or subtract.

a. $\dfrac{x}{4} + \dfrac{5x}{4}$

b. $\dfrac{x^2}{x + 7} - \dfrac{49}{x + 7}$

c. $\dfrac{x}{3y^2} - \dfrac{x + 1}{3y^2}$

7. Divide $3x^4 + 2x^3 - 8x + 6$ by $x^2 - 1$.

8. Solve: $\dfrac{2x}{2x - 1} + \dfrac{1}{x} = \dfrac{1}{2x - 1}$

9. Steve Deitmer takes $1\dfrac{1}{2}$ times as long to go 72 miles upstream in his boat as he does to return. If the boat cruises at 30 mph in still water, what is the speed of the current?

10. Simplify the following expressions.

a. $\sqrt[4]{81}$

b. $\sqrt[5]{-243}$

c. $-\sqrt{25}$

d. $\sqrt[4]{-81}$

e. $\sqrt[3]{64x^3}$

11. Use rational exponents to write as a single radical.

a. $\sqrt{x} \cdot \sqrt[4]{x}$

b. $\dfrac{\sqrt{x}}{\sqrt[3]{x}}$

c. $\sqrt[3]{3} \cdot \sqrt{2}$

12. Multiply.

a. $\sqrt{3}(5 + \sqrt{30})$

b. $(\sqrt{5} - \sqrt{6})(\sqrt{7} + 1)$

c. $(7\sqrt{x} + 5)(3\sqrt{x} - \sqrt{5})$

d. $(4\sqrt{3} - 1)^2$

e. $(\sqrt{2x} - 5)(\sqrt{2x} + 5)$

13. Rationalize the denominator of $\dfrac{\sqrt[4]{x}}{\sqrt[4]{81y^5}}$.

14. Solve $\sqrt{4 - x} = x - 2$.

15. Solve $3x^2 - 9x + 8 = 0$ by completing the square.

16. Solve $\dfrac{3x}{x - 2} - \dfrac{x + 1}{x} = \dfrac{6}{x(x - 2)}$.

17. Solve $x^2 - 4x \le 0$.

18. Graph $F(x) = (x - 3)^2 + 1$.

19. Find the midpoint of the line segment that joins points $P(-3, 3)$ and $Q(1, 0)$.

20. Graph the equation $4x^2 + 16y^2 = 64$.

21. Solve the system:
$$\begin{cases} x^2 + y^2 = 4 \\ x + y = 3 \end{cases}$$

22. Graph the system:
$$\begin{cases} x \le 1 - 2y \\ y \le x^2 \end{cases}$$

23. If $f(x) = x - 1$ and $g(x) = 2x - 3$, find

   a. $(f + g)(x)$

   b. $(f - g)(x)$

   c. $(f \cdot g)(x)$

   d. $\left(\dfrac{f}{g}\right)(x)$

24. Find an equation of the inverse of $f(x) = x + 3$.

25. Find the value of each logarithmic expression.

   a. $\log_4 16$

   b. $\log_{10} \dfrac{1}{10}$

   c. $\log_9 3$

A certified financial planner works with clients to develop a sound financial plan that helps the client reach his or her life goals. Financial planning is a growing field: As Baby Boomers approach retirement age and life spans lengthen overall, more and more people will seek professional assistance with financial management.

Financial planners work for investment firms, accounting firms, insurance companies, banks, credit counseling organizations, law firms, or in private practice. Through interviews and discussions, they assess clients' current financial positions. Planners then give advice on retirement planning, insurance needs, investment options, estate planning, tax strategies, and employee benefits. Financial planners may then help clients implement their new financial plans. Certified financial planners use math and problem-solving skills in such tasks as analyzing clients' current cash flow, estimating cash needs for future goals, and calculating investment returns.

For more information about a career as a certified financial planner, visit the Certified Financial Planner Board of Standards Web site by first going to www.prenhall.com/martin-gay.

In the Spotlight on Decision Making feature on page 651, you will have the opportunity to make a decision about reaching a client's retirement goals as a certified financial planner.

Appendix A

REVIEW OF ANGLES, LINES, AND SPECIAL TRIANGLES

The word **geometry** is formed from the Greek words, **geo**, meaning earth, and **metron**, meaning measure. Geometry literally means to measure the earth.

This section contains a review of some basic geometric ideas. It will be assumed that fundamental ideas of geometry such as point, line, ray, and angle are known. In this appendix, the notation $\angle 1$ is read "angle 1" and the notation $m\angle 1$ is read "the measure of angle 1."

We first review types of angles.

ANGLES

A **right angle** is an angle whose measure is 90°. A right angle can be indicated by a square drawn at the vertex of the angle, as shown below.
An angle whose measure is more than 0° but less than 90° is called an **acute angle**.
An angle whose measure is greater than 90° but less than 180° is called an **obtuse angle**.
An angle whose measure is 180° is called a **straight angle**.
Two angles are said to be **complementary** if the sum of their measures is 90°. Each angle is called the **complement** of the other.
Two angles are said to be **supplementary** if the sum of their measures is 180°. Each angle is called the **supplement** of the other.

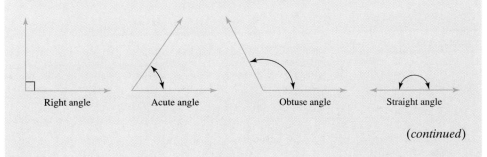

Right angle   Acute angle   Obtuse angle   Straight angle

(continued)

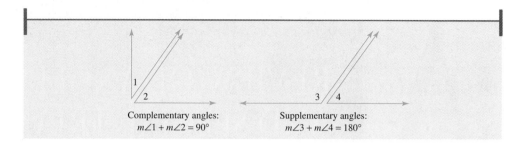

Complementary angles:
$m\angle 1 + m\angle 2 = 90°$

Supplementary angles:
$m\angle 3 + m\angle 4 = 180°$

Example 1 If an angle measures 28°, find its complement.

Solution Two angles are complementary if the sum of their measures is 90°. The complement of a 28° angle is an angle whose measure is $90° - 28° = 62°$. To check, notice that $28° + 62° = 90°$.

Plane is an undefined term that we will describe. A plane can be thought of as a flat surface with infinite length and width, but no thickness. A plane is two dimensional. The arrows in the following diagram indicate that a plane extends indefinitely and has no boundaries.

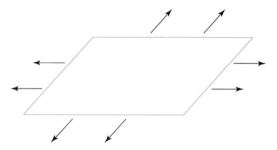

Figures that lie on a plane are called **plane figures**. (See the description of common plane figures in Appendix B.) Lines that lie in the same plane are called **coplanar**.

LINES

Two lines are **parallel** if they lie in the same plane but never meet.
Intersecting lines meet or cross in one point.
Two lines that form right angles when they intersect are said to be **perpendicular**.

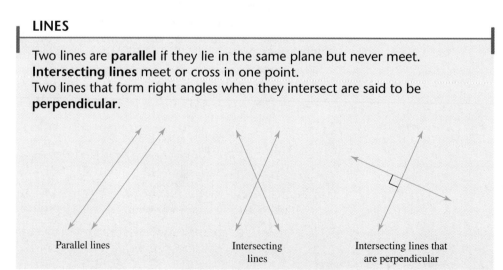

Parallel lines

Intersecting lines

Intersecting lines that are perpendicular

Two intersecting lines form **vertical angles**. Angles 1 and 3 are vertical angles. Also, angles 2 and 4 are vertical angles. It can be shown that **vertical angles have equal measures**.

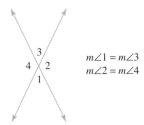

$$m\angle 1 = m\angle 3$$
$$m\angle 2 = m\angle 4$$

Adjacent angles have the same vertex and share a side but have no interior points in common. Angles 1 and 2 are adjacent angles. Other pairs of adjacent angles are angles 2 and 3, angles 3 and 4, and angles 4 and 1.

A **transversal** is a line that intersects two or more lines in the same plane. Line l is a transversal that intersects lines m and n. The eight angles formed are numbered and certain pairs of these angles are given special names.

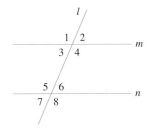

Corresponding angles: $\angle 1$ and $\angle 5$, $\angle 3$ and $\angle 7$, $\angle 2$ and $\angle 6$, $\angle 4$ and $\angle 8$.

Exterior angles: $\angle 1, \angle 2, \angle 7, \angle 8$.

Interior angles: $\angle 3, \angle 4, \angle 5, \angle 6$.

Alternate interior angles: $\angle 3$ and $\angle 6$, $\angle 4$ and $\angle 5$.

These angles and parallel lines are related in the following manner:

PARALLEL LINES CUT BY A TRANSVERSAL

1. If two parallel lines are cut by a transversal, then
   a. **corresponding angles are equal** and
   b. **alternate interior angles are equal.**
2. If corresponding angles formed by two lines and a transversal are equal, then the lines are parallel.
3. If alternate interior angles formed by two lines and a transversal are equal, then the lines are parallel.

Example 2 Given that lines m and n are parallel and that the measure of angle 1 is 100°, find the measures of angles 2, 3, and 4.

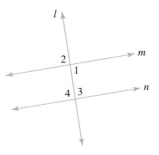

Solution $m\angle 2 = 100°$, since angles 1 and 2 are vertical angles.
$m\angle 4 = 100°$, since angles 1 and 4 are alternate interior angles.
$m\angle 3 = 180° - 100° = 80°$, since angles 4 and 3 are supplementary angles. ▬

A **polygon** is the union of three or more coplanar line segments that intersect each other only at each end point, with each end point shared by exactly two segments.
A **triangle** is a polygon with three sides. The sum of the measures of the three angles of a triangle is 180°. In the following figure, $m\angle 1 + m\angle 2 + m\angle 3 = 180°$.

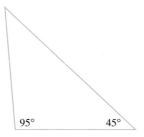

Example 3 Find the measure of the third angle of the triangle shown.

Solution The sum of the measures of the angles of a triangle is 180°. Since one angle measures 45° and the other angle measures 95°, the third angle measures $180° - 45° - 95° = 40°$. ▬

Two triangles are **congruent** if they have the same size and the same shape. In congruent triangles, the measures of corresponding angles are equal and the lengths of corresponding sides are equal. The following triangles are congruent:

Corresponding angles are equal: $m\angle 1 = m\angle 4$, $m\angle 2 = m\angle 5$, and $m\angle 3 = m\angle 6$. Also, lengths of corresponding sides are equal: $a = x$, $b = y$, and $c = z$.

Any one of the following may be used to determine whether two triangles are congruent:

CONGRUENT TRIANGLES

1. If the measures of two angles of a triangle equal the measures of two angles of another triangle and the lengths of the sides between each pair of angles are equal, the triangles are congruent.

2. If the lengths of the three sides of a triangle equal the lengths of corresponding sides of another triangle, the triangles are congruent.

3. If the lengths of two sides of a triangle equal the lengths of corresponding sides of another triangle, and the measures of the angles between each pair of sides are equal, the triangles are congruent.

Two triangles are **similar** if they have the same shape. In similar triangles, the measures of corresponding angles are equal and corresponding sides are in proportion. The following triangles are similar. (All similar triangles drawn in this appendix will be oriented the same.)

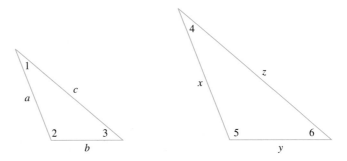

Corresponding angles are equal: $m\angle 1 = m\angle 4$, $m\angle 2 = m\angle 5$, and $m\angle 3 = m\angle 6$. Also, corresponding sides are proportional: $\dfrac{a}{x} = \dfrac{b}{y} = \dfrac{c}{z}$.

Any one of the following may be used to determine whether two triangles are similar:

SIMILAR TRIANGLES

1. If the measures of two angles of a triangle equal the measures of two angles of another triangle, the triangles are similar.

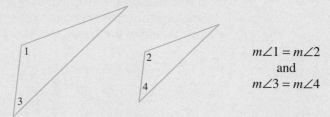

$$m\angle 1 = m\angle 2$$
and
$$m\angle 3 = m\angle 4$$

2. If three sides of one triangle are proportional to three sides of another triangle, the triangles are similar.

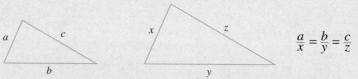

$$\frac{a}{x} = \frac{b}{y} = \frac{c}{z}$$

3. If two sides of a triangle are proportional to two sides of another triangle and the measures of the included angles are equal, the triangles are similar.

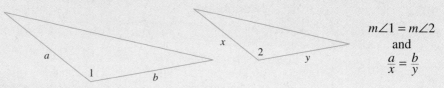

$$m\angle 1 = m\angle 2$$
and
$$\frac{a}{x} = \frac{b}{y}$$

Example 4 Given that the following triangles are similar, find the missing length x.

Solution Since the triangles are similar, corresponding sides are in proportion. Thus, $\frac{2}{3} = \frac{10}{x}$. To solve this equation for x, we multiply both sides by the LCD, $3x$.

$$3x\left(\frac{2}{3}\right) = 3x\left(\frac{10}{x}\right)$$
$$2x = 30$$
$$x = 15$$

The missing length is 15 units.

A **right triangle** contains a right angle. The side opposite the right angle is called the **hypotenuse**, and the other two sides are called the **legs**. The **Pythagorean theorem** gives a formula that relates the lengths of the three sides of a right triangle.

THE PYTHAGOREAN THEOREM

If a and b are the lengths of the legs of a right triangle, and c is the length of the hypotenuse, then $a^2 + b^2 = c^2$.

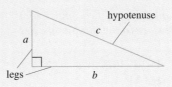

Example 5   Find the length of the hypotenuse of a right triangle whose legs have lengths of 3 centimeters and 4 centimeters.

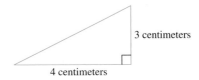

Solution   Because we have a right triangle, we use the Pythagorean theorem. The legs are 3 centimeters and 4 centimeters, so let $a = 3$ and $b = 4$ in the formula.

$$a^2 + b^2 = c^2$$
$$3^2 + 4^2 = c^2$$
$$9 + 16 = c^2$$
$$25 = c^2$$

Since c represents a length, we assume that c is positive. Thus, if c^2 is 25, c must be 5. The hypotenuse has a length of 5 centimeters.

Appendix A Exercise Set

Find the complement of each angle. See Example 1.

1. $19°$

2. $65°$

3. $70.8°$

4. $45\frac{2}{3}°$

5. $11\frac{1}{4}°$

6. $19.6°$

Find the supplement of each angle.

7. $150°$

8. $90°$

9. $30.2°$

10. $81.9°$

11. $79\frac{1}{2}°$

12. $165\frac{8}{9}°$

13. If lines m and n are parallel, find the measures of angles 1 through 7. See Example 2.

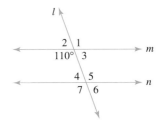

14. If lines *m* and *n* are parallel, find the measures of angles 1 through 5. See Example 2.

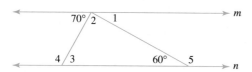

In each of the following, the measures of two angles of a triangle are given. Find the measure of the third angle. See Example 3.

15. 11°, 79°   **16.** 8°, 102°
17. 25°, 65°   **18.** 44°, 19°
19. 30°, 60°   **20.** 67°, 23°

In each of the following, the measure of one angle of a right triangle is given. Find the measures of the other two angles.

21. 45°   **22.** 60°
23. 17°   **24.** 30°
25. $39\frac{3}{4}°$ **26.** 72.6°

Given that each of the following pairs of triangles is similar, find the missing lengths. See Example 4.

27.

28.

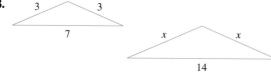

29.

30.

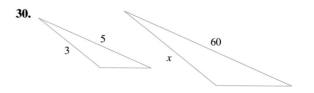

Use the Pythagorean theorem to find the missing lengths in the right triangles. See Example 5.

31.

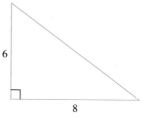

32.

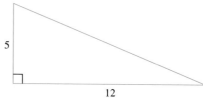

33.

34.

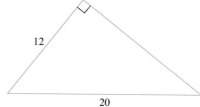

Appendix B
REVIEW OF GEOMETRIC FIGURES

Plane figures have length and width but no thickness or depth.

Name	Description	Figure
POLYGON	Union of three or more coplanar line segments that intersect with each other only at each endpoint, with each endpoint shared by two segments.	
TRIANGLE	Polygon with three sides (sum of measures of three angles is 180°).	
SCALENE TRIANGLE	Triangle with no sides of equal length.	
ISOSCELES TRIANGLE	Triangle with two sides of equal length.	
EQUILATERAL TRIANGLE	Triangle with all sides of equal length.	
RIGHT TRIANGLE	Triangle that contains a right angle.	leg, hypotenuse, leg

Plane figures have length and width but no thickness or depth.

Name	Description	Figure
QUADRILATERAL	Polygon with four sides (sum of measures of four angles is 360°).	
TRAPEZOID	Quadrilateral with exactly one pair of opposite sides parallel.	
ISOSCELES TRAPEZOID	Trapezoid with legs of equal length.	
PARALLELOGRAM	Quadrilateral with both pairs of opposite sides parallel and equal in length.	
RHOMBUS	Parallelogram with all sides of equal length.	
RECTANGLE	Parallelogram with four right angles.	
SQUARE	Rectangle with all sides of equal length.	
CIRCLE	All points in a plane the same distance from a fixed point called the **center**.	

Solids have length, width, and depth.

Name	Description	Figure
RECTANGULAR SOLID	A solid with six sides, all of which are rectangles.	
CUBE	A rectangular solid whose six sides are squares.	
SPHERE	All points the same distance from a fixed point, called the center.	
RIGHT CIRCULAR CYLINDER	A cylinder with two circular bases that are perpendicular to its altitude.	
RIGHT CIRCULAR CONE	A cone with a circular base that is perpendicular to its altitude.	

REVIEW OF VOLUME AND SURFACE AREA

A **convex solid** is a set of points, S, not all in one plane, such that for any two points A and B in S, all points between A and B are also in S. In this appendix, we will find the volume and surface area of special types of solids called polyhedrons. A solid formed by the intersection of a finite number of planes is called a **polyhedron**. The box below is an example of a polyhedron.

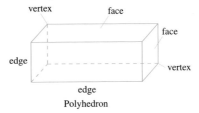

Polyhedron

Each of the plane regions of the polyhedron is called a **face** of the polyhedron. If the intersection of two faces is a line segment, this line segment is an **edge** of the polyhedron. The intersections of the edges are the **vertices** of the polyhedron.

    Volume is a measure of the space of a solid. The volume of a box or can, for example, is the amount of space inside. Volume can be used to describe the amount of juice in a pitcher or the amount of concrete needed to pour a foundation for a house.

    The volume of a solid is the number of **cubic units** in the solid. A cubic centimeter and a cubic inch are illustrated.

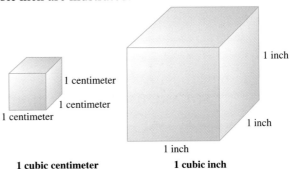

1 cubic centimeter   **1 cubic inch**

    The **surface area** of a polyhedron is the sum of the areas of the faces of the polyhedron. For example, each face of the cube to the left above has an area of 1 square centimeter. Since there are 6 faces of the cube, the sum of the areas of the faces is 6 square centimeters. Surface area can be used to describe the amount of material needed to cover or form a solid. Surface area is measured in square units.

Formulas for finding the volumes, V, and surface areas, SA, of some common solids are given next.

VOLUME AND SURFACE AREA FORMULAS OF COMMON SOLIDS

Solid   *Formulas*

RECTANGULAR SOLID

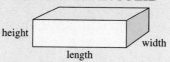

$V = lwh$
$SA = 2lh + 2wh + 2lw$
where h = height, w = width, l = length

CUBE

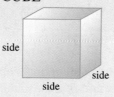

$V = s^3$
$SA = 6s^2$
where s = side

SPHERE

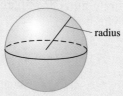

$V = \dfrac{4}{3}\pi r^3$
$SA = 4\pi r^2$
where r = radius

CIRCULAR CYLINDER

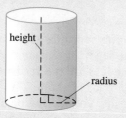

$V = \pi r^2 h$
$SA = 2\pi rh + 2\pi r^2$
where h = height, r = radius

CONE

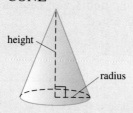

$V = \dfrac{1}{3}\pi r^2 h$

$SA = \pi r\sqrt{r^2 + h^2} + \pi r^2$
where h = height, r = radius

SQUARE-BASED PYRAMID

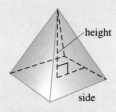

$V = \dfrac{1}{3}s^2 h$

$SA = B + \dfrac{1}{2}pl$

where B = area of base, p = perimeter of base, h = height, s = side, l = slant height

> **HELPFUL HINT**
> Volume is measured in cubic units. Surface area is measured in square units.

Example 1 Find the volume and surface area of a rectangular box that is 12 inches long, 6 inches wide, and 3 inches high.

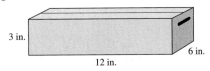

3 in.

6 in.

12 in.

Solution Let $h = 3$ in., $l = 12$ in., and $w = 6$ in.

$V = lwh$

$V = 12$ inches $\cdot$ 6 inches $\cdot$ 3 inches $= 216$ cubic inches

The volume of the rectangular box is 216 cubic inches.

$SA = 2lh + 2wh + 2lw$

$= 2(12\text{ in.})(3\text{ in.}) + 2(6\text{ in.})(3\text{ in.}) + 2(12\text{ in.})(6\text{ in.})$

$= 72$ sq. in. $+ 36$ sq. in. $+ 144$ sq. in.

$= 252$ sq. in.

The surface area of the rectangular box is 252 square inches.

Example 2 Find the volume and surface area of a ball of radius 2 inches. Give the exact volume and surface area and then use the approximation $\dfrac{22}{7}$ for π.

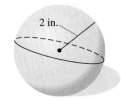

2 in.

Solution

$V = \dfrac{4}{3}\pi r^3$ Formula for volume of a sphere.

$V = \dfrac{4}{3}\pi(2\text{ in.})^3$ Let $r = 2$ inches.

$= \dfrac{32}{3}\pi$ cu. in.   Simplify.

$\approx \dfrac{32}{3} \cdot \dfrac{22}{7}$ cu. in.   Approximate π with $\dfrac{22}{7}$.

$= \dfrac{704}{21}$ or $33\dfrac{11}{21}$ cu. in.

The volume of the sphere is exactly $\dfrac{32}{3}\pi$ cubic inches or approximately $33\dfrac{11}{21}$ cubic inches.

$SA = 4\pi r^2$ Formula for surface area.

$SA = 4\pi(2\text{ in.})^2$ Let $r = 2$ inches.

$= 16\pi$ sq. in.   Simplify.

$\approx 16 \cdot \dfrac{22}{7}$ sq. in.   Approximate π with $\dfrac{22}{7}$.

$= \dfrac{352}{7}$ or $50\dfrac{2}{7}$ sq. in.

The surface area of the sphere is exactly 16π square inches or approximately $50\dfrac{2}{7}$ square inches.

Appendix C Exercise Set

Find the volume and surface area of each solid. See Examples 1 and 2. For formulas that contain π, give an exact answer and then approximate using $\frac{22}{7}$ for π.

1.

4 in.

3 in.

6 in.

2.

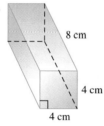

3 mi

3.

8 cm

8 cm

8 cm

4.

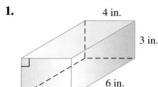

8 cm

4 cm

4 cm

5. (For surface area, use 3.14 for π and approximate to two decimal places.)

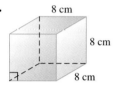

3 yd

2 yd

6.

10 ft

6 ft

7.

10 in.

8. Find the volume only.

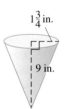

$1\frac{3}{4}$ in.

9 in.

9.

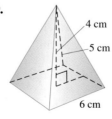

4 cm

5 cm

6 cm

10.

1 ft

Solve.

11. Find the volume of a cube with edges of $1\frac{1}{3}$ inches.

$1\frac{1}{3}$ in.

12. A water storage tank is in the shape of a cone with the pointed end down. If the radius is 14 ft and the depth of the tank is 15 ft, approximate the volume of the tank in cubic feet. Use $\frac{22}{7}$ for π.

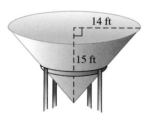

14 ft

15 ft

13. Find the surface area of a rectangular box 2 ft by 1.4 ft by 3 ft.

14. Find the surface area of a box in the shape of a cube that is 5 ft on each side.

15. Find the volume of a pyramid with a square base 5 in. on a side and a height of 1.3 in.

16. Approximate to the nearest hundredth the volume of a sphere with a radius of 2 cm. Use 3.14 for π.

17. A paperweight is in the shape of a square-based pyramid 20 cm tall. If an edge of the base is 12 cm, find the volume of the paperweight.

18. A bird bath is made in the shape of a hemisphere (half-sphere). If its radius is 10 in., approximate the volume. Use $\dfrac{22}{7}$ for π.

19. Find the exact surface area of a sphere with a radius of 7 in.

20. A tank is in the shape of a cylinder 8 ft tall and 3 ft in radius. Find the exact surface area of the tank.

21. Find the volume of a rectangular block of ice 2 ft by $2\dfrac{1}{2}$ ft by $1\dfrac{1}{2}$ ft.

22. Find the capacity (volume in cubic feet) of a rectangular ice chest with inside measurements of 3 ft by $1\dfrac{1}{2}$ ft by $1\dfrac{3}{4}$ ft.

23. An ice cream cone with a 4-cm diameter and 3-cm depth is filled exactly level with the top of the cone. Approximate how much ice cream (in cubic centimeters) is in the cone. Use $\dfrac{22}{7}$ for π.

24. A child's toy is in the shape of a square-based pyramid 10 in. tall. If an edge of the base is 7 in., find the volume of the toy.

Appendix D

AN INTRODUCTION TO USING A GRAPHING UTILITY

The Viewing Window and Interpreting Window Settings

In this appendix, we will use the term **graphing utility** to mean a graphing calculator or a computer software graphing package. All graphing utilities graph equations by plotting points on a screen. While plotting several points can be slow and sometimes tedious for us, a graphing utility can quickly and accurately plot hundreds of points. How does a graphing utility show plotted points? A computer or calculator screen is made up of a grid of small rectangular areas called **pixels**. If a pixel contains a point to be plotted, the pixel is turned "on"; otherwise, the pixel remains "off." The graph of an equation is then a collection of pixels turned "on." The graph of $y = 3x + 1$ from a graphing calculator is shown in Figure A-1. Notice the irregular shape of the line caused by the rectangular pixels.

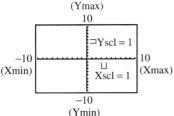

Figure A-1

$y = 3x + 1$

The portion of the coordinate plane shown on the screen in Figure A-1 is called the **viewing window** or the **viewing rectangle.** Notice the *x*-axis and the *y*-axis on the graph. While tick marks are shown on the axes, they are not labeled. This means that from this screen alone, we do not know how many units each tick mark represents. To see what each tick mark represents and the minimum and maximum values on the axes, check the *window setting* of the graphing utility. It defines the viewing window. The window of the graph of $y = 3x + 1$ shown in Figure A-1 has the following setting (Figure A-2):

Xmin = −10	The minimum *x*-value is −10.
Xmax = 10	The maximum *x*-value is 10.
Xscl = 1	The *x*-axis scale is 1 unit per tick mark.
Ymin = −10	The minimum *y*-value is −10.
Ymax = 10	The maximum *y*-value is 10.
Yscl = 1	The *y*-axis scale is 1 unit per tick mark.

Figure A-2

(Ymax) 10
(Ymin) −10
(Xmin) −10
(Xmax) 10
Yscl = 1
Xscl = 1

By knowing the scale, we can find the minimum and the maximum values on the axes simply by counting tick marks. For example, if both the Xscl (*x*-axis scale) and the Yscl are 1 unit per tick mark on the graph in Figure A-3, we can count the tick marks and find that the minimum *x*-value is −10 and the maximum *x*-value is 10. Also, the minimum *y*-value is −10 and the maximum *y*-value is 10. If the Xscl (*x*-axis scale) changes to 2 units per tick mark (shown in Figure A-4), by counting tick marks, we see that the minimum x-value is now -20 and the maximum x-value is now 20.

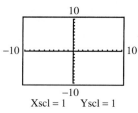

Xscl = 1   Yscl = 1

Figure A-3

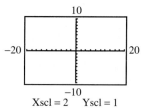

Xscl = 2   Yscl = 1

Figure A-4

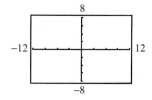

Figure A-5

It is also true that if we know the Xmin and the Xmax values, we can calculate the Xscl by the displayed axes. For example, the Xscl of the graph in Figure A-5 must be 3 units per tick mark for the maximum and minimum x-values to be as shown. Also, the Yscl of that graph must be 2 units per tick mark for the maximum and minimum y-values to be as shown.

We will call the viewing window in Figure A-3 a *standard* viewing window or rectangle. Although a standard viewing window is sufficient for much of this text, special care must be taken to ensure that all key features of a graph are shown. Figures A-6, A-7, and A-8 show the graph of $y = x^2 + 11x - 1$ on three different viewing windows. Note that certain viewing windows for this equation are misleading.

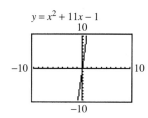

$y = x^2 + 11x - 1$

Figure A-6

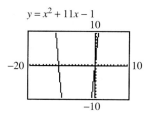

$y = x^2 + 11x - 1$

Figure A-7

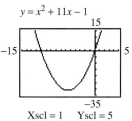

$y = x^2 + 11x - 1$

Xscl = 1   Yscl = 5

Figure A-8

How do we ensure that all distinguishing features of the graph of an equation are shown? It helps to know about the equation that is being graphed. For example, the equation $y = x^2 + 11x - 1$ is not a linear equation and its graph is not a line. This equation is a quadratic equation and, therefore, its graph is a parabola. By knowing this information, we know that the graph shown in Figure A-6, although correct, is misleading. Of the three viewing rectangles shown, the graph in Figure A-8 is best because it shows more of the distinguishing features of the parabola. Properties of equations needed for graphing will be studied in this text.

Viewing Window and Interpreting Window Settings Exercise Set

In Exercises 1–4, determine whether all ordered pairs listed will lie within a standard viewing rectangle.

1. $(-9, 0), (5, 8), (1, -8)$
2. $(4, 7), (0, 0), (-8, 9)$
3. $(-11, 0), (2, 2), (7, -5)$
4. $(3, 5), (-3, -5), (15, 0)$

In Exercises 5–10, choose an Xmin, Xmax, Ymin, and Ymax so that all ordered pairs listed will lie within the viewing rectangle.

5. $(-90, 0), (55, 80), (0, -80)$
6. $(4, 70), (20, 20), (-18, 90)$
7. $(-11, 0), (2, 2), (7, -5)$

8. $(3, 5), (-3, -5), (15, 0)$
9. $(200, 200), (50, -50), (70, -50)$
10. $(40, 800), (-30, 500), (15, 0)$.

Write the window setting for each viewing window shown. Use the following format:

11.

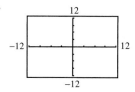

12.

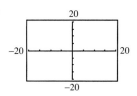

13.

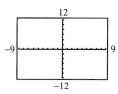

14.

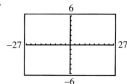

15.

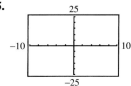

16.

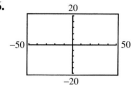

17.

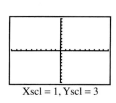

Xscl = 1, Yscl = 3

18.

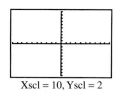

Xscl = 10, Yscl = 2

19.

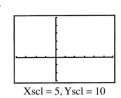

Xscl = 5, Yscl = 10

20.

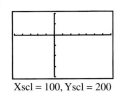

Xscl = 100, Yscl = 200

Graphing Equations and Square Viewing Window

In general, the following steps may be used to graph an equation on a standard viewing window.

GRAPHING AN EQUATION IN x AND y WITH A GRAPHIING UTILITY ON A STANDARD VIEWING WINDOW

Step 1: Solve the equation for y.
Step 2: Use your graphing utility and enter the equation in the form
$Y = expression\ involving\ x$
Step 3: Activate the graphing utility.

Special care must be taken when entering the *expression involving x* in Step 2. You must be sure that the graphing utility you are using interprets the expression as you want it to. For example, let's graph $3y = 4x$. To do so,

Step 1: Solve the equation for y.

$$3y = 4x$$

$$\frac{3y}{3} = \frac{4x}{3}$$

$$y = \frac{4}{3}x$$

Step 2: Using your graphing utility, enter the expression $\frac{4}{3}x$ after the

Y = prompt. In order for your graphing utility to correctly interpret the expression, you may need to enter $(4/3)x$ or $(4 \div 3)x$.

Step 3: Activate the graphing utility. The graph should appear as in Figure A-9.

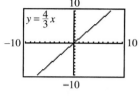

Figure A-9

Distinguishing features of the graph of a line include showing all the intercepts of the line. For example, the window of the graph of the line in Figure A-10 does not show both intercepts of the line, but the window of the graph of the same line in Figure A-11 does show both intercepts. Notice the notation below each graph. This is a shorthand notation of the range setting of the graph. This notation means [Xmin, Xmax] by [Ymin, Ymax].

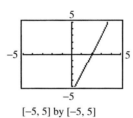

[−5, 5] by [−5, 5]

Figure A-10

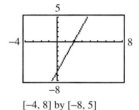

[−4, 8] by [−8, 5]

Figure A-11

On a standard viewing window, the tick marks on the y-axis are closer together than the tick marks on the x-axis. This happens because the viewing window is a rectangle, and so 10 equally spaced tick marks on the positive y-axis will be closer together than 10 equally spaced tick marks on the positive x-axis. This causes the appearance of graphs to be distorted.

For example, notice the different appearances of the same line graphed using different viewing windows. The line in Figure A-12 is distorted because the tick marks along the x-axis are farther apart than the tick marks along the y-axis. The graph of the same line in Figure A-13 is not distorted because the viewing rectangle has been selected so that there is equal spacing between tick marks on both axes.

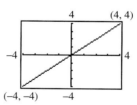

Figure A-12

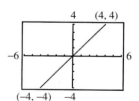

Figure A-13

We say that the line in Figure A-13 is graphed on a *square* setting. Some graphing utilities have a built-in program that, if activated, will automatically provide a square setting. A square setting is especially helpful when we are graphing perpendicular lines, circles, or when a true geometric perspective is desired. Some examples of square screens are shown in Figures A-14 and A-15.

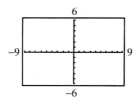

Figure A-14

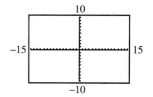

Figure A-15

Other features of a graphing utility such as Trace, Zoom, Intersect, and Table are discussed in appropriate Graphing Calculator Explorations in this text.

Graphing Equations and Square Viewing Window Exersise Set

Graph each linear equation in two variables, using the two different range settings given. Determine which setting shows all intercepts of a line.

1. $y = 2x + 12$

Setting A: $[-10, 10]$ by $[-10, 10]$
Setting B: $[-10, 10]$ by $[-10, 15]$

2. $y = -3x + 25$

Setting A: $[-5, 5]$ by $[-30, 10]$
Setting B: $[-10, 10]$ by $[-10, 30]$

3. $y = -x - 41$

Setting A: $[-50, 10]$ by $[-10, 10]$
Setting B: $[-50, 10]$ by $[-50, 15]$

4. $y = 6x - 18$

Setting A: $[-10, 10]$ by $[-20, 10]$
Setting B: $[-10, 10]$ by $[-10, 10]$

5. $y = \dfrac{1}{2}x - 15$

Setting A: $[-10, 10]$ by $[-20, 10]$
Setting B: $[-10, 35]$ by $[-20, 15]$

6. $y = -\dfrac{2}{3}x - \dfrac{29}{3}$

Setting A: $[-10, 10]$ by $[-10, 10]$
Setting B: $[-15, 5]$ by $[-15, 5]$

The graph of each equation is a line. Use a graphing utility and a standard viewing window to graph each equation.

7. $3x = 5y$ **8.** $7y = -3x$ **9.** $9x - 5y = 30$

10. $4x + 6y = 20$ **11.** $y = -7$ **12.** $y = 2$

13. $x + 10y = -5$ **14.** $x - 5y = 9$

Graph the following equations using the square setting given. Some keystrokes that may be helpful are given.

15. $y = \sqrt{x}$ $[-12, 12]$ by $[-8, 8]$

Suggested keystrokes: $\sqrt{\ }\ x$

16. $y = \sqrt{2x}$ $[-12, 12]$ by $[-8, 8]$

Suggested keystrokes: $\sqrt{\ }\ (2x)$

17. $y = x^2 + 2x + 1$ $[-15, 15]$ by $[-10, 10]$

Suggested keystrokes: $x \wedge 2 + 2\,x + 1$

18. $y = x^2 - 5$ $[-15, 15]$ by $[-10, 10]$

Suggested keystrokes: $x \wedge 2 - 5$

19. $y = |x|$ $[-9, 9]$ by $[-6, 6]$

Suggested keystrokes: $ABS\,(x)$

20. $y = |x - 2|$ $[-9, 9]$ by $[-6, 6]$

Suggested keystrokes: $ABS\,(x - 2)$

Graph each line. Use a standard viewing window; then, if necessary, change the viewing window so that all intercepts of each line show.

21. $x + 2y = 30$ **22.** $1.5x - 3.7y = 40.3$

ANSWERS TO SELECTED EXERCISES

■ CHAPTER 1 REAL NUMBERS AND ALGEBRAIC EXPRESSIONS

Exercise Set 1.2 **1.** 35 **3.** 30.38 **5.** $\dfrac{3}{8}$ **7.** 22 **9.** 2000 mi **11.** 20.4 sq. ft **13.** \$36,909.60 **15.** $\{1, 2, 3, 4, 5\}$

17. $\{11, 12, 13, 14, 15, 16\}$ **19.** $\{0\}$ **21.** $\{0, 2, 4, 6, 8\}$ **23.** (number line from -2 to 6) **25.** (number line from -1 to 1 with $\frac{1}{2}$ $\frac{2}{3}$)

27. (number line from -12 to 4) **29.** Answers may vary. **31.** $\{3, 0, \sqrt{36}\}$ **33.** $\{3, \sqrt{36}\}$ **35.** $\{\sqrt{7}\}$ **37.** $\in$ **39.** $\notin$ **41.** $\notin$

43. $\notin$ **45.** true **47.** true **49.** false **51.** false **53.** true **55.** false **57.** Answers may vary. **59.** -2 **61.** 4 **63.** 0

65. -3 **67.** Answers may vary. **69.** 6.2 **71.** $-\dfrac{4}{7}$ **73.** $\dfrac{2}{3}$ **75.** 0 **77.** $2x$ **79.** $2x + 5$ **81.** $x - 10$ **83.** $x + 2$

85. $\dfrac{x}{11}$ **87.** $3x + 12$ **89.** $x - 17$ **91.** $2(x + 3)$ **93.** $\dfrac{5}{4 - x}$ **95.** 137; 102; 93; 71; 59

Exercise Set 1.3 **1.** 5 **3.** -24 **5.** -11 **7.** -4 **9.** $\dfrac{4}{3}$ **11.** -2 **13.** -60 **15.** 80 **17.** 3 **19.** 0 **21.** -8 **23.** $-\dfrac{3}{7}$

25. $\dfrac{1}{21}$ **27.** -49 **29.** 36 **31.** -8 **33.** Answers may vary. **35.** 7 **37.** $\dfrac{1}{3}$ **39.** 4 **41.** 3 **43.** 48 **45.** -1 **47.** -3

49. 14.4 **51.** -2.1 **53.** $-\dfrac{1}{3}$ **55.** 17 **57.** $-\dfrac{79}{15}$ **59.** $-\dfrac{5}{14}$ **61.** -0.5876 **63.** 13 **65.** 65 **67.** -2 **69.** $\dfrac{5}{2}$

71. a. 18; 22; 28; 208 **b.** increase **73. a.** 600; 150; 105 **b.** decrease **75.** $\dfrac{13}{35}$ **77.** 4205 m **79.** b **81.** d **83.** Yes.
Two players have 6 points each (the third player has 0 points) or two players have 5 points each (the third has 2 points).
85. 16.5227 **87.** 4.4272 **89.** 13.2% **91.** 10.8%

Exercise Set 1.4 **1.** $4c = 7$ **3.** $3(x + 1) = 7$ **5.** $\dfrac{n}{5} = 4n$ **7.** $z - 2 = 2z$ **9.** $>$ **11.** $=$ **13.** $<$ **15.** $7x \le -21$

17. $-2 + x \ne 10$ **19.** $2(x - 6) > \dfrac{1}{11}$ **21.** $y - 7 = 6$ **23.** $2(x - 6) = -27$ **25.** $-5; \dfrac{1}{5}$ **27.** $8; -\dfrac{1}{8}$

29. $\dfrac{1}{4}; -4$ **31.** 0; undefined **33.** $-\dfrac{7}{8}, \dfrac{8}{7}$ **35.** Zero. For every real number x, $0 \cdot x \ne 1$, so 0 has no reciprocal.

It is the only real number that has no reciprocal because if $x \ne 0$, then $x \cdot \dfrac{1}{x} = 1$ by definition. **37.** $y + 7x$ **39.** $w \cdot z$

41. $\dfrac{x}{5} \cdot \dfrac{1}{3}$ **43.** no **45.** $(5 \cdot 7)x$ **47.** $x + (1.2 + y)$ **49.** $14(z \cdot y)$ **51.** 10 and 4. Subtraction is not associative.

53. $3x + 15$ **55.** $-2a - b$ **57.** $12x + 10y + 4z$ **59.** $2y - 6 = \dfrac{1}{8}$ **61.** $\dfrac{n + 5}{2} > 2n$ **63.** $6 + 3x$ **65.** 0

A-1

67. 7   **69.** $(10 \cdot 2)y$ **71.** $a(b + c) = ab + ac$ **73.** $0.1d$ **75.** $112 - x$ **77.** $90 - 5x$ **79.** $\$35.61y$ **81.** $2x + 2$
83. $-8y - 14$ **85.** $-9c - 4$ **87.** $4 - 8y$ **89.** $-11y - 11$ **91.** $3t - 14$ **93.** 0   **95.** $13n - 20$
97. $-180.96y - 74.33$ **99.** $6.5y - 7.92x + 25.47$ **101.** no   **103.** 70 million   **105.** 35 million   **107.** 12.3%

Chapter 1 Review   **1.** 21   **3.** 324,000   **5.** $\{-2, 0, 2, 4, 6\}$ **7.** $\varnothing$ **9.** $\{\ldots, -1, 0, 1, 2\}$ **11.** false   **13.** true   **15.** true
17. true   **19.** true   **21.** true   **23.** true   **25.** true   **27.** true   **29.** $\left\{5, \frac{8}{2}, \sqrt{9}\right\}$ **31.** $\{\sqrt{7}, \pi\}$ **33.** $\left\{5, \frac{8}{2}, \sqrt{9}, -1\right\}$
35. -0.6 **37.** -1 **39.** $\frac{1}{0.6}$ **41.** 1   **43.** -35 **45.** 0.31   **47.** 13.3   **49.** 0   **51.** 0   **53.** -5 **55.** 4   **57.** 9   **59.** 3
61. $-\frac{32}{135}$ **63.** $-\frac{5}{4}$ **65.** $\frac{5}{8}$ **67.** -1 **69.** 1   **71.** -4 **73.** $\frac{5}{7}$ **75.** $\frac{1}{5}$ **77.** -5 **79.** 5   **81.** $-xy + 1$ **83.** $2x^2 - 2$
85. $-1.1x - 0.3$ **87. a.** $6.28; 62.8; 628$ **b.** increase   **89.** $n + 2n = -15$ **91.** $6(t - 5) = 4$ **93.** $9x - 10 = 5$
95. $-4 < 7y$ **97.** $t + 6 \le -12$ **99.** distributive property   **101.** commutative property of addition
103. multiplicative inverse property   **105.** associative property of multiplication   **107.** multiplicative identity property
109. $(3 + x) + (7 + y)$ **111.** $2 \cdot \frac{1}{2}$, for example   **113.** $7 + 0$ **115.** $>$ **117.** $=$ **119.** $>$

Chapter 1 Test   **1.** true   **2.** false   **3.** false   **4.** false   **5.** true   **6.** false   **7.** -3 **8.** 43   **9.** -225 **10.** -2 **11.** 1
12. 12   **13.** 1   **14. a.** $5.75; 17.25; 57.50; 115.00$ **b.** increase   **15.** $2|x + 5| = 30$ **16.** $\frac{(6 - y)^2}{7} < -2$ **17.** $\frac{9z}{|-12|} \ne 10$
18. $3\left(\frac{n}{5}\right) = -n$ **19.** $20 = 2x - 6$ **20.** $-2 = \frac{x}{x + 5}$ **21.** distributive property   **22.** associative property of addition
23. additive inverse property   **24.** multiplication property of zero   **25.** $0.05n + 0.1d$ **26.** $2y^2 - 10$ **27.** $-1.3x + 1.9$

CHAPTER 2   EQUATIONS, INEQUALITIES, AND PROBLEM SOLVING

Mental Math   **1.** $8x + 21$ **3.** $6n - 7$ **5.** $-4x - 1$
Exercise Set 2.1   **1.** -12 **3.** -0.9 **5.** 6   **7.** -5 **9.** -1.1 **11.** -5 **13.** 0   **15.** 2   **17.** -9
19. $-\frac{10}{7}$ **21. a.** $4x + 5$ **b.** -3 **c.** Answers may vary.   **23.** $\frac{1}{6}$ **25.** 4   **27.** 1   **29.** 5   **31.** all real numbers   **33.** $\varnothing$
35. Answers may vary.   **37.** 8   **39.** -5.9 **41.** 7   **43.** 4.2   **45.** 2   **47.** -2 **49.** 0   **51.** 5   **53.** $\varnothing$ **55.** $\frac{1}{8}$ **57.** 0   **59.** 29
61. -8 **63.** all real numbers   **65.** 4   **67.** 8   **69.** all real numbers   **71.** $\frac{40}{3}$ **73.** 17   **75.** $\frac{3}{5}$ **77.** $\frac{4}{5}$ **79.** $K = -11$
81. $K = 24$ **83.** -4.86 **85.** 1.53   **87.** not a fair game   **89.** $8 + x$ **91.** $8 - x$ **93.** $2x - 5$ **95.** $-\frac{3}{22}$ **97.** 4

Exercise Set 2.2   **1.** $4y$ **3.** $3z + 3$ **5.** $15x + 30$ **7.** $10x + 3$ **9.** -5 **11.** $45, 225$ **13.** 78   **15.** 1.92
17. approximately 658.59 million acres   **19.** 51,700 homes   **21.** 20%   **23.** 117 automobile loans
25. Dallas/Ft. Worth, 60.5; Atlanta, 68.2; Chicago, 70.3   **27.** B767-300ER, 216 seats; B737-200, 112 seats   **29.** $\$430.00$
31. a. 49,057 telephone company operators   **b.** Answers may vary.   **33.** 5 years   **35.** 17 million returns
37. square: each side, 18 cm; triangle: each side, 24 cm   **39.** length, 14 cm; width, 6 cm   **41.** width: 8.4 m; height: 47 m
43. $64°, 32°, 84°$ **45.** $80°, 100°$ **47.** $15°, 75°$ **49.** $40°, 140°$ **51.** $75, 76, 77$ **53.** Fallon's zip code is 89406; Fernley's zip
code is 89408; Gardnerville Ranchos' zip code is 89410   **55.** any three consecutive integers   **57.** 25 skateboards
59. 800 books   **61.** Answers may vary.   **63.** 11 million trees   **65.** 6   **67.** 208   **69.** -55 **71.** 3195   **73.** 121.8152

Mental Math   **1.** $y = 5 - 2x$ **3.** $a = 5b + 8$ **5.** $k = h - 5j + 6$

Exercise Set 2.3   **1.** $t = \frac{D}{r}$ **3.** $R = \frac{I}{PT}$ **5.** $y = \frac{9x - 16}{4}$ **7.** $W = \frac{P - 2L}{2}$ **9.** $A = \frac{J + 3}{C}$ **11.** $g = \frac{W}{h - 3t^2}$
13. $B = \frac{T - 2C}{AC}$ **15.** $r = \frac{C}{2\pi}$ **17.** $r = \frac{E - IR}{I}$ **19.** $L = \frac{2s - an}{n}$ **21.** $v = \frac{3st^4 - N}{5s}$ **23.** $H = \frac{S - 2LW}{2L + 2W}$
25. $\$4703.71; \$4713.99; \$4719.22; \$4722.74; \$4724.45$ **27.** 12 times a year; you earn more interest
29. a. $\$7313.97$ **b.** $\$7321.14$ **c.** $\$7325.98$ **31.** $40°C$ **33.** 3.6 hr, or 3 hr and 36 min   **35.** 171 packages   **37.** 0.42 ft
39. 0.25 sec   **41.** 41.125π ft ≈ 129.1325 ft   **43.** Estimates will vary; actual cost was $\$6.80$ each.   **45.** $\$1831.96$
47. 2 gal   **49. a.** 1174.86 cu. m   **b.** 310.34 cu. m   **c.** 1485.20 cu. m   **51.** 2.25 hr, or 2 hr and 15 min

53. approximately 34,507 mph   **55.** 0.388; 0.723; 1.00; 1.523; 5.202; 9.538; 19.193; 30.065; 39.505

57. $\frac{1}{4}$ **59.** $\frac{3}{8}$ **61.** $\frac{3}{8}$ **63.** $\frac{3}{4}$ **65.** 1   **67.** 1   **69.** $\{2, 3\}$ **71.** $\{-3, -2, -1, 0, 1, 2, 3\}$ **73.** Answers may vary.

Mental Math **1.** $\{x \mid x < 6\}$ **3.** $\{x \mid x \geq 10\}$ **5.** $\{x \mid x > 4\}$ **7.** $\{x \mid x \leq 2\}$

Exercise Set 2.4 **1.** $;(-\infty, -3)$ **3.** $;[0.3, \infty)$ **5.** $;(5, \infty)$

7. $;(-2, 5)$ **9.** $;(-1, 5)$ **11.** Answers may vary.   **13.** 100   **15.** $-5, -1{,}000{,}000$

17. $;[-2, \infty)$ **19.** $;(-\infty, 1)$ **21.** $;(-\infty, 2]$

23. $;(-\infty, -4)$ **25.** $;\left[\frac{8}{3}, \infty\right)$ **27.** $;(-\infty, -4.7)$

29. $;(-\infty, -3]$ **31.** $;(4, \infty)$ **33.** $(-\infty, -1]$ **35.** $(-\infty, 11]$ **37.** $(-13, \infty)$ **39.** $(-\infty, 7]$

41. $(-\infty, \infty)$ **43.** $\varnothing$ **45.** $(0, \infty)$ **47.** $(-2, \infty)$ **49.** $\left[-\frac{3}{5}, \infty\right]$ **51.** $[-9.6, \infty)$ **53.** $(38, \infty)$ **55.** Answers may vary.

57. $[0, \infty)$ **59.** $(-\infty, -5]$ **61.** $\left(-\infty, \frac{1}{4}\right)$ **63.** $(-\infty, -1)$ **65.** $\left[-\frac{79}{3}, \infty\right)$ **67.** $(-\infty, -15)$ **69.** $[3, \infty)$

71. $\left[-\frac{37}{3}, \infty\right)$ **73.** $(-\infty, 5)$ **75.** 30   **77.** 1040 lb   **79.** 16 oz   **81.** more than 200 calls   **83.** $F \geq 932°$

85. a. 2002 **b.** Answers may vary.   **87.** decreasing   **89.** 6.74 gal   **91.** 2004   **93.** Answers may vary.   **95.** 2001

97. $0, 1, 2, 3, 4, 5, 6, 7$ **99.** $-6, -7, -8, \ldots$ **101.** $;(-7, 1]$ **103.** $;[-2.5, 5.3)$

Exercise Set 2.5 **1.** $\{2, 3, 4, 5, 6, 7\}$ **3.** $\{4, 6\}$ **5.** $\{\ldots, -2, -1, 0, 1, \ldots\}$ **7.** $\{5, 7\}$

9. $\{x \mid x \text{ is an odd integer or } x = 2 \text{ or } x = 4\}$ **11.** $\{2, 4\}$ **13.** $;(-2, 5)$ **15.** $;[6, \infty)$

17. $;(-\infty, -3]$ **19.** $;(11, 17)$ **21.** $;[1, 4]$

23. $;\left[-3, \frac{3}{2}\right]$ **25.** $;[-21, -9]$ **27.** $;(-\infty, -1) \cup (0, \infty)$

29. $;[2, \infty)$ **31.** $;(-\infty, \infty)$ **33.** Answers may vary.   **35.** $;(-1, 2)$

37. $;(-\infty, \infty)$ **39.** $;[-1, \infty)$ **41.** $;[-5, \infty)$ **43.** $;\left[\frac{3}{2}, 6\right]$

45. $;\left(\frac{5}{4}, \frac{11}{4}\right)$ **47.** $;\varnothing$ **49.** $;(-7, \infty)$ **51.** $;\left(-5, \frac{5}{2}\right)$

53. $;\left(0, \frac{14}{3}\right]$ **55.** $;(-\infty, -3]$ **57.** $;(-\infty, 1] \cup \left(\frac{29}{7}, \infty\right)$

59. $;\varnothing$ **61.** $;\left[-\frac{1}{2}, \frac{3}{2}\right)$ **63.** $;\left(-\frac{4}{3}, \frac{7}{3}\right)$ **65.** $;(6, 12)$

67. $-20.2° \leq F \leq 95°$ **69.** $67 \leq \text{final score} \leq 94$ **71.** 1993, 1994, 1995   **73.** -12 **75.** -4 **77.** $-7, 7$ **79.** 0

81. $;(6, \infty)$ **83.** $;[3, 7]$ **85.** $;(-\infty, -1)$

Mental Math **1.** 7   **3.** -5 **5.** -6 **7.** 12

Exercise Set 2.6 **1.** $7, -7$ **3.** $4.2, -4.2$ **5.** $7, -2$ **7.** $8, 4$ **9.** $5, -5$ **11.** $3, -3$ **13.** 0   **15.** $\varnothing$ **17.** $\frac{1}{5}$ **19.** $|x| = 5$

21. $9, -\frac{1}{2}$ **23.** $-\frac{5}{2}$ **25.** Answers may vary.   **27.** $4, -4$ **29.** 0   **31.** $\varnothing$ **33.** $0, \frac{14}{3}$ **35.** $2, -2$ **37.** $\varnothing$ **39.** $7, -1$

41. $\varnothing$ **43.** $\varnothing$ **45.** $-\dfrac{1}{8}$ **47.** $\dfrac{1}{2}, -\dfrac{5}{6}$ **49.** $2, -\dfrac{12}{5}$ **51.** $3, -2$ **53.** $-8, \dfrac{2}{3}$ **55.** $\varnothing$ **57.** 4   **59.** $13, -8$ **61.** $3, -3$

63. $8, -7$ **65.** $2, 3$ **67.** $2, -\dfrac{10}{3}$ **69.** $\dfrac{3}{2}$ **71.** $\varnothing$ **73.** Answers may vary.   **75.** 13%   **77.** \$1.088 billion

79. Answers may vary.   **81.** no solution

Exercise Set 2.7   **1.** ; $[-4, 4]$ **3.** ; $(1, 5)$ **5.** ; $(-5, -1)$

7. ; $[-10, 3]$ **9.** ; $[-5, 5]$ **11.** ; $\varnothing$ **13.** ; $[0, 12]$

15. ; $(-\infty, -3) \cup (3, \infty)$ **17.** ; $(-\infty, -24] \cup [4, \infty)$

19. ; $(-\infty, -4) \cup (4, \infty)$ **21.** ; $(-\infty, \infty)$ **23.** ; $\left(-\infty, \dfrac{2}{3}\right) \cup (2, \infty)$

25. ; $\{0\}$ **27.** ; $\left(-\infty, -\dfrac{3}{8}\right) \cup \left(-\dfrac{3}{8}, \infty\right)$ **29.** $|x| < 7$ **31.** $|x| \le 5$

33. ; $[-2, 2]$ **35.** ; $(-\infty, -1) \cup (1, \infty)$ **37.** ; $(-5, 11)$

39. ; $(-\infty, 4) \cup (6, \infty)$ **41.** ; $\varnothing$ **43.** ; $(-\infty, \infty)$

45. ; $[-2, 9]$ **47.** ; $(-\infty, -11] \cup [1, \infty)$ **49.** ; $(-\infty, 0) \cup (0, \infty)$

51. ; $(-\infty, \infty)$ **53.** ; $\left[-\dfrac{1}{2}, 1\right]$ **55.** ; $(-\infty, -3) \cup (0, \infty)$

57. ; $\varnothing$ **59.** ; $(-\infty, \infty)$ **61.** ; $\left(-\dfrac{2}{3}, 0\right)$ **63.** ; $(-\infty, \infty)$

65. ; $(-\infty, -1) \cup (1, \infty)$ **67.** ; $(-\infty, -12) \cup (0, \infty)$

69. ; $(-\infty, -6) \cup (0, \infty)$ **71.** ; $\left(-\dfrac{31}{5}, \dfrac{11}{5}\right)$ **73.** ; $[-1, 8]$

75. ; $\left[-\dfrac{23}{8}, \dfrac{17}{8}\right]$ **77.** $(-2, 5)$ **79.** $5, -2$ **81.** $(-\infty, -7] \cup [17, \infty)$ **83.** $-\dfrac{9}{4}$ **85.** $(-2, 1)$ **87.** $2, \dfrac{4}{3}$

89. $\varnothing$ **91.** $\dfrac{19}{2}, -\dfrac{17}{2}$ **93.** $\left(-\infty, -\dfrac{25}{3}\right) \cup \left(\dfrac{35}{3}, \infty\right)$ **95.** Answers may vary.   **97.** $3.45 < x < 3.55$ **99.** $\dfrac{1}{6}$ **101.** 0

103. $\dfrac{1}{3}$ **105.** -1.5 **107.** 0

Chapter 2 Review   **1.** 3   **3.** $-\dfrac{45}{14}$ **5.** 0   **7.** 6   **9.** all real numbers   **11.** $\varnothing$ **13.** -3 **15.** $\dfrac{96}{5}$ **17.** 32   **19.** 8   **21.** $\varnothing$

23. 2   **25.** -7 **27.** 52   **29.** \$22,896   **31.** No such odd integers exist.   **33.** 358 mi   **35.** 5 plants, \$200   **37.** $r = \dfrac{C}{2\pi}$

39. $x = \dfrac{4y - 12}{5}$ **41.** $x = \dfrac{y - y_1 + mx_1}{m}$ **43.** $g = \dfrac{s - vt}{t^2}$ **45.** $P = \dfrac{I}{1 + rt}$ **47.** $h = \dfrac{3V}{\pi r^2}$ **49.** $T_2 = \dfrac{T_1 V_2}{V_1}$

51. $\left(\dfrac{290}{9}\right)°C \approx 32.2°C$ **53.** 16 packages   **55.** 58 mph   **57.** $(-\infty, -4]$ **59.** $(-17, \infty)$ **61.** $(-\infty, 4]$ **63.** $(-\infty, 1)$

65. $(2, \infty)$ **67.** $260° \le C \le 538°C$ **69.** \$1750 to \$3750   **71.** $\left[-2, -\dfrac{9}{5}\right)$ **73.** $\left(-\dfrac{3}{5}, 0\right)$ **75.** $\left[-\dfrac{4}{3}, \dfrac{7}{6}\right]$ **77.** $(-\infty, \infty)$

79. $(5, \infty)$ **81.** 5, 11 **83.** $-1, \dfrac{11}{3}$ **85.** $-\dfrac{1}{6}$ **87.** $\varnothing$ **89.** 1, 5 **91.** $\varnothing$ **93.** $-10, -\dfrac{4}{3}$

95. 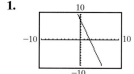 ; $(-\infty, -4] \cup [1, \infty)$ **97.** 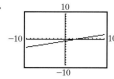 ; $(-3, 3)$ **99.** 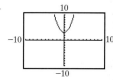 ; $(-\infty, \infty)$

101. 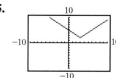 ; $\left(-\dfrac{1}{2}, 2\right)$ **103.** ; $\varnothing$

Chapter 2 Test **1.** 10 **2.** 1 **3.** $\varnothing$ **4.** all real numbers **5.** 12 **6.** $-\dfrac{80}{29}$ **7.** 1, $\dfrac{2}{3}$ **8.** $\varnothing$ **9.** $y = \dfrac{3x - 8}{4}$

10. $n = \dfrac{9}{7}m$ **11.** $g = \dfrac{S}{t^2 + vt}$ **12.** $C = \dfrac{5}{9}(F - 32)$ **13.** $(5, \infty)$ **14.** $[2, \infty)$ **15.** $\left(\dfrac{3}{2}, 5\right]$ **16.** $(-\infty, -2) \cup \left(\dfrac{4}{3}, \infty\right)$

17. $[5, \infty)$ **18.** $[4, \infty)$ **19.** $[-3, -1)$ **20.** $(-\infty, \infty)$ **21.** 9.6 **22.** 211,468 people **23.** approximately 8
24. more than 850 sunglasses **25.** \$3542.27 **26.** \$0.87 per lb **27.** 1402 watts

Chapter 2 Cumulative Review **1. a.** $\{2, 3, 4, 5\}$ **b.** $\{101, 102, 103, \dots\}$; Sec. 1.2, Ex. 3 **2. a.** 3 **b.** 5 **c.** -2 **d.** -8

e. 0; Sec. 1.2, Ex. 6 **3. a.** -14 **b.** -4 **c.** 5 **d.** -10.2 **e.** $-\dfrac{5}{21}$; Sec. 1.3, Ex. 1 **4. a.** 3 **b.** 5 **c.** $\dfrac{1}{2}$; Sec. 1.3, Ex. 7

5. a. -2 **b.** 9 **c.** -1; Sec. 1.3, Ex. 10 **6. a.** $x + 5 = 20$ **b.** $2(3 + y) = 4$ **c.** $x - 8 = 2x$

d. $\dfrac{z}{9} = 3(z - 5)$; Sec. 1.4, Ex. 1 **7.** $5 + 7x$; Sec. 1.4, Ex. 6 **8.** 2; Sec. 2.1, Ex. 1 **9.** all real numbers; Sec. 2.1, Ex. 9

10. a. $2x + 1$ **b.** $12x - 3$; Sec. 2.2, Ex. 1 **11.** 23, 49; Sec. 2.2, Ex. 3 **12.** $y = \dfrac{2x + 7}{3}$ or $y = \dfrac{2x}{3} + \dfrac{7}{3}$; Sec. 2.3, Ex. 2

13. $b = \dfrac{2A - Bh}{h}$; Sec. 2.3, Ex. 3 **14. a.** ; $[2, \infty)$ **b.** ; $(-\infty, -1)$

c. ; $(0.5\ 3]$; Sec. 2.4, Ex. 1 **15.** $\left[\dfrac{5}{2}, \infty\right)$; Sec. 2.4, Ex. 5 **16.** $(-\infty, \infty)$; Sec. 2.4, Ex. 7

17. $\{4, 6\}$; Sec. 2.5, Ex. 1 **18.** $(-\infty, 4)$; Sec. 2.5, Ex. 2 **19.** $\{2, 3, 4, 5, 6, 8\}$; Sec. 2.5, Ex. 6 **20.** $(-\infty, \infty)$; Sec. 2.5, Ex. 8
21. 2, -2; Sec. 2.6, Ex. 1 **22.** 24, -20; Sec. 2.6, Ex. 3 **23.** 4; Sec. 2.6, Ex. 9 **24.** $[-3, 3]$; Sec. 2.7, Ex. 1
25. $(-\infty, \infty)$; Sec. 2.7, Ex. 1

■ CHAPTER 3   GRAPHS AND FUNCTIONS

Graphing Calculator Explorations
1. **3.** **5.** **7.**

Mental Math **1.** $(5, 2)$ **3.** $(3, -1)$ **5.** $(-5, -2)$ **7.** $(-1, 0)$

Exercise Set 3.1
1. Quadrant I   **3.** Quadrant II   **5.** Quadrant IV   **7.** y-axis   **9.** Quadrant III

11. Quadrant IV   **13.** x-axis   **15.** Quadrant III   **17.** no; yes   **19.** yes; yes   **21.** yes; yes   **23.** yes; no   **25.** yes; yes

27. linear

29. linear

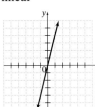

31. linear

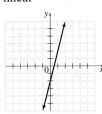

33. not linear

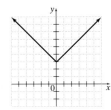

35. linear

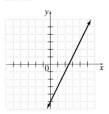

37. not linear

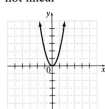

39. not linear

41. linear

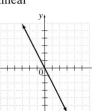

43. linear

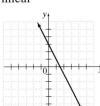

45. not linear

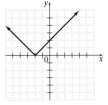

47. not linear

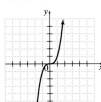

49. not linear

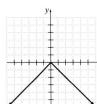

51. linear

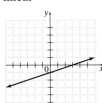

53. linear

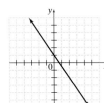

55.

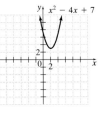

y $x^2 - 4x + 7$

57. a.

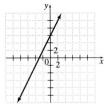

b. 14 in.   **59.** 1991   **61.** Answers may vary.   **63.** $7000   **65.** $500

67. Depreciation is the same from year to year.   **69.** B   **71.** C

73.

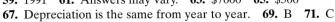
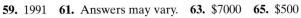
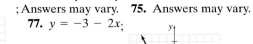

; Answers may vary.   **75.** Answers may vary.

77. $y = -3 - 2x$;

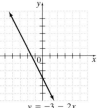

$y = -3 - 2x$

79. $y = 5 - x^2$;

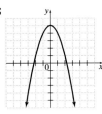

81.

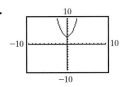

83.

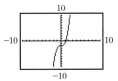

85. 0   **87.** $\dfrac{1}{4}$ **89.** $(-\infty, -6)$ **91.** $(-\infty, -4]$

Graphing Calculator Explorations   **1.**

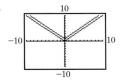

3.

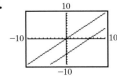

5.

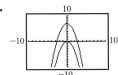

Exercise Set 3.2   1. domain: $\{-1, 0, -2, 5\}$; range: $\{7, 6, 2\}$; function   **3.** domain: $\{-2, 6, -7\}$; range: $\{4, -3, -8\}$; not a function   **5.** domain: $\{1\}$; range: $\{1, 2, 3, 4\}$; not a function   **7.** domain: $\left\{\dfrac{3}{2}, 0\right\}$; range: $\left\{\dfrac{1}{2}, -7, \dfrac{4}{5}\right\}$; not a function

9. domain: $\{-3, 0, 3\}$; range: $\{-3, 0, 3\}$; function   **11.** domain: $\{-1, 1, 2, 3\}$; range: $\{2, 1\}$; function
13. domain: $\{$Colorado, Alaska, Delaware, Illinois, Connecticut, Texas$\}$; range: $\{6, 1, 20, 30\}$; function
15. domain: $\{32°, 104°, 212°, 50°\}$; range: $\{0°, 40°, 10°, 100°\}$; function   **17.** domain: $\{2, -1, 5, 100\}$; range: $\{0\}$; function
19. function   **21.** Answers may vary.   **23.** function   **25.** not a function   **27.** function
29. domain: $[0, \infty)$; range: $(-\infty, \infty)$; not a function   **31.** domain: $[-1, 1]$; range: $(-\infty, \infty)$; not a function
33. domain: $(-\infty, \infty)$; range: $(-\infty, -3] \cup [3, \infty)$; not a function   **35.** domain: $[2, 7]$; range $[1, 6]$; not a function
37. domain: $\{-2\}$; range: $(-\infty, \infty)$; not a function   **39.** domain: $(-\infty, \infty)$; range: $(-\infty, 3]$; function
41. Answers may vary.   **43.** yes   **45.** no   **47.** yes   **49.** yes   **51.** yes   **53.** no   **55.** 15   **57.** 38   **59.** 7   **61.** 3

63. a. 0   **b.** 1   **c.** -1 **65. a.** 246   **b.** 6   **c.** $\dfrac{9}{2}$ **67. a.** -5 **b.** -5 **c.** -5 **69. a.** 5.1   **b.** 15.5   **c.** 9.533   **71.** $(1, -10)$

73. $f(-1) = -2$ **75.** $-4, 0$ **77.** infinite number   **79. a.** \$13.4 billion   **b.** \$13.672 billion   **81.** \$34.374 billion
83. $f(x) = x + 7$ **85.** 25π sq. cm   **87.** 2744 cu. in.   **89.** 166.38 cm   **91.** 163.2 mg
93. a. 91.4; The per capita consumption of poultry was 91.4 pounds in 1997.   **b.** 106.7 lb

95. $5, -5, 6$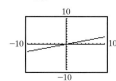
97. $2, \dfrac{8}{7}, \dfrac{12}{7}$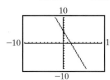
99. $0, 0, -6$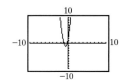
101. yes; 170 m

103. a. $-3s + 12$
b. $-3r + 12$
105. a. 132   **b.** $a^2 - 12$

Graphing Calculator Explorations

1. $y = \dfrac{x}{3.5}$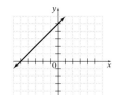
3. $y = -\dfrac{5.78}{2.31}x + \dfrac{10.98}{2.31}$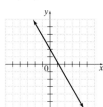
5. $y = |x| + 3.78$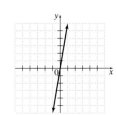
7. $y = 5.6x^2 + 7.7x + 1.5$

Exercise Set 3.3   1. $y = -2x$ 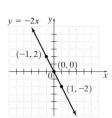   **3.** $y = -2x + 3$ 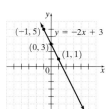   **5.** $y = \dfrac{1}{2}x$ 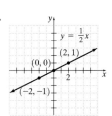   **7.** $y = \dfrac{1}{2}x - 4$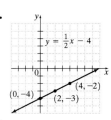

9. C   **11.** D   **13.** 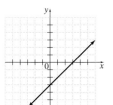   **15.** 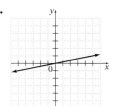   **17.** 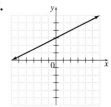   **19.**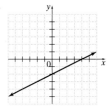

21. Answers may vary.   **23.** 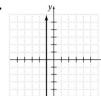   **25.** 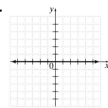   **27.**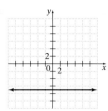

29. C   **31.** A   **33.** The vertical line $x = 0$ has y-intercepts.

35. 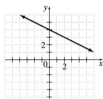   **37.** 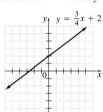   **39.** 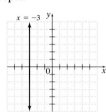   **41.**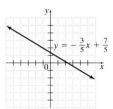

43. 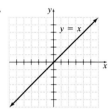   **45.** 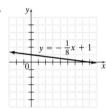   **47.** 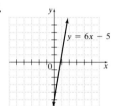   **49.**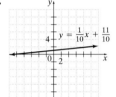

51. 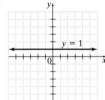   **53.** 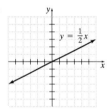   **55.** 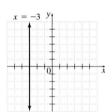   **57.**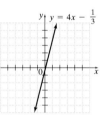

59.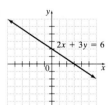

61. a. $(0, 500)$; if no tables are produced, 500 chairs can be produced
b. $(750, 0)$; if no chairs are produced, 750 tables can be produced
c. 466 chairs

63. a. \$64
b.

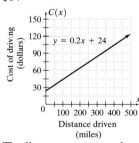

c. The line moves upward from left to right.

65. a. \$2243.20
b. 2007
c. Answers may vary.

67. 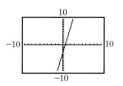   **69.**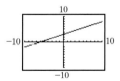

71. $9, -3$ **73.** $(-\infty, -4) \cup (-1, \infty)$
75. $\left[\dfrac{2}{3}, 2\right]$ **77.** $\dfrac{3}{2}$ **79.** 6   **81.** $-\dfrac{6}{5}$

Graphing Calculator Explorations   **1.** 18.4   **3.** −1.5   **5.** 14.0; 4.2, −9.4

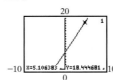 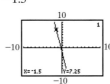 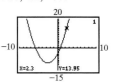

Mental Math   **1.** upward   **3.** horizontally

Exercise Set 3.4   **1.** $\dfrac{9}{5}$ **3.** $-\dfrac{7}{2}$ **5.** $-\dfrac{5}{6}$ **7.** $\dfrac{1}{3}$ **9.** $-\dfrac{4}{3}$ **11.** 0   **13.** undefined   **15.** 2   **17.** −1   **19.** l_2 **21.** l_2 **23.** l_2

25. a. l_1: −2, l_2: −1, l_3: $-\dfrac{2}{3}$ **b.** lesser   **27.** $m = -2, b = 6$ **29.** $m = 5, b = 10$ **31.** $m = -\dfrac{3}{4}, b = -\dfrac{3}{2}$

33. $m = -\dfrac{1}{4}, b = 0$ **35.** D   **37.** C   **39.** 0   **41.** undefined   **43.** 0   **45.** Answers may vary.   **47.** $m = 1, b = 2$

49. $m = \dfrac{4}{7}, b = -4$ **51.** $m = \dfrac{1}{2}, b = \dfrac{7}{2}$ **53.** slope is undefined, no *y*-intercept   **55.** $m = \dfrac{1}{7}, b = 0$

57. slope is undefined, no *y*-intercept   **59.** $m = 0, b = -\dfrac{11}{2}$ **61.** parallel   **63.** perpendicular   **65.** neither

67. Answers may vary.   **69.** −3   **71.** 1   **73.** $\dfrac{3}{25}$ **75.** $\dfrac{3}{20}$

77. a. $28,559.40   **b.** $m = 1054.7$; The annual average income increases $1054.70 every year   **c.** $b = 23,285.9$; At year $x = 0$ or 1991, the annual average income was $23,285.90.   **79. a.** $m = 7.6, b = 113$ **b.** The number of people employed as paralegals increases 7.6 thousand for every 1 year.   **c.** There were 113 thousand paralegals employed in 1996.
81. a. The yearly cost of tuition increases $72.90 every 1 year.   **b.** The yearly cost of tuition in 1990 was $785.20.   **83.** 1
85. −1   **87.** $\dfrac{3}{4}$ **89. a.** $(6, 20)$ **b.** $(10, 13)$ **c.** $-\dfrac{7}{4}$ or −1.75 yd per sec   **d.** $\dfrac{3}{2}$ or 1.5 yd per sec

91. 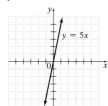   **93. a.** 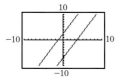   **b.** 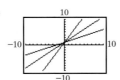   **c.** true   **95.** $\dfrac{2}{11}$ **97.** $\dfrac{3}{11}$

99. $\dfrac{4}{11}$
101. $y = -3x - 30$
103. $y = -8x - 23$

Mental Math   **1.** $m = -4, b = 12$ **3.** $m = 5, b = 0$ **5.** $m = \dfrac{1}{2}, b = 6$ **7.** parallel   **9.** neither

Exercise Set 3.5   **1.** $y = -x + 1$ **3.** $y = 2x + \dfrac{3}{4}$ **5.** $y = \dfrac{2}{7}x$

7. $y = 5x$ **9.** $x + y = 7$ **11.** $-3x + 2y = 3$ **13.** $y = 3x - 1$ **15.** $y = -2x - 1$

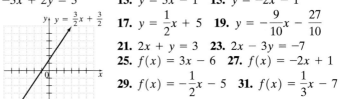

17. $y = \dfrac{1}{2}x + 5$ **19.** $y = -\dfrac{9}{10}x - \dfrac{27}{10}$

21. $2x + y = 3$ **23.** $2x - 3y = -7$
25. $f(x) = 3x - 6$ **27.** $f(x) = -2x + 1$
29. $f(x) = -\dfrac{1}{2}x - 5$ **31.** $f(x) = \dfrac{1}{3}x - 7$
33. Answers may vary.   **35.** −2   **37.** 2

39. −2   **41.** $y = -4$ **43.** $x = 4$ **45.** $y = 5$ **47.** $f(x) = 4x - 4$ **49.** $f(x) = -3x + 1$ **51.** $f(x) = -\dfrac{3}{2}x - 6$
53. $2x - y = -7$ **55.** $f(x) = -x + 7$ **57.** $x + 2y = 22$ **59.** $2x + 7y = -42$ **61.** $4x + 3y = -20$ **63.** $x = -2$

65. $x + 2y = 2$ **67.** $y = 12$ **69.** $8x - y = 47$ **71.** $x = 5$ **73.** $f(x) = -\dfrac{3}{8}x - \dfrac{29}{4}$

75. a. $P(x) = 12{,}000x + 18{,}000$ **b.** \$102,000 **c.** end of the ninth yr **77. a.** $y = -1000x + 13{,}000$
b. 9500 Fun Noodles **79. a.** $4625x + 109{,}900$ **b.** \$174,650.67 **81. a.** $y = 16.6x + 225$ **b.** 357.8 thousand people

83. 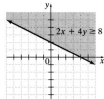 **85.** 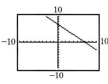 **87.** 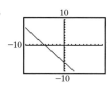, $(-\infty, 14]$ **89.** , $\left[\dfrac{7}{2}, \infty\right)$

91. 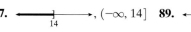, $\left(-\infty, -\dfrac{1}{4}\right)$ **93.** $-4x + y = 4$

95. $2x + y = -23$ **97.** $3x - 2y = -13$

Exercise Set 3.6 **1.** 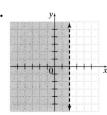 **3.** 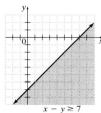 **5.** 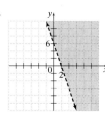 **7.**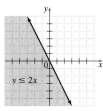

9. 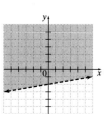 **11.** 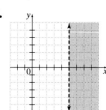 **13.** Answers may vary. **15.**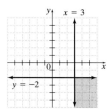

17. 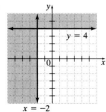 **19.** 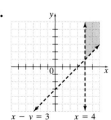 **21.** 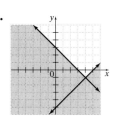 **23.**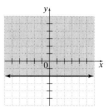

25. 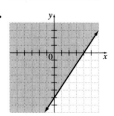 **27.** 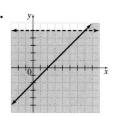 **29.** 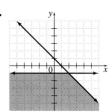 **31.**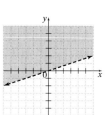

33. 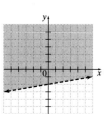 **35.** 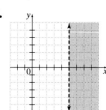 **37.** 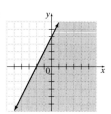 **39.**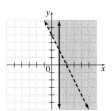

41. 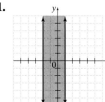   **43.** 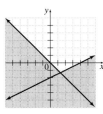   **45.** 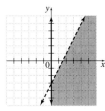   **47.** D   **49.** A
51. $x \geq 2$ **53.** $y \leq -3$
55. $y > 4$ **57.** $x < 1$

59. $x \leq 20$ and $y \geq 10$.   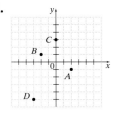   **61.** 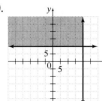   **63.** 9   **65.** 25   **67.** -16 **69.** $\dfrac{4}{49}$

71. domain: $(-\infty, -2] \cup [2, \infty)$;
range: $(-\infty, \infty)$; no

Chapter 3 Review   **1.** 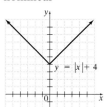   **3.** no, yes   **5.** yes, yes   **7.** linear   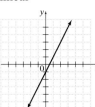   **9.** linear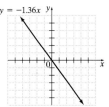

11. nonlinear   **13.** linear   **15.** linear   **17.** linear
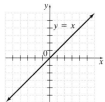   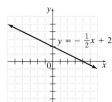   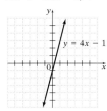   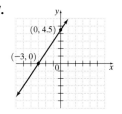

19. domain: $\left\{-\dfrac{1}{2}, 6, 0, 25\right\}$; range: $\left\{\dfrac{3}{4} \text{ or } 0.75, -12, 25\right\}$; function   **21.** domain: $\{2, 4, 6, 8\}$; range: $\{2, 4, 5, 6\}$; not a function
23. domain: $(-\infty, \infty)$; range: $(-\infty, -1] \cup [1, \infty)$; not a function   **25.** domain: $(-\infty, \infty)$; range: $\{4\}$; function   **27.** -3
29. 18   **31.** -3 **33.** 381 lb   **35.** 0   **37.** $-2, 4$
39. 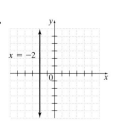   **41.** 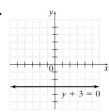   **43.** A   **45.** D   **47.** 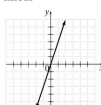   **49.**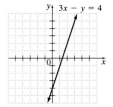

51.   **53.**   **55.** -3 **57.** $\dfrac{5}{2}$ **59.** $m = \dfrac{2}{5}, b = -\dfrac{4}{3}$
61. 0   **63.** l_2 **65.** l_2

67. a. $m = 0.3$; The cost increases by \$0.30 for each additional mile driven.   **b.** $b = 42$; The cost for 0 miles driven is \$42.
69. parallel   **71.** 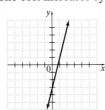   **73.** 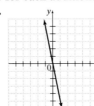   **75.** $x = -2$ **77.** $y = 5$ **79.** $2x - y = 12$
81. $11x + y = -52$ **83.** $y = -5$ **85.** $f(x) = -x - 2$
87. $f(x) = -\dfrac{3}{2}x - 8$ **89.** $f(x) = -\dfrac{3}{2}x - 1$
91. a. $y = \dfrac{17}{22}x + 43$ **b.** 52 million

93. 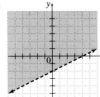   **95.** 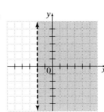   **97.** 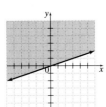   **99.**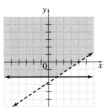

Chapter 3 Test   **1.** 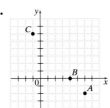   **2.** $(-6, -3)$ **3.** 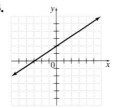   **4.**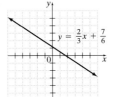

5. 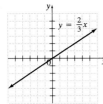   **6.** 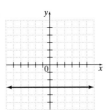   **7.** $-\dfrac{3}{2}$ **8.** $m = -\dfrac{1}{4}, b = \dfrac{2}{3}$ **9.**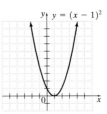

10. 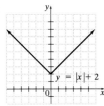   **11.** $y = -8$ **12.** $x = -4$ **13.** $y = -2$ **14.** $3x + y = 11$ **15.** $5x - y = 2$
16. $f(x) = -\dfrac{1}{2}x$ **17.** $f(x) = -\dfrac{1}{3}x + \dfrac{5}{3}$ **18.** $f(x) = -\dfrac{1}{2}x - \dfrac{1}{2}$ **19.** neither
20. 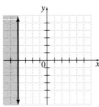   **21.** 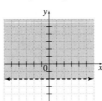   **22.** 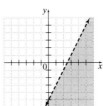   **23.**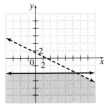

24. domain: $(-\infty, \infty)$; range: $\{5\}$; function   **25.** domain: $\{-2\}$; range: $(-\infty, \infty)$; not a function
26. domain: $(-\infty, \infty)$; range: $[0, \infty)$; function   **27.** domain: $(-\infty, \infty)$; range: $(-\infty, \infty)$; function
28. a. \$22,892   **b.** \$28,016   **c.** 2008   **d.** The average yearly earnings for high school graduates increases \$732 per year.
e. The average yearly earnings for a high school graduate in 1996 was \$21,428.

Chapter 3 Cumulative Review   **1.** 41; Sec. 1.2, Ex. 2   **2. a.** true   **b.** false   **c.** false   **d.** false; Sec. 1.2, Ex. 5
3. a. -6 **b.** -7 **c.** -16 **d.** 20.5   **e.** $\dfrac{1}{6}$ **f.** 0.94   **g.** -3; Sec. 1.3, Ex. 2   **4. a.** 9   **b.** $\dfrac{1}{16}$ **c.** -25 **d.** 25   **e.** -125
f. -125; Sec. 1.3, Ex. 6   **5. a.** $>$ **b.** $=$ **c.** $<$ **d.** $<$; Sec. 1.4, Ex. 2   **6. a.** $\dfrac{1}{11}$ **b.** $-\dfrac{1}{9}$ **c.** $\dfrac{4}{7}$; Sec. 1.4, Ex. 5

7. 0.4; Sec. 2.1, Ex. 2   **8.** { } or $\varnothing$; Sec. 2.1, Ex. 8   **9.** 4; Sec. 2.2, Ex. 4   **10.** 86 and 88; Sec. 2.2, Ex. 7

11. $\dfrac{V}{lw} = h$; Sec. 2.3, Ex. 1   **12.** $\{x \mid x < 7\}$; ; Sec. 2.4, Ex. 2   **13.** $\left(-\infty, -\dfrac{7}{3}\right]$; Sec. 2.4, Ex. 6

14. $\varnothing$; Sec. 2.5, Ex. 3   **15.** $\left(-\infty, \dfrac{13}{5}\right] \cup [4, \infty)$; Sec. 2.5, Ex. 7   **16.** $-2, \dfrac{4}{5}$; Sec. 2.6, Ex. 2   **17.** $\dfrac{3}{4}, 5$; Sec. 2.6, Ex. 8

18. $\left[-2, \dfrac{8}{5}\right]$; Sec. 2.7, Ex. 3   **19.** $(-\infty, -4) \cup (10, \infty)$; Sec. 2.7, Ex. 5   **20.** solutions: $(2, -6), (0, -12)$; not a solution $(1, 9)$;

Sec. 3.1, Ex. 2   **21.** yes; Sec. 3.2, Ex. 3   **22. a.** $\left(0, \dfrac{3}{7}\right)$ **b.** $(0, -3.2)$; Sec. 3.3, Ex. 3   **23.** $\dfrac{2}{3}$; Sec. 3.4, Ex.3

24. $y = \dfrac{1}{4}x - 3$; Sec. 3.5 Ex. 1   **25.**

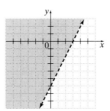

■ CHAPTER 4   SYSTEMS OF EQUATIONS

Graphing Calculator Explorations   **1.** $(2.11, 0.17)$ **3.** $(0.57, -1.97)$

Mental Math   **1.** B   **3.** A

Exercise Set 4.1   **1.** yes   **3.** no   **5.** yes
7. $(2, -1)$ **9.** $(1, 2)$ **11.** $\varnothing$ **13.** No   **15.** $(2, 8)$ **17.** $(0, -9)$

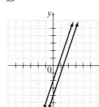

19. $(1, -1)$ **21.** $(-5, 3)$

23. $\left(\dfrac{5}{2}, \dfrac{5}{4}\right)$ **25.** $(1, -2)$ **27.** $(9, 9)$

29. $(7, 2)$ **31.** $\varnothing$

33. $\{(x, y) \mid 3x + y = 1\}$

35. Answers may vary; One possibility: $\begin{cases} -2x + y = 1 \\ x - 2y = -8 \end{cases}$ **37.** $\left(\dfrac{3}{2}, 1\right)$ **39.** $(2, -1)$ **41.** $(-5, 3)$

43. $\{(x, y) \mid 3x + 9y = 12\}$ **45.** $\varnothing$ **47.** $\left(\dfrac{1}{2}, \dfrac{1}{5}\right)$ **49.** $(8, 2)$ **51.** $\{(x, y) \mid x = 3y + 2\}$ **53.** $\left(-\dfrac{1}{4}, \dfrac{1}{2}\right)$ **55.** $(3, 2)$

57. $(7, -3)$ **59.** $\varnothing$ **61.** $(3, 4)$ **63.** $(-2, 1)$ **65.** $(1.2, -3.6)$ **67.** 5000 ties; $21   **69.** Supply is greater than demand.
71. $(1875; 4687.5)$ **73.** makes money   **75.** for x-values greater than 1875
77. a. Consumption of red meat is decreasing while consumption of poultry is increasing.   **b.** $(14, 113)$
c. In the year 2009, red meat and poultry consumption will each be about 113 pounds per person.   **79.** 1993   **81.** false
83. true   **85.** $3x - 7z = 3$ **87.** $-4y - 2z = 43$ **89.** $\left(-3, \dfrac{1}{5}\right)$ **91.** $(1, 1)$ **93.** $\left(-\dfrac{1}{4}, \dfrac{1}{3}\right)$ **95.** $\varnothing$

Exercise Set 4.2   **1.** $(-2, 5, 1)$ **3.** $(-2, 3, -1)$ **5.** $\{(x, y, z) \mid x - 2y + z = -5\}$ **7.** $\varnothing$

9. Answers may vary; One possibility is: $\begin{cases} 3x = -3 \\ 2x + 4y = 6 \\ x - 3y + z = -11 \end{cases}$ **11.** $(0, 0, 0)$ **13.** $(-3, -35, -7)$ **15.** $(6, 22, -20)$

17. $\varnothing$ **19.** $(3, 2, 2)$ **21.** $\{(x, y, z) \mid x + 2y - 3z = 4\}$ **23.** $(-3, -4, -5)$ **25.** $(12, 6, 4)$ **27.** $(1, 1, -1)$
29. 15 and 30   **31.** 5   **33.** $-\dfrac{5}{3}$ **35.** $(1, 1, 0, 2)$ **37.** $(1, -1, 2, 3)$

Exercise Set 4.3 **1.** 10 and 8 **3.** plane, 520 mph; wind, 40 mph **5.** 20 quarts of 4%; 40 quarts of 1%
7. 9 large frames; 13 small frames **9.** −10 and −8 **11.** tablets, $0.80; pens, $0.20 **13.** plane, 630 mph; wind, 90 mph
15. 5 in., 7 in., 7 in., and 10 in. **17.** 18, 13, and 9 **19.** $2000 in sales **21.** $1.90 for a template; $0.75 for a pencil;
$2.25 for a pad of paper **23.** 750 units **25.** 750 units **27.** 500 units **29. a.** $R(x) = 31x$ **b.** $C(x) = 15x + 500$
c. 31.25, or 32 baskets **31.** $x = 40; y = 70$ **33.** 40 oz of the 20% solution and 20 oz of the 50% solution
35. 120 liters of 25%, 60 liters of 40%, 20 liters of 50% **37.** 4 free throws; 8 two-point field goals; 2 three-point field goals
39. Answers may vary. **41.** $a = 1, b = -2, c = 3$ **43.** $x = 95; y = 123; z = 70$ **45.** $a = 0.28, b = -3.71, c = 12.83$;
2.12 inches in September **47.** $3y + 8z = 18$ **49.** $-5x - 5z = -16$ **51.** $\dfrac{3}{8}$ **53.** $\dfrac{5}{8}$

Exercise Set 4.4 **1.** $(2, -1)$ **3.** $(-4, 2)$ **5.** ∅ **7.** $\{(x, y)|x - y = 3\}$ **9.** $(-2, 5, -2)$ **11.** $(1, -2, 3)$ **13.** $(4, -3)$
15. $(2, 1, -1)$ **17.** $(9, 9)$ **19.** ∅ **21.** ∅ **23.** $(1, -4, 3)$ **25.** Answers may vary. **27.** function **29.** not a function
31. −13 **33.** −36 **35.** 0

Exercise Set 4.5 **1.** 26 **3.** −19 **5.** 0 **7.** $(1, 2)$ **9.** $\{(x, y)|3x + y = 1\}$ **11.** $(9, 9)$ **13.** 8 **15.** 0 **17.** 54
19. $(-2, 0, 5)$ **21.** $(6, -2, 4)$ **23.** 16 **25.** 15 **27.** $\dfrac{13}{6}$ **29.** 0 **31.** 56 **33.** 0 **35.** 5 **37.** $(-3, -2)$ **39.** ∅
41. $(-2, 3, -1)$ **43.** $(3, 4)$ **45.** $(-2, 1)$ **47.** $\{(x, y, z)|x - 2y + z = -3\}$ **49.** $(0, 2, -1)$
51.
```
 + − + −
 − + − +
 + − + −
 − + − +
```
53. $6x - 18$ **55.** $9x - 15$ **57.** 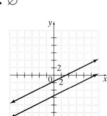 **59.**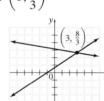

61. −125 **63.** 24

Chapter 4 Review **1.** $(-3, 1)$ 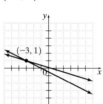 **3.** ∅ 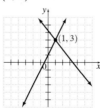 **5.** $\left(3, \dfrac{8}{3}\right)$ 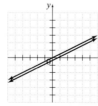 **7.** $(2, 0, 2)$

9. $\left(-\dfrac{1}{2}, \dfrac{3}{4}, 1\right)$

11. ∅

13. $(1, 1, -2)$

15. 10, 40, and 48

17. 58 mph, 65 mph

19. 20 liters of 10% solution, 30 liters of 60% solution **21.** 17 pennies, 20 nickels, and 16 dimes **23.** Two sides are 22 cm
each; third side is 29 cm. **25.** $(-3, 1)$ **27.** $\left(-\dfrac{2}{3}, 3\right)$ **29.** $\left(\dfrac{5}{4}, \dfrac{5}{8}\right)$ **31.** $(1, 3)$ **33.** $(1, 2, 3)$ **35.** $(3, -2, 5)$
37. $(1, 1, -2)$ **39.** −17 **41.** 34 **43.** $\left(-\dfrac{2}{3}, 3\right)$ **45.** $(-3, 1)$ **47.** ∅ **49.** $(1, 2, 3)$ **51.** $(2, 1, 0)$ **53.** ∅

Chapter 4 Test **1.** 34 **2.** −6 **3.** $(1, 3)$ **4.** ∅ **5.** $(2, -3)$ **6.** $\{(x, y)|10x + 4y = 10\}$
7. $(1, 2, 4)$ **8.** ∅
9. $\left(\dfrac{7}{2}, -10\right)$ **10.** $(2, -1)$ **11.** $(3, 6)$
12. $(3, -1, 2)$ **13.** $(5, 0, -4)$
14. $\{(x, y)|x - y = -2\}$
15. $(5, -3)$ **16.** $(-1, -1, 0)$
17. ∅ **18.** 275 frames

19. 53 double rooms and 27 single rooms **20.** 5 gal of 10%, 15 gal of 20% **21.** 800 packages

Chapter 4 Cumulative Review   **1. a.** true   **b.** true; Sec. 1.2, Ex. 4   **2. a.** 6   **b.** -7; Sec. 1.3, Ex. 3

3. a. -8 **b.** $-\dfrac{1}{5}$ **c.** 9.6; Sec. 1.4, Ex. 4   **4. a.** $6x + 3y$ **b.** $-3x + 1$; Sec. 1.4, Ex. 8   **5. a.** $-2x + 4$ **b.** $8yz$

c. $4z + 6.1$; Sec. 1.4, Ex. 11   **6.** -4; Sec. 2.1, Ex. 3   **7.** -4; Sec. 2.1, Ex. 7   **8.** 25 cm, 62 cm, 62 cm; Sec. 2.2, Ex. 6

9. $\{x \mid x \geq -10\}$

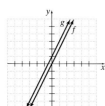

; Sec. 2.4, Ex. 3

10. $(-3, 2)$; Sec 2.5, Ex. 4
11. $1, -1$; Sec. 2.6, Ex. 4
12. $(4, 8)$; Sec. 2.7, Ex. 2

13. a. IV   **b.** y-axis   **c.** II   **d.** x-axis   **e.** III   **f.** I;   ; Sec. 3.1, Ex. 1

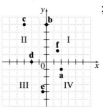

14. a. $1580   **b.** greater than $1000; Sec. 3.1, Ex. 3   **15. a.** 5   **b.** 1   **c.** 35   **d.** -2; Sec 3.2, Ex. 7

16.

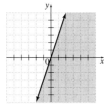

; Sec. 3.3, Ex. 1
17. slope: $\dfrac{3}{4}$; y-intercept: $(0, -1)$; Sec 3.4, Ex. 4

18. a. parallel   **b.** neither; Sec. 3.4, Ex. 8

19. $f(x) = \dfrac{5}{8}x - \dfrac{5}{2}$; Sec. 3.5, Ex. 5

20.

; Sec. 3.6, Ex. 2   **21. a.** yes   **b.** no; Sec 4.1, Ex. 1   **22.** $(-4, 2, 1)$; Sec. 4.2, Ex. 1

23. $(-1, 2)$; Sec. 4.4, Ex. 1   **24. a.** -2 **b.** -10; Sec. 4.5, Ex. 1

■ CHAPTER 5   EXPONENTS, POLYNOMIALS, AND POLYNOMIAL FUNCTIONS

Graphing Calculator Explorations   **1.** 6×10^{43} **3.** 3.796×10^{28}

Mental Math   **1.** $\dfrac{5}{xy^2}$ **3.** $\dfrac{a^2}{bc^5}$ **5.** $\dfrac{x^4}{y^2}$

Exercise Set 5.1   **1.** 4^5 **3.** x^8 **5.** $-140x^{12}$ **7.** $-20x^2y$ **9.** $-16x^6y^3p^2$ **11.** -1 **13.** 1   **15.** 6   **17.** Answers may vary.

19. a^3 **21.** x **23.** $-13z^4$ **25.** $-6a^4b^4c^6$ **27.** $\dfrac{1}{16}$ **29.** $\dfrac{1}{x^8}$ **31.** $\dfrac{5}{a^4}$ **33.** $\dfrac{1}{x^7}$ **35.** $4r^8$ **37.** 1   **39.** $\dfrac{13}{36}$ **41.** 9   **43.** x^{15}

45. $10x^{10}$ **47.** $\dfrac{1}{z^3}$ **49.** y^4 **51.** $\dfrac{3}{x}$ **53.** -2 **55.** r^8 **57.** $\dfrac{1}{x^9y^4}$ **59.** $\dfrac{b^7}{9a^7}$ **61.** $\dfrac{6x^{16}}{5}$ **63.** 3.125×10^7 **65.** 1.6×10^{-2}

67. 6.7413×10^4 **69.** 1.25×10^{-2} **71.** 5.3×10^{-5} **73.** 0.0000000036   **75.** 93,000,000   **77.** 1,278,000

79. 7,350,000,000,000   **81.** 0.000000403   **83.** Answers may vary.   **85. a, c, d**   **87.** 7.783×10^8 **89.** 4.3141×10^7

91. 1.13×10^9 **93.** 1.0×10^{-3} **95.** x^{7a+5} **97.** x^{2t-1} **99.** x^{4a+7} **101.** z^{6x-7} **103.** x^{6t-1} **105.** x^{3a+9} **107.** 7^{13}

109. 7^{-11} **111.** 100   **113.** $\dfrac{27}{64}$ **115.** 64   **117.** $\dfrac{1}{16}$

Mental Math   **1.** x^{20} **3.** x^9 **5.** y^{42} **7.** z^{20} **9.** z^{18}

Exercise Set 5.2   **1.** $\dfrac{1}{9}$ **3.** $\dfrac{1}{x^{36}}$ **5.** $\dfrac{1}{y^5}$ **7.** $9x^4y^6$ **9.** $16x^{20}y^{12}$ **11.** $\dfrac{c^{18}}{a^{12}b^6}$ **13.** $\dfrac{y^{15}}{x^{35}z^{20}}$ **15.** $\dfrac{1}{a^2}$ **17.** $4a^8b^4$ **19.** $\dfrac{x^4}{4z^2}$

21. yes; $a = \pm 1$ **23.** $\dfrac{1}{125}$ **25.** $\dfrac{1}{x^{63}}$ **27.** $\dfrac{343}{512}$ **29.** $16x^4$ **31.** $-\dfrac{y^3}{64}$ **33.** $4^8x^2y^6$ **35.** $\dfrac{36}{p^{12}}$ **37.** $-\dfrac{a^6}{512x^3y^9}$ **39.** $\dfrac{x^{14}y^{14}}{a^{21}}$

41. $\dfrac{x^4}{16}$ **43.** 64 **45.** $\dfrac{1}{y^{15}}$ **47.** $\dfrac{2}{p^2}$ **49.** $\dfrac{3}{8x^8y^7}$ **51.** $\dfrac{1}{x^{30}b^6c^6}$ **53.** $\dfrac{25}{8x^5y^4}$ **55.** $\dfrac{2}{x^4y^{10}}$ **57.** 1.45×10^9 **59.** 8×10^{15}
61. 4×10^{-7} **63.** 3×10^{-1} **65.** 2×10^1 **67.** 1×10^1 **69.** 8×10^{-5} **71.** 1.1×10^7 **73.** 1.5×10^{22}
75. $0.002 = 2 \times 10^{-3}$ sec   **77.** 1.331928×10^{13} tons   **79.** $\dfrac{8}{x^6y^3}$ cu. m   **81.** 2.5808×10^{-5} sq. m   **83.** Answers may vary.
85. 7 times   **87.** x^{4b+14} **89.** x^{-3y+1} **91.** c^{6a+9} **93.** y^{26a+1} **95.** $9y^{12a-2}$ **97.** y^{3b-a} **99.** $x^{-3a-3b}y^{b-a}$ **101.** $-3m - 15$
103. $-3y - 5$ **105.** $-3x + 5$

Graphing Calculator Explorations   **1.** $x^3 - 4x^2 + 7x - 8$ **3.** $-2.1x^2 - 3.2x - 1.7$ **5.** $7.69x^2 - 1.26x + 5.3$

Exercise Set 5.3   **1.** 0   **3.** 2   **5.** 3   **7.** degree 1; binomial   **9.** degree 2; trinomial   **11.** degree 3; monomial
13. degree 3; none of these   **15.** Answers may vary.   **17.** 57   **19.** 499   **21.** 1   **23.** 989 ft   **25.** 477 ft   **27.** $6y$
29. $11x - 3$ **31.** $xy + 2x - 1$ **33.** $18y^2 - 17$ **35.** $3x^2 - 3xy + 6y^2$ **37.** $x^2 - 4x + 8$ **39.** $y^2 + 3$
41. $-2x^2 + 5x$ **43.** $-2x^2 - 4x + 15$ **45.** $4x - 13$ **47.** $x^2 + 2$ **49.** $12x^3 + 8x + 8$ **51.** $7x^3 + 4x^2 + 8x - 10$
53. $-18y^2 + 11yx + 14$ **55.** $-x^3 + 8a - 12$ **57.** $5x^2 - 9x - 3$ **59.** $-3x^2 + 3$ **61.** $8xy^2 + 2x^3 + 3x^2 - 3$
63. $7y^2 - 3$ **65.** $5x^2 + 22x + 16$ **67.** $-q^4 + q^2 - 3q + 5$ **69.** $15x^2 + 8x - 6$ **71.** $x^4 - 7x^2 + 5$
73. $4x^{2y} + 2x^y - 11$ **75.** 404 ft per sec   **77. a.** \$1783.05   **b.** \$3515.05   **c.** \$6274.30   **d.** No, $f(x)$ is not linear.
79. \$26,000   **81. a.** 284 ft   **b.** 536 ft   **c.** 756 ft   **d.** 944 ft   **83.** 19 sec   **85. a.** 578 HMO's   **b.** 545 HMO's
c. 1732 HMO's   **87.** $4x^2 - 3x + 6$ **89.** $-x^2 - 6x + 10$ **91.** $3x^2 - 12x + 13$ **93.** $15x^2 + 12x - 9$
95. $43x^2 - 12x - 43$ **97.** B   **99.** C   **101.** $(z^3 + 2z^2 - 2z + 3)$ units   **103.** $-14z + 42y$ **105.** $-15y^2 - 10y + 35$
107. a. $8a + 3$ **b.** $-8x + 3$ **c.** $8x + 8h + 3$ **109. a.** $-4a$ **b.** $4x$ **c.** $-4x - 4h$ **111. a.** $3a - 2$ **b.** $-3x - 2$
c. $3x + 3h - 2$

Graphing Calculator Explorations   **1.** $x^2 - 16$ **3.** $9x^2 - 42x + 49$ **5.** $5x^3 - 14x^2 - 13x - 2$

Exercise Set 5.4   **1.** $-12x^5$ **3.** $12x^2 + 21x$ **5.** $-24x^2y - 6xy^2$ **7.** $-4a^3bx - 4a^3by + 12ab$ **9.** $2x^2 - 2x - 12$
11. $2x^4 + 3x^3 - 2x^2 + x + 6$ **13.** $15x^2 - 7x - 2$ **15.** $15m^3 + 16m^2 - m - 2$ **17.** Answers may vary.
19. $x^2 + x - 12$ **21.** $10x^2 + 11xy - 8y^2$ **23.** $3x^2 + 8x - 3$ **25.** $9x^2 - \dfrac{1}{4}$ **27.** $x^2 + 8x + 16$ **29.** $36y^2 - 1$
31. $9x^2 - 6xy + y^2$ **33.** $9b^2 - 36y^2$ **35.** $16b^2 + 32b + 16$ **37.** $4s^2 - 12s + 8$ **39.** $x^2y^2 - 4xy + 4$
41. Answers may vary.   **43.** $9x^2 + 18x + 5$ **45.** $10x^5 + 8x^4 + 2x^3 + 25x^2 + 20x + 5$ **47.** $49x^2 - 9$
49. $9x^3 + 30x^2 + 12x - 24$ **51.** $16x^2 - \dfrac{2}{3}x - \dfrac{1}{6}$ **53.** $36x^2 + 12x + 1$ **55.** $x^4 - 4y^2$ **57.** $-30a^4b^4 + 36a^3b^2 + 36a^2b^3$
59. $2a^2 - 12a + 16$ **61.** $49a^2b^2 - 9c^2$ **63.** $m^2 - 8m + 16$ **65.** $9x^2 + 6x + 1$ **67.** $y^2 - 7y + 12$
69. $2x^3 + 2x^2y + x^2 + xy - x - y$ **71.** $9x^4 + 12x^3 - 2x^2 - 4x + 1$ **73.** $12x^3 - 2x^2 + 13x + 5$ **75.** $5x^2 + 25x$
77. $x^4 - 4x^2 + 4$ **79.** $x^3 + 5x^2 - 2x - 10$ **81. a.** $6x + 12$ **b.** $9x^2 + 36x + 35$ **83.** $\pi(25x^2 - 20x + 4)$sq. km
85. $a^2 - 3a$ **87.** $a^2 + 2ah + h^2 - 3a - 3h$ **89.** $b^2 - 7b + 10$ **91. a.** $a^2 + 2ah + h^2 + 3a + 3h + 2$

b. $a^2 + 3a + 2$ **c.** $2ah + h^2 + 3h$ **93.** $30x^2y^{2n+1} - 10x^2y^n$ **95.** $x^{3a} + 5x^{2a} - 3x^a - 15$ **97.** -2 **99.** $\dfrac{3}{5}$ **101.** function

Mental Math   **1.** 6   **3.** 5   **5.** x **7.** $7x$

Exercise Set 5.5   **1.** a^3 **3.** y^2z^2 **5.** $3x^2y$ **7.** $5xz^3$ **9.** $6(3x - 2)$ **11.** $4y^2(1 - 4xy)$ **13.** $2x^3(3x^2 - 4x + 1)$
15. $4ab(2a^2b^2 - ab + 1 + 4b)$ **17.** $(x + 3)(6 + 5a)$ **19.** $(z + 7)(2x + 1)$ **21.** $(x^2 + 5)(3x - 2)$
23. Answers may vary.   **25.** $(a + 2)(b + 3)$ **27.** $(a - 2)(c + 4)$ **29.** $(x - 2)(2y - 3)$ **31.** $(4x - 1)(3y - 2)$
33. $3(2x^3 + 3)$ **35.** $x^2(x + 3)$ **37.** $4a(2a^2 - 1)$ **39.** $-4xy(5x - 4y^2)$ **41.** $5ab^2(2ab + 1 - 3b)$
43. $3b(3ac^2 + 2a^2c - 2a + c)$ **45.** $(y - 2)(4x - 3)$ **47.** $(2x + 3)(3y + 5)$ **49.** $(x + 3)(y - 5)$
51. $(2a - 3)(3b - 1)$ **53.** $(6x + 1)(2y + 3)$ **55.** $(n - 8)(2m - 1)$ **57.** $3x^2y^2(5x - 6)$ **59.** $(2x + 3y)(x + 2)$
61. $(5x - 3)(x + y)$ **63.** $(x^2 + 4)(x + 3)$ **65.** $(x^2 - 2)(x - 1)$ **67.** $2\pi r(r + h)$ **69.** $A = P(1 + RT)$
71. a. $h(t) = -16t(t - 4)$ **b.** 48 ft   **c.** Answers may vary.   **73.** none   **75.** a   **77.** $-14y^4$ **79.** $16y^{12}$
81. $x^2 - 8x + 7$ **83.** $x^2 - 2x - 8$ **85.** $s^2 + 18s + 80$ **87.** $y^n(3 + 3y^n + 5y^{7n})$ **89.** $3x^{2a}(x^{3a} - 2x^a + 3)$

Mental Math   **1.** 5 and 2   **3.** 8 and 3

Exercise Set 5.6 **1.** $(x + 3)(x + 6)$ **3.** $(x - 8)(x - 4)$ **5.** $(x + 12)(x - 2)$ **7.** $(x - 6)(x + 4)$
9. $3(x - 2)(x - 4)$ **11.** $4z(x + 2)(x + 5)$ **13.** $2(x + 18)(x - 3)$ **15.** $\pm5, \pm7$ **17.** $(5x + 1)(x + 3)$
19. $(2x - 3)(x - 4)$ **21.** prime polynomial **23.** $(2x - 3)^2$ **25.** $2(3x - 5)(2x + 5)$ **27.** $y^2(3y + 5)(y - 2)$
29. $2x(3x^2 + 4x + 12)$ **31.** $(x + 7z)(x + z)$ **33.** $(2x + y)(x - 3y)$ **35.** $(x - 4)(x + 3)$ **37.** $2(7y + 2)(2y + 1)$
39. $(2x - 3)(x + 9)$ **41.** $\pm8, \pm16$ **43.** $(x^2 + 3)(x^2 - 2)$ **45.** $(5x + 8)(5x + 2)$ **47.** $(x^3 - 4)(x^3 - 3)$
49. $(a - 3)(a + 8)$ **51.** $x(3x + 4)(x - 2)$ **53.** $(x - 27)(x + 3)$ **55.** $(x - 18)(x + 3)$ **57.** $3(x - 1)^2$
59. $(3x + 1)(x - 2)$ **61.** $(4x - 3)(2x - 5)$ **63.** $3x^2(2x + 1)(3x + 2)$ **65.** $3(a + 2b)^2$ **67.** prime polynomial
69. $(2x + 13)(x + 3)$ **71.** $(3x - 2)(2x - 15)$ **73.** $(x^2 - 6)(x^2 + 1)$ **75.** $x(3x + 1)(2x - 1)$
77. $(4a - 3b)(3a - 5b)$ **79.** $(3x + 5)^2$ **81.** $y(3x - 8)(x - 1)$ **83.** $2(x + 3)(x - 2)$ **85.** $(x + 2)(x - 7)$
87. $(2x^3 - 3)(x^3 + 3)$ **89.** $2x(6y^2 - z)^2$ **91.** $x^2(x + 5)(x + 1)$ **93.** $3x(5x - 1)(2x + 1)$ **95.** $x^3 - 8$ **97.** -9
99. -8 **101.** $(x^n + 8)(x^n + 2)$ **103.** $(x^n - 6)(x^n + 3)$ **105.** $(2x^n + 1)(x^n + 5)$ **107.** $(2x^n - 3)^2$

Exercise Set 5.7 **1.** $(x + 3)^2$ **3.** $(2x - 3)^2$ **5.** $3(x - 4)^2$ **7.** $x^2(3y + 2)^2$ **9.** $(x + 5)(x - 5)$ **11.** $(3 + 2z)(3 - 2z)$
13. $(y + 9)(y - 5)$ **15.** $4(4x + 5)(4x - 5)$ **17.** $(x + 3)(x^2 - 3x + 9)$ **19.** $(z - 1)(z^2 + z + 1)$
21. $(m + n)(m^2 - mn + n^2)$ **23.** $y^2(x - 3)(x^2 + 3x + 9)$ **25.** $b(a + 2b)(a^2 - 2ab + 4b^2)$
27. $(5y - 2x)(25y^2 + 10yx + 4x^2)$ **29.** $(x + 3 + y)(x + 3 - y)$ **31.** $(x - 5 + y)(x - 5 - y)$
33. $(2x + 1 + z)(2x + 1 - z)$ **35.** $(3x + 7)(3x - 7)$ **37.** $(x - 6)^2$ **39.** $(x^2 + 9)(x + 3)(x - 3)$
41. $(x + 4 + 2y)(x + 4 - 2y)$ **43.** $(x + 2y + 3)(x + 2y - 3)$ **45.** $(x - 6)(x^2 + 6x + 36)$
47. $(x + 5)(x^2 - 5x + 25)$ **49.** prime polynomial **51.** $(2a + 3)^2$ **53.** $2y(3x + 1)(3x - 1)$
55. $(2x + y)(4x^2 - 2xy + y^2)$ **57.** $(x^2 - y)(x^4 + x^2y + y^2)$ **59.** $(x + 8 + x^2)(x + 8 - x^2)$
61. $3y^2(x^2 + 3)(x^4 - 3x^2 + 9)$ **63.** $(x + y + 5)(x^2 + 2xy + y^2 - 5x - 5y + 25)$ **65.** $(2x - 1)(4x^2 + 20x + 37)$

67. $\pi R^2 - \pi r^2 = \pi(R + r)(R - r)$ **69.** $V = \frac{4}{3}\pi R^3 - \frac{4}{3}\pi6^3 = \frac{4}{3}\pi(R - 6)(R^2 + 6R + 36)$ **71.** $(1 - y)(1 + y + y^2)$

73. $(3x + 1)^2$ **75.** $(x - 4 + y)(x - 4 - y)$ **77.** $x(x - 1)(x^2 + x + 1)$ **79.** $2xy(7x - 1)$ **81.** $4(x + 2)(x - 2)$
83. $2(4a - b)(16a^2 + 4ab + b^2)$ **85.** $(3x - 11)(x + 1)$ **87.** $4(x + 3)(x - 1)$ **89.** $(2x + 9)^2$
91. $(2x + 3y)(4x^2 - 6xy + 9y^2)$ **93.** $8x^2(2y - 1)(4y^2 + 2y + 1)$ **95.** $(x + 5 + y)(x^2 + 10x + 25 - xy - 5y + y^2)$
97. $(5a - 6)^2$ **99.** $c = 9$ **101.** $c = 49$ **103.** $c = \pm8$ **105. a.** $(x + 1)(x^2 - x + 1)(x - 1)(x^2 + x + 1)$
b. $(x + 1)(x - 1)(x^4 + x^2 + 1)$ **107.** -7 **109.** 3 **111.** 0 **113.** -4 **115.** $(x^n + 6)(x^n - 6)$
117. $(5x^n + 9)(5x^n - 9)$ **119.** $(x^{2n} + 25)(x^n + 5)(x^n - 5)$

Graphing Calculator Explorations **1.** $-3.562, 0.562$ **3.** $-0.874, 2.787$ **5.** $-0.465, 1.910$

Mental Math **1.** $3, -5$ **3.** $3, -7$ **5.** $0, 9$

Exercise Set 5.8 **1.** $-3, \frac{4}{3}$ **3.** $\frac{5}{2}, -\frac{3}{4}$ **5.** $-3, -8$ **7.** $\frac{1}{4}, -\frac{2}{3}$ **9.** $1, 9$ **11.** $\frac{3}{5}, -1$ **13.** 0 **15.** $6, -3$ **17.** $\frac{2}{5}, -\frac{1}{2}$

19. $\frac{3}{4}, -\frac{1}{2}$ **21.** $-2, 7, \frac{8}{3}$ **23.** $0, 3, -3$ **25.** $2, 1, -1$ **27.** Answers may vary. **29.** $-\frac{7}{2}, 10$ **31.** $0, 5$ **33.** $-3, 5$ **35.** $-\frac{1}{2}, \frac{1}{3}$

37. $-4, 9$ **39.** $\frac{4}{5}$ **41.** $-5, 0, 2$ **43.** $-3, 0, \frac{4}{5}$ **45.** $\varnothing$ **47.** $-7, 4$ **49.** $4, 6$ **51.** $-\frac{1}{2}$ **53.** $-4, -3, 3$ **55.** $-5, 0, 5$

57. $-6, 5$ **59.** $-\frac{1}{3}, 0, 1$ **61.** $-\frac{1}{3}, 0$ **63.** $-\frac{7}{8}$ **65.** $\frac{31}{4}$ **67.** 1 **69. a.** incorrect **b.** correct **c.** correct **d.** incorrect

71. -11 and -6 or 6 and 11 **73.** 75 ft **75.** 105 units **77.** 12 cm and 9 cm **79.** 2 in. **81.** 10 sec
83. width: 7 ft; length: 13 ft **85.** 10 in. sq. tier **87.** E **89.** F **91.** B
93. Answers may vary. Ex.: $f(x) = x^2 - 8x + 15$ **95.** Answers may vary. Ex.: $f(x) = x^2 - x - 2$
97. $(-3, 0), (0, 2)$; function **99.** $(-4, 0), (0, 2), (4, 0), (0, -2)$; not a function **101.** Answers may vary.

Mental Math **1.** upward **3.** downward

Exercise Set 5.9 **1. a.** domain: $(-\infty, \infty)$; range: $(-\infty, 5]$ **b.** x-intercepts: $(-2, 0), (6, 0)$; y-intercept: $(0, 5)$ **c.** $(0, 5)$
d. There is no such point. **e.** $-2, 6$ **f.** between $x = -2$ and $x = 6$ **g.** $-2, 6$ **3. a.** domain: $(-\infty, \infty)$; range: $[-4, \infty)$
b. x-intercepts: $(-3, 0), (1, 0)$; y-intercept: $(0, -3)$ **c.** There is no such point. **d.** $(-1, -4)$ **e.** $-3, 1$ **f.** $x < -3$ or $x > 1$
g. $-3, 1$ **5. a.** domain: $(-\infty, \infty)$; range: $(-\infty, \infty)$ **b.** x-intercepts: $(-2, 0), (0, 0), (2, 0)$; y-intercept: $(0, 0)$
c. There is no such point. **d.** There is no such point. **e.** $-2, 0, 2$ **f.** between $x = -2$ and 0; $x > 2$ **g.** $-2, 0, 2$

9. no; Sec. 3.2, Ex. 4   **10.** 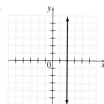 ; Sec. 3.3, Ex. 6   **11.** 0; Sec. 3.4, Ex. 7   **12.** $y = 3$; Sec. 3.5, Ex. 7

13. 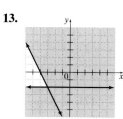 ; Sec. 3.6, Ex. 4   **14.** $\left(-4, \dfrac{1}{2}\right)$; Sec. 4.1, Ex. 3   **15.** $\left(\dfrac{1}{2}, 0, \dfrac{3}{4}\right)$; Sec. 4.2, Ex. 3

16. 7, 11; Sec. 4.3, Ex. 1   **17.** $\varnothing$; Sec. 4.4, Ex. 2   **18.** $(1, -2, -1)$; Sec. 4.5, Ex. 4

19. a. 7.3×10^5 **b.** 1.04×10^{-6}; Sec. 5.1, Ex. 8

20. a. $\dfrac{y^6}{4}$ **b.** x^9 **c.** $\dfrac{49}{4}$ **d.** $\dfrac{y^{16}}{25x^5}$; Sec. 5.2, Ex. 3   **21.** 4; Sec. 5.3, Ex. 3

22. a. $10x^9$ **b.** $-7xy^{15}z^9$; Sec. 5.4, Ex. 1   **23.** $17x^3y^2(1 - 2x)$; Sec. 5.5, Ex. 3

24. $(x + 2)(x + 8)$; Sec. 5.6, Ex. 1   **25.** $-5, \dfrac{1}{2}$; Sec. 5.8, Ex. 2

■ CHAPTER 6   RATIONAL EXPRESSIONS

Graphing Calculator Explorations   **1.** $\{x | x \text{ is a real number and } x \neq -2, x \neq 2\}$

3. $\left\{ x \,\middle|\, x \text{ is a real number and } x \neq -4, x \neq \dfrac{1}{2} \right\}$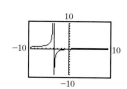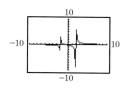

Exercise Set 6.1   **1.** $\dfrac{10}{3}, -8, -\dfrac{7}{3}$ **3.** $-\dfrac{17}{48}, \dfrac{2}{7}, -\dfrac{3}{8}$ **5.** $\{x | x \text{ is a real number}\}$ **7.** $\{t | t \text{ is a real number and } t \neq 0\}$

9. $\{x | x \text{ is a real number and } x \neq 7\}$ **11.** $\{x | x \text{ is a real number and } x \neq -2, x \neq 0, x \neq 1\}$

13. $\{x | x \text{ is a real number and } x \neq 2, x \neq -2\}$ **15.** Answers may vary.   **17.** $\dfrac{4}{3}$ **19.** -2 **21.** $\dfrac{x + 1}{x - 3}$ **23.** $\dfrac{2(x + 3)}{x - 3}$

25. $\dfrac{3}{x}$ **27.** $\dfrac{x + 1}{x^2 + 1}$ **29.** $\dfrac{1}{2(q - 1)}$ **31.** $x - 4$ **33.** $-x^2 - 5x - 25$ **35.** $\dfrac{4x^2 + 6x + 9}{2}$ **37.** $-\dfrac{2}{3x^3y^2}$ **39.** $\dfrac{4}{ab^6}$

41. $\dfrac{1}{4a(a - b)}$ **43.** $\dfrac{(x + 2)(x + 3)}{4}$ **45.** $\dfrac{3}{2(x - 1)}$ **47.** $\dfrac{4a^2}{a - b}$ **49.** $\dfrac{2(x + 3)(x - 3)}{5(x^2 - 8x - 15)}$ **51.** $\dfrac{x + 2}{x + 3}$ **53.** $\dfrac{3b}{a - b}$

55. $\dfrac{3a}{a - b}$ **57.** $\dfrac{1}{4}$ **59.** -1 **61.** $\dfrac{8}{3}$ **63.** $\dfrac{8(a - 2)}{3(a + 2)}$ **65.** $\dfrac{8}{x^2y}$ **67.** $\dfrac{(y + 5)(2x - 1)}{(y + 2)(5x + 1)}$ **69.** $\dfrac{5(3a + 2)}{a}$ **71.** $\dfrac{5x^2 - 2}{(x - 1)^2}$

73. $\dfrac{5}{x - 2}$ sq. m   **75.** Answers may vary.   **77.** $\dfrac{(x + 2)(x - 1)^2}{x^5}$ ft

79. $0, \dfrac{20}{9}, \dfrac{60}{7}, 20, \dfrac{140}{3}, 180, 380, 1980;$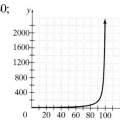

81. a. $\{x | 0 \leq x < 100\}$
b. \$42,857.14
c. \$150,000; \$400,000
d. \$900,000; \$1,900,000; \$9,900,000; Answers may vary.

83. $\dfrac{7}{5}$ **85.** $\dfrac{1}{12}$ **87.** $\dfrac{11}{16}$ **89.** $2x^2(x^n + 2)$

91. $\dfrac{1}{10y(y^n + 3)}$ **93.** $\dfrac{y^n + 1}{2(y^n - 1)}$

Exercise Set 6.2 **1.** $-\dfrac{3}{x}$ **3.** $\dfrac{x+2}{x-2}$ **5.** $x-2$ **7.** $\dfrac{1}{2-x}$ **9.** $\dfrac{4x}{x+5}$ ft; $\dfrac{x^2}{x^2+10x+25}$ sq. ft **11.** $35x$ **13.** $x(x+1)$

15. $(x+7)(x-7)$ **17.** $6(x+2)(x-2)$ **19.** $(3x-1)(x+2)$ **21.** $(a+b)(a-b)^2$ **23.** $-4x(x+3)(x-3)$

25. Answers may vary. **27.** $\dfrac{17}{6x}$ **29.** $\dfrac{35-4y}{14y^2}$ **31.** $\dfrac{-13x+4}{(x+4)(x-4)}$ **33.** $\dfrac{2x+4}{(x-5)(x+4)}$ **35.** 0 **37.** $-\dfrac{x}{x-1}$

39. $\dfrac{-x+1}{x-2}$ **41.** $\dfrac{y^2+2y+10}{(y+4)(y-4)(y-2)}$ **43.** $\dfrac{5(x^2+x-4)}{(3x+2)(x+3)(2x-5)}$ **45.** $\dfrac{x^2+5x+21}{(x-2)(x+1)(x+3)}$

47. $\dfrac{-2x+5}{2(x+1)}$ **49.** $\dfrac{2(x^2+x-21)}{(x+3)^2(x-3)}$ **51.** $\dfrac{3}{x^2y^3}$ **53.** $-\dfrac{5}{x}$ **55.** $\dfrac{25}{6(x+5)}$ **57.** $\dfrac{-2x-1}{x^2(x-3)}$ **59.** $\dfrac{2ab-b^2}{(a+b)(a-b)}$

61. $\dfrac{2x+16}{(x+2)^2(x-2)}$ **63.** $\dfrac{5a+1}{(a+1)^2(a-1)}$ **65.** Answers may vary. **67.** Answers may vary. **69.** $\dfrac{2x^2+9x-18}{6x^2}$

71. $\dfrac{4}{3}$ **73.** $\dfrac{4a^2}{9(a-1)}$ **75.** 4 **77.** $\dfrac{6x}{(x+3)(x-3)^2}$ **79.** $-\dfrac{4}{x-1}$ **81.** $-\dfrac{32}{x(x+2)(x-2)}$

83. 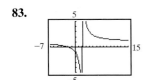 **85.** **87.** 10 **89.** $4+x^2$ **91.** 10 **93.** 2 **95.** 3 **97.** 5 m

99. $\dfrac{3}{2x}$ **101.** $\dfrac{4-3x}{x^2}$ **103.** $\dfrac{1-3x}{x^3}$

Exercise Set 6.3 **1.** $\dfrac{5}{6}$ **3.** $\dfrac{8}{5}$ **5.** 4 **7.** $\dfrac{7}{13}$ **9.** $\dfrac{4}{x}$ **11.** $\dfrac{9x-18}{9x^2-4}$ **13.** $\dfrac{1-x}{1+x}$ **15.** $\dfrac{xy^2}{x^2+y^2}$ **17.** $\dfrac{2b^2+3a}{b^2-ab}$ **19.** $\dfrac{x}{x^2-1}$

21. $\dfrac{x+1}{x+2}$ **23.** $\dfrac{10}{69}$ **25.** $\dfrac{2(x+1)}{2x-1}$ **27.** $\dfrac{x(x+1)}{6}$ **29.** $\dfrac{x}{2-3x}$ **31.** $-\dfrac{y}{x+y}$ **33.** $-\dfrac{2x^3}{y(x-y)}$ **35.** $\dfrac{2x+1}{y}$

37. $\dfrac{x-3}{9}$ **39.** $\dfrac{1}{x+2}$ **41.** $\dfrac{x}{5x-10}$ **43.** $\dfrac{x-2}{2x-1}$ **45.** $-\dfrac{x^2+4}{4x}$ **47.** $\dfrac{x-3y}{x+3y}$ **49.** $\dfrac{1+a}{1-a}$ **51.** $\dfrac{x^2+6xy}{2y}$

53. $\dfrac{5a}{2a+4}$ **55.** $5xy^2+2x^2y$ **57.** $\dfrac{xy}{2x+5y}$ **59.** $\dfrac{xy}{x+y}$ **61.** x^2+x **63.** $\dfrac{770a}{770-s}$ **65. a.** $\dfrac{1}{a+h}$ **b.** $\dfrac{1}{a}$

c. $\dfrac{\dfrac{1}{a+h}-\dfrac{1}{a}}{h}$ **d.** $\dfrac{-1}{a(a+h)}$ **67. a.** $\dfrac{3}{a+h+1}$ **b.** $\dfrac{3}{a+1}$ **c.** $\dfrac{\dfrac{3}{a+h+1}-\dfrac{3}{a+1}}{h}$ **d.** $\dfrac{-3}{(a+h+1)(a+1)}$

69. $\dfrac{x^2y^2}{4}$ **71.** $-9x^3y^4$ **73.** $-4, 14$ **75.** $(-4, 14)$ **77.** $\dfrac{x-1}{x}$ **79.** $2x$ **81.** $3a^2+4a+4$

Exercise Set 6.4 **1.** $2a+4$ **3.** $3ab+4$ **5.** $2y+\dfrac{3y}{x}-\dfrac{2y}{x^2}$ **7.** x^2+2x+1 **9.** (x^4+2x^2-6) m **11.** $x+1$

13. $2x-8$ **15.** $x-\dfrac{1}{2}$ **17.** $2x^2-\dfrac{1}{2}x+5$ **19.** $(3x-7)$ in. **21.** $\dfrac{5b^5}{2a^3}$ **23.** x^3y^3-1 **25.** $a+3$ **27.** $2x+5$

29. $4y-6y^2$ **31.** $2x+23+\dfrac{130}{x-5}$ **33.** $10x+3y-6x^2y^2$ **35.** $2x+4$ **37.** $y+5$ **39.** $2x+3$

41. $2x^2-8x+38-\dfrac{156}{x+4}$ **43.** $3x+3-\dfrac{1}{x-1}$ **45.** $-2x^3+3x^2-x+4$ **47.** $3x^3+5x+4-\dfrac{2x}{x^2-2}$

49. $x-\dfrac{5}{3x^2}$ **51.** 4 **53.** 372 **55.** Answers may vary. **57.** $3x^2+10x+8+\dfrac{4}{x-2}$ **59.** $=$ **61.** $=$ **63.** $(-9,-1)$

65. $(-\infty,-8]\cup[1,\infty)$ **67.** $x^3+\dfrac{5}{3}x^2+\dfrac{5}{3}x+\dfrac{8}{3}+\dfrac{8}{3(x-1)}$ **69.** $\dfrac{3}{2}x^3+\dfrac{1}{4}x^2+\dfrac{1}{8}x-\dfrac{7}{16}+\dfrac{1}{16(2x-1)}$

71. $x^3-\dfrac{2}{5}x$

Exercise Set 6.5   **1.** $x + 8$ **3.** $x - 1$ **5.** $x^2 - 5x - 23 - \dfrac{41}{x - 2}$ **7.** $4x + 8 + \dfrac{7}{x - 2}$ **9.** 3   **11.** 73   **13.** −8

15. $x^2 + \dfrac{2}{x - 3}$ **17.** $6x + 7 + \dfrac{1}{x + 1}$ **19.** $2x^3 - 3x^2 + x - 4$ **21.** $3x - 9 + \dfrac{12}{x + 3}$

23. $3x^2 - \dfrac{9}{2}x + \dfrac{7}{4} + \dfrac{47}{8(x - 1/2)}$ **25.** $3x^2 + 3x - 3$ **27.** $3x^2 + 4x - 8 + \dfrac{20}{x + 1}$ **29.** $x^2 + x + 1$ **31.** $x - 6$

33. 1   **35.** −133   **37.** 3   **39.** $-\dfrac{187}{81}$ **41.** $\dfrac{95}{32}$ **43.** Answers may vary.

45. $(x + 3)(x^2 + 4) = x^3 + 3x^2 + 4x + 12$ **47.** 0   **49.** $x^3 + 2x^2 + 7x + 28$ **51.** $(x - 1)$ m   **53.** $\dfrac{13}{3}$ **55.** −3, 1

57. −1   **59.** $(2y + 1)(4y^2 - 2y + 1)$ **61.** $(a - 3)(a^2 + 3a + 9)$ **63.** $(x - 1)(x + y)$ **65.** $2x(x + 4)(x - 4)$

Exercise Set 6.6   **1.** 72   **3.** 2   **5.** 6   **7.** 2   **9.** 3   **11.** ∅   **13.** 15   **15.** 4   **17.** ∅   **19.** 1   **21.** −1   **23.** −3   **25.** $\dfrac{5}{3}$

27. 10, 2   **29.** 2   **31.** 3   **33.** ∅   **35.** ∅   **37.** −1   **39.** 9   **41.** 1, 7   **43.** $\dfrac{1}{10}$ **45.** 800 pencil sharpeners   **47.** $\dfrac{1}{9}, -\dfrac{1}{4}$

49. 3, 2   **51.** 1.39   **53.** −0.08   **55.**   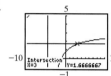   **57.**   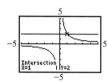   **59.** 73 and 74   **61.** $\dfrac{1}{2}$ and 2

63. 3%   **65.** 54%   **67.** −1, 0

69. −2

Supplementary Exercises on Expressions and Equations   **1.** $\dfrac{1}{2}$ **3.** $\dfrac{1 + 2x}{8}$ **5.** $\dfrac{2(x - 4)}{(x + 2)(x - 1)}$ **7.** 4   **9.** −5

11. $\dfrac{2x + 5}{x(x - 3)}$ **13.** −2   **15.** $\dfrac{(a + 3)(a + 1)}{a + 2}$ **17.** $-\dfrac{1}{5}$ **19.** $\dfrac{4a + 1}{(3a + 1)(3a - 1)}$ **21.** $-1, \dfrac{3}{2}$ **23.** $\dfrac{3}{x + 1}$ **25.** −1

Exercise Set 6.7   **1.** $C = \dfrac{5}{9}(F - 32)$ **3.** $I = A - QL$ **5.** $R = \dfrac{R_1 R_2}{R_1 + R_2}$ **7.** $n = \dfrac{2S}{a + L}$ **9.** $b = \dfrac{2A - ah}{h}$

11. $T_2 = \dfrac{P_2 V_2 T_1}{P_1 V_1}$ **13.** $f_2 = \dfrac{f_1 f}{f_1 - f}$ **15.** $L = \dfrac{n\lambda}{2}$ **17.** $c = \dfrac{2L\omega}{\theta}$ **19.** 1 and 5   **21.** 5   **23.** 6 ohms

25. $\dfrac{1}{R} = \dfrac{1}{R_1} + \dfrac{1}{R_2} + \dfrac{1}{R_3}$; $R = \dfrac{15}{13}$ ohms   **27.** 12 hr   **29.** $1\dfrac{1}{3}$ hr   **31.** 50 mph   **33.** 6 mph   **35.** 9 and 11   **37.** $3\dfrac{1}{3}$ hr

39. 13 mph   **41.** $\dfrac{6}{10}$ **43.** 10 mph; 8 mph   **45.** 3 hr   **47.** 22,500 mi   **49.** $2\dfrac{2}{9}$ hr   **51.** 2 hr   **53.** $108   **55.** $2\dfrac{2}{9}$ days

57. 1 hr   **59.** 60 in. or 5 ft   **61.** −5   **63.** 2

Exercise Set 6.8   **1.** $k = \dfrac{1}{5}$; $y = \dfrac{1}{5}x$ **3.** $k = \dfrac{3}{2}$; $y = \dfrac{3}{2}x$ **5.** $k = 14$; $y = 14x$ **7.** $k = 0.25$; $y = 0.25x$ **9.** 4.05 lb

11. $P = 566,222$ tons   **13.** $k = 30$; $y = \dfrac{30}{x}$ **15.** $k = 700$; $y = \dfrac{700}{x}$ **17.** $k = 2$; $y = \dfrac{2}{x}$ **19.** $k = 0.14$; $y = \dfrac{0.14}{x}$

21. 54 mph   **23.** 72 amps   **25.** divided by 4   **27.** $x = kyz$ **29.** $r = kst^3$ **31.** 22.5 tons   **33.** 15π cu. in.

35. 90 hp   **37.** 800 millibars   **39.** multiplied by 2   **41.** multiplied by 4

43.   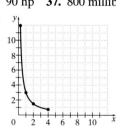   **45.**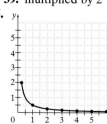

47. $C = 12\pi$ cm; $A = 36\pi$ sq. cm

49. $C = 14\pi$ m; $A = 49\pi$ sq. m

51. 6   **53.** 2   **55.** $\dfrac{1}{5}$ **57.** $\dfrac{5}{11}$

Chapter 6 Review   **1.** $\{x|x \text{ is a real number}\}$ **3.** $\{x|x \text{ is a real number and } x \neq 5\}$

5. $\{x|x \text{ is a real number and } x \neq 0, x \neq -8\}$ **7.** $\dfrac{x^2}{3}$ **9.** $\dfrac{9m^2p}{5}$ **11.** $\dfrac{1}{5}$ **13.** $\dfrac{1}{x-1}$ **15.** $\dfrac{2(x-3)}{x-4}$ **17. a.** \$119   **b.** \$77

c. decrease   **19.** $\dfrac{2x^3}{z^3}$ **21.** $\dfrac{2}{5}$ **23.** $\dfrac{1}{6}$ **25.** $\dfrac{3x}{16}$ **27.** $\dfrac{3c^2}{14a^2b}$ **29.** $\dfrac{(x+4)(x+5)}{3}$ **31.** $\dfrac{7(x-4)}{2(x-2)}$ **33.** $-\dfrac{1}{x}$ **35.** $\dfrac{8}{9a^2}$

37. $\dfrac{6}{a}$ **39.** $60x^2y^5$ **41.** $5x(x-5)$ **43.** $\dfrac{2}{5}$ **45.** $\dfrac{2}{x^2}$ **47.** $\dfrac{1}{x-2}$ **49.** $\dfrac{5x^2-3y^2}{15x^4y^3}$ **51.** $\dfrac{-x+5}{(x+1)(x-1)}$

53. $\dfrac{2x^2-5x-4}{x-3}$ **55.** $\dfrac{3x^2-7x-4}{(3x-4)(9x^2+12x+16)}$ **57.** $-\dfrac{12}{x(x+1)(x-3)}$ **59.** $\dfrac{14x-40}{(x+4)^2(x-4)}$ **61.** $\dfrac{2}{3}$

63. $\dfrac{2}{15-2x}$ **65.** $\dfrac{y}{2}$ **67.** $\dfrac{20x-15}{10x^2-4}$ **69.** $\dfrac{5xy+x}{3y}$ **71.** $\dfrac{1+x}{1-x}$ **73.** $\dfrac{x-1}{3x-1}$ **75.** $-\dfrac{x^2+9}{6x}$ **77. a.** $\dfrac{3}{a+h}$ **b.** $\dfrac{3}{a}$

c. $\dfrac{\dfrac{3}{a+h}-\dfrac{3}{a}}{h}$ **d.** $\dfrac{-3}{a(a+h)}$ **79.** $\dfrac{9b^2z^3}{4a}$ **81.** $\dfrac{3}{b}+4b$ **83.** $2x^3-4x^2+7x-9+\dfrac{6}{x+2}$ **85.** $2x^2-2+\dfrac{5}{x+3/2}$

87. $3x^2+6$ **89.** $3x^2-\dfrac{5}{2}x-\dfrac{1}{4}-\dfrac{5}{8\left(x+\dfrac{3}{2}\right)}$ **91.** $x^2+3x+9-\dfrac{54}{x-3}$ **93.** $3x^3-6x^2+10x-20+\dfrac{50}{x+2}$

95. -9323 **97.** $\dfrac{365}{32}$ **99.** 6   **101.** 2   **103.** $\dfrac{3}{2}$ **105.** $\dfrac{5}{3}$ **107.** $-\dfrac{1}{3}, 2$ **109.** $a=\dfrac{2A-hb}{h}$ **111.** $R=\dfrac{E-Ir}{I}$

113. $A=\dfrac{HL}{k(T_1-T_2)}$ **115.** 7   **117.** -10 and -8 **119.** 12 hr   **121.** 490 mph   **123.** 8 mph   **125.** 4 mph   **127.** 9

129. 3.125 cu. ft

Chapter 6 Test   **1.** $\{x \mid x \text{ is a real number and } x \neq 1\}$ **2.** $\{x \mid x \text{ is a real number and } x \neq -3, x \neq -1\}$ **3.** $\dfrac{5x^3}{3}$

4. $-\dfrac{7}{8}$ **5.** $\dfrac{x}{x+9}$ **6.** $\dfrac{x+2}{5}$ **7.** $\dfrac{5}{3x}$ **8.** $\dfrac{4a^3b^4}{c^6}$ **9.** $\dfrac{x+2}{2(x+3)}$ **10.** $-\dfrac{4(2x+9)}{5}$ **11.** $\dfrac{3}{x^3}$ **12.** -1

13. $\dfrac{5x-2}{(x-3)(x+2)(x-2)}$ **14.** $-\dfrac{x+30}{6(x-7)}$ **15.** $\dfrac{3}{2}$ **16.** $\dfrac{1}{5}$ **17.** $\dfrac{64}{3}$ **18.** $\dfrac{(x-3)^2}{x-2}$ **19.** $\dfrac{4xy}{3z}+\dfrac{3}{z}+\dfrac{1}{3x}$

20. $x^5+5x^4+8x^3+16x^2+33x+63+\dfrac{128}{x-2}$ **21.** $4x^3-15x^2+47x-142+\dfrac{425}{x+3}$ **22.** 91   **23.** 7

24. $2, -2$ **25.** 8   **26.** $x=\dfrac{7a^2+b^2}{4a-b}$ **27.** 5   **28.** $\dfrac{6}{7}$ hr   **29.** 16   **30.** 9   **31.** 256 ft

Chapter 6 Cumulative Review   **1. a.** $8x$ **b.** $8x+3$ **c.** $x \div -7$ or $\dfrac{x}{-7}$ **d.** $2x-1.6$; Sec. 1.2, Ex. 8   **2.** 2; Sec. 2.1, Ex. 5

3. after 2013; Sec. 2.4, Ex. 9   **4.** 0; Sec. 2.6, Ex. 7   **5.** -1; Sec. 2.7, Ex. 8

6. 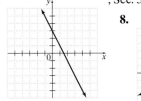 ; Sec. 3.1, Ex. 4   **7. a.** function   **b.** not a function   **c.** function; Sec. 3.2, Ex. 2

8. 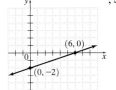 ; Sec. 3.3, Ex. 4   **9.** $y=-3x-2$; Sec. 3.5, Ex. 4

10. 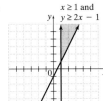 ; Sec. 3.6, Ex. 3

11. $(0, -5)$; Sec. 4.1, Ex. 6
12. $\varnothing$; Sec. 4.2, Ex. 2
13. $30°, 110°, 40°$; Sec. 4.3, Ex. 5
14. $(1, -1, 3)$; Sec. 4.4, Ex. 3

15. a. 1   **b.** -1 **c.** 1   **d.** 2; Sec. 5.1, Ex. 3   **16. a.** $4x^b$ **b.** y^{5a+6}; Sec 5.2, Ex. 5

17. a. 2   **b.** 5   **c.** 1   **d.** 6   **e.** 0; Sec. 5.3, Ex. 1   **18.** $9+12a+6b+4a^2+4ab+b^2$; Sec. 5.4, Ex. 9

19. $(b - 6)(a + 2)$; Sec 5.5, Ex. 7   **20.** prime polynomial; Sec. 5.6, Ex. 4

21. $(x + 2 + y)(x + 2 - y)$; Sec. 5.7, Ex. 5   **22.** $-2, 6$; Sec. 5.8, Ex. 1

23. 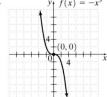 $f(x) = -x^3$; Sec. 5.9, Ex. 6   **24.** $\dfrac{5k^2 - 7k + 4}{(k + 2)(k - 2)(k - 1)}$; Sec. 6.2, Ex. 4   **25.** -2; Sec. 6.6, Ex. 2

■ CHAPTER 7   RATIONAL EXPONENTS, RADICALS, AND COMPLEX NUMBERS

Exercise Set 7.1   **1.** 10   **3.** $\dfrac{1}{2}$ **5.** 0.01   **7.** -6 **9.** x^5 **11.** $4y^3$ **13.** 2.646   **15.** 6.164   **17.** 14.142   **19.** 4   **21.** $\dfrac{1}{2}$

23. -1 **25.** x^4 **27.** $-3x^3$ **29.** -2 **31.** not a real number   **33.** -2 **35.** x^4 **37.** $2x^2$ **39.** $9x^2$ **41.** $4x^2$ **43.** 8

45. -8 **47.** $2|x|$ **49.** x **51.** $|x - 5|$ **53.** $|x + 2|$ **55.** -11 **57.** $2x$ **59.** y^6 **61.** $5ab^{10}$ **63.** $-3x^4y^3$ **65.** a^4b

67. $-2x^2y$ **69.** $\dfrac{5}{7}$ **71.** $\dfrac{x}{2y}$ **73.** $-\dfrac{z^7}{3x}$ **75.** $\dfrac{x}{2}$ **77.** $\sqrt{3}$ **79.** -1 **81.** -3 **83.** $\sqrt{7}$

85. $[0, \infty)$;   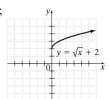   **87.** $[3, \infty)$;   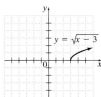   **89.** $(-\infty, \infty)$;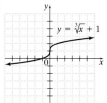

91. $(-\infty, \infty)$; $0, 1, -1, 2, -2$ 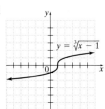   **93.** Answers may vary.   **95.**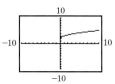

97.   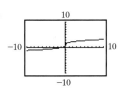   **99.** $-32x^{15}y^{10}$ **101.** $-60x^7y^{10}z^5$ **103.** $\dfrac{x^9y^5}{2}$

Exercise Set 7.2   **1.** 7   **3.** 3   **5.** $\dfrac{1}{2}$ **7.** 13   **9.** $2\sqrt[3]{m}$ **11.** $3x^2$ **13.** -3 **15.** -2 **17.** 8   **19.** 16   **21.** not a real number

23. $\sqrt[5]{(2x)^3}$ **25.** $\sqrt[3]{(7x + 2)^2}$ **27.** $\dfrac{64}{27}$ **29.** $\dfrac{1}{16}$ **31.** $\dfrac{1}{16}$ **33.** not a real number   **35.** $\dfrac{1}{x^{1/4}}$ **37.** $a^{2/3}$ **39.** $\dfrac{5x^{3/4}}{7}$

41. Answers may vary.   **43.** $a^{7/3}$ **45.** x **47.** $3^{5/8}$ **49.** $y^{1/6}$ **51.** $8u^3$ **53.** $-b$ **55.** $27x^{2/3}$ **57.** $y - y^{7/6}$

59. $2x^{5/3} - 2x^{2/3}$ **61.** $4x^{2/3} - 9$ **63.** $x^{8/3}(1 + x^{2/3})$ **65.** $x^{1/5}(x^{1/5} - 3)$ **67.** $x^{-1/3}(5 + x)$ **69.** $\sqrt{x}$ **71.** $\sqrt[3]{2}$ **73.** $2\sqrt{x}$

75. $\sqrt{xy}$ **77.** $\sqrt[15]{y^{11}}$ **79.** $\sqrt[12]{b^5}$ **81.** $\sqrt{a}$ **83.** $\sqrt[6]{432}$ **85.** $\sqrt[15]{343y^5}$ **87.** $\dfrac{t^{1/2}}{u^{1/2}}$ **89.** 1316 calories

91. a. \$43,340 million   **b.** \$63,374 million   **93.** $x^{3/8}$ **95.** $y^{1/4}$ **97.** 1.8206   **99.** 22.0515   **101.** $4 \cdot 5$ **103.** $9 \cdot 5$

105. $8 \cdot 7$ **107.** $8 \cdot 10$

Exercise Set 7.3 **1.** $\sqrt{14}$ **3.** 2 **5.** $\sqrt[3]{36}$ **7.** $\sqrt{6x}$ **9.** $\sqrt{\dfrac{14}{xy}}$ **11.** $\sqrt[4]{20x^3}$ **13.** $\dfrac{\sqrt{6}}{7}$ **15.** $\dfrac{\sqrt{2}}{7}$ **17.** $\dfrac{\sqrt[4]{x^3}}{2}$ **19.** $\dfrac{\sqrt[3]{4}}{3}$

21. $\dfrac{\sqrt[4]{8}}{x^2}$ **23.** $\dfrac{\sqrt[3]{2x}}{3y^4\sqrt[3]{3}}$ **25.** $\dfrac{x\sqrt{y}}{10}$ **27.** $\dfrac{\sqrt{5x}}{2y}$ **29.** $-\dfrac{z^2\sqrt[3]{z}}{3x}$ **31.** $4\sqrt{2}$ **33.** $4\sqrt[3]{3}$ **35.** $25\sqrt{3}$ **37.** $2\sqrt{6}$ **39.** $10x^2\sqrt{x}$

41. $2y^2\sqrt[3]{2y}$ **43.** $a^2b\sqrt[4]{b^3}$ **45.** $y^2\sqrt{y}$ **47.** $5ab\sqrt{b}$ **49.** $-2x^2\sqrt[5]{y}$ **51.** $x^4\sqrt[3]{50x^2}$ **53.** $-4a^4b^3\sqrt{2b}$ **55.** $3x^3y^4\sqrt{xy}$

57. $5r^3s^4$ **59.** $\sqrt{2}$ **61.** 2 **63.** 10 **65.** x^2y **67.** $24m^2$ **69.** $\dfrac{15x\sqrt{2x}}{2}$ or $\dfrac{15x}{2}\sqrt{2x}$ **71.** $2a^2$

73. a. 20π sq. cm **b.** 211.57 sq. ft **75. a.** 3.8 times **b.** 2.9 times **c.** Answers may vary. **77.** $48x^2$
79. $3x - 2$ **81.** $-72y^4$ **83.** $x + 2$ **85.** $4x^2 + 4x + 1$

Mental Math **1.** $6\sqrt{3}$ **3.** $3\sqrt{x}$ **5.** $12\sqrt[3]{x}$

Exercise Set 7.4 **1.** $-2\sqrt{2}$ **3.** $10x\sqrt{2x}$ **5.** $17\sqrt{2} - 15\sqrt{5}$ **7.** $-\sqrt[3]{2x}$ **9.** $5b\sqrt{b}$ **11.** $\dfrac{31\sqrt{2}}{15}$ **13.** $\dfrac{\sqrt[3]{11}}{3}$ **15.** $\dfrac{5\sqrt{5x}}{9}$

17. $14 + \sqrt{3}$ **19.** $7 - 3y$ **21.** $6\sqrt{3} - 6\sqrt{2}$ **23.** $-23\sqrt[3]{5}$ **25.** $2b\sqrt{b}$ **27.** $20y\sqrt{2y}$ **29.** $2y\sqrt[3]{2x}$ **31.** $6\sqrt[3]{11} - 4\sqrt{11}$

33. $4x\sqrt[4]{x^3}$ **35.** $\dfrac{2\sqrt{3}}{3}$ **37.** $\dfrac{5x\sqrt[3]{x}}{7}$ **39.** $\dfrac{5\sqrt{7}}{2x}$ **41.** $\dfrac{\sqrt[3]{2}}{6}$ **43.** $\dfrac{14x\sqrt[3]{2x}}{9}$ **45.** $15\sqrt{3}$ in. **47.** $\sqrt{35} + \sqrt{21}$

49. $7 - 2\sqrt{10}$ **51.** $3\sqrt{x} - x\sqrt{3}$ **53.** $6x - 13\sqrt{x} - 5$ **55.** $\sqrt[3]{a^2} + \sqrt[3]{a} - 20$ **57.** $6\sqrt{2} - 12$ **59.** $2 + 2x\sqrt{3}$
61. $-16 - \sqrt{35}$ **63.** $x - y^2$ **65.** $3 + 2x\sqrt{3} + x^2$ **67.** $5x - 3\sqrt{15x} - 3\sqrt{10x} + 9\sqrt{6}$ **69.** $2\sqrt[3]{2} - \sqrt[3]{4}$
71. $-4\sqrt[6]{x^5} + \sqrt[3]{x^2} + 8\sqrt[3]{x} - 4\sqrt{x} + 7$ **73. a.** $22\sqrt{5}$ ft **b.** 150 sq. ft **75.** Answers may vary. **77.** $x - 7$

79. $\dfrac{7}{x + y}$ **81.** $2a - 3$ **83.** $\dfrac{-2 + \sqrt{3}}{3}$

Mental Math **1.** $\sqrt{2} - x$ **3.** $5 + \sqrt{a}$ **5.** $7\sqrt{5} - 8\sqrt{x}$

Exercise Set 7.5 **1.** $\dfrac{\sqrt{14}}{7}$ **3.** $\dfrac{\sqrt{5}}{5}$ **5.** $\dfrac{\sqrt[3]{6}}{2}$ **7.** $\dfrac{4\sqrt[3]{9}}{3}$ **9.** $\dfrac{3\sqrt{2x}}{4x}$ **11.** $\dfrac{3\sqrt[3]{2x}}{2x}$ **13.** $\dfrac{2\sqrt{x}}{x}$ **15.** $\dfrac{3\sqrt{3a}}{a}$ **17.** $\dfrac{3\sqrt[3]{4}}{2}$

19. $\dfrac{2\sqrt{21}}{7}$ **21.** $\dfrac{\sqrt{10xy}}{5y}$ **23.** $\dfrac{3\sqrt[4]{2}}{2}$ **25.** $\dfrac{2\sqrt[4]{9x}}{3x^2}$ **27.** $\dfrac{5a\sqrt[5]{4ab^4}}{2a^2b^3}$ **29.** $\dfrac{5}{\sqrt{15}}$ **31.** $\dfrac{6}{\sqrt{10}}$ **33.** $\dfrac{2x}{7\sqrt{x}}$ **35.** $\dfrac{5y}{\sqrt[3]{100xy}}$

37. $\dfrac{2}{\sqrt{10}}$ **39.** $\dfrac{2x}{11\sqrt{2x}}$ **41.** $\dfrac{7}{2\sqrt[3]{49}}$ **43.** $\dfrac{3x^2}{10\sqrt[3]{9x}}$ **45.** $\dfrac{6x^2y^3}{\sqrt{6z}}$ **47.** Answers may vary. **49.** $-2(2 + \sqrt{7})$

51. $\dfrac{7(3 + \sqrt{x})}{9 - x}$ **53.** $-5 + 2\sqrt{6}$ **55.** $\dfrac{2a + 2\sqrt{a} + \sqrt{ab} + \sqrt{b}}{4a - b}$ **57.** $-\dfrac{8(1 - \sqrt{10})}{9}$ **59.** $\dfrac{x - \sqrt{xy}}{x - y}$ **61.** $\dfrac{5 + 3\sqrt{2}}{7}$

63. $\dfrac{-7}{12 + 6\sqrt{11}}$ **65.** $\dfrac{3}{10 + 5\sqrt{7}}$ **67.** $\dfrac{x - 9}{x - 3\sqrt{x}}$ **69.** $\dfrac{1}{3 + 2\sqrt{2}}$ **71.** $\dfrac{x - 1}{x - 2\sqrt{x} + 1}$ **73.** $r = \dfrac{\sqrt{A\pi}}{2\pi}$

75. Answers may vary. **77.** 5 **79.** $-\dfrac{1}{2}, 6$ **81.** 2, 6

Graphing Calculator Explorations **1.** 3.19 **3.** $\varnothing$ **5.** 3.23

Exercise Set 7.6 **1.** 8 **3.** 7 **5.** $\varnothing$ **7.** 7 **9.** 6 **11.** $-\dfrac{9}{2}$ **13.** 29 **15.** 4 **17.** -4 **19.** $\varnothing$

21. 7 **23.** 9 **25.** 50 **27.** $\varnothing$ **29.** $\dfrac{15}{4}$ **31.** 13 **33.** 5 **35.** -12 **37.** 9 **39.** -3 **41.** 1

43. 1 **45.** $\dfrac{1}{2}$ **47.** 0, 4 **49.** $\dfrac{37}{4}$ **51.** Answers may vary. **53.** $3\sqrt{5}$ ft **55.** $2\sqrt{10}$ m **57.** $2\sqrt{131}$ m $\approx$ 22.9 m

59. $\sqrt{100.84}$ mm $\approx$ 10.0 mm **61.** 17 ft **63.** 13 ft **65.** 14,657,415 sq. mi **67.** 100 ft **69.** 1 **71.** 2743 deliveries

73. a. Answers may vary. **b.** Answers may vary. **75.** not a function **77.** not a function **79.** not a function

81. $-\dfrac{20 + 16y}{3y}$ **83.** $\dfrac{x + y}{x - y}$ **85.** $-1, 2$ **87.** $-8, -6, 0, 2$

Mental Math   1. $9i$ **3.** $i\sqrt{7}$ **5.** -4 **7.** $8i$

Exercise Set 7.7   1. $2i\sqrt{6}$ **3.** $-6i$ **5.** $24i\sqrt{7}$ **7.** $-3\sqrt{6}$ **9.** $-\sqrt{14}$ **11.** $-5\sqrt{2}$ **13.** $4i$ **15.** $i\sqrt{3}$ **17.** $2\sqrt{2}$

19. $6 - 4i$ **21.** $-2 + 6i$ **23.** $-2 - 4i$ **25.** $18 + 12i$ **27.** 7 **29.** $12 - 16i$ **31.** $-4i$ **33.** $\dfrac{28}{25} - \dfrac{21}{25}i$

35. $4 + i$ **37.** $\dfrac{17}{13} + \dfrac{7}{13}i$ **39.** 63 **41.** $2 - i$ **43.** 20 **45.** 10 **47.** 2 **49.** $-5 - \dfrac{16}{3}i$ **51.** $17 + 144i$

53. $\dfrac{3}{5} - \dfrac{1}{5}i$ **55.** $5 - 10i$ **57.** $\dfrac{1}{5} - \dfrac{8}{5}i$ **59.** $8 - i$ **61.** 1 **63.** i **65.** $-i$ **67.** -1 **69.** $1 - i$ **71.** 0

73. $2 + 3i$ **75.** $2 + i\sqrt{2}$ **77.** $\dfrac{1}{2} - \dfrac{\sqrt{3}}{2}i$ **79.** Answers may vary.   **81.** $6 - 6i$ **83.** yes   **85.** $33°$

87. $5x^3 - 10x^2 + 17x - 34 + \dfrac{70}{x + 2}$ **89.** 5 **91.** 11 **93.** 16.7%

Chapter 7 Review   1. 9 **3.** -2 **5.** $-\dfrac{1}{7}$ **7.** -6 **9.** $-a^2b^3$ **11.** $2ab^2$ **13.** $\dfrac{x^6}{6y}$ **15.** $|-x|$ **17.** -27 **19.** $-x$

21. $5|(x - y)^5|$ **23.** $-x$ **25.** $(-\infty, \infty); -2, -1, 0, 1, 2$ **27.** $-\dfrac{1}{3}$ **29.** $-\dfrac{1}{4}$ **31.** $\dfrac{1}{4}$ **33.** $\dfrac{343}{125}$

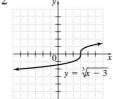

35. not a real number   **37.** $5^{1/5}x^{2/5}y^{3/5}$ **39.** $5\sqrt[3]{xy^2z^5}$ **41.** $a^{13/6}$ **43.** $\dfrac{1}{a^{9/2}}$ **45.** a^4b^6 **47.** $\dfrac{b^{5/6}}{49a^{1/4}c^{5/3}}$ **49.** 4.472

51. 5.191 **53.** -26.246 **55.** $\sqrt[6]{1372}$ **57.** $2\sqrt{6}$ **59.** $2x$ **61.** $2\sqrt{15}$ **63.** $3\sqrt[3]{6}$ **65.** $6x^3\sqrt{x}$ **67.** $\dfrac{p^8\sqrt{p}}{11}$ **69.** $\dfrac{y\sqrt[4]{xy^2}}{3}$

71. a. $\dfrac{5}{\sqrt{\pi}}$ m or $\dfrac{5\sqrt{\pi}}{\pi}$ m   **b.** 5.75 in.   **73.** $xy\sqrt{2y}$ **75.** $3a\sqrt[4]{2a}$ **77.** $\dfrac{3\sqrt{2}}{4x}$ **79.** $-4ab\sqrt[4]{2b}$ **81.** $x - 6\sqrt{x} + 9$

83. $4x - 9y$ **85.** $\sqrt[3]{a^2} + 4\sqrt[3]{a} + 4$ **87.** $a + 64$ **89.** $\dfrac{\sqrt{3x}}{6}$ **91.** $\dfrac{2x^2\sqrt{2x}}{y}$ **93.** $-\dfrac{10 + 5\sqrt{7}}{3}$ **95.** $-5 + 2\sqrt{6}$

97. $\dfrac{6}{\sqrt{2y}}$ **99.** $\dfrac{4x^3}{y\sqrt{2x}}$ **101.** $\dfrac{x - 25}{-3\sqrt{x} + 15}$ **103.** $\varnothing$ **105.** $\varnothing$ **107.** 16 **109.** $\sqrt{241}$ **111.** 4.24 ft   **113.** $-i\sqrt{6}$

115. $-\sqrt{10}$ **117.** $-13 - 3i$ **119.** $10 + 4i$ **121.** $1 + 5i$ **123.** 87 **125.** $-\dfrac{1}{3} + \dfrac{1}{3}i$

Chapter 7 Test   1. $6\sqrt{6}$ **2.** $-x^{16}$ **3.** $\dfrac{1}{5}$ **4.** 5 **5.** $\dfrac{4x^2}{9}$ **6.** $-a^6b^3$ **7.** $\dfrac{8a^{1/3}c^{2/3}}{b^{5/12}}$ **8.** $a^{7/12} - a^{7/3}$ **9.** $|4xy|$ or $4|xy|$

10. -27 **11.** $\dfrac{3\sqrt{y}}{y}$ **12.** $\dfrac{8 - 6\sqrt{x} + x}{8 - 2x}$ **13.** $\dfrac{\sqrt[3]{b^2}}{b}$ **14.** $\dfrac{6 - x^2}{8(\sqrt{6} - x)}$ **15.** $-x\sqrt{5x}$ **16.** $4\sqrt{3} - \sqrt{6}$

17. $x + 2\sqrt{x} + 1$ **18.** $\sqrt{6} - 4\sqrt{3} + \sqrt{2} - 4$ **19.** -20 **20.** 23.685 **21.** 0.019 **22.** $2, 3$ **23.** $\varnothing$ **24.** 6 **25.** $i\sqrt{2}$

26. $-2i\sqrt{2}$ **27.** $-3i$ **28.** 40 **29.** $7 + 24i$ **30.** $-\dfrac{3}{2} + \dfrac{5}{2}i$ **31.** $x = \dfrac{5\sqrt{2}}{2}$

32. $[-2, \infty);$ $; 0, 1, 2, 3$ **33.** 27 mph   **34.** 360 ft

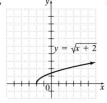

Chapter 7 Cumulative Review   **1. a.** $2xy - 2$ **b.** $2x^2 + 23$ **c.** $3.1x - 0.3$; Sec. 1.4, Ex. 12   **2.** $\dfrac{21}{11}$; Sec. 2.1, Ex. 6

3. \$4500 per month; Sec. 2.4, Ex. 8   **4.** $\varnothing$; Sec. 2.6, Ex. 6   **5.** $(-\infty, -3] \cup [9, \infty)$; Sec. 2.7, Ex. 7

6. ; Sec. 3.1, Ex. 7   **7. a.** domain: $\{2, 0, 3\}$; range: $\{3, 4, -1\}$

  b. domain: $\{-4, -3, -2, -1, 0, 1, 2, 3\}$; range: $\{1\}$

  c. domain: $\{$Erie, Escondido, Gary, Miami, Waco$\}$; range: $\{104, 109, 117, 359\}$;
    Sec. 3.2, Ex. 1

8. 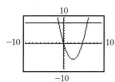 ; Sec. 3.3, Ex. 7   **9.** udefined; Sec. 3.4, Ex. 6   **10.** $\left(-\dfrac{21}{10}, \dfrac{3}{10}\right)$; Sec. 4.1, Ex. 4   **11. a.** 2^7 **b.** x^{10}

  c. y^7; Sec. 5.1, Ex. 1   **12.** 6×10^{-5}; Sec. 5.2, Ex. 7   **13. a.** -4

  b. 11; Sec. 5.3, Ex. 4   **14. a.** $2x^2 + 11x + 15$

  b. $10x^3 - 27x^2 + 32x - 21$; Sec. 5.4, Ex. 3   **15.** $5x^2$; Sec. 5.5, Ex. 1

  16. a. $x^2 - 2x + 4$ **b.** $\dfrac{2}{y - 5}$; Sec. 6.1, Ex. 5

17. a. $\dfrac{6x + 5}{3x^3 y}$ **b.** $\dfrac{5x^2 - 2x}{(x + 2)(x - 2)}$ **c.** $\dfrac{x + 4}{x - 1}$; Sec. 6.2, Ex. 3   **18. a.** $\dfrac{x(x - 2)}{2(x + 2)}$ **b.** $\dfrac{x^2}{y^2}$; Sec. 6.3, Ex. 2

19. $2x^2 - x + 4$; Sec. 6.4, Ex. 1   **20.** $2x^2 + 5x + 2 + \dfrac{7}{x - 3}$; Sec. 6.5, Ex. 1   **21.** $\varnothing$; Sec. 6.6, Ex. 3

22. $x = \dfrac{yz}{y - z}$; Sec. 6.7, Ex. 1   **23.** constant of variation: 15; $u = \dfrac{15}{w}$; Sec. 6.8, Ex. 3   **24. a.** $\dfrac{1}{8}$ **b.** $\dfrac{1}{9}$; Sec. 7.2, Ex. 3

25. $\dfrac{x - 4}{5(\sqrt{x} - 2)}$; Sec. 7.5, Ex. 7

■ CHAPTER 8   QUADRATIC EQUATIONS AND FUNCTIONS

Graphing Calculator Explorations

1. $-1.27, 6.27$ **3.** $-1.10, 0.90$ **5.** $\varnothing$

Exercise Set 8.1   **1.** $-4, 4$ **3.** $-\sqrt{7}, \sqrt{7}$ **5.** $-3\sqrt{2}, 3\sqrt{2}$ **7.** $-\sqrt{10}, \sqrt{10}$ **9.** $-8, -2$ **11.** $6 - 3\sqrt{2}, 6 + 3\sqrt{2}$

13. $\dfrac{3 - 2\sqrt{2}}{2}, \dfrac{3 + 2\sqrt{2}}{2}$ **15.** $-3i, 3i$ **17.** $-\sqrt{6}, \sqrt{6}$ **19.** $-2i\sqrt{2}, 2i\sqrt{2}$ **21.** $1 - 4i, 1 + 4i$ **23.** $-7 - \sqrt{5}, -7 + \sqrt{5}$

25. $-3 - 2i\sqrt{2}, -3 + 2i\sqrt{2}$ **27.** $x^2 + 16x + 64 = (x + 8)^2$ **29.** $z^2 - 12z + 36 = (z - 6)^2$

31. $p^2 + 9p + \dfrac{81}{4} = \left(p + \dfrac{9}{2}\right)^2$ **33.** $x^2 + x + \dfrac{1}{4} = \left(x + \dfrac{1}{2}\right)^2$ **35.** $-8x, 8x$ **37.** $-5z, 5z$ **39.** $-5, -3$

41. $-3 - \sqrt{7}, -3 + \sqrt{7}$ **43.** $\dfrac{-1 - \sqrt{5}}{2}, \dfrac{-1 + \sqrt{5}}{2}$ **45.** $-1 - \sqrt{6}, -1 + \sqrt{6}$ **47.** $\dfrac{6 - \sqrt{30}}{3}, \dfrac{6 + \sqrt{30}}{3}$

49. $\dfrac{3 - \sqrt{11}}{2}, \dfrac{3 + \sqrt{11}}{2}$ **51.** $-4, \dfrac{1}{2}$ **53.** $-1, 5$ **55.** $-4 - \sqrt{15}, -4 + \sqrt{15}$ **57.** $\dfrac{-3 - \sqrt{21}}{3}, \dfrac{-3 + \sqrt{21}}{3}$ **59.** $-1, \dfrac{5}{2}$

61. $-1 - i, -1 + i$ **63.** $3 - \sqrt{6}, 3 + \sqrt{6}$ **65.** $-2 - i\sqrt{2}, -2 + i\sqrt{2}$ **67.** $\dfrac{-15 - 7\sqrt{5}}{10}, \dfrac{-15 + 7\sqrt{5}}{10}$

69. $\dfrac{1 - i\sqrt{47}}{4}, \dfrac{1 + i\sqrt{47}}{4}$ **71.** $-5 - i\sqrt{3}, -5 + i\sqrt{3}$ **73.** $-4, 1$ **75.** $\dfrac{2 - i\sqrt{2}}{2}, \dfrac{2 + i\sqrt{2}}{2}$ **77.** $\dfrac{-3 - \sqrt{69}}{6}, \dfrac{-3 + \sqrt{69}}{6}$

79. 20%   **81.** 11%   **83.** Answers may vary.   **85.** simple   **87.** 8.11 sec   **89.** 6.73 sec   **91.** 6 in.   **93.** $\dfrac{27\sqrt{2}}{2}$ in.

95. 2.828 thousand units   **97.** $\dfrac{7}{5}$ **99.** $\dfrac{1}{5}$ **101.** $5 - 10\sqrt{3}$ **103.** $\dfrac{3 - 2\sqrt{7}}{4}$ **105.** $2\sqrt{7}$ **107.** $\sqrt{13}$

Exercise Set 8.2   **1.** $-6, 1$ **3.** $-\dfrac{3}{5}, 1$ **5.** 3 **7.** $\dfrac{-7 - \sqrt{33}}{2}, \dfrac{-7 + \sqrt{33}}{2}$ **9.** $\dfrac{1 - \sqrt{57}}{8}, \dfrac{1 + \sqrt{57}}{8}$

11. $\dfrac{7 - \sqrt{85}}{6}, \dfrac{7 + \sqrt{85}}{6}$ **13.** $1 - \sqrt{3}, 1 + \sqrt{3}$ **15.** $-\dfrac{3}{2}, 1$ **17.** $\dfrac{3 - \sqrt{11}}{2}, \dfrac{3 + \sqrt{11}}{2}$ **19.** Answers may vary.

21. $\dfrac{3 - i\sqrt{87}}{8}, \dfrac{3 + i\sqrt{87}}{8}$ **23.** $-2 - \sqrt{11}, -2 + \sqrt{11}$ **25.** $\dfrac{-5 - i\sqrt{5}}{10}, \dfrac{-5 + i\sqrt{5}}{10}$ **27.** Answers may vary.

29. two real solutions   **31.** one real solution   **33.** two real solutions   **35.** two complex but not real solutions

37. $\dfrac{-5 - \sqrt{17}}{2}, \dfrac{-5 + \sqrt{17}}{2}$ **39.** $\dfrac{5}{2}, 1$ **41.** $\dfrac{3 - \sqrt{29}}{2}, \dfrac{3 + \sqrt{29}}{2}$ **43.** $\dfrac{-1 - \sqrt{19}}{6}, \dfrac{-1 + \sqrt{19}}{6}$

45. $-3 - 2i, -3 + 2i$ **47.** $\dfrac{-1 - i\sqrt{23}}{4}, \dfrac{-1 + i\sqrt{23}}{4}$ **49.** 1 **51.** $\dfrac{19 - \sqrt{345}}{2}, \dfrac{19 + \sqrt{345}}{2}$ **53.** 14 ft

55. $2 + 2\sqrt{2}$ cm, $2 + 2\sqrt{2}$ cm, $4 + 2\sqrt{2}$ cm   **57.** width: $-5 + 5\sqrt{17}$ ft; length: $5 + 5\sqrt{17}$ ft

59. a. $50\sqrt{2}$ m   **b.** 5000 sq. m   **61.** $\dfrac{1 + \sqrt{5}}{2}$ **63.** 8.9 sec   **65.** 2.8 sec   **67.** Sunday to Monday.   **69.** Wednesday

71. 32; yes   **73. a.** \$3056 million   **b.** 2005
75. 8.9 sec: 1200   ; 2.8 sec: 200

77. two real solutions   **79.** $\dfrac{11}{5}$ **81.** 15   **83.** $(x^2 + 5)(x + 2)(x - 2)$ **85.** $(z + 3)(z - 3)(z + 2)(z - 2)$

87. $\dfrac{\sqrt{3}}{3}$ **89.** $\dfrac{-\sqrt{2} - i\sqrt{2}}{2}, \dfrac{-\sqrt{2} + i\sqrt{2}}{2}$ **91.** $\dfrac{\sqrt{3} - \sqrt{11}}{4}, \dfrac{\sqrt{3} + \sqrt{11}}{4}$

Exercise Set 8.3   **1.** 2 **3.** 16 **5.** $1, 4$ **7.** $3 - \sqrt{7}, 3 + \sqrt{7}$ **9.** $\dfrac{3 - \sqrt{57}}{4}, \dfrac{3 + \sqrt{57}}{4}$ **11.** $\dfrac{1 - \sqrt{29}}{2}, \dfrac{1 + \sqrt{29}}{2}$

13. $-2, 2, -2i, 2i$ **15.** $-\dfrac{1}{2}, \dfrac{1}{2}, -i\sqrt{3}, i\sqrt{3}$ **17.** $-3, 3, -2, 2$ **19.** $125, -8$ **21.** $-\dfrac{4}{5}, 0$ **23.** $-\dfrac{1}{8}, 27$ **25.** $-\dfrac{2}{3}, \dfrac{4}{3}$

27. $-\dfrac{1}{125}, \dfrac{1}{8}$ **29.** $-\sqrt{2}, \sqrt{2}, -\sqrt{3}, \sqrt{3}$ **31.** $\dfrac{-9 - \sqrt{201}}{6}, \dfrac{-9 + \sqrt{201}}{6}$ **33.** $2, 3$ **35.** 3 **37.** $27, 125$ **39.** $1, -3i, 3i$

41. $\dfrac{1}{8}, -8$ **43.** $-\dfrac{1}{2}, \dfrac{1}{3}$ **45.** 4 **47.** -3 **49.** $-\sqrt{5}, \sqrt{5}, -2i, 2i$ **51.** $-3, \dfrac{3 - 3i\sqrt{3}}{2}, \dfrac{3 + 3i\sqrt{3}}{2}$ **53.** $6, 12$

55. $-\dfrac{1}{3}, \dfrac{1}{3}, -\dfrac{i\sqrt{6}}{3}, \dfrac{i\sqrt{6}}{3}$ **57.** 5 mph, then 4 mph   **59.** inlet pipe, 15.5 hr; hose, 16.5 hr   **61.** 55 mph, 66 mph

63. 8.5 hr.   **65.** 12 or -8 **67. a.** $x - 6$ **b.** $300 = (x - 6) \cdot (x - 6) \cdot 3$ **c.** 16 cm by 16 cm

69. a. 281.0 ft per sec   **b.** 284.8 ft per sec   **c.** Papis: 191.6 mph; Montoya: 194.2 mph   **71.** Answers may vary.

73. $(-\infty, 3]$ **75.** $(-5, \infty)$ **77.** domain: $\{x | x$ is a real number$\}$; range: $\{y | y$ is a real number$\}$; function

79. domain: $\{x | x$ is a real number$\}$; range: $\{y | y \geq -1\}$; function

Exercise Set 8.4   **1.** 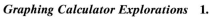 ; $(-\infty, -5) \cup (-1, \infty)$ **3.** ; $[-4, 3]$ **5.** ; $[2, 5]$

7. ; $\left(-5, -\dfrac{1}{3}\right)$ **9.** ; $(2, 4) \cup (6, \infty)$

11. ; $(-\infty, -4] \cup [0, 1]$ **13.** ; $(-\infty, -3) \cup (-2, 2) \cup (3, \infty)$

15. ; $(-7, 2)$ **17.** ; $(-1, \infty)$ **19.** ; $(-\infty, -1] \cup (4, \infty)$

21. Answers may vary.   **23.** ; $(-\infty, 2) \cup \left(\dfrac{11}{4}, \infty\right)$ **25.** ; $(0, 2] \cup [3, \infty)$

27. ; $(-\infty, -7) \cup (8, \infty)$ **29.** ; $\left[-\dfrac{5}{4}, \dfrac{3}{2}\right]$ **31.** ; $(-\infty, 0) \cup (1, \infty)$

33. ; $(-\infty, -4] \cup [4, 6]$ **35.** ; $\left(-\infty, -\dfrac{2}{3}\right] \cup \left[\dfrac{3}{2}, \infty\right)$

37. ; $\left(-4, -\dfrac{3}{2}\right) \cup \left(\dfrac{3}{2}, \infty\right)$ **39.** ; $(-\infty, -5] \cup [-1, 1] \cup [5, \infty)$

41. ; $\left(-\infty, -\dfrac{5}{3}\right) \cup \left(\dfrac{7}{2}, \infty\right)$ **43.** ; $(0, 10)$ **45.** ; $(-\infty, -4) \cup [5, \infty)$

47. ; $(-\infty, -6] \cup (-1, 0] \cup (7, \infty)$ **49.** ; $(-\infty, 1) \cup (2, \infty)$

51. ; $(-\infty, -8] \cup (-4, \infty)$ **53.** ; $(-\infty, 0] \cup \left(5, \dfrac{11}{2}\right]$

55. ; $(0, \infty)$ **57.** Any number less than -1 or between 0 and 1   **59.** x is between 2 and 11

61. 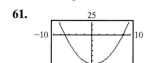   **63.** 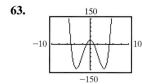   **65.** 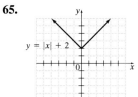   **67.**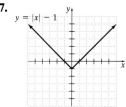

69. 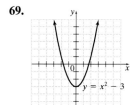   **71.**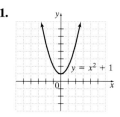

Graphing Calculator Explorations   **1.** 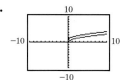   **3.** 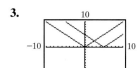   **5.**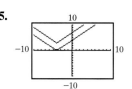

Mental Math   **1.** $(0, 0)$ **3.** $(2, 0)$ **5.** $(0, 3)$ **7.** $(-1, 5)$

Exercise Set 8.5   **1.**

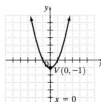

3.

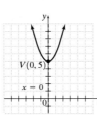

5.

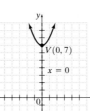

7.

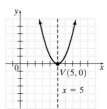

9.

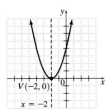

11.

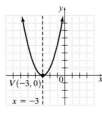

13.

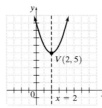

15.

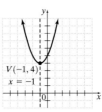

17.

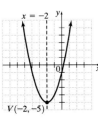

19.

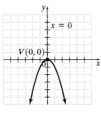

21.

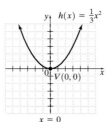

23.

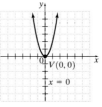

25.

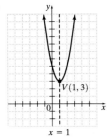

27.

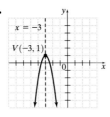

29.

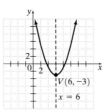

31.

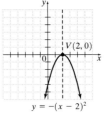

33.

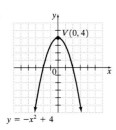

35.

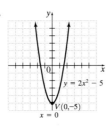

37.

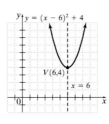

39.

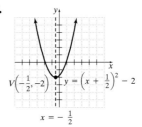

41.

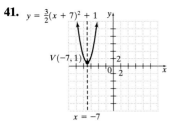

43.

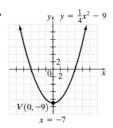

45.

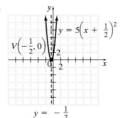

47.

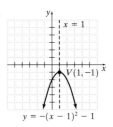

49. $y = \sqrt{3}(x + 5)^2 + \frac{3}{4}$

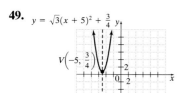

$V\left(-5, \frac{3}{4}\right)$

$x = -5$

51.

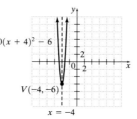

$y = 10(x + 4)^2 - 6$

$V(-4, -6)$

$x = -4$

53.

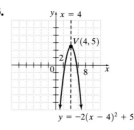

$x = 4$

$V(4, 5)$

$y = -2(x - 4)^2 + 5$

55. $f(x) = 5(x - 2)^2 + 3$ **57.** $f(x) = 5(x + 3)^2 + 6$

59.

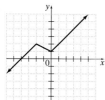

61.

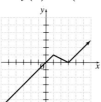

63.

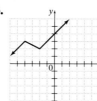

65. $x^2 + 8x + 16$

67. $z^2 - 16z + 64$

69. $y^2 + y + \dfrac{1}{4}$

71. $-6, 2$

73. $-5 - \sqrt{26}, -5 + \sqrt{26}$

75. $4 - 3\sqrt{2}, 4 + 3\sqrt{2}$

Exercise Set 8.6   **1.** $(-4, -9)$ **3.** $(5, 30)$ **5.** $(1, -2)$ **7.** $\left(\dfrac{1}{2}, \dfrac{5}{4}\right)$ **9.** D   **11.** B

13.

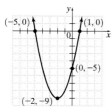

$(-5, 0)$ $(1, 0)$

$(0, -5)$

$(-2, -9)$

15.

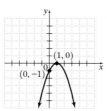

$(1, 0)$

$(0, -1)$

17.

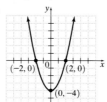

$(-2, 0)$ $(2, 0)$

$(0, -4)$

19.

$\left(-\dfrac{3}{2}, 0\right)$ $\left(\dfrac{1}{2}, 0\right)$

$(0, -3)$

$\left(-\dfrac{1}{2}, -4\right)$

21. $y = x^2 + 8x + 15$

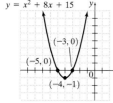

$(-3, 0)$

$(-5, 0)$

$(-4, -1)$

23. $y = x^2 - 6x + 5$

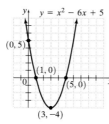

$(0, 5)$

$(1, 0)$

$(5, 0)$

$(3, -4)$

25.

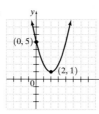

$(0, 5)$

$(2, 1)$

27.

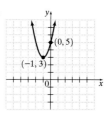

$(0, 5)$

$(-1, 3)$

29.

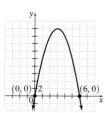

$(0, 0)$ $(6, 0)$

31.

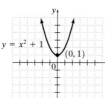

$y = x^2 + 1$

$(0, 1)$

33. $y = x^2 - 2x - 15$

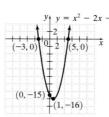

$(-3, 0)$ $(5, 0)$

$(0, -15)$

$(1, -16)$

35.

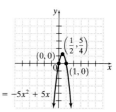

$\left(\dfrac{1}{2}, \dfrac{5}{4}\right)$

$(0, 0)$

$(1, 0)$

$y = -5x^2 + 5x$

37.

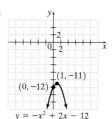

$(1, -11)$

$(0, -12)$

$y = -x^2 + 2x - 12$

39.

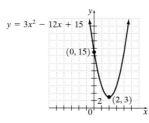

$y = 3x^2 - 12x + 15$

$(0, 15)$

$(2, 3)$

41. $y = x^2 + x - 6$

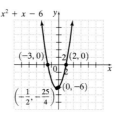

$(-3, 0)$ $(2, 0)$

$(0, -6)$

$\left(-\dfrac{1}{2}, -\dfrac{25}{4}\right)$

43.

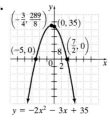

$\left(-\dfrac{3}{4}, \dfrac{289}{8}\right)$ $(0, 35)$

$\left(\dfrac{7}{2}, 0\right)$

$(-5, 0)$

$y = -2x^2 - 3x + 35$

45. a. 200 bicycles   **b.** \$12,000   **47.** 16 ft   **49.** 30 and 30   **51.** 5, −5   **53.** length, 20 units; width, 20 units

55. a. 135.27 million metric tons   **b.** 1996   **c.** 184.39 million metric tons

57.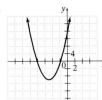

59.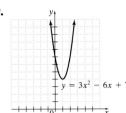
$$y = 3x^2 - 6x + 7$$

61.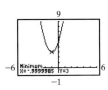

63.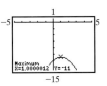

65. −0.84 **67.** 1.43 **69.**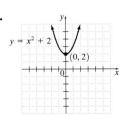
$$y = x^2 + 2$$
$(0, 2)$

71.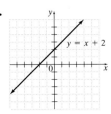
$y = x + 2$

73. $y = (x + 5)^2 + 2$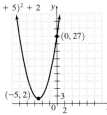
$(0, 27)$
$(-5, 2)$

75.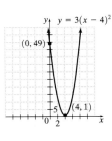
y $y = 3(x - 4)^2 + 1$
$(0, 49)$
$(4, 1)$

77.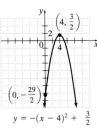
$\left(4, \dfrac{3}{2}\right)$
$\left(0, -\dfrac{29}{2}\right)$
$y = -(x - 4)^2 + \dfrac{3}{2}$

Chapter 8 Review **1.** 14, 1 **3.** $\dfrac{4}{5}, -\dfrac{1}{2}$ **5.** −7, 7 **7.** $-\dfrac{4}{9}, \dfrac{2}{9}$ **9.** $\dfrac{-3 - \sqrt{5}}{2}, \dfrac{-3 + \sqrt{5}}{2}$ **11.** $\dfrac{-3 - i\sqrt{7}}{8}, \dfrac{-3 + i\sqrt{7}}{8}$

13. 4.25% **15.** two complex but not real solutions **17.** two real solutions **19.** 8 **21.** $-i\sqrt{11}, i\sqrt{11}$

23. $\dfrac{5 - i\sqrt{143}}{12}, \dfrac{5 + i\sqrt{143}}{12}$ **25.** $\dfrac{21 - \sqrt{41}}{50}, \dfrac{21 + \sqrt{41}}{50}$ **27. a.** 20 ft **b.** $\dfrac{15 + \sqrt{321}}{16}$ sec; 2.1 sec

29. $3, \dfrac{-3 + 3i\sqrt{3}}{2}, \dfrac{-3 - 3i\sqrt{3}}{2}$ **31.** $\dfrac{2}{3}, 5$ **33.** −5, 5, −2i, 2i **35.** 1, 125 **37.** −1, 1, −i, i **39.** Jerome: 10.5 hr; Tim: 9.5 hr

41. ⟵[────]⟶; [−5, 5] **43.** ⟵───] [───⟶; $\left(-\infty, -\dfrac{5}{4}\right] \cup \left[\dfrac{3}{2}, \infty\right)$ **45.** ⟵(────)⟶; (5, 6)

47. ⟵───(───)───(───⟶; $(-\infty, -6) \cup \left(-\dfrac{3}{4}, 0\right) \cup (5, \infty)$ **49.** ⟵(───)───(───⟶; $(-5, -3) \cup (5, \infty)$

51. ⟵(─) (─)⟶; $\left(-\dfrac{6}{5}, 0\right) \cup \left(\dfrac{5}{6}, 3\right)$ **53.**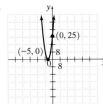
$(0, -4)$
$x = 0$

55.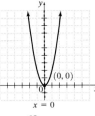
$(0, 0)$
$x = 0$

57.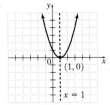
$(1, 0)$
$x = 1$

59.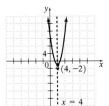
$(4, -2)$
$x = 4$

61.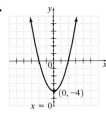
$(0, 25)$
$(-5, 0)$

63.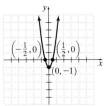
$\left(-\dfrac{1}{2}, 0\right)$ $\left(\dfrac{1}{2}, 0\right)$
$(0, -1)$

65.

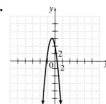

67. The numbers are both 210.

Chapter 8 Test   **1.** $\dfrac{7}{5}, -1$ **2.** $-1 - \sqrt{10}, -1 + \sqrt{10}$ **3.** $\dfrac{1 + i\sqrt{31}}{2}, \dfrac{1 - i\sqrt{31}}{2}$ **4.** $3 - \sqrt{7}, 3 + \sqrt{7}$ **5.** $-\dfrac{1}{7}, -1$

6. $\dfrac{3 + \sqrt{29}}{2}, \dfrac{3 - \sqrt{29}}{2}$ **7.** $-2 - \sqrt{11}, -2 + \sqrt{11}$ **8.** $-3, 3, -i, i$ **9.** $-1, 1, -i, i$ **10.** $6, 7$ **11.** $3 - \sqrt{7}, 3 + \sqrt{7}$

13. 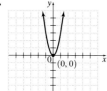 $; \left(-\infty, -\dfrac{3}{2}\right) \cup (5, \infty)$ **14.** 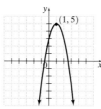 $; (-\infty, -5) \cup (-4, 4) \cup (5, \infty)$

15. 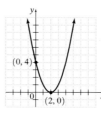 $; (-\infty, -3) \cup (2, \infty)$ **16.** 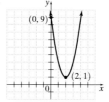 $; (-\infty, -3) \cup [2, 3)$

17.   **18.**   **19.**   **20.**

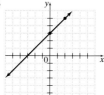

21. $(2 + \sqrt{46})$ ft ≈ 8.8 ft   **22.** $(5 + \sqrt{17})$ hr ≈ 9.12 hr   **23. a.** 272 ft   **b.** 5.12 sec   **24.** 7 ft

Chapter 8 Cumulative Review   **1. a.** $5 + y \geq 7$ **b.** $11 \neq z$ **c.** $20 < 5 - 2x$; Sec. 1.4, Ex. 3
2. slope: 1; 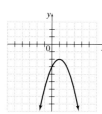 ; Sec. 3.4, Ex. 1   **3.** $(-2, 2)$; Sec. 4.1, Ex. 5
4. a. $6x^2 - 29x + 28$ **b.** $15x^2 - xy - 2y^2$; Sec. 5.4, Ex. 6
5. a. $4(2x^2 + 1)$ **b.** prime polynomial   **c.** $3x^2(2 - x)$; Sec. 5.5, Ex. 2
6. $(x - 5)(x - 7)$; Sec. 5.6, Ex. 2
7. $3x(a - 2b)^2$; Sec. 5.7, Ex. 2
8. $-\dfrac{2}{3}$; Sec. 5.8, Ex. 4

9.  ; Sec. 5.9, Ex. 2   **10.** $\dfrac{1}{5x - 1}$; Sec. 6.1, Ex. 3   **11.** $\dfrac{7x^2 - 9x - 13}{(2x + 1)(x - 5)(3x - 2)}$; Sec. 6.2, Ex. 5
12. $\dfrac{xy + 2x^3}{y - 1}$; Sec. 6.3, Ex. 3   **13.** $3x^3y - 15x - 1 - \dfrac{6}{xy}$; Sec. 6.4, Ex. 2
14. a. 5   **b.** 5; Sec. 6.5, Ex. 3   **15.** -3; Sec. 6.6, Ex. 1   **16.** 2; Sec. 6.7, Ex. 2
17. $\dfrac{1}{6}; y = \dfrac{1}{6}x$; Sec. 6.8, Ex. 1

18. a. 3   **b.** $|x|$ **c.** $|x - 2|$ **d.** -5 **e.** $2x - 7$; Sec. 7.1, Ex. 5
19. a. $\sqrt[3]{5}$ **b.** $\sqrt{x}$ **c.** $\sqrt{rs^3}$; Sec. 7.2, Ex. 7   **20. a.** $5x\sqrt{x}$ **b.** $3x^2y^2\sqrt[3]{2y^2}$ **c.** $3z^2\sqrt[4]{z^3}$; Sec. 7.3, Ex. 4
21. a. $\dfrac{2\sqrt{5}}{5}$ **b.** $\dfrac{8\sqrt{x}}{3x}$ **c.** $\dfrac{\sqrt[3]{4}}{2}$; Sec. 7.5, Ex. 1   **22.** $\dfrac{2}{9}$; Sec. 7.6, Ex. 5   **23. a.** $\dfrac{1}{2} + \dfrac{3}{2}i$ **b.** $-\dfrac{7}{3}i$; Sec. 7.7, Ex. 5
24. $-1 + 2\sqrt{3}, -1 - 2\sqrt{3}$; Sec. 8.1, Ex. 3   **25.** 9; Sec. 8.3, Ex. 1

■ CHAPTER 9   CONIC SECTIONS

Graphing Calculator Explorations **1.** 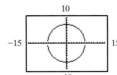 **3.** 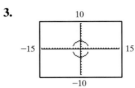 **5.**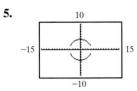

7.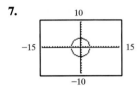

Mental Math **1.** upward **3.** to the left **5.** downward

Exercise Set 9.1 **1.** 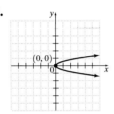 **3.** 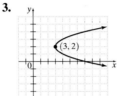 **5.** 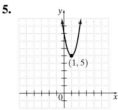 **7.**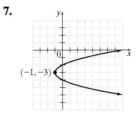

9. 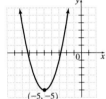 **11.** **13.** 5 units **15.** $\sqrt{41}$ units **17.** $\sqrt{10}$ units
19. $\sqrt{5}$ units **21.** 13.88 units **23.** 9 units **25.** $(4, -2)$
27. $\left(-5, \dfrac{5}{2}\right)$ **29.** $(3, 0)$ **31.** $\left(-\dfrac{1}{2}, \dfrac{1}{2}\right)$ **33.** $\left(\sqrt{2}, \dfrac{\sqrt{5}}{2}\right)$
35. $(6.2, -6.65)$

37. 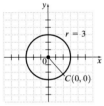 **39.** 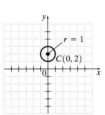 **41.** 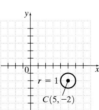 **43.**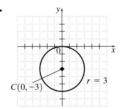

45. 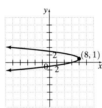 **47.** 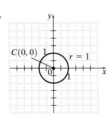 **49.** $(x - 2)^2 + (y - 3)^2 = 36$ **57.**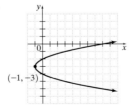
51. $x^2 + y^2 = 3$
53. $(x + 5)^2 + (y - 4)^2 = 45$
55. Answers may vary.

59. 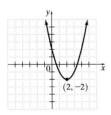 **61.** 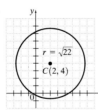 **63.** 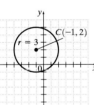 **65.**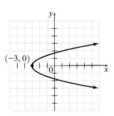

67.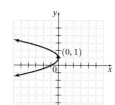

69.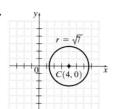

71.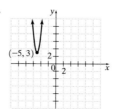

73.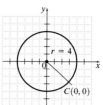

75.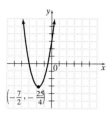

77.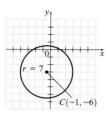

79.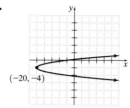

81.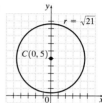

83.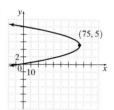

85.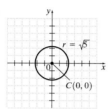

87.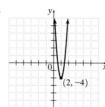

89. Yes, it is.   **91.** $y = -\dfrac{2}{125}x^2 + 40$

93.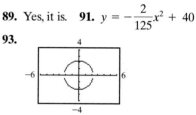

95.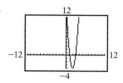

97.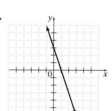

99.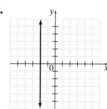

101. $\dfrac{\sqrt{10}}{4}$ **103.** $2\sqrt{5}$

Graphing Calculator Explorations   **1.** 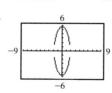   **3.** 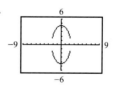   **5.**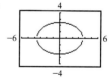

Exercise Set 9.2   **1.** 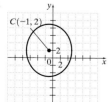   **3.** 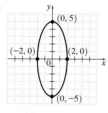   **5.** 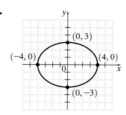   **7.**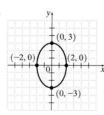

9.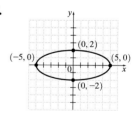

11.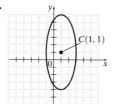

13.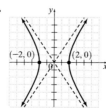

15.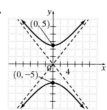

17.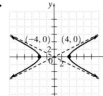

19.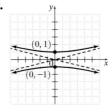

21. Answers may vary. **23.** parabola

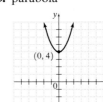

25. ellipse

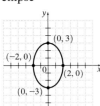

27. hyperbola

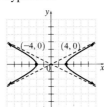

29. circle

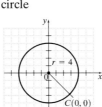

31. parabola

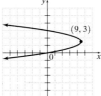

33. ellipse

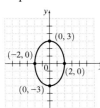

35. hyperbola

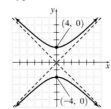

37. parabola

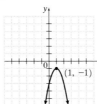

39. A: 36, 13; B: 4, 4; C: 25, 16; D: 39, 25;
E: 17, 81; F: 36, 36; G: 16, 65; H: 144, 140

41. A: 6; B: 2; C: 5; D: 5; E: 9; F: 6; G: 4; H: 12
43. greater than zero and less than one
45. greater than one
47. (1,782,000,000 356,400,000)

49.   **51.** $(-\infty, 1)$ **53.** $[2, \infty)$ **55.** $-2x^3$ **57.** $-5x^4$

59.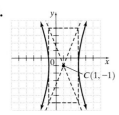

61.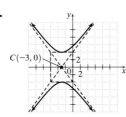

63.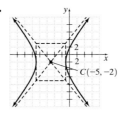

Exercise Set 9.3 **1.** $(3, -4), (-3, 4)$ **3.** $(\sqrt{2}, \sqrt{2}), (-\sqrt{2}, -\sqrt{2})$ **5.** $(4, 0), (0, -2)$
7. $(-\sqrt{5}, -2), (-\sqrt{5}, 2), (\sqrt{5}, -2), (\sqrt{5}, 2)$ **9.** $\varnothing$ **11.** $(1, -2), (3, 6)$ **13.** $(2, 4), (-5, 25)$ **15.** $\varnothing$
17. $(1, -3)$ **19.** $(-1, -2), (-1, 2), (1, -2), (1, 2)$ **21.** $(0, -1)$ **23.** $(-1, 3), (1, 3)$ **25.** $(\sqrt{3}, 0), (-\sqrt{3}, 0)$
27. $\varnothing$ **29.** $(-6, 0), (6, 0), (0, -6)$ **31.** 0, 1, 2, 3, or 4   **33.** 9 and 7; 9 and -7; -9 and 7; -9 and -7
35. 15 cm by 19 cm   **37.** 15 thousand compact discs; price: \$3.75

39.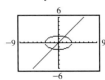

41.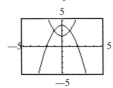

43.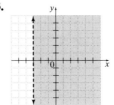

45.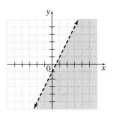

47. $(8x - 25)$ in.   **49.** $(4x^2 + 6x + 2)$ m

Exercise Set 9.4   **1.**

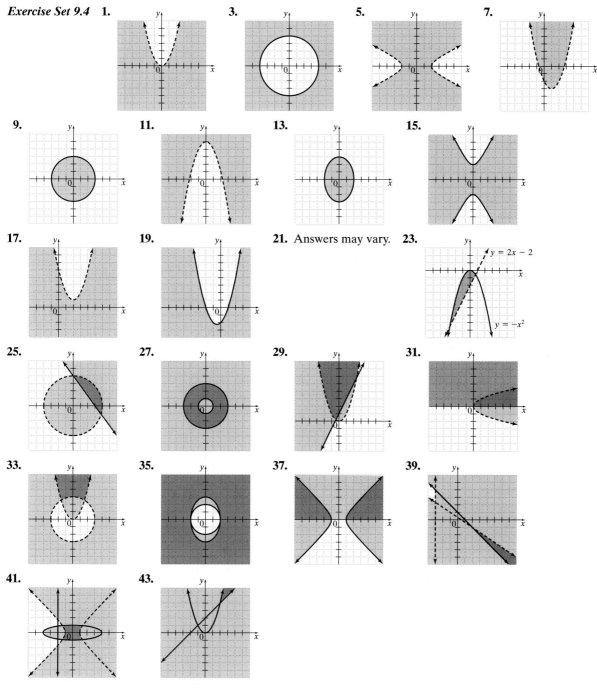

21. Answers may vary.

23. $y = 2x - 2$ $y = -x^2$

45. function   **47.** not a function   **49.** 25   **51.** $3b^2 - 2$

Chapter 9 Review   **1.** $\sqrt{197}$ units   **3.** $\sqrt{130}$ units   **5.** $7\sqrt{2}$ units   **7.** 16.60 units   **9.** $(-5, 5)$ **11.** $\left(-\dfrac{15}{2}, 1\right)$

13. $\left(\dfrac{1}{20}, -\dfrac{3}{16}\right)$ **15.** $(\sqrt{3}, -3\sqrt{6})$ **17.** $(x + 4)^2 + (y - 4)^2 = 9$ **19.** $(x + 7)^2 + (y + 9)^2 = 11$

21.
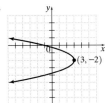

23.
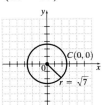

25.
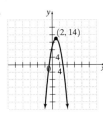

27.
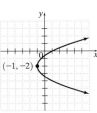

29.
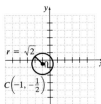

31.
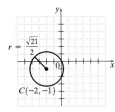

33.
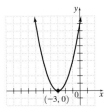

35. $(x - 5.6)^2 + (y + 2.4)^2 = 9.61$

37.
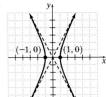

39.
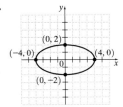

41.
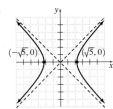

43.
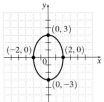

45.
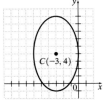

47.
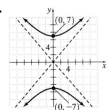

49.
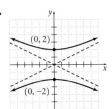

51.
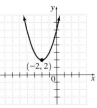

53.
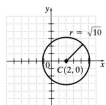

55.
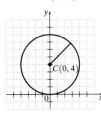

57.
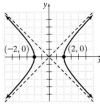

59.
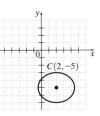

61.
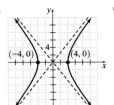

63.
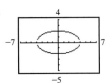

65.
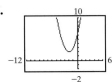

67. $(1, -2), (4, 4)$
69. $(-1, 1), (2, 4)$
71. $(2, 2\sqrt{2}), (2, -2\sqrt{2})$
73. $(-1, 3), (-1, -3), (1, 3), (1, -3)$
75. $(1, 4)$
77. 15 ft by 10 ft

79. 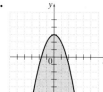   **81.** 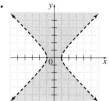   **83.** 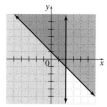   **85.**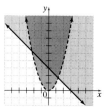

87.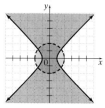

Chapter 9 Test   **1.** $2\sqrt{26}$ units   **2.** $\sqrt{95}$ units   **3.** $\left(-4, \dfrac{7}{2}\right)$ **4.** $\left(-\dfrac{1}{2}, \dfrac{3}{10}\right)$

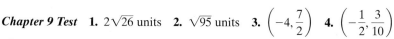

5. 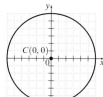   **6.** 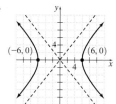   **7.** 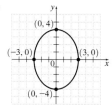   **8.**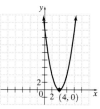

9. 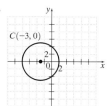   **10.** 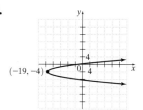   **11.** 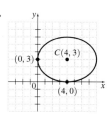   **12.**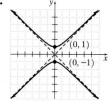

13. $(-12, 5), (12, -5)$ **14.** $(-5, -1), (-5, 1), (5, -1), (5, 1)$ **15.** $(6, 12), (1, 2)$ **16.** $(1, 1), (-1, -1)$

17. 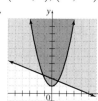   **18.** 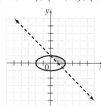   **19.** 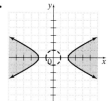   **20.**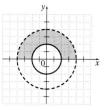

21. B   **22.** height: 10 ft; width: 30 ft

Chapter 9 Cumulative Review   **1.** $(4 \cdot 9)y = 36y$; Sec. 1.4, Ex. 7   **2.**   ; Sec. 3.3, Ex. 5

3. $\varnothing$; Sec. 4.1, Ex. 7

4. a. $125x^6$ **b.** $\dfrac{8}{27}$ **c.** $\dfrac{9p^8}{q^{10}}$ **d.** $64y^2$ **e.** $\dfrac{y^{14}}{x^{35}z^7}$; Sec. 5.2, Ex. 8

5. $-\dfrac{1}{6}, 3$; Sec. 5.8, Ex. 5   **6.** $\dfrac{12}{x-1}$; Sec. 6.2, Ex. 6

7. a. $\dfrac{1}{9xy^2}$ **b.** $\dfrac{x(x-2)}{2(x+2)}$ **c.** $\dfrac{x^2}{y^2}$; Sec. 6.3, Ex. 1   **8.** $2x - 5$; Sec. 6.4, Ex. 3   **9.** 16; Sec. 6.5, Ex. 4

10. $-6, -1$; Sec. 6.6, Ex. 5   **11.** $2\frac{2}{9}$ hr; no; Sec. 6.7, Ex. 4   **12. a.** 1   **b.** -4 **c.** $\frac{2}{5}$ **d.** x^2

e. $-2x^3$; Sec. 7.1, Ex. 3   **13. a.** $z - z^{17/3}$ **b.** $x^{2/3} - 3x^{1/3} - 10$; Sec. 7.2, Ex. 5   **14. a.** 2   **b.** $\frac{5}{2}\sqrt{x}$

c. $14xy^2\sqrt[3]{x}$; Sec. 7.3, Ex. 5   **15. a.** $\frac{5\sqrt{5}}{12}$ **b.** $\frac{5\sqrt[3]{7x}}{2}$; Sec. 7.4, Ex. 2   **16.** $\frac{\sqrt{21xy}}{3y}$; Sec. 7.5, Ex. 2   **17.** 42; Sec. 7.6, Ex. 1

18. a. $-i$ **b.** 1   **c.** -1 **d.** 1; Sec. 7.7, Ex. 6   **19.** $-1 + \sqrt{5}, -1 - \sqrt{5}$; Sec. 8.1, Ex. 5

20. $2 + \sqrt{2}, 2 - \sqrt{2}$; Sec. 8.2, Ex. 3   **21.** $2, -2, i, -i$; Sec. 8.3, Ex. 3   **22.** $[-2, 3)$; Sec. 8.4, Ex. 4

23. 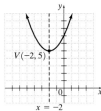 ; Sec. 8.5, Ex. 8   **24.** $(2, -16)$; Sec. 8.6, Ex. 4   **25.** $\sqrt{2} \approx 1.414$; Sec. 9.1, Ex. 5

$V(-2, 5)$

$x = -2$

■ CHAPTER 10   EXPONENTIAL AND LOGARITHMIC FUNCTIONS

Exercise Set 10.1   **1. a.** $3x - 6$ **b.** $-x - 8$ **c.** $2x^2 - 13x - 7$ **d.** $\frac{x - 7}{2x + 1}$, where $x \neq -\frac{1}{2}$ **3. a.** $x^2 + 5x + 1$

b. $x^2 - 5x + 1$ **c.** $5x^3 + 5x$ **d.** $\frac{x^2 + 1}{5x}$, where $x \neq 0$ **5. a.** $\sqrt{x} + x + 5$ **b.** $\sqrt{x} - x - 5$ **c.** $x\sqrt{x} + 5\sqrt{x}$

d. $\frac{\sqrt{x}}{x + 5}$, where $x \neq -5$ **7. a.** $5x^2 - 3x$ **b.** $-5x^2 - 3x$ **c.** $-15x^3$ **d.** $-\frac{3}{5x}$, where $x \neq 0$ **9.** 42   **11.** -18 **13.** 0

15. $(f \circ g)(x) = 25x^2 + 1; (g \circ f)(x) = 5x^2 + 5$ **17.** $(f \circ g)(x) = 2x + 11; (g \circ f)(x) = 2x + 4$

19. $(f \circ g)(x) = -8x^3 - 2x - 2; (g \circ f)(x) = -2x^3 - 2x + 4$ **21.** $(f \circ g)(x) = \sqrt{-5x + 2}; (g \circ f)(x) = -5\sqrt{x} + 2$

23. $H(x) = (g \circ h)(x)$ **25.** $F(x) = (h \circ f)(x)$ **27.** $G(x) = (f \circ g)(x)$ **29.** Answers may vary.

31. Answers may vary.   **33.** Answers may vary.   **35.** 6   **37.** 4   **39.** 48   **41.** -1 **43.** $P(x) = R(x) - C(x)$

45. $y = x - 2$ **47.** $y = \frac{x}{3}$ **49.** $y = -\frac{x + 7}{2}$

Exercise Set 10.2   **1.** one-to-one; $f^{-1} = \{(-1, -1), (1, 1), (2, 0), (0, 2)\}$ **3.** one-to-one; $h^{-1} = \{(10, 10)\}$

5. one-to-one; $f^{-1} = \{(12, 11), (3, 4), (4, 3), (6, 6)\}$ **7.** not one-to-one

9. one-to-one;

Rank in Population (Input)	1	49	12	2	45
State (Output)	CA	VT	VA	TX	SD

11. a. 3   **b.** 1   **13. a.** 1   **b.** -1
15. one-to-one   **17.** not one-to-one
19. one-to-one   **21.** not one-to-one

23. $f^{-1}(x) = \frac{x - 2}{5}$ **25.** $f^{-1}(x) = \frac{x + 3}{2}$ **27.** $f^{-1}(x) = 2x + 2$ **29.** $f^{-1}(x) = \sqrt[3]{x}$

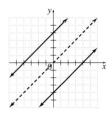 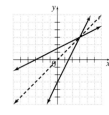 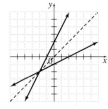 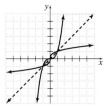

31. $f^{-1}(x) = \frac{x - 2}{5}$ **33.** $f^{-1}(x) = 5x + 2$ **35.** $f^{-1}(x) = x^3$ **37.** $f^{-1}(x) = \frac{5 - x}{3x}$ **39.** $f^{-1}(x) = \sqrt[3]{x} - 2$

41. 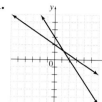   **43.** 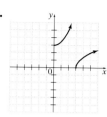   **45.**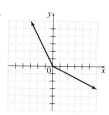

47. $(f \circ f^{-1})(x) = x; (f^{-1} \circ f)(x) = x$ **49.** $(f \circ f^{-1})(x) = x; (f^{-1} \circ f)(x) = x$

51. a. $\left(-2, \dfrac{1}{4}\right), \left(-1, \dfrac{1}{2}\right), (0, 1), (1, 2), (2, 5)$ **b.** $\left(\dfrac{1}{4}, -2\right), \left(\dfrac{1}{2}, -1\right), (1, 0), (2, 1), (5, 2)$

c. 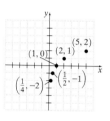   **d.** 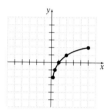   **53.** $f^{-1}(x) = \dfrac{x - 1}{3};$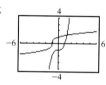

55. $f^{-1}(x) = x^3 - 1;$ 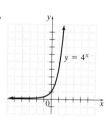   **57.** 5   **59.** 8   **61.** $\dfrac{1}{27}$ **63.** 9   **65.** $3^{1/2} \approx 1.73$

Graphing Calculator Explorations: **1.** 81.98%;   **3.** 22.54%;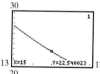

Exercise Set 10.3   **1.** 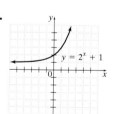   **3.** 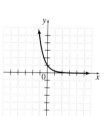   **5.** 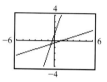   **7.**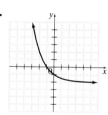

9. 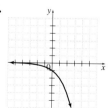   **11.** 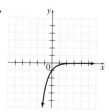   **13.** 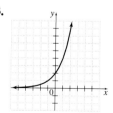   **15.**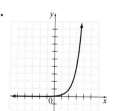

■ CHAPTER 11   SEQUENCES, SERIES, AND THE BINOMIAL THEOREM

Exercise Set 11.1   **1.** $5, 6, 7, 8, 9$ **3.** $-1, 1, -1, 1, -1$ **5.** $\dfrac{1}{4}, \dfrac{1}{5}, \dfrac{1}{6}, \dfrac{1}{7}, \dfrac{1}{8}$ **7.** $2, 4, 6, 8, 10$ **9.** $-1, -4, -9, -16, -25$

11. $2, 4, 8, 16, 32$ **13.** $7, 9, 11, 13, 15$ **15.** $-1, 4, -9, 16, -25$ **17.** 75 **19.** 118 **21.** $\dfrac{6}{5}$ **23.** 729 **25.** $\dfrac{4}{7}$ **27.** $\dfrac{1}{8}$

29. -95 **31.** $-\dfrac{1}{25}$ **33.** $a_n = 4n - 1$ **35.** $a_n = -2^n$ **37.** $a_n = \dfrac{1}{3^n}$ **39.** 48 ft, 80 ft, and 112 ft

41. $a_n = 0.10(2)^{n-1}$; $819.20   **43.** 2400 cases; 75 cases   **45.** 50 sparrows in 2000: extinct in 2006 or 2007
47. $1, 0.7071, 0.5774, 0.5, 0.4472$ **49.** $2, 2.25, 2.3704, 2.4414, 2.4883$ **51.**   **53.**
55. $\sqrt{13}$ units   **57.** $\sqrt{41}$ units

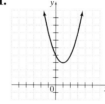

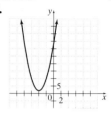

Exercise Set 11.2   **1.** $4, 6, 8, 10, 12$ **3.** $6, 4, 2, 0, -2$ **5.** $1, 3, 9, 27, 81$ **7.** $48, 24, 12, 6, 3$ **9.** 33 **11.** -875 **13.** -60

15. 96 **17.** -28 **19.** 1250 **21.** 31 **23.** 20 **25.** $a_1 = \dfrac{2}{3}; r = -2$ **27.** Answers may vary.   **29.** $a_1 = 2; d = 2$

31. $a_1 = 5; r = 2$ **33.** $a_1 = \dfrac{1}{2}; r = \dfrac{1}{5}$ **35.** $a_1 = x; r = 5$ **37.** $a_1 = p; d = 4$ **39.** 19 **41.** $-\dfrac{8}{9}$ **43.** $\dfrac{17}{2}$ **45.** $\dfrac{8}{81}$

47. -19 **49.** $a_n = 4n + 50$; 130 seats   **51.** $a_n = 6(3)^{n-1}$ **53.** $486, 162, 54, 18, 6$; $a_n = \dfrac{486}{3^{n-1}}$; 6 bounces

55. $a_n = 4000 + 125(n - 1)$ or $a_n = 3875 + 125n$; $5375   **57.** 25 grams   **59.** $11,782.40, $5891.20, $2945.60, $1472.80

61. $19.652, 19.618, 19.584, 19.55$ **63.** Answers may vary.   **65.** $\dfrac{11}{18}$ **67.** 40 **69.** $\dfrac{907}{495}$

Exercise Set 11.3   **1.** -2 **3.** 60 **5.** 20 **7.** $\dfrac{73}{168}$ **9.** $\dfrac{11}{36}$ **11.** 60 **13.** 74 **15.** 62 **17.** $\dfrac{241}{35}$ **19.** $\displaystyle\sum_{i=1}^{5}(2i - 1)$

21. $\displaystyle\sum_{i=1}^{4}4(3)^{i-1}$ **23.** $\displaystyle\sum_{i=1}^{6}(-3i + 15)$ **25.** $\displaystyle\sum_{i=1}^{4}\dfrac{4}{3^{i-2}}$ **27.** $\displaystyle\sum_{i=1}^{7}i^2$ **29.** -24 **31.** -13 **33.** 82 **35.** -20 **37.** -2
39. $1, 2, 3, \ldots, 10$; 55 trees   **41.** $a_n = 6(2)^{n-1}$; 96 units   **43.** $a_n = 50(2)^n$; n represents the number of 12-hour periods;
800 bacteria   **45.** 30 opossums; 68 opossums   **47.** 6.25 lb; 93.75 lb   **49.** 16.4 in.; 134.5 in.
51. a. $2 + 6 + 12 + 20 + 30 + 42 + 56$ **b.** $1 + 2 + 3 + 4 + 5 + 6 + 7 + 1 + 4 + 9 + 16 + 25 + 36 + 49$

c. Answers may vary.   **d.** true   **53.** 10 **55.** $\dfrac{10}{27}$ **57.** 45 **59.** 90

Exercise Set 11.4   **1.** 36 **3.** 484 **5.** 63 **7.** 2.496 **9.** 55 **11.** 16 **13.** 24 **15.** $\dfrac{1}{9}$ **17.** -20 **19.** $\dfrac{16}{9}$ **21.** $\dfrac{4}{9}$ **23.** 185

25. $\dfrac{381}{64}$ **27.** $-\dfrac{33}{4}$, or -8.25 **29.** $-\dfrac{75}{2}$ **31.** $\dfrac{56}{9}$ **33.** $4000, 3950, 3900, 3850, 3800$: 3450 cars; $44,700$ cars
35. Firm A (Firm A, $265,000; Firm B, $254,000)   **37.** $39,930; $139,230   **39.** 20 min; 123 min   **41.** 180 ft

43. Player A, 45 points; Player B, 75 points   **45.** $3050   **47.** $10,737,418.23   **49.** $\dfrac{8}{10} + \dfrac{8}{100} + \dfrac{8}{1000} + \cdots; \dfrac{8}{9}$

51. Answers may vary.   **53.** 720 **55.** 3 **57.** $x^2 + 10x + 25$ **59.** $8x^3 - 12x^2 + 6x - 1$

Exercise Set 11.5   **1.** $m^3 + 3m^2n + 3mn^2 + n^3$ **3.** $c^5 + 5c^4d + 10c^3d^2 + 10c^2d^3 + 5cd^4 + d^5$
5. $y^5 - 5y^4x + 10y^3x^2 - 10y^2x^3 + 5yx^4 - x^5$ **7.** Answers may vary.   **9.** 8 **11.** 42 **13.** 360 **15.** 56
17. $a^7 + 7a^6b + 21a^5b^2 + 35a^4b^3 + 35a^3b^4 + 21a^2b^5 + 7ab^6 + b^7$ **19.** $a^5 + 10a^4b + 40a^3b^2 + 80a^2b^3 + 80ab^4 + 32b^5$
21. $q^9 + 9q^8r + 36q^7r^2 + 84q^6r^3 + 126q^5r^4 + 126q^4r^5 + 84q^3r^6 + 36q^2r^7 + 9qr^8 + r^9$
23. $1024a^5 + 1280a^4b + 640a^3b^2 + 160a^2b^3 + 20ab^4 + b^5$ **25.** $625a^4 - 1000a^3b + 600a^2b^2 - 160ab^3 + 16b^4$
27. $8a^3 + 36a^2b + 54ab^2 + 27b^3$ **29.** $x^5 + 10x^4 + 40x^3 + 80x^2 + 80x + 32$ **31.** $5cd^4$ **33.** d^7 **35.** $-40r^2s^3$

37. $6x^2y^2$ **39.** $30a^9b$ **41.** 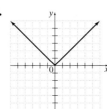   **43.** 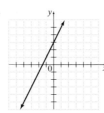   **45.**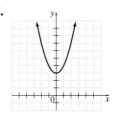

Chapter 11 Review   **1.** $-3, -12, -27, -48, -75$ **3.** $\dfrac{1}{100}$ **5.** $a_n = \dfrac{1}{6n}$ **7.** 144 ft, 176 ft, 208 ft

9. 450, 1350, 4050, 12,150, 36,450; 36,450 infected people in 1999   **11.** $-2, -\dfrac{4}{3}, -\dfrac{8}{9}, -\dfrac{16}{27}, -\dfrac{32}{81}$ **13.** 111   **15.** -83

17. $a_1 = 3; d = 5$ **19.** $a_n = \dfrac{3}{10^n}$ **21.** $a_1 = \dfrac{8}{3}, r = \dfrac{3}{2}$ **23.** $a_1 = 7x, r = -2$ **25.** 8, 6, 4.5, 3.4, 2.5, 1.9; good   **27.** $a_n = 2^{n-1}$, \$512, \$536,870,912   **29.** $a_n = 900 + (n-1)150$ or $a_n = 150n + 750$; \$1650/month

31. $1 + 3 + 5 + 7 + 9 = 25$ **33.** $\dfrac{1}{4} - \dfrac{1}{6} + \dfrac{1}{8} = \dfrac{5}{24}$ **35.** -4 **37.** -10 **39.** $\displaystyle\sum_{i=1}^{6} 3^{i-1}$ **41.** $\displaystyle\sum_{i=1}^{4} \dfrac{1}{4^i}$

43. $a_n = 20(2)^n$; n represents the number of 8-hour periods; 1280 yeast   **45.** Job A, \$48,300; Job B, \$46,000   **47.** 150

49. 900   **51.** -410 **53.** 936   **55.** 10   **57.** -25 **59.** \$30,418; \$99,868   **61.** \$58; \$553   **63.** 2696 mosquitoes   **65.** $\dfrac{5}{9}$
67. $x^5 + 5x^4z + 10x^3z^2 + 10x^2z^3 + 5xz^4 + z^5$ **69.** $16x^4 + 32x^3y + 24x^2y^2 + 8xy^3 + y^4$
71. $b^8 + 8b^7c + 28b^6c^2 + 56b^5c^3 + 70b^4c^4 + 56b^3c^5 + 28b^2c^6 + 8bc^7 + c^8$
73. $256m^4 - 256m^3n + 96m^2n^2 - 16mn^3 + n^4$ **75.** $35a^4b^3$

Chapter 11 Test   **1.** $-\dfrac{1}{5}, \dfrac{1}{6}, -\dfrac{1}{7}, \dfrac{1}{8}, -\dfrac{1}{9}$ **2.** $-3, 3, -3, 3, -3$ **3.** 247   **4.** 39,999   **5.** $a_n = \dfrac{2}{5}\left(\dfrac{1}{5}\right)^{n-1}$ **6.** $a_n = (-1)^n 9n$

7. 155   **8.** -330 **9.** $\dfrac{144}{5}$ **10.** 1   **11.** 10   **12.** -60 **13.** $a^6 - 6a^5b + 15a^4b^2 - 20a^3b^3 + 15a^2b^4 - 6ab^5 + b^6$

14. $32x^5 + 80x^4y + 80x^3y^2 + 40x^2y^3 + 10xy^4 + y^5$
15. $y^8 + 8y^7z + 28y^6z^2 + 56y^5z^3 + 70y^4z^4 + 56y^3z^5 + 28y^2z^6 + 8yz^7 + z^8$
16. $128p^7 + 448p^6r + 672p^5r^2 + 560p^4r^3 + 280p^3r^4 + 84p^2r^5 + 14pr^6 + r^7$ **17.** 925 people; 250 people initially

18. $1 + 3 + 5 + 7 + 9 + 11 + 13 + 15$; 64 shrubs   **19.** 33.75 cm, 218.75 cm   **20.** 320 cm   **21.** 304 ft; 1600 ft   **22.** $\dfrac{14}{33}$

Chapter 11 Cumulative Review   **1. a.** -5 **b.** 3   **c.** $-\dfrac{1}{8}$ **d.** -4 **e.** $\dfrac{1}{4}$ **f.** undefined; Sec. 1.3, Ex. 5

2. \$2350; Sec. 2.2, Ex. 5   **3. a.** $(-5, 2)$ **b.** $(1, 0)$; Sec. 4.5, Ex. 2   **4. a.** $15x^7$ **b.** $-8x^4p^{12}$

5. $x^3 - 4x^2 - 3x + 11 + \dfrac{12}{x+2}$; Sec. 6.5, Ex. 2   **6. a.** $5\sqrt{2}$ **b.** $2\sqrt[3]{3}$ **c.** $\sqrt{26}$ **d.** $2\sqrt[4]{2}$; Sec. 7.3, Ex. 3

7. 10%; Sec. 8.1, Ex. 9   **8.** 2, 7; Sec. 8.3, Ex. 4   **9.** $\left(-\dfrac{7}{2}, -1\right)$; Sec. 8.4, Ex. 5   **10.** $\dfrac{25}{4}$ ft; $\dfrac{5}{8}$ sec; Sec. 8.6, Ex. 5

11. 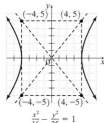 ; Sec. 9.2, Ex. 4   **12.** $(2, \sqrt{2})$; Sec. 9.3, Ex. 2

13. 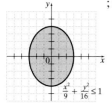 ; Sec. 9.4, Ex. 1

14. a. $25; 7$ **b.** $x^2 + 6x + 9; x^2 + 3$; Sec. 10.1, Ex. 2 **15.** $f^{-1} = \{(1, 0), (7, -2), (-6, 3), (4, 4)\}$; Sec. 10.2, Ex. 3

16. a. 4 **b.** $\dfrac{3}{2}$ **c.** 6; Sec. 10.3, Ex. 4 **17. a.** 2 **b.** -1 **c.** 3 **d.** 6; Sec. 10.4, Ex. 5 **18. a.** $\log_{11}30$ **b.** $\log_3 6$

   c. $\log_2(x^2 + 2x)$; Sec. 10.5, Ex. 1 **19.** $\$2509.30$; Sec. 10.6, Ex. 8 **20.** $\dfrac{\log 7}{\log 3} \approx 1.7712$; Sec. 10.7, Ex. 1

21. 18; Sec. 10.7, Ex. 2 **22.** $0, 3, 8, 15, 24$; Sec. 11.1, Ex. 1 **23.** 72; Sec. 11.2, Ex. 3 **24. a.** $\dfrac{7}{2}$ **b.** 56; Sec. 11.3, Ex. 1

25. 465; Sec. 11.4, Ex. 2

APPENDIX A   REVIEW OF ANGLES, LINES, AND SPECIAL TRIANGLES

1. $71°$ **3.** $19.2°$ **5.** $78\frac{3}{4}°$ **7.** $30°$ **9.** $149.8°$ **11.** $100\frac{1}{2}°$
13. $m\angle 1 = m\angle 5 = m\angle 7 = 110°, m\angle 2 = m\angle 3 = m\angle 4 = m\angle 6 = 70°$ **15.** $90°$ **17.** $90°$ **19.** $90°$ **21.** $45°, 90°$
23. $78°, 90°$ **25.** $50\frac{1}{4}°, 90°$ **27.** $x = 6$ **29.** $x = 4.5$ **31.** 10 **33.** 12

APPENDIX C   REVIEW OF VOLUME AND SURFACE AREA

1. $V = 72$ cu. in.; $SA = 108$ sq. in. **3.** $V = 512$ cu. cm; $SA = 384$ sq. cm **5.** $V = 4\pi$ cu. yd $\approx 12\dfrac{4}{7}$ cu. yd;

$SA = (2\sqrt{13}\pi + 4\pi)$ sq yd ≈ 35.20 sq. yd **7.** $V = \dfrac{500}{3}\pi$ cu. in. $\approx 523\dfrac{17}{21}$ cu. in.; $SA = 100\pi$ sq. in. $\approx 314\dfrac{2}{7}$ sq. in.

9. $V = 48$ cu. cm; $SA = 96$ sq. cm **11.** $2\dfrac{10}{27}$ cu. in. **13.** 26 sq. ft **15.** $10\dfrac{5}{6}$ cu. in. **17.** 960 cu. cm **19.** 196π sq. in.

21. $7\dfrac{1}{2}$ cu. ft **23.** $12\dfrac{4}{7}$ cu. cm

APPENDIX D   AN INTRODUCTION TO USING A GRAPHING UTILITY

Viewing Window and Interpreting Window Settings Exercise Set
1. yes **3.** no **5.** Answers may vary. **7.** Answers may vary. **9.** Answers may vary.
11. Xmin $= -12$ Ymin $= -12$ **13.** Xmin $= -9$ Ymin $= -12$ **15.** Xmin $= -10$ Ymin $= -25$
         Xmax $= 12$ Ymax $= 12$ Xmax $= 9$ Ymax $= 12$ Xmax $= 10$ Ymax $= 25$
         Xscl $= 3$ Yscl $= 3$ Xscl $= 1$ Yscl $= 2$ Xscl $= 2$ Yscl $= 5$
17. Xmin $= -10$ Ymin $= -30$ **19.** Xmin $= -20$ Ymin $= -30$
         Xmax $= 10$ Ymax $= 30$ Xmax $= 30$ Ymax $= 50$
         Xscl $= 1$ Yscl $= 3$ Xscl $= 5$ Yscl $= 10$

Graphing Equations and Square Viewing Window Exercise Set

1. Setting B   **3.** Setting B   **5.** Setting B

7.
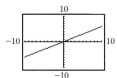

9.
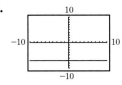

11.
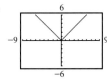

13.
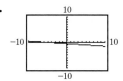

15.
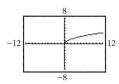

17.
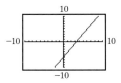

19.
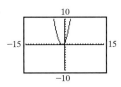

21.
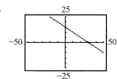

SUBJECT INDEX

Photo Credits

Chapter 1 CO Kerry Sieh/California Institute of Technology/Palomar/Hale Observatory, (p.5) John A. Rizzo/PhotoDisc, Inc.

Chapter 2 CO Robert Brenner/PhotoEdit, (p.57) Peter J. Schulz/Liaison Agency, Inc., (p.60) Michael Newman/PhotoEdit, (p.62) Jeremy Woodhouse/PhotoDisc, Inc., (p.73) Jeffrey Stevenson Studio, (p.74) Photo Researchers, Inc., (p.114) © Mark Downey/Lucid Images/PictureQuest

Chapter 3 CO © Bernard Boutril/Woodfin Camp/PictureQuest, (p.118) Porter Gifford/Liaison Agency, Inc., (p.165) Bill Bachmann/Photo Researchers, Inc., (p.186) Photo Courtesy of Motorola, Inc.

Chapter 4 CO Frank Fisher/Liaison Agency, Inc., (p.218) Doug Densinger/Allsport Photography (USA), Inc., (p.218) Tony Gutierrez/AP/Wide World Photos, (p.233) T.A. Wiewandt/DRK Photo

Chapter 5 CO © Jagdish Agarwal/Stock Connection/PictureQuest, (p.250) Corbis Digital Stock, (p.252) Chris Butler/Science Photo Library/Photo Researchers, Inc., (p.252) Alan Schen/The Stock Market, (p.307) PhotoDisc, Inc.

Chapter 6 CO Bryan F. Peterson/The Stock Market, (p.353) Gary Benson/Gary J. Benson Photography, (p.359) Courtesy Gateway 2000, Inc., (p.369) Spike Matford/PhotoDisc, Inc., (p.376) Amy C. Etra/PhotoEdit, (p.377) John Serafin/Pearson Education Corporate Digital Archive, (p.380) Michael Gadomski/Photo Researchers, Inc., (p.380) Tardos Camesi/The Stock Market, (p.381) Ed Lallo/Liaison Agency, Inc., (p.381) Treat Davidson/National Audubon Society/Photo Researchers, Inc., (p.385) Richard A. Cooke III/Stone, (p.389) Mary Teresa Giancoli

Chapter 7 CO David Young-Wolff/PhotoEdit, (p.418) John Henley/The Stock Market, (p.441) Steve Gottlieb/FPG International LLC

Chapter 8 CO Henley & Savage/The Stock Market, (p.471) Tony Freeman/PhotoEdit, (p.491) Tim Flach/Stone, (p.491) Arthur S. Aubry Photography/PhotoDisc, Inc., (p.514) Jody Dole/The Image Bank, (p.514) Simon Fraser/Northumbrian Environmental Management, LTD/SPL/Photo Researchers, Inc., (p.520) AP/Wide World Photos

Chapter 9 CO Telegraph Colour Library/FPG International LLC

Chapter 10 CO Gary Landsman/The Stock Market, (p.589) PhotoDisc, Inc.

Chapter 11 CO Steve Smith/FPG International LLC

Trigonometric Functions

Have you had days where your physical, intellectual, and emotional potentials were all at their peak? Then there are those other days when we feel we should not even bother getting out of bed. Do our potentials run in oscillating cycles like the tides? Can they be described mathematically? In this chapter you will encounter functions that enable us to model phenomena that occur in cycles.

What a day! It started when you added two miles to your morning run. You've experienced a feeling of peak physical well-being ever since. College was wonderful: You actually enjoyed two difficult lectures and breezed through a math test that had you worried. Now you're having dinner with an old group of friends. You experience the warmth from bonds of friendship filling the room.

SECTION 5.1 *Angles and Their Measure*

Objectives

1. Recognize and use the vocabulary of angles.
2. Use degree measure.
3. Draw angles in standard position.
4. Find coterminal angles.
5. Find complements and supplements.
6. Use radian measure.
7. Convert between degrees and radians.
8. Find the length of a circular arc.
9. Use linear and angular speed to describe motion on a circular path.

The San Francisco Museum of Modern Art was constructed in 1996 to illustrate how art and architecture can enrich one another. The exterior involves geometric shapes, symmetry, and unusual facades. Although there are no windows, natural light streams in through a truncated cylindrical skylight that crowns the building. The architect worked with a scale model of the museum at the site and observed how light hit it during different times of the day. These observations were used to cut the cylindrical skylight at an angle that maximizes sunlight entering the interior.

Angles play a critical role in creating modern architecture. They are also fundamental in trigonometry. In this section, we begin our study of trigonometry by looking at angles and methods for measuring them.

1   Recognize and use the vocabulary of angles.

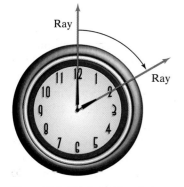

Figure 5.1 Clock with hands forming an angle

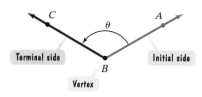

Figure 5.2 An angle; two rays with a common endpoint

Angles

The hour hand of a clock suggests a **ray**, a part of a line that has only one endpoint and extends forever in the opposite direction. An **angle** is formed by two rays that have a common endpoint. One ray is called the **initial side** and the other the **terminal side**.

A rotating ray is often a useful way to think about angles. The ray in Figure 5.1 rotates from 12 to 2. The ray pointing to 12 is the **initial side** and the ray pointing to 2 is the **terminal side**. The common endpoint of an angle's initial side and terminal side is the **vertex** of the angle.

Figure 5.2 shows an angle. The arrow near the vertex shows the direction and the amount of rotation from the initial side to the terminal side. Several methods can be used to name an angle. Lowercase Greek letters, such as α (alpha), β (beta), γ (gamma), and θ (theta), are often used.

An angle is in **standard position** if

- its vertex is at the origin of a rectangular coordinate system

and

- its initial side lies along the positive x-axis.

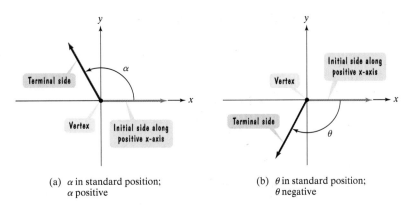

(a) α in standard position;
α positive

(b) θ in standard position;
θ negative

Figure 5.3 Two angles in standard position

The angles in Figure 5.3 are both in standard position.

When we see an initial side and a terminal side in place, there are two kinds of rotation that could have generated it. The arrow in Figure 5.3(a) indicates that the rotation from the initial side to the terminal side is in the counterclockwise direction. **Positive angles** are generated by counterclockwise rotation. Thus, angle α is positive. By contrast, the arrow in Figure 5.3(b) shows that the rotation from the initial side to the terminal side is in the clockwise direction. **Negative angles** are generated by clockwise rotation. Thus, angle θ is negative.

When an angle is in standard position, its terminal side can lie in a quadrant. We say that the angle **lies in that quadrant**. For example, in Figure 5.3(a), the terminal side of angle α lies in quadrant II. Thus, angle α lies in quadrant II. By contrast, in Figure 5.3(b), the terminal side of angle θ lies in quadrant III. Thus, angle θ lies in quadrant III.

Must all angles in standard position lie in a quadrant? The answer is no. The terminal side can lie on the x-axis or the y-axis. For example, angle β in Figure 5.4 has a terminal side that lies on the negative y-axis. An angle is called a **quadrantal angle** if its terminal side lies on the x-axis or the y-axis. Angle β in Figure 5.4 is an example of a quadrantal angle.

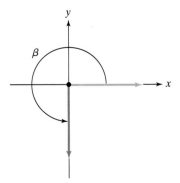

Figure 5.4 β is a quadrantal angle.

2 Use degree measure.

A complete 360° rotation

Measuring Angles Using Degrees

Angles are measured by determining the amount of rotation from the initial side to the terminal side. One way to measure angles is in **degrees**, symbolized by a small, raised circle °. Think of the hour hand of a clock. From 12 noon to 12 midnight, the hour hand moves around in a complete circle. By definition, the ray has rotated through 360 degrees, or 360°. Using 360° as the amount of rotation of a ray back onto itself, a degree, 1°, is $\frac{1}{360}$ of a complete rotation.

Figure 5.5 shows angles classified by their degree measurement. An **acute angle** measures less than 90° [see Figure 5.5(a)]. A **right angle**, one quarter of a complete rotation, measures 90° [Figure 5.5(b)]. Examine the right angle—do you see a small square at the vertex? This symbol is used to indicate a right angle. An **obtuse angle** measures more than 90°, but less than 180° [Figure 5.5(c)]. Finally, a **straight angle**, one-half a complete rotation, measures 180° [Figure 5.5(d)].

Figure 5.5 Classifying angles by their degree measurement

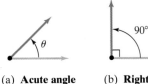

(a) **Acute angle**
($0° < \theta < 90°$)

(b) **Right angle**
($\frac{1}{4}$ rotation)

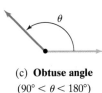

(c) **Obtuse angle**
($90° < \theta < 180°$)

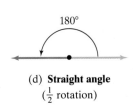

(d) **Straight angle**
($\frac{1}{2}$ rotation)

3 Draw angles in standard position.

We will be using notation such as $\theta = 60°$ to refer to an angle θ whose measure is 60°. We also refer to *an angle of 60°* or a *60°angle*, instead of using the more precise (but cumbersome) phrase *an angle whose measure is 60°*.

Technology

Fractional parts of degrees are measured in minutes and seconds. One minute, written $1'$, is $\frac{1}{60}$ degree.
   One second, written $1''$, is $\frac{1}{3600}$ degree.
   For example,

$31°47'12''$

$= \left(31 + \dfrac{47}{60} + \dfrac{12}{3600}\right)^{\circ}$

$= 31.787°$.

Many calculators have keys for changing an angle from degree, minute, second notation ($D°M'S''$) to a decimal form and vice versa.

EXAMPLE 1   Drawing Angles in Standard Position

Draw each angle in standard position.

a. a 45° angle   **b.** a 225° angle   **c.** a −135° angle   **d.** a 405° angle

Solution   Because we are drawing angles in standard position, each vertex is at the origin and each initial side lies along the positive x-axis.

a. A 45° angle is half of a right angle. The angle lies in quadrant I and is shown in Figure 5.6(a).

b. A 225° angle is a positive angle. It has a counterclockwise rotation of 180° followed by a counterclockwise rotation of 45°. The angle lies in quadrant III and is shown in Figure 5.6(b).

c. A −135° angle is negative angle. It has a clockwise rotation of 90° followed by a clockwise rotation of 45°. The angle lies in quadrant III and is shown in Figure 5.6(c).

d. A 405° angle is a positive angle. It has a counterclockwise rotation of 360°, one complete rotation, followed by a counterclockwise rotation of 45°. The angle lies in quadrant I and is shown in Figure 5.6(d).

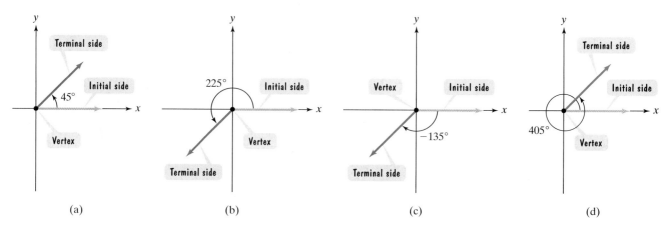

(a)   (b)   (c)   (d)

Figure 5.6 Four angles in standard position

Check Point 1   Draw each angle in standard position.
   a. a 30° angle   **b.** a 210° angle
   c. a −120° angle   **d.** a 390° angle

4 Find coterminal angles.

Look at Figure 5.6 again. The 45° and 405° angles in parts (a) and (d) have the same initial and terminal sides. Similarly, the 225° and −135° angles in parts (b) and (c) have the same initial and terminal sides. Two angles with the same initial and terminal sides are called **coterminal angles**.

Every angle has infinitely many coterminal angles. Why? Think of an angle in standard position. One or more complete rotations of 360°, clockwise or counterclockwise, result in angles with the same initial and terminal sides as the original angle.

> **Coterminal Angles**
>
> An angle of $x°$ is coterminal with angles of
> $$x° + k \cdot 360°$$
> where k is an integer.

Two coterminal angles for an angle of $x°$ can be found by adding 360° to $x°$ and subtracting 360° from $x°$.

EXAMPLE 2   Finding Coterminal Angles

Assume the following angles are in standard position. Find a positive angle less than 360° that is coterminal with:

a. a 420° angle   **b.** a −120° angle.

Solution   We obtain the coterminal angle by adding or subtracting 360°. Our need to obtain a positive angle less than 360° determines whether we should add or subtract.

a. For a 420° angle, subtract 360° to find a positive coterminal angle.
$$420° − 360° = 60°$$

A 60° angle is coterminal with a 420° angle. Figure 5.7(a) illustrates that these angles have the same initial and terminal sides.

b. For a −120° angle, add 360° to find a positive coterminal angle.
$$−120° + 360° = 240°$$

A 240° angle is coterminal with a −120° angle. Figure 5.7(b) illustrates that these angles have the same initial and terminal sides.

Counterclockwise Clocks

The counterclockwise rotation associated with positive angles was used in England to manufacture counterclockwise clocks. They ran backward but told the time perfectly correctly.

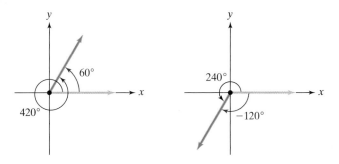

(a) Angles of 420° and 60° are coterminal.

(b) Angles of −120° and 240° are coterminal.

Figure 5.7 Pairs of coterminal angles

> **Check Point 2** Find a positive angle less than 360° that is coterminal with:
> **a.** a 400° angle   **b.** a −135° angle.

5 Find complements and supplements.

Two positive angles are **complements** if their sum is 90°. For example, angles of 70° and 20° are complements because 70° + 20° = 90°.

Two positive angles are **supplements** if their sum is 180°. For example, angles of 130° and 50° are supplements because 130° + 50° = 180°.

Finding Complements and Supplements

- For an $x°$ angle, the complement is a $90° - x°$ angle. Thus, the complement's measure is found by subtracting the angle's measure from 90°.
- For an $x°$ angle, the supplement is a $180° - x°$ angle. Thus, the supplement's measure is found by subtracting the angle's measure from 180°.

Because we use only positive angles for complements and supplements, some angles do not have complements and supplements.

EXAMPLE 3   Complements and Supplements

If possible, find the complement and the supplement of the given angle.

    a. $\theta = 62°$ **b.** $\alpha = 123°$

Solution   We find the complement by subtracting the angle's measure from 90°. We find the supplement by subtracting the angle's measure from 180°.

    a. We begin with $\theta = 62°$.

$$\text{complement} = 90° - 62° = 28°$$
$$\text{supplement} = 180° - 62° = 118°$$

For a 62° angle, the complement is a 28° angle and the supplement is a 118° angle.

    b. Now we turn to $\alpha = 123°$. For the angle's complement, we consider subtracting 123° from 90°. The difference is negative. Because we use only positive angles for complements, a 123° angle has no complement. It does, however, have a supplement.

$$\text{supplement} = 180° - 123° = 57°$$

The supplement of a 123° angle is a 57° angle.

> **Check Point 3** If possible, find the complement and the supplement of the given angle.
> **a.** $\theta = 78°$ **b.** $\alpha = 150°$

6 Use radian measure.

Measuring Angles Using Radians

Another way to measure angles is in *radians*. Let's first define an angle measuring **1 radian**. We use a circle of radius r. In Figure 5.8, we've constructed an angle

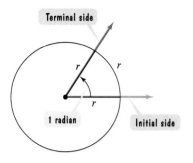

whose vertex is at the center of the circle. Such an angle is called a **central angle**. Notice that the central angle intercepts an arc along the circle measuring r units. The radius of the circle is also r units. The measure of such an angle is 1 radian.

Figure 5.8 For a 1-radian angle, the intercepted arc and the radius are equal.

Definition of a Radian

One radian is the measure of the central angle of a circle that intercepts an arc equal in length to the radius of the circle.

The **radian measure** of any central angle is the length of the intercepted arc divided by the circle's radius. In Figure 5.9(a), the length of the arc intercepted by angle β is double the radius, r. We find the measure of angle β in radians by dividing the length of the intercepted arc by the radius.

$$\beta = \frac{\text{length of the intercepted arc}}{\text{radius}} = \frac{2r}{r} = 2$$

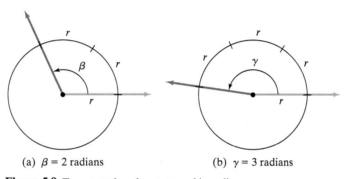

(a) $\beta = 2$ radians   (b) $\gamma = 3$ radians

Figure 5.9 Two central angles measured in radians

Thus, angle β measures 2 radians. In Figure 5.9(b), the length of the intercepted arc is triple the radius, r. Let us find the measure of angle γ:

$$\gamma = \frac{\text{length of the intercepted arc}}{\text{radius}} = \frac{3r}{r} = 3$$

Thus, angle γ measures 3 radians.

Radian Measure

Consider an arc of length s on a circle of radius r. The measure of the central angle θ that intercepts the arc is

$$\theta = \frac{s}{r} \text{ radians.}$$

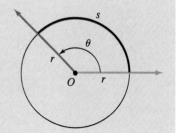

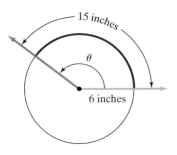

Figure 5.10

EXAMPLE 4   Computing Radian Measure

A central angle θ in a circle of radius 6 inches intercepts an arc of length 15 inches. What is the radian measure of θ?

Solution   Angle θ is shown in Figure 5.10. The radian measure of a central angle is the length of the intercepted arc, s, divided by the circle's radius, r. The length of the intercepted arc is 15 inches: $s = 15$ inches. The circle's radius is 6 inches: $r = 6$ inches. Now we use the formula for radian measure to find the radian measure of θ.

$$\theta = \frac{s}{r} = \frac{15 \text{ inches}}{6 \text{ inches}} = 2.5$$

Thus, the radian measure of θ is 2.5.

Study Tip

Before applying the formula for radian measure, be sure that the same unit of length is used for the intercepted arc, s, and the radius, r.

In Example 4, notice that the units (inches) cancel when we use the formula for radian measure. We are left with a number with no units. Thus, if an angle θ has a measure of 2.5 radians, we can write $\theta = 2.5$ radians or $\theta = 2.5$. We will often include the word *radians* simply for emphasis. There should be no confusion as to whether radian or degree measure is being used. Why is this so? If θ has degree measure 2.5°, we must include the degree symbol and write $\theta = 2.5°$, and *not* $\theta = 2.5$.

Check Point 4   A central angle θ in a circle of radius 12 feet intercepts an arc of length 42 feet. What is the radian measure of θ?

7 Convert between degrees and radians.

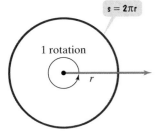

Figure 5.11 A complete rotation

Relationship between Degrees and Radians

How can we obtain a relationship between degrees and radians? We compare the number of degrees and the number of radians in one complete rotation, shown in Figure 5.11. We know that 360° is the amount of rotation of a ray back onto itself. The length of the intercepted arc is equal to the circumference of the circle. Thus, the radian measure of this central angle is the circumference of the circle divided by the circle's radius, r. The circumference of a circle of radius r is $2\pi r$. We use the formula for radian measure to find the radian measure of the 360° angle.

$$\theta = \frac{s}{r} = \frac{\text{the circle's circumference}}{r} = \frac{2\pi r}{r} = 2\pi$$

Because one complete rotation measures 360° and 2π radians,

$$360° = 2\pi \text{ radians.}$$

Dividing both sides by 2, we have

$$180° = \pi \text{ radians.}$$

Dividing this last equation by 180° or π gives the following conversion rules.

Study Tip

The unit you are converting *to* appears in the *numerator* of the conversion factor.

Conversion between Degrees and Radians

Using the basic relationship π radians $= 180°$,

1. To convert degrees to radians, multiply degrees by $\dfrac{\pi \text{ radians}}{180°}$.

2. To convert radians to degrees, multiply radians by $\dfrac{180°}{\pi \text{ radians}}$.

Angles that are fractions of a complete rotation are usually expressed in radian measure as fractional multiples of π, rather than as decimal approximations. For example, we write $\theta = \dfrac{\pi}{2}$ rather than using the decimal approximation $\theta \approx 1.57$.

EXAMPLE 5   Converting from Degrees to Radians

Convert each angle in degrees to radians.

    a. $30°$ **b.** $90°$ **c.** $-135°$

Solution   To convert degrees to radians, multiply by $\dfrac{\pi \text{ radians}}{180°}$. Observe how the degree units cancel.

  a. $30° = 30° \cdot \dfrac{\pi \text{ radians}}{180°} = \dfrac{30\pi}{180} \text{ radians} = \dfrac{\pi}{6} \text{ radians}$

  b. $90° = 90° \cdot \dfrac{\pi \text{ radians}}{180°} = \dfrac{90\pi}{180} \text{ radians} = \dfrac{\pi}{2} \text{ radians}$

  c. $-135° = -135° \cdot \dfrac{\pi \text{ radians}}{180°} = -\dfrac{135\pi}{180} \text{ radians} = -\dfrac{3\pi}{4} \text{ radians}$

> Divide the numerator and denominator by 45.

Check Point 5   Convert each angle in degrees to radians.
    a. $60°$ **b.** $270°$ **c.** $-300°$

EXAMPLE 6   Converting from Radians to Degrees

Convert each angle in radians to degrees.

    a. $\dfrac{\pi}{3}$ radians   **b.** $-\dfrac{5\pi}{3}$ radians   **c.** 1 radian

Solution   To convert radians to degrees, multiply by $\dfrac{180°}{\pi \text{ radians}}$. Observe how the radian units cancel.

Study Tip

In Example 6(c), we see that 1 radian is approximately 57°. Keep in mind that a radian is much larger than a degree.

a. $\dfrac{\pi}{3}$ radians $= \dfrac{\pi \text{ radians}}{3} \cdot \dfrac{180°}{\pi \text{ radians}} = \dfrac{180°}{3} = 60°$

b. $-\dfrac{5\pi}{3}$ radians $= -\dfrac{5\pi \text{ radians}}{3} \cdot \dfrac{180°}{\pi \text{ radians}} = -\dfrac{5 \cdot 180°}{3} = -300°$

c. 1 radian $= 1$ radian $\cdot \dfrac{180°}{\pi \text{ radians}} = \dfrac{180°}{\pi} \approx 57.3°$

Check Point 6

Convert each angle in radians to degrees.

a. $\dfrac{\pi}{4}$ radians   **b.** $-\dfrac{4\pi}{3}$ radians   **c.** 6 radians

Figure 5.12 illustrates the degree and radian measures of angles that you will commonly see in trigonometry. Each angle is in standard position, so that the initial side lies along the positive *x*-axis. We will be using both degree and radian measure for these angles.

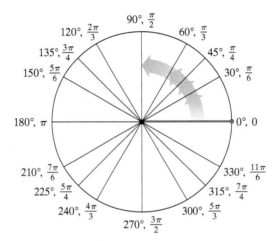

Figure 5.12 Degree and radian measures of selected angles

8 Find the length of a circular arc.

The Length of a Circular Arc

We can use the radian measure formula, $\theta = \dfrac{s}{r}$, to find the length of the arc of a circle. How do we do this? Remember that *s* represents the length of the arc intercepted by the central angle θ. Thus, by solving the formula for *s*, we have an equation for arc length.

The Length of a Circular Arc

Let *r* be the radius of a circle and θ the non-negative radian measure of a central angle of the circle. The length of the arc intercepted by the central angle is

$$s = r\theta.$$

EXAMPLE 7   Finding the Length of a Circular Arc

A circle has a radius of 10 inches. Find the length of the arc intercepted by a central angle of 120°.

Study Tip

The unit used to describe the length of a circular arc is the same unit that is given in the circle's radius.

Solution   The formula $s = r\theta$ can be used only when θ is expressed in radians. Thus, we begin by converting 120° to radians. Multiply by $\dfrac{\pi \text{ radians}}{180°}$.

$$120° = 120° \cdot \frac{\pi \text{ radians}}{180°} = \frac{120\pi}{180} \text{ radians} = \frac{2\pi}{3} \text{ radians}$$

Now we can use the formula $s = r\theta$ to find the length of the arc. The circle's radius is 10 inches: $r = 10$ inches. The measure of the central angle, in radians, is $\dfrac{2\pi}{3} : \theta = \dfrac{2\pi}{3}$. The length of the arc intercepted by this central angle is

$$s = r\theta = (10 \text{ inches})\left(\frac{2\pi}{3}\right) = \frac{20\pi}{3} \text{ inches} \approx 20.94 \text{ inches.}$$

> **Check Point 7**   A circle has a radius of 6 inches. Find the length of the arc intercepted by a central angle of 45°. Express arc length in terms of π. Then round your answer to two decimal places.

9 Use linear and angular speed to describe motion on a circular path.

Linear and Angular Speed

A carousel contains four circular rows of animals. As the carousel revolves, the animals in the outer row travel a greater distance per unit of time than those in the inner rows. These animals have a greater *linear speed* than those in the inner rows. By contrast, all animals, regardless of the row, complete the same number of revolutions per unit of time. All animals in the four circular rows travel at the same *angular speed*.

Using v for linear speed and ω (omega) for angular speed, we define these two kinds of speeds along a circular path as follows.

Definitions of Linear and Angular Speed

If a point is in motion on a circle of radius r through an angle of θ radians in time t, then its **linear speed** is

$$v = \frac{s}{t},$$

where s is the arc length given by $s = r\theta$, and its **angular speed** is

$$\omega = \frac{\theta}{t}.$$

The hard drive in a computer rotates at 3600 revolutions per minute. This angular speed, expressed in revolutions per minute, can also be expressed in revolutions per second, radians per minute, and radians per second. Using 2π radians = 1 revolution, we express the angular speed of a hard drive in radians per minute as follows:

3600 revolutions per minute

$$= \frac{3600 \text{ revolutions}}{1 \text{ minute}} \cdot \frac{2\pi \text{ radians}}{1 \text{ revolution}} = \frac{7200\pi \text{ radians}}{1 \text{ minute}}$$

$$= 7200\pi \text{ radians per minute.}$$

We can establish a relationship between the two kinds of speed by dividing both sides of the arc length formula, $s = r\theta$, by t:

$$\frac{s}{t} = \frac{r\theta}{t} = r\frac{\theta}{t}.$$

This expression defines linear speed.

This expression defines angular speed.

Thus, linear speed is the product of the radius and the angular speed.

Linear Speed in Terms of Angular Speed

The linear speed, v, of a point a distance r from the center of rotation is given by

$$v = r\omega$$

where ω is the angular speed in radians per unit of time.

EXAMPLE 8 Finding Linear Speed

A wind machine used to generate electricity has blades that are 10 feet in length (see Figure 5.13). The propeller is rotating at four revolutions per second. Find the linear speed, in feet per second, of the tips of the blades.

10 feet

Figure 5.13

Solution We are given ω, the angular speed.

$$\omega = 4 \text{ revolutions per second}$$

We use the formula $v = r\omega$ to find v, the linear speed. Before applying the formula, we must express ω in radians per second.

$$\omega = \frac{4 \text{ revolutions}}{1 \text{ second}} \cdot \frac{2\pi \text{ radians}}{1 \text{ revolution}} = \frac{8\pi \text{ radians}}{1 \text{ second}} \quad \text{or} \quad \frac{8\pi}{1 \text{ second}}$$

The angular speed of the propeller is 8π radians per second. The linear speed is

$$v = r\omega = 10 \text{ feet} \cdot \frac{8\pi}{1 \text{ second}} = \frac{80\pi \text{ feet}}{\text{second}}.$$

The linear speed of the tips of the blades is 80π feet per second, which is approximately 251 feet per second.

Check Point 8 A 45-rpm record has an angular speed of 45 revolutions per minute. Find the linear speed, in inches per minute, at the point where the needle is 1.5 inches from the record's center.

EXERCISE SET 5.1

Practice Exercises

In Exercises 1–6, each angle is in standard position. Determine the quadrant in which the angle lies.

1. $145°$

2. $285°$

3. $-100°$

4. $-110°$

5. $362°$

6. $364°$

In Exercises 7–10, classify the angle as acute, right, straight, or obtuse.

7.

8.

9.

10.

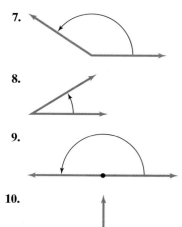

In Exercises 11–18, draw each angle in standard position.

11. $135°$

12. $120°$

13. $-150°$

14. $-240°$

15. $420°$

16. $450°$

17. $-90°$

18. $-270°$

In Exercises 19–24, find a positive angle less than $360°$ that is coterminal with the given angle.

19. $395°$

20. $415°$

21. $-150°$

22. $-160°$

23. $-45°$

24. $-40°$

In Exercises 25–30, if possible, find the complement and the supplement of the given angle.

25. $52°$

26. $85°$

27. $37.4°$

28. $47.6°$

29. $111°$

30. $95°$

In Exercises 31–36, find the radian measure of the central angle of a circle of radius r that intercepts an arc of length s.

	Radius, r	Arc length, s
31.	10 inches	40 inches
32.	5 feet	30 feet
33.	6 yards	8 yards
34.	8 yards	18 yards
35.	1 meter	400 centimeters
36.	1 meter	600 centimeters

In Exercises 37–44, convert each angle in degrees to radians. Express your answer as a multiple of π.

37. 45°

38. 18°

39. 135°

40. 150°

41. 300°

42. 330°

43. −225°

44. −270°

In Exercises 45–52, convert each angle in radians to degrees.

45. $\dfrac{\pi}{2}$

46. $\dfrac{\pi}{9}$

47. $\dfrac{2\pi}{3}$

48. $\dfrac{3\pi}{4}$

49. $\dfrac{7\pi}{6}$

50. $\dfrac{11\pi}{6}$

51. −3π

52. −4π

In Exercises 53–58, convert each angle in degrees to radians. Round to two decimal places.

53. 18°

54. 76°

55. −40°

56. −50°

57. 200°

58. 250°

In Exercises 59–64, convert each angle in radians to degrees. Round to two decimal places.

59. 2 radians

60. 3 radians

61. $\dfrac{\pi}{13}$ radians

62. $\dfrac{\pi}{17}$ radians

63. −4.8 radians

64. −5.2 radians

In Exercises 65–68, find the length of the arc on a circle of radius r intercepted by a central angle θ. Express arc length in terms of π. Then round your answer to two decimal places.

Radius, *r*	Central angle, *θ*
65. 12 inches	$\theta = 45°$
66. 16 inches	$\theta = 60°$
67. 8 feet	$\theta = 225°$
68. 9 yards	$\theta = 315°$

In Exercises 69–70, express each angular speed in radians per second.

69. 6 revolutions per second

70. 20 revolutions per second

 Application Exercises

71. The minute hand of a clock moves from 12 to 2 o'clock, or $\frac{1}{6}$ of a complete revolution. Through how many degrees does it move? Through how many radians does it move?

72. The minute hand of a clock moves from 12 to 4 o'clock, or $\frac{1}{3}$ of a complete revolution. Through how many degrees does it move? Through how many radians does it move?

73. The minute hand of a clock is 8 inches long and moves from 12 to 2 o'clock. How far does the tip of the minute hand move? Express your answer in terms of π and then round to two decimal places.

74. The minute hand of a clock is 6 inches long and moves from 12 to 4 o'clock. How far does the tip of the minute hand move? Express your answer in terms of π and then round to two decimal places.

75. The figure shows a highway sign that warns of a railway crossing. The lines that form the cross pass through the circle's center and intersect at right angles. If the radius of the circle is 24 inches, find the length of each of the four arcs formed by the cross. Express your answer in terms of π and then round to two decimal places.

76. The radius of a wheel is 80 centimeters. If the wheel rotates through an angle of 60°, how many centimeters does it move? Express your answer in terms of π and then round to two decimal places.

How do we measure the distance between two points A and B on Earth? We measure along a circle with a center, C, at the center of Earth. The radius of the circle is equal to the distance from C to the surface. Use the fact that Earth is a sphere of radius equal to approximately 4000 miles to solve Exercises 77–80.

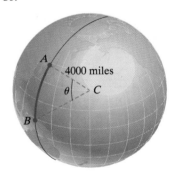

77. If two points A and B are 8000 miles apart, express angle θ in radians and in degrees.

78. If two points A and B are 10,000 miles apart, express angle θ in radians and in degrees.

79. If $\theta = 30°$, find the distance between A and B to the nearest mile.

80. If $\theta = 10°$, find the distance between A and B to the nearest mile.

81. The angular speed of a point on the Earth is $\frac{\pi}{12}$ radians per hour. The Equator lies on a circle of radius approximately 4000 miles. Find the linear velocity, in miles per hour, of a point on the Equator.

82. A Ferris wheel has a radius of 25 feet. The wheel is rotating at three revolutions per minute. Find the linear speed, in feet per minute, of this Ferris wheel.

83. A water wheel has a radius of 12 feet. The wheel is rotating at 20 revolutions per minute. Find the linear speed, in feet per minute, of the water.

84. On a carousel, the outer row of animals is 20 feet from the center. The inner row of animals is 10 feet from the center. The carousel is rotating at 2.5 revolutions per minute. What is the difference, in feet per minute, in the linear speeds of the animals in the outer and inner rows? Round to the nearest foot per second.

Writing in Mathematics

85. What is an angle?

86. What determines the size of an angle?

87. Describe an angle in standard position.

88. Explain the difference between positive and negative angles. What are coterminal angles?

89. Explain what is meant by one radian.

90. Explain how to find the radian measure of a central angle.

91. Describe how to convert an angle in degrees to radians.

92. Explain how to convert an angle in radians to degrees.

93. Explain how to find the length of a circular arc.

94. If a carousel is rotating at 2.5 revolutions per minute, explain how to find the linear speed of a child seated on one of the animals.

95. The angular velocity of a point on the Earth is $\frac{\pi}{12}$ radians per hour. Describe what happens every 24 hours.

96. Have you ever noticed that we use the vocabulary of angles in everyday speech? Here is an example:

> My opinion about art museums took a 180° turn after visiting the San Francisco Museum of Modern Art.

Explain what this means. Then give another example of the vocabulary of angles in everyday use.

Technology Exercises

In Exercises 97–100, use the keys on your calculator or graphing utility for converting an angle in degrees, minutes, and seconds (D°M′S″) into decimal form, and vice versa.

In Exercises 97–98, convert each angle to a decimal in degrees. Round your answer to two decimal places.

97. $30°15'10''$ **98.** $65°45'20''$

In Exercises 99–100, convert each angle to D°M′S″ form. Round your answer to the nearest second.

99. $30.42°$ **100.** $50.42°$

Critical Thinking Exercises

101. If $\theta = \frac{3}{2}$, is this angle larger or smaller than a right angle?

102. A railroad curve is laid out on a circle. What radius should be used if the track is to change direction by 20° in a distance of 100 miles? Round your answer to the nearest mile.

103. Assuming the Earth to be a sphere of radius 4000 miles, how many miles north of the Equator is Miami, Florida, if it is 26° north from the Equator? Round your answer to the nearest mile.

SECTION 5.2   *Right Triangle Trigonometry*

Objectives

1. Use right triangles to evaluate trigonometric functions.

2. Find function values for $30°\left(\dfrac{\pi}{6}\right)$, $45°\left(\dfrac{\pi}{4}\right)$, and $60°\left(\dfrac{\pi}{3}\right)$.

3. Recognize and use fundamental identities.

4. Use equal cofunctions of complements.

5. Evaluate trigonometric functions with a calculator.

6. Use right triangle trigonometry to solve applied problems.

In the last century, Ang Rita Sherpa climbed Mount Everest eight times, all without the use of bottled oxygen.

Mountain climbers have forever been fascinated by reaching the top of Mount Everest, sometimes with tragic results. The mountain, on Asia's Tibet-Nepal border, is Earth's highest, peaking at an incredible 29,029 feet. The heights of mountains can be found using **trigonometry**. The word *trigonometry* means *measurement of triangles*. Trigonometry is used in navigation, building, and engineering. For centuries, Muslims have used trigonometry and the stars to navigate across the Arabian desert to Mecca, the birthplace of the prophet Muhammad, the founder of Islam. The ancient Greeks used trigonometry to record the locations of thousands of stars and worked out the motion of the Moon relative to the Earth. Today, trigonometry is used to study the structure of DNA, the master molecule that determines how we grow from a single cell to a complex, fully developed adult.

1 Use right triangles to evaluate trigonometric functions.

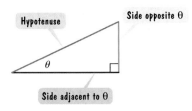

Figure 5.14 Naming a right triangle's sides from the point of view of an acute angle θ

The Six Trigonometric Functions

We begin the study of trigonometry by defining six functions, the six *trigonometric functions*. The inputs for these functions are measures of acute angles in right triangles. The outputs are the ratios of the lengths of the sides of right triangles.

Figure 5.14 shows a right triangle with one of its acute angles labeled θ. The side opposite the right angle is known as the **hypotenuse**. The other sides of the triangle are described by their position relative to the acute angle θ. One side is opposite θ and one is adjacent to θ.

The trigonometric functions have names that are words, rather than single letters such as f, g, and h. For example, the **sine of θ** is the length of the side opposite θ divided by the length of the hypotenuse:

$$\sin\theta = \frac{\text{length of side opposite }\theta}{\text{length of hypotenuse}}.$$

Input is the measure of an acute angle.

Output is the ratio of the lengths of the sides.

The ratio of lengths depends on angle θ and thus is a function of θ. The expression $\sin\theta$ really means $\sin(\theta)$, where sine is the name of the function and θ, the measure of an acute angle, is an input.

Here are the names of the six trigonometric functions, along with their abbreviations.

Name	Abbreviation	Name	Abbreviation
sine	sin	cosecant	csc
cosine	cos	secant	sec
tangent	tan	cotangent	cot

Now, let θ be an acute angle in a right triangle, shown in Figure 5.15. The length of the side opposite θ is a, the length of the side adjacent to θ is b, and the length of the hypotenuse is c.

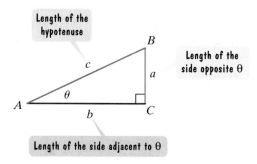

Figure 5.15

Length of the hypotenuse

Length of the side opposite θ

Length of the side adjacent to θ

Right Triangle Definitions of Trigonometric Functions

See Figure 5.15. The six **trigonometric functions of the acute angle θ** are defined as follows.

$$\sin\theta = \frac{\text{length of side opposite angle }\theta}{\text{length of hypotenuse}} = \frac{a}{c}$$

$$\csc\theta = \frac{\text{length of hypotenuse}}{\text{length of side opposite angle }\theta} = \frac{c}{a}$$

$$\cos\theta = \frac{\text{length of side adjacent to angle }\theta}{\text{length of hypotenuse}} = \frac{b}{c}$$

$$\sec\theta = \frac{\text{length of hypotenuse}}{\text{length of side adjacent to angle }\theta} = \frac{c}{b}$$

$$\tan\theta = \frac{\text{length of side opposite angle }\theta}{\text{length of side adjacent to angle }\theta} = \frac{a}{b}$$

$$\cot\theta = \frac{\text{length of side adjacent to angle }\theta}{\text{length of side opposite angle }\theta} = \frac{b}{a}$$

Each of the trigonometric functions of the acute angle θ is positive. Observe that the functions in the second column in the box are the reciprocals of the corresponding functions in the first column.

Figure 5.16 on page 432 shows four right triangles of varying sizes. In each of the triangles, θ is the same acute angle, measuring approximately 56.3°. All four of these similar triangles have the same shape and the lengths of corresponding sides are in the same ratio. In each triangle, the tangent function has the same value: $\tan\theta = \frac{3}{2}$.

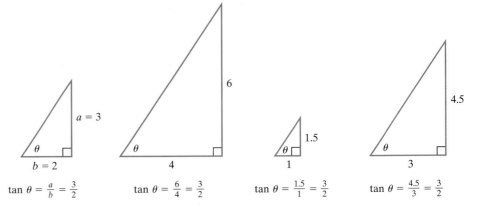

$$\tan \theta = \frac{a}{b} = \frac{3}{2} \qquad \tan \theta = \frac{6}{4} = \frac{3}{2} \qquad \tan \theta = \frac{1.5}{1} = \frac{3}{2} \qquad \tan \theta = \frac{4.5}{3} = \frac{3}{2}$$

Figure 5.16 A particular acute angle always gives the same ratio of opposite to adjacent sides.

In general, **the trigonometric function values of θ depend only on the size of angle θ, and not on the size of the triangle.**

EXAMPLE 1   Evaluating Trigonometric Functions

Find the value of each of the six trigonometric functions of θ in Figure 5.17.

Solution   We need to find the values of the six trigonometric functions of θ. However, we must know the lengths of all three sides of the triangle (a, b, and c) to evaluate all six functions. The values of a and b are given. We can use the Pythagorean Theorem, $c^2 = a^2 + b^2$, to find c.

$$\boxed{a = 5} \quad \boxed{b = 12}$$

$$c^2 = a^2 + b^2 = 5^2 + 12^2 = 25 + 144 = 169$$
$$c = \sqrt{169} = 13$$

Now that we know the lengths of the three sides of the triangle, we apply the definitions of the six trigonometric functions of θ. Referring to these lengths as opposite, adjacent, and hypotenuse, we have

$$\sin \theta = \frac{\text{opposite}}{\text{hypotenuse}} = \frac{5}{13} \qquad \csc \theta = \frac{\text{hypotenuse}}{\text{opposite}} = \frac{13}{5}$$

$$\cos \theta = \frac{\text{adjacent}}{\text{hypotenuse}} = \frac{12}{13} \qquad \sec \theta = \frac{\text{hypotenuse}}{\text{adjacent}} = \frac{13}{12}$$

$$\tan \theta = \frac{\text{opposite}}{\text{adjacent}} = \frac{5}{12} \qquad \cot \theta = \frac{\text{adjacent}}{\text{opposite}} = \frac{12}{5}.$$

Figure 5.17

Study Tip

The functions in the second column are reciprocals of those in the first column. You can obtain their values by exchanging the numerator and denominator of the corresponding ratios in the first column.

Check Point 1   Find the value of each of the six trigonometric functions of θ in the figure.

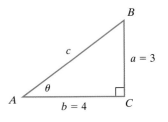

2 Find function values for $30°\left(\dfrac{\pi}{6}\right)$, $45°\left(\dfrac{\pi}{4}\right)$, and $60°\left(\dfrac{\pi}{3}\right)$.

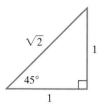

Figure 5.18 An isosceles right triangle

Function Values for Some Special Angles

A 45°, or $\dfrac{\pi}{4}$ radian, angle occurs frequently in trigonometry. How do we find the values of the trigonometric functions of 45°? We construct a right triangle with a 45° angle, shown in Figure 5.18. The triangle actually has two 45° angles. Thus, the triangle is isosceles—that is, it has two sides of the same length. Assume that each leg of the triangle has a length equal to 1. We can find the length of the hypotenuse using the Pythagorean Theorem.

$$(\text{length of hypotenuse})^2 = 1^2 + 1^2 = 2$$
$$\text{length of hypotenuse} = \sqrt{2}$$

With Figure 5.18, we can determine the trigonometric function values for 45°.

EXAMPLE 2 Evaluating Trigonometric Functions of 45°

Use Figure 5.18 to find $\sin 45°$, $\cos 45°$, and $\tan 45°$.

Solution We apply the definitions of these three trigonometric functions.

$$\sin 45° = \frac{\text{length of side opposite } 45°}{\text{length of hypotenuse}} = \frac{1}{\sqrt{2}}$$

$$\cos 45° = \frac{\text{length of side adjacent to } 45°}{\text{length of hypotenuse}} = \frac{1}{\sqrt{2}}$$

$$\tan 45° = \frac{\text{length of side opposite } 45°}{\text{length of side adjacent to } 45°} = \frac{1}{1} = 1$$

Check Point 2 Use Figure 5.18 to find $\csc 45°$, $\sec 45°$, and $\cot 45°$.

When you worked Checkpoint 2, did you actually use Figure 5.18 or did you use reciprocals to find the values?

$$\csc 45° = \sqrt{2} \qquad \sec 45° = \sqrt{2} \qquad \cot 45° = 1$$

Take the reciprocal of $\sin 45° = \dfrac{1}{\sqrt{2}}$.   Take the reciprocal of $\cos 45° = \dfrac{1}{\sqrt{2}}$.   Take the reciprocal of $\tan 45° = \dfrac{1}{1}$.

We found that $\sin 45° = \dfrac{1}{\sqrt{2}}$ and $\cos 45° = \dfrac{1}{\sqrt{2}}$. This value is often expressed by rationalizing the denominator:

$$\frac{1}{\sqrt{2}} = \frac{1}{\sqrt{2}} \cdot \frac{\sqrt{2}}{\sqrt{2}} = \frac{\sqrt{2}}{2}.$$

We are multiplying by 1 and not changing the value of $\dfrac{1}{\sqrt{2}}$.

Thus, $\sin 45° = \dfrac{\sqrt{2}}{2}$ and $\cos 45° = \dfrac{\sqrt{2}}{2}$.

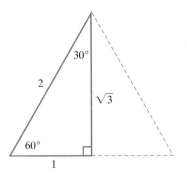

Figure 5.19 30°-60°-90° triangle

Two other angles that occur frequently in trigonometry are 30°, or $\frac{\pi}{6}$ radian, and 60°, or $\frac{\pi}{3}$ radian, angles. We can find the values of the trigonometric functions of 30° and 60° by using a right triangle. To form this right triangle, draw an equilateral triangle—that is a triangle with all sides the same length. Assume that each side has a length equal to 2. Now take half of the equilateral triangle. We obtain the right triangle in Figure 5.19. This right triangle has a hypotenuse of length 2 and a leg of length 1. The other leg has length a, which can be found using the Pythagorean Theorem.

$$a^2 + 1^2 = 2^2$$
$$a^2 + 1 = 4$$
$$a^2 = 3$$
$$a = \sqrt{3}$$

With the right triangle in Figure 5.19, we can determine the trigonometric functions for 30° and 60°.

EXAMPLE 3 Evaluating Trigonometric Functions of 30° and 60°

Use Figure 5.19 to find $\sin 60°$, $\cos 60°$, $\sin 30°$, and $\cos 30°$.

Solution We begin with 60°. Use the angle on the lower left in Figure 5.19.

$$\sin 60° = \frac{\text{length of side opposite } 60°}{\text{length of hypotenuse}} = \frac{\sqrt{3}}{2}$$

$$\cos 60° = \frac{\text{length of side adjacent to } 60°}{\text{length of hypotenuse}} = \frac{1}{2}$$

To find $\sin 30°$ and $\cos 30°$, use the angle on the upper right in Figure 5.19.

$$\sin 30° = \frac{\text{length of side opposite } 30°}{\text{length of hypotenuse}} = \frac{1}{2}$$

$$\cos 30° = \frac{\text{length of side adjacent to } 30°}{\text{length of hypotenuse}} = \frac{\sqrt{3}}{2}$$

Use Figure 5.19 to find $\tan 60°$ and $\tan 30°$. If necessary, express the value without a square root in the denominator by rationalizing the denominator.

Because we will often use the function values of 30°, 45°, and 60°, you should learn to construct the right triangles shown in Figure 5.18 and 5.19. With sufficient practice, you will memorize the following values.

Sines, Cosines, and Tangents of Special Angles

$$\sin 30° = \sin \frac{\pi}{6} = \frac{1}{2} \qquad \cos 30° = \cos \frac{\pi}{6} = \frac{\sqrt{3}}{2} \qquad \tan 30° = \tan \frac{\pi}{6} = \frac{\sqrt{3}}{3}$$

$$\sin 45° = \sin \frac{\pi}{4} = \frac{\sqrt{2}}{2} \qquad \cos 45° = \cos \frac{\pi}{4} = \frac{\sqrt{2}}{2} \qquad \tan 45° = \tan \frac{\pi}{4} = 1$$

$$\sin 60° = \sin \frac{\pi}{3} = \frac{\sqrt{3}}{2} \qquad \cos 60° = \cos \frac{\pi}{3} = \frac{1}{2} \qquad \tan 60° = \tan \frac{\pi}{3} = \sqrt{3}$$

3 Recognize and use fundamental identities.

Fundamental Identities

Many relationships exist among the six trigonometric functions. These relationships are described using **trigonometric identities**. For example, $\csc \theta$ is defined as the reciprocal of $\sin \theta$. This relationship can be expressed by the identity

$$\csc \theta = \frac{1}{\sin \theta}.$$

This identity is one of six **reciprocal identities**.

Reciprocal Identities

$$\sin \theta = \frac{1}{\csc \theta} \qquad \cos \theta = \frac{1}{\sec \theta} \qquad \tan \theta = \frac{1}{\cot \theta}$$

$$\csc \theta = \frac{1}{\sin \theta} \qquad \sec \theta = \frac{1}{\cos \theta} \qquad \cot \theta = \frac{1}{\tan \theta}$$

Two other relationships that follow from the definitions of the trigonometric functions are called the **quotient identities.**

Quotient Identities

$$\tan \theta = \frac{\sin \theta}{\cos \theta} \qquad \cot \theta = \frac{\cos \theta}{\sin \theta}$$

If $\sin \theta$ and $\cos \theta$ are known, a quotient identity and three reciprocal identities make it possible to find the value of each of the four remaining trigonometric functions.

EXAMPLE 4 Using Quotient and Reciprocal Identities

Given $\sin \theta = \frac{1}{2}$ and $\cos \theta = \frac{\sqrt{3}}{2}$, find the value of each of the four remaining trigonometric functions.

Solution   We can find $\tan\theta$ by using the quotient identity that describes $\tan\theta$ as the quotient of $\sin\theta$ and $\cos\theta$.

$$\tan\theta = \frac{\sin\theta}{\cos\theta} = \frac{\frac{1}{2}}{\frac{\sqrt{3}}{2}} = \frac{1}{2} \cdot \frac{2}{\sqrt{3}} = \frac{1}{\sqrt{3}} = \frac{1}{\sqrt{3}} \cdot \frac{\sqrt{3}}{\sqrt{3}} = \frac{\sqrt{3}}{3}$$

> Rationalize the denominator.

We use the reciprocal identities to find the value of each of the remaining three functions.

$$\csc\theta = \frac{1}{\sin\theta} = \frac{1}{\frac{1}{2}} = 2$$

$$\sec\theta = \frac{1}{\cos\theta} = \frac{1}{\frac{\sqrt{3}}{2}} = \frac{2}{\sqrt{3}} = \frac{2}{\sqrt{3}} \cdot \frac{\sqrt{3}}{\sqrt{3}} = \frac{2\sqrt{3}}{3}$$

> Rationalize the denominator.

$$\cot\theta = \frac{1}{\tan\theta} = \frac{1}{\frac{1}{\sqrt{3}}} = \sqrt{3}$$

Check Point 4   Given $\sin\theta = \dfrac{2}{3}$, $\cos\theta = \dfrac{\sqrt{5}}{3}$, find the value of each of the four remaining trigonometric functions.

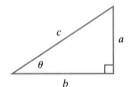

Figure 5.20

Other relationships among trigonometric functions follow from the Pythagorean Theorem. Using Figure 5.20, the Pythagorean Theorem states that

$$a^2 + b^2 = c^2.$$

To obtain ratios that correspond to trigonometric functions, divide both sides of this equation by c^2.

$$\frac{a^2}{c^2} + \frac{b^2}{c^2} = 1 \quad \text{or} \quad \left(\frac{a}{c}\right)^2 + \left(\frac{b}{c}\right)^2 = 1$$

> In Figure 5.20 $\sin\theta = \frac{a}{c}$, so this is $(\sin\theta)^2$.

> In Figure 5.20 $\cos\theta = \frac{b}{c}$, so this is $(\cos\theta)^2$.

Based on the observations in the voice balloons, we see that

$$(\sin\theta)^2 + (\cos\theta)^2 = 1.$$

We will eliminate the parentheses in this identity by writing $\sin^2\theta$ instead of $(\sin\theta)^2$ and $\cos^2\theta$ instead of $(\cos\theta)^2$. With this notation, we can write the identity as

$$\sin^2\theta + \cos^2\theta = 1.$$

Two additional identities can be obtained from $a^2 + b^2 = c^2$ by dividing both sides by b^2 and a^2, respectively. The three identities are called the **Pythagorean identities.**

Pythagorean Identities

$$\sin^2\theta + \cos^2\theta = 1 \qquad 1 + \tan^2\theta = \sec^2\theta \qquad 1 + \cot^2\theta = \csc^2\theta$$

EXAMPLE 5 Using a Pythagorean Identity

Given that $\sin\theta = \frac{3}{5}$ and θ is an acute angle, find the value of $\cos\theta$ using a trigonometric identity.

Solution We can find the value of $\cos\theta$ by using the Pythagorean identity

$$\sin^2\theta + \cos^2\theta = 1.$$

$$\left(\frac{3}{5}\right)^2 + \cos^2\theta = 1 \qquad \text{We are given that } \sin\theta = \frac{3}{5}.$$

$$\frac{9}{25} + \cos^2\theta = 1 \qquad \text{Square } \frac{3}{5}: \left(\frac{3}{5}\right)^2 = \frac{3^2}{5^2} = \frac{9}{25}.$$

$$\cos^2\theta = 1 - \frac{9}{25} \qquad \text{Subtract } \frac{9}{25} \text{ from both sides.}$$

$$\cos^2\theta = \frac{16}{25} \qquad \text{Simplify: } 1 - \frac{9}{25} = \frac{25}{25} - \frac{9}{25} = \frac{16}{25}.$$

$$\cos\theta = \sqrt{\frac{16}{25}} = \frac{4}{5} \qquad \text{Because } \theta \text{ is an acute angle, } \cos\theta \text{ is positive.}$$

Thus, $\cos\theta = \frac{4}{5}$.

Check Point 5 Given that $\sin\theta = \frac{1}{2}$ and θ is an acute angle, find the value of $\cos\theta$ using a trigonometric identity.

4 Use equal cofunctions of complements.

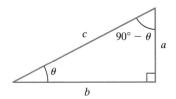

Figure 5.21

Trigonometric Functions and Complements

Another relationship among trigonometric functions is based on angles that are complements. Refer to Figure 5.21. Because the sum of the angles of any triangle is 180°, in a right triangle the sum of the acute angles is 90°. Thus, the acute angles are complements. If the degree measure of one acute angle is θ, then the degree measure of the other acute angle is $(90° - \theta)$. This angle is shown on the upper right in Figure 5.21.

Let's use Figure 5.21 to compare $\sin\theta$ and $\cos(90° - \theta)$.

$$\sin\theta = \frac{\text{length of side opposite }\theta}{\text{length of hypotenuse}} = \frac{a}{c}$$

$$\cos(90° - \theta) = \frac{\text{length of side adjacent to }(90° - \theta)}{\text{length of hypotenuse}} = \frac{a}{c}$$

Thus, $\sin\theta = \cos(90° - \theta)$. If two angles are complements, the sine of one equals the cosine of the other. Because of this relationship, the sine and cosine are called *cofunctions* of each other. The name *cosine* is a shortened form of the phrase *complement's sine*.

Any pair of trigonometric functions f and g for which

$$f(\theta) = g(90° - \theta) \quad \text{and} \quad g(\theta) = f(90° - \theta)$$

are called **cofunctions**. Using Figure 5.21, we can show that the tangent and cotangent are cofunctions of each other. So are the secant and cosecant.

Cofunction Identities

The value of a trigonometric function of θ is equal to the cofunction of the complement of θ.

$$\sin\theta = \cos(90° - \theta) \qquad \cos\theta = \sin(90° - \theta)$$
$$\tan\theta = \cot(90° - \theta) \qquad \cot\theta = \tan(90° - \theta)$$
$$\sec\theta = \csc(90° - \theta) \qquad \csc\theta = \sec(90° - \theta)$$

If θ is in radians, replace $90°$ with $\dfrac{\pi}{2}$.

EXAMPLE 6

Find a cofunction with the same value as the given expression.

    a. $\sin 72°$ **b.** $\csc\dfrac{\pi}{3}$

Solution Because the value of a trigonometric function of θ is equal to the cofunction of the complement of θ, we need to find the complement of each angle. We do this by subtracting the angle's measure from $90°$ or its radian equivalent, $\dfrac{\pi}{2}$.

    a. $\sin 72° = \cos(90° - 72°) = \cos 18°$

> We have a function and its cofunction.

    b. $\csc\dfrac{\pi}{3} = \sec\left(\dfrac{\pi}{2} - \dfrac{\pi}{3}\right) = \sec\left(\dfrac{3\pi}{6} - \dfrac{2\pi}{6}\right) = \sec\dfrac{\pi}{6}$

> We have a cofunction and its function.

> Perform the subtraction using the least common denominator, 6.

Check Point 6 Find a cofunction with the same value as the given expression.

    a. $\sin 46°$ **b.** $\cot\dfrac{\pi}{12}$

5 Evaluate trigonometric functions with a calculator.

Using a Calculator to Evaluate Trigonometric Functions

The values of the trigonometric functions obtained with the special triangles are exact values. For most angles other than $30°$, $45°$, and $60°$, we approximate the value of each of the trigonometric functions using a calculator. The first step is to set the calculator to the correct *mode*, degrees or radians, depending on how the acute angle is measured.

Most calculators have keys marked $\boxed{\text{SIN}}$, $\boxed{\text{COS}}$, and $\boxed{\text{TAN}}$. For example, to find the value of sin 30°, set the calculator to the degree mode and enter 30 $\boxed{\text{SIN}}$ on most scientific calculators and $\boxed{\text{SIN}}$ 30 $\boxed{\text{ENTER}}$ on most graphing calculators. Consult the manual for your calculator.

To evaluate the cosecant, secant, and cotangent functions, use the key for the respective reciprocal function, $\boxed{\text{SIN}}$, $\boxed{\text{COS}}$, or $\boxed{\text{TAN}}$, and then use the reciprocal key. The reciprocal key is $\boxed{1/x}$ on most scientific calculators and $\boxed{x^{-1}}$ on most graphing calculators. For example, we can evaluate $\sec \dfrac{\pi}{12}$ using the following reciprocal relationship:

$$\sec \frac{\pi}{12} = \frac{1}{\cos \dfrac{\pi}{12}}.$$

Using the radian mode, enter one of the following keystroke sequences.

Most Scientific Calculators

$$\boxed{\pi} \boxed{\div} 12 \boxed{=} \boxed{\text{COS}} \boxed{1/x}$$

Most Graphing Calculators

$$\boxed{(} \boxed{\text{COS}} \boxed{(} \boxed{\pi} \boxed{\div} 12 \boxed{)} \boxed{)} \boxed{x^{-1}} \boxed{\text{ENTER}}$$

Rounding the display to four decimal places, we obtain $\sec \dfrac{\pi}{12} = 1.0353$.

EXAMPLE 7   Evaluating Trigonometric Functions with a Calculator

Use a calculator to find the value to four decimal places of:

a. cos 48.2°   **b.** cot 1.2.

Solution

Scientific Calculator Solution

Function	Mode	Keystrokes	Display, rounded to four decimal places
a. cos 48.2°	Degree	48.2 $\boxed{\text{COS}}$	0.6665
b. cot 1.2	Radian	1.2 $\boxed{\text{TAN}}$ $\boxed{1/x}$	0.3888

Graphing Calculator Solution

Function	Mode	Keystrokes	Display, rounded to four decimal places
a. cos 48.2°	Degree	$\boxed{\text{COS}}$ 48.2 $\boxed{\text{ENTER}}$	0.6665
b. cot 1.2	Radian	$\boxed{(}$ $\boxed{\text{TAN}}$ 1.2 $\boxed{)}$ $\boxed{x^{-1}}$ $\boxed{\text{ENTER}}$	0.3888

Check Point 7

Use a calculator to find the value to four decimal places of:
a. sin 72.8°   **b.** csc 1.5.

6 Use right triangle trigonometry to solve applied problems.

Applications

Many applications of right triangle trigonometry involve the angle made with an imaginary horizontal line. As shown in Figure 5.22, an angle formed by a horizontal line and the line of sight to an object that is above the horizontal line is called the **angle of elevation**. The angle formed by a horizontal line and the line of sight to an object that is below the horizontal line is called the **angle of depression**. Transits and sextants are instruments used to measure such angles.

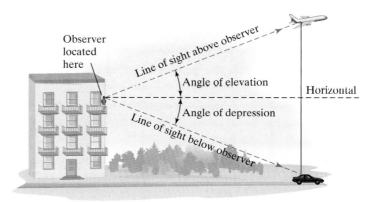

Figure 5.22

EXAMPLE 8   Problem Solving Using an Angle of Elevation

Sighting the top of a building, a surveyor measured the angle of elevation to be 22°. The transit is 5 feet above the ground and 300 feet from the building. Find the building's height.

Solution   The situation is illustrated in Figure 5.23. Let a be the height of the portion of the building that lies above the transit. The height of the building is the transit's height, 5 feet, plus a. Thus, we need to identify a trigonometric function that will make it possible to find a. In terms of the 22° angle, we are looking for the side opposite the angle. The transit is 300 feet from the building, so the side adjacent to the 22° angle is 300 feet. Because we have a known angle, an unknown opposite side, and a known adjacent side, we select the tangent function.

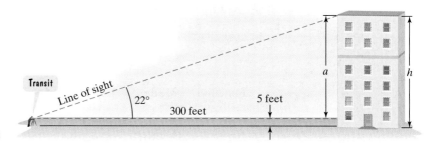

Figure 5.23

$$\tan 22° = \frac{a}{300} \quad \boxed{\text{Length of side opposite the 22° angle}}$$
$$\boxed{\text{Length of side adjacent to the 22° angle}}$$

$$a = 300 \tan 22° \qquad \text{Multiply both sides of the equation by 300.}$$

$$a \approx 300(0.4040) \approx 121 \qquad \text{Find } \tan 22° \text{ with a calculator}$$
$$\text{in the degree mode.}$$

The height of the part of the building above the transit is approximately 121 feet. Thus, the height of the building is determined by adding the transit's height, 5 feet, to 121 feet.

$$h \approx 5 + 121 = 126$$

The building's height is approximately 126 feet.

Check Point 8 The irregular blue shape in Figure 5.24 represents a lake. The distance across the lake, a, is unknown. To find this distance, a surveyor took the measurements shown in the figure. What is the distance across the lake?

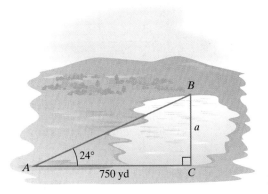

Figure 5.24

If two sides of a right triangle are known, an appropriate trigonometric function can be used to find an acute angle θ in the triangle. You will also need to use the *inverse key* on a calculator. This key uses a function value to display the acute angle θ. For example, suppose that $\sin \theta = 0.866$. We can find θ in the degree mode by using the *inverse sine* key, usually labeled $\boxed{\text{SIN}^{-1}}$.

Scientific Calculator   **Graphing Calculator**

$.866 \boxed{\text{SIN}^{-1}}$ $\boxed{\text{SIN}^{-1}} .866 \boxed{\text{ENTER}}$

The display shows approximately 59.99, which we can round to 60. Thus, if $\sin \theta = 0.866$, then $\theta \approx 60°$.

EXAMPLE 9   Determining the Angle of Elevation

A building that is 21 meters tall casts a shadow 25 meters long. Find the angle of elevation of the sun to the nearest degree.

Solution   The situation is illustrated in Figure 5.25. We are asked to find θ. We begin with the tangent function.

$$\tan \theta = \frac{\text{side opposite } \theta}{\text{side adjacent to } \theta} = \frac{21}{25}$$

We use a calculator in the degree mode to find θ.

Scientific Calculator

21 ÷ 25 = TAN⁻¹

Graphing Calculator

TAN⁻¹ (21 ÷ 25) ENTER

The display should show approximately 40. Thus, the angle of elevation of the sun is approximately 40°.

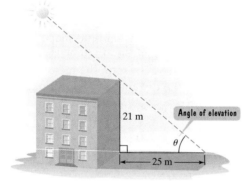

21 m

Angle of elevation

θ

25 m

Figure 5.25

Check Point 9

A flagpole that is 14 meters tall casts a shadow 10 meters long. Find the angle of elevation of the sun to the nearest degree.

The Mountain Man

In the 1930s, a *National Geographic* team headed by Brad Washburn used trigonometry to create a map of the 5000-square-mile region of the Yukon, near the Canadian border. The team started with aerial photography. By drawing a network of angles on the photographs, the approximate locations of the major mountains and their rough heights were determined. The expedition then spent three months on foot to find the exact heights. Team members established two base points a known distance apart, one directly under the mountain's peak. By measuring the angle of elevation from one of the base points to the peak, the tangent function was used to determine the peak's height. The Yukon expedition was a major advance in the way maps are made.

EXERCISE SET 5.2

✓ Practice Exercises

In Exercises 1–8, use the Pythagorean Theorem to find the length of the missing side of each right triangle. Then find the value of each of the six trigonometric functions of θ.

1.

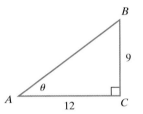

2.

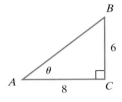

3.

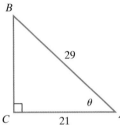

4.

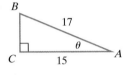

5.

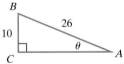

6.

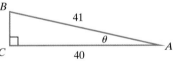

7.

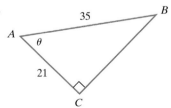

8.

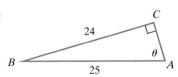

In Exercises 9–16, use the given triangles to evaluate each expression. If necessary, express the value without a square root in the denominator by rationalizing the denominator.

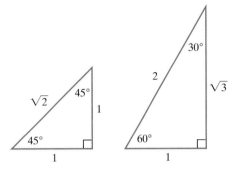

9. $\cos 30°$

10. $\tan 30°$

11. $\sec 45°$

12. $\csc 45°$

13. $\tan \dfrac{\pi}{3}$

14. $\cot \dfrac{\pi}{3}$

15. $\sin \dfrac{\pi}{4} - \cos \dfrac{\pi}{4}$

16. $\tan \dfrac{\pi}{4} + \csc \dfrac{\pi}{6}$

In Exercises 17–20, θ is an acute angle and $\sin θ$ and $\cos θ$ are given. Use identities to find $\tan θ$, $\csc θ$, $\sec θ$, and $\cot θ$. Where necessary, rationalize denominators.

17. $\sin \theta = \dfrac{8}{17}, \quad \cos \theta = \dfrac{15}{17}$

18. $\sin \theta = \dfrac{3}{5}, \quad \cos \theta = \dfrac{4}{5}$

19. $\sin \theta = \dfrac{1}{3}, \quad \cos \theta = \dfrac{2\sqrt{2}}{3}$

20. $\sin \theta = \dfrac{2}{3}, \quad \cos \theta = \dfrac{\sqrt{5}}{3}$

In Exercises 21–24, θ is an acute angle and $\sin θ$ is given. Use the Pythagorean identity $\sin^2 θ + \cos^2 θ = 1$ to find $\cos θ$.

21. $\sin \theta = \dfrac{6}{7}$

22. $\sin \theta = \dfrac{7}{8}$

23. $\sin \theta = \dfrac{\sqrt{39}}{8}$

24. $\sin \theta = \dfrac{\sqrt{21}}{5}$

In Exercises 25–30, use an identity to find the value of each expression. Do not use a calculator.

25. $\sin 37° \csc 37°$

26. $\cos 53° \sec 53°$

27. $\sin^2 \dfrac{\pi}{9} + \cos^2 \dfrac{\pi}{9}$

28. $\sin^2 \dfrac{\pi}{10} + \cos^2 \dfrac{\pi}{10}$

29. $\sec^2 23° - \tan^2 23°$

30. $\csc^2 63° - \cot^2 63°$

In Exercises 31–38, find a cofunction with the same value as the given expression.

31. $\sin 7°$

32. $\sin 19°$

33. $\csc 25°$

34. $\csc 35°$

35. $\tan \dfrac{\pi}{9}$

36. $\tan \dfrac{\pi}{7}$

37. $\cos \dfrac{2\pi}{5}$

38. $\cos \dfrac{3\pi}{8}$

In Exercises 39–48, use a calculator to find the value of the trigonometric function to four decimal places.

39. $\sin 38°$

40. $\cos 21°$

41. $\tan 32.7°$

42. $\tan 52.6°$

43. $\csc 17°$

44. $\sec 55°$

45. $\cos \dfrac{\pi}{10}$

46. $\sin \dfrac{3\pi}{10}$

47. $\cot \dfrac{\pi}{12}$

48. $\cot \dfrac{\pi}{18}$

In Exercises 49–54, find the measure of the side of the right triangle whose length is designated by a lowercase letter. Round answers to the nearest whole number.

49.

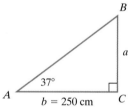

50.

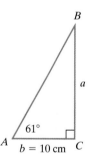

51.

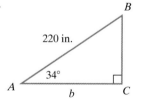

52.

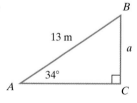

53.

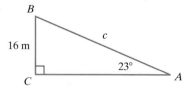

54.

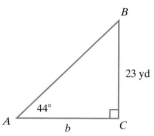

In Exercises 55–58, use a calculator to find the value of the acute angle θ to the nearest degree.

55. $\sin \theta = 0.2974$

56. $\cos \theta = 0.8771$

57. $\tan \theta = 4.6252$

58. $\tan \theta = 26.0307$

In Exercises 59–62, use a calculator to find the value of the acute angle θ in radians, rounded to three decimal places.

59. $\cos \theta = 0.4112$

60. $\sin \theta = 0.9499$

61. $\tan \theta = 0.4169$

62. $\tan \theta = 0.5117$

 Application Exercises

63. To find the distance across a lake, a surveyor took the measurements in the figure shown. Use these measurements to determine how far it is across the lake. Round to the nearest yard.

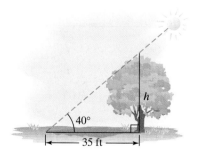

64. At a certain time of day, the angle of elevation of the sun is 40°. To the nearest foot, find the height of a tree whose shadow is 35 feet long.

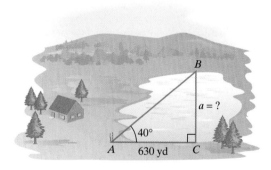

65. A tower that is 125 feet tall casts a shadow 172 feet long. Find the angle of elevation of the sun to the nearest degree.

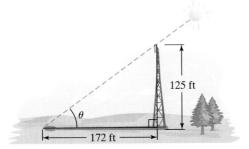

66. The Washington Monument is 555 feet high. If you stand one quarter of a mile, or 1320 feet, from the base of the monument and look to the top, find the angle of elevation to the nearest degree.

Washington Monument

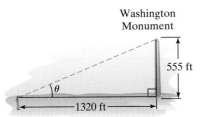

67. A plane rises from take-off and flies at an angle of 10° with the horizontal runway. When it has gained 500 feet, find the distance, to the nearest foot, the plane has flown.

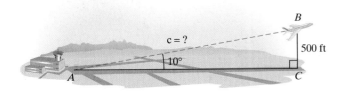

68. A road is inclined at an angle of 5°. After driving 5000 feet along this road, find the driver's increase in altitude. Round to the nearest foot.

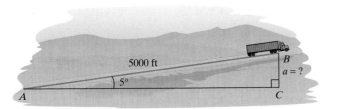

69. A telephone pole is 60 feet tall. A guy wire 75 feet long is attached from the ground to the top of the pole. Find the angle between the wire and the pole to the nearest degree.

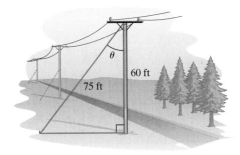

70. A telephone pole is 55 feet tall. A guy wire 80 feet long is attached from the ground to the top of the pole. Find the angle between the wire and the pole to the nearest degree.

Writing in Mathematics

71. If you are given the lengths of the sides of a right triangle, describe how to find the sine of either acute angle.

72. Describe one similarity and one difference between the definitions of $\sin \theta$ and $\cos \theta$, where θ is an acute angle of a right triangle.

73. Describe the triangle used to find the trigonometric functions of 45°.

74. Describe the triangle used to find the trigonometric functions of 30° and 60°.

75. What is a trigonometric identity?

76. Use words (not an equation) to describe one of the reciprocal identities.

77. Use words (not an equation) to describe one of the quotient identities.

78. Use words (not an equation) to describe one of the Pythagorean identities.

79. Describe a relationship among trigonometric functions that is based on angles that are complements.

80. Describe what is meant by an angle of elevation and an angle of depression.

81. Stonehenge, the famous "stone circle" in England, was built between 2750 B.C. and 1300 B.C. using solid stone blocks weighing over 99,000 pounds each. It required 550 people to pull a single stone up a ramp inclined at a 9° angle. Describe how right triangle trigonometry can be used to determine the distance the 550 workers had to drag a stone in order to raise it to a height of 30 feet.

Technology Exercises

82. Use a calculator in the radian mode to fill in the values in the following table. Then draw a conclusion about $\frac{\sin\theta}{\theta}$ as θ approaches 0.

θ	0.4	0.3	0.2	0.1	0.01	0.001	0.0001	0.00001
$\sin\theta$								
$\dfrac{\sin\theta}{\theta}$								

83. Use a calculator in the radian mode to fill in the values in the following table. Then draw a conclusion about $\frac{\cos\theta-1}{\theta}$ as θ approaches 0.

θ	0.4	0.3	0.2	0.1	0.01	0.001	0.0001	0.00001
$\cos\theta$								
$\dfrac{\cos\theta-1}{\theta}$								

Critical Thinking Exercises

84. Which one of the following is true?

a. $\dfrac{\tan 45°}{\tan 15°} = \tan 3°$

b. $\tan^2 15° - \sec^2 15° = -1$

c. $\sin 45° + \cos 45° = 1$

d. $\tan^2 5° = \tan 25°$

85. Explain why the sine or cosine of an acute angle cannot be greater than or equal to 1.

86. Describe what happens to the tangent of an acute angle as the angle gets close to 90°. What happens at 90°?

87. From the top of a 250-foot lighthouse, a plane is sighted overhead and a ship is observed directly below the plane. The angle of elevation of the plane is 22° and the angle of depression of the ship is 35°. Find **a.** the distance of the ship from the lighthouse; **b.** the plane's height above the water. Round to the nearest foot.

SECTION 5.3 *Trigonometric Functions of Any Angle*

Objectives

1. Use the definitions of trigonometric functions of any angle.
2. Use the signs of the trigonometric functions.
3. Find reference angles.
4. Use reference angles to evaluate trigonometric functions.

There is something comforting in the repetition of some of nature's patterns. The ocean level at a beach varies between high and low tide approximately every 12 hours. The number of hours of daylight oscillates from a maximum on the summer solstice, June 21; it decreases slowly until the minimum daylight occurs on the winter solstice, December 21, and then increases to the same maximum the following June 21. Some believe that cycles, called biorhythms, represent physical, emotional, and intellectual aspects of our lives. Throughout the remainder of this chapter, we will see how the trigonometric functions are used to model phenomena that occur again and again. To do this, we need to move beyond right triangles.

1 Use the definitions of trigonometric functions of any angle.

Trigonometric Functions of Any Angle

In the last section we evaluated trigonometric functions of acute angles, such as that shown in Figure 5.26(a). Note that this angle is in standard position. The point $P = (x, y)$ is a point r units from the origin on the terminal side of θ. A right triangle is formed by drawing a perpendicular from $P = (x, y)$ to the x-axis. Note that y is the length of the side opposite θ and x is the length of the side adjacent to θ.

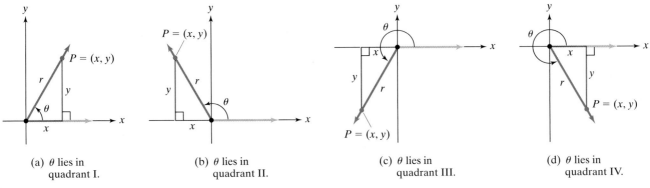

(a) θ lies in quadrant I.

(b) θ lies in quadrant II.

(c) θ lies in quadrant III.

(d) θ lies in quadrant IV.

Figure 5.26

Figures 5.26(b), (c), and (d) show angles in standard position, but they are not acute. We can extend our definitions of the six trigonometric functions to include such angles, as well as quadrantal angles. (Recall that a quadrantal angle has its terminal side on the x-axis or y-axis; such angles are *not* shown in Figure 5.26.) The point $P = (x, y)$ may be any point on the terminal side of the angle θ other than the origin $(0, 0)$.

Study Tip

If θ is acute, we have the right triangle shown in Figure 5.26(a). In this situation, the definitions in the box are the right triangle definitions of the trigonometric functions. This should make it easier for you to remember the six definitions.

Definitions of Trigonometric Functions of Any Angle

Let θ be any angle in standard position, and let $P = (x, y)$ be a point on the terminal side of θ. If $r = \sqrt{x^2 + y^2}$ is the distance from $(0, 0)$ to (x, y), as shown in Figure 5.26, the **six trigonometric functions of θ** are defined by the following ratios.

$$\sin \theta = \frac{y}{r} \qquad \cos \theta = \frac{x}{r} \qquad \tan \theta = \frac{y}{x}, x \neq 0$$

$$\csc \theta = \frac{r}{y}, y \neq 0 \qquad \sec \theta = \frac{r}{x}, x \neq 0 \qquad \cot \theta = \frac{x}{y}, y \neq 0$$

Because the point $P = (x, y)$ is any point on the terminal side of θ other than the origin $(0, 0)$, $r = \sqrt{x^2 + y^2}$ cannot be zero. Examine the six trigonometric functions defined previously. Note that the denominator of the sine and cosine functions is r. Because $r \neq 0$, the sine and cosine functions are defined for any real value of the angle θ. This is not true for the other four trigonometric functions. Note that the denominator of the tangent and secant functions is x. These functions are not defined if $x = 0$. If the point $P = (x, y)$ is on the y-axis, then $x = 0$. Thus, the tangent and secant functions are undefined for all quadrantal angles with terminal sides on the positive or negative y-axis. Likewise, if $P = (x, y)$ is on the x-axis, then $y = 0$, and the cotangent and cosecant functions

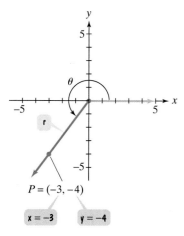

Figure 5.27

are undefined. The cotangent and cosecant functions are undefined for all quadrantal angles with terminal sides on the positive or negative x-axis.

EXAMPLE 1   Evaluating Trigonometric Functions

Let $P = (-3, -4)$ be a point on the terminal side of θ. Find each of the six trigonometric functions of θ.

Solution   The situation is shown in Figure 5.27. We need values for x, y, and r to evaluate all six trigonometric functions. We are given the values of x and y. Because $P = (-3, -4)$ is a point on the terminal side of θ, $x = -3$ and $y = -4$. Furthermore,

$$r = \sqrt{x^2 + y^2} = \sqrt{(-3)^2 + (-4)^2} = \sqrt{9 + 16} = \sqrt{25} = 5.$$

Now that we know x, y, and r, we can find the six trigonometric functions of θ.

$$\sin\theta = \frac{y}{r} = \frac{-4}{5} = -\frac{4}{5}, \qquad \cos\theta = \frac{x}{r} = \frac{-3}{5} = -\frac{3}{5}, \qquad \tan\theta = \frac{y}{x} = \frac{-4}{-3} = \frac{4}{3}$$

$$\csc\theta = \frac{r}{y} = \frac{5}{-4} = -\frac{5}{4}, \qquad \sec\theta = \frac{r}{x} = \frac{5}{-3} = -\frac{5}{3}, \qquad \cot\theta = \frac{x}{y} = \frac{-3}{-4} = \frac{3}{4}$$

> These ratios are the reciprocals of those shown directly above.

Check Point 1   Let $P = (4, -3)$ be a point on the terminal side of θ. Find each of the six trigonometric functions of θ.

How do we find the values of the trigonometric functions for a quadrantal angle? First, draw the angle in standard position. Second, choose a point P on the angle's terminal side. The trigonometric function values of θ depend only on the size of θ and not on the distance of point P from the origin. Thus, we choose a point that is 1 unit from the origin. Finally, apply the definition of the appropriate trigonometric function.

EXAMPLE 2   Trigonometric Functions of Quadrantal Angles

Evaluate, if possible, the sine function and the tangent function at the following four quadrantal angles:

a. $\theta = 0° = 0$ **b.** $\theta = 90° = \dfrac{\pi}{2}$ **c.** $\theta = 180° = \pi$ **d.** $\theta = 270° = \dfrac{3\pi}{2}$

Solution

a. If $\theta = 0° = 0$ radians, then the terminal side of the angle is on the positive x-axis. Let us select the point $P = (1, 0)$ with $x = 1$ and $y = 0$. This point is 1 unit from the origin, so $r = 1$. Now that we know x, y, and r, we can apply the definitions of the sine and tangent functions.

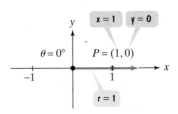

$$\sin 0° = \sin 0 = \frac{y}{r} = \frac{0}{1} = 0$$

$$\tan 0° = \tan 0 = \frac{y}{x} = \frac{0}{1} = 0$$

b. If $\theta = 90° = \dfrac{\pi}{2}$ radians, then the terminal side of the angle is on the positive y-axis. Let us select the point $P = (0, 1)$ with $x = 0$ and $y = 1$. This point is 1 unit from the origin, so $r = 1$. Now that we know x, y, and r, we can apply the definitions of the sine and tangent functions.

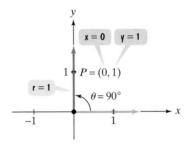

$$\sin 90° = \sin \frac{\pi}{2} = \frac{y}{r} = \frac{1}{1} = 1$$

$$\tan 90° = \tan \frac{\pi}{2} = \frac{y}{x} = \frac{1}{0}$$

Because division by 0 is undefined, $\tan 90°$ is undefined.

c. If $\theta = 180° = \pi$ radians, then the terminal side of the angle is on the negative x-axis. Let us select the point $P = (-1, 0)$ with $x = -1$ and $y = 0$. This point is 1 unit from the origin, so $r = 1$. Now that we know x, y, and r, we can apply the definitions of the sine and tangent functions.

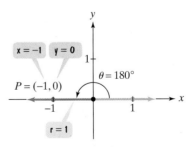

$$\sin 180° = \sin \pi = \frac{y}{r} = \frac{0}{1} = 0$$

$$\tan 180° = \tan \pi = \frac{y}{x} = \frac{0}{-1} = 0$$

d. If $\theta = 270° = \dfrac{3\pi}{2}$ radians, then the terminal side of the angle is on the negative y-axis. Let us select the point $P = (0, -1)$ with $x = 0$ and $y = -1$. This point is 1 unit from the origin, so $r = 1$. Now that we know x, y, and r, we can apply the definitions of the sine and tangent functions.

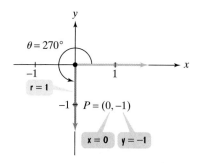

$$\sin 270° = \sin \frac{3\pi}{2} = \frac{y}{r} = \frac{-1}{1} = -1$$

$$\tan 270° = \tan \frac{3\pi}{2} = \frac{y}{x} = \frac{-1}{0}$$

Because division by 0 is undefined, $\tan 270°$ is undefined.

Check Point 2

Evaluate, if possible, the cosine function and the cosecant function at the following four quadrantal angles:

a. $\theta = 0° = 0$ **b.** $\theta = 90° = \dfrac{\pi}{2}$

c. $\theta = 180° = \pi$ **d.** $\theta = 270° = \dfrac{3\pi}{2}$

---

2 Use the signs of the trigonometric functions.

The Signs of the Trigonometric Functions

In Example 2, we evaluated trigonometric functions of quadrantal angles. However, we will now return to the trigonometric functions of nonquadrantal angles. **If θ is not a quadrantal angle, the sign of a trigonometric function depends on the quadrant in which θ lies.** In all four quadrants, r is positive. However, x and y can be positive or negative. For example, if θ lies in quadrant II, x is negative and y is positive. Thus, the only positive ratios in this quadrant are $\dfrac{y}{r}$ and its reciprocal, $\dfrac{r}{y}$. These ratios are the function values for the sine and cosecant, respectively. In short, if θ lies in quadrant II, $\sin\theta$ and $\csc\theta$ are positive. The other four trigonometric functions are negative.

Figure 5.28 summarizes the signs of the trigonometric functions. If θ lies in quadrant I, all six functions are positive. If θ lies in quadrant II, only $\sin\theta$ and $\csc\theta$ are positive. If θ lies in quadrant III, only $\tan\theta$ and $\cot\theta$ are positive. Finally, if θ lies in quadrant IV, only $\cos\theta$ and $\sec\theta$ are positive. Observe that the positive functions in each quadrant occur in reciprocal pairs.

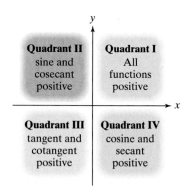

Figure 5.28 The signs of the trigonometric functions

EXAMPLE 3   Finding the Quadrant in Which an Angle Lies

If $\tan \theta < 0$ and $\cos \theta > 0$, name the quadrant in which angle θ lies.

Solution   Because $\tan \theta < 0, \theta$ cannot lie in quadrant I; all the functions are positive in quadrant I. Furthermore, θ cannot lie in quadrant III; $\tan \theta$ is positive in quadrant III. Thus, with $\tan \theta < 0, \theta$ lies in quadrant II or quadrant IV. We are also given that $\cos \theta > 0$. Because quadrant IV is the only quadrant in which the cosine is positive and the tangent is negative, we conclude that θ lies in quadrant IV.

> **Check Point 3**   If $\sin \theta < 0$ and $\cos \theta < 0$, name the quadrant in which angle θ lies.

EXAMPLE 4   Evaluating Trigonometric Functions

Given $\tan \theta = -\frac{2}{3}$ and $\cos \theta > 0$, find $\cos \theta$ and $\csc \theta$.

Solution   Because the tangent is negative and the cosine is positive, θ lies in quadrant IV. This will help us to determine whether the negative sign in $\tan \theta = -\frac{2}{3}$ should be associated with the numerator or the denominator. Keep in mind that in quadrant IV, x is positive and y is negative. Thus,

> In quadrant IV, y is negative.

$$\tan \theta = -\frac{2}{3} = \frac{y}{x} = \frac{-2}{3}$$

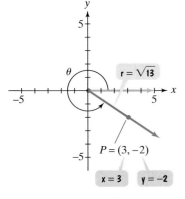

Figure 5.29 $\tan \theta = -\frac{2}{3}$ and $\cos \theta > 0$

(See Figure 5.29). Thus, $x = 3$ and $y = -2$. Furthermore,

$$r = \sqrt{x^2 + y^2} = \sqrt{3^2 + (-2)^2} = \sqrt{9 + 4} = \sqrt{13}.$$

Now that we know $x, y,$ and r, we can find $\cos \theta$ and $\csc \theta$.

$$\cos \theta = \frac{x}{r} = \frac{3}{\sqrt{13}} = \frac{3}{\sqrt{13}} \cdot \frac{\sqrt{13}}{\sqrt{13}} = \frac{3\sqrt{13}}{13} \qquad \csc \theta = \frac{r}{y} = \frac{\sqrt{13}}{-2} = -\frac{\sqrt{13}}{2}$$

> **Check Point 4**   Given $\tan \theta = -\frac{1}{3}$ and $\cos \theta < 0$, find $\sin \theta$ and $\sec \theta$.

3 Find reference angles.

Reference Angles

We will often evaluate trigonometric functions of positive angles greater than 90° and all negative angles by making use of a positive acute angle. This positive acute angle is called a *reference angle*.

> ### Definition of a Reference Angle
> Let θ be a nonacute angle in standard position that lies in a quadrant. Its **reference angle** is the positive acute angle θ' formed by the terminal side of θ and the x-axis.

Figure 5.30 shows the reference angle for θ lying in quadrants II, III, and IV. Notice that the formula used to find θ, the reference angle, varies according to the quadrant in which θ lies. You may find it easier to find the reference angle for a given angle by making a figure that shows the angle in standard position. The acute angle formed by the terminal side of this angle and the *x*-axis is the reference angle.

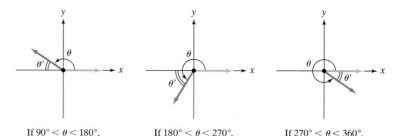

Figure 5.30 Reference angles for positive angles in quadrants II, III, and IV

If $90° < \theta < 180°$, then $\theta' = 180° - \theta$.

If $180° < \theta < 270°$, then $\theta' = \theta - 180°$.

If $270° < \theta < 360°$, then $\theta' = 360° - \theta$.

EXAMPLE 5   Finding Reference Angles

Find the reference angle, θ', for each of the following angles:

a. $\theta = 345°$ **b.** $\theta = \dfrac{5\pi}{6}$ **c.** $\theta = -135°$ **d.** $\theta = 2.5$.

Solution

a. A 345° angle in standard position is shown in Figure 5.31. Because 345° lies in quadrant IV, the reference angle is

$$\theta' = 360° - 345° = 15°.$$

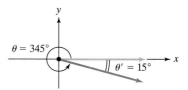

Figure 5.31

b. Because $\dfrac{5\pi}{6}$ lies between $\dfrac{\pi}{2} = \dfrac{3\pi}{6}$ and

$\pi = \dfrac{6\pi}{6}$, $\theta = \dfrac{5\pi}{6}$ lies in quadrant II. The angle is shown in Figure 5.32. The reference angle is

$$\theta' = \pi - \dfrac{5\pi}{6} = \dfrac{6\pi}{6} - \dfrac{5\pi}{6} = \dfrac{\pi}{6}.$$

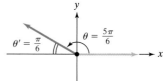

Figure 5.32

c. A −135° angle in standard position is shown in Figure 5.33. The figure indicates that the positive acute angle formed by the terminal side of θ and the *x*-axis is 45°. The reference angle is

$$\theta' = 45°.$$

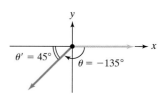

Figure 5.33

d. The angle $\theta = 2.5$ lies between $\dfrac{\pi}{2} \approx 1.57$

and $\pi \approx 3.14$. This means that $\theta = 2.5$ is in quadrant II, shown in Figure 5.34. The reference angle is

$$\theta' = \pi - 2.5 \approx 0.64.$$

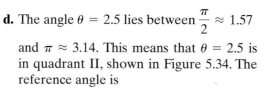

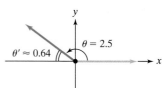

Figure 5.34

Check Point 5

Find the reference angle, θ', for each of the following angles:

a. $\theta = 210°$ **b.** $\theta = \dfrac{7\pi}{4}$ **c.** $\theta = -240°$ **d.** $\theta = 3.6$.

4 Use reference angles to evaluate trigonometric functions.

The way that reference angles are defined makes them useful in evaluating trigonometric functions.

Using Reference Angles to Evaluate Trigonometric Functions

The values of the trigonometric functions of a given angle, θ, are the same as the values of the trigonometric functions of the reference angle, θ', except possibly for the sign. A function value of the acute angle, θ', is always positive. However, the same function value for θ may be positive or negative.

For example, we can use a reference angle, θ', to obtain an exact value for $\tan 120°$. The reference angle for $\theta = 120°$ is $\theta' = 180° - 120° = 60°$. We know the exact value for the tangent function of the reference angle: $\tan 60° = \sqrt{3}$. We also know that the value of a trigonometric function for a given angle, θ, is the same as that for its reference angle, θ', except possibly for the sign. Thus, we can conclude that $\tan 120°$ equals $-\sqrt{3}$ or $\sqrt{3}$.

What sign should we attach to $\sqrt{3}$? A $120°$ angle lies in quadrant II, where sine and cosecant are positive. Thus, the tangent function is negative for a $120°$ angle. Therefore,

Prefix by a negative sign to
show tangent is negative in
quadrant II.

$$\tan 120° = -\tan 60° = -\sqrt{3}.$$

The reference angle
for $120°$ is $60°$.

In the previous section, we used two right triangles to find exact trigonometric values of $30°, 45°$, and $60°$. Using a procedure similar to finding $\tan 120°$, we can now find the function values of all angles for which $30°, 45°$, or $60°$ are reference angles.

A Procedure for Using Reference Angles to Evaluate Trigonometric Functions

The value of a trigonometric function of any angle θ is found as follows:

1. Find the associated reference angle, θ', and the function value for θ'.
2. Use the quadrant in which θ lies to prefix the appropriate sign to the function value in step 1.

Discovery

Draw the two right triangles involving $30°, 45°$, and $60°$. Indicate the length of each side. Use these lengths to verify the function values for the reference angles in the solution to Example 6.

EXAMPLE 6 Using Reference Angles to Evaluate Trigonometric Functions

Use reference angles to find the exact value of each of the following trigonometric functions.

a. $\sin 135°$ **b.** $\cos \dfrac{4\pi}{3}$ **c.** $\cot\left(-\dfrac{\pi}{3}\right)$

Solution

a. We use our two-step procedure to find $\sin 135°$.

Step 1 Find the reference angle, θ', and $\sin\theta'$. Figure 5.35 shows $135°$ lies in quadrant II. The reference angle is

$$\theta' = 180° - 135° = 45°.$$

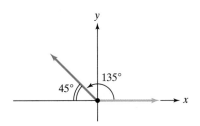

The function value for the reference angle is $\sin 45° = \dfrac{\sqrt{2}}{2}$.

Figure 5.35 Reference angle for 135°

Step 2 Use the quadrant in which θ lies to prefix the appropriate sign to the function value in step 1. The angle $\theta = 135°$ lies in quadrant II. Because the sine is positive in quadrant II, we put a + sign before the function value of the reference angle. Thus,

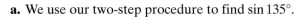

The sine is positive in quadrant II.

$$\sin 135° = +\sin 45° = \frac{\sqrt{2}}{2}.$$

The reference angle for 135° is 45°.

b. We use our two-step procedure to find $\cos\dfrac{4\pi}{3}$.

Step 1 Find the reference angle, θ', and $\cos\theta'$. Figure 5.36 shows that $\theta = \dfrac{4\pi}{3}$ lies in quadrant III. The reference angle is

$$\theta' = \frac{4\pi}{3} - \pi = \frac{4\pi}{3} - \frac{3\pi}{3} = \frac{\pi}{3}.$$

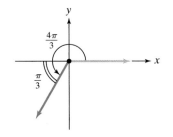

The function value for the reference angle is

$$\cos\frac{\pi}{3} = \frac{1}{2}.$$

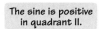

Figure 5.36 Reference angle for $\dfrac{4\pi}{3}$

Step 2 Use the quadrant in which θ lies to prefix the appropriate sign to the function value in step 1. The angle $\theta = \dfrac{4\pi}{3}$ lies in quadrant III. Because only the tangent and cotangent are positive in quadrant III, the cosine is negative in this quadrant. We put a − sign before the function value of the reference angle. Thus,

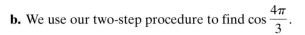

The cosine is negative in quadrant III.

$$\cos\frac{4\pi}{3} = -\cos\frac{\pi}{3} = -\frac{1}{2}.$$

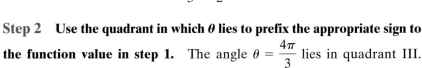

The reference angle for $\dfrac{4\pi}{3}$ is $\dfrac{\pi}{3}$.

c. We use our two-step procedure to find $\cot\left(-\dfrac{\pi}{3}\right)$.

Step 1   Find the reference angle, θ', and $\cot\theta'$.   Figure 5.37 shows that $\theta = -\dfrac{\pi}{3}$ lies in quadrant IV. The reference angle is $\theta' = \dfrac{\pi}{3}$. The function value for the reference angle is $\cot\dfrac{\pi}{3} = \dfrac{\sqrt{3}}{3}$.

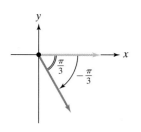

Figure 5.37 Reference angle for $-\dfrac{\pi}{3}$

Step 2   Use the quadrant in which θ lies to prefix the appropriate sign to the function value in step 1.   The angle $\theta = -\dfrac{\pi}{3}$ lies in quadrant IV. Because only the cosine and secant are positive in quadrant IV, the cotangent is negative in this quadrant. We put a $-$ sign before the function value of the reference angle. Thus,

The cotangent is negative in quadrant IV.

$$\cot\left(-\frac{\pi}{3}\right) = -\cot\frac{\pi}{3} = -\frac{\sqrt{3}}{3}.$$

The reference angle for $-\dfrac{\pi}{3}$ is $\dfrac{\pi}{3}$.

Check Point 6   Use reference angles to find the exact value of the following trigonometric functions.

a. $\sin 300°$ **b.** $\tan\dfrac{5\pi}{4}$ **c.** $\sec\left(-\dfrac{\pi}{6}\right)$

EXERCISE SET 5.3

Practice Exercises

In Exercises 1–8, a point on the terminal side of angle θ is given. Find the exact value of each of the six trigonometric functions of θ.

1. $(-4, 3)$ **2.** $(-12, 5)$
3. $(2, 3)$ **4.** $(3, 7)$
5. $(3, -3)$ **6.** $(5, -5)$
7. $(-2, -5)$ **8.** $(-1, -3)$

In Exercises 9–16, evaluate the trigonometric function at the quadrantal angle, or state that the expression is undefined.

9. $\cos\pi$ **10.** $\tan\pi$
11. $\sec\pi$ **12.** $\csc\pi$
13. $\tan\dfrac{3\pi}{2}$ **14.** $\cos\dfrac{3\pi}{2}$
15. $\cot\dfrac{\pi}{2}$ **16.** $\tan\dfrac{\pi}{2}$

In Exercises 17–22, let θ be an angle in standard position. Name the quadrant in which θ lies.

17. $\sin\theta > 0,\quad \cos\theta > 0$

18. $\sin\theta < 0,\quad \cos\theta > 0$
19. $\sin\theta < 0,\quad \cos\theta < 0$
20. $\tan\theta < 0,\quad \sin\theta < 0$
21. $\tan\theta < 0,\quad \cos\theta < 0$
22. $\cot\theta > 0,\quad \sec\theta < 0$

In Exercises 23–34, find the exact value of each of the remaining trigonometric functions of θ.

23. $\cos\theta = -\dfrac{3}{5},\quad \theta$ in quadrant III
24. $\sin\theta = -\dfrac{12}{13},\quad \theta$ in quadrant III
25. $\sin\theta = \dfrac{5}{13},\quad \theta$ in quadrant II
26. $\cos\theta = \dfrac{4}{5},\quad \theta$ in quadrant IV
27. $\cos\theta = \dfrac{8}{17},\quad 270° < \theta < 360°$
28. $\cos\theta = \dfrac{1}{3},\quad 270° < \theta < 360°$
29. $\tan\theta = -\dfrac{2}{3},\quad \sin\theta > 0$
30. $\tan\theta = -\dfrac{1}{3},\quad \sin\theta > 0$
31. $\tan\theta = \dfrac{4}{3},\quad \cos\theta < 0$
32. $\tan\theta = \dfrac{5}{12},\quad \cos\theta < 0$
33. $\sec\theta = -3,\quad \tan\theta > 0$
34. $\csc\theta = -4,\quad \tan\theta > 0$

In Exercises 35–50, find the reference angle for each angle.

35. 160°

36. 170°

37. 205°

38. 210°

39. 355°

40. 351°

41. $\dfrac{7\pi}{4}$

42. $\dfrac{5\pi}{4}$

43. $\dfrac{5\pi}{6}$

44. $\dfrac{5\pi}{7}$

45. −150°

46. −250°

47. −335°

48. −359°

49. 4.7

50. 5.5

In Exercises 51–66, use reference angles to find the exact value of each expression. Do not use a calculator.

51. $\cos 225°$

52. $\sin 300°$

53. $\tan 210°$

54. $\sec 240°$

55. $\tan 420°$

56. $\tan 405°$

57. $\sin \dfrac{2\pi}{3}$

58. $\cos \dfrac{3\pi}{4}$

59. $\csc \dfrac{7\pi}{6}$

60. $\cot \dfrac{7\pi}{4}$

61. $\tan \dfrac{9\pi}{4}$

62. $\tan \dfrac{9\pi}{2}$

63. $\sin(-240°)$

64. $\sin(-225°)$

65. $\tan\left(-\dfrac{\pi}{4}\right)$

66. $\tan\left(-\dfrac{\pi}{6}\right)$

Writing in Mathematics

67. If you are given a point on the terminal side of angle θ, explain how to find $\sin\theta$.

68. Explain why $\tan 90°$ is undefined.

69. If $\cos\theta > 0$ and $\tan\theta < 0$, explain how to find the quadrant in which θ lies.

70. What is a reference angle? Give an example with your description.

71. Explain how reference angles are used to evaluate trigonometric functions. Give an example with your description.

SECTION 5.4 Trigonometric Functions of Real Numbers; Periodic Functions

Objectives

1. Use a unit circle to define trigonometric functions of real numbers.
2. Recognize the domain and range of sine and cosine functions.
3. Use even and odd trigonometric functions.
4. Use periodic properties.

Cycles govern many aspects of life—heartbeats, sleep patterns, seasons, and tides all follow regular, predictable cycles. In this section we will see why trigonometric functions are used to model phenomena that occur in cycles. To do this, we need to move beyond angles and consider trigonometric functions of real numbers.

1 Use a unit circle to define trigonometric functions of real numbers.

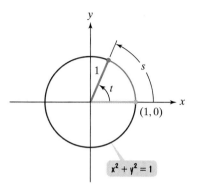

Figure 5.38 Unit circle with a central angle measuring t radians

Trigonometric Functions of Real Numbers

Thus far, we have considered trigonometric functions of angles measured in degrees or radians. To define trigonometric functions of real numbers, rather than angles, we use a unit circle. A **unit circle** is a circle of radius 1, with center at the origin of a rectangular coordinate system. The equation of this unit circle is $x^2 + y^2 = 1$. Figure 5.38 shows a unit circle in which the central angle measures t radians. We can use the formula for the length of a circular arc, $s = r\theta$, to find the length of the intercepted arc.

$$s = r\theta = 1 \cdot t = t$$

| The radius of a unit circle is 1. | The radian measure of the central angle is t. |

Thus, the length of the intercepted arc is t. This is also the radian measure of the central angle. Thus, **in a unit circle, the radian measure of the angle is equal to the measure of the intercepted arc.** Both are given by the same *real number t*.

In Figure 5.39, the radian measure of the angle and the length of the intercepted arc are both shown by t. Let $P = (x, y)$ denote the point on the unit circle that has arc length t from $(1, 0)$. Figure 5.39(a) shows that if t is positive, point P is reached by moving counterclockwise along the unit circle from $(1, 0)$. Figure 5.39(b) shows that if t is negative, point P is reached by moving clockwise along the unit circle from $(1, 0)$. For each real number t there corresponds a point $P = (x, y)$ on the unit circle.

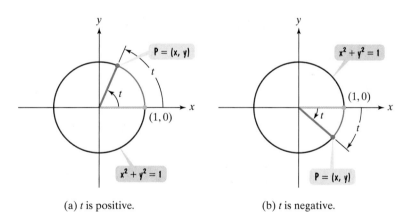

Figure 5.39   (a) t is positive.   (b) t is negative.

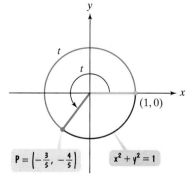

Figure 5.40

Using Figure 5.39, we define the cosine function at t as the x-coordinate of P and the sine function at t as the y-coordinate of P. Thus,

$$x = \cos t \quad \text{and} \quad y = \sin t.$$

For example, a point $P = (x, y)$ on the unit circle corresponding to a real number t is shown in Figure 5.40 for $\pi < t < \dfrac{3\pi}{2}$. We see that the coordinates of $P = (x, y)$ are $x = -\frac{3}{5}$ and $y = -\frac{4}{5}$. Because the cosine function is the x-coordinate of P and the sine function is the y-coordinate of P, the values of these trigonometric functions at the real number t are

$$\cos t = -\frac{3}{5} \quad \text{and} \quad \sin t = -\frac{4}{5}.$$

> **Definitions of the Trigonometric Functions in Terms of a Unit Circle**
>
> If t is a real number and $P = (x, y)$ is a point on the unit circle that corresponds to t, then
>
> $$\sin t = y \qquad\qquad \cos t = x \qquad\qquad \tan t = \frac{y}{x}, x \neq 0$$
>
> $$\csc t = \frac{1}{y}, y \neq 0 \qquad \sec t = \frac{1}{x}, x \neq 0 \qquad \cot t = \frac{x}{y}, y \neq 0$$

Because this definition expresses function values in terms of coordinates of a point on a unit circle, the trigonometric functions are sometimes called the **circular functions.**

EXAMPLE 1   Finding Values of the Trigonometric Functions

Use Figure 5.41 to find the values of the trigonometric functions at $t = \dfrac{\pi}{2}$.

Solution   The point P on the unit circle that corresponds to $t = \dfrac{\pi}{2}$ has coordinates $(0, 1)$. We use $x = 0$ and $y = 1$ to find the values of the trigonometric functions.

$$\sin \frac{\pi}{2} = y = 1 \qquad\qquad \cos \frac{\pi}{2} = x = 0$$

$$\csc \frac{\pi}{2} = \frac{1}{y} = \frac{1}{1} = 1 \qquad\qquad \cot \frac{\pi}{2} = \frac{x}{y} = \frac{0}{1} = 0$$

By definition, $\tan t = \dfrac{y}{x}$ and $\sec t = \dfrac{1}{x}$. Because $x = 0$, $\tan \dfrac{\pi}{2}$ and $\sec \dfrac{\pi}{2}$, are undefined.

Figure 5.41

(figure at left: unit circle with $P = (0, 1)$, angle $\frac{\pi}{2}$, point $(1,0)$, and $x^2 + y^2 = 1$)

> **Check Point 1**   Use the figure on the right to find the values of the trigonometric functions at $t = \pi$.

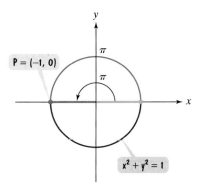

2   Recognize the domain and range of sine and cosine functions.

Domain and Range of Sine and Cosine Functions

The value of a trigonometric function at the real number t is its value at an angle of t radians. However, using real number domains, we can observe properties of trigonometric functions that are not as apparent using the angle approach. For example, the domain and range of each trigonometric function can be found from the unit circle definition. At this point, let's look only at the sine and cosine functions,

$$\sin t = y \quad \text{and} \quad \cos t = x.$$

Because t can be the radian measure of any angle or, equivalently, the measure of any intercepted arc, the domain of the sine function and the cosine function is the set of all real numbers. Because the radius of the unit circle is 1, we have

$$-1 \le x \le 1 \quad \text{and} \quad -1 \le y \le 1.$$

Therefore, with $x = \cos t$ and $y = \sin t$, we obtain

$$-1 \le \cos t \le 1 \quad \text{and} \quad -1 \le \sin t \le 1.$$

The range of the cosine and sine functions is $[-1, 1]$.

The Domain and Range of the Sine and Cosine Functions

The domain of the sine function and the cosine function is the set of all real numbers. The range of these functions is the set of all real numbers from -1 to 1, inclusive.

---

3 Use even and odd trigonometric functions.

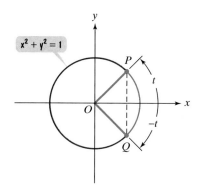

Figure 5.42

Even and Odd Trigonometric Functions

In Chapter 2, we saw that a function is even if $f(-t) = f(t)$ and odd if $f(-t) = -f(t)$. We can use Figure 5.42 to show that the cosine is an even function and the sine is an odd function. By definition, the coordinates of the points P and Q in Figure 5.42 are as follows:

$$P: \quad (\cos t, \sin t)$$

$$Q: \quad (\cos(-t), \sin(-t)).$$

In Figure 5.42, the x-coordinates of P and Q are the same. Thus,

$$\cos(-t) = \cos t.$$

This shows that cosine is an even function. By contrast, the y-coordinates of P and Q are negatives of each other. Thus,

$$\sin(-t) = -\sin t.$$

This shows that the sine is an odd function.

This argument is valid regardless of the length of t. Thus, the arc may terminate in any of the four quadrants. Using the unit circle definition of the trigonometric functions, we obtain the following results.

Even and Odd Trigonometric Functions

The cosine and secant functions are *even*.

$$\cos(-t) = \cos t \qquad \sec(-t) = \sec t$$

The sine, cosecant, tangent, and cotangent functions are *odd*.

$$\sin(-t) = -\sin t \qquad \csc(-t) = -\csc t$$

$$\tan(-t) = -\tan t \qquad \cot(-t) = -\cot t$$

EXAMPLE 2 Using Even and Odd Functions to Find Exact Values

Find the exact value of:

a. $\cos(-45°)$ **b.** $\tan\left(-\dfrac{\pi}{3}\right)$.

Solution

a. $\cos(-45°) = \cos 45° = \dfrac{\sqrt{2}}{2}$ **b.** $\tan\left(-\dfrac{\pi}{3}\right) = -\tan\dfrac{\pi}{3} = -\sqrt{3}$

Check Point 2

Find the exact value of:

a. $\cos(-60°)$ **b.** $\tan\left(-\dfrac{\pi}{6}\right)$.

4 Use periodic properties.

Periodic Functions

Certain patterns in nature repeat again and again. For example, the ocean level at a beach varies between low tide and high tide approximately every 12 hours. If low tide occurs at noon, then high tide will be around 6 P.M. and low tide will occur again around midnight, and so on infinitely. If $f(t)$ represents the ocean level at the beach at any time t, then the level is the same 12 hours later. Thus,

$$f(t + 12) = f(t).$$

The word *periodic* means that this tidal behavior repeats infinitely. The *period*, 12 hours, is the time it takes to complete one full cycle.

Definition of a Periodic Function

A function f is **periodic** if there exists a positive number p such that

$$f(t + p) = f(t)$$

for all t in the domain of f. The smallest number p for which f is periodic is called the **period** of f.

The trigonometric functions are used to model periodic phenomena. Why? If we begin at any point P on the unit circle and travel a distance of 2π units along the perimeter, we will return to the same point P. Because the trigonometric functions are defined in terms of the coordinates of that point P, we obtain the following results.

Periodic Properties of the Sine and Cosine Functions

$$\sin(t + 2\pi) = \sin t \quad \text{and} \quad \cos(t + 2\pi) = \cos t$$

The sine and cosine functions are periodic functions and have period 2π.

EXAMPLE 3   **Using Periodic Properties to Find Exact Values**

Find the exact value of: **a.** $\tan 420°$ **b.** $\sin \dfrac{9\pi}{4}$.

Solution

a. $\tan 420° = \tan(360° + 60°) = \tan 60° = \sqrt{3}$

b. $\sin \dfrac{9\pi}{4} = \sin\left(2\pi + \dfrac{\pi}{4}\right) = \sin \dfrac{\pi}{4} = \dfrac{\sqrt{2}}{2}$

Check Point 3   Find the exact value of:

a. $\cos 405°$ **b.** $\tan \dfrac{7\pi}{3}$.

Like the sine and cosine functions, the secant and cosecant functions have period 2π. However, this is not true for the tangent and cotangent functions. If we begin at any point $P(x, y)$ on the unit circle and travel a distance of π units along the perimeter, we arrive at the point $(-x, -y)$. The tangent function, defined in terms of the coordinates of a point, is the same at (x, y) and $(-x, -y)$.

Tangent function at (x, y) $\dfrac{y}{x} = \dfrac{-y}{-x}$ Tangent function π radians later

We see that $\tan(t + \pi) = \tan t$. The same observations apply to the cotangent function.

Periodic Properties of the Tangent and Cotangent Functions

$$\tan(t + \pi) = \tan t \quad \text{and} \quad \cot(t + \pi) = \cot t$$

The tangent and cotangent functions are periodic functions and have period π.

Why do the trigonometric functions model phenomena that repeat *indefinitely*? By starting at point P on the unit circle and traveling a distance of 2π units, 4π units, 6π units, and so on, we return to the starting point P. Because the trigonometric functions are defined in terms of the coordinates of that point P, if we add (or subtract) multiples of 2π, the trigonometric values do not change.

Furthermore, the trigonometric values for the tangent and cotangent functions do not change if we add (or subtract) multiples of π.

Repetitive Behavior of the Sine, Cosine, and Tangent Functions

For any integer n and real number t,

$$\sin(t + 2\pi n) = \sin t, \quad \cos(t + 2\pi n) = \cos t, \quad \text{and} \quad \tan(t + \pi n) = \tan t$$

EXERCISE SET 5.4

Practice Exercises

In Exercises 1–4, a point $P(x, y)$ is shown on the unit circle corresponding to a real number t. Find the values of the trigonometric functions at t.

1.

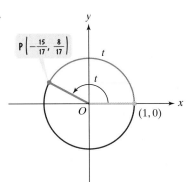

2.

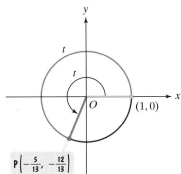

3.

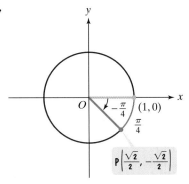

4.

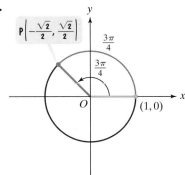

In Exercises 5–8, use even and odd properties of the trigonometric functions to find the exact value of each expression.

5. $\sin(-45°)$

6. $\tan(-45°)$

7. $\sec\left(-\dfrac{\pi}{3}\right)$

8. $\sec\left(-\dfrac{\pi}{6}\right)$

In Exercises 9–12, use periodic properties to find the exact value of each expression.

9. $\cos 585°$

10. $\cos 570°$

11. $\cot \dfrac{7\pi}{3}$

12. $\cot \dfrac{9\pi}{4}$

Application Exercises

13. The number of hours of daylight, H, on day t of any given year (on January 1, $t = 1$) in Fairbanks, Alaska, can be modeled by the function

$$H = 12 + 8.3 \sin\left[\frac{2\pi}{365}(t - 80)\right].$$

a. March 21, the 80th day of the year, is the spring equinox. Find the number of hours of daylight in Fairbanks on this day.

b. June 21, the 172nd day of the year, is the summer solstice, the day with the maximum number of hours of daylight. To the nearest tenth of an hour, find the number of hours of daylight in Fairbanks on this day.

c. December 21, the 355th day of the year, is the winter solstice, the day with the minimum number of hours of daylight. Find, to the nearest tenth of an hour, the number of hours of daylight in Fairbanks on this day.

14. The number of hours of daylight, H, on day t of any given year (on January 1, $t = 1$) in San Diego, California, can be modeled by the function

$$H = 12 + 2.4 \sin\left[\frac{2\pi}{365}(t - 80)\right].$$

a. March 21, the 80th day of the year, is the spring equinox. Find the number of hours of daylight in San Diego on this day.

b. June 21, the 172nd day of the year, is the summer solstice, the day with the maximum number of hours of daylight. Find, to the nearest tenth of an hour, the number of hours of daylight in San Diego on this day.

c. December 21, the 355th day of the year, is the winter solstice, the day with the minimum number of hours of daylight. To the nearest tenth of an hour, find the number of hours of daylight in San Diego on this day.

15. People who believe in biorhythms claim that there are three cycles that rule our behavior—the physical, emotional, and mental. Each is a sine function of a certain period. The function for our emotional fluctuations is

$$E = \sin\frac{\pi}{14}t$$

where t is measured in days starting at birth. Emotional fluctuations, E, are measured from -1 to 1, inclusive, with 1 representing peak emotional well-being, -1 representing the low for emotional well-being, and 0 representing feeling neither emotionally high or low.

a. Find E corresponding to $t = 7, 14, 21, 28$, and 35. Describe what you observe.

b. What is the period of the emotional cycle?

16. The height of the water, H, in feet, at a boat dock t hours after 6 A.M. is given by

$$H = 10 + 4 \sin\frac{\pi}{6}t.$$

a. Find the height of the water at the dock at 6 A.M., 9 A.M., noon, 6 P.M., midnight, and 3 A.M.

b. When is low tide and when is high tide?

c. What is the period of this function and what does this mean about the tides?

Writing in Mathematics

17. Why are the trigonometric functions sometimes called circular functions?

18. What is the range of the sine function? Use the unit circle to explain where this range comes from.

19. What do we mean by even trigonometric functions? Which of the six functions fall into this category?

20. What is a periodic function? Why are the sine and cosine functions periodic?

21. Explain how you can use the function for emotional fluctuations in Exercise 15 to determine good days for having dinner with your moody boss.

22. Describe a phenomenon that repeats infinitely. What is its period?

Critical Thinking Exercises

23. Find the exact value of $\cos 0° + \cos 1° + \cos 2° + \cos 3° + \cdots + \cos 179° + \cos 180°$.

24. If $f(x) = \sin x$ and $f(a) = \frac{1}{4}$, find the value of

$$f(a) + f(a + 2\pi) + f(a + 4\pi) + f(a + 6\pi).$$

25. If $f(x) = \sin x$ and $f(a) = \frac{1}{4}$, find the value of $f(a) + 2f(-a)$.

26. The seats of a ferris wheel are 40 feet from the wheel's center. When you get on the ride, your seat is 5 feet above the ground. How far above the ground are you after rotating through an angle of 765°?

SECTION 5.5 *Graphs of Sine and Cosine Functions*

Objectives

1. Understand the graph of $y = \sin x$.
2. Graph variations of $y = \sin x$.
3. Understand the graph of $y = \cos x$.
4. Graph variations of $y = \cos x$.
5. Use vertical shifts of sine and cosine curves.
6. Model periodic behavior.

Take a deep breath and relax. Many relaxation exercises involve slowing down our breathing. Some people suggest that the way we breathe affects every part of our lives. Did you know that graphs of trigonometric functions can be used to analyze the breathing cycle, which is our closest link to both life and death?

In this section, we use graphs of sine and cosine functions to visualize their properties. We use the traditional symbol x, rather than θ or t, to represent the independent variable. We use the symbol y for the dependent variable, or the function's value at x. Thus, we will be graphing $y = \sin x$ and $y = \cos x$ in rectangular coordinates. In all graphs of trigonometric functions, the independent variable, x, is measured in radians.

1 Understand the graph of $y = \sin x$.

The Graph of $y = \sin x$

The trigonometric functions can be graphed in a rectangular coordinate system by plotting points whose coordinates belong to the function. Thus, we graph $y = \sin x$ by listing some points on the graph. Because the period of the sine function is 2π, we will graph the function on the interval $[0, 2\pi]$. The rest of the graph is made up of repetitions of this portion.

Table 5.1 lists some values of (x, y) on the graph of $y = \sin x, 0 \le x \le 2\pi$.

Table 5.1 Values of (x, y) on $y = \sin x$

x	0	$\dfrac{\pi}{6}$	$\dfrac{\pi}{3}$	$\dfrac{\pi}{2}$	$\dfrac{2\pi}{3}$	$\dfrac{5\pi}{6}$	π	$\dfrac{7\pi}{6}$	$\dfrac{4\pi}{3}$	$\dfrac{3\pi}{2}$	$\dfrac{5\pi}{3}$	$\dfrac{11\pi}{6}$	2π
$y = \sin x$	0	$\dfrac{1}{2}$	$\dfrac{\sqrt{3}}{2}$	1	$\dfrac{\sqrt{3}}{2}$	$\dfrac{1}{2}$	0	$-\dfrac{1}{2}$	$-\dfrac{\sqrt{3}}{2}$	-1	$-\dfrac{\sqrt{3}}{2}$	$-\dfrac{1}{2}$	0

As x increases from 0 to $\frac{\pi}{2}$, y increases from 0 to 1.

As x increases from $\frac{\pi}{2}$ to π, y decreases from 1 to 0.

As x increases from π to $\frac{3\pi}{2}$, y decreases from 0 to -1.

As x increases from $\frac{3\pi}{2}$ to 2π, y increases from -1 to 0.

In plotting the points obtained in Table 5.1, we will use the approximation $\dfrac{\sqrt{3}}{2} \approx 0.87$. Rather than approximating π, we will mark off units on the x-axis in terms of π. If we connect these points with a smooth curve, we obtain the graph shown in Figure 5.43. The figure shows one period of the graph of $y = \sin x$.

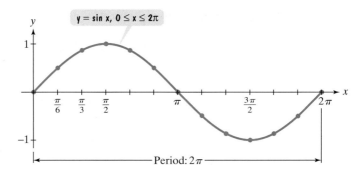

Figure 5.43 One period of the graph of $y = \sin x$

We can obtain a more complete graph of $y = \sin x$ by continuing the portion shown in Figure 5.43 to the left and right. The graph of the sine function, called a **sine curve**, is shown in Figure 5.44. Any part of the graph that corresponds to one period (2π) is one cycle of the graph of $y = \sin x$.

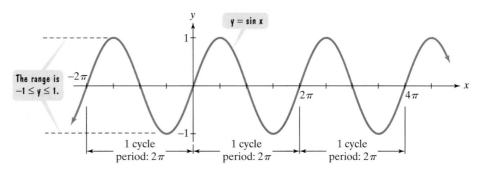

Figure 5.44 The graph of $y = \sin x$

The graph of $y = \sin x$ allows us to visualize some of the properties of the sine function.

- The domain is the set of all real numbers. The graph extends indefinitely to the left and to the right with no gaps or holes.
- The range consists of all numbers between -1 and 1 inclusive. The graph never rises above 1 or falls below -1.
- The period is 2π. The graph's pattern repeats in every interval of length 2π.
- The function is an odd function: $\sin(-x) = -\sin x$. This can be seen by observing that the graph is symmetric with respect to the origin.

2 Graph variations of $y = \sin x$.

Graphing Variations of $y = \sin x$

To graph variations of $y = \sin x$ by hand, it is helpful to find x-intercepts, maximum points, and minimum points. One complete cycle of the sine curve includes three x-intercepts, one maximum point, and one minimum point. The graph of $y = \sin x$ has x-intercepts at the beginning, middle, and end of its full period, shown in Figure 5.45. The curve reaches its maximum point $\frac{1}{4}$ of the way through the period. It reaches its minimum point $\frac{3}{4}$ of the way through the period. Thus, key points in graphing sine functions are obtained by dividing the

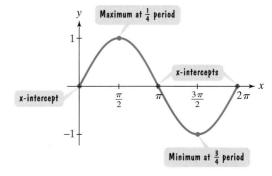

Figure 5.45 Key points in graphing the sine function

period into four equal parts. The x-coordinates of the five key points are as follows:

$$x_1 = \text{value of } x \text{ where the cycle begins}$$

$$x_2 = x_1 + \frac{\text{period}}{4}$$

$$x_3 = x_2 + \frac{\text{period}}{4}$$

$$x_4 = x_3 + \frac{\text{period}}{4}$$

$$x_5 = x_4 + \frac{\text{period}}{4}.$$

> Add "quarter-periods" to find successive value of x.

The y-coordinates of the five key points are obtained by evaluating the given function at each of these values of x.

The graph of $y = \sin x$ forms the basis for graphing functions of the form

$$y = A \sin x.$$

For example, consider $y = 2 \sin x$, in which $A = 2$. We can obtain the graph of $y = 2 \sin x$ from that of $y = \sin x$ if we multiply each y-coordinate on the graph of $y = \sin x$ by 2. Figure 5.46 shows the graphs. The basic sine curve is *stretched* and ranges between -2 and 2 rather than between -1 and 1. However, both $y = \sin x$ and $y = 2 \sin x$ have a period of 2π.

In general, the graph of $y = A \sin x$ ranges between $-A$ and A. Thus, the range of the function is $-A \leq y \leq A$. If $A > 1$, the basic sine curve is *stretched*, as in Figure 5.46. If $A < 1$, the basic sine curve is *shrunk*. We call $|A|$ the **amplitude** of $y = A \sin x$. The maximum value of y on the graph of $y = A \sin x$ is $|A|$, the amplitude.

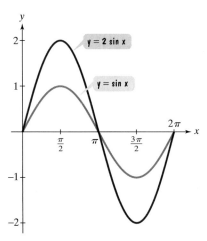

Figure 5.46 Comparing the graphs of $y = \sin x$ and $y = 2 \sin x$

Graphing Variations of $y = \sin x$

1. Identify the amplitude and the period.
2. Find the values of x for the five key points—the three x-intercepts, the maximum point, and the minimum point. Start with the value of x where the cycle begins and add quarter-periods—that is, $\dfrac{\text{period}}{4}$—to find successive values of x.
3. Find the values of y for the five key points by evaluating the function at each value of x from step 2.
4. Connect the five key points with a smooth curve and graph one complete cycle of the given function.
5. Extend the graph in step 4 to the left or right as desired.

EXAMPLE 1 Graphing a Variation of $y = \sin x$

Determine the amplitude of $y = \frac{1}{2} \sin x$. Then graph $y = \sin x$ and $y = \frac{1}{2} \sin x$ for $0 \leq x \leq 2\pi$.

Solution

Step 1 Identify the amplitude and the period. The equation $y = \frac{1}{2} \sin x$ is of the form $y = A \sin x$ with $A = \frac{1}{2}$. Thus, the amplitude is $|A| = \frac{1}{2}$. This means that the maximum value of y is $\frac{1}{2}$ and the minimum value of y is $-\frac{1}{2}$. The period for both $y = \frac{1}{2} \sin x$ and $y = \sin x$ is 2π.

Step 2 Find the values of x for the five key points. We need to find the three x-intercepts, the maximum point, and the minimum point on the interval $[0, 2\pi]$. To do so, we begin by dividing the period, 2π, by 4.

$$\frac{\text{period}}{4} = \frac{2\pi}{4} = \frac{\pi}{2}$$

We start with the value of x where the cycle begins: $x = 0$. Now we add quarter-periods, $\frac{\pi}{2}$, to generate x-values for each of the key points. The five x-values are

$$x = 0, \quad x = 0 + \frac{\pi}{2} = \frac{\pi}{2}, \quad x = \frac{\pi}{2} + \frac{\pi}{2} = \pi,$$

$$x = \pi + \frac{\pi}{2} = \frac{3\pi}{2}, \quad x = \frac{3\pi}{2} + \frac{\pi}{2} = 2\pi.$$

Step 3 Find the values of y for the five key points. We evaluate the function at each value of x from step 2.

Value of x	Value of y: $y = \frac{1}{2} \sin x$	Coordinates of key point	
0	$y = \dfrac{1}{2} \sin 0 = \dfrac{1}{2} \cdot 0 = 0$	$(0, 0)$	
$\dfrac{\pi}{2}$	$y = \dfrac{1}{2} \sin \dfrac{\pi}{2} = \dfrac{1}{2} \cdot 1 = \dfrac{1}{2}$	$\left(\dfrac{\pi}{2}, \dfrac{1}{2}\right)$	maximum point
π	$y = \dfrac{1}{2} \sin \pi = \dfrac{1}{2} \cdot 0 = 0$	$(\pi, 0)$	
$\dfrac{3\pi}{2}$	$y = \dfrac{1}{2} \sin \dfrac{3\pi}{2} = \dfrac{1}{2}(-1) = -\dfrac{1}{2}$	$\left(\dfrac{3\pi}{2}, -\dfrac{1}{2}\right)$	minimum point
2π	$y = \dfrac{1}{2} \sin 2\pi = \dfrac{1}{2} \cdot 0 = 0$	$(2\pi, 0)$	

There are x-intercepts at 0, π, and 2π. The maximum and minimum points are indicated by the voice balloons.

Step 4 Connect the five key points with a smooth curve and graph one complete cycle of the given function. The five key points for $y = \frac{1}{2} \sin x$ are shown in Figure 5.47. By connecting the points with a smooth curve, the figure shows one complete cycle of $y = \frac{1}{2} \sin x$. Also shown is the graph of $y = \sin x$. The graph of $y = \frac{1}{2} \sin x$ shrinks the graph of $y = \sin x$.

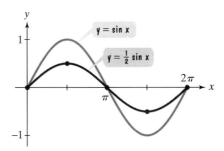

Figure 5.47 The graphs of $y = \sin x$ and $y = \frac{1}{2} \sin x$, $0 \le x \le 2\pi$

> **Check Point 1** Determine the amplitude of $y = 3 \sin x$. Then graph $y = \sin x$ and $y = 3 \sin x$ for $0 \le x \le 2\pi$.

EXAMPLE 2   Graphing a Variation of $y = \sin x$

Determine the amplitude of $y = -2 \sin x$. Then graph $y = \sin x$ and $y = -2 \sin x$ for $-\pi \le x \le 3\pi$.

Solution

Step 1   Identify the amplitude and the period.   The equation $y = -2 \sin x$ is of the form $y = A \sin x$ with $A = -2$. Thus, the amplitude is $|A| = |-2| = 2$. This means that the maximum value of y is 2 and the minimum value of y is -2. Both $y = \sin x$ and $y = -2 \sin x$ have a period of 2π.

Step 2   Find the x-values for the five key points.   Begin by dividing the period, 2π, by 4.

$$\frac{\text{period}}{4} = \frac{2\pi}{4} = \frac{\pi}{2}$$

Start with the value of x where the cycle begins: $x = 0$. Adding quarter-periods, $\frac{\pi}{2}$, the five x-values for the key points are

$$x = 0, \quad x = 0 + \frac{\pi}{2} = \frac{\pi}{2}, \quad x = \frac{\pi}{2} + \frac{\pi}{2} = \pi,$$

$$x = \pi + \frac{\pi}{2} = \frac{3\pi}{2}, \quad x = \frac{3\pi}{2} + \frac{\pi}{2} = 2\pi.$$

Step 3   Find the values of y for the five key points.   We evaluate the function at each value of x from step 2.

Value of x	Value of y: $y = -2 \sin x$	Coordinates of key point	
0	$y = -2 \sin 0 = -2 \cdot 0 = 0$	$(0, 0)$	
$\dfrac{\pi}{2}$	$y = -2 \sin \dfrac{\pi}{2} = -2 \cdot 1 = -2$	$\left(\dfrac{\pi}{2}, -2\right)$	minimum point
π	$y = -2 \sin \pi = -2 \cdot 0 = 0$	$(\pi, 0)$	
$\dfrac{3\pi}{2}$	$y = -2 \sin \dfrac{3\pi}{2} = -2(-1) = 2$	$\left(\dfrac{3\pi}{2}, 2\right)$	maximum point
2π	$y = -2 \sin 2\pi = -2 \cdot 0 = 0$	$(2\pi, 0)$	

There are x-intercepts at 0, π, and 2π. The minimum and maximum points are indicated by the voice balloons.

Step 4   Connect the five key points with a smooth curve and graph one complete cycle of the given function.   The five key points for $y = -2 \sin x$ are shown in Figure 5.48. By connecting the points with a smooth curve, the red portion shows one complete cycle of $y = -2 \sin x$. Also shown in blue is one complete cycle of the graph of $y = \sin x$.

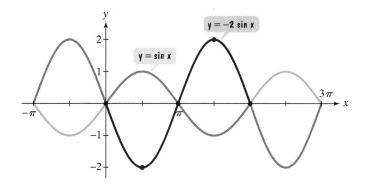

Figure 5.48 The graphs of $y = \sin x$ and $y = -2 \sin x$, $-\pi \le x \le 3\pi$

Step 5 Extend the graph in step 4 to the left or right as desired. The red and blue portions of the graphs in Figure 5.48 are from 0 to 2π. In order to graph for $-\pi \le x \le 3\pi$, continue the pattern of each graph to the left and right. These extensions are shown in the lighter colors in Figure 5.48.

> **Check Point 2** Determine the amplitude of $y = -\frac{1}{2} \sin x$. Then graph $y = \sin x$ and $y = -\frac{1}{2} \sin x$ for $-\pi \le x \le 3\pi$.

Now let us examine the graphs of functions of the form $y = A \sin Bx$, where B is the coefficient of x. How do such graphs compare to those of functions of the form $y = A \sin x$? We know that $y = A \sin x$ completes one cycle from $x = 0$ to $x = 2\pi$. Thus, $y = A \sin Bx$ completes one cycle from $Bx = 0$ to $Bx = 2\pi$. Solve each of these equations for x.

$$Bx = 0 \qquad\qquad Bx = 2\pi$$

$$x = 0 \qquad\qquad x = \frac{2\pi}{B} \qquad \text{Divide both sides of each equation by } B.$$

This means that $y = A \sin Bx$ completes one cycle from 0 to $\frac{2\pi}{B}$. The period is $\frac{2\pi}{B}$.

Amplitudes and Periods
The graph of $y = A \sin Bx$ has

$$\text{amplitude} = |A|$$

$$\text{period} = \frac{2\pi}{B}.$$

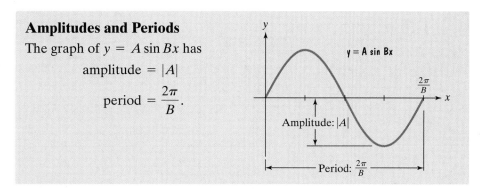

EXAMPLE 3   Graphing a Function of the Form $y = A \sin Bx$

Determine the amplitude and period of $y = 3 \sin 2x$. Then graph the function for $0 \le x \le 2\pi$.

Solution

Step 1 Identify the amplitude and the period. The equation $y = 3 \sin 2x$ is of the form $y = A \sin Bx$ with $A = 3$ and $B = 2$.

$$\text{amplitude:} \quad |A| = |3| = 3$$

$$\text{period:} \quad \frac{2\pi}{B} = \frac{2\pi}{2} = \pi$$

The amplitude, 3, tells us that the maximum value of y is 3 and the minimum value of y is -3.

Step 2 Find the x-values for the five key points. Begin by dividing the period, π, by 4.

$$\frac{\text{period}}{4} = \frac{\pi}{4}$$

Start with the value of x where the cycle begins: $x = 0$. Adding quarter-periods, $\frac{\pi}{4}$, the five x-values for the key points are

$$x = 0, \quad x = 0 + \frac{\pi}{4} = \frac{\pi}{4}, \quad x = \frac{\pi}{4} + \frac{\pi}{4} = \frac{\pi}{2},$$

$$x = \frac{\pi}{2} + \frac{\pi}{4} = \frac{3\pi}{4}, \quad x = \frac{3\pi}{4} + \frac{\pi}{4} = \pi.$$

Step 3 Find the values of y for the five key points. We evaluate the function at each value of x from step 2.

Value of x	Value of y: $y = 3 \sin 2x$	Coordinates of key point	
0	$y = 3 \sin 2 \cdot 0$ $= 3 \sin 0 = 3 \cdot 0 = 0$	$(0, 0)$	
$\dfrac{\pi}{4}$	$y = 3 \sin 2 \cdot \dfrac{\pi}{4}$ $= 3 \sin \dfrac{\pi}{2} = 3 \cdot 1 = 3$	$\left(\dfrac{\pi}{4}, 3\right)$	maximum point
$\dfrac{\pi}{2}$	$y = 3 \sin 2 \cdot \dfrac{\pi}{2}$ $= 3 \sin \pi = 3 \cdot 0 = 0$	$\left(\dfrac{\pi}{2}, 0\right)$	
$\dfrac{3\pi}{4}$	$y = 3 \sin 2 \cdot \dfrac{3\pi}{4}$ $= 3 \sin \dfrac{3\pi}{2} = 3(-1) = -3$	$\left(\dfrac{3\pi}{4}, -3\right)$	minimum point
π	$y = 3 \sin 2 \cdot \pi$ $= 3 \sin 2\pi = 3 \cdot 0 = 0$	$(\pi, 0)$	

In the interval $[0, \pi]$, there are x-intercepts at $0, \dfrac{\pi}{2}$, and π. The maximum and minimum points are indicated by the voice balloons.

Step 4 Connect the five key points with a smooth curve and graph one complete cycle of the given function. The five key points for $y = 3 \sin 2x$ are shown in

Technology

The graph of $y = 3 \sin 2x$ in a $\left[0, 2\pi, \dfrac{\pi}{2}\right]$ by $[-4, 4, 1]$ viewing rectangle verifies our hand-drawn graph in Figure 5.49.

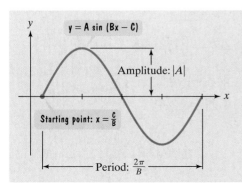

Figure 5.49. By connecting the points with a smooth curve, the blue portion shows one complete cycle of $y = 3 \sin 2x$ from 0 to π.

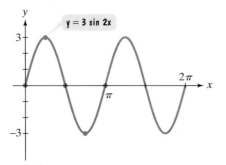

Figure 5.49

Step 5   Extend the graph in step 4 to the left or right as desired.   The blue portion of the graph in Figure 5.49 is from 0 to π. In order to graph for $0 \le x \le 2\pi$, we continue this portion and extend the graph another full period to the right. This extension is shown in black in Figure 5.49.

> **Check Point 3**   Determine the amplitude and period of $y = 2 \sin \frac{1}{2} x$. Then graph the function for $0 \le x \le 8\pi$.

Now let us examine the graphs of functions of the form $y = A \sin (Bx - C)$. How do such graphs compare to those of functions of the form $y = A \sin Bx$? In both cases, the amplitude is $|A|$ and the period is $\dfrac{2\pi}{B}$. One complete cycle occurs if $Bx - C$ increases from 0 to 2π. This means that we can find an interval containing one cycle by solving the equations

$$Bx - C = 0 \quad \text{and} \quad Bx - C = 2\pi$$
$$Bx = C \qquad\qquad\qquad Bx = C + 2\pi \qquad \text{Add } C \text{ to both sides in each equation.}$$
$$x = \frac{C}{B} \qquad\qquad\qquad x = \frac{C}{B} + \frac{2\pi}{B}. \qquad \text{Divide both sides by } B \text{ in each equation.}$$

This is the x-coordinate on the left where the cycle begins.

This is the x-coordinate on the right where the cycle ends. $\dfrac{2\pi}{B}$ is the period.

The voice balloon on the left indicates that $y = A \sin (Bx - C)$ shifts the graph of $y = A \sin Bx$ horizontally by $\dfrac{C}{B}$. Thus, the number $\dfrac{C}{B}$ is the **phase shift** associated with the graph.

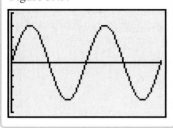

The Graph of $y = A \sin (Bx - C)$

The graph of $y = A \sin (Bx - C)$ is obtained by horizontally shifting the graph of $y = A \sin Bx$ so that the starting point of the cycle is shifted from $x = 0$ to $x = \dfrac{C}{B}$. The number $\dfrac{C}{B}$ is called the **phase shift**.

$$\text{amplitude} = |A|$$

$$\text{period} = \frac{2\pi}{B}$$

EXAMPLE 4 **Graphing a Function of the Form** $y = A \sin(Bx - C)$

Determine the amplitude, period, and phase shift of $y = 4 \sin\left(2x - \dfrac{2\pi}{3}\right)$. Then graph one period of the function.

Solution

Step 1 Identify the amplitude, the period, and the phase shift.   We must first identify values for A, B, and C.

> This equation is of the form
> $y = A \sin(Bx - C)$.

$$y = 4 \sin\left(2x - \frac{2\pi}{3}\right)$$

Using the voice balloon, we see that $A = 4$, $B = 2$, and $C = \dfrac{2\pi}{3}$.

amplitude: $|A| = |4| = 4$ > The maximum y is 4 and the minimum is −4.

period: $\dfrac{2\pi}{B} = \dfrac{2\pi}{2} = \pi$ > Each cycle is completed in π radians.

phase shift: $\dfrac{C}{B} = \dfrac{\frac{2\pi}{3}}{2} = \dfrac{2\pi}{3} \cdot \dfrac{1}{2} = \dfrac{\pi}{3}$ > A cycle starts at $x = \frac{\pi}{3}$.

Step 2 Find the x-values for the five key points.   Begin by dividing the period, π, by 4.

$$\frac{\text{period}}{4} = \frac{\pi}{4}$$

Start with the value of x where the cycle begins: $x = \dfrac{\pi}{3}$. Adding quarter-periods, $\dfrac{\pi}{4}$, the five x-values for the key points are

$$x = \frac{\pi}{3}, \quad x = \frac{\pi}{3} + \frac{\pi}{4} = \frac{4\pi}{12} + \frac{3\pi}{12} = \frac{7\pi}{12},$$

$$x = \frac{7\pi}{12} + \frac{\pi}{4} = \frac{7\pi}{12} + \frac{3\pi}{12} = \frac{10\pi}{12} = \frac{5\pi}{6},$$

$$x = \frac{5\pi}{6} + \frac{\pi}{4} = \frac{10\pi}{12} + \frac{3\pi}{12} = \frac{13\pi}{12},$$

$$x = \frac{13\pi}{12} + \frac{\pi}{4} = \frac{13\pi}{12} + \frac{3\pi}{12} = \frac{16\pi}{12} = \frac{4\pi}{3}.$$

Study Tip

You can speed up the additions on the right by first writing the starting point and the quarter-period with a common denominator.

starting point
$= \dfrac{\pi}{3} = \dfrac{4\pi}{12}$

quarter-period
$= \dfrac{\pi}{4} = \dfrac{3\pi}{12}$

Step 3 Find the values of y for the five key points.   We evaluate the function at each value of x from step 2.

Value of x	Value of y: $y = 4\sin\left(2x - \dfrac{2\pi}{3}\right)$	Coordinates of key point	
$\dfrac{\pi}{3}$	$y = 4\sin\left(2\cdot\dfrac{\pi}{3} - \dfrac{2\pi}{3}\right)$ $= 4\sin 0 = 4\cdot 0 = 0$	$\left(\dfrac{\pi}{3}, 0\right)$	
$\dfrac{7\pi}{12}$	$y = 4\sin\left(2\cdot\dfrac{7\pi}{12} - \dfrac{2\pi}{3}\right)$ $= 4\sin\left(\dfrac{7\pi}{6} - \dfrac{2\pi}{3}\right)$ $= 4\sin\dfrac{3\pi}{6} = 4\sin\dfrac{\pi}{2} = 4\cdot 1 = 4$	$\left(\dfrac{7\pi}{12}, 4\right)$	maximum point
$\dfrac{5\pi}{6}$	$y = 4\sin\left(2\cdot\dfrac{5\pi}{6} - \dfrac{2\pi}{3}\right)$ $= 4\sin\left(\dfrac{5\pi}{3} - \dfrac{2\pi}{3}\right)$ $= 4\sin\dfrac{3\pi}{3} = 4\sin\pi = 4\cdot 0 = 0$	$\left(\dfrac{5\pi}{6}, 0\right)$	
$\dfrac{13\pi}{12}$	$y = 4\sin\left(2\cdot\dfrac{13\pi}{12} - \dfrac{2\pi}{3}\right)$ $= 4\sin\left(\dfrac{13\pi}{6} - \dfrac{4\pi}{6}\right)$ $= 4\sin\dfrac{9\pi}{6} = 4\sin\dfrac{3\pi}{2} = 4(-1) = -4$	$\left(\dfrac{13\pi}{12}, -4\right)$	minimum point
$\dfrac{4\pi}{3}$	$y = 4\sin\left(2\cdot\dfrac{4\pi}{3} - \dfrac{2\pi}{3}\right)$ $= 4\sin\dfrac{6\pi}{3} = 4\sin 2\pi = 4\cdot 0 = 0$	$\left(\dfrac{4\pi}{3}, 0\right)$	

In the interval $\left[\dfrac{\pi}{3}, \dfrac{4\pi}{3}\right]$, there are x-intercepts at $\dfrac{\pi}{3}, \dfrac{5\pi}{6}$, and $\dfrac{4\pi}{3}$. The maximum and minimum points are indicated by the voice balloons.

Step 4   Connect the five key points with a smooth curve and graph one complete cycle of the given function.   The key points and the graph of $y = 4\sin\left(2x - \dfrac{2\pi}{3}\right)$ are shown in Figure 5.50.

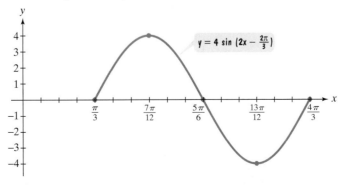

Figure 5.50

> **Check Point 4** Determine the amplitude, period, and phase shift of $y = 3 \sin\left(2x - \dfrac{\pi}{3}\right)$. Then graph one period of the function.

3 Understand the graph of $y = \cos x$.

The Graph of $y = \cos x$

We graph $y = \cos x$ by listing some points on the graph. Because the period of the cosine function is 2π, we will concentrate on the graph of the basic cosine curve on the interval $[0, 2\pi]$. The rest of the graph is made up of repetitions of this portion. Table 5.2 lists some values of (x, y) on the graph of $y = \cos x$.

Table 5.2 Values of (x, y) on $y = \cos x$

x	0	$\dfrac{\pi}{6}$	$\dfrac{\pi}{3}$	$\dfrac{\pi}{2}$	$\dfrac{2\pi}{3}$	$\dfrac{5\pi}{6}$	π	$\dfrac{7\pi}{6}$	$\dfrac{4\pi}{3}$	$\dfrac{3\pi}{2}$	$\dfrac{5\pi}{3}$	$\dfrac{11\pi}{6}$	2π
$y = \cos x$	1	$\dfrac{\sqrt{3}}{2}$	$\dfrac{1}{2}$	0	$-\dfrac{1}{2}$	$-\dfrac{\sqrt{3}}{2}$	-1	$-\dfrac{\sqrt{3}}{2}$	$-\dfrac{1}{2}$	0	$\dfrac{1}{2}$	$\dfrac{\sqrt{3}}{2}$	1

As x increases from 0 to $\dfrac{\pi}{2}$, y decreases from 1 to 0.

As x increases from $\dfrac{\pi}{2}$ to π, y decreases from 0 to -1.

As x increases from π to $\dfrac{3\pi}{2}$, y increases from -1 to 0.

As x increases from $\dfrac{3\pi}{2}$ to 2π, y increases from 0 to 1.

Plotting the points in Table 5.2 and connecting them with a smooth curve, we obtain the graph shown in Figure 5.51. The portion of the graph in dark blue shows one complete period. We can obtain a more complete graph of $y = \cos x$ by extending this dark blue portion to the left and right.

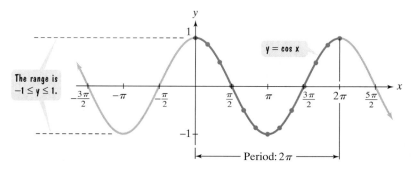

Figure 5.51 The graph of $y = \cos x$

The graph of $y = \cos x$ allows us to visualize some of the properties of the cosine function.

- The domain is the set of all real numbers. The graph extends indefinitely to the left and to the right with no gaps or holes.
- The range consists of all numbers between -1 and 1 inclusive. The graph never rises above 1 or falls below -1.
- The period is 2π. The graph's pattern repeats in every interval of length 2π.
- The function is an even function: $\cos(-x) = \cos x$. This can be seen by observing that the graph is symmetric with respect to the y-axis.

Take a second look at Figure 5.51. Can you see that the graph of $y = \cos x$ is the graph of $y = \sin x$ with a phase shift of $-\dfrac{\pi}{2}$ radians? If you trace along the curve from $x = -\dfrac{\pi}{2}$ to $x = \dfrac{3\pi}{2}$, you are tracing one complete cycle of the sine curve. This can be expressed as an identity:

$$\cos x = \sin\left(x + \frac{\pi}{2}\right).$$

Because of this similarity, the graphs of sine functions and cosine functions are called **sinusoidal graphs**.

4 Graph variations of $y = \cos x$.

Graphing Variations of $y = \cos x$

We use the same steps to graph variations of $y = \cos x$ as we did for graphing variations of $y = \sin x$. We will continue finding key points by dividing the period into four equal parts. Amplitudes, periods, and phase shifts play an important role when graphing by hand.

The Graph of $y = A \cos Bx$

The graph of $y = A \cos Bx$ has

$$\text{amplitude} = |A|$$

$$\text{period} = \frac{2\pi}{B}.$$

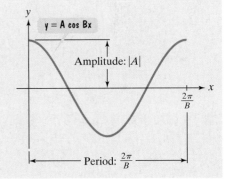

EXAMPLE 5   Graphing a Function of the Form $y = A \cos Bx$

Determine the amplitude and period of $y = -3 \cos \dfrac{\pi}{2} x$. Then graph the function for $-4 \le x \le 4$.

Solution

Step 1   Identify the amplitude and the period.   The equation $y = -3 \cos \dfrac{\pi}{2} x$ is of the form $y = A \cos Bx$ with $A = -3$ and $B = \dfrac{\pi}{2}$.

amplitude: $|A| = |-3| = 3$ The maximum y is 3 and the minimum is -3.

period: $\dfrac{2\pi}{B} = \dfrac{2\pi}{\dfrac{\pi}{2}} = 2\pi \cdot \dfrac{2}{\pi} = 4$ Each cycle is completed in 4 radians.

Step 2   Find the x-values for the five key points.   Begin by dividing the period, 4, by 4.

$$\frac{\text{period}}{4} = \frac{4}{4} = 1$$

Start with the value of x where the cycle begins: $x = 0$. Adding quarter-periods, 1, the five x-values for the key points are

$$x = 0, \quad x = 0 + 1 = 1, \quad x = 1 + 1 = 2, \quad x = 2 + 1 = 3, \quad x = 3 + 1 = 4$$

Step 3 Find the values of y for the five key points. We evaluate the function at each value of x from step 2.

Value of x	Value of y: $y = -3 \cos \dfrac{\pi}{2} x$	Coordinates of key point	
0	$y = -3 \cos \dfrac{\pi}{2} \cdot 0$ $= -3 \cos 0 = -3 \cdot 1 = -3$	$(0, -3)$	minimum point
1	$y = -3 \cos \dfrac{\pi}{2} \cdot 1$ $= -3 \cos \dfrac{\pi}{2} = -3 \cdot 0 = 0$	$(1, 0)$	
2	$y = -3 \cos \dfrac{\pi}{2} \cdot 2$ $= -3 \cos \pi = -3(-1) = 3$	$(2, 3)$	maximum point
3	$y = -3 \cos \dfrac{\pi}{2} \cdot 3$ $= -3 \cos \dfrac{3\pi}{2} = -3(0) = 0$	$(3, 0)$	
4	$y = -3 \cos \dfrac{\pi}{2} \cdot 4$ $= -3 \cos 2\pi = -3(1) = -3$	$(4, -3)$	minimum point

In the interval $[0, 4]$, there are x-intercepts at 1 and 3. The minimum and maximum points are indicated by the voice balloons.

Step 4 Connect the five key points with a smooth curve and graph one complete cycle of the given function. The five key points for $y = -3 \cos \dfrac{\pi}{2} x$ are shown in Figure 5.52. By connecting the points with a smooth curve, the blue portion shows one complete cycle of $y = -3 \cos \dfrac{\pi}{2} x$ from 0 to 4.

Technology

The graph of $y = -3 \cos \dfrac{\pi}{2} x$ in a $[-4, 4, 1]$ by $[-4, 4, 1]$ viewing rectangle verifies our hand-drawn graph in Figure 5.52.

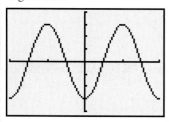

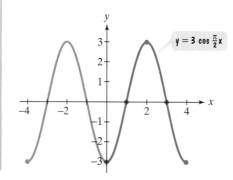

Figure 5.52

Step 5   Extend the graph in step 4 to the left or right as desired.   The blue portion of the graph in Figure 5.52 is from 0 to 4. In order to graph for $-4 \le x \le 4$, we continue this portion and extend the graph another full period to the left. This extension is shown in black in Figure 5.52.

Check Point 5	Determine the amplitude and period of $y = -4 \cos \pi x$. Then graph the function for $-2 \le x \le 2$.

Finally, let us examine the graphs of functions of the form $y = A \cos(Bx - C)$. Graphs of these functions shift the graph of $y = A \cos Bx$ horizontally by $\dfrac{C}{B}$.

The Graph of $y = A \cos(Bx - C)$

The graph of $y = A \cos(Bx - C)$ is obtained by horizontally shifting the graph of $y = A \cos Bx$ so that the starting point of the cycle is shifted from $x = 0$ to $x = \dfrac{C}{B}$. The number $\dfrac{C}{B}$ is called the **phase shift**.

$$\text{amplitude} = |A|$$

$$\text{period} = \frac{2\pi}{B}$$

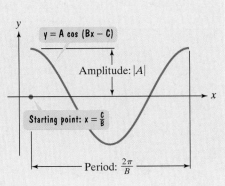

EXAMPLE 6   Graphing a Function of the Form $y = A \cos(Bx - C)$

Determine the amplitude, period, and phase shift of $y = \frac{1}{2}\cos(4x + \pi)$. Then graph one period of the function.

Solution

Step 1   Identify the amplitude, the period, and the phase shift.   We must first identify values for A, B, and C. To do this, we need to express the equation in the form $y = A \cos(Bx - C)$. Thus, we write $y = \frac{1}{2}\cos(4x + \pi)$ as $y = \frac{1}{2}\cos(4x - (-\pi))$. Now we can identify values for A, B, and C.

> This equation is of the form $y = A \cos(Bx - C)$.

$$y = \frac{1}{2}\cos\big(4x - (-\pi)\big)$$

Using the voice balloon, we see that $A = \frac{1}{2}$, $B = 4$, and $C = -\pi$.

amplitude: $|A| = \left|\dfrac{1}{2}\right| = \dfrac{1}{2}$ The maximum y is $\frac{1}{2}$ and the minimum is $-\frac{1}{2}$.

period: $\dfrac{2\pi}{B} = \dfrac{2\pi}{4} = \dfrac{\pi}{2}$ Each cycle is completed in $\frac{\pi}{2}$ radians.

phase shift: $\dfrac{C}{B} = -\dfrac{\pi}{4}$ A cycle starts at $x = -\frac{\pi}{4}$.

Step 2   Find the x-values for the five key points.   Begin by dividing the period, $\frac{\pi}{2}$, by 4.

$$\frac{\text{period}}{4} = \frac{\frac{\pi}{2}}{4} = \frac{\pi}{8}$$

Start with the value of x where the cycle begins: $x = -\frac{\pi}{4}$. Adding quarter-periods, $\frac{\pi}{8}$, the five x-values for the key points are

$$x = -\frac{\pi}{4}, \quad x = -\frac{\pi}{4} + \frac{\pi}{8} = -\frac{2\pi}{8} + \frac{\pi}{8} = -\frac{\pi}{8}, \quad x = -\frac{\pi}{8} + \frac{\pi}{8} = 0,$$

$$x = 0 + \frac{\pi}{8} = \frac{\pi}{8}, \quad x = \frac{\pi}{8} + \frac{\pi}{8} = \frac{2\pi}{8} = \frac{\pi}{4}.$$

Step 3   Find the values of y for the five key points.   Take a few minutes and use your calculator to evaluate the function at each value of x from step 2. Show that the key points are

$$\left(-\frac{\pi}{4}, \frac{1}{2}\right), \quad \left(-\frac{\pi}{8}, 0\right), \quad \left(0, -\frac{1}{2}\right), \quad \left(\frac{\pi}{8}, 0\right), \quad \text{and} \quad \left(\frac{\pi}{4}, \frac{1}{2}\right).$$

| maximum point | x-intercept | minimum point | y-intercept | maximum point |

Step 4   Connect the five key points with a smooth curve and graph one complete cycle of the given function.   The key points and the graph of $y = \frac{1}{2}\cos(4x + \pi)$ are shown in Figure 5.53.

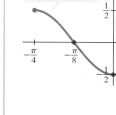

Figure 5.53

Technology

The graph of

$$y = \frac{1}{2}\cos(4x + \pi)$$

in a $\left[-\frac{\pi}{4}, \frac{\pi}{4}, \frac{\pi}{8}\right]$ by $[-1, 1, 1]$ viewing rectangle verifies our hand-drawn graph in Figure 5.53.

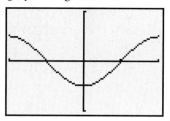

Check Point 6   Determine the amplitude, period, and phase shift of $y = \frac{3}{2}\cos(2x + \pi)$. Then graph one period of the function.

5   Use vertical shifts of sine and cosine curves.

Vertical Shifts of Sinusoidal Graphs

We now look at sinusoidal graphs of

$$y = A\sin(Bx - C) + D \quad \text{and} \quad y = A\cos(Bx - C) + D.$$

The constant D causes vertical shifts in the graphs of $y = A\sin(Bx - C)$ and $y = A\cos(Bx - C)$. If D is positive, the shift is D units upward. If D is negative, the shift is D units downward. These vertical shifts result in sinusoidal graphs oscillating about the horizontal line $y = D$ rather than about the x-axis. Thus, the maximum y is $D + |A|$ and the minimum y is $D - |A|$.

EXAMPLE 7 A Vertical Shift

Graph one period of the function $y = \frac{1}{2} \cos x - 1$.

Solution The graph of $y = \frac{1}{2} \cos x - 1$ is the graph of $y = \frac{1}{2} \cos x$ shifted one unit downward. The period of $y = \frac{1}{2} \cos x$ is 2π, which is also the period for the vertically shifted graph. The key points on the interval $[0, 2\pi]$ for $y = \frac{1}{2} \cos x - 1$ are found by first determining their x-coordinates. The quarter-period is $\frac{2\pi}{4}$ or $\frac{\pi}{2}$.

The cycle begins at $x = 0$. As always, we add quarter-periods to generate x-values for each of the key points. The five x-values are

$$x = 0, \quad x = 0 + \frac{\pi}{2} = \frac{\pi}{2}, \quad x = \frac{\pi}{2} + \frac{\pi}{2} = \pi,$$

$$x = \pi + \frac{\pi}{2} = \frac{3\pi}{2}, \quad x = \frac{3\pi}{2} + \frac{\pi}{2} = 2\pi.$$

The values of y for the five key points and their coordinates are determined as follows.

Value of x	Value of y: $y = \dfrac{1}{2} \cos x - 1$	Coordinates of key point
0	$y = \dfrac{1}{2} \cos 0 - 1$ $= \dfrac{1}{2} \cdot 1 - 1 = -\dfrac{1}{2}$	$\left(0, -\dfrac{1}{2}\right)$
$\dfrac{\pi}{2}$	$y = \dfrac{1}{2} \cos \dfrac{\pi}{2} - 1$ $= \dfrac{1}{2} \cdot 0 - 1 = -1$	$\left(\dfrac{\pi}{2}, -1\right)$
π	$y = \dfrac{1}{2} \cos \pi - 1$ $= \dfrac{1}{2}(-1) - 1 = -\dfrac{3}{2}$	$\left(\pi, -\dfrac{3}{2}\right)$
$\dfrac{3\pi}{2}$	$y = \dfrac{1}{2} \cos \dfrac{3\pi}{2} - 1$ $= \dfrac{1}{2} \cdot 0 - 1 = -1$	$\left(\dfrac{3\pi}{2}, -1\right)$
2π	$y = \dfrac{1}{2} \cos 2\pi - 1$ $= \dfrac{1}{2} \cdot 1 - 1 = -\dfrac{1}{2}$	$\left(2\pi, -\dfrac{1}{2}\right)$

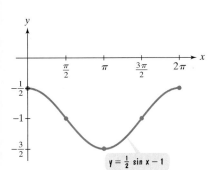

$y = \frac{1}{2} \sin x - 1$

Figure 5.54

The five key points for $y = \frac{1}{2} \cos x - 1$ are shown in Figure 5.54. By connecting the points with a smooth curve, we obtain one period of the graph.

Check Point 7 Graph one period of the function $y = 2 \cos x + 1$.

6 Model periodic behavior.

Modeling Periodic Behavior

Our breathing consists of alternating periods of inhaling and exhaling. Each complete pumping cycle of the human heart can be described using a sine function. Our brain waves during deep sleep are sinusoidal. Viewed in this way, trigonometry becomes an intimate experience.

Some graphing utilities have a SINe REGression feature. This feature gives the sine function of best fit of wavelike data with the form of a sinusoidal function. However, it is not always necessary to use technology. In our next example, we use our understanding of sinusoidal graphs to model the process of breathing.

EXAMPLE 8 A Trigonometric Breath of Life

The graph in Figure 5.55 shows one complete normal breathing cycle. The cycle consists of inhaling and exhaling. It takes place every 5 seconds. Velocity of air flow is positive when we inhale and negative when we exhale. It is measured in liters per second. If y represents velocity of air flow after x seconds, find a function of the form $y = A \sin Bx$ that models air flow in a normal breathing cycle.

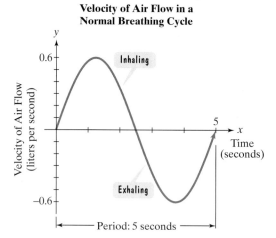

Velocity of Air Flow in a Normal Breathing Cycle

Figure 5.55

Solution We need to determine values for A and B in the equation $y = A \sin Bx$. A, the amplitude, is the maximum value of y. Figure 5.55 shows that this maximum value is 0.6. Thus, $A = 0.6$.

The value of B in $y = A \sin Bx$ can be found using the formula for the period: period $= \dfrac{2\pi}{B}$. The period of our breathing cycle is 5 seconds. Thus,

$$5 = \frac{2\pi}{B} \qquad \text{\textit{Our goal is to solve this equation for B.}}$$

$$5B = 2\pi \qquad \text{\textit{Multiply both sides of the equation by B.}}$$

$$B = \frac{2\pi}{5} \qquad \text{\textit{Divide both sides of the equation by 5.}}$$

We see that $A = 0.6$ and $B = \dfrac{2\pi}{5}$. Substitute these values into $y = A \sin Bx$. The breathing cycle is modeled by

$$y = 0.6 \sin \frac{2\pi}{5} x.$$

Check Point 8

Find an equation of the form $y = A \sin Bx$ that produces the graph shown in the figure on the right.

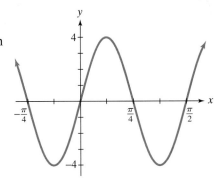

EXAMPLE 9 Modeling a Tidal Cycle

Figure 5.56 shows that the depth of water at a boat dock varies with the tides. The depth is 5 feet at low tide and 13 feet at high tide. On a certain day, low tide occurs at 4 A.M. and high tide at 10 A.M. If y represents the depth of the water x hours after midnight, use a sine function of the form $y = A \sin(Bx - C) + D$ to model the water's depth.

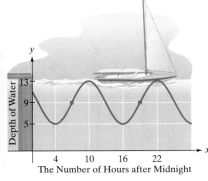

Figure 5.56

Solution   We need to determine values for $A, B, C,$ and D in the equation $y = A \sin(Bx - C) + D$. We can find these values using Figure 5.56. We begin with D.

To find D, we use the vertical shift. Because the water's depth ranges from a minimum of 5 feet to a maximum of 13 feet, the curve oscillates about the middle value, 9 feet. Thus, $D = 9$, which is the vertical shift.

At maximum depth, the water is 4 feet above 9 feet. Thus, A, the amplitude, is 4: $A = 4$.

To find B, we use the period. The blue portion of the graph shows that one complete tidal cycle occurs in $19 - 7$, or 12 hours. The period is 12. Thus,

$$12 = \frac{2\pi}{B} \qquad \textit{Our goal is to solve this equation for B.}$$

$$12B = 2\pi \qquad \textit{Multiply both sides by B.}$$

$$B = \frac{2\pi}{12} = \frac{\pi}{6}. \qquad \textit{Divide both sides by 12.}$$

To find C, we use the phase shift. The blue portion of the graph shows that the starting point of the cycle is shifted from 0 to 7. The phase shift, $\frac{C}{B}$, is 7.

$$7 = \frac{C}{B} \qquad \textit{The phase shift of } y = A \sin(Bx - C) \textit{ is } \frac{C}{B}.$$

$$7 = \frac{C}{\frac{\pi}{6}} \qquad \textit{From above, we have } B = \frac{\pi}{6}.$$

$$\frac{7\pi}{6} = C \qquad \textit{Multiply both sides of the equation by } \frac{\pi}{6}.$$

We see that $A = 4$, $B = \dfrac{\pi}{6}$, $C = \dfrac{7\pi}{6}$, and $D = 9$. Substitute these values into $y = A\sin(Bx - C) + D$. The water's depth x hours after midnight is modeled by

$$y = 4\sin\left(\frac{\pi}{6}x - \frac{7\pi}{6}\right) + 9.$$

Check Point 9

The figure shows the number of hours of daylight for a region that is 30° north of the equator. Hours of daylight are at a minimum of 10 hours in January and December. Hours of daylight are at a maximum of 14 hours in June. Let x represent the month of the year, with 1 for January, 2 for February, 3 for March, and 12 for December. If y represents the number of hours of daylight in month x, use a sine function of the form $y = A\sin(Bx - C) + D$ to model the hours of daylight.

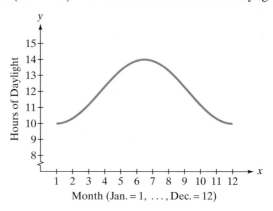

Month (Jan. = 1, ... , Dec. = 12)

EXERCISE SET 5.5

Practice Exercises

In Exercises 1–6, determine the amplitude of each function. Then graph the function and $y = \sin x$ in the same rectangular coordinate system for $0 \le x \le 2\pi$.

1. $y = 4\sin x$

2. $y = 5\sin x$

3. $y = \frac{1}{3}\sin x$

4. $y = \frac{1}{4}\sin x$

5. $y = -3\sin x$

6. $y = -4\sin x$

In Exercises 7–16, determine the amplitude and period of each function. Then graph one period of the function.

7. $y = \sin 2x$

8. $y = \sin 4x$

9. $y = 3\sin\frac{1}{2}x$

10. $y = 2\sin\frac{1}{4}x$

11. $y = 4\sin\pi x$

12. $y = 3\sin 2\pi x$

13. $y = -3\sin 2\pi x$

14. $y = -2\sin\pi x$

15. $y = -\sin\frac{2}{3}x$

16. $y = -\sin\frac{4}{3}x$

In Exercises 17–30, determine the amplitude, period, and phase shift of each function. Then graph one period of the function.

17. $y = \sin(x - \pi)$

18. $y = \sin\left(x - \dfrac{\pi}{2}\right)$

19. $y = \sin(2x - \pi)$

20. $y = \sin\left(2x - \dfrac{\pi}{2}\right)$

21. $y = 3 \sin (2x - \pi)$

22. $y = 3 \sin \left(2x - \dfrac{\pi}{2} \right)$

23. $y = \frac{1}{2} \sin \left(x + \dfrac{\pi}{2} \right)$

24. $y = \frac{1}{2} \sin (x + \pi)$

25. $y = -2 \sin \left(2x + \dfrac{\pi}{2} \right)$

26. $y = -3 \sin \left(2x + \dfrac{\pi}{2} \right)$

27. $y = 3 \sin (\pi x + 2)$

28. $y = 3 \sin (2\pi x + 4)$

29. $y = -2 \sin (2\pi x + 4\pi)$

30. $y = -3 \sin (2\pi x + 4\pi)$

In Exercises 31–34, determine the amplitude of each function. Then graph the function and $y = \cos x$ in the same rectangular coordinate system for $0 \le x \le 2\pi$.

31. $y = 2 \cos x$

32. $y = 3 \cos x$

33. $y = -2 \cos x$

34. $y = -3 \cos x$

In Exercises 35–42, determine the amplitude and period of each function. Then graph one period of the function.

35. $y = \cos 2x$

36. $y = \cos 4x$

37. $y = 4 \cos 2\pi x$

38. $y = 5 \cos 2\pi x$

39. $y = -4 \cos \frac{1}{2} x$

40. $y = -3 \cos \frac{1}{3} x$

41. $y = -\frac{1}{2} \cos \dfrac{\pi}{3} x$

42. $y = -\frac{1}{2} \cos \dfrac{\pi}{4} x$

In Exercises 43–50, determine the amplitude, period, and phase shift of each function. Then graph one period of the function.

43. $y = 3 \cos (2x - \pi)$

44. $y = 4 \cos (2x - \pi)$

45. $y = \frac{1}{2} \cos \left(3x + \dfrac{\pi}{2} \right)$

46. $y = \frac{1}{2} \cos (2x + \pi)$

47. $y = -3 \cos \left(2x - \dfrac{\pi}{2} \right)$

48. $y = -4 \cos \left(2x - \dfrac{\pi}{2} \right)$

49. $y = 2 \cos (2\pi x + 8\pi)$

50. $y = 3 \cos (2\pi x + 4\pi)$

In Exercises 51–58, use a vertical shift to graph one period of the function.

51. $y = \sin x + 2$

52. $y = \sin x - 2$

53. $y = \cos x - 3$

54. $y = \cos x + 3$

55. $y = 2 \sin \frac{1}{2} x + 1$

56. $y = 2 \cos \frac{1}{2} x + 1$

57. $y = -3 \cos 2\pi x + 2$

58. $y = -3 \sin 2\pi x + 2$

Application Exercises

In the theory of biorhythms, sine functions are used to measure a person's potential. You can obtain your biorhythm chart online by simply entering your date of birth, the date you want your biorhythm chart to begin, and the number of months you wish to be included in the plot. The following is your author's chart, beginning January 25, 2000, when he was 19,998 days old. We all have cycles with the same amplitudes and periods as those shown here. Each of our three basic cycles begins at birth. Use the biorhythm chart shown to solve Exercises 59–66.

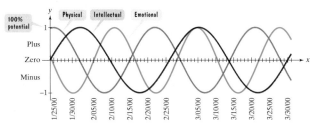

59. What is the period of the physical cycle?

60. What is the period of the emotional cycle?

61. What is the period of the intellectual cycle?

62. For the period shown, what is the worst day in February for your author to run in a marathon?

63. For the period shown, what is the best day in March for your author to meet an online friend for the first time?

64. For the period shown, what is the best day in January for your author to begin writing this trigonometry chapter?

65. If you extend these sinusoidal graphs to the end of the year, is there a day when your author should not even bother getting out of bed?

66. If you extend these sinusoidal graphs to the end of the year, are there any days where your author is at near-peak physical, emotional, and intellectual potential?

67. Rounded to the nearest hour, Los Angeles averages 14 hours of daylight in June, 10 hours in December, and 12 hours in March and September. Let x represent the number of months after June and y represent the number of hours of daylight in month x. Make a graph that displays the information from June of one year to June of the following year.

68. A clock with an hour hand that is 15 inches long is hanging on a wall. At noon, the distance between the tip of the hour hand and the ceiling is 23 inches. At 3 P.M., the distance is 38 inches; at 6 P.M., 53 inches; at 9 P.M., 38 inches; and at midnight the distance is again 23 inches. If y represents the distance between the tip of the hour hand and the ceiling x hours after noon, make a graph that displays the information for $0 \le x \le 24$.

69. The number of hours of daylight in Boston is given by

$$y = 3 \sin \dfrac{2\pi}{365} (x - 79) + 12$$

where x is the number of days after January 1.
a. What is the amplitude of this function?
b. What is the period of this function?

c. How many hours of daylight are there on the longest day of the year?

d. How many hours of daylight are there on the shortest day of the year?

e. Graph the function for one period, starting on January 1.

70. The average monthly temperature, y, in degrees Fahrenheit, for Juneau, Alaska, can be modeled by $y = 16 \sin\left(\frac{\pi}{6}x - \frac{2\pi}{3}\right) + 40$, where x is the month of the year (January = 1, February = 2, ..., December = 12). Graph the function for $1 \le x \le 12$. What is the highest average monthly temperature? In which month does this occur?

71. The figure shows the depth of water at the end of a boat dock. The depth is 6 feet at low tide and 12 feet at high tide. On a certain day, low tide occurs at 6 A.M. and high tide at noon. If y represents the depth of the water x hours after midnight, use a cosine function of the form $y = A \cos Bx + D$ to model the water's depth.

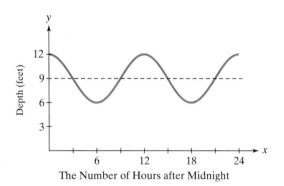

The Number of Hours after Midnight

72. The figure shows the depth of water at the end of a boat dock. The depth is 5 feet at high tide and 3 feet at low tide. On a certain day, high tide occurs at noon and low tide at 6 P.M. If y represents the depth of the water x hours after noon, use a cosine function of the form $y = A \cos Bx + D$ to model the water's depth.

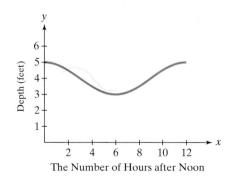

The Number of Hours after Noon

Writing in Mathematics

73. Without drawing a graph, describe the behavior of the basic sine curve.

74. What is the amplitude of the sine function? What does this tell you about the graph?

75. If you are given the equation of a sine function, how do you determine the period?

76. What does a phase shift indicate about the graph of a sine function? How do you determine the phase shift from the function's equation?

77. Describe a general procedure for obtaining the graph of $y = A \sin(Bx - C)$.

78. Without drawing a graph, describe the behavior of the basic cosine curve.

79. Describe a relationship between the graphs of $y = \sin x$ and $y = \cos x$.

80. Describe the relationship between the graphs of $y = A \cos(Bx - C)$ and $y = A \cos(Bx - C) + D$.

81. Biorhythm cycles provide interesting applications of sinusoidal graphs. But do you believe in the validity of biorhythms? Write a few sentences explaining why or why not.

Technology Exercises

82. Use a graphing utility to verify any five of the sine curves that you drew by hand in Exercises 7–30. The amplitude, period, and phase shift should help you to determine appropriate range settings.

83. Use a graphing utility to verify any five of the cosine curves that you drew by hand in Exercises 31–50.

84. Use a graphing utility to verify any two of the sinusoidal curves with vertical shifts that you drew in Exercises 51–58.

In Exercises 85–88, use a graphing utility to graph two periods of the function.

85. $y = 3 \sin(2x + \pi)$ **86.** $y = -2 \cos\left(2\pi x - \frac{\pi}{2}\right)$

87. $y = 0.2 \sin\left(\frac{\pi}{10}x + \pi\right)$ **88.** $y = 3 \sin(2x - \pi) + 5$

89. Use a graphing utility to graph $y = \sin x$ and $y = x - \frac{x^3}{6} + \frac{x^5}{120}$ in a $\left[-\pi, \pi, \frac{\pi}{2}\right]$ by $[-2, 2, 1]$ viewing rectangle. How do the graphs compare?

90. Use a graphing utility to graph $y = \cos x$ and $y = 1 - \dfrac{x^2}{2} + \dfrac{x^4}{24}$ in a $\left[-\pi, \pi, \dfrac{\pi}{2} \right]$ by $[-2, 2, 1]$ viewing rectangle. How do the graphs compare?

91. Use a graphing utility to graph

$$y = \sin x + \frac{\sin 2x}{2} + \frac{\sin 3x}{3} + \frac{\sin 4x}{4}$$

in a $\left[-2\pi, 2\pi, \dfrac{\pi}{2} \right]$ by $[-2, 2, 1]$ viewing rectangle. How do these waves compare to the smooth rolling waves of the basic sine curve?

92. Use a graphing utility to graph

$$y = \sin x - \frac{\sin 3x}{9} + \frac{\sin 5x}{25}$$

in a $\left[-2\pi, 2\pi, \dfrac{\pi}{2} \right]$ by $[-2, 2, 1]$ viewing rectangle. How do these waves compare to the smooth rolling waves of the basic sine curve?

93. The data show the average monthly temperatures for Washington, D.C.
a. Use your graphing utility to draw a scatter plot of the data from $x = 1$ through $x = 12$.
b. Use the SINe REGression feature to find the sinusoidal function of the form $y = A \sin(Bx + C) + D$ that best fits the data.
c. Use your graphing utility to draw the sinusoidal function of best fit on the scatter plot.

x Month		Average Monthly Temperature, °F
1	(January)	34.6
2	(February)	37.5
3	(March)	47.2
4	(April)	56.5
5	(May)	66.4
6	(June)	75.6
7	(July)	80.0
8	(August)	78.5
9	(September)	71.3
10	(October)	59.7
11	(November)	49.8
12	(December)	39.4

Source: U.S. National Oceanic and Atmospheric Administration.

94. Repeat Exercise 93 for data of your choice. The data can involve the average monthly temperatures for the region where you live or any data whose scatter plot takes the form of a sinusoidal function.

 Critical Thinking Exercises

Graph the function in Exercises 95–96 by hand.

95. $y = \sin x + \cos x$ for $0 \le x \le 2\pi$

96. $y = x + \cos x$ for $0 \le x \le \dfrac{5\pi}{2}$

97. Use the cosine function to find an equation of the graph in the figure shown.

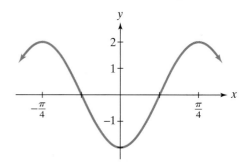

 Group Exercise

98. This exercise is intended to provide some fun with biorhythms, regardless of whether you believe they have any validity. We will use each member's chart to determine biorhythmic compatibility. Before meeting, each group member should go online and obtain his or her biorhythm chart. The date of the group meeting is the date on which your chart should begin. Include 12 months in the plot. At the meeting, compare differences and similarities among the intellectual sinusoidal curves. Using these comparisons, each person should find the one other person with whom he or she would be most intellectually compatible.

SECTION 5.6 *Graphs of Other Trigonometric Functions*

Objectives

1. Understand the graph of $y = \tan x$.
2. Graph variations of $y = \tan x$.
3. Understand the graph of $y = \cot x$.
4. Graph variations of $y = \cot x$.
5. Understand the graphs of $y = \csc x$ and $y = \sec x$.
6. Graph variations of $y = \csc x$ and $y = \sec x$.

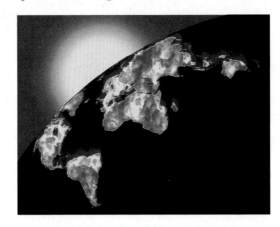

Recent advances in our understanding of climate have changed global warming from a subject for a disaster movie (the Statue of Liberty up to its chin in water) to a serious but manageable scientific and policy issue. Global warming may be related to the burning of fossil fuels, which adds carbon dioxide to the atmosphere. In the new millennium, we will see whether our use of fossil fuels will add enough carbon dioxide to the atmosphere to change it (and our climate) in significant ways. In this section's exercise set, you will see how trigonometric graphs reveal interesting patterns in carbon dioxide concentration from 1990 to 2000. In the section itself, trigonometric graphs will reveal patterns involving the tangent, cotangent, secant, and cosecant functions.

1 Understand the graph of $y = \tan x$.

The Graph of $y = \tan x$

The properties of the tangent function discussed in Section 5.4 will help us determine its graph. Because the tangent function has properties that are different from sinusoidal functions, its graph differs significantly from those of sine and cosine. Properties of the tangent function include the following:

- The period is π. It is only necessary to graph $y = \tan x$ over an interval of length π. The remainder of the graph consists of repetitions of that graph at intervals of π.
- The tangent function is an odd function: $\tan(-x) = -\tan x$. The graph is symmetric with respect to the origin.
- The tangent function is undefined at $\frac{\pi}{2}$. The graph of $y = \tan x$ has a vertical asymptote at $x = \frac{\pi}{2}$.

We obtain the graph of $y = \tan x$ using some points on the graph and origin symmetry. Table 5.3 lists some values of (x, y) on the graph of $y = \tan x$ on the interval $\left[0, \frac{\pi}{2}\right)$.

Table 5.3 Values of (x, y) on $y = \tan x$

x	0	$\frac{\pi}{6}$	$\frac{\pi}{4}$	$\frac{\pi}{3}$	$\frac{5\pi}{12} (75°)$	$\frac{17\pi}{36} (85°)$	$\frac{89\pi}{180} (89°)$	1.57	$\frac{\pi}{2}$
$y = \tan x$	0	$\frac{\sqrt{3}}{3} \approx 0.6$	1	$\sqrt{3} \approx 1.7$	3.7	11.4	57.3	1255.8	undefined

As x increases from 0 to $\frac{\pi}{2}$, y increases slowly at first, then more and more rapidly.

The graph in Figure 5.57(a) is based on our observation in the voice balloon. Notice that y increases without bound as x approaches $\dfrac{\pi}{2}$. As the figure shows, the graph of $y = \tan x$ has a vertical asymptote at $x = \dfrac{\pi}{2}$.

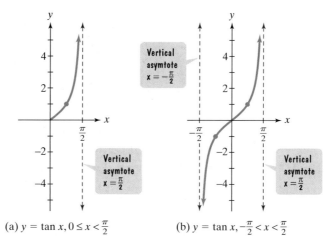

Figure 5.57 Graphing the tangent function

(a) $y = \tan x, 0 \leq x < \dfrac{\pi}{2}$ (b) $y = \tan x, -\dfrac{\pi}{2} < x < \dfrac{\pi}{2}$

The graph of $y = \tan x$ can be completed for the interval $\left(-\dfrac{\pi}{2}, \dfrac{\pi}{2}\right)$ by using origin symmetry. Figure 5.57(b) shows the result of reflecting the graph in Figure 5.57(a) about the origin. The graph of $y = \tan x$ has another vertical asymptote at $x = -\dfrac{\pi}{2}$. Notice that y decreases without bound as x approaches $-\dfrac{\pi}{2}$.

Because the period of the tangent function is π radians, the graph in Figure 5.57(b) shows one complete period of $y = \tan x$. We obtain the complete graph of $y = \tan x$ by repeating the graph in Figure 5.57(b) to the left and right over intervals of π. The resulting graph and its main characteristics are shown in the following box.

The Tangent Curve: The Graph of $y = \tan x$ and Its Characteristics

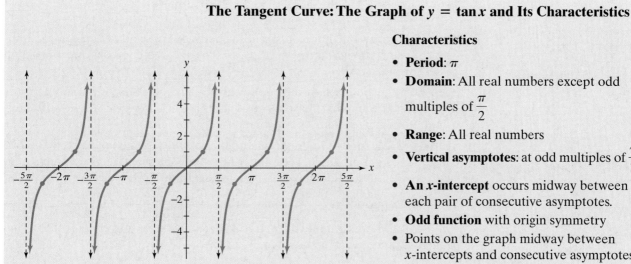

Characteristics

- **Period:** π
- **Domain:** All real numbers except odd multiples of $\dfrac{\pi}{2}$
- **Range:** All real numbers
- **Vertical asymptotes:** at odd multiples of $\dfrac{\pi}{2}$
- An **x-intercept** occurs midway between each pair of consecutive asymptotes.
- **Odd function** with origin symmetry
- Points on the graph midway between x-intercepts and consecutive asymptotes have y-coordinates of -1 and 1.

2 Graph variations of $y = \tan x$.

Graphing Variations of $y = \tan x$

We use the characteristics of the tangent curve to graph tangent functions of the form $y = A \tan(Bx - C)$.

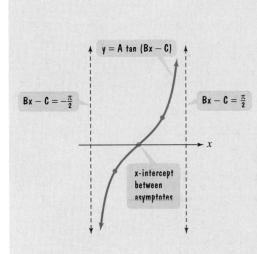

Graphing $y = A \tan(Bx - C)$

1. Find two consecutive asymptotes by setting the variable expression in the tangent equal to $-\dfrac{\pi}{2}$ and $\dfrac{\pi}{2}$ and solving

$$Bx - C = -\frac{\pi}{2} \text{ and } Bx - C = \frac{\pi}{2}.$$

2. Identify an x-intercept, midway between consecutive asymptotes.

3. Find the points on the graph midway between an x-intercept and the asymptotes. These points have y coordinates of $-A$ and A.

4. Use steps 1–3 to graph one full period of the function. Add additional cycles to the left or right as needed.

EXAMPLE 1   Graphing a Tangent Function

Graph $y = 2 \tan \dfrac{x}{2}$ for $-\pi < x < 3\pi$.

Solution

Step 1   Find two consecutive asymptotes. We solve the equations

$$\frac{x}{2} = -\frac{\pi}{2} \quad \text{and} \quad \frac{x}{2} = \frac{\pi}{2}. \quad \text{\small Set the variable expression in the tangent equal to } -\frac{\pi}{2} \text{ and } \frac{\pi}{2}.$$

$$x = -\pi \qquad\qquad x = \pi \quad \text{\small Multiply both sides of each equation by 2.}$$

Thus, two consecutive asymptotes occur at $x = -\pi$ and $x = \pi$.

Step 2   Identify an x-intercepts, midway between consecutive asymptotes. Midway between $x = -\pi$ and $x = \pi$ is $x = 0$. An x-intercept is 0 and the graph passes through $(0, 0)$.

Step 3   Find points on the graph midway between an x-intercept and the asymptotes. These points have y-coordinates of $-A$ and A. Because A, the coefficient of the tangent, is 2, these points have y-coordinates of -2 and 2.

Step 4   Use steps 1–3 to graph one full period of the function. We use the two consecutive asymptotes, $x = -\pi$ and $x = \pi$, an x-intercept of 0, and points midway between the x-intercept and asymptotes with y-coordinates of -2 and 2. We graph one period of $y = 2 \tan \dfrac{\pi}{2}$ from $-\pi$ to π. In order to graph for $-\pi < x < 3\pi$, we continue the pattern and extend the graph another full period to the right. The graph is shown in Figure 5.58.

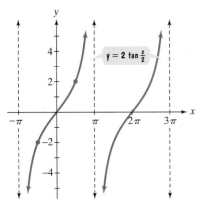

Figure 5.58 The graph is shown for two full periods

Check Point 1   Graph $y = 3 \tan 2x$ for $-\dfrac{\pi}{4} < x < \dfrac{3\pi}{4}$.

EXAMPLE 2   Graphing a Tangent Function

Graph two full periods of $y = \tan\left(x + \dfrac{\pi}{4}\right)$.

Solution   The graph of $y = \tan\left(x + \dfrac{\pi}{4}\right)$ is the graph of $y = \tan x$ shifted horizontally to the left $\dfrac{\pi}{4}$ units.

Step 1   Find two consecutive asymptotes. We solve the equations

$$x + \frac{\pi}{4} = -\frac{\pi}{2} \quad \text{and} \quad x + \frac{\pi}{4} = \frac{\pi}{2}$$

Set the variable expression in the tangent equal to $-\dfrac{\pi}{2}$ and $\dfrac{\pi}{2}$.

$$x = -\frac{\pi}{4} - \frac{\pi}{2} \qquad\qquad x = -\frac{\pi}{4} + \frac{\pi}{2}$$ Subtract $\dfrac{\pi}{4}$ from both sides in each equation.

$$x = -\frac{3\pi}{4} \qquad\qquad\qquad x = \frac{\pi}{4}$$ Simplify.

Thus, two consecutive asymptotes occur at $x = -\dfrac{3\pi}{4}$ and $x = \dfrac{\pi}{4}$.

Step 2   Identify an x-intercept, midway between consecutive asymptotes.

$$x\text{-intercept} = \frac{-\dfrac{3\pi}{4} + \dfrac{\pi}{4}}{2} = \frac{-\dfrac{2\pi}{4}}{2} = -\frac{2\pi}{8} = -\frac{\pi}{4}$$

An x-intercept is $-\dfrac{\pi}{4}$ and the graph passes through $\left(-\dfrac{\pi}{4}, 0\right)$.

Step 3   Find points on the graph midway between an x-intercept and the asymptotes. Because A, the coefficient of the tangent, is 1, these points have y-coordinates of -1 and 1.

Step 4   Use steps 1–3 to graph one full period of the function. We use the two consecutive asymptotes, $x = -\dfrac{3\pi}{4}$ and $x = \dfrac{\pi}{4}$, to graph one full period of $y = \tan\left(x + \dfrac{\pi}{4}\right)$ from $-\dfrac{3\pi}{4}$ to $\dfrac{\pi}{4}$. We graph two full periods by continuing the pattern and extending the graph another full period to the right. The graph is shown in Figure 5.59.

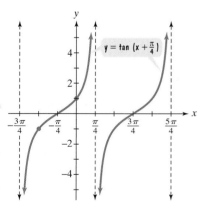

$y = \tan\left(x + \frac{\pi}{4}\right)$

Figure 5.59 The graph is shown for two full periods.

Check Point 2   Graph two full periods of $y = \tan\left(x - \dfrac{\pi}{2}\right)$.

3 Understand the graph of $y = \cot x$.

The Graph of $y = \cot x$

Like the tangent function, the cotangent function, $y = \cot x$, has a period of π. The graph and its main characteristics are shown in the following box.

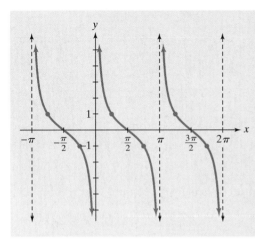

The Cotangent Curve: The Graph of $y = \cot x$ and Its Characteristics

Characteristics

- **Period**: π
- **Domain**: All real numbers except integral multiples of π
- **Range**: All real numbers
- **Vertical asymptotes** at integral multiples of π
- An **x-intercept** occurs midway between each pair of consecutive asymptotes.
- **Odd function** with origin symmetry
- Points on the graph midway between x-intercepts and consecutive asymptotes have y-coordinates of 1 and -1.

4 Graph variations of $y = \cot x$.

Graphing Variations of $y = \cot x$

We use the characteristics of the cotangent curve to graph cotangent functions of the form $y = A \cot(Bx - C)$.

$y = A \cot(Bx - C)$

y-coordinate is A.

$Bx - C = 0$ $Bx - C = \pi$

x-intercept between asymptotes

y-coordinate is –A.

Graphing $y = A \cot(Bx - C)$

1. Find two consecutive asymptotes by setting the variable expression in the cotangent equal to 0 and π and solving

$$Bx - C = 0 \text{ and } Bx - C = \pi.$$

2. Identify an x-intercept, midway between consecutive asymptotes.

3. Find the points on the graph midway between an x-intercept and the asymptotes. These points have y-coordinates of A and $-A$.

4. Use steps 1-3 to graph one full period of the function. Add additional cycles to the left or right as needed.

EXAMPLE 3   Graphing a Cotangent Function

Graph $y = 3 \cot 2x$.

Solution

Step 1   Find two consecutive asymptotes. We solve the equations

$2x = 0$ and $2x = \pi$.   *Set the variable expression in the cotangent equal to 0 and π.*

$x = 0$ $x = \dfrac{\pi}{2}$ *Divide both sides of each equation by 2.*

Two consecutive asymptotes occur at $x = 0$ and $x = \dfrac{\pi}{2}$.

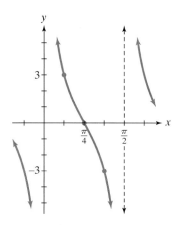

Figure 5.60 The graph of $y = 3 \cot 2x$

5 Understand the graphs of $y = \csc x$ and $y = \sec x$.

Step 2   Identify an *x*-intercept, midway between consecutive asymptotes. Midway between $x = 0$ and $x = \dfrac{\pi}{2}$ is $x = \dfrac{\pi}{4}$. An *x*-intercept is $\dfrac{\pi}{4}$ and the graph passes through $\left(\dfrac{\pi}{4}, 0\right)$.

Step 3   Find points on the graph midway between an *x*-intercept and the asymptotes. These points have *y*-coordinates of *A* and −*A*. Because A, the coefficient of the cotangent, is 3, these points have *y*-coordinates of 3 and −3.

Step 4   Use steps 1–3 to graph one full period of the function. We use the two consecutive asymptotes, $x = 0$ and $x = \dfrac{\pi}{2}$, to graph one full period of $y = 3 \cot 2x$. This curve is repeated to the left and right, as shown in Figure 5.60.

Check Point 3   Graph $y = \dfrac{1}{2} \cot \dfrac{\pi}{2} x.$

The Graphs of $y = \csc x$ and $y = \sec x$

We obtain the graphs of the cosecant and secant curves by using the reciprocal identities

$$\csc x = \frac{1}{\sin x} \quad \text{and} \quad \sec x = \frac{1}{\cos x}.$$

The identity on the left tells us that the value of the cosecant function $y = \csc x$ at a given value of x equals the reciprocal of the corresponding value of the sine function, provided that the value of the sine function is not 0. If the value of $\sin x$ is 0, then at each of these values of x, the cosecant function is not defined. A vertical asymptote is associated with each of these values on the graph of $y = \csc x$.

We obtain the graph of $y = \csc x$ by taking reciprocals of the *y*-values in the graph of $y = \sin x$. Vertical asymptotes of $y = \csc x$ occur at the *x*-intercepts of $y = \sin x$. Likewise, we obtain the graph of $y = \sec x$ by taking the reciprocal of $y = \cos x$. Vertical asymptotes of $y = \sec x$ occur at the *x*-intercepts of $y = \cos x$. The graphs of $y = \csc x$ and $y = \sec x$ and their key characteristics are shown in the following boxes. We have used dashed red lines to first graph $y = \sin x$ and $y = \cos x$, drawing vertical asymptotes through the *x*-intercepts.

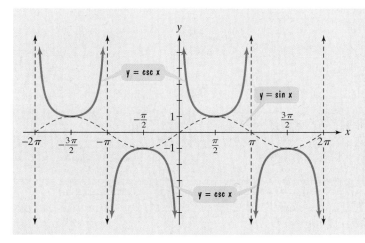

The Cosecant Curve: The Graph of $y = \csc x$ and Its Characteristics

Characteristics

- **Period**: 2π
- **Domain**: All real numbers except integral multiples of π
- **Range**: All real numbers y such that $y \leq -1$ or $y \geq 1$
- **Vertical asymptotes** at integral multiples of π
- **Odd function**, $\csc(-x) = -\csc x$, with origin symmetry

The Secant Curve: The Graph of $y = \sec x$ and Its Characteristics

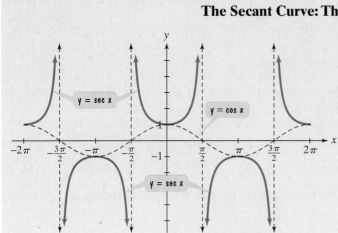

Characteristics

- **Period**: 2π
- **Domain**: All real numbers except odd multiples of $\dfrac{\pi}{2}$
- **Range**: All real numbers y such that $y \le -1$ or $y \ge 1$
- **Vertical asymptotes** at odd multiples of $\dfrac{\pi}{2}$
- **Even function**, $\sec(-x) = \sec x$, with y-axis symmetry

---

6 Graph variations of $y = \csc x$ and $y = \sec x$.

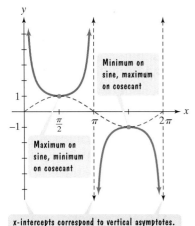

Figure 5.61

Graphing Variations of $y = \csc x$ and $y = \sec x$

We use graphs of reciprocal functions to obtain graphs of cosecant and secant functions. To graph a cosecant or secant curve, begin by graphing the reciprocal function. For example, to graph $y = 2 \csc 2x$, we use the graph of $y = 2 \sin 2x$. Likewise, to graph $y = -3 \sec \dfrac{x}{2}$, we use the graph of $y = -3 \cos \dfrac{x}{2}$.

Figure 5.61 illustrates how we use a sine curve to obtain a cosecant curve. Notice that

- x-intercepts on the sine curve correspond to vertical asymptotes of the cosecant curve.
- A maximum point on the sine curve corresponds to a minimum point on a continuous portion of the cosecant curve.
- A minimum point on the sine curve corresponds to a maximum point on a continuous portion of the cosecant curve.

EXAMPLE 4   Using a Sine Curve to Obtain a Cosecant Curve

Use the graph of $y = 2 \sin 2x$ in Figure 5.62 to obtain the graph of $y = 2 \csc 2x$.

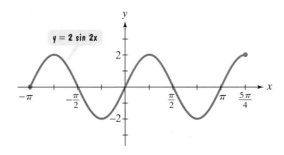

Figure 5.62

Solution   The x-intercepts of $y = 2 \sin 2x$ correspond to the vertical asymptotes of $y = 2 \csc 2x$. Thus, we draw vertical asymptotes through the x-intercepts, shown in Figure 5.63. Using the asymptotes as guides, we sketch the graph of $y = 2 \csc 2x$ in Figure 5.63.

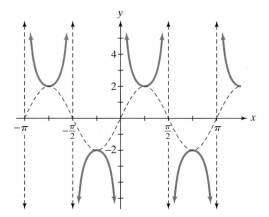

Figure 5.63 Using a sine curve to graph $y = 2 \csc 2x$

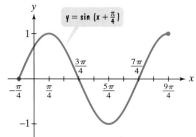

> **Check Point 4**
>
> Use the graph of $y = \sin\left(x + \dfrac{\pi}{4}\right)$ shown on the left to obtain the graph of $y = \csc\left(x + \dfrac{\pi}{4}\right)$.

We use a cosine curve to obtain a secant curve in exactly the same way we used a sine curve to obtain a cosecant curve. Thus,

- x-intercepts on the cosine curve correspond to vertical asymptotes on the secant curve.
- A maximum point on the cosine curve corresponds to a minimum point on a continuous portion of the secant curve.
- A minimum point on the cosine curve corresponds to a maximum point on a continuous portion of the secant curve.

EXAMPLE 5   Graphing a Secant Function

Graph $y = -3 \sec \dfrac{x}{2}$ for $-\pi < x < 5\pi$.

Solution   We begin by graphing the reciprocal cosine function, $y = -3 \cos \dfrac{x}{2}$. This equation is of the form $y = A \cos Bx$ with $A = -3$ and $B = \frac{1}{2}$.

amplitude: $|A| = |-3| = 3$ The maximum y is 3 and the minimum is −3.

period: $\dfrac{2\pi}{B} = \dfrac{2\pi}{\frac{1}{2}} = 4\pi$ Each cycle is completed in 4π radians.

We use quarter-periods, $\dfrac{4\pi}{4}$ or π, to find the x-values for the five key points. Starting with $x = 0$, the x-values are $0, \pi, 2\pi, 3\pi$, and 4π. Evaluating the function at each of these values of x, the key points are

$$(0, -3), (\pi, 0), (2\pi, 3), (3\pi, 0), \text{ and } (4\pi, -3).$$

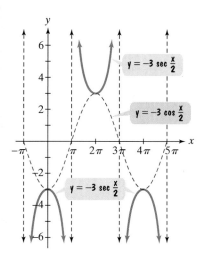

Figure 5.64 Using a cosine curve to graph $y = -3 \sec \dfrac{x}{2}$

We use these key points to graph $y = -3 \cos \dfrac{x}{2}$ from 0 to 4π. In order to graph for $-\pi \le x \le 5\pi$, extend the graph π units to the left and π units to the right. The graph is shown using a dashed red line in Figure 5.64. Now use this dashed red graph to obtain the graph of the reciprocal function. Draw vertical asymptotes through the x-intercepts. Using these asymptotes as guides, the graph of $y = -3 \sec \dfrac{x}{2}$ is shown in blue in Figure 5.64.

Check
Point
5

Graph $y = 2 \sec 2x$ for $-\dfrac{3\pi}{4} < x < \dfrac{3\pi}{4}$.

The Six Curves of Trigonometry

Table 5.4 summarizes the graphs of the six trigonometric functions. Below each of the graphs is a description of the domain, range, and period of the function.

Table 5.4   Graphs of the Six Trigonometric Functions

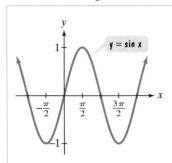

Domain: all real numbers

Range: $[-1, 1]$
Period: 2π

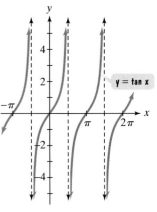

Domain: all real numbers

Range: $[-1, 1]$
Period: 2π

Domain: all real numbers

   except odd multiples of $\dfrac{\pi}{2}$

Range: all real numbers
Period: π

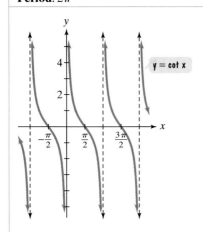

Domain: all real numbers

   except integral multiples of π

Range: all real numbers
Period: π

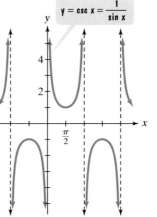

Domain: all real numbers

   except integral multiples of π

Range: $(-\infty, -1]$ or $[1, \infty)$
Period: 2π

Domain: all real numbers

   except odd multiples of $\dfrac{\pi}{2}$

Range: $(-\infty, -1]$ or $[1, \infty)$
Period: 2π

EXERCISE SET 5.6

Practice Exercises

In Exercises 1–4, the graph of a tangent function is given. Select the equation for each graph from the following options.

$$y = \tan\left(x + \frac{\pi}{2}\right), \quad y = \tan(x + \pi), \quad y = -\tan x, \quad y = -\tan\left(x - \frac{\pi}{2}\right)$$

1.

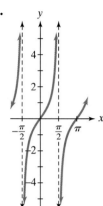

2.

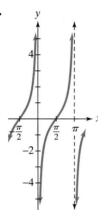

3.

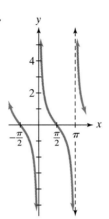

4.

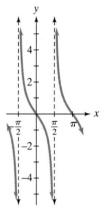

In Exercises 5–12, graph two periods of the given tangent function.

5. $y = 3\tan\dfrac{x}{4}$

6. $y = 2\tan\dfrac{x}{4}$

7. $y = \frac{1}{2}\tan 2x$

8. $y = 3\tan 2x$

9. $y = -2\tan\frac{1}{2}x$

10. $y = -3\tan\frac{1}{2}x$

11. $y = \tan(x - \pi)$

12. $y = \tan\left(x + \dfrac{\pi}{2}\right)$

In Exercises 13–16, the graph of a cotangent function is given. Select the equation for each graph from the following options.

$$y = \cot\left(x + \frac{\pi}{2}\right), \quad y = \cot(x + \pi), \quad y = -\cot x, \quad y = -\cot\left(x - \frac{\pi}{2}\right)$$

13.

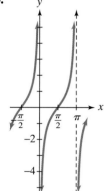

14.

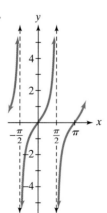

15.

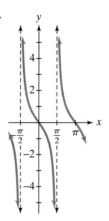

16.

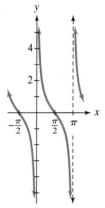

In Exercises 17–24, graph two periods of the given cotangent function.

17. $y = 2\cot x$

18. $y = \frac{1}{2}\cot x$

19. $y = \frac{1}{2}\cot 2x$

20. $y = 2\cot 2x$

21. $y = -3\cot\dfrac{\pi}{2}x$

22. $y = -2\cot\dfrac{\pi}{4}x$

23. $y = 3\cot\left(x + \dfrac{\pi}{2}\right)$

24. $y = 3\cot\left(x + \dfrac{\pi}{4}\right)$

In Exercises 25–28, use each graph to obtain the graph of the reciprocal function. Give the equation of the function for the graph that you obtain.

25.

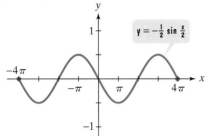

$y = -\frac{1}{2} \sin \frac{x}{2}$

26.

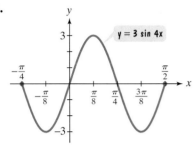

$y = 3 \sin 4x$

27.

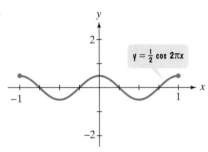

$y = \frac{1}{2} \cos 2\pi x$

28.

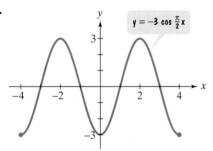

$y = -3 \cos \frac{\pi}{2} x$

In Exercises 29–44, graph two periods of the given cosecant or secant function.

29. $y = 3 \csc x$

30. $y = 2 \csc x$

31. $y = \frac{1}{2} \csc \frac{x}{2}$

32. $y = \frac{3}{2} \csc \frac{x}{4}$

33. $y = 2 \sec x$

34. $y = 3 \sec x$

35. $y = \sec \frac{x}{3}$

36. $y = \sec \frac{x}{2}$

37. $y = -2 \csc \pi x$

38. $y = -\frac{1}{2} \csc \pi x$

39. $y = -\frac{1}{2} \sec \pi x$

40. $y = -\frac{3}{2} \sec \pi x$

41. $y = \csc(x - \pi)$

42. $y = \csc\left(x - \frac{\pi}{2}\right)$

43. $y = 2 \sec(x + \pi)$

44. $y = 2 \sec\left(x + \frac{\pi}{2}\right)$

 Application Exercises

45. An ambulance with a rotating beacon of light is parked 12 feet from a building. The function

$$d = 12 \tan 2\pi t$$

describes the distance, d, in feet, of the rotating beacon from point C after t seconds.
  a. Graph the function on the interval $[0, 2]$.
  b. For what values of t in $[0, 2]$ is the function undefined? What does this mean in terms of the rotating beacon in the figure shown?

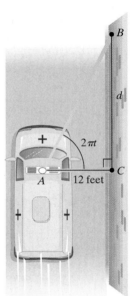

46. The angle of elevation from the top of a house to a jet flying 2 miles above the house is x radians. If d represents the horizontal distance of the jet from the house, express d in terms of a trigonometric function of x. Then graph the function for $0 < x < \pi$.

47. Your best friend is marching with a band and has asked you to film her. The figure on page 497 shows that you have set yourself up 10 feet from the street where your friend will be passing from left to right. If d represents your distance from your friend and x is the radian measure of the angle shown, express d in terms of a trigonometric function of *x*. Then graph the function for $-\dfrac{\pi}{2} < x < \dfrac{\pi}{2}$. Negative angles indicate that your marching buddy is on your left.

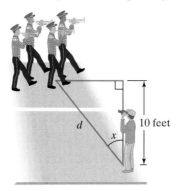

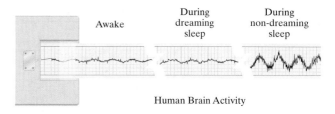

Human Brain Activity

In Exercises 48–50, sketch a reasonable graph that models the given situation.

48. The number of hours of daylight per day in your hometown over a two-year period

49. The motion of a diving board vibrating 10 inches in each direction per second just after someone has dived off

50. The distance of a rotating beacon of light from a point on a wall (See the figure for Exercise 45.)

Writing in Mathematics

51. Without drawing a graph, describe the behavior of the basic tangent curve.

52. If you are given the equation of a tangent function, how do you find consecutive asymptotes?

53. If you are given the equation of a tangent function, how do you identify an *x*-intercept?

54. Without drawing a graph, describe the behavior of the basic cotangent curve.

55. If you are given the equation of a cotangent function, how do you find consecutive asymptotes?

56. Explain how to determine the range of $y = \csc x$ from the graph. What is the range?

57. Explain how to use a sine curve to obtain a cosecant curve. Why can the same procedure be used to obtain a secant curve from a cosine curve?

58. Scientists record brain activity by attaching electrodes to the scalp and then connecting these electrodes to a machine. The record of brain activity recorded with this machine is shown in the three graphs at the top of the next column. Which trigonometric functions would be most appropriate for describing the oscillations in brain activity? Describe similarities and differences among these functions when modeling brain activity when awake, during dreaming sleep, and during non-dreaming sleep.

Technology Exercises

In working Exercises 59–62, describe what happens at the asymptotes on the graphing utility. Compare the graphs in the connected and dot modes.

59. Use a graphing utility to verify any two of the tangent curves that you drew by hand in Exercises 5–12.

60. Use a graphing utility to verify any two of the cotangent curves that you drew by hand in Exercises 17–24.

61. Use a graphing utility to verify any two of the cosecant curves that you drew by hand in Exercises 29–44.

62. Use a graphing utility to verify any two of the secant curves that you drew by hand in Exercises 29–44.

In Exercises 63–68, use a graphing utility to graph each function. Use a range setting so that the graph is shown for at least two periods.

63. $y = \tan \dfrac{x}{4}$

64. $y = \tan 4x$

65. $y = \cot 2x$

66. $y = \cot \dfrac{x}{2}$

67. $y = \frac{1}{2}\tan \pi x$

68. $y = \frac{1}{2}\tan(\pi x + 1)$

In Exercises 69–72, use a graphing utility to graph each pair of functions in the same viewing rectangle. Use a range setting so that the graphs are shown for at least two periods.

69. $y = 0.8 \sin \dfrac{x}{2}$ and $y = 0.8 \csc \dfrac{x}{2}$

70. $y = -2.5 \sin \dfrac{\pi}{3} x$ and $y = -2.5 \csc \dfrac{\pi}{3} x$

71. $y = 4 \cos\left(2x - \dfrac{\pi}{6}\right)$ and $y = 4 \sec\left(2x - \dfrac{\pi}{6}\right)$

72. $y = -3.5 \cos\left(\pi x - \dfrac{\pi}{6}\right)$ and $y = -3.5 \sec\left(\pi x - \dfrac{\pi}{6}\right)$

73. Carbon dioxide particles in our atmosphere trap heat and raise the planet's temperature. The resultant gradually increasing temperature is called the greenhouse effect. Carbon dioxide accounts for about half of global warming. The function

$$y = 2.5 \sin 2\pi x + 0.0216x^2 + 0.654x + 316$$

models carbon dioxide concentration, *y*, in parts per million, where $x = 0$ represents January 1960; $x = \frac{1}{12}$, February 1960; $x = \frac{2}{12}$, March 1960; ... , $x = 1$, January 1961; $x = \frac{13}{12}$, February 1961; and so on. Use a graphing utility to graph the function in a $[30, 40, 5]$ by $[310, 380, 5]$ viewing rectangle. Describe what the graph reveals about carbon dioxide concentration from 1990 to 2000.

74. Graph $y = \sin \dfrac{1}{x}$ in a $[-0.2, 0.2, 0.01]$ by $[-1.2, 1.2, 0.01]$

viewing rectangle. What is happening as x approaches 0 from the left or the right? Explain this behavior.

Critical Thinking Exercises

In Exercises 75–76, write an equation for each blue graph.

75.

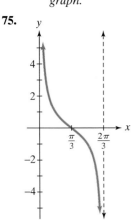

76.

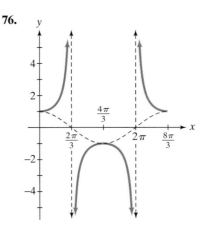

77. For $x > 0$, what effect does 2^{-x} in $y = 2^{-x} \sin x$ have on the graph of $y = \sin x$? What kind of behavior can be modeled by a function such as $y = 2^{-x} \sin x$?

SECTION 5.7   Inverse Trigonometric Functions

Objectives

1. Understand and use the inverse sine function.
2. Understand and use the inverse cosine function.
3. Understand and use the inverse tangent function.
4. Use a calculator to evaluate inverse trigonometric functions.
5. Find exact values of composite functions with inverse trigonometric functions.

You watched *The Matrix* on video and were impressed by the elaborate computer-generated effects. The movie is being shown again at a local theater, where you can experience its stunning visual force on a large screen. Where in the theater should you sit to maximize the film's visual impact? In this section you will see how an inverse trigonometric function can enhance your movie-going experiences.

Study Tip

Here are some helpful things to remember from our discussion of inverse functions in Section 2.6.

- If no horizontal line intersects the graph of a function more than once, the function is one-to-one and has an inverse function.
- If the point (a, b) is on the graph of f, then the point (b, a) is on the graph of the inverse function, denoted f^{-1}. The graph of f^{-1} is a reflection of the graph of f about the line $y = x$.

1 Understand and use the inverse sine function.

The Inverse Sine Function

Figure 5.65 shows the graph of $y = \sin x$. Can you see that every horizontal line that can be drawn between -1 and 1 intersects the graph infinitely many times? Thus, the sine function is not one-to-one and has no inverse function.

In Figure 5.66, we have taken a portion of the sine curve, restricting the domain of the sine function to $-\dfrac{\pi}{2} \le x \le \dfrac{\pi}{2}$. With this restricted domain, every horizontal line that can be drawn between -1 and 1 intersects the graph exactly once. Thus, the restricted function passes the horizontal line test and is one-to-one.

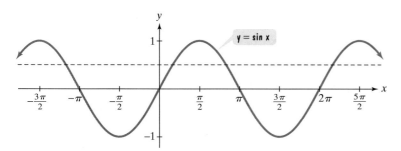

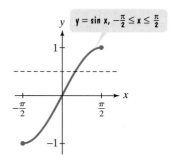

Figure 5.65 The horizontal line test shows that the sine function is not one to one and has no inverse function.

Figure 5.66 The restricted sine function passes the horizontal line test. It is one-to-one and has an inverse function.

On the restricted domain $-\dfrac{\pi}{2} \le x \le \dfrac{\pi}{2}$, $y = \sin x$ has an inverse function. The inverse of the restricted sine function is called the **inverse sine function**. Two notations are commonly used to denote the inverse sine function:

$$y = \sin^{-1} x \quad \text{or} \quad y = \arcsin x.$$

In this book, we will use $y = \sin^{-1} x$. This notation has the same symbol as the inverse function notation $f^{-1}(x)$.

The Inverse Sine Function

The **inverse sine function**, denoted by $\sin^{-1}$, is the inverse of the restricted sine function $y = \sin x$, $-\dfrac{\pi}{2} \le x \le \dfrac{\pi}{2}$. Thus,

$$y = \sin^{-1} x \quad \text{means} \quad \sin y = x,$$

where $-\dfrac{\pi}{2} \le y \le \dfrac{\pi}{2}$ and $-1 \le x \le 1$. We read $y = \sin^{-1} x$ as "y equals the inverse sine at x."

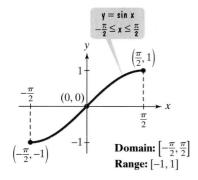

Figure 5.67 The restricted sine function

One way to graph $y = \sin^{-1} x$ is to take points on the graph of the restricted sine function and reverse the order of the coordinates. For example, Figure 5.67 shows that $\left(-\dfrac{\pi}{2}, -1\right)$, $(0, 0)$, and $\left(\dfrac{\pi}{2}, 1\right)$ are on the graph of the restricted sine function. Reversing the order of the coordinates gives $\left(-1, -\dfrac{\pi}{2}\right)$, $(0, 0)$, and

$\left(1, \dfrac{\pi}{2}\right)$. We now use these three points to sketch the inverse sine function. The graph of $y = \sin^{-1} x$ is shown in Figure 5.68.

Another way to obtain the graph of $y = \sin^{-1} x$ is to reflect the graph of the restricted sine function about the line $y = x$, shown in Figure 5.69. The blue graph is the graph of $y = \sin^{-1} x$.

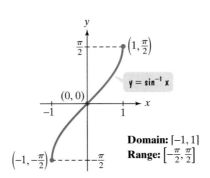

Figure 5.68 The graph of the inverse sine function

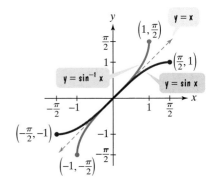

Figure 5.69 Using a reflection to obtain the graph of the inverse sine function

Table 5.5   Exact Values for
$$\sin\theta, \; -\frac{\pi}{2} \le \theta \le \frac{\pi}{2}$$

θ	$\sin\theta$
$-\dfrac{\pi}{2}$	-1
$-\dfrac{\pi}{3}$	$-\dfrac{\sqrt{3}}{2}$
$-\dfrac{\pi}{4}$	$-\dfrac{\sqrt{2}}{2}$
$-\dfrac{\pi}{6}$	$-\dfrac{1}{2}$
0	0
$\dfrac{\pi}{6}$	$\dfrac{1}{2}$
$\dfrac{\pi}{4}$	$\dfrac{\sqrt{2}}{2}$
$\dfrac{\pi}{3}$	$\dfrac{\sqrt{3}}{2}$
$\dfrac{\pi}{2}$	1

Exact values of $\sin^{-1} x$ can be found by thinking of **$\sin^{-1} x$ as the angle in the interval** $\left[-\dfrac{\pi}{2}, \dfrac{\pi}{2} \right]$ **whose sine is x.** For example, we can use the two points on the blue graph of the inverse sine function in Figure 5.69 and write

$$\sin^{-1}(-1) = -\frac{\pi}{2} \quad \text{and} \quad \sin^{-1} 1 = \frac{\pi}{2}.$$

The angle whose sine is -1 is $-\dfrac{\pi}{2}$.

The angle whose sine is 1 is $\dfrac{\pi}{2}$.

Because we are thinking of $\sin^{-1} x$ in terms of an angle, we will represent such an angle by θ.

Finding Exact Values of $\sin^{-1} x$.

1. Let $\theta = \sin^{-1} x$.
2. Rewrite step 1 as $\sin\theta = x$.
3. Use the exact values in Table 5.5 to find the value of θ in $\left[-\dfrac{\pi}{2}, \dfrac{\pi}{2} \right]$ that satisfies $\sin\theta = x$.

EXAMPLE 1   Finding the Exact Value of an Inverse Sine Function

Find the exact value of $\sin^{-1} \dfrac{\sqrt{2}}{2}$.

Solution

Step 1 Let $\theta = \sin^{-1}x$. Thus,

$$\theta = \sin^{-1}\frac{\sqrt{2}}{2}.$$

We must find the angle θ, $-\frac{\pi}{2} \le \theta \le \frac{\pi}{2}$, whose sine equals $\frac{\sqrt{2}}{2}$.

Step 2 Rewrite $\theta = \sin^{-1}x$ as $\sin\theta = x$. Using the definition of the inverse sine function, we rewrite $\theta = \sin^{-1}\frac{\sqrt{2}}{2}$ as

$$\sin\theta = \frac{\sqrt{2}}{2}.$$

Step 3 Use the exact values in Table 5.5 to find the value of θ in $\left[-\frac{\pi}{2}, \frac{\pi}{2}\right]$ that satisfies $\sin\theta = x$. Table 5.5 shows that the only angle in the interval $\left[-\frac{\pi}{2}, \frac{\pi}{2}\right]$ that satisfies $\sin\theta = \frac{\sqrt{2}}{2}$ is $\frac{\pi}{4}$. Thus, $\theta = \frac{\pi}{4}$. Because θ, in step 1, represents $\sin^{-1}\frac{\sqrt{2}}{2}$, we conclude that

$$\sin^{-1}\frac{\sqrt{2}}{2} = \frac{\pi}{4}. \quad \text{\small The angle in } \left[-\frac{\pi}{2}, \frac{\pi}{2}\right] \text{ \small whose sine is } \frac{\sqrt{2}}{2} \text{ \small is } \frac{\pi}{4}$$

Study Tip

If you have not already done so, you should memorize the values in Table 5.5, as well as those in the forthcoming Tables 5.6 and 5.7.

Check Point 1 Find the exact value of $\sin^{-1}\frac{\sqrt{3}}{2}$.

EXAMPLE 2 Finding the Exact Value of an Inverse Sine Function

Find the exact value of $\sin^{-1}\left(-\frac{1}{2}\right)$.

Solution

Step 1 Let $\theta = \sin^{-1}x$. Thus,

$$\theta = \sin^{-1}\left(-\frac{1}{2}\right).$$

We must find the angle θ, $-\frac{\pi}{2} \le \theta \le \frac{\pi}{2}$, whose sine equals $-\frac{1}{2}$.

Step 2 Rewrite $\theta = \sin^{-1}x$ as $\sin\theta = x$. We obtain

$$\sin\theta = -\frac{1}{2}$$

Step 3 Use the exact values in Table 5.5 to find the value of θ in $\left[-\dfrac{\pi}{2}, \dfrac{\pi}{2}\right]$ that satisfies $\sin\theta = x$. The table on page 500 shows that the only angle in the interval $\left[-\dfrac{\pi}{2}, \dfrac{\pi}{2}\right]$ that satisfies $\sin\theta = -\frac{1}{2}$ is $-\dfrac{\pi}{6}$. Thus,

$$\sin^{-1}\left(-\frac{1}{2}\right) = -\frac{\pi}{6}$$

> **Check Point 2** Find the exact value of $\sin^{-1}\left(-\dfrac{\sqrt{2}}{2}\right)$.

Some inverse sine expressions cannot be evaluated. Because the domain of the inverse sine function is $[-1, 1]$, it is only possible to evaluate $\sin^{-1}x$ for values of x in this domain. Thus, $\sin^{-1}3$ cannot be evaluated. There is no angle whose sine is 3.

2 Understand and use the inverse cosine function.

The Inverse Cosine Function

Figure 5.70 shows how we restrict the domain of the cosine function so that it becomes one-to-one and has an inverse function. Restrict the domain to the interval $[0, \pi]$, shown by the dark blue graph. Over this interval, the restricted cosine function passes the horizontal line test and has an inverse function.

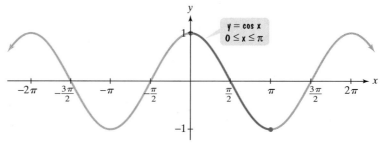

Figure 5.70 $y = \cos x$ is one-to-one on the interval $[0, \pi]$.

The Inverse Cosine Function

The **inverse cosine function**, denoted by $\cos^{-1}$, is the inverse of the restricted cosine function $y = \cos x, 0 \le x \le \pi$. Thus,

$$y = \cos^{-1}x \quad \text{means} \quad \cos y = x,$$

where $0 \le y \le \pi$ and $-1 \le x \le 1$.

One way to graph $y = \cos^{-1} x$ is to take points on the graph of the restricted cosine function and reverse the order of the coordinates. For example, Figure 5.71 shows that $(0, 1)$, $\left(\dfrac{\pi}{2}, 0\right)$ and $(\pi, -1)$ are on the graph of the restricted cosine function. Reversing the order of the coordinates gives $(1, 0)$, $\left(0, \dfrac{\pi}{2}\right)$, and $(-1, \pi)$. We now use these three points to sketch the inverse cosine function. The graph of $y = \cos^{-1} x$ is shown in Figure 5.72. You can also obtain this graph by reflecting the graph of the restricted cosine function about the line $y = x$.

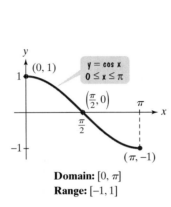

Domain: $[0, \pi]$
Range: $[-1, 1]$

Figure 5.71 The restricted cosine function

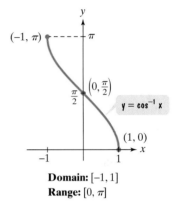

Domain: $[-1, 1]$
Range: $[0, \pi]$

Figure 5.72 The graph of the inverse cosine function

Table 5.6 Exact Values for $\cos\theta, 0 \leq \theta \leq \pi$

θ	$\cos\theta$
0	1
$\dfrac{\pi}{6}$	$\dfrac{\sqrt{3}}{2}$
$\dfrac{\pi}{4}$	$\dfrac{\sqrt{2}}{2}$
$\dfrac{\pi}{3}$	$\dfrac{1}{2}$
$\dfrac{\pi}{2}$	0
$\dfrac{2\pi}{3}$	$-\dfrac{1}{2}$
$\dfrac{3\pi}{4}$	$-\dfrac{\sqrt{2}}{2}$
$\dfrac{5\pi}{6}$	$-\dfrac{\sqrt{3}}{2}$
π	-1

Exact values of $\cos^{-1} x$ can be found by thinking of $\cos^{-1} x$ as **the angle in the interval $[0, \pi]$ whose cosine is x.** This time we will use Table 5.6, which shows exact values for $\cos\theta$ for θ in the interval $[0, \pi]$.

EXAMPLE 3 Finding the Exact Value of an Inverse Cosine Function

Find the exact value of $\cos^{-1}\left(-\dfrac{\sqrt{3}}{2}\right)$.

Solution

Step 1 Let $\theta = \cos^{-1} x$. Thus,

$$\theta = \cos^{-1}\left(-\frac{\sqrt{3}}{2}\right).$$

We must find the angle $\theta, 0 \leq \theta \leq \pi$, whose cosine equals $-\dfrac{\sqrt{3}}{2}$.

Step 2 Rewrite $\theta = \cos^{-1} x$ as $\cos\theta = x$. We obtain

$$\cos\theta = -\frac{\sqrt{3}}{2}.$$

Step 3 Use the exact values in Table 5.6 to find the value of θ in $[0, \pi]$ that satisfies $\cos\theta = x$. The table on page 503 shows that the only angle in the interval $[0, \pi]$ that satisfies $\cos\theta = -\dfrac{\sqrt{3}}{2}$ is $\dfrac{5\pi}{6}$. Thus, $\theta = \dfrac{5\pi}{6}$ and

$$\cos^{-1}\left(-\frac{\sqrt{3}}{2}\right) = \frac{5\pi}{6}.$$ *The angle in $[0,\pi]$ whose cosine is $-\dfrac{\sqrt{3}}{2}$ is $\dfrac{5\pi}{6}$.*

Check Point 3 Find the exact value of $\cos^{-1}\left(-\dfrac{1}{2}\right)$.

3 Understand and use the inverse tangent function.

The Inverse Tangent Function

Figure 5.73 shows how we restrict the domain of the tangent function so that it becomes one-to-one and has an inverse function. Restrict the domain to the interval $\left(-\dfrac{\pi}{2}, \dfrac{\pi}{2}\right)$, shown by the solid blue graph. Over this interval, the restricted tangent function passes the horizontal line test and has an inverse function.

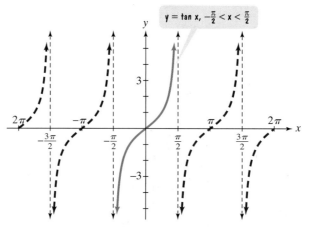

Figure 5.73 $y = \tan x$ is one-to-one on the interval $\left(-\dfrac{\pi}{2}, \dfrac{\pi}{2}\right)$.

The Inverse Tangent Function

The **inverse tangent function**, denoted by $\tan^{-1}$, is the inverse of the restricted tangent function $y = \tan x$, $-\dfrac{\pi}{2} < x < \dfrac{\pi}{2}$. Thus,

$$y = \tan^{-1}x \quad \text{means} \quad \tan y = \infty,$$

where $-\dfrac{\pi}{2} < y < \dfrac{\pi}{2}$ and $-\infty < x < \infty$.

We graph $y = \tan^{-1}x$ by taking points on the graph of the restricted function and reversing the order of the coordinates. Figure 5.74 shows that $\left(-\dfrac{\pi}{4}, -1\right)$, $(0, 0)$, and $\left(\dfrac{\pi}{4}, 1\right)$ are on the graph of the restricted tangent function. Reversing the order gives $\left(-1, -\dfrac{\pi}{4}\right)$, $(0, 0)$, and $\left(1, \dfrac{\pi}{4}\right)$. We now use these three points to graph the inverse tangent function. The graph of $y = \tan^{-1} x$ is shown in Figure 5.75. Notice that the vertical asymptotes become horizontal asymptotes for the graph of the inverse function.

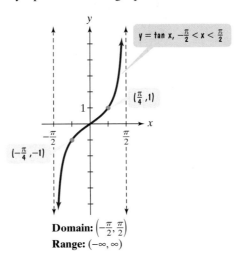

Domain: $\left(-\dfrac{\pi}{2}, \dfrac{\pi}{2}\right)$
Range: $(-\infty, \infty)$

Figure 5.74 The restricted tangent function

Domain: $(-\infty, \infty)$
Range: $\left(-\dfrac{\pi}{2}, \dfrac{\pi}{2}\right)$

Figure 5.75 The graph of the inverse tangent function

Exact values of $\tan^{-1} x$ can be found by thinking of **$\tan^{-1}x$ as the angle in the interval** $\left(-\dfrac{\pi}{2}, \dfrac{\pi}{2}\right)$ **whose tangent is x.** We use Table 5.7, which shows exact values for $\tan \theta$ for θ in the interval $\left(-\dfrac{\pi}{2}, \dfrac{\pi}{2}\right)$.

Table 5.7 Exact Values for $\tan \theta, -\dfrac{\pi}{2} < \theta < \dfrac{\pi}{2}$

θ	$\tan \theta$
$-\dfrac{\pi}{2}$	Undefined
$-\dfrac{\pi}{3}$	$-\sqrt{3}$
$-\dfrac{\pi}{4}$	-1
$-\dfrac{\pi}{6}$	$-\dfrac{\sqrt{3}}{3}$
0	0
$\dfrac{\pi}{6}$	$\dfrac{\sqrt{3}}{3}$
$\dfrac{\pi}{4}$	1
$\dfrac{\pi}{3}$	$\sqrt{3}$
$\dfrac{\pi}{2}$	Undefined

EXAMPLE 4 **Finding the Exact Value of an Inverse Tangent Function**

Find the exact value of $\tan^{-1} \sqrt{3}$.

Solution

Step 1 **Let $\theta = \tan^{-1}x$.** Thus,
$$\theta = \tan^{-1} \sqrt{3}.$$

We must find the angle $\theta, -\dfrac{\pi}{2} < \theta < \dfrac{\pi}{2}$, whose tangent equals $\sqrt{3}$.

Step 2 **Rewrite $\theta = \tan^{-1}x$ as $\tan \theta = x$.** We obtain $\tan \theta = \sqrt{3}$.

Step 3 **Use the exact values in Table 5.7 to find the value of θ in $\left(-\dfrac{\pi}{2}, \dfrac{\pi}{2}\right)$ that satisfies $\tan \theta = x$.** The table shows that the only angle in the interval $\left(-\dfrac{\pi}{2}, \dfrac{\pi}{2}\right)$ that satisfies $\tan \theta = \sqrt{3}$ is $\dfrac{\pi}{3}$. Thus, $\theta = \dfrac{\pi}{3}$ and

$$\tan^{-1} \sqrt{3} = \dfrac{\pi}{3}. \quad \text{The angle in } \left(-\dfrac{\pi}{2}, \dfrac{\pi}{2}\right) \text{ whose tangent is } \sqrt{3} \text{ is } \dfrac{\pi}{3}.$$

> **Check Point 4** Find the exact value of $\tan^{-1}(-1)$.

Table 5.8 summarizes the graphs of the three basic inverse trigonometric functions. Below each of the graphs is a description of the function's domain and range.

Table 5.8 Graphs of the Three Basic Inverse Trigonometric Functions

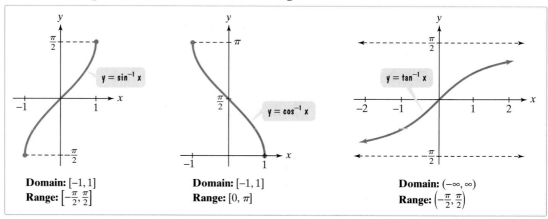

Domain: $[-1, 1]$	**Domain:** $[-1, 1]$	**Domain:** $(-\infty, \infty)$
Range: $\left[-\frac{\pi}{2}, \frac{\pi}{2}\right]$	**Range:** $[0, \pi]$	**Range:** $\left(-\frac{\pi}{2}, \frac{\pi}{2}\right)$

4 Use a calculator to evaluate inverse trigonometric functions.

Using a Calculator to Evaluate Inverse Trigonometric Functions

Calculators give approximate values of inverse trigonometric functions. Use the keys marked $\boxed{\text{SIN}^{-1}}$, $\boxed{\text{COS}^{-1}}$, and $\boxed{\text{TAN}^{-1}}$. Consult your manual for the location of this feature.

EXAMPLE 5 Calculators and Inverse Trigonometric Functions

Use a calculator to find the value to four decimal places of:

a. $\sin^{-1}\dfrac{1}{4}$ **b.** $\tan^{-1}(-9.65)$.

Solution

Scientific Calculator Solution

Function	Mode	Keystrokes	Display, rounded to four places
a. $\sin^{-1}\dfrac{1}{4}$	Radian	$1\,\boxed{\div}\,4\,\boxed{=}\,\boxed{\text{SIN}^{-1}}$	0.2527
b. $\tan^{-1}(-9.65)$	Radian	$9.65\,\boxed{^{+}/_{-}}\,\boxed{\text{TAN}^{-1}}$	-1.4675

Graphing Calculator Solution

Function	Mode	Keystrokes	Display, rounded to four places
a. $\sin^{-1}\dfrac{1}{4}$	Radian	$\boxed{\text{SIN}^{-1}}\,\boxed{(}\,\boxed{1}\,\boxed{\div}\,\boxed{4}\,\boxed{)}\,\boxed{\text{ENTER}}$	0.2527
b. $\tan^{-1}(-9.65)$	Radian	$\boxed{\text{TAN}^{-1}}\,\boxed{(-)}\,9.65\,\boxed{\text{ENTER}}$	-1.4675

> **Check Point 5**
>
> Use a calculator to find the value to four decimal places of:
>
> **a.** $\cos^{-1}\dfrac{1}{3}$ **b.** $\tan^{-1}(-35.85)$.

What happens if you attempt to evaluate an inverse trigomometric function at a value that is not in its domain? In real number mode, most calculators will display an error message. For example, an error message can result if you attempt to approximate $\cos^{-1}3$. There is no angle whose cosine is 3. The domain of the inverse cosine function is $[-1, 1]$, and 3 does not belong to this domain.

5 Find exact values of composite functions with inverse trigonometric functions.

Composition of Functions Involving Inverse Trigonometric Functions

In our discussion of functions and their inverses in Section 2.6, we saw that

$$f(f^{-1}(x)) = x \quad \text{and} \quad f^{-1}(f(x)) = x.$$

x must be in the domain of f^{-1}.   x must be in the domain of f.

We apply these properties to the sine, cosine, tangent, and their inverse functions to obtain the following properties.

Inverse Properties

The Sine Function and Its Inverse

$\sin(\sin^{-1}x) = x$ for every x in the interval $[-1, 1]$

$\sin^{-1}(\sin x) = x$ for every x in the interval $\left[-\dfrac{\pi}{2}, \dfrac{\pi}{2}\right]$

The Cosine Function and Its Inverse

$\cos(\cos^{-1}x) = x$ for every x in the interval $[-1, 1]$

$\cos^{-1}(\cos x) = x$ for every x in the interval $[0, \pi]$

The Tangent Function and Its Inverse

$\tan(\tan^{-1}x) = x$ for every real number x

$\tan^{-1}(\tan x) = x$ for every x in the interval $\left(-\dfrac{\pi}{2}, \dfrac{\pi}{2}\right)$

The restrictions on x in the inverse properties are a bit tricky. For example,

$$\sin^{-1}\left(\sin\dfrac{\pi}{4}\right) = \dfrac{\pi}{4}$$

$\sin^{-1}(\sin x) = x$ for x in $\left[-\dfrac{\pi}{2}, \dfrac{\pi}{2}\right]$.
Observe that $\dfrac{\pi}{4}$ is in this interval.

Can we use $\sin^{-1}(\sin x) = x$ to find the exact value of $\sin^{-1}\left(\sin\dfrac{5\pi}{4}\right)$? Is $\dfrac{5\pi}{4}$ in the interval $\left[-\dfrac{\pi}{2}, \dfrac{\pi}{2}\right]$? No. Thus to evaluate $\sin^{-1}\left(\sin\dfrac{5\pi}{4}\right)$, we must first find $\sin\dfrac{5\pi}{4}$.

$\dfrac{5\pi}{4}$ is in quadrant III where the sine is negative.

$$\sin \dfrac{5\pi}{4} = -\sin \dfrac{\pi}{4} = -\dfrac{\sqrt{2}}{2}$$

The reference angle for $\dfrac{5\pi}{4}$ is $\dfrac{\pi}{4}$.

We evaluate $\sin^{-1}\left(\sin \dfrac{5\pi}{4}\right)$ as follows.

$$\sin^{-1}\left(\sin \dfrac{5\pi}{4}\right) = \sin^{-1}\left(-\dfrac{\sqrt{2}}{2}\right) = -\dfrac{\pi}{4} \qquad \textit{If necessary, see Table 5.5 on page 500.}$$

To determine how to evaluate the composition of functions involving inverse trigonometric functions, first examine the value of x. You can use the inverse properties in the box on page 507 only if x is in the specified interval.

EXAMPLE 6 Evaluating Compositions of Functions and Their Inverses

Find the exact value, if possible, of:

a. $\cos(\cos^{-1} 0.6)$ **b.** $\sin^{-1}\left(\sin \dfrac{3\pi}{2}\right)$ **c.** $\cos(\cos^{-1} 2\pi)$.

Solution

a. The inverse property $\cos(\cos^{-1} x) = x$ applies for every x in $[-1, 1]$. To evaluate $\cos(\cos^{-1} 0.6)$, observe that $x = 0.6$. This value of x lies in $[-1, 1]$, which is the domain of the inverse cosine function. This means that we can use the inverse property $\cos(\cos^{-1} x) = x$. Thus,

$$\cos(\cos^{-1} 0.6) = 0.6.$$

b. The inverse property $\sin^{-1}(\sin x) = x$ applies for every x in $\left[-\dfrac{\pi}{2}, \dfrac{\pi}{2}\right]$. To evaluate $\sin^{-1}\left(\sin \dfrac{3\pi}{2}\right)$, observe that $x = \dfrac{3\pi}{2}$. This value of x does not lie in $\left[-\dfrac{\pi}{2}, \dfrac{\pi}{2}\right]$. To evaluate this expression, we first find $\sin \dfrac{3\pi}{2}$.

$$\sin^{-1}\left(\sin \dfrac{3\pi}{2}\right) = \sin^{-1}(-1) = -\dfrac{\pi}{2} \qquad \textit{The angle in } \left[-\dfrac{\pi}{2}, \dfrac{\pi}{2}\right] \textit{ whose sine is } -1 \textit{ is } -\dfrac{\pi}{2}.$$

c. The inverse property $\cos(\cos^{-1} x) = x$ applies for every x in $[-1, 1]$. To attempt to evaluate $\cos(\cos^{-1} 2\pi)$, observe that $x = 2\pi$. This value of x does not lie in $[-1, 1]$, which is the domain of the inverse cosine function. Thus, the expression $\cos(\cos^{-1} 2\pi)$ is not defined because $\cos^{-1} 2\pi$ is not defined.

Check Point 6 Find the exact value, if possible, of:
a. $\cos(\cos^{-1} 0.7)$ **b.** $\sin^{-1}(\sin \pi)$ **c.** $\cos(\cos^{-1} \pi)$.

We can use points on terminal sides of angles in standard position to find exact values of expressions involving the composition of a function and a different inverse function. Here are two examples.

$$\cos\left(\tan^{-1}\frac{5}{12}\right) \qquad \cot\left[\sin^{-1}\left(-\frac{1}{3}\right)\right]$$

Inner part involves the angle in $\left(-\frac{\pi}{2},-\frac{\pi}{2}\right)$ whose tangent is $\frac{5}{12}$.

Inner part involves the angle in $\left(-\frac{\pi}{2},\frac{\pi}{2}\right)$ whose sine is $-\frac{1}{3}$.

The inner part of each expression involves an angle. To evaluate such expressions, we represent such angles by θ. Then we use a sketch that illustrates our representation. Examples 7 and 8 show how to carry out such evaluations.

EXAMPLE 7   Evaluating a Composite Trigonometric Expression

Find the exact value of $\cos\left(\tan^{-1}\frac{5}{12}\right)$.

Solution   We let θ represent the angle in $\left(-\frac{\pi}{2},\frac{\pi}{2}\right)$ whose tangent is $\frac{5}{12}$. Thus,

$$\theta = \tan^{-1}\frac{5}{12}.$$

Using the definition of the inverse tangent function, we can rewrite this as

$$\tan\theta = \frac{5}{12}.$$

Because $\tan\theta$ is positive, θ must be an angle in $\left(0,\frac{\pi}{2}\right)$. Thus, θ is a first-quadrant angle. Figure 5.76 shows a right triangle in quadrant I with

$$\tan\theta = \frac{5}{12} \quad \text{Side opposite } \theta.$$

Side adjacent to θ.

The hypotenuse of the triangle can be found using the Pythagorean Theorem.

$$r^2 = 12^2 + 5^2 = 144 + 25 = 169 \quad \text{and} \quad r = \sqrt{169} = 13$$

We use this right triangle to find the exact value of $\cos\left(\tan^{-1}\frac{5}{12}\right)$.

$$\cos\left(\tan^{-1}\frac{5}{12}\right) = \cos\theta = \frac{\text{side adjacent to }\theta}{\text{hypotenuse}} = \frac{12}{13}$$

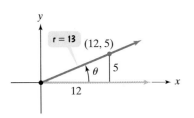

Figure 5.76 Representing $\tan\theta = \frac{5}{12}$

Check Point 7   Find the exact value of $\sin\left(\tan^{-1}\frac{3}{4}\right)$.

EXAMPLE 8   Evaluating a Composite Trigonometric Expression

Find the exact value of $\cot\left[\sin^{-1}\left(-\frac{1}{3}\right)\right]$.

Solution   We let θ represent the angle in $\left[-\frac{\pi}{2},\frac{\pi}{2}\right]$ whose sine is $-\frac{1}{3}$. Thus,

$$\theta = \sin^{-1}\left(-\frac{1}{3}\right) \quad \text{and} \quad \sin\theta = -\frac{1}{3}.$$

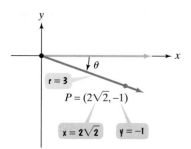

Figure 5.77 Representing $\sin\theta = -\frac{1}{3}$

Because $\sin\theta$ is negative, θ must be an angle in $\left[-\frac{\pi}{2}, 0\right]$. Thus, θ is a negative angle that lies in quadrant IV. Figure 5.77 shows angle θ in quadrant IV with

> In quadrant IV, y is negative

$$\sin\theta = -\frac{1}{3} = \frac{y}{r} = \frac{-1}{3}.$$

The value of x can be found using $x^2 + y^2 = r^2$.

$$x^2 + (-1)^2 = 3^2$$
$$x^2 + 1 = 9$$
$$x^2 = 8$$
$$x = \sqrt{8} = \sqrt{4\cdot 2} = 2\sqrt{2} \quad \text{Remember that x is positive in quadrant IV.}$$

We use values for x and y to find the exact value of $\cot\left[\sin^{-1}\left(-\frac{1}{3}\right)\right]$.

$$\cot\left[\sin^{-1}\left(-\frac{1}{3}\right)\right] = \cot\theta = \frac{x}{y} = \frac{2\sqrt{2}}{-1} = -2\sqrt{2}$$

Check Point 8 Find the exact value of $\cos\left[\sin^{-1}\left(-\frac{1}{2}\right)\right]$.

Some composite functions with inverse trigonometric functions can be simplified to algebraic expressions. To simplify such an expression, we represent the inverse trigonometric function in the expression by θ. Then we use a right triangle.

EXAMPLE 9   Simplifying an Expression Involving $\sin^{-1}x$

If $0 < x \le 1$, write $\cos\left(\sin^{-1}x\right)$ as an algebraic expression in x.

Solution   We let θ represent the angle in $\left[-\frac{\pi}{2}, \frac{\pi}{2}\right]$ whose sine is x. Thus,

$$\theta = \sin^{-1}x, \quad \text{and} \quad \sin\theta = x.$$

Because $0 < x \le 1$, $\sin\theta$ is positive. Thus, θ is a first-quadrant angle. Figure 5.78 shows a right triangle in quadrant I with

$$\sin\theta = x = \frac{x}{1}. \quad \begin{array}{l}\text{Side opposite }\theta\\ \text{Hypotenuse}\end{array}$$

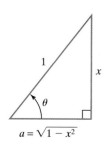

Figure 5.78 Representing $\sin\theta = x$

The third side, a, can be found using the Pythagorean Theorem.

$$a^2 + x^2 = 1^2 \quad \text{Apply the Pythagorean Theorem to the right triangle in Figure 5.78.}$$

$$a^2 = 1 - x^2 \quad \text{Subtract } x^2 \text{ from both sides.}$$

$$a = \sqrt{1 - x^2} \quad \text{Solve for a.}$$

We use the right triangle in Figure 5.78 to write $\cos(\sin^{-1} x)$ as an algebraic expression.

$$\cos(\sin^{-1} x) = \cos\theta = \frac{\text{side adjacent to } \theta}{\text{hypotenuse}} = \frac{\sqrt{1-x^2}}{1} = \sqrt{1-x^2}$$

Check Point 9 If $x > 0$, write $\sec(\tan^{-1} x)$ as an algebraic expression in x.

The inverse secant function, $y = \sec^{-1} x$, is used in calculus. However, inverse cotangent and inverse cosecant functions are rarely used. Two of these remaining inverse trigonometric functions are briefly developed in the exercise set that follows.

EXERCISE SET 5.7

Practice Exercises

In Exercises 1–18, use the values in the table shown to find the exact value of each expression.

θ	$-\dfrac{\pi}{2}$	$-\dfrac{\pi}{3}$	$-\dfrac{\pi}{4}$	$-\dfrac{\pi}{6}$	0	$\dfrac{\pi}{6}$	$\dfrac{\pi}{4}$	$\dfrac{\pi}{3}$	$\dfrac{\pi}{2}$	$\dfrac{2\pi}{3}$	$\dfrac{3\pi}{4}$	$\dfrac{5\pi}{6}$	π
$\sin\theta$	-1	$-\dfrac{\sqrt3}{2}$	$-\dfrac{\sqrt2}{2}$	$-\dfrac{1}{2}$	0	$\dfrac{1}{2}$	$\dfrac{\sqrt2}{2}$	$\dfrac{\sqrt3}{2}$	1	$\dfrac{\sqrt3}{2}$	$\dfrac{\sqrt2}{2}$	$\dfrac{1}{2}$	0
$\cos\theta$	0	$\dfrac{1}{2}$	$\dfrac{\sqrt2}{2}$	$\dfrac{\sqrt3}{2}$	1	$\dfrac{\sqrt3}{2}$	$\dfrac{\sqrt2}{2}$	$\dfrac{1}{2}$	0	$-\dfrac{1}{2}$	$-\dfrac{\sqrt2}{2}$	$-\dfrac{\sqrt3}{2}$	-1
$\tan\theta$	undef.	$-\sqrt3$	-1	$-\dfrac{\sqrt3}{3}$	0	$\dfrac{\sqrt3}{3}$	1	$\sqrt3$	undef.	$-\sqrt3$	-1	$\dfrac{-\sqrt3}{3}$	0

1. $\sin^{-1}\frac{1}{2}$

2. $\sin^{-1} 0$

3. $\sin^{-1}\dfrac{\sqrt2}{2}$

4. $\sin^{-1}\dfrac{\sqrt3}{2}$

5. $\sin^{-1}\left(-\dfrac{1}{2}\right)$

6. $\sin^{-1}\left(-\dfrac{\sqrt3}{2}\right)$

7. $\cos^{-1}\dfrac{\sqrt3}{2}$

8. $\cos^{-1}\dfrac{\sqrt2}{2}$

9. $\cos^{-1}\left(-\dfrac{\sqrt2}{2}\right)$

10. $\cos^{-1}\left(-\dfrac{\sqrt3}{2}\right)$

11. $\cos^{-1} 0$

12. $\cos^{-1} 1$

13. $\tan^{-1}\dfrac{\sqrt3}{3}$

14. $\tan^{-1} 1$

15. $\tan^{-1} 0$

16. $\tan^{-1}(-1)$

17. $\tan^{-1}(-\sqrt3)$

18. $\tan^{-1}\left(-\dfrac{\sqrt3}{3}\right)$

In Exercises 19–30, use a calculator to find the value of each expression rounded to two decimal places.

19. $\sin^{-1} 0.3$

20. $\sin^{-1} 0.47$

21. $\sin^{-1}(-0.32)$

22. $\sin^{-1}(-0.625)$

23. $\cos^{-1}\frac{3}{8}$

24. $\cos^{-1}\frac{4}{9}$

25. $\cos^{-1}\dfrac{\sqrt5}{7}$

26. $\cos^{-1}\dfrac{\sqrt7}{10}$

27. $\tan^{-1}(-20)$

28. $\tan^{-1}(-30)$

29. $\tan^{-1}(-\sqrt{473})$

30. $\tan^{-1}(-\sqrt{5061})$

In Exercises 31–46, find the exact value of each expression, if possible. Do not use a calculator.

31. $\sin(\sin^{-1} 0.9)$

32. $\cos(\cos^{-1} 0.57)$

33. $\sin^{-1}\left(\sin\dfrac{\pi}{3}\right)$

34. $\cos^{-1}\left(\cos\dfrac{2\pi}{3}\right)$

35. $\sin^{-1}\left(\sin\dfrac{5\pi}{6}\right)$

36. $\cos^{-1}\left(\cos\dfrac{4\pi}{3}\right)$

37. $\tan(\tan^{-1} 125)$

38. $\tan(\tan^{-1} 380)$

39. $\tan^{-1}\left[\tan\left(-\dfrac{\pi}{6}\right)\right]$

40. $\tan^{-1}\left[\tan\left(-\dfrac{\pi}{3}\right)\right]$

41. $\tan^{-1}\left(\tan\dfrac{2\pi}{3}\right)$ **42.** $\tan^{-1}\left(\tan\dfrac{3\pi}{4}\right)$

43. $\sin^{-1}(\sin\pi)$ **44.** $\cos^{-1}(\cos 2\pi)$

45. $\sin(\sin^{-1}\pi)$ **46.** $\cos(\cos^{-1}3\pi)$

In Exercises 47–60, use a sketch to find the exact value of each expression.

47. $\cos(\sin^{-1}\tfrac{4}{5})$ **48.** $\sin(\tan^{-1}\tfrac{7}{24})$

49. $\tan(\cos^{-1}\tfrac{5}{13})$ **50.** $\cot(\sin^{-1}\tfrac{5}{13})$

51. $\tan[\sin^{-1}(-\tfrac{3}{5})]$ **52.** $\cos[\sin^{-1}(-\tfrac{4}{5})]$

53. $\sin\left(\cos^{-1}\dfrac{\sqrt{2}}{2}\right)$ **54.** $\cos(\sin^{-1}\tfrac{1}{2})$

55. $\sec[\sin^{-1}(-\tfrac{1}{4})]$ **56.** $\sec[\sin^{-1}(-\tfrac{1}{2})]$

57. $\tan[\cos^{-1}(-\tfrac{1}{3})]$ **58.** $\tan[\cos^{-1}(-\tfrac{1}{4})]$

59. $\csc\left[\cos^{-1}\left(-\dfrac{\sqrt{3}}{2}\right)\right]$ **60.** $\sec\left[\sin^{-1}\left(-\dfrac{\sqrt{2}}{2}\right)\right]$

In Exercises 61–66, use a right triangle to write each expression as an algebraic expression. Assume that x is positive and in the domain of the given inverse trigonometric function.

61. $\tan(\cos^{-1}x)$ **62.** $\sin(\tan^{-1}x)$

63. $\cos\left(\sin^{-1}\dfrac{1}{x}\right)$ **64.** $\sec\left(\cos^{-1}\dfrac{1}{x}\right)$

65. $\sec\left(\sin^{-1}\dfrac{x}{\sqrt{x^2+4}}\right)$ **66.** $\cot\left(\sin^{-1}\dfrac{\sqrt{x^2-9}}{x}\right)$

67. a. Graph the restricted secant function, $y = \sec x$, by restricting x to the intervals $\left[0, \dfrac{\pi}{2}\right)$ and $\left(\dfrac{\pi}{2}, \pi\right]$.

  b. Use the horizontal line test and explain why the restricted secant function has an inverse function.

  c. Use the graph of the restricted secant function to graph $y = \sec^{-1}x$.

68. a. Graph the restricted cotangent function, $y = \cot x$, by restricting x to the interval $(0, \pi)$.

  b. Use the horizontal line test and explain why the restricted cotangent function has an inverse function.

  c. Use the graph of the restricted cotangent function to graph $y = \cot^{-1}x$.

 Application Exercises

69. Your neighborhood movie theater has a 25-foot-high screen located 8 feet above your eye level. If you sit too close to the screen, your viewing angle is too small, resulting in a distorted picture. By contrast, if you sit too far back, the image is quite small, diminishing the movie's visual impact. If you sit x feet back from the screen, your viewing angle θ is given by

$$\theta = \tan^{-1}\dfrac{33}{x} - \tan^{-1}\dfrac{8}{x}.$$

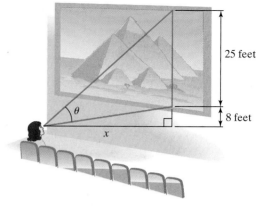

25 feet

8 feet

Find the viewing angle, in radians, at distances of 5 feet, 10 feet, 15 feet, 20 feet, and 25 feet.

70. The function $\theta = \tan^{-1}\dfrac{33}{x} - \tan^{-1}\dfrac{8}{x}$ is graphed below in a $[0, 50, 10]$ by $[0, 1, 0.1]$ viewing rectangle. Use the graph to describe what happens to your viewing angle as you move farther back from the screen. How far back from the screen, to the nearest foot, should you sit to maximize your viewing angle? Verify this observation by finding the viewing angle one foot closer to the screen and one foot farther from the screen for this ideal viewing distance.

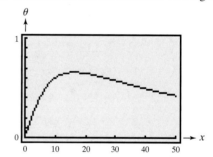

The formula

$$\theta = 2\tan^{-1}\dfrac{21.634}{x}$$

gives the viewing angle, in radians, for a camera whose lens is x millimeters wide. Use this formula to solve Exercises 71–72.

71. Find the viewing angle, in radians and in degrees (to the nearest tenth of a degree), of a 28-millimeter lens.

72. Find the viewing angle, in radians and degrees (to the nearest tenth of a degree), of a 300-millimeter telephoto lens.

For years, mathematicians were challenged by the following problem: What is the area of a region under a curve between two values of x? The problem was solved in the seventeenth century with the development of integral calculus. Using calculus, the area of the region under $y = \dfrac{1}{x^2 + 1}$, above the x-axis, and between $x = a$ and $x = b$ is $\tan^{-1} b - \tan^{-1} a$. Use this result, shown in the figure, to find the area of the region under $y = \dfrac{1}{x^2 + 1}$ and between a and b given in Exercises 73–74.

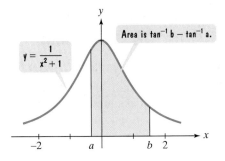

73. $a = 0$ and $b = 2$

74. $a = -2$ and $b = 1$

Writing in Mathematics

75. Explain why, without restrictions, no trigonometric function has an inverse function.

76. Describe the restriction on the sine function so that it has an inverse function.

77. How can the graph of $y = \sin^{-1} x$ be obtained from the graph of the restricted sine function?

78. Without drawing a graph, describe the behavior of the graph of $y = \sin^{-1} x$. Mention the function's domain and range in your description.

79. Describe the restriction on the cosine function so that it has an inverse function.

80. Without drawing a graph, describe the behavior of the graph of $y = \cos^{-1} x$. Mention the function's domain and range in your description.

81. Describe the restriction on the tangent function so that it has an inverse function.

82. Without drawing a graph, describe the behavior of the graph of $y = \tan^{-1} x$. Mention the function's domain and range in your description.

83. If $\sin^{-1}\left(\sin\dfrac{\pi}{3}\right) = \dfrac{\pi}{3}$, is $\sin^{-1}\left(\sin\dfrac{5\pi}{6}\right) = \dfrac{5\pi}{6}$? Explain your answer.

84. Explain how a right triangle can be used to find the exact value of $\sec\left(\sin^{-1}\frac{4}{5}\right)$.

85. Find the height of the screen and the number of feet that it is located above eye level in your favorite movie theater. Modify the formula given in Exercise 69 so that it applies to your theater. Then describe where in the theater you should sit so that a movie creates the greatest visual impact.

Technology Exercises

In Exercises 86–89, graph each pair of functions in the same viewing rectangle. Use your knowledge of the domain and range for the inverse trigonometric functions to select an appropriate viewing rectangle. What does the graph of the second equation in each exercise do to the graph of the first equation?

86. $y = \sin^{-1} x$ and $y = \sin^{-1} x + 2$

87. $y = \cos^{-1} x$ and $y = \cos^{-1}(x - 1)$

88. $y = \tan^{-1} x$ and $y = -2 \tan^{-1} x$

89. $y = \sin^{-1} x$ and $y = \sin^{-1}(x + 2) + 1$

90. Graph $y = \tan^{-1} x$ and its two horizontal asymptotes in a $[-3, 3, 1]$ by $\left[-\pi, \pi, \dfrac{\pi}{2}\right]$ viewing rectangle. Then change the range setting to $[-50, 50, 5]$ by $\left[-\pi, \pi, \dfrac{\pi}{2}\right]$. What do you observe?

91. Graph $y = \sin^{-1} x + \cos^{-1} x$ in a $[-2, 2, 1]$ by $[0, 3, 11]$ viewing rectangle. What appears to be true about the sum of the inverse sine and inverse cosine for values between -1 and 1 inclusive?

Critical Thinking Exercises

92. Solve $y = 2\sin^{-1}(x - 5)$ for x in terms of y.

93. Solve for x: $2\sin^{-1} x = \dfrac{\pi}{4}$.

94. Prove that if $x > 0$, $\tan^{-1} x + \tan^{-1}\dfrac{1}{x} = \dfrac{\pi}{2}$.

95. Derive the formula for θ, your viewing angle at the movie theater, in Exercise 69. *Hint*: Use the figure shown and represent the acute angle on the left in the smaller right triangle by α. Find expressions for $\tan \alpha$ and $\tan(\alpha + \theta)$.

SECTION 5.8 *Applications of Trigonometric Functions*

Objectives

1. Solve a right triangle.
2. Solve problems involving bearings.
3. Model simple harmonic motion.

In the late 1960s, popular musicians were searching for new sounds. Film composers were looking for ways to create unique sounds as well. From these efforts, synthesizers that electronically reproduce musical sounds were born. From providing the backbone of today's most popular music to providing the strange sounds for the most experimental music, synthesizers are at the forefront of today's music technology.

If we did not understand the periodic nature of sinusoidal functions, the synthesizers used in almost all forms of music would not exist. In this section, we look at applications of trigonometric functions in right triangles and in modeling periodic phenomena such as sound.

1 Solve a right triangle.

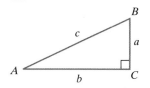

Figure 5.79 Labeling right triangles

Solving Right Triangles

Solving a right triangle means finding the missing lengths of its sides and the measurements of its angles. We will label right triangles so that side a is opposite angle A, side b is opposite angle B, and side c is the hypotenuse opposite right angle C. Figure 5.79 illustrates this labeling.

When solving a right triangle, we will use the sine, cosine, and tangent functions, rather than their reciprocals. Example 1 shows how to solve a right triangle when we know the length of a side and the measure of an acute angle.

EXAMPLE 1 Solving a Right Triangle

Solve the right triangle shown in Figure 5.80.

Solution   We begin by finding the measure of angle B. We do not need a trigonometric function to do so. Because $C = 90°$ and the sum of a triangle's angles is $180°$, we see that $A + B = 90°$. Thus,

$$B = 90° - A = 90° - 34.5° = 55.5°.$$

Now we need to find a. Because we have a known angle, an unknown opposite side, and a known adjacent side, we use the tangent function.

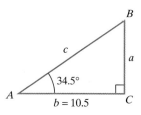

Figure 5.80 Find B, a, and c

$$\tan 34.5° = \frac{a}{10.5}$$

Side opposite the 34.5° angle

Side adjacent to the 34.5° angle

Discovery

There is often more than one correct way to solve a right triangle. In Example 1, find a using angle $B = 55.5°$. Find c using the Pythagorean Theorem.

Now we solve for a.

$$a = 10.5 \tan 34.5° \approx 7.22$$

Finally, we need to find c. Because we have a known angle, a known adjacent side, and an unknown hypotenuse, we use the cosine function.

$$\cos 34.5° = \frac{10.5}{c}$$

Side adjacent to the 34.5° angle

hypotenuse

Now we solve for c.

$$c = \frac{10.5}{\cos 34.5°} \approx 12.74$$

In summary, $B = 55.5°$, $a \approx 7.22$, and $c \approx 12.74$.

Check Point 1   In Figure 5.79, let $A = 62.7°$ and $a = 8.4$. Solve the right triangle, rounding lengths to two decimal places.

Trigonometry was first developed to measure heights and distances that are inconvenient or impossible to measure. In solving application problems, begin by making a sketch involving a right triangle that illustrates the problem's conditions. Then put your knowledge of solving right triangles to work and find the required distance or height.

EXAMPLE 2   Finding the Side of a Triangle

From a point on level ground 125 feet from the base of a tower, the angle of elevation is $57.2°$. Approximate the height of the tower to the nearest foot.

Solution   A sketch is shown in Figure 5.81, where a represents the height of the tower. In the right triangle, we have a known angle, an unknown opposite side, and a known adjacent side. Therefore, we use the tangent function.

$$\tan 57.2° = \frac{a}{125}$$

Side opposite the 57.2° angle

Side adjacent to the 57.2° angle

Solving for a,

$$a = 125 \tan 57.2° \approx 194.$$

The tower is approximately 194 feet high.

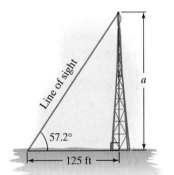

Figure 5.81 Determining height without using direct measurement

Check Point 2   From a point on level ground 80 feet from the base of the Eiffel Tower, the angle of elevation is $85.4°$. Approximate the height of the Eiffel Tower to the nearest foot.

Example 3 illustrates how to find the measure of an acute angle of a right triangle if the length of two sides is known.

EXAMPLE 3   Finding the Angle of a Triangle

A kite flies at a height of 30 feet when 65 feet of string is out. If the string is in a straight line, find the angle that it makes with the ground. Round to the nearest tenth of a degree.

Solution   A sketch is shown in Figure 5.82, where A represents the angle the string makes with the ground. In the right triangle, we have an unknown angle, a known opposite side, and a known hypotenuse. Therefore, we use the sine function.

$$\sin A = \frac{30}{65} \quad \text{Side opposite } A \\ \text{hypotenuse}$$

$$A = \sin^{-1} \frac{30}{65} \approx 27.5°$$

The string makes an angle of approximately 27.5° with the ground.

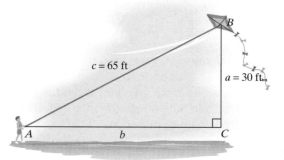

$c = 65$ ft

$a = 30$ ft

A b C

Figure 5.82 Flying a kite

Check Point 3   A guy wire is 13.8 yards long and is attached from the ground to a pole 6.7 yards above the ground. Find the angle, to the nearest tenth of a degree, that the wire makes with the ground.

EXAMPLE 4   Using Two Right Triangles to Solve a Problem

You are taking your first hot-air balloon ride. Your friend is standing on level ground, 100 feet away from your point of launch, making a video of the terrified look on your rapidly ascending face. How rapidly? At one instant, the angle of elevation from the video camera to your face is 31.7°. One minute later, the angle of elevation is 76.2°. How far did you travel during that minute?

Solution   A sketch that illustrates the problem is shown in Figure 5.83. We need to determine $b - a$, the distance traveled during the one-minute period. We find a using the small right triangle. Because we have a known angle, an unknown opposite side, and a known adjacent side, we use the tangent function.

$$\tan 31.7° = \frac{a}{100} \quad \text{Side opposite the 31.7° angle} \\ \text{Side adjacent to the 31.7° angle}$$

$$a = 100 \tan 31.7° \approx 61.8$$

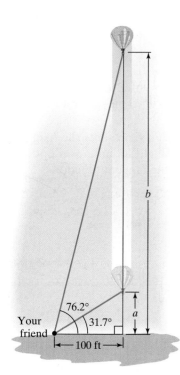

76.2°

Your friend   31.7°

b

a

← 100 ft →

Figure 5.83 Ascending in a hot-air balloon

We find b using the tangent function in the large right triangle.

$$\tan 76.2° = \frac{b}{100}$$

Side opposite the 76.2° angle

Side adjacent to the 76.2° angle

$$b = 100 \tan 76.2° \approx 407.1$$

The balloon traveled $407.1 - 61.8$, or approximately 345.3 feet, during the minute.

> **Check Point 4**
>
> You are standing on level ground 800 feet from Mt. Rushmore, looking at the sculpture of Abraham Lincoln's face. The angle of elevation to the bottom of the sculpture is 32° and the angle of elevation to the top is 35°. Find the height of the sculpture of Lincoln's face to the nearest tenth of a foot.

2 Solve problems involving bearings.

Trigonometry and Bearings

In navigation and surveying problems, the term *bearing* is used to specify the location of one point relative to another. The **bearing** from point O to point P is the acute angle between ray OP and a north-south line. Figure 5.84 illustrates some examples of bearings. The north-south line and the east-west line intersect at right angles.

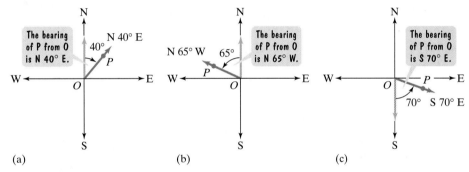

Figure 5.84 An illustration of three bearings

(a)　　　　　(b)　　　　　(c)

Each bearing has three parts: a letter (N or S), the measure of an acute angle, and a letter (E or W). Here's how we write a bearing:

- If the acute angle is measured from the *north side* of the north-south line, then we write N first. [See Figure 5.84(a).] If the acute angle is measured from the *south side* of the north-south line, then we write S first. [See Figure 5.84(c).]
- Second, we write the measure of the acute angle.
- If the acute angle is measured on the *east side* of the north-south line, then we write E last. [See Figure 5.84(a)]. If the acute angle is measured on the *west side* of the north-south line, then we write W last. [See Figure 5.84(b).]

EXAMPLE 5　Understanding Bearings

Use Figure 5.85 on page 518 to find:

a. the bearing from O to B.

b. the bearing from O to A.

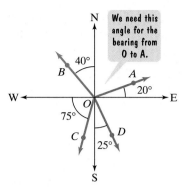

Figure 5.85 Finding bearings

Solution

a. To find the bearing from O to B, we need the acute angle between the ray OB and the north-south line through O. The measurement of this angle is given to be 40°. Figure 5.85 shows that the angle is measured from the north side of the north-south line and lies west of the north-south line. Thus, the bearing from O to B is N 40° W.

b. To find the bearing from O to A, we need the acute angle between the ray OA and the north-south line through O. This angle is specified by the voice balloon in Figure 5.85. The figure shows that this angle measures 90° − 20°, or 70°. This angle is measured from the north side of the north-south line. This angle is also east of the north-south line. Thus, the bearing from O to A is N 70° E.

Check Point 5

Use Figure 5.85 to find:

a. the bearing from O to D.

b. the bearing from O to C.

EXAMPLE 6 Finding the Bearing of a Boat

A boat leaves the entrance to a harbor and travels 25 miles on a bearing of N 42° E. Figure 5.86 shows that the captain then turns the boat 90° and travels 18 miles on a bearing of S 48° E. At that time:

a. How far is the boat from the harbor entrance?

b. What is the bearing of the boat from the harbor entrance?

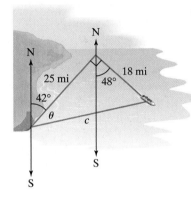

Figure 5.86 Finding a boat's bearing from the harbor entrance

Study Tip

When making a diagram showing bearings, draw a north-south line through each point at which a change in course occurs. The north side of the line lies above each point. The south side of the line lies below each point.

Solution

a. The boat's distance from the harbor entrance is represented by c in Figure 5.86. Because we know the length of two sides of the right triangle, we find c using the Pythagorean Theorem. We have

$$c^2 = a^2 + b^2 = 25^2 + 18^2 = 949$$
$$c = \sqrt{949} \approx 30.8.$$

The boat is approximately 30.8 miles from the harbor entrance.

b. To find the bearing of the boat from the harbor entrance, look at the north-south line passing through the harbor entrance on the left in Figure 5.86. The acute angle from this line to the ray on which the boat lies is $42° + \theta$. Because we are measuring the angle from the north side of the line and the boat is east of the harbor, its bearing from the harbor entrance is N($42° + \theta$)E. To find θ, we use the right triangle shown in Figure 5.86 and the tangent function.

$$\tan \theta = \frac{\text{side opposite } \theta}{\text{side adjacent to } \theta} = \frac{18}{25}$$

$$\theta = \tan^{-1} \frac{18}{25}$$

We can use a calculator in degree mode to find the value of θ: $\theta \approx 35.8°$. Thus, $42° + \theta = 42° + 35.8° = 77.8°$. The bearing of the boat from the harbor entrance is N 77.8° E.

Check Point 6 You leave the entrance to a system of hiking trails and hike 2.3 miles on a bearing of S 31° W. You then turn and hike 3.5 miles on a bearing of N 59° W. At that time:

a. How far are you from the entrance to the trail system?

b. What is your bearing from the entrance to the trail system?

3 Model simple harmonic motion.

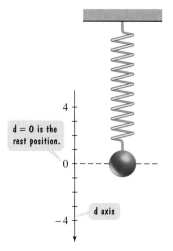

d = 0 is the rest position.

d axis

Figure 5.87 Using a *d*-axis to describe a ball's distance from its rest position

Simple Harmonic Motion

Because of their periodic nature, trigonometric functions are used to model phenomena that occur again and again. This includes vibratory or oscillatory motion, such as the motion of a vibrating guitar string, the swinging of a pendulum, or the bobbing of an object attached to a spring. Trigonometric functions are also used to describe radio waves from your favorite FM station, television waves from your not-to-be-missed weekly sitcom, and sound waves from your most-prized CDs.

To see how trigonometric functions are used to model vibratory motion, consider this: A ball is attached to a spring hung from the ceiling. You pull the ball down 4 inches and then release it. If we neglect the effects of friction and air resistance, the ball will continue bobbing up and down on the end of the spring. These up-and-down oscillations are called **simple harmonic motion**.

To better understand this motion, we use a *d*-axis, where *d* represents distance. This axis is shown in Figure 5.87. On this axis, the position of the ball before you pull it down is $d = 0$. This rest position is called the **equilibrium position**. Now you pull the ball down 4 inches to $d = -4$ and release it. Figure 5.88 shows a sequence of "photographs" taken at one-second time intervals illustrating the distance of the ball from its rest position, *d*.

The curve in Figure 5.88 shows how the ball's distance from its rest position changes over time. The curve is sinusoidal and the motion can be described using a cosine or a sine function.

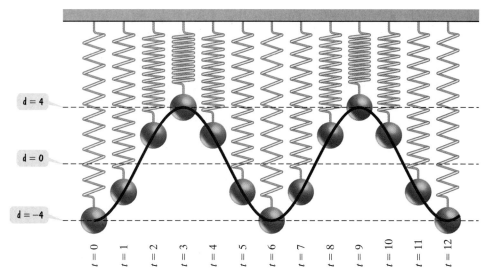

Figure 5.88 A sequence of "photographs" showing the bobbing ball's distance from the rest position, taken at one-second intervals

Simple Harmonic Motion

An object that moves on a coordinate axis is in **simple harmonic motion** if its distance from the origin, d, at time t is given by either

$$d = a \cos \omega t \text{ or } d = a \sin \omega t.$$

The motion has **amplitude** $|a|$, the maximum displacement of the object from its rest position. The **period** of the motion is $\dfrac{2\pi}{\omega}$, where $\omega > 0$. The period gives the time it takes for the motion to go through one complete cycle.

In describing simple harmonic motion, the equation with the cosine function is used if the object is at its greatest distance from rest position, the origin, at $t = 0$. By contrast, the equation with the sine function is used if the object is at its rest position, the origin, at $t = 0$.

Diminishing Motion with Increasing Time

Due to friction and other resistive forces, the motion of an oscillating object decreases over time. The function

$$d = 3e^{-0.1t} \cos 2t$$

models this type of motion. The graph of the function is shown in a $t = [0, 10, 1]$ by $d = [-3, 3, 1]$ viewing rectangle. Notice how the amplitude is decreasing with time as the moving object loses energy.

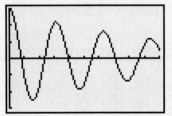

EXAMPLE 7 Finding an Equation for an Object in Simple Harmonic Motion

A ball on a spring is pulled 4 inches below its rest position and then released. The period of the motion is 6 seconds. Write the equation for the ball's simple harmonic motion.

Solution We need to write an equation that describes d, the distance of the ball from its rest position, after t seconds. (The motion is illustrated by the "photo" sequence in Figure 5.88 on page 519.) When the object is released ($t = 0$), the ball's distance from its rest position is 4 inches down. Because it is *down* 4 inches, d is negative: When $t = 0$, $d = -4$. Notice the greatest distance from rest position occurs at $t = 0$. Thus, we will use the equation with the cosine function,

$$d = a \cos \omega t,$$

to model the ball's simple harmonic motion.

Now we determine values for a and ω. Recall that $|a|$ is the maximum displacement. Because the ball initially moves down, $a = -4$.

The value of ω in $d = a \cos \omega t$ can be found using the formula for the period.

$$\text{period} = \frac{2\pi}{\omega} = 6 \qquad \textit{We are given that the period of the motion is 6 seconds.}$$

$$2\pi = 6\omega \qquad \textit{Multiply both sides by } \omega.$$

$$\omega = \frac{2\pi}{6} = \frac{\pi}{3} \qquad \textit{Divide both sides by 6 and solve for } \omega.$$

We see that $a = -4$ and $\omega = \dfrac{\pi}{3}$. Substitute these values into $d = a \cos \omega t$.

The equation for the ball's simple harmonic motion is

$$d = -4 \cos \frac{\pi}{3} t.$$

Modeling Music

Sounds are caused by vibrating objects that result in variations in pressure in the surrounding air. Areas of high and low pressure moving through the air are modeled by the harmonic motion formulas. When these vibrations reach our eardrums, the eardrums' vibrations send signals to our brains which create the sensation of hearing.

French mathematician John Fourier (1768–1830) proved that all musical sounds—instrumental and vocal—could be modeled by sums involving sine functions. Modeling musical sounds with sinusoidal functions is used by synthesizers to electronically produce sounds unobtainable from ordinary musical instruments.

Check Point 7 A ball on a spring is pulled 6 inches below its rest position and then released. The period for the motion is 4 seconds. Write the equation for the ball's simple harmonic motion.

The period of the harmonic motion in Example 7 was 6 seconds. It takes 6 seconds for the moving object to complete one cycle. Thus, $\frac{1}{6}$ of a cycle is completed every second. We call $\frac{1}{6}$ the *frequency* of the moving object. **Frequency** describes the number of complete cycles per unit time and is the reciprocal of the period.

Frequency of an Object in Simple Harmonic Motion

An object in simple harmonic motion given by

$$d = a \cos \omega t \text{ or } d = a \sin \omega t$$

has **frequency** f given by

$$f = \frac{\omega}{2\pi}, \omega > 0.$$

Equivalently,

$$f = \frac{1}{\text{period}}.$$

EXAMPLE 8 Analyzing Simple Harmonic Motion

Figure 5.89 shows a mass on a smooth table attached to a spring. The mass moves in simple harmonic motion described by

$$d = 10 \cos \frac{\pi}{6} t$$

with t measured in seconds and d in centimeters. Find (a) the maximum displacement, (b) the frequency, and (c) the time required for one cycle.

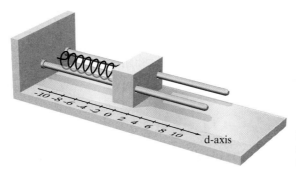

Figure 5.89 A mass attached to a spring, moving in simple harmonic motion

Solution We begin by identifying values for a and ω.

$$d = 10 \cos \frac{\pi}{6} t$$

The form of this equation is
$$d = a \cos \omega t$$
with $a = 10$ and $\omega = \frac{\pi}{6}$.

a. The maximum displacement from the rest position is the amplitude. Because $a = 10$, the maximum displacement is 10 centimeters.

b. The frequency, f, is

$$f = \frac{\omega}{2\pi} = \frac{\frac{\pi}{6}}{2\pi} = \frac{\pi}{6} \cdot \frac{1}{2\pi} = \frac{1}{12}.$$

The frequency is $\frac{1}{12}$ centimeter per second.

c. The time required for one cycle is the period.

$$\text{period} = \frac{2\pi}{\omega} = \frac{2\pi}{\frac{\pi}{6}} = 2\pi \cdot \frac{6}{\pi} = 12$$

The time required for one cycle is 12 seconds.

Check Point 8

An object moves in simple harmonic motion described by $d = 12 \cos\frac{\pi}{4}t$, where t is measured in seconds and d in centimeters. Find (a) the maximum displacement, (b) the frequency, and (c) the time required for one cycle.

Resisting Damage of Simple Harmonic Motion

Simple harmonic motion from an earthquake caused this highway in Oakland, California to collapse. By studying the harmonic motion of the soil under the highway, engineers learn to build structures that can resist damage.

EXERCISE SET 5.8

✓ Practice Exercises

In Exercises 1–12, solve the right triangle shown in the figure. Round lengths to two decimal places and express angles to the nearest tenth of a degree.

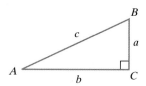

1. $A = 23.5°, b = 10$
2. $A = 41.5°, b = 20$
3. $A = 52.6°, c = 54$
4. $A = 54.8°, C = 80$
5. $B = 16.8°, b = 30.5$
6. $B = 23.8°, b = 40.5$
7. $a = 30.4, c = 50.2$
8. $a = 11.2, c = 65.8$
9. $a = 10.8, b = 24.7$
10. $a = 15.3, b = 17.6$
11. $b = 2, c = 7$
12. $b = 4, c = 9$

Use the figure shown to solve Exercises 13–16.

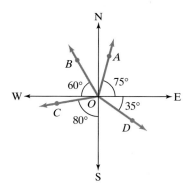

13. Find the bearing from O to A.
14. Find the bearing from O to B.
15. Find the bearing from O to C.
16. Find the bearing from O to D.

In Exercises 17–20, an object is attached to a coiled spring. The object is pulled down (negative direction from the rest position) and then released. Write an equation for the distance of the object from its rest position after t seconds.

	Distance from rest position at $t = 0$	Amplitude	Period
17.	6 centimeters	6 centimeters	4 seconds
18.	8 inches	8 inches	2 seconds
19.	0	3 inches	1.5 seconds
20.	0	5 centimeters	2.5 seconds

In Exercises 21–28, an object moves in simple harmonic motion described by the given equation, where t is measured in seconds and d in inches. In each exercise, find:

a. *the maximum displacement.*

b. *the frequency.*

c. *the time required for one cycle.*

21. $d = 5 \cos \dfrac{\pi}{2} t$
22. $d = 10 \cos 2\pi t$
23. $d = -6 \cos 2\pi t$
24. $d = -8 \cos \dfrac{\pi}{2} t$
25. $d = \frac{1}{2} \sin 2t$
26. $d = \frac{1}{3} \sin 2t$
27. $d = -5 \sin \dfrac{2\pi}{3} t$
28. $d = -4 \sin \dfrac{3\pi}{2} t$

★ Application Exercises

29. The tallest television transmitting tower in the world is in North Dakota. From a point on level ground 5280 feet (one mile) from the base of the tower, the angle of elevation is 21.3°. Approximate the height of the tower to the nearest foot.

30. From a point on level ground 30 yards from the base of a building, the angle of elevation is 38.7°. Approximate the height of the building to the nearest foot.

31. The Statue of Liberty is approximately 305 feet tall. If the angle of elevation of a ship to the top of the statue is 23.7°, how far, to the nearest foot, is the ship from the statue's base?

32. A 200-foot cliff drops vertically into the ocean. If the angle of elevation of a ship to the top of the cliff is 22.3°, how far off shore, to the nearest foot, is the ship?

33. A helicopter hovers 1000 feet above a small island. The figure shows that the angle of depression from the helicopter to point P is 36°. How far off the coast, to the nearest foot, is the island?

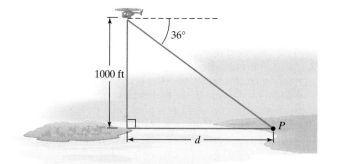

34. A police helicopter is flying at 800 feet. A stolen car is sighted at an angle of depression of 72°. Find the distance of the stolen car, to the nearest foot, from a point directly below the helicopter.

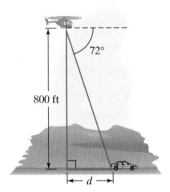

35. A wheelchair ramp is to be built beside the steps to the campus library. Find the angle of elevation of the 23-foot ramp, to the nearest tenth of a degree, if its final height is 6 feet.

36. A building that is 250 feet high casts a shadow 40 feet long. Find the angle of elevation, to the nearest tenth of a degree, of the sun at this time.

37. A hot-air balloon is rising vertically. The angle of elevation from a point on level ground 125 feet from the balloon to a point directly under the passenger compartment changes from 19.2° to 31.7°. How far, to the nearest tenth of a foot, does the balloon rise during this period?

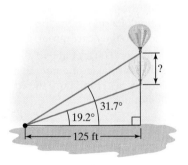

38. A flagpole is situated on top of a building. The angle of elevation from a point on level ground 330 feet from the building to the top of the flagpole is 63°. The angle of elevation from the same point to the bottom of the flagpole is 53°. Find the height of the flagpole to the nearest tenth of a foot.

39. A boat leaves the entrance to a harbor and travels 150 miles on a bearing of N 53° E. How many miles north and how many miles east from the harbor has the boat traveled?

40. A boat leaves the entrance to a harbor and travels 40 miles on a bearing of S 64° E. How many miles south and how many miles east from the harbor has the boat traveled?

41. A forest ranger sights a fire directly to the south. A second ranger, 7 miles east of the first ranger, also sights the fire. The bearing from the second ranger to the fire is S 28° W. How far, to the nearest tenth of a mile, is the first ranger from the fire?

42. A ship sights a lighthouse directly to the south. A second ship, 9 miles east of the first ship, also sights the lighthouse. The bearing from the second ship to the lighthouse is S 34° W. How far, to the nearest tenth of a mile, is the first ship from the lighthouse?

43. You leave your house and run 2 miles due west followed by 1.5 miles due north. At that time, what is your bearing from your house?

44. A ship is 9 miles east and 6 miles south of a harbor. What bearing should be taken to sail directly to the harbor?

45. A jet leaves a runway whose bearing is N 35° E from the control tower. After flying 5 miles, the jet turns 90° and flies on a bearing of S 55° E for 7 miles. At that time, what is the bearing of the jet from the control tower?

46. A ship leaves port with a bearing of S 40° W. After traveling 7 miles, the ship turns 90° and travels on a bearing of N 60° W for 11 miles. At that time, what is the bearing of the ship from port?

47. An object in simple harmonic motion has a frequency of $\frac{1}{2}$ oscillation per minute and an amplitude of 6 feet. Write an equation in the form $d = a \sin \omega t$ for the object's simple harmonic motion.

48. An object in simple harmonic motion has a frequency of $\frac{1}{4}$ oscillation per minute and an amplitude of 8 feet. Write an equation in the form $d = a \sin \omega t$ for the object's simple harmonic motion.

49. A piano tuner uses a tuning fork. If middle C has a frequency of 264 vibrations per second, write an equation in the form $d = \sin \omega t$ for the simple harmonic motion.

50. A radio station, 98.1 on the FM dial, has radio waves with a frequency of 98.1 million cycles per second. Write an equation in the form $d = \sin \omega t$ for the simple harmonic motion of the radio waves.

Writing in Mathematics

51. What does it mean to solve a right triangle?

52. Explain how to find one of the acute angles of a right triangle if two sides are known.

53. Describe a situation in which a right triangle and a trigonometric function are used to measure a height or distance that would otherwise be inconvenient or impossible to measure.

54. What is meant by the bearing from point O to point P? Give an example with your description.

55. What is simple harmonic motion? Give an example with your description.

56. Explain the period and the frequency of simple harmonic motion. How are they related?

57. Explain how the photograph of the damaged highway on page 522 illustrates simple harmonic motion.

 ## Technology Exercises

The functions in Exercises 58–59 model motion in which the amplitude decreases with time due to friction or other resistive forces. Graph each function in the given viewing rectangle. How many complete oscillations occur on the time interval $0 \le x \le 10$?

58. $y = 4e^{-0.1x} \cos 2x$ $[0, 10, 1]$ by $[-4, 4, 1]$

59. $y = -6e^{-0.09x} \cos 2\pi x$ $[0, 10, 1]$ by $[-6, 6, 1]$

 ## Critical Thinking Exercises

60. The figure shows a satellite circling 112 miles above Earth. When the satellite is directly above point B, angle A measures 76.6°. Find Earth's radius to the nearest mile.

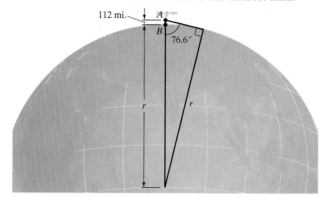

61. The figure shows that the angle of elevation to the top of the building changes from 20° to 40° as an observer advances 75 feet toward the building. Find the height of the building to the nearest foot.

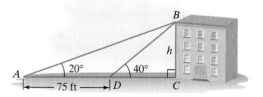

 ## Group Exercise

62. Music and mathematics have been linked over the centuries. Group members should research and present a seminar to the class on music and mathematics. Be sure to include the role of trigonometric functions in the music-mathematics link.

CHAPTER SUMMARY, REVIEW, AND TEST

Summary

5.1 Angles and Their Measure

a. An angle consists of two rays with a common endpoint, the vertex.

b. An angle is in standard position if its vertex is at the origin and its initial side lies along the positive x-axis. Figure 5.3 on page 417 shows positive and negative angles in standard position.

c. A quadrantal angle is one with its terminal side on the x-axis or the y-axis.

d. Angles can be measured in degrees. 1° is $\frac{1}{360}$ of a complete rotation.

e. Acute angles measure less than 90°, right angles 90°, obtuse angles more than 90° but less than 180°, and straight angles 180°.

f. Two angles with the same initial and terminal sides are called coterminal angles.

g. Two angles are complements if their sum is 90° and supplements if their sum is 180°. Only positive angles are used.

h. Angles can be measured in radians. One radian is the measure of the central angle if the intercepted arc and radius have the same length. In general, the radian measure of a central angle is the length of the intercepted arc divided by the circle's radius: $\theta = \dfrac{s}{r}$.

i. To convert degrees to radians, multiply degrees by $\dfrac{\pi \text{ radians}}{180°}$. To convert from radians to degrees, multiply radians by $\dfrac{180°}{\pi \text{ radians}}$.

j. The arc length formula, $s = r\theta$, is described in the box on page 424.

k. The definitions of linear speed, $v = \dfrac{s}{t}$, and angular speed, $\omega = \dfrac{\theta}{t}$, are given in the box on page 425.

l. Linear speed is expressed in terms of angular speed by $v = r\omega$, where v is the linear speed of a point a distance r from the center of rotation and ω is the angular speed in radians per unit of time.

5.2 Right Triangle Trigonometry

a. The right triangle definitions of the six trigonometric functions are given in the box on page 431.

b. Function values for 30°, 45°, and 60° can be obtained using these special triangles.

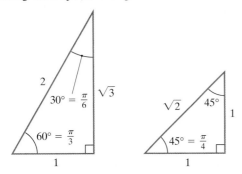

c. Fundamental Identities

1. Reciprocal Identities

$$\sin\theta = \frac{1}{\csc\theta} \quad \cos\theta = \frac{1}{\sec\theta} \quad \tan\theta = \frac{1}{\cot\theta}$$

$$\csc\theta = \frac{1}{\sin\theta} \quad \sec\theta = \frac{1}{\cos\theta} \quad \cot\theta = \frac{1}{\tan\theta}$$

2. Quotient Identities

$$\tan\theta = \frac{\sin\theta}{\cos\theta} \quad \cot\theta = \frac{\cos\theta}{\sin\theta}$$

3. Pythagorean Identities

$$\sin^2\theta + \cos^2\theta = 1$$
$$1 + \tan^2\theta = \sec^2\theta$$
$$1 + \cot^2\theta = \csc^2\theta$$

d. The value of a trigonometric function of θ is equal to the cofunction of the complement of θ. Cofunction identities are listed in the box on page 438.

5.3 Trigonometric Functions of Any Angle

a. Definitions of the trigonometric functions of any angle are given in the box on page 447.

b. Signs of the trigonometric functions: All functions are positive in quadrant I. If θ lies in quadrant II, $\sin\theta$ and $\csc\theta$ are positive. If θ lies in quadrant III, $\tan\theta$ and $\cot\theta$ are positive. If θ lies in quadrant IV, $\cos\theta$ and $\sec\theta$ are positive.

c. If θ is a nonacute angle in standard position that lies in a quadrant, its reference angle is the positive acute angle θ' formed by the terminal side of θ and the x-axis. The reference angle for a given angle can be found by making a sketch that shows the angle in standard position. Figure 5.30 on page 452 shows reference angles for θ in quadrants II, III, and IV.

d. The values of the trigonometric functions of a given angle are the same as the values of the functions of the reference angle, except possibly for the sign. A procedure for using reference angles to evaluate trigonometric functions is given in the box on page 453.

5.4 Trigonometric Functions of Real Numbers; Periodic Functions

a. Definitions of the trigonometric functions in terms of a unit circle are given in the box on page 458.

b. The cosine and secant functions are even:
$$\cos(-t) = \cos t, \quad \sec(-t) = \sec t.$$
The other trigonometric functions are odd:
$$\sin(-t) = -\sin t, \quad \tan(-t) = -\tan t,$$
$$\cot(-t) = -\cot t, \quad \csc(-t) = -\csc t.$$

c. If $f(t + p) = f(t)$, function f is periodic. The smallest p for which f is periodic is the period of f. The tangent and cotangent functions have period π. The other four trigonometric functions have period 2π.

5.5 and 5.6 Graphs of the Trigonometric Functions

a. Graphs of the six trigonometric functions, with a description of the domain, range, and period of each function, are given in Table 5.4 on page 494.

b. The graph of $y = A\sin(Bx - C)$ can be obtained using amplitude $= |A|$, period $= \dfrac{2\pi}{B}$ and phase shift $= \dfrac{C}{B}$. See the illustration in the box on page 471.

c. The graph of $y = A\cos(Bx - C)$ can be obtained using amplitude $= |A|$, period $= \dfrac{2\pi}{B}$, and phase shift $= \dfrac{C}{B}$. See the illustration in the box on page 477.

d. The constant D in $y = A \sin(Bx - C) + D$ and $y = A \cos(Bx - C) + D$ causes vertical shifts in the graphs in the preceding items (b) and (c). If $D > 0$, the shift is D units upward and if $D < 0$, the shift is D units downward. Oscillation is about $y = D$.

e. The graph of $y = A \tan(Bx - C)$ is obtained using the procedure in the box on page 488. Consecutive asymptotes (solve $Bx - C = -\dfrac{\pi}{2}$ and $Bx - C = \dfrac{\pi}{2}$) and an x-intercept midway between them play a key role in the graphing process.

f. The graph of $y = A \cot(Bx - C)$ is obtained using the procedure in the box on page 490. Consecutive asymptotes (solve $Bx - C = 0$ and $Bx - C = \pi$) and an x-intercept midway between them play a key role in the graphing process.

g. To graph a cosecant curve, begin by graphing the reciprocal sine curve. Draw vertical asymptotes through x-intercepts, using asymptotes as guides to sketch the graph. To graph a secant curve, first graph the reciprocal cosine curve and use the same procedure.

5.7 Inverse Trigonometric Functions

a. On the restricted domain $-\dfrac{\pi}{2} \le x \le \dfrac{\pi}{2}$, $y = \sin x$ has an inverse function, defined in the box on page 499. Think of $\sin^{-1} x$ as the angle in $\left[-\dfrac{\pi}{2}, \dfrac{\pi}{2} \right]$ whose sine is x.

b. On the restricted domain $0 \le x \le \pi$, $y = \cos x$ has an inverse function, defined in the box on page 502. Think of $\cos^{-1} x$ as the angle in $[0, \pi]$ whose cosine is x.

c. On the restricted domain $-\dfrac{\pi}{2} < x < \dfrac{\pi}{2}$, $y = \tan x$ has an inverse function, defined in the box on page 504. Think of $\tan^{-1} x$ as the angle in $\left(-\dfrac{\pi}{2}, \dfrac{\pi}{2} \right)$ whose tangent is x.

d. Graphs of the three basic inverse trigonometric functions, with a description of the domain and range of each function, are given in Table 5.8 on page 506.

e. Inverse properties are given in the box on page 507. Points on terminal sides of angles in standard position are used to find exact values of the composition of a function and a different inverse function.

5.8 Applications of Trigonometric Functions

a. Solving a right triangle means finding the missing lengths of its sides and the measurements of its angles. The Pythagorean Theorem, two acute angles whose sum is $90°$, and appropriate trigonometric functions are used in this process.

b. The bearing from point O to point P is the acute angle between ray OP and a north-south line.

c. Simple harmonic motion, described in the box on page 520, is modeled by $d = a \cos \omega t$ or $d = a \sin \omega t$, with amplitude $= |a|$, period $= \dfrac{2\pi}{\omega}$ and frequency $= \dfrac{\omega}{2\pi} = \dfrac{1}{\text{period}}$.

Review Exercises

5.1

In Exercises 1–4, draw each angle in standard position.

1. $190°$

2. $-135°$

3. $\dfrac{5\pi}{6}$

4. $-\dfrac{2\pi}{3}$

In Exercises 5–6, find a positive angle less than $360°$ that is coterminal with the given angle.

5. $400°$

6. $-85°$

In Exercises 7–8, if possible, find the complement and the supplement of the given angle.

7. $73°$

8. $\dfrac{2\pi}{3}$

9. Find the radian measure of the central angle of a circle of radius 6 centimeters that intercepts an arc of length 27 centimeters.

In Exercises 10–12, convert each angle in degrees to radians. Express your answer as a multiple of π.

10. $15°$

11. $120°$

12. $315°$

In Exercises 13–15, convert each angle in radians to degrees.

13. $\dfrac{5\pi}{3}$

14. $\dfrac{7\pi}{5}$

15. $-\dfrac{5\pi}{6}$

16. Find the length of the arc on a circle of radius 10 feet intercepted by a $135°$ central angle. Express arc length in terms of π. Then round your answer to two decimal places.

17. The angular speed of a propeller on a wind generator is 10.3 revolutions per minute. Express this angular speed in radians per minute.

18. The propeller of an airplane has a radius of 3 feet. The propeller is rotating at 2250 revolutions per minute. Find the linear speed, in feet per minute, of the tip of the propeller.

5.2

19. Use the triangle to find each of the six trigonometric functions of θ.

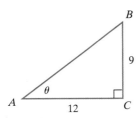

In Exercises 20–23, find the exact value of each expression. Do not use a calculator.

20. $\tan 60°$

21. $\cos \dfrac{\pi}{4}$

22. $\sec \dfrac{\pi}{6}$

23. $\sin^2 \dfrac{\pi}{5} + \cos^2 \dfrac{\pi}{5}$

24. If θ is an acute angle and $\sin\theta = \dfrac{2}{\sqrt{7}}$, use the identity $\sin^2\theta + \cos^2\theta = 1$ to find $\cos\theta$.

In Exercises 25–26, find a cofunction with the same value as the given expression.

25. $\sin 70°$

26. $\cos \dfrac{\pi}{2}$

In Exercises 27–29, find the measure of the side of the right triangle whose length is designated by a lowercase letter. Round answers to the nearest whole number.

27.

28.

29.

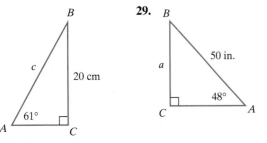

30. A hiker climbs for a half mile up a slope whose inclination is 17°. How many feet of altitude, to the nearest foot, does the hiker gain?

31. To find the distance across a lake, a surveyor took the measurements in the figure shown. What is the distance across the lake? Round to the nearest meter.

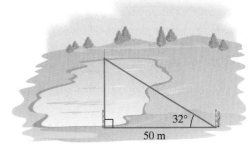

32. When a six-foot pole casts a four-foot shadow, what is the angle of elevation of the sun? Round to the nearest whole degree.

5.3 and 5.4

In Exercises 33–34, a point on the terminal side of angle θ is given. Find the exact value of each of the six trigonometric functions of θ, or state that the function is undefined.

33. $(-1, -5)$

34. $(0, -1)$

In Exercises 35–36, let θ be an angle in standard position. Name the quadrant in which θ lies.

35. $\tan\theta > 0$ and $\sec\theta > 0$

36. $\tan\theta > 0$ and $\cos\theta < 0$

In Exercises 37–38, find the exact value of each of the remaining trigonometric functions of θ.

37. $\cos\theta = \frac{2}{5}$, $\sin\theta < 0$

38. $\tan\theta = -\frac{1}{3}$, $\sin\theta > 0$

In Exercises 39–41, find the reference angle for each angle.

39. $265°$

40. $\dfrac{5\pi}{8}$

41. $-410°$

In Exercises 42–50, find the exact value of each expression. Do not use a calculator.

42. $\sin 240°$

43. $\tan 120°$

44. $\sec \dfrac{7\pi}{4}$

45. $\cos \dfrac{11\pi}{6}$

46. $\cot(-210°)$

47. $\csc\left(-\dfrac{2\pi}{3}\right)$

48. $\sin\left(-\dfrac{\pi}{3}\right)$

49. $\sin 495°$

50. $\tan \dfrac{13\pi}{4}$

5.5

In Exercises 51–56, determine the amplitude and period of each function. Then graph one period of the function.

51. $y = 3 \sin 4x$

52. $y = -2 \cos 2x$

53. $y = 2 \cos\frac{1}{2}x$

54. $y = \dfrac{1}{2} \sin \dfrac{\pi}{3}x$

55. $y = -\sin \pi x$

56. $y = 3 \cos \dfrac{x}{3}$

In Exercises 57–61, determine the amplitude, period, and phase shift of each function. Then graph one period of the function.

57. $y = 2 \sin(x - \pi)$

58. $y = -3 \cos(x + \pi)$

59. $y = \frac{3}{2} \cos\left(2x + \frac{\pi}{4}\right)$

60. $y = \frac{5}{2} \sin\left(2x + \frac{\pi}{2}\right)$

61. $y = -3 \sin\left(\frac{\pi}{3} x - 3\pi\right)$

In Exercises 62–63, use a vertical shift to graph one period of the function.

62. $y = \sin 2x + 1$

63. $y = 2 \cos\frac{1}{3} x - 2$

64. The equation

$$y = 98.6 + 0.3 \sin\left(\frac{\pi}{12} x - \frac{11\pi}{12}\right)$$

models variation in body temperature, y, in °F, x hours after midnight.
   a. What is body temperature at midnight?
   b. What is the period of the body temperature cycle?
   c. When is body temperature highest? What is the body temperature at this time?
   d. When is body temperature lowest? What is the body temperature at this time?
   e. Graph one period of the body temperature function.

5.6

In Exercises 65–71, graph two full periods of the given tangent or cotangent function.

65. $y = 4 \tan 2x$

66. $y = -2 \tan\frac{\pi}{4} x$

67. $y = \tan(x + \pi)$

68. $y = -\tan\left(x - \frac{\pi}{4}\right)$

69. $y = 2 \cot 3x$

70. $y = -\frac{1}{2} \cot\frac{\pi}{2} x$

71. $y = 2 \cot\left(x + \frac{\pi}{2}\right)$

In Exercises 72–75, graph two full periods of the given cosecant or secant function.

72. $y = 3 \sec 2\pi x$

73. $y = -2 \csc \pi x$

74. $y = 3 \sec(x + \pi)$

75. $y = \frac{5}{2}\csc(x - \pi)$

5.7

In Exercises 76–93, find the exact value of each expression. Do not use a calculator.

76. $\sin^{-1} 1$

77. $\cos^{-1} 1$

78. $\tan^{-1} 1$

79. $\sin^{-1}\left(-\frac{\sqrt{3}}{2}\right)$

80. $\cos^{-1}\left(-\frac{1}{2}\right)$

81. $\tan^{-1}\left(-\frac{\sqrt{3}}{3}\right)$

82. $\cos\left(\sin^{-1}\frac{\sqrt{2}}{2}\right)$

83. $\sin\left(\cos^{-1} 0\right)$

84. $\tan\left[\sin^{-1}\left(-\frac{1}{2}\right)\right]$

85. $\tan\left[\cos^{-1}\left(-\frac{\sqrt{3}}{2}\right)\right]$

86. $\csc\left(\tan^{-1}\frac{\sqrt{3}}{3}\right)$

87. $\cos\left(\tan^{-1}\frac{3}{4}\right)$

88. $\sin\left(\cos^{-1}\frac{3}{5}\right)$

89. $\tan\left[\sin^{-1}\left(-\frac{3}{5}\right)\right]$

90. $\tan\left[\cos^{-1}\left(-\frac{4}{5}\right)\right]$

91. $\sin^{-1}\left(\sin\frac{\pi}{3}\right)$

92. $\sin^{-1}\left(\sin\frac{2\pi}{3}\right)$

93. $\sin^{-1}\left(\cos\frac{2\pi}{3}\right)$

In Exercises 94–95, use a right triangle to write each expression as an algebraic expression. Assume that x is positive and in the domain of the given inverse trigonometric function.

94. $\cos\left(\tan^{-1}\frac{x}{2}\right)$

95. $\sec\left(\sin^{-1}\frac{1}{x}\right)$

5.8

In Exercises 96–99, solve the right triangle shown in the figure. Round lengths to two decimal places and express angles to the nearest tenth of a degree.

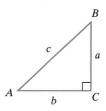

96. $A = 22.3°, c = 10$

97. $B = 37.4°, b = 6$

98. $a = 2, c = 7$

99. $a = 1.4, b = 3.6$

100. From a point on level ground 80 feet from the base of a building, the angle of elevation is 25.6°. Approximate the height of the building to the nearest foot.

101. Two buildings with flat roofs are 60 yards apart. The height of the shorter building is 40 yards. From its roof, the angle of elevation to the edge of the roof of the taller building is 40°. Find the height of the taller building to the nearest yard.

102. You want to measure the height of an antenna on the top of a 125-foot building. From a point in front of the building, you measure the angle of elevation to the top of the building to be 68° and the angle of elevation to the top of the antenna to be 71°. How tall is the antenna, to the nearest tenth of a foot?

In Exercises 103–104, use the figure shown to find the bearing from O to A.

103.

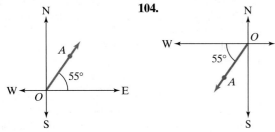

104.

105. A ship is due west of a lighthouse. A second ship is 12 miles south of the first ship. The bearing from the second ship to the lighthouse is N 64° E. How far, to the nearest tenth of a mile, is the first ship from the lighthouse?

106. From city A to city B, a plane flies 850 miles at a bearing of N 58° E. From city B to city C, the plane flies 960 miles at a bearing of S 32° E.
  a. Find, to the nearest tenth of a mile, the distance from city A to city C.
  b. What is the bearing from city A to city C?

In Exercises 107–108, an object moves in simple harmonic motion described by the given equation, where t is measured in seconds and d in centimeters. In each exercise, find:
  a. *the maximum displacement.*
  b. *the frequency.*
  c. *the time required for one cycle.*

107. $d = 20 \cos \dfrac{\pi}{4} t$

108. $d = \frac{1}{2} \sin 4t$

In Exercises 109–110, an object is attached to a coiled spring. The object is pulled down (negative direction from the rest position) and then released. Write an equation for the distance of the object from its rest position after t seconds.

	Distance from rest position at $t = 0$	Amplitude	Period
109.	30 inches	30 inches	2 seconds
110.	0	$\frac{1}{4}$ inches	5 seconds

Chapter 5 Test

1. Convert 135° to exact radian measure.

2. Find the supplement of the angle whose radian measure is $\dfrac{9\pi}{13}$. Express the answer in terms of π.

3. Find the length of the arc on a circle of radius 20 feet intercepted by a 75° central angle. Express arc length in terms of π. Then round your answer to two decimal places.

4. If $(-2, 5)$ is a point on the terminal side of angle θ, find the exact value of each of the six trigonometric functions of θ.

5. Determine the quadrant in which θ lies if $\cos < 0$ and $\cot \theta > 0$.

6. If $\cos \theta = \frac{1}{3}$ and $\tan \theta < 0$, find the exact value of each of the remaining trigonometric functions of θ.

In Exercises 7–9, find the exact value of each expression. Do not use a calculator.

7. $\tan \dfrac{\pi}{6} \cos \dfrac{\pi}{3} - \cos \dfrac{\pi}{2}$

8. $\tan 300°$

9. $\sin \dfrac{7\pi}{4}$

In Exercises 10–13, graph one period of each function.

10. $y = 3 \sin 2x$

11. $y = -2 \cos \left(x - \dfrac{\pi}{2} \right)$

12. $y = 2 \tan \dfrac{x}{2}$

13. $y = -\frac{1}{2} \csc \pi x$

14. Find the exact value of $\tan\left[\cos^{-1}\left(-\frac{1}{2}\right)\right]$.

15. Solve the right triangle in the figure shown. Round lengths to one decimal place.

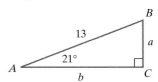

16. The angle of elevation of a building from a point on the ground 30 yards from its base is 37°. Find the height of the building to the nearest yard.

17. A 73-foot rope from the top of a circus tent pole is anchored to the flat ground 43 feet from the bottom of the pole. Find the angle, to the nearest tenth of a degree, that the rope makes with the pole.

18. Use the figure to find the bearing from O to P.

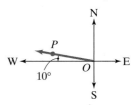

19. An object moves in simple harmonic motion described by $d = -6 \cos \pi t$, where t is measured in seconds and d in inches. Find (a) the maximum displacement, (b) the frequency, and (c) the time required for one oscillation.

20. Why are trigonometric functions ideally suited to model phenomena that repeat in cycles?

Cumulative Review Exercises (Chapters 1–5)

Solve each equation or inequality in Exercises 1–6.

1. $x^2 = 18 + 3x$

2. $x^3 + 5x^2 - 4x - 20 = 0$

3. $\log_2 x + \log_2(x - 2) = 3$

4. $\sqrt{x - 3} + 5 = x$

5. $x^3 - 4x^2 + x + 6 = 0$

6. $|2x - 5| \le 11$

7. If $f(x) = \sqrt{x - 6}$, find $f^{-1}(x)$.

8. Divide $20x^3 - 6x^2 - 9x + 10$ by $5x + 2$.

9. Write as a single logarithm and evaluate: $\log 25 + \log 40$.

10. Convert $\dfrac{14\pi}{9}$ radians to degrees.

11. Find the maximum number of positive and negative real roots of the equation $3x^4 - 2x^3 + 5x^2 + x - 9 = 0$.

In Exercises 12–16, graph each equation.

12. $f(x) = \dfrac{x}{x^2 - 1}$

13. $(x - 2)^2 + y^2 = 1$

14. $y = (x - 1)(x + 2)^2$

15. $y = \sin\left(2x + \dfrac{\pi}{2}\right)$, from 0 to 2π

16. $y = 2\tan 3x$; graph two complete cycles.

17. You invest in a new play. The cost includes an overhead of $30,000, plus production costs of $2500 per performance. A sold-out performance brings you $3125. How many sold-out performances must be played in order for you to break even?

18. Use the exponential growth model $A = A_0 e^{kt}$ to solve this exercise. Data from the Federal Communication Commission show that the use of toll-free 800 numbers has grown exponentially. In 1991 there were 10.2 billion such calls and by 1998, there were 86.7 billion.
   a. Find the exponential function that models the data.
   b. By what year will the number of toll-free 800 numbers reach 200 billion?

19. The rate of heat lost through insulation varies inversely as the thickness of the insulation. The rate of heat lost through a 3.5-inch thickness of insulation is 2200 Btu per hour. What is the rate of heat lost through a 5-inch thickness of the same insulation?

20. A tower is 200 feet tall. To the nearest degree, find the angle of elevation from a point 50 feet from the base of the tower to the top of the tower.

Analytic Trigonometry

This chapter emphasizes the algebraic aspects of trigonometry. We derive important categories of identities involving trigonometric functions. These identities are used to simplify and analyze expressions that model phenomena as diverse as the distance achieved when throwing an object and musical sounds on a touch-tone phone. For example, we can find out critical information about an athlete's performance by using an identity to analyze an expression involving throwing distance. You will learn how to use trigonometric identities to better understand your periodic world.

You enjoy watching your friend participate in the shot put at college track and field events. After a few full turns in a circle, she throws ("puts") a 16-pound shot from the shoulder. The range of her throwing distance continues to improve. Knowing that you are studying trigonometry, she asks if there is some way that a trigonometric expression might help achieve the best distance possible in the event.

32.

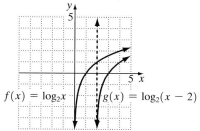

$f(x) = \log_2 x$ $g(x) = \log_2(x - 2)$

x-intercept: $(3, 0)$
vertical asymptote: $x = 2$

33.

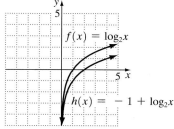

$f(x) = \log_2 x$

$h(x) = -1 + \log_2 x$

x-intercept: $(2, 0)$
vertical asymptote: $x = 0$

34.

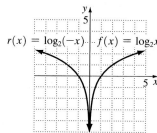

$r(x) = \log_2(-x)$ $f(x) = \log_2 x$

x-intercept: $(-1, 0)$
vertical asymptote: $x = 0$

35. $(-5, \infty)$ **36.** $(-\infty, 3)$ **37.** $(-\infty, 1) \cup (1, \infty)$ **38.** $6x$ **39.** $\sqrt{x}$ **40.** $4x^2$ **41.** 3.0

42. a. 76

b. $\approx 67, \approx 63, \approx 61, \approx 59, \approx 56$

c.

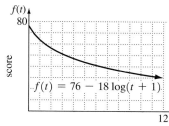

$f(t) = 76 - 18 \log(t + 1)$

time (months)
Retention decreases as time passes.

43. about 9 weeks   **44.** $2 + 3 \log_6 x$ **45.** $\frac{1}{2} \log_4 x - 3$

46. $\log_2 x + 2 \log_2 y - 6$ **47.** $\frac{1}{3} \ln x - \frac{1}{3}$ **48.** $\log_b 21$ **49.** $\log \frac{3}{x^3}$

50. $\ln(x^3 y^4)$ **51.** $\ln \frac{\sqrt{x}}{y}$ **52.** 6.2448 **53.** -0.1063

54. $\left\{ \frac{\ln 12{,}143}{\ln 8} \right\}; \approx 4.523$ **55.** $\left\{ \frac{1}{5} \ln 141 \right\}; \approx 0.990$

56. $\left\{ \frac{12 - \ln 130}{5} \right\}; \approx 1.426$ **57.** $\left\{ \frac{\ln 37{,}500 - 2 \ln 5}{4 \ln 5} \right\}; \approx 1.136$

58. $\{\ln 3\}; \approx 1.099$ **59.** $\{23\}$ **60.** $\{5\}$ **61.** $\varnothing$ **62.** $\left\{ \frac{1}{e} \right\}$ or $\{0.368\}$

63. $\left\{ \frac{e^3}{2} \right\}$ or $\{10.043\}$ **64.** 2042 **65.** 2086 **66.** 2005 **67.** 7.3 yr

68. 14.6 yr   **69.** about 21.97% **70. a.** 0.041 **b.** 40.7 million   **c.** 2010 **71.** about $15{,}679$ years old   **72. a.** about 9 people
b. about 104 people   **c.** 171 people; yes; The limiting size is 171; however, 178 people died.   **73.** $y = 73e^{(\ln 2.6)x}; y = 73e^{0.956x}$
74. $y = 6.5e^{(\ln 0.43)x}; y = 6.5e^{-0.844x}$ **75.** high: exponential; medium: linear; low: quadratic; Explanations will vary; negative;
The parabola opens downward.   **76.** The exponential model, $y = (3.38051786)(1.0235357)^x$, is the best fit; 113.4 million

Chapter 4 Test

1.

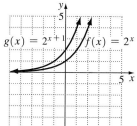

$g(x) = 2^{x+1}$ $f(x) = 2^x$

2.

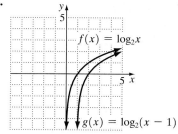

$f(x) = \log_2 x$

$g(x) = \log_2(x - 1)$

3. $5^3 = 125$ **4.** $\log_{36} 6 = \frac{1}{2}$ **5.** $(-\infty, 3)$

6. $3 + 5 \log_4 x$ **7.** $\frac{1}{3} \log_3 x - 4$ **8.** $\log(x^6 y^2)$

9. $\ln \frac{7}{x^3}$ **10.** 1.5741 **11.** $\left\{ \frac{\ln 1.4}{\ln 5} \right\}$ or $\{0.2091\}$

12. $\left\{ \frac{\ln 4}{0.005} \right\}$ or $\{277.2589\}$ **13.** $\{0, \ln 5\}$ or $\{0, 1.6094\}$

14. $\{54.25\}$ **15.** $\{5\}$ **16.** $\left\{ \frac{e^4}{3} \right\}$ or $\{18.1993\}$

17. 6.5% compounded semiannually; $\$221.15$ more   **18.** 120 db   **19. a.** about 89% **b.** decreasing; $k = -0.004 < 0$ **c.** 1995
20. $A = 484e^{0.005t}$ **21.** about $24{,}758$ years ago   **22. a.** 14 elk   **b.** about 51 elk   **c.** 140 elk

Cumulative Review Exercises (Chapters 1–4)

1. $\left\{ \frac{2}{3}, 2 \right\}$ **2.** $\{3, 7\}$ **3.** $\{-2, -1, 1\}$ **4.** $\{0.9704\}$ **5.** $\{3\}$ **6.** $(-\infty, 4]$ **7.** $[1, 3]$

8. using $(1, 3)$, $y - 3 = -3(x - 1); y = -3x + 6$ **9.** $(f \circ g)(x) = (x + 2)^2; (g \circ f)(x) = x^2 + 2$ **10.** $f^{-1}(x) = \frac{1}{2}x + \frac{7}{2}$

11. $x^2 + 3x - 3 + \frac{-4}{x + 2}$ **12.** $\pm 1, \pm \frac{1}{2}, \pm \frac{1}{4}, \pm 3, \pm \frac{3}{2}, \pm \frac{3}{4}$ **13.** 300 **14.** $\{1 + i, 1 - i, 2\}$

15.

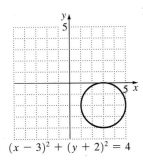

$(x - 3)^2 + (y + 2)^2 = 4$

16.

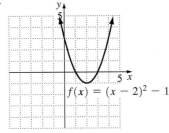

$f(x) = (x - 2)^2 - 1$

17.

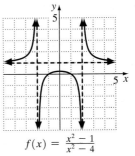

$f(x) = \frac{x^2 - 1}{x^2 - 4}$

18.

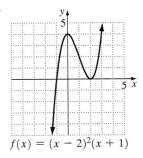

$f(x) = (x - 2)^2(x + 1)$

19. $12 per hr   **20.** $\dfrac{0.5}{\ln 4} \approx 0.361$; about $\dfrac{3}{10}$ of the people

CHAPTER 5

Section 5.1

Check Point Exercises

1. a.

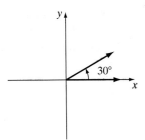

b.

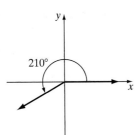

c.

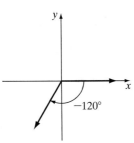

d.

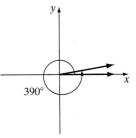

2. a. $40°$ **b.** $225°$ **3. a.** $12°; 102°$ **b.** no complementary angle; $30°$ **4.** 3.5 radians   **5. a.** $\dfrac{\pi}{3}$ radians   **b.** $\dfrac{3\pi}{2}$ radians

c. $-\dfrac{5\pi}{3}$ radians   **6. a.** $45°$ **b.** $-240°$ **c.** $343.8°$ **7.** $\dfrac{3\pi}{2}$ in. ≈ 4.71 in.   **8.** 135π in./min ≈ 424 in./min

Exercise Set 5.1

1. quadrant II   **3.** quadrant III   **5.** quadrant I   **7.** obtuse   **9.** straight

11.

13.

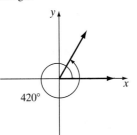

15.

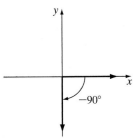

17.

19. $35°$ **21.** $210°$ **23.** $315°$ **25.** $38°; 128°$ **27.** $52.6°; 142.6°$ **29.** no complement; $69°$ **31.** 4 radians   **33.** $\dfrac{4}{3}$ radians

35. 4 radians   **37.** $\dfrac{\pi}{4}$ radians   **39.** $\dfrac{3\pi}{4}$ radians   **41.** $\dfrac{5\pi}{3}$ radians   **43.** $-\dfrac{5\pi}{4}$ radians   **45.** $90°$ **47.** $120°$ **49.** $210°$

51. $-540°$ **53.** 0.31 radians   **55.** -0.70 radians   **57.** 3.49 radians   **59.** $114.59°$ **61.** $13.85°$ **63.** $-275.02°$

65. 3π in. ≈ 9.42 in.   **67.** 10π ft ≈ 31.42 ft   **69.** $\dfrac{12\pi \text{ radians}}{\text{second}}$ **71.** $60°; \dfrac{\pi}{3}$ radians   **73.** $\dfrac{8\pi}{3}$ in. ≈ 8.38 in.

75. 12π in. ≈ 37.70 in.   **77.** 2 radians; $114.59°$ **79.** 2094 mi   **81.** 1047 mph   **83.** 1508 ft/min   **97.** $30.25°$ **99.** $30° \, 25' \, 12''$

101. smaller than a right angle   **103.** 1815 mi

Section 5.2

Check Point Exercises

1. $\sin\theta = \dfrac{3}{5}; \cos\theta = \dfrac{4}{5}; \tan\theta = \dfrac{3}{4}; \csc\theta = \dfrac{5}{3}; \sec\theta = \dfrac{5}{4}; \cot\theta = \dfrac{4}{3}$ **2.** $\sqrt{2}; \sqrt{2}; 1$ **3.** $\sqrt{3}; \dfrac{\sqrt{3}}{3}$ **4.** $\tan\theta = \dfrac{2\sqrt{5}}{5}; \csc\theta = \dfrac{3}{2};$ $\sec\theta = \dfrac{3\sqrt{5}}{5}; \cot\theta = \dfrac{\sqrt{5}}{2}$ **5.** $\dfrac{\sqrt{3}}{2}$ **6. a.** $\cos 44°$ **b.** $\tan\dfrac{5\pi}{12}$ **7. a.** 0.9553 **b.** 1.0025 **8.** 333.9 yd **9.** $54°$

Exercise Set 5.2

1. $15; \sin\theta = \dfrac{3}{5}; \cos\theta = \dfrac{4}{5}; \tan\theta = \dfrac{3}{4}; \csc\theta = \dfrac{5}{3}; \sec\theta = \dfrac{5}{4}; \cot\theta = \dfrac{4}{3}$ **3.** $20; \sin\theta = \dfrac{20}{29}; \cos\theta = \dfrac{21}{29}; \tan\theta = \dfrac{20}{21}; \csc\theta = \dfrac{29}{20};$ $\sec\theta = \dfrac{29}{21}; \cot\theta = \dfrac{21}{20}$ **5.** $24; \sin\theta = \dfrac{5}{13}; \cos\theta = \dfrac{12}{13}; \tan\theta = \dfrac{5}{12}; \csc\theta = \dfrac{13}{5}; \sec\theta = \dfrac{13}{12}; \cot\theta = \dfrac{12}{5}$ **7.** $28; \sin\theta = \dfrac{4}{5}; \cos\theta = \dfrac{3}{5};$ $\tan\theta = \dfrac{4}{3}; \csc\theta = \dfrac{5}{4}; \sec\theta = \dfrac{5}{3}; \cot\theta = \dfrac{3}{4}$ **9.** $\dfrac{\sqrt{3}}{2}$ **11.** $\sqrt{2}$ **13.** $\sqrt{3}$ **15.** 0 **17.** $\tan\theta = \dfrac{8}{15}; \csc\theta = \dfrac{17}{8}; \sec\theta = \dfrac{17}{15};$ $\cot\theta = \dfrac{15}{8}$ **19.** $\tan\theta = \dfrac{\sqrt{2}}{4}; \csc\theta = 3; \sec\theta = \dfrac{3\sqrt{2}}{4}; \cot\theta = 2\sqrt{2}$ **21.** $\dfrac{\sqrt{13}}{7}$ **23.** $\dfrac{5}{8}$ **25.** 1 **27.** 1 **29.** 1 **31.** $\cos 83°$

33. $\sec 65°$ **35.** $\cot\dfrac{7\pi}{18}$ **37.** $\sin\dfrac{\pi}{10}$ **39.** 0.6157 **41.** 0.6420 **43.** 3.4203 **45.** 0.9511 **47.** 3.7321 **49.** 188 cm
51. 182 in. **53.** 41 m **55.** $17°$ **57.** $78°$ **59.** 1.147 radians **61.** 0.3950 radians **63.** 529 yd **65.** $36°$ **67.** 2879 ft
69. $37°$ **83.** $0.92106, -0.19735; 0.95534, -0.148878; 0.98007, -0.099667; 0.99500, -0.04996; 0.99995, -0.005; 0.9999995, -0.0005;$
$0.999999995, -0.00005; 1, -0.000005; \dfrac{\cos\theta - 1}{\theta}$ approaches 0 as θ approaches 0. **85.** In a right triangle, the hypotenuse is greater than
either other side. Therefore, both $\dfrac{\text{opposite}}{\text{hypotenuse}}$ and $\dfrac{\text{adjacent}}{\text{hypotenuse}}$ must be less than 1 for an acute angle in a right triangle.
87. a. 357 ft **b.** 394 ft

Section 5.3

Check Point Exercises

1. $\sin\theta = -\dfrac{3}{5}; \cos\theta = \dfrac{4}{5}; \tan\theta = -\dfrac{3}{4}; \csc\theta = -\dfrac{5}{3}; \sec\theta = \dfrac{5}{4}; \cot\theta = -\dfrac{4}{3}$ **2. a.** $1;$ undefined **b.** $0; 1$ **c.** $-1;$ undefined

d. $0; -1$ **3.** quadrant III **4.** $\dfrac{\sqrt{10}}{10}; -\dfrac{\sqrt{10}}{3}$ **5. a.** $30°$ **b.** $\dfrac{\pi}{4}$ **c.** $60°$ **d.** 0.46 **6. a.** $-\dfrac{\sqrt{3}}{2}$ **b.** 1 **c.** $\dfrac{2\sqrt{3}}{3}$

Exercise Set 5.3

1. $\sin\theta = \dfrac{3}{5}; \cos\theta = -\dfrac{4}{5}; \tan\theta = -\dfrac{3}{4}; \csc\theta = \dfrac{5}{3}; \sec\theta = -\dfrac{5}{4}; \cot\theta = -\dfrac{4}{3}$ **3.** $\sin\theta = \dfrac{3\sqrt{13}}{13}; \cos\theta = \dfrac{2\sqrt{13}}{13}; \tan\theta = \dfrac{3}{2}; \csc\theta = \dfrac{\sqrt{13}}{3};$ $\sec\theta = \dfrac{\sqrt{13}}{2}; \cot\theta = \dfrac{2}{3}$ **5.** $\sin\theta = -\dfrac{\sqrt{2}}{2}; \cos\theta = \dfrac{\sqrt{2}}{2}; \tan\theta = -1; \csc\theta = -\sqrt{2}; \sec\theta = \sqrt{2}; \cot\theta = -1$

7. $\sin\theta = -\dfrac{5\sqrt{29}}{29}; \cos\theta = -\dfrac{2\sqrt{29}}{29}; \tan\theta = \dfrac{5}{2}; \csc\theta = -\dfrac{\sqrt{29}}{5}; \sec\theta = -\dfrac{\sqrt{29}}{2}; \cot\theta = \dfrac{2}{5}$ **9.** -1 **11.** -1 **13.** undefined

15. 0 **17.** quadrant I **19.** quadrant III **21.** quadrant II **23.** $\sin\theta = -\dfrac{4}{5}; \tan\theta = \dfrac{4}{3}; \csc\theta = -\dfrac{5}{4}; \sec\theta = -\dfrac{5}{3}; \cot\theta = \dfrac{3}{4}$

25. $\cos\theta = -\dfrac{12}{13}; \tan\theta = -\dfrac{5}{12}; \csc\theta = \dfrac{13}{5}; \sec\theta = -\dfrac{13}{12}; \cot\theta = -\dfrac{12}{5}$ **27.** $\sin\theta = -\dfrac{15}{17}; \tan\theta = -\dfrac{15}{8}; \csc\theta = -\dfrac{17}{15}; \sec\theta = \dfrac{17}{8};$

$\cot\theta = -\dfrac{8}{15}$ **29.** $\sin\theta = \dfrac{2\sqrt{13}}{13}; \cos\theta = -\dfrac{3\sqrt{13}}{13}; \csc\theta = \dfrac{\sqrt{13}}{2}; \sec\theta = -\dfrac{\sqrt{13}}{3}; \cot\theta = -\dfrac{3}{2}$ **31.** $\sin\theta = -\dfrac{4}{5}; \cos\theta = -\dfrac{3}{5};$

$\csc\theta = -\dfrac{5}{4}; \sec\theta = -\dfrac{5}{3}; \cot\theta = \dfrac{3}{4}$ **33.** $\sin\theta = -\dfrac{2\sqrt{2}}{3}; \cos\theta = -\dfrac{1}{3}; \tan\theta = 2\sqrt{2}; \csc\theta = -\dfrac{3\sqrt{2}}{4}; \cot\theta = \dfrac{\sqrt{2}}{4}$ **35.** $20°$

37. $25°$ **39.** $5°$ **41.** $\dfrac{\pi}{4}$ **43.** $\dfrac{\pi}{6}$ **45.** $30°$ **47.** $25°$ **49.** 1.56 **51.** $-\dfrac{\sqrt{2}}{2}$ **53.** $\dfrac{\sqrt{3}}{3}$ **55.** $\sqrt{3}$ **57.** $\dfrac{\sqrt{3}}{2}$ **59.** -2

61. 1 **63.** $\dfrac{\sqrt{3}}{2}$ **65.** -1

Section 5.4

Check Point Exercises

1. $\sin \pi = 0$; $\cos \pi = -1$; $\tan \pi = 0$; $\csc \pi$ is undefined; $\sec \pi = -1$; $\cot \pi$ is undefined   **2. a.** $\dfrac{1}{2}$ **b.** $-\dfrac{\sqrt{3}}{3}$ **3. a.** $\dfrac{\sqrt{2}}{2}$ **b.** $\sqrt{3}$

Exercise Set 5.4

1. $\sin t = \dfrac{8}{17}$; $\cos t = -\dfrac{15}{17}$; $\tan t = -\dfrac{8}{15}$; $\csc t = \dfrac{17}{8}$; $\sec t = -\dfrac{17}{15}$; $\cot t = -\dfrac{15}{8}$

3. $\sin\left(-\dfrac{\pi}{4}\right) = -\dfrac{\sqrt{2}}{2}$; $\cos\left(-\dfrac{\pi}{4}\right) = \dfrac{\sqrt{2}}{2}$; $\tan\left(-\dfrac{\pi}{4}\right) = -1$; $\csc\left(-\dfrac{\pi}{4}\right) = -\sqrt{2}$; $\sec\left(-\dfrac{\pi}{4}\right) = \sqrt{2}$; $\cot\left(-\dfrac{\pi}{4}\right) = -1$

5. $-\dfrac{\sqrt{2}}{2}$ **7.** 2   **9.** $-\dfrac{\sqrt{2}}{2}$ **11.** $\dfrac{\sqrt{3}}{3}$ **13. a.** 12 hr   **b.** 20.3 hr   **c.** 3.7 hr   **15. a.** $1; 0; -1; 0; 1$ **b.** 28 days

23. 0   **25.** $-\dfrac{1}{4}$

Section 5.5

Check Point Exercises

1. 3

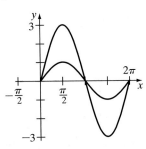

2. $\dfrac{1}{2}$

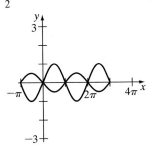

3. $2; 4\pi$

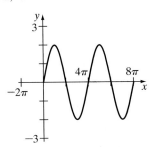

4. $3; \pi; \dfrac{\pi}{6}$

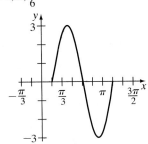

5. $4; 2$

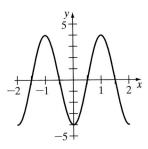

6. $\dfrac{3}{2}; \pi; -\dfrac{\pi}{2}$

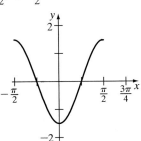

7.

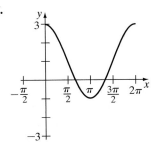

8. $y = 4 \sin 4x$

9. $y = 2 \sin\left(\dfrac{\pi}{6}x - \dfrac{\pi}{2}\right) + 12$

Exercise Set 5.5

1. 4

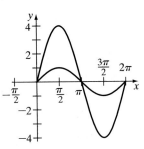

3. $\dfrac{1}{3}$

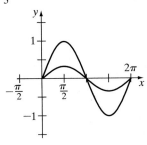

5. 3

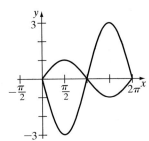

7. $1; \pi$

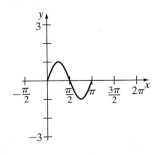

9. $3; 4\pi$

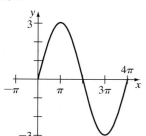

11. $4; 2$

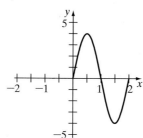

13. $3; 1$

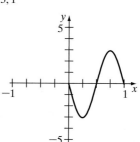

15. $1; 3\pi$

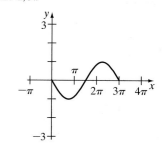

17. $1; 2\pi; \pi$

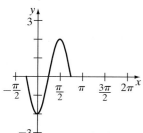

19. $1; \pi; \dfrac{\pi}{2}$

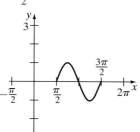

21. $3; \pi; \dfrac{\pi}{2}$

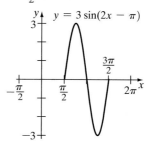
$y = 3\sin(2x - \pi)$

23. $\dfrac{1}{2}; 2\pi; -\dfrac{\pi}{2}$

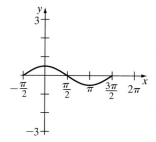

25. $2; \pi; -\dfrac{\pi}{4}$

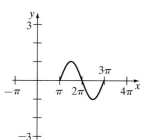

27. $3; 2; -\dfrac{2}{\pi}$

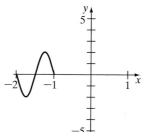

29. $2; 1; -2$

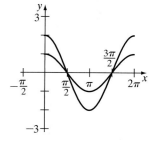

31. 2

33. 2

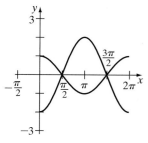

35. $1; \pi$

37. $4; 1$

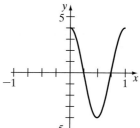

39. $4; 4\pi$

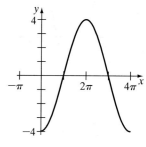

41. $\dfrac{1}{2}; 6$

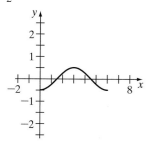

43. $3; \pi; \dfrac{\pi}{2}$

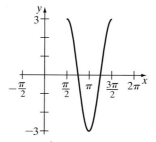

45. $\dfrac{1}{2}; \dfrac{2\pi}{3}; -\dfrac{\pi}{6}$

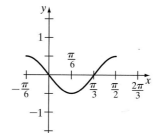

47. $3; \pi; \dfrac{\pi}{4}$

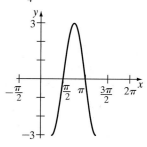

49. $2; 1; -4$

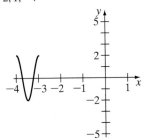

51.

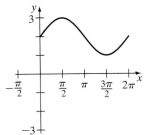

53.

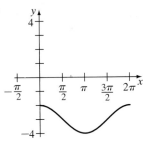

55.

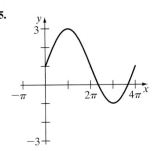

57.

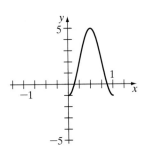

59. 33 days   **61.** 23 days   **63.** March 21

65. No

67.

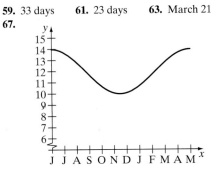

69. a. 3   **b.** 365 days

c. 15 hours of daylight

d. 9 hours of daylight

e.

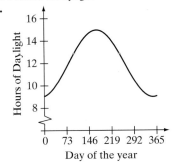

71. $y = 3 \cos \dfrac{\pi x}{6} + 9$

85.

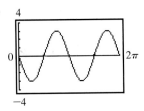

87.

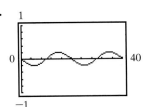

89.

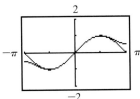

The graphs appear to be the same from $-\dfrac{\pi}{2}$ to $\dfrac{\pi}{2}$.

91.

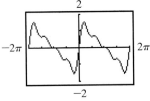

The graph is similar to $y = \sin x$, except the amplitude is greater and the curve is less smooth.

93. a.

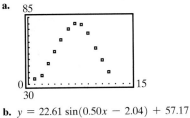

b. $y = 22.61 \sin(0.50x - 2.04) + 57.17$

c.

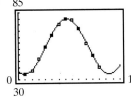

95.

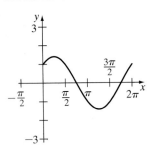

97. $y = 2 \cos(4x + \pi)$

Section 5.6

Check Point Exercises

1.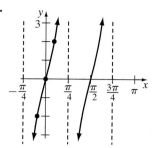

2.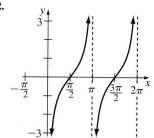

3.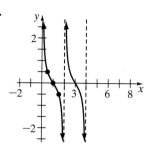

4.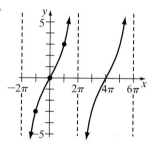

5.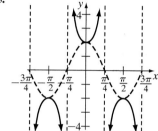

Exercise Set 5.6

1. $y = \tan(x + \pi)$ **3.** $y = -\tan\left(x - \dfrac{\pi}{2}\right)$

5.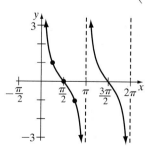

7.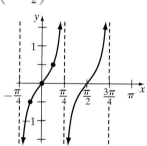

9.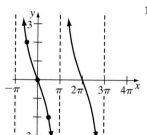

11.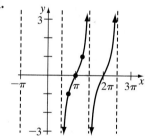

13. $y = -\cot x$ **15.** $y = \cot\left(x + \dfrac{\pi}{2}\right)$

17.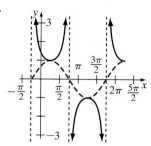

19.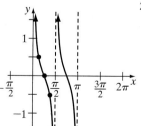

21.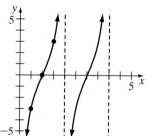

23.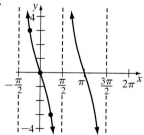

25. $y = -\dfrac{1}{2} \csc \dfrac{x}{2}$;

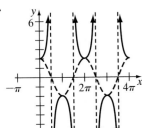

27. $y = \dfrac{1}{2} \sec 2\pi x$;

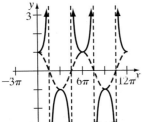

29.

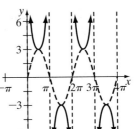

31.

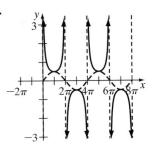

33.

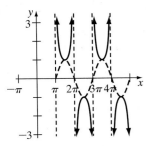

35.

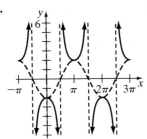

37.

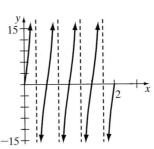

39.

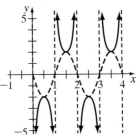

41.

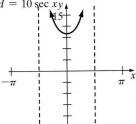

43.

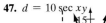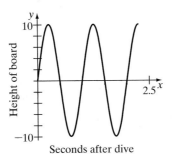

45. a.

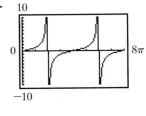

b. 0.25, 0.75, 1.25, 1.75; The beacon is shining parallel to the wall at these times.

47. $d = 10 \sec xy$

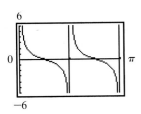

49.

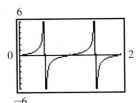

63.

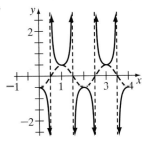

65.

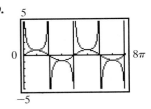

67.

69.

71.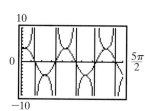

73.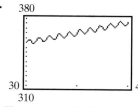

The concentration is increasing.

75. $y = \cot \frac{3}{2}x$

77. 2^{-x} decreases the amplitude as x gets larger.

Section 5.7

Check Point Exercises

1. $\frac{\pi}{3}$ **2.** $-\frac{\pi}{4}$ **3.** $\frac{2\pi}{3}$ **4.** $-\frac{\pi}{4}$ **5. a.** 1.2310 **b.** −1.5429 **6. a.** 0.7 **b.** 0 **c.** not defined **7.** $\frac{3}{5}$ **8.** $\frac{\sqrt{3}}{2}$
9. $\sqrt{x^2 + 1}$

Exercise Set 5.7

1. $\frac{\pi}{6}$ **3.** $\frac{\pi}{4}$ **5.** $-\frac{\pi}{6}$ **7.** $\frac{\pi}{6}$ **9.** $\frac{3\pi}{4}$ **11.** $\frac{\pi}{2}$ **13.** $\frac{\pi}{6}$ **15.** 0 **17.** $-\frac{\pi}{3}$ **19.** 0.30 **21.** −0.33 **23.** 1.19

25. 1.25 **27.** −1.52 **29.** −1.52 **31.** 0.9 **33.** $\frac{\pi}{3}$ **35.** $\frac{\pi}{6}$ **37.** 125 **39.** $-\frac{\pi}{6}$ **41.** $-\frac{\pi}{3}$ **43.** 0 **45.** not defined

47. $\frac{3}{5}$ **49.** $\frac{12}{5}$ **51.** $-\frac{3}{4}$ **53.** $\frac{\sqrt{2}}{2}$ **55.** $\frac{4\sqrt{15}}{15}$ **57.** $-2\sqrt{2}$ **59.** 2 **61.** $\frac{\sqrt{1-x^2}}{x}$ **63.** $\frac{\sqrt{x^2-1}}{x}$ **65.** $\frac{\sqrt{x^2+4}}{2}$

67. a.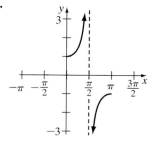

b. No horizontal line intersects the graph of $y = \sec x$ more than once, so the function is one-to-one and has an inverse function.

c.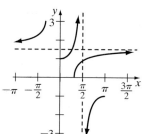

69. 0.408 radians; 0.602 radians; 0.654 radians; 0.645 radians; 0.613 radians
71. 1.3157 radians or 75.4°
73. 1.1071 sq units
87.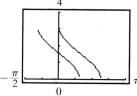

Shifted right 1 unit

89.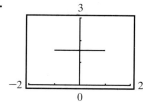

Shifted left 2 units and up 1 unit

91.

It seems $\sin^{-1} x + \cos^{-1} x = \frac{\pi}{2}$ for $-1 \le x \le 1$

93. $x = \sin \frac{\pi}{8}$

95. $\tan \alpha = \frac{8}{x}$, so $\tan^{-1} \frac{8}{x} = \alpha$.

$\tan(\alpha + \theta) = \frac{33}{x}$, so $\tan^{-1} \frac{33}{x} = \alpha + \theta$.

$\theta = \alpha + \theta - \alpha = \tan^{-1} \frac{33}{x} - \tan^{-1} \frac{8}{x}$.

Section 5.8

Check Point Exercises

1. $B = 27.3°; b \approx 4.34; c \approx 9.45$ **2.** 998 ft **3.** $\theta \approx 29.0$ **4.** 60.3 ft **5. a.** S 25° E **b.** S 15° W
6. a. 4.2 mi **b.** S87.7°W **7.** $d = -6 \cos \frac{\pi}{2}t$ **8. a.** 12 cm **b.** $\frac{1}{8}$ cm per sec **c.** 8 sec

Exercise Set 5.8

1. $B = 66.5°; a \approx 4.35; c \approx 10.90$ **3.** $B = 37.4°; a \approx 42.90; b \approx 32.80$ **5.** $A = 73.2°; a \approx 101.02; c \approx 105.52$

7. $b \approx 39.95$; $A \approx 37.3°$; $B \approx 52.7°$ **9.** $c \approx 26.96$; $A \approx 23.6°$; $B \approx 66.4°$ **11.** $a \approx 6.71$; $B \approx 16.6°$; $A \approx 73.4°$

13. N 15° E   **15.** S 80° W   **17.** $d = -6 \cos \frac{\pi}{2} t$ **19.** $d = 3 \sin \frac{4\pi}{3} t$ **21. a.** 5 in.   **b.** $\frac{1}{4}$ in. per sec   **c.** 4 sec

23. a. 6 in.   **b.** 1 in. per sec   **c.** 1 sec   **25. a.** $\frac{1}{2}$ in.   **b.** 0.32 in. per sec   **c.** 3.14 sec   **27. a.** 5 in.   **b.** $\frac{1}{3}$ in. per sec

c. 3 sec   **29.** $h \approx 2059$ ft   **31.** $d \approx 695$ ft   **33.** 1376 ft   **35.** 15.1°   **37.** 33.7 ft   **39.** 90 mi north and 120 mi east

41. 13.2 mi   **43.** N 53° W   **45.** N 89.5° E   **47.** $d = 6 \sin \pi t$ **49.** $d = \sin 528 \pi t$

59.   ; 10 complete oscillations   **61.** 48 ft

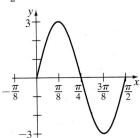

Chapter 5 Review Exercises

1.
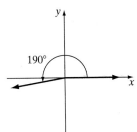

2.
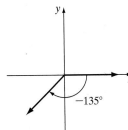

3.
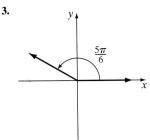

4.
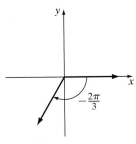

5. 40°   **6.** 275°   **7.** 17°; 107°   **8.** no complement; $\frac{\pi}{3}$ radians   **9.** 4.5 radians   **10.** $\frac{\pi}{12}$ radians   **11.** $\frac{2\pi}{3}$ radians

12. $\frac{7\pi}{4}$ radians   **13.** 300°   **14.** 252°   **15.** −150°   **16.** $\frac{15\pi}{2}$ ft ≈ 23.56 ft   **17.** 20.6π radians per min   **18.** 42,412 ft per min

19. $\sin \theta = \frac{3}{5}$; $\cos \theta = \frac{4}{5}$; $\tan \theta = \frac{3}{4}$; $\csc \theta = \frac{5}{3}$; $\sec \theta = \frac{5}{4}$; $\cot \theta = \frac{4}{3}$ **20.** $\sqrt{3}$ **21.** $\frac{\sqrt{2}}{2}$ **22.** $\frac{2\sqrt{3}}{3}$ **23.** 1   **24.** $\frac{\sqrt{21}}{7}$

25. $\cos 20°$ **26.** $\sin 0$ **27.** 42 mm   **28.** 23 cm   **29.** 37 in.   **30.** 772 ft   **31.** 31 m   **32.** 56°

33. $\sin \theta = -\frac{5\sqrt{26}}{26}$; $\cos \theta = -\frac{\sqrt{26}}{26}$; $\tan \theta = 5$; $\csc \theta = -\frac{\sqrt{26}}{5}$; $\sec \theta = -\sqrt{26}$; $\cot \theta = \frac{1}{5}$

34. $\sin \theta = -1$; $\cos \theta = 0$; $\tan \theta$ is undefined; $\csc \theta = -1$; $\sec \theta$ is undefined; $\cot \theta = 0$ **35.** quadrant I   **36.** quadrant III

37. $\sin \theta = -\frac{\sqrt{21}}{5}$; $\tan \theta = -\frac{\sqrt{21}}{2}$; $\csc \theta = -\frac{5\sqrt{21}}{21}$; $\sec \theta = \frac{5}{2}$; $\cot \theta = -\frac{2\sqrt{21}}{21}$

38. $\sin \theta = \frac{\sqrt{10}}{10}$; $\cos \theta = -\frac{3\sqrt{10}}{10}$; $\csc \theta = \sqrt{10}$; $\sec \theta = -\frac{\sqrt{10}}{3}$; $\cot \theta = -3$ **39.** 85°   **40.** $\frac{3\pi}{8}$ **41.** 50°   **42.** $-\frac{\sqrt{3}}{2}$

43. $-\sqrt{3}$ **44.** $\sqrt{2}$ **45.** $\frac{\sqrt{3}}{2}$ **46.** $-\sqrt{3}$ **47.** $-\frac{2\sqrt{3}}{3}$ **48.** $-\frac{\sqrt{3}}{2}$ **49.** $\frac{\sqrt{2}}{2}$ **50.** 1

51. $3; \frac{\pi}{2}$ **52.** $2; \pi$ **53.** $2; 4\pi$ **54.** $\frac{1}{2}; 6$

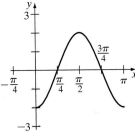

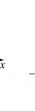

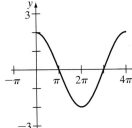

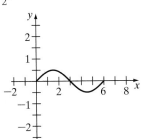

55. $1; 2$

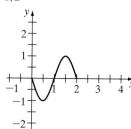

56. $3; 6\pi$

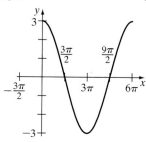

57. $2; 2\pi; \pi$

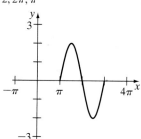

58. $3; 2\pi; -\pi$

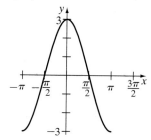

59. $\dfrac{3}{2}; \pi; -\dfrac{\pi}{8}$

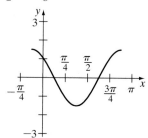

60. $\dfrac{5}{2}; \pi; -\dfrac{\pi}{4}$

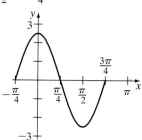

61. $3; 6; 9$

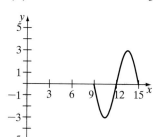

62.

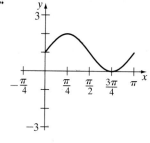

63.

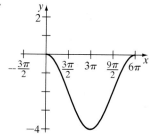

64. a. $\approx 98.52°$ **b.** 24 hr   **c.** 5:00 P.M.; $98.9°$
d. 5:00 A.M.; $98.3°$ **e.**

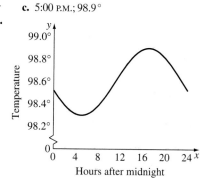

65.

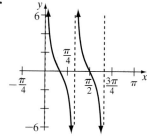

66.

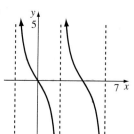

67.

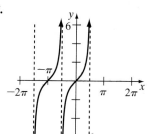

68.

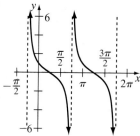

69.

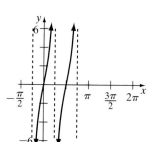

70.

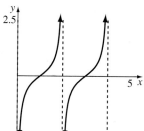

71.

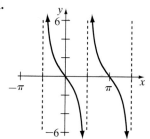

72.

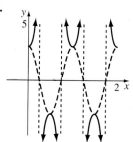

73.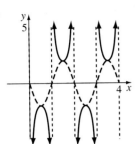

74.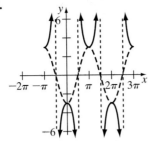

75.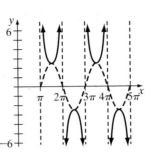

76. $\dfrac{\pi}{2}$ **77.** 0   **78.** $\dfrac{\pi}{4}$

79. $-\dfrac{\pi}{3}$ **80.** $\dfrac{2\pi}{3}$

81. $-\dfrac{\pi}{6}$ **82.** $\dfrac{\sqrt{2}}{2}$

83. 1   **84.** $-\dfrac{\sqrt{3}}{3}$

85. $-\dfrac{\sqrt{3}}{3}$ **86.** 2

87. $\dfrac{4}{5}$ **88.** $\dfrac{4}{5}$ **89.** $-\dfrac{3}{4}$ **90.** $-\dfrac{3}{4}$ **91.** $\dfrac{\pi}{3}$ **92.** $\dfrac{\pi}{3}$ **93.** $-\dfrac{\pi}{6}$ **94.** $\dfrac{2}{\sqrt{x^2+4}}$ **95.** $\dfrac{x}{\sqrt{x^2-1}}$

96. $B \approx 67.7°; a \approx 3.79; b \approx 9.25$ **97.** $A \approx 52.6°; a \approx 7.85; c \approx 9.88$ **98.** $A \approx 16.6°; B \approx 73.4°; b \approx 6.71$

99. $A \approx 21.3°; B \approx 68.7°; c \approx 3.86$ **100.** 38 ft   **101.** 90 yd   **102.** 21.7 ft   **103.** N 35° E   **104.** S 35° W

105. 24.6 mi   **106. a.** 1282.2 mi   **b.** S74°E   **107. a.** 20 cm   **b.** $\dfrac{1}{8}$ cm per sec   **c.** 8 sec

108. a. $\dfrac{1}{2}$ cm   **b.** 0.64 cm per sec   **c.** 1.57 sec   **109.** $d = -30 \cos \pi t$ **110.** $d = \dfrac{1}{4} \sin \dfrac{2\pi}{5} t$

Chapter 5 Test

1. $\dfrac{3\pi}{4}$ radians   **2.** $\dfrac{4\pi}{13}$ **3.** $\dfrac{25\pi}{3}$ ft ≈ 26.18 ft

4. $\sin \theta = \dfrac{5\sqrt{29}}{29}; \cos \theta = -\dfrac{2\sqrt{29}}{29}; \tan \theta = -\dfrac{5}{2}; \csc \theta = \dfrac{\sqrt{29}}{5}; \sec \theta = -\dfrac{\sqrt{29}}{2}; \cot \theta = -\dfrac{2}{5}$ **5.** quadrant III

6. $\sin \theta = -\dfrac{2\sqrt{2}}{3}; \tan \theta = -2\sqrt{2}; \csc \theta = -\dfrac{3\sqrt{2}}{4}; \sec \theta = 3; \cot \theta = -\dfrac{\sqrt{2}}{4}$ **7.** $\dfrac{\sqrt{3}}{6}$ **8.** $-\sqrt{3}$ **9.** $-\dfrac{\sqrt{2}}{2}$

10.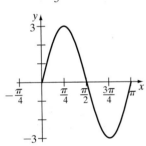

11.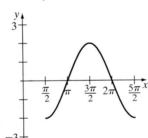

12.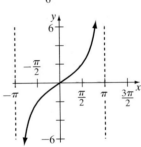

13.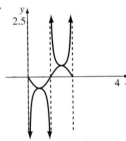

14. $-\sqrt{3}$ **15.** $B = 69°; a = 4.7; b = 12.1$ **16.** 23 yd   **17.** 36.1°   **18.** N 80° W   **19. a.** 6 in.   **b.** $\dfrac{1}{2}$ in. per sec   **c.** 2 sec

20. Trigonometric functions are periodic.

Cumulative Review Exercises (Chapters 1–5)

1. $\{-3, 6\}$ **2.** $\{-5, -2, 2\}$ **3.** $\{4\}$ **4.** $\{7\}$ **5.** $\{-1, 2, 3\}$

6. $-3 \le x \le 8$ **7.** $f^{-1}(x) = x^2 + 6$ **8.** $4x^2 - \dfrac{14}{5}x - \dfrac{17}{25} + \dfrac{284}{125x + 50}$ **9.** $\log 1000 = 3$ **10.** 280°

11. 3 positive real roots; 1 negative real root

12.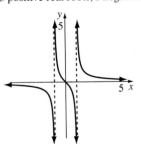

13.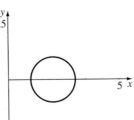

14.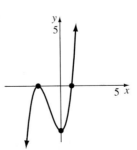

15.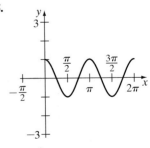

16.

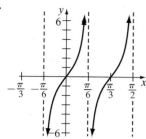

17. 48 performances   **18. a.** $A = 10.2^{0.3057t}$ **b.** 2001   **19.** 1540 Btu per hr   **20.** 76°

CHAPTER 6

Section 6.1

Check Point Exercises

1. $\csc x \tan x = \dfrac{1}{\sin x} \cdot \dfrac{\sin x}{\cos x} = \dfrac{1}{\cos x} = \sec x$ **2.** $\cos x \cot x + \sin x = \cos x \cdot \dfrac{\cos x}{\sin x} + \sin x = \dfrac{\cos^2 x}{\sin x} + \sin x \cdot \dfrac{\sin x}{\sin x} = \dfrac{\cos^2 x + \sin^2 x}{\sin x}$

$= \dfrac{1}{\sin x} = \csc x$ **3.** $\sin x - \sin x \cos^2 x = \sin x(1 - \cos^2 x) = \sin x \cdot \sin^2 x = \sin^3 x$ **4.** $\dfrac{\sin x}{1 + \cos x} + \dfrac{1 + \cos x}{\sin x}$

$= \dfrac{\sin x(\sin x)}{(1 + \cos x)(\sin x)} + \dfrac{(1 + \cos x)(1 + \cos x)}{(\sin x)(1 + \cos x)} = \dfrac{\sin^2 x + 1 + 2 \cos x + \cos^2 x}{(1 + \cos x)(\sin x)} = \dfrac{\sin^2 x + \cos^2 x + 1 + 2 \cos x}{(1 + \cos x)(\sin x)}$

$= \dfrac{1 + 1 + 2 \cos x}{(1 + \cos x)(\sin x)} = \dfrac{2 + 2 \cos x}{(1 + \cos x)(\sin x)} = \dfrac{2(1 + \cos x)}{(1 + \cos x)(\sin x)} = \dfrac{2}{\sin x} = 2 \csc x$

5. $\dfrac{\cos x}{1 + \sin x} = \dfrac{\cos x(1 - \sin x)}{(1 + \sin x)(1 - \sin x)} = \dfrac{\cos x(1 - \sin x)}{1 - \sin^2 x} = \dfrac{\cos x(1 - \sin x)}{\cos^2 x} = \dfrac{1 - \sin x}{\cos x}$ **6.** $\dfrac{\sec x + \csc(-x)}{\sec x \csc x} = \dfrac{\sec x - \csc x}{\sec x \csc x}$

$= \dfrac{\dfrac{1}{\cos x} - \dfrac{1}{\sin x}}{\dfrac{1}{\cos x} \cdot \dfrac{1}{\sin x}} = \dfrac{\dfrac{\sin x}{\cos x \cdot \sin x} - \dfrac{\cos x}{\cos x \cdot \sin x}}{\dfrac{1}{\cos x \cdot \sin x}} = \dfrac{\dfrac{\sin x - \cos x}{\cos x \cdot \sin x}}{\dfrac{1}{\cos x \cdot \sin x}} = \dfrac{\sin x - \cos x}{\cos x \cdot \sin x} \cdot \dfrac{\cos x \cdot \sin x}{1} = \sin x - \cos x$

7. Left side: $\dfrac{1}{1 + \sin \theta} + \dfrac{1}{1 - \sin \theta} = \dfrac{1(1 - \sin \theta)}{(1 + \sin \theta)(1 - \sin \theta)} + \dfrac{1(1 + \sin \theta)}{(1 - \sin \theta)(1 + \sin \theta)} = \dfrac{1 - \sin \theta + 1 + \sin \theta}{(1 + \sin \theta)(1 - \sin \theta)} = \dfrac{2}{1 - \sin^2 \theta};$

Right side: $2 + 2 \tan^2 \theta = 2 + 2\left(\dfrac{\sin^2 \theta}{\cos^2 \theta}\right) = \dfrac{2 \cos^2 \theta}{\cos^2 \theta} + \dfrac{2 \sin^2 \theta}{\cos^2 \theta} = \dfrac{2 \cos^2 \theta + 2 \sin^2 \theta}{\cos^2 \theta} = \dfrac{2(\cos^2 \theta + \sin^2 \theta)}{\cos^2 \theta} = \dfrac{2}{\cos^2 \theta} = \dfrac{2}{1 - \sin^2 \theta}$

Exercise Set 6.1

For Exercises 1–59, proofs may vary.

65.

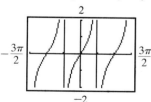

Proofs may vary.

67.

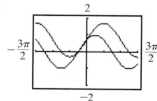

Values for x may vary.

69.

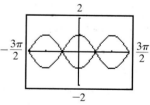

Values for x may vary.

71.

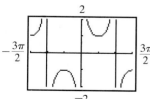

Proofs may vary.

73.

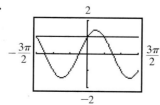

Values for x may vary.

75. Proofs may vary.
77. Answers may vary.

Section 6.2

Check Point Exercises

1. $\dfrac{\sqrt{3}}{2}$ **2.** $\dfrac{\sqrt{3}}{2}$ **3.** $\dfrac{\cos(\alpha - \beta)}{\cos \alpha \cos \beta} = \dfrac{\cos \alpha \cos \beta + \sin \alpha \sin \beta}{\cos \alpha \cos \beta} = \dfrac{\cos \alpha}{\cos \alpha} \cdot \dfrac{\cos \beta}{\cos \beta} + \dfrac{\sin \alpha}{\cos \alpha} \cdot \dfrac{\sin \beta}{\cos \beta} = 1 + \tan \alpha \tan \beta$ **4.** $\dfrac{\sqrt{2} + \sqrt{6}}{4}$

5. a. $\cos \alpha = -\dfrac{3}{5}$ **b.** $\cos \beta = \dfrac{\sqrt{3}}{2}$ **c.** $\dfrac{-3\sqrt{3} - 4}{10}$ **d.** $\dfrac{4\sqrt{3} - 4}{10}$ **6. a.** $y = \sin x$

b. $\cos\left(x + \dfrac{3\pi}{2}\right) = \cos x \cos \dfrac{3\pi}{2} - \sin x \sin \dfrac{3\pi}{2} = \cos x \cdot 0 - \sin x \cdot (-1) = \sin x$

7. $\tan(x + \pi) = \dfrac{\tan x + \tan \pi}{1 - \tan x \tan \pi} = \dfrac{\tan x + 0}{1 - \tan x \cdot 0} = \dfrac{\tan x}{1} = \tan x$

Exercise Set 6.2

1. $\dfrac{\sqrt{6} + \sqrt{2}}{4}$ **3.** $\dfrac{\sqrt{2} - \sqrt{6}}{4}$ **5. a.** $\alpha = 50°, \beta = 20°$ **b.** $\cos 30°$ **c.** $\dfrac{\sqrt{3}}{2}$ **7. a.** $\alpha = \dfrac{5\pi}{12}, \beta = \dfrac{\pi}{12}$ **b.** $\cos\left(\dfrac{\pi}{3}\right)$ **c.** $\dfrac{1}{2}$

For Exercises 9–11, proofs may vary.   **13.** $\dfrac{\sqrt{6} - \sqrt{2}}{4}$ **15.** $\dfrac{\sqrt{6} + \sqrt{2}}{4}$ **17.** $\sqrt{3} + 2$ **19.** $2 - \sqrt{3}$ **21.** $-\dfrac{\sqrt{6} + \sqrt{2}}{4}$

23. $\dfrac{\sqrt{6} - \sqrt{2}}{4}$ **25.** $\sin 30°; \dfrac{1}{2}$ **27.** $\tan 45°; 1$ **29.** $\sin \dfrac{\pi}{6}; \dfrac{1}{2}$ **31.** $\tan \dfrac{\pi}{6}; \dfrac{\sqrt{3}}{3}$ For Exercises 33–55, proofs may vary.

57. a. $-\dfrac{63}{65}$ **b.** $-\dfrac{16}{65}$ **c.** $\dfrac{16}{63}$ **59. a.** $-\dfrac{4 + 6\sqrt{2}}{15}$ **b.** $\dfrac{3 - 8\sqrt{2}}{15}$ **c.** $\dfrac{54 - 25\sqrt{2}}{28}$ **61. a.** $-\dfrac{8\sqrt{3} + 15}{34}$ **b.** $\dfrac{15\sqrt{3} - 8}{34}$

c. $\dfrac{480 - 289\sqrt{3}}{33}$ **63. a.** $y = \sin x$ **b.** $\sin(\pi - x) = \sin \pi \cos x - \cos \pi \sin x = 0 \cdot \cos x - (-1) \sin x = \sin x$ **65. a.** $y = 2 \cos x$

b. $\sin\left(x + \dfrac{\pi}{2}\right) + \sin\left(\dfrac{\pi}{2} - x\right) = \sin x \cos \dfrac{\pi}{2} + \cos x \sin \dfrac{\pi}{2} + \sin \dfrac{\pi}{2} \cos x - \cos \dfrac{\pi}{2} \sin x = \sin x \cdot 0 + \cos x \cdot 1 + 1 \cdot \cos x - 0 \cdot \sin x$

$= \cos x + \cos x = 2 \cos x$ **67.** Proofs may vary.; amplitude is $\sqrt{13}$; period is 2π

77.

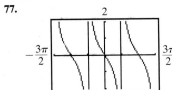

Proofs may vary.

79.

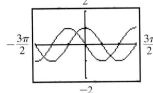

Values for x may vary.

81.

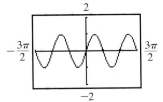

$\sin 1.2x \cos 0.8x + \cos 1.2x \sin 0.8x = \sin(1.2x + 0.8x)$
$= \sin 2x$

83. Proofs may vary.   **85.** $y\sqrt{1 - x^2} + x\sqrt{1 - y^2}$

Section 6.3

Check Point Exercises

1. a. $-\dfrac{24}{25}$ **b.** $-\dfrac{7}{25}$ **c.** $\dfrac{24}{7}$ **2.** $\dfrac{\sqrt{3}}{2}$ **3.** $\sin 3\theta = \sin(2\theta + \theta) = \sin 2\theta \cos \theta + \cos 2\theta \sin \theta = 2 \sin \theta \cos \theta \cos \theta$

$+ (2 \cos^2 \theta - 1)\sin \theta = 2 \sin \theta \cos^2 \theta + 2 \sin \theta \cos^2 \theta - \sin \theta = 4 \sin \theta \cos^2 \theta - \sin \theta = 4 \sin \theta(1 - \sin^2 \theta) - \sin \theta = 4 \sin \theta - 4 \sin^3 \theta$

$- \sin \theta = 3 \sin \theta - 4 \sin^3 \theta$ **4.** $\sin^4 x = (\sin^2 x)^2 = \left(\dfrac{1 - \cos 2x}{2}\right)^2 = \dfrac{1 - 2 \cos 2x + \cos^2 2x}{4} = \dfrac{1}{4} - \dfrac{1}{2}\cos 2x + \dfrac{1}{4}\cos^2 2x$

$= \dfrac{1}{4} - \dfrac{1}{2}\cos 2x + \dfrac{1}{4}\left(\dfrac{1 + \cos 2(2x)}{2}\right) = \dfrac{1}{4} - \dfrac{1}{2}\cos 2x + \dfrac{1}{8} + \dfrac{1}{8}\cos 4x = \dfrac{3}{8} - \dfrac{1}{2}\cos 2x + \dfrac{1}{8}\cos 4x$ **5.** $-\dfrac{\sqrt{2 + \sqrt{3}}}{2}$

6. $\dfrac{\sin 2\theta}{1 + \cos 2\theta} = \dfrac{2 \sin \theta \cos \theta}{1 + (1 - 2 \sin^2 \theta)} = \dfrac{2 \sin \theta \cos \theta}{2 - 2 \sin^2 \theta} = \dfrac{2 \sin \theta \cos \theta}{2(1 - \sin^2 \theta)} = \dfrac{2 \sin \theta \cos \theta}{2 \cos^2 \theta} = \dfrac{\sin \theta}{\cos \theta} = \tan \theta$

7. $\dfrac{\sec \alpha}{\sec \alpha \csc \alpha + \csc \alpha} = \dfrac{\dfrac{1}{\cos \alpha}}{\dfrac{1}{\cos \alpha} \cdot \dfrac{1}{\sin \alpha} + \dfrac{1}{\sin \alpha}} = \dfrac{\dfrac{1}{\cos \alpha}}{\dfrac{1}{\cos \alpha \sin \alpha} + \dfrac{\cos \alpha}{\cos \alpha \sin \alpha}} = \dfrac{\dfrac{1}{\cos \alpha}}{\dfrac{1 + \cos \alpha}{\cos \alpha \sin \alpha}} = \dfrac{1}{\cos \alpha} \cdot \dfrac{\cos \alpha \sin \alpha}{1 + \cos \alpha} = \dfrac{\sin \alpha}{1 + \cos \alpha} = \tan \dfrac{\alpha}{2}$